INDIA AND PAKISTAN

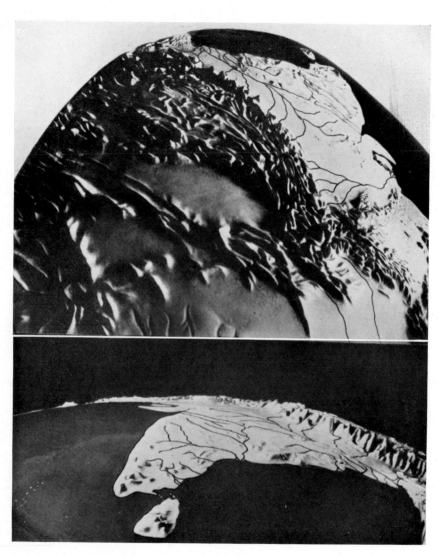

INDIA: APPROACHES BY LAND AND SEA.

INDIA
AND PAKISTAN

A General and Regional Geography

By

O. H. K. SPATE

Professor of Geography in the Australian National University;
sometime Lecturer in Geography, University of Rangoon

With a chapter on CEYLON by
B. H. FARMER
Fellow of St. John's College, Cambridge

We must hear accounts of India with indulgence, for
not only is it very far away, but even those who have
seen it saw only some parts of it, and most of what they
tell us is from hearsay.   Moreover, what they saw
they learnt during a passage along it with an army,
on rapid marches.   Wherefore they do not give consistent information. . . .

STRABO, *Geography* (*c*. AD 20)

LONDON: METHUEN & CO. LTD
NEW YORK: E. P. DUTTON & CO. INC.

First published in 1954

CATALOGUE No. 4255/U [METHUEN]

PRINTED AND BOUND IN ENGLAND BY
HAZELL WATSON AND VINEY LTD
AYLESBURY AND LONDON

PREFACE

AMONG ruminant animals, writers on Indian affairs form a special class; some refreshing exceptions apart, they chew over and over again the cud of Royal Commissions, Tariff Enquiries, Gazetteers, and the like. However rich the original material, nutritional returns soon diminish; hence the writer's vow, made in India, never to add to the mass of Indian literature; of which rash determination this volume is the natural nemesis.

Yet there is some justification, at least for the attempt, in the extraordinary fact that there has been no serious geography of India in English since Holdich's *India* of 1904. Like all Holdich's work, this has many merits: not least a vivid style and an admirable welding of history and geography. But there is surely something odd about a book which purports to be a geography of India and, in its regional sections, actually devotes 48 pages to Afghanistan and 28 to the Indo-Gangetic Plains and the Peninsula put together; a complete failure to subordinate local interest and special knowledge to the demands of a wider architecture. My own all too slight direct acquaintance with India at least shields me from this error. Apart from Krebs' admirable but not very accessible German work, for a really balanced geography of India on an adequate scale we must go back to Elisée Reclus' *Nouvelle Géographie Universelle*, of which the Indian volume was published in 1883. One does not—or at least nowadays one should not—go to *L'Inde* for details other than historical; but for grasp of fundamental relationships, for really masterly presentation of broad essentials, I know of no geographer superior to Reclus. "That Providence so often unacknowledged", as Febvre calls his book, shall not go unacknowledged here.

Although this book has occupied me, sometimes to the point of obsession, for six years, it had at the last to be somewhat rushed owing to my appointment to the Australian National University. For this reason Part 3 —The Economy—which was the last written, owes more than I could wish to secondary authorities, excellent as some of these are, and grateful as I am to such writers as Sharma, Jathar and Beri, and Vakil. In other directions I have been most painfully conscious of deficient technical equipment; notably in climatology and pedology. Despite its length, the book is to a large degree no more than a reconnaissance, so rich is the material which awaits synthesis. I cannot claim to have done more than follow a few trodden paths through the vast jungle—so often arid and thorny—of the literature; yet I may hope that the scattered traverses have been pulled together into some sort of coherent survey. At least I have pointed to some promising fields for further exploration; and the heavy documentation of some chapters is designed to give some idea of the abundant resources, almost untapped by Western geographers, which lie for instance in the publications of the Geological Survey of India, in the Gazetteers, and in the *Indian Geographical Journal*.

I am aware that a good deal of this book is "not geography". One could of course defend this, without undue difficulty, by a discussion of the true content of geography, or could shelter behind the indubitable fact that in Asia, where so much of life is ruled by ancient concepts entirely novel to most Western students, no human geography could be intelligible without much presentation of purely social factors. I prefer a shorter answer: "I am a man, and think nothing human indifferent to me."

If anything in this book should give undesigned offence to Indian or Pakistani readers, may I say that I have written in good faith and with good will; and with the conviction that some things which should be said, but which before 1947 might have appeared arrogance or condescension from a member of a ruling caste, can now be said as friendly criticism between equals; and it is in this spirit that I have written. Similarly, it is no disparagement of the devotion of thousands of British 'servants of India' to point out that the results of their actions were at times socially ambivalent.

I think that there is good work in this book, and I know that there is honest; but no-one can realise more keenly than I do its manifold imperfections, and none but myself can know how great is the gulf between conception and execution. I console myself by recalling those nobly measured periods in which Samuel Johnson, at the end of the *Plan* and *Preface* of his Dictionary, expresses so exactly how the author of a large work should regard his labours; though I cannot claim that indifference which I doubt if Johnson himself felt. Here too are implied the canons of criticism which every reviewer of a work of large scope should carry in his heart. Error there is and must be in such a book; constructive criticism and factual corrections will be received with gratitude proportioned to their relevance.

For the rest, the drudgery and delight of six years are ended, doubtless to the relief of my friends no less than of myself; certainly to the unspeakable relief of my long-suffering family:

To-morrow to fresh Woods, and Pastures new.

London, *April 1951*   O. H. K. S.

ACKNOWLEDGEMENTS

FOR information and for permission to reprint extracts or to reproduce maps my thanks are due to many official agencies in *India* and Pakistan: the Surveys of both countries; the Geological Survey of India; the Forest Research Institute at Dehra Dun, the Central Board of Irrigation, the Damodar Valley Corporation. Both in England and in Australia the Information Officers attached to the Offices of the High Commissioners for *India* and Pakistan were most helpful. Information on Goa was supplied by the Agencia Geral das Colonias, Lisbon.

Quotations of generous length were kindly allowed by: Chatto and Windus (Aldous Huxley's *Jesting Pilate*), the Cambridge University Press (G. E. Hutchinson's *The Clear Mirror*); Vora Bros., Bombay (Vakil's *Economic Consequences of Divided India*). Map credits are separately listed. Sections of the book have appeared in *Eastern World, Geography*, and *The Indian Geographical Journal*, and thanks are due to their editors for permission to reprint.

My large debts to such writers as Sir Malcolm Darling, Helmut de Terra, Radhakamal Mukerjee, and Jathar and Beri is evident, and is I trust amply acknowledged in the appropriate contexts. Mr E. S. Lindley and Sir Robert Bristow kindly gave me first-hand unpublished details on the Punjab canals and the port of Cochin respectively.

From Indian academic colleagues, friends or strangers, I received the most generous assistance. Prof. C. N. Vakil of Bombay and Prof. T. L. Sharma of Agra gave me liberty to base myself solidly on their works. I received also useful information from Prof. M. B. Pithawala of Karachi, Prof. S. P. Chatterjee of Calcutta, and Mr Nafis Ahmad of Dacca. To Prof. George Kuriyan of Madras I owe not only carte blanche for material from *The Indian Geographical Journal*, but a detailed check on the Tamilnad and Kerala sections; and a special word is due to the very friendly assistance of Mr C. D. Deshpande of Dharwar. My Indian students at LSE were teachers as well as pupils: E. Ahmad, H. L. Dayal, P. K. Dutt, M. Guha, S. A. Majid, Binapani Mukerjee. I trust that they will accept this recognition as some apology for my too-frequent impatiences, irascibilities, and unpunctualities.

I doubt if this book could have been written had it not been for the facilities of the London School of Economics; not least of which is its proximity to the library of India House, where Miss W. Thorne's kindness and encyclopaedic guidance have been main factors in the achievement of many Indian and other students of the sub-continent. This book owes much also to discussion with many colleagues at LSE, especially Prof. L. Dudley Stamp. Prof. R. Ogilvie Buchanan very kindly made the cartographical facilities of the LSE Geography Department available to me even after my departure. Most of the maps were redrawn or scripted by Miss Webb and Miss West, cartographers at LSE, and I also received much help from our technician Mr Judd. Mr W. T. W. Morgan compiled most of the crop distribution maps, and my friend Miss Marjory Fowler drew the vignettes of house types. But my chief debt is due to my colleague Mr D. J. Sinclair, who, on my departure for Australia, very generously offered to take over the supervision of the maps from my sketches—some very rough—to the blocks. It will be obvious that this was no light burden, and without his help the task would have been almost insuperable.

For discussions and criticism I should like to thank also Prof. Pierre Gourou of Paris, Prof. S. W. Wooldridge of London, and Prof. Raymond Firth, a colleague both in London and in Canberra. My friend Mr B. H. Farmer of St John's College, Cambridge, stepped into the breach when it became clear to me that I could not hope to deal adequately with Ceylon in the time available.

A very special service was rendered me by Sir Douglas Copland, the Vice-Chancellor, Prof. Marcus Oliphant, and Prof. W. R. Crocker, all of the ANU—the last in his other capacity of Australian High Commissioner at New Delhi. With them were associated Mr C. Rajagopalachariar, Mr K. P. S. Menon, Prof. S. Bhatnagar, and Dr D. N. Wadia: to all of them my gratitude. And to Mr J. N. L. Baker for the inception of the book.

Invaluable secretarial assistance was given by Miss Donne Shirwin at LSE, Miss Joan Binns in Canberra; the latter greatly lightened the labour of indexing.

Lastly, I should like to place on record the inspiration I have received from Reclus' *L'Inde* and Preston James's *Latin America*; the latter is the best regional geography in English known to me. Their value has been immense, however far I have fallen short of such exemplars.

O. H. K. S.

Canberra, *July 1952*

I wish to make it clear that the responsibility for the delay in the appearance of this book does not fall upon the publishers: pressure of work at the ANU is the only, but sufficient, reason.

O. H. K. S.

Canberra, *July 1953*

CONTENTS

MAPS AND DIAGRAMS

India: Approaches by Land and Sea   *Frontispiece*

Grateful acknowledgement is made to the following authors, editors, and publishers for permission to use or adapt maps as indicated by the initials above; fuller references will be found in the map captions. Apologies are offered for any inadvertent omissions.

BM   Dr Binapani Mukerjee, Calcutta.
CBI   Central Board of Irrigation, New Delhi.
CDD   C. D. Deshpande, Dharwar.
CE   *Chambers's Encyclopædia* (George Newnes Limited, London (1950)).
EA   Dr Enayat Ahmad, Patna.
ES/GA   Miss Ethel Simkins and The Geographical Association, Sheffield.
FRI   Forest Research Institution, Dehra Dun.
GK   Prof. George Kuriyan, *The Indian Geographical Journal*, and the University of Madras.
GR   *The Geographical Review*, New York.
GSI   Geological Survey of India, Calcutta.
KR   Dr K. Ramamurthy, Madras.
LDS   Prof. L. Dudley Stamp (maps from *Asia*, Methuen's).
LH/*GJ* Mr L. Hoffmann and *The Geographical Journal*, London.
MBP   Prof. Maneck B. Pithawala, Karachi.
OUP   Oxford University Press.
SAM   Dr S. A. Majid, Patna.
SOC   Survey of Ceylon, Colombo.
SOI   Survey of India, Mussoorie.
SOP   Survey of Pakistan, Karachi.
SP   S. Pandyan, Madras.
SPC   Prof. S. P. Chatterjee and Messrs. Orient Longmans Ltd, Calcutta.

TABLES

(Excluding short tabular statements in the text. All Tables are grouped together at the end of Part 3, The Economy.)

xix

CONVENTIONS AND PRELIMINARY DATA

Nomenclature

Recent political changes are likely to give rise to some terminological confusions; to avoid ambiguity the following conventions have been adopted.

1. The adoption by a part of the old political entity 'India' of the name formerly applied to the whole is unfortunate, since one cannot always write 'the Indian sub-continent' with convenience (and still less the official Karachi version 'the Indo-Pakistanian sub-continent'), and 'India' is still the most suitable geographical expression for the whole area from K2 to Cape Comorin and from Baluchistan to Assam. Hence **wherever reference is made to the new political entity of the Union or Republic of India, the words '*India*' or '*Indian*' are italicised.**

'Bharat' is apparently a legal alternative to *India*, but it is used mainly by Pakistanis or the more romantic Hindus, and is avoided here.

2. Both the Republic of *India* and the Dominion of Pakistan are in form federations; the units of Pakistan are Provinces; those of *India*, whether formerly British Provinces or princely territories, are known officially as States. **In this book 'State' when capitalised refers to these units of the Republic; when printed with initial lower case it refers to old princely territories.** The use of such phrases as 'state control of industry' is avoided except in a few places where no ambiguity can arise. 'Province' is used in historical contexts where appropriate.

3. **The word 'Government' refers to the Central authorities at New Delhi and Karachi, 'government' (initial lower case) to the local authorities of States or Provinces.**

4. There have been some changes of nomenclature in *India*, mainly owing to the formation of the following unions of states from the older groups indicated in parentheses: Rajasthan (Rajputana Agency), Saurashtra (Western India Agency), Madhya Bharat and Vindhya Pradesh (Central India Agency), Himachal Pradesh (Punjab Hill states), Patiala and East Punjab States Union (Punjab states adhering to *India*). (See Fig. 1.) The last of these is referred to in official publications as **Pepsu. The new names are used in this book when referring to the political territories, old regional names (Rajputana, Kathiawar, etc.) as geographical expressions.**

The United Provinces are now **Uttar Pradesh** (UP); the old Central Provinces are now **Madhya Pradesh**—the abbreviation CP is added for the convenience of British memories. **Bengal and Punjab without 'E' or 'W' imply the old undivided Provinces or are simply regional names.**

xxi

5. There have been a few slight changes in town names: Cawnpore into Kanpur, Benares into Banaras, Trichinopoly into Tiruchirapalli. In these cases the form familiar to British readers is retained; similarly Kistna is preferred to Krishna for the Deccan river. But two Indian regional names are used in preference to less correct British usages: **'Malabar' is referred to as Kerala, 'the Carnatic' as Tamilnad.** (See also p. 488.)

6. The spelling of place-names, with one or two exceptions, follows the Survey of India.

Other Conventions

7. Undated population figures in ordinary type are those of the 1941 Census; all in **bold face** are for 1951. Figures of density of population should be read as including the words "per square mile in 1941" (or 1951).

8. The place of publication of works cited, unless otherwise stated, is London. Apart from accidental omissions, the only exceptions to this rule are for official publications by local governments, in which case it is the capital of the State or Province; and publications of the Central Government of India (or *India*) are ascribed to New Delhi, although they are often issued by the Manager of Publications, Civil Lines, (Old) Delhi.

9. The writer favours the increasingly standard practice of omitting points in abbreviations composed of initials (e.g. NWFP not N.-W.F.P.) or in which the last letter of the abbreviation is the same as that of the complete word (e.g. Rly not Rly.).

10. The use of a stroke (/) or hyphen (-) is not fortuitous, though doubtless inconsistencies will be found. In directions the hyphen indicates movement, the stroke mere alignment; e.g. the river Tongawadi flows N–S, but the area is bounded by a line N/S through Tongawallahpur. Elsewhere the hyphen is conjunctive, the stroke disjunctive; e.g. the Assam-Burma Ranges (continuity), the Assam/Burma boundary (division); or the Kistna-Tungabhadra basin, but the Kistna/Godavari watershed.

11. Similarly, there is a slight nuance in the use of single or of double quotes for single words or short phrases; double quotes indicating that the writer's acceptance of the propriety or accuracy of the phrase is not unqualified.

12. Indian topographical or technical terms of frequent occurrence, such as 'doab', 'terai', 'sal', are italicised at the first mention only; those which occur in only a few passages are italicised wherever used. As such terms, if not explained by their context, are fully explained at their first occurrence, the index serves the purpose of a glossary.

13. 'Western' and 'Eastern', when spelled in full, have a cultural connotation, equivalent to Occidental and Oriental.

Administrative Units

14. The States of *India* and the Provinces of Pakistan are divided (if large enough) into Divisions, and these into Districts, of which there are about 277 in *India* (after states' mergers) and 55 in Pakistan. The Districts may be taken as roughly equivalent to English Counties; in Uttar Pradesh, for example, they have an average area of 2213 sq. mls. and population (1951) of *c.* 1,235,000. Some Districts, especially perhaps in the Gangetic Plains, represent entities which go back to Mogul times, but the great majority are merely *ad hoc* units for administrative convenience, as is suggested by the fact that all but a handful are named after their headquarters town. Districts are sub-divided into *taluks* (*taluqs*) or *tahsils* (*tehsils*), normally from 3 to 8 to a District. In Bengal, however, the next unit to the District is the *thana* or police-station area, which is much smaller than the average tahsil or taluk.

Numeration, etc.

15. The writer admires those who give metric equivalents with British units, but frankly blenched at the labours of conversion involved. Indian units, except rupees, have invariably been converted into British, but for the benefit of non-Indian readers who may follow up some of the references a short note on Indian numeration follows.

Indian numeration differs from European decimal or duodecimal systems, or British chaos; it is binary (i.e. proceeding by halving and halving again) for lower figures, and for larger is essentially decimal. It has two useful terms, which might well be borrowed: a *lakh* or *lac* = 100,000 and a *crore* = 100 lakhs or 10,000,000.

Thus the rupee (*Indian* = 1s. 6d., Pakistani since Devaluation = 2s. 2d.) is divided into 16 annas, and this division is often used where we would use a rough percentage: 'an 8-anna share' = 'a fifty-fifty share.' Large figures are often set out in lakhs and crores; thus 1,581,000 in European notation becomes in Indian 15,81,000 (15·8 lakhs), and the 1941 population of 388,997,955 may be written 38,89,97,955 (38 crores 89·98 lakhs). It is useful to remember that a lakh of *Indian* rupees is very roughly £7500 or $21,000 (more precisely £7471).

The words lakh and crore are occasionally used in this book, but not the Indian notation. Figures of over 6 digits are normally expressed in the useful convention of *The Times*, 25,621,000 being written 25·62 m.; with some exceptions for the sake of emphasis.

16. The only Indian measure very likely to be met is the *maund* of 40 *seers*. There is still some local variation in the value of the maund, but the standard is 82·28 lbs avoirdupois. The unit of area is the *bigha*, but this varies so greatly that areas are practically always given in acres.

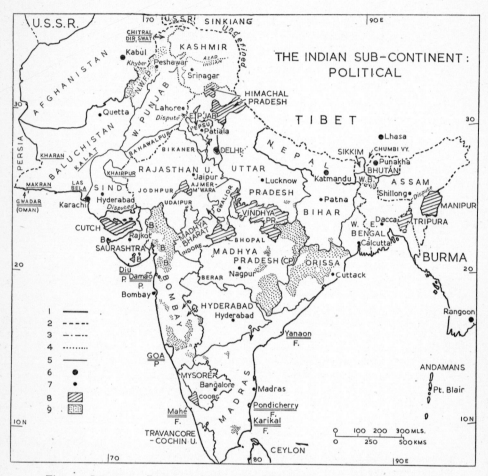

Fig. 1.—*INDIA* AND PAKISTAN: TERRITORIAL STRUCTURE. 1–5, boundaries: 1, international; 2, international, undemarcated; 3, Indo-Pakistani; 4, of Kashmir, and cease-fire line; 5, internal; 6, capitals of countries; 7, of States or provinces; 8, class "C" States (centrally administered); 9, unadministered tribal areas in NWFP (Pakistan) and merged states in India. Old states joining Pakistan underlined, surviving foreign holdings double-underlined (P, Portuguese, F, French).

ABBREVIATIONS

Standard abbreviations, such as ac. (acres), fn. (footnote), are not given here.

Bibliographical:
CGR   *Calcutta Geographical Review.*
Gaz.   *Gazetteer.*
GJ   *Geographical Journal.*
GR   *Geographical Review.*
HJ   *Himalayan Journal.*
IGJ   *Indian Geographical Journal.*
IR   *India Record.*
ISC   Indian Science Congress.
JMGA Journal of the Madras Geographical Association.
n.d.   no date, no data.
ND   New Delhi.
NY   New York.
OPIA   Oxford Pamphlets on Indian Affairs.
RCAI   (Report of) Royal Commission on Agriculture in India.
Mem. (Rec.) GSI Memoirs (Records) of the Geological Survey of India.
SOI (P) Survey of India (Pakistan).

Railway:
BG   broad gauge.
DT   double track.
ST   single track.
BB&CI Bombay, Baroda & Central India.
BNR   Bengal–Nagpur Rly.
GPI   Great Peninsular of India.
M&SM Madras & Southern Mahratta.
NWR   North-Western Rly.
SIR   South Indian Rly.

Other:
CP   Central Provinces (now Madhya Pradesh).
NWFP North-West Frontier Province.
UP   United Provinces (now Uttar Pradesh).
CBI   Central Board of Irrigation.
NSA   Net Sown Area.
TSA   Total Sown Area.

Dt   District.

INTRODUCTION

India as a Unit of Geographical Study

THE lands which until August 15th, 1947, formed the Indian Empire, and are now divided into the Republic of *India* and the Dominion of Pakistan, were never one country until welded together by British power. At long intervals, indeed, a single dynast secured loose but nearly universal sway; nor did the British themselves administer the sub-continent as a whole, large areas and populations remaining under vassal Indian rulers. But the British connection brought to most of India a common system of administration and law, railways, a common language for the intelligentsia, new forms of economic organisation, new ideals of polity. To the extent that these transcended the fantastically interlocking internal divisions, India became one country; in that lay the British achievement.

Persians and Greeks extended the name Sindhu—'the river'—from the Indus, to which it belonged, to cover such of the land as they knew; and hence the Muslim name Hindustan, properly applied to the area of most firmly based Islamic power in the north. Beyond the Narbada and the Chota Nagpur jungles, which lie across the root of the Peninsula, was the Deccan, the Sanskrit Dakshinapatha or 'Southland'; beyond the Kistna again Tamilnad lived its own life, inheriting the most ancient traditions of Hinduism, perhaps affiliated to the pre-Aryan Indus civilisation, itself contemporary with the early empires of Mesopotamia and Egypt. In Hindu literature the sub-continent as a whole is styled Bharata-Varsha, the land of the legendary King Bharata; but it seems safe to say that there was little feeling of identity over the whole country.

Yet for twenty-five centuries at least the entire area, a few margins and enclaves apart, has received the impress of the complex, hardly definable, but always easily recognisable culture of Hinduism, which indeed, with Buddhism, once stretched beyond the Wn borders to the Hindu Kush. Those regions where the cultural landscape displays few or none of the tokens of Hinduism are for the most part mountainous and arid, mountainous and cold, or mountainous and jungle-clad: the Islamic hill country of the Wn Borderlands, the Buddhist high Himalaya in the N, in the E the hills of the Burma border inhabited by a congeries of spirit-worshipping Mongoloid tribes.

Historically, then, it seems pointless to stress the facts that 'India' was rarely (if ever) a single political entity and that its peoples, in common speech at least, had no one name for the whole For at least two centuries there has been sufficient definiteness about the idea of 'India' to make the area so connoted a feasible unit of study; and despite its partition into two great states, 'India' remains valid as a geographical expression for all the lands between Cape Comorin and the towering peak K2, respectively in 8° and 36° N.

Isolation and Contact by Land and Sea

Geographically also India is an intelligible isolate. The huge salient of the Peninsula, the keystone of the arch of the Indian Ocean shores, strikes the eye at once; and on the inland borders are the ramparts and fosses of the giant ranges which in large measure wall off the sub-continent from the rest of Asia. These are, however, by no means complete barriers: in that role they are most important as insulating India from the Polar air masses which rule so much of the climate of central Asia, and so ensuring to the sub-continent a practically self-contained monsoon system of its own. But from a human point of view the values of the mountain wall are often determined as much by what lies beyond as by its own topography.

Behind the stupendous bulwarks of the Himalayas lie the vast and all but empty plateaus of wind-swept Tibet, home of a twisted in-bred culture peculiar to itself. Clearly the contacts on this side will be few: a little trade creeping painfully through the high passes—many higher than the loftiest Alpine peaks—and, far more important, seekers of many faiths. To the E the ranges of Assam are much lower, but rain-swept for half the year, and guarded by thick jungle: contact with the Irrawaddy trough is far easier by sea, and it was by sea that the germs of civilisation were brought from India to the ancestors of the Burmese, who had gradually filtered down from the marches of Tibet and China.[1] On the W the great arcs of Baluchistan, loop on loop of sharp arid ridges cleft by the narrowest and wildest of gorges, are backed by the burning deserts of Seistan; Makran in the S was once more fertile, and through it the Arabs passed to conquer Sind in the 8th century AD. But the great entry lies farther N, guarded on the Indian side by Peshawar and the Indus crossing at Attock.

Here the belt of mountains narrows to under 250 miles between Turkestan and the Punjab, and the core of the mountain zone, the Hindu Kush, is pierced by numerous passes, blocked by snow in winter but in other seasons practicable without great difficulty. Over this Oxus/Indus watershed lies the major passage through which people after people has pressed into the plains of Hindustan, whether impelled by desiccation in the steppe or by the political pressures of the constantly shifting fortunes

---

[1] There was some cultural influence of Mahayana Buddhism through Manipur in Burmese proto-dynastic times (*c.* 9th–11th centuries AD), but it amounted to little; see G. E. Harvey, *History of Burma* (1924), Ch. I.

of central Asian war. Of all these incursions, those of prime importance are the organised invasions of various Muslim leaders, culminating in the Mogul Babur's conquest of Hindustan in AD 1526; and the distant folk-wandering of the Aryan-speaking people of the steppes, who had entered certainly by 1000 BC and may have been in at the death of the Indus civilisation a few centuries earlier. Horsemen, meat-eaters, mighty drinkers, they contrast strongly with the dark-skinned 'snub-nosed Dasyus', the Dravidian heirs of Indus culture. From the millennial interaction of these two great groups is woven much of the rich tapestry of Hindu myth, and probably also of the darker fabric of caste.

On the whole, then, India is clearly marked off from the rest of Asia by a broad no-man's-land of mountains, whether jungle-covered, ice-bound, or desert; though obviously among the mountain-dwellers themselves no hard and fast line can be drawn dividing those solely or mainly Indian in history and cultural affinity from those solely Burmese, Tibetan, Afghan, or Iranian. The critical area is in the NW hills, and here we find in the past great empires slung across the mountains like saddle-bags, with bases of power on the plateau at Kabul or Ghazni or Kandahar, and also in the Punjab plains.

The significance of the mountain barrier, and especially of this great gateway, is clear enough, and more than amply stressed in the British literature, since the Afghan disaster of 1842 almost obsessed with 'the Frontier'. The question of maritime relations is more difficult, and indeed they are often slurred over by easy generalisations about harbourless coasts. But for small craft the W coast at least is not lacking in harbourage, nor should the delta creeks of the Bay of Bengal be overlooked: Portuguese keels were far from the first to plough the Indian seas. It is true that, until the coming of European seamen, no considerable power was founded *in* India from the sea; but some were founded *from* India.

An active trade linked the Graeco-Roman world with Ceylon and Sn India, and to Ceylon also came trading fleets from China. In the W —the significantly 'Arabian' Sea—the active agents were Arabs, who may indeed have been the intermediaries for the trade which indubitably existed between the Indus civilisation and Sumeria. From the later Middle Ages onwards not only commercial but also political contacts with SW Asia, and even NE Africa, were important: an 'African' party played a prominent role in the politics of the Muslim Deccani Kingdoms, and to this day a tiny exclave of Oman territory, the Gwadar Peninsula, survives on the Baluchistan coast.

To the E the initiative came from India. Hindu traders and colonisers took their civilisation by sea to the SE Asian lands, and in the first centuries of the Christian era history in Burma, Indonesia, and Indo-China begins with these pioneers. A few years before William the Conqueror impressed Europe with the organising ability displayed in crossing the English Channel, the fleets of the Chola Kingdom in Madras and the equally Indian Kingdom of Sailendra or Sri Vijaya in Sumatra entered upon a century-long struggle across 1000 miles of open ocean. So much for isolation by sea!

The actual node of shipping, however, was and is not in India itself but in Ceylon, and the full exploitation of the key position of India waited until the Indian Ocean was as it were subsumed into the World-Ocean by Vasco da Gama; a reminder of the importance of human and technological elements in locational relations. The reasons for the rapid supersession of Portuguese power by the less spectacular but more efficient Dutch and British are a matter of general European rather than Indian history. But it is worthy of note that the Portuguese, consciously pursuing a Crusade against the Moors, concentrated on the W coast, hemmed in by the Ghats and later by the Marathas, so that they had greater impediments to territorial acquisition than their rivals, even had the pattern of dominion laid down by their second and greatest Viceroy, Afonso de Albuquerque, called for landward expansion. Though Surat, seaward terminal of the great route to Hindustan, was bitterly contested by all three powers, the British were more active on the E coast: and when the Mogul Empire collapsed the land lay open before them.

Diversity and Unity in the Sub-Continent

The isolation of India, then, is but relative; yet isolation there is, and within the girdle of mountains and seas has developed the almost incredibly complex culture of Hinduism: not unaffected by outside influences, certainly, but, in so far as we can dimly descry the origins of some of its yet existing cults in the earliest Indus civilisation, native to this soil. Hinduism gives, or until very recently has given, a certain common tone to most of the sub-continent, but it contains within itself a vast range of diversities, not to mention the enclaves of primitive tribes and the fossils of ancient faiths, such as the Jains, the Parsees, the Jews of Cochin, the 'Syrian' Nestorian Christians whose traditions go back to St Thomas the Apostle. Confronting it, and ever drawing strength from its bases in arid Asia, is the great rival creed of Islam. For millennia the Peninsula has been virtually a cul-de-sac into which peoples and cultures have infiltrated or been driven, retaining much of their ancient rules of life and yet ceaselessly reacting upon one another, and, for the most part, if not welded together at least held together in the iron clasp of the caste system, a unique solution[2] to the problems of plural society, which are in essence resolved by recognising, canalising, and in fact sanctifying the plurality. It is no exaggeration to say that among the peoples of

[2] Unique at least in degree of development.

India are groups at all levels of economic development from that of jungle-folk barely out of the Stone Age to that of monopoly capitalism, with a tinge at least of state planning. The difficulties of building no more than two nations out of this heterogeneous human stuff are obvious.

This human heterogeneity is seconded by more purely geographical factors, which give some colour to the generally accepted description of India as a 'sub-continent'. The concept of a sub-continent is far from clear, but the term has its uses, especially now that '*India*' as the name of a state is the name of but a part of the old India, and it will often recur in the following pages. So far as it has a meaning distinct from the short-hand usage just mentioned, 'sub-continent' conveys an idea of size and numbers, and these India certainly has: the Empire covered an area of 1,581,410 square miles and the 1951 population of *India* and Pakistan together was about 438,000,000. This is possibly more than that of China, so that what Herodotus wrote may still be true: "of all the nations that we know, India has the largest population." This great population is of course unequally distributed: the sub-continent contains, in the deserts of Baluchistan and the Thar and in the high desolation of outer Kashmir, tens of thousands of square miles almost devoid of inhabitants, while in Bengal Dacca Division has twice the population of Belgium on an area one-third greater, and this with only four towns of any size and with practically no industry.

It is only to be expected that so vast an area, bordered by incomparably the most massive mountains of the world, intersected by rivers of the first rank, should contain very considerable physical diversity. In essence the sub-continent falls into only three macro-regions: the Extra-Peninsular Mountain Wall; the Indo-Gangetic Plains; the old Peninsular Block. But these contain a multitude of distinctive *pays* within themselves. Even in the broad alluvial monotony of the Indo-Gangetic Plains factors of climate, soil, aspect, and hydrology give rise to clear, if not clearly-marked, regional divisions; and although the transitions, like those in a suite of fossil echinoderms, are almost imperceptibly gradual, the extremes are extreme indeed: from the desert environs of Karachi to the almost unbelievably dense stipple of homesteads between Calcutta and Dacca.

Yet there is a sort of massive architectural simplicity in the pattern of the three great divisions: the old Peninsular platform, wrapped round by the great trough from the Indus to the Ganges Delta, a trough filled with the debris of the mountains which again enfold it on three sides. This is not accidental, since it is the rigid resistance of the old block which has moulded the frozen waves of the mountains, though their onset has in turn warped the root of the Peninsula to form the scarps and ranges from Gujarat to Chota Nagpur. It is aesthetically fitting that the historic heart of India should lie on the divide between Indus and Ganges, which is also the passage between the Aravallis and the Himalayas, perhaps the oldest surviving and the youngest ranges on the globe. This is the great node of Delhi, for over two thousand years, since the far-off legendary battles of the *Mahabharata* epic, the key to power in Hindustan.

Underlying the life of India is one great common factor, expressed it is true in divers modalities and degrees: the rhythm of the monsoonal year. The peoples of India are predominantly agrarian, and even most o the industrialisation of to-day, like the great dynastic achievements of the past, is after all built upon the ancient foundation, the toil of the dwellers in 650,000 villages. The tapestries of their lives are wrought in various colours—the lush green of the deltas, the drab khaki of the deserts—but nearly everywhere the fundamental lineaments of the pattern are similar, and are controlled by the seasonal cycle in which the great bulk of the rainfall comes in the warmer half of the year: this is so whether the annual fall is 450 ins. on the Assam Plateau, or under 15 in the Punjab, the only really large exception being the Tamilnad coast in the SE. There is also—away from mountains—a certain sameness in the régimes of temperature, annual or diurnal; but here, though we commonly think of India as 'tropical', it must be remembered that half of the area and over half of the population are N of the Tropic of Cancer. To a large extent, however, this is offset by the mountain wall forming an insulated compartment; and although in the Punjab night frosts bring the mean January temperatures down to the level of an English May, clear skies and intense insolation raise day temperatures to a tropical level, so that all beneath the Himalayas is essentially tropical, despite latitudes of 25–30°. Outside the Himalayas agriculture is nearly everywhere tropical in type, and it is rain, not temperature, that essentially decides what crops shall be grown.

Problems of Economy

Rain, or at least water: for of all the physical problems of India those of soil and water are supreme, and in many areas life depends on canal, tank, or well. Two-thirds of the people live directly from the soil, and the cultivated area is less than one acre to each dweller in the countryside. This simple ratio is the core-problem of *India* and Pakistan; the extension of agriculture (if that is possible to any large degree) and the security of much existing cultivation depends on a better use of the water which falls directly onto the face of the land and that which is locked in snow-fields or sealed within the earth. The improvement of the pitifully low yields from a cultivated area barely adequate to present population depends in part on better water-control, in part on better treatment of the soil itself, in general inadequately manured and exploited for generations without ceasing, so that in many areas it seems to have reached the irreducible minimum of fertility. Here the 'peculiar institution' of cow-sanctity, with consequent bovine over-population, raises issues special to *India*.

Apart from food the resources of the sub-continent, and especially *India*, are extensive indeed: a wide range of minerals, of fibres, of vegetable raw materials, of timber products; wealth almost incalculable in iron and manganese. Yet it may be questioned whether, in relation to numbers, even *India* is really a rich country, and Pakistan on the whole is definitely a poor one, as well as being split into two very ill-balanced sections 1000 miles apart. Power resources are as yet a weak link in the chain of industrialisation: the really good coalfields are concentrated in one corner of the Peninsula, and while the hydro-electric resources are great, many potential sites are ill-placed for development, and exploitation is rendered costly by the great seasonal variation in the flow of the rivers. And in the last resort a prosperous industry must depend on a prosperous countryside: the agrarian problem is central to all the problems of development. On all fronts, progress depends on real co-operation between *India* and Pakistan, not just the present avoidance of war, and on a refashioning of social relationships, which still too often violate human dignity and in the long run imperil social order and decency.

A vast tropical land, mountain-ringed, the immeasurably old plateaus and warped eroded hills of the Peninsula girdled by rain-swept deltas, arid wastes, and the long leagues of tillage in the Gangetic Plain; a landscape clad naturally by dense jungle or open thorny scrub, but profoundly changed by the toil of generations of peasants whose prosperity or dearth depends primarily on the secular rhythm of the monsoon; home of a diversity of cultures under the hegemony of Hinduism—one of the greatest, most individual, and most self-contained of human institutions; open on one side to wave after wave of peoples from the steppe, for a thousand years bringing with them a more rigid and more austere creed; subjugated by the alien strength, military and economic, of modern imperialism, and now newly free, though divided, to build if it can of its own strength and for its own purposes, to marry its ancient philosophies to new techniques: such is the skeleton of Indian geography which we shall endeavour to clothe with living flesh.

GENERAL BIBLIOGRAPHICAL NOTE

The amount of specifically geographical writing about India is small, though *Indian* and Pakistani geographers are rapidly increasing it. But the amount of literature with a geographical bearing is vast. It is inevitable that any book on India will owe much of its background to works not cited or even, perhaps, consciously remembered.

Specific Geographical Works

There is no modern geography in English, other than school texts, devoted to India alone. Sir T. H. Holdich's *India* (Regions of the World Series, 1904), is discussed in the Preface; his introductory sketch in *The Imperial Gazetteer of India*, Vol. I (1908) is clear and stimulating, as is Sir H. J. Mackinder's brilliant opening chapter in *The Cambridge History of India*, Vol. I (1922), though it contains a few questionable statements.

Reclus is also discussed in the Preface; other general works which deal at some length with India are:

> J. Sion, *Asie des Moussons* (*Géographie Universelle*, Tome IX, 2me Partie, 1929). Has the merits of the French school, chiefly a luminous ease in regional description, but weak on economic matters.
>
> L. W. Lyde, *The Continent of Asia* (1933, 1938). Stimulating, but erratic as to facts.
>
> L. D. Stamp, *Asia* (8th ed., 1950).
>
> G. B. Cressey, *Asia's Lands and Peoples* (1944).
>
> A. D. C. Peterson, *The Far East* (1949).

These contain clear and well-organised factual introductions, Cressey a useful bibliography.

In German N. Krebs' *Vorder Indien und Ceylon* (Stuttgart, 1939) is a good text, with admirable photographs and interesting maps; but there is a certain lack of systematic treatment, and the Himalayas and Baluchistan are omitted.

Periodicals

The leading geographical periodicals in India and Pakistan are:

> *The Indian Geographical Journal* (formerly *Journal of the Madras Geographical Association*);
>
> *The Calcutta Geographical Review* (now *Geographical Review of India*);
>
> *Pakistan Geographical Review* (formerly *Panjab Geographical Review*), Lahore;
>
> *The Geographer*, Aligarh (Muslim University);
>
> *The Bulletin of the Karachi Geographical Society.*

These are obtainable from the appropriate University Departments of Geography. They are uneven, but all contain some articles of value, and standards are improving.

There are many official and quasi-official publications, most of them issued from New Delhi or Karachi: *The Indian Forester, Indian Agriculture, Indian Trade and Industry, Indian Minerals, Pakistan Trade*, and so on. A useful weekly (in convenient quarto format) is *Indian Record*, published in London by the High Commissioner for India.

Of British journals, perhaps the most consistently useful are *The Asiatic Review* and *Eastern World*; *Asian Horizon* and *The Journal of the Royal Society of Arts* also contain good material, as does *Pacific Affairs* in USA.

Official Publications

Those which have some relevance are too numerous to be listed; but there are five fundamental sources which must be mentioned. These are:

(a) the Census Reports, both the general and the provincial volumes; the 1931 Census is especially valuable, far more so than 1941;

(b) the *Records* and *Memoirs* of the Geological Survey of India (Calcutta);

(c) the *Report of the Royal Commission on Agriculture in India* (1928);

(d) the *Gazetteers*;

(e) the *Settlement Reports*.

The *Gazetteers* are issued in three series: (i) the *Imperial Gazetteer of India* (Oxford, 1908)—four introductory volumes covering geography, history, ethnography, economics, etc.—containing much information of permanent value—followed by 20 volumes with alphabetical entries, and an atlas volume; (ii) the *Provincial Gazetteers* (1908–09), one or two volumes to each major political unit (including States and Agencies); (iii) the *District Gazetteers* (various dates). Despite their age the *Gazetteers* are still of much use, though the District volumes, on which the others are based, are very unequal indeed, excellent or the reverse according to the conscience, enthusiasm, and ability of the local District Commissioners. They have been at once a blessing and a curse to Indian geographers; no comparable area of the world has anything like this survey of all aspects of life, county by county as it were, on a standard pattern which facilitates reference—a Domesday and much more; but they have to some extent fostered a gazetteer habit of mind—enumerating rather than selective— and the repetition of stereotyped statements long out of date; and since "It's all in the *Gazetteer*" they have to some extent inhibited the essential geographical attitude of going to see for one's self. I have used the four general volumes and the Provincial series extensively, but not as a rule the District volumes, which are on a scale more appropriate to regional monograph work.

This remark applies also to the *Settlement Reports*, which are minute surveys of agricultural possibilities and development, made for the assessment of Land Revenue.

Maps

The most useful general series is the Survey of India "India and Adjacent Countries", 1/1,000,000, published in various styles at various dates. Larger-scale SOI maps are on 1/253,440, 1/126,720, and 1/63,360: the modern full-coloured sheets are beautiful and astonishingly accurate productions giving an immense amount of information on vegetation, land use, and the cultural landscape; most major regions of the sub-continent have at least fair coverage in this style, though for some areas there are only poor $\frac{1}{4}$-in. uncoloured maps with hachures and a generally archaic style. The SOI also publishes 'Guide Maps' to the major cities and hill stations on scale 1/21,120 or larger. Purchase of large-scale Indian maps, however, may be restricted.

The Geological Survey has a general map (rather out-of-date) on the 1/2,000,000 scale; $\frac{1}{4}$-in. maps will be found in the *Records* and *Memoirs* on selected areas.

Some special atlases and maps are referred to in the appropriate chapters. The best one-sheet map is Bartholomew's "India and Pakistan" (1/4,000,000); there appear to be some inaccuracies in the contours, but on this scale they are not very serious. Maps in official publications are in general very poor indeed; but the SOI has a political map, giving the new external and internal boundaries on the scale 1/4,435,200 (70 miles to the in.)—a very useful outline. The 1941 Census contained an extremely useful base-map on this scale, coloured to show forest, scrub, and irrigated areas, and with District boundaries—about the only improvement on the 1931 Census.

Background

Almost any book on India, with the exception of the 'Mystic East' and pornographic schools, and such oddly-balanced works as those of Katharine Mayo and Beverley Nichols, adds something to the general picture. Of travel books (excluding Himalayan travel), however, the only one of much value is Aldous Huxley's *Jesting Pilate* (1924), which contains excellent descriptive writing and acute social observation: the critical faculties displayed here seem to have become softened somewhat in the atmosphere of Hollywood Orientalism. Perhaps the most useful single volume on India before the recent upheavals is L. S. S. O'Malley (ed.), *Modern India and the West* (1941); slighter but excellent is G. T. Garratt's *An Indian Commentary* (1933). O'Malley's book and Sir W. Blunt (ed.), *Social Service in India* (1938), are more or less 'official' in outlook, with all that implies; extremist views which yet have much point are those of R. P. Dutt, *India To-day* (1940; Communist) and K. S. Shelvankar, *The Problem of India* (Penguins, 1940; left-wing Congress). On politics R. Coupland, *The Indian Problem* (1943) is again 'unofficial official'; the autobiographies of Gandhi and Nehru are essential to an understanding of the Indian scene, with W. C. Smith, *Modern Islam in India* (1947) for the Muslim side. G. T. Garratt (ed.), *The Legacy of India* (1937), is perhaps the best introduction to the vast intellectual and aesthetic history of India. More specialised works are cited in the appropriate Bibliographical Notes below.

The judicious student will not neglect more creative writers: *Kim* (despite its romantic view of the Raj) and *A Passage to India* retain their classic value as interpretations of India. More recent novelists of insight include Philip Woodruff (especially in *Call the Next Witness*), Christine Weston, Rumer Godden. Of Indian writers Mulk Raj Anand is best-known and perhaps over-estimated: his view of India suffers from being that of a political expatriate, though at his best he is very moving. The only Muslim novelist of note (in English) is Ahmed Ali, whose *Twilight in Delhi* is an exceedingly subtle study of a society in decay; to be confronted, perhaps, with Mohammed Iqbal's *Secrets of the Self*, great philosophical verse with a biting edge which makes Tagore's poems look as soft and spiritless as Ganges mud. Bharati Sarabhai welds together the hopes of young India and the harking-back to ancestral tradition in the rather Audenesque verse of her *The Well of the People*. For the Dravidian South the novels and tales of R. K. Narayan give the very feel of small-town life with delicate and rather wistful artistry.

PART I

THE LAND

CHAPTER I

STRUCTURE AND RELIEF

The Triple Tectonic Division

THE familiar division of India into three major geomorphological components—the ancient block of Peninsular India, the Himalayas and their associated young fold-mountains E and W, and the Indo-Gangetic Plains lying between these two—is generally valid. The physiographic contrasts between these macro-regions are most striking; broadly speaking the Peninsula is dominated by an open senile topography, witness to vast periods of geological quiescence, while the Himalayas display the most youthful and highly differentiated relief on the face of the earth, and the Indo-Gangetic Plains present a monotonous aggradational surface of great extent. Nevertheless the Peninsula has its youthful, or rather rejuvenated, landforms and the Himalayas their worn-down erosion surfaces, and structurally also the division is not entirely clear-cut. The Peninsula has not been entirely immune from the impulses of the great Tertiary orogeny, while conversely concealed extensions of the old block have exerted an important influence on the direction of folding, on both local and regional scales, in the NW and probably also in the NE Himalaya. Again, despite the sharpness (on the map) of the Nn border of the Indo-Gangetic Plains, the outermost Himalayan foothills—the Siwaliks—represent a late buckling of the erosion products of the mountains themselves, deposits not essentially different from some of those now forming. The three great divisions are therefore related in a rather more intimate way than is implied by the mere statement that the Himalayan folding is the resultant of the relative moving together of the old blocks of Gondwanaland, of which Peninsular India is a part, and Angaraland, the core of the Siberian table.

I. THE PENINSULA

Geology (Figs. 2–4)

The Nn boundary of the Peninsular block may be taken as an irregular line running from Cutch along the Wn flank of the Aravalli Range to the neighbourhood of Delhi, and thence roughly parallel to the Jumna and the Ganges as far as the Rajmahal Hills and the Ganges Delta. Embayments of the Indo-Gangetic alluvium naturally penetrate S of this line, which in detail is very ragged in the W, in sharp contrast to the long smooth line of the Himalayan front; and the ancient Peninsular rocks

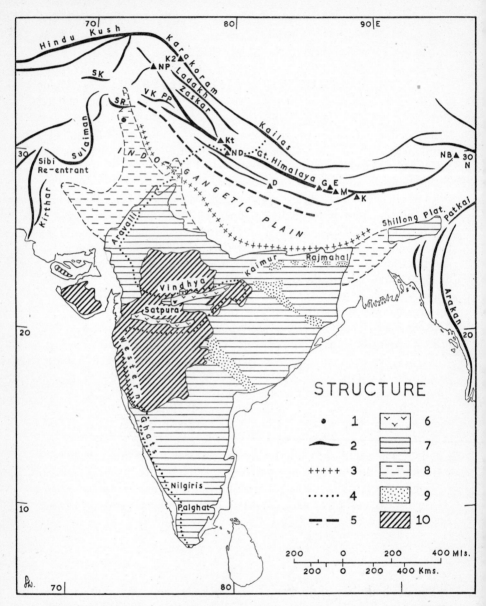

Fig. 2.—STRUCTURAL OUTLINES. 1, most Nly Aravalli outcrops; 2, trend of main
Tertiary fold ranges; 3, boundary of Indo-Gangetic trough (Wadia); 4, Bay of Bengal/
Arabian Sea watershed; 5, Siwalik Hills; 6, Narbada and Tapti troughs; 7, Peninsular
Block; 8, concealed extensions of 7; 9, Gondwana troughs; 10, Deccan Lavas. SK,
Safed Koh; SR, Salt Range; PP, Pir Panjal; VK, Vale of Kashmir. Peaks not on Fig. 5:
G, Gaurisankar; Kt, Kamet; M, Makalu.

are relatively close to the surface at least in the gap between the Rajmahal Hills and the Shillong Plateau (an outlying fragment of the Peninsular block), and in a Nly wedge indicated by the Kirana Hills in the Punjab (Figs. 2, 6).

The Peninsula is essentially formed by a great complex of very ancient gneisses and granites, which form the surface over more than half its area. The relations of this complex with the oldest metamorphosed sedimentary rocks are not clear; the old view that the gneisses formed a floor on which the sedimentaries were deposited has been considerably modified, as it is now known that much of the gneiss is intrusive into the Dharwar rocks. But at all events the Peninsula has been a great land-mass from very early times and, except for the Deccan Lavas, rocks younger than pre-Cambrian have a relatively small extension in synclinal and faulted troughs and basins.

The Peninsular formations, with their approximate ages, are:

Coastal Alluvium, and that of Narbada and Tapti basins
Coastal Tertiaries
Deccan Lavas . . . late Cretaceous–? early Tertiary
Coastal Cretaceous and Jurassic
Upper Gondwana . . Jurassic
Middle Gondwana . . Triassic
Lower Gondwana . . Permian to Carboniferous
Vindhyan . . . Cambrian, Torridonian, Algonkian
Cuddapah and Delhi . Algonkian
Dharwar and Aravalli . Huronian
Gneisses and Granites . Lewisian (at least in part)[1]

The *Dharwar* and *Aravalli* formations "possess the most diverse lithological characters, being a complex of all kinds of rocks—plastic sediments, chemically precipitated rocks, volcanic and plutonic rocks—all of which generally show an intense degree of metamorphism".[2] The chief occurrences are in a series of narrow belts, the troughs of tight-packed synclines, in the Mysore-Dharwar-Bellary area; flanking the Chota Nagpur Plateau on the N and S, and in patches Wwds as far as Nagpur city; and in the Aravallis. Those of the Bihar-Orissa area are of great economic importance as they contain the most valuable iron ores of India. The Aravalli Range was probably originally formed in the close of Dharwar times, and has since been peneplaned and again uplifted in the Cambrian, and possibly again before the Permo-Carboniferous

[1] The Indian formations are sometimes classified in four great groups—Archaean (including the Dharwars and Aravallis), Purana (Cuddapah and Vindhyan), Dravidian (Upper Vindhyan), and Aryan (Gondwana upwards); but these terms are not necessary to our purpose and will not be used.
[2] D. N. Wadia, *Geology of India* (2nd ed., 1939), 70.

glaciation; it may perhaps claim to be the oldest mountain system, still recognisable as such by its relief, on the earth's surface.

The earth-movements responsible for the folding of the Aravallis and other Dharwarian areas were succeeded by a prolonged period of erosion and subsidence—the Eparchaean interval, which is thought to have been as long as the total of the succeeding periods. A great unconformity separates the Dharwarian from the 20,000 ft of slates, quartzites, and limestones which form the marine *Cuddapah* system, deposited presumably in great synclinal basins. The Cuddapah rocks are preserved mainly in a big belt on the E of the Deccan, between the Kistna and Penner Rivers, and in the valley of the upper Mahanadi; except in the

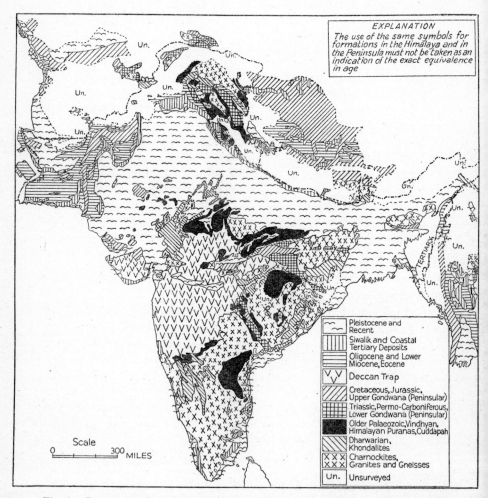

EXPLANATION
The use of the same symbols for formations in the Himalaya and in the Peninsula must not be taken as an indication of the exact equivalence in age

Pleistocene and Recent
Siwalik and Coastal Tertiary Deposits
Oligocene and Lower Miocene, Eocene
Deccan Trap
Cretaceous, Jurassic, Upper Gondwana (Peninsular)
Triassic, Permo-Carboniferous, Lower Gondwana (Peninsular)
Older Palaeozoic, Vindhyan, Himalayan Puranas, Cuddapah
Dharwarian, Khondalites
Charnockites, Granites and Gneisses
Un.   Unsurveyed

Scale
0   300 MILES

Fig. 3.—GEOLOGICAL OUTLINES; after D. N. Wadia; courtesy *Chambers's Encyclopædia*.

long border-ridges of the Nallamalai and Velikonda Hills they are little disturbed. The Delhi quartzites occur in narrow tightly-packed belts in the centre of the great Aravalli synclinorium; they form the rocky echelonned ridges, low but persistent, which terminate in the famous Ridge at Delhi.

Vindhyan rocks overlie the Cuddapahs in the lowest part of the Kistna-Penner trough, but their main occurrence is in a belt along the Nn flank of the Peninsula from the Chambal to the Son, broken by the expanse of ancient Bundelkhand Gneiss around Jhansi; W of the Aravallis patches of lavas of Lower Vindhyan age are found around Jodhpur. In the lower part of the system marine shales, limestones, and sandstones are found, but above these are great thicknesses of nearly horizontal fluviatile and estuarine sandstones, including the famous red sandstone used for many of the best Mogul buildings. In general the Vindhyans are little disturbed or metamorphosed, except in the isolated patches W of the Aravallis. The most striking feature formed by the Vindhyan rocks is the scarp which marks the Nn flank of the Narbada and Son Valleys; in the W this is largely formed of Deccan Lavas, but Vindhyan rocks occur between Bhopal and Itarsi and dominate farther E in the remarkably even and continuous scarp of the Kaimur Hills, overlooking the Son.[3]

The *Gondwanas* consist of great thicknesses of sandstones with some shales and clays; they are of continental origin, fluviatile and lacustrine deposits laid down in great troughs which were probably formed on the old plateau-surface by tensional faults and consequent subsidence.[4] They show a striking parallelism to sequences of similar age in South Africa, Australia, and South America, notably in the presence of glacial basal conglomerates (in India probably formed by glaciers radiating from the Aravallis) and the famous *Glossopteris* flora; this parallelism is of fundamental significance in discussions of continental drift and cognate subjects. More immediately important, perhaps, is the fact that nearly all India's coal comes from Gondwana formations, nearly 90% of it from the Damodar Valley on the flanks of the Chota Nagpur Plateau. More or less continuous belts of Gondwana rocks are found along the lower Penganga and Godavari Rivers, and between the Mahanadi and the Brahmani from Talchir (on the lower Brahmani) to the headstreams of the Narbada and the Son, while the Damodar Valley is marked by a string of outcrops.

[3] The geographical and geological usages of the word Vindhyan must be distinguished. The Vindhyan *Hills* are taken as extending roughly from 75 to 78° E, and are mostly Deccan Lavas; Ewds the same general line is continued by the Bhanrer and Kaimur Hills, which are formed of Vindhyan *rocks*. Vindhyan rocks are also found e.g. in the Bhima Valley about half-way between Sholapur and Raichur and probably underlie much of the Deccan Lava country.

[4] There is an isolated occurrence of marine Permo-Carboniferous limestone at Umaria (Vindhya Pradesh), "a solitary record of an evanescent transgression of the sea-waters into the heart of the Peninsula" (Wadia, 164).

This disposition strongly suggests that these rivers, in contrast to the Narbada and the Tapti, occupy ancient structural troughs.

The Deccan Lavas (styled Deccan Traps in the older literature) are generally from 2000 to 5000 ft thick and reach a maximum of 10,000 ft; they cover some 200,000 sq mls with their mesa-like terrain. These practically horizontal and remarkably homogeneous basalts were probably extruded from fissures towards the end of the Cretaceous, though a flora which seems to be of early Eocene age is found between some of the flows. The lavas were poured out onto a land surface which had already attained an advanced stage of maturity, and form a most striking feature in the geomorphology of the Peninsula, with an obvious family likeness, seized upon by Joly, to the great basaltic flows of the Colombia Plateau and of Sn Brazil.

Finally, in Cutch and Kathiawar and along the SE coast, patches of marine Jurassic, Cretaceous, and Tertiary rocks bear witness to marginal transgressions of the sea.

Structural History

After the deposition of the earlier Peninsular sedimentaries the first recognisable event seems to be the folding of the Aravallis in the earlier Vindhyan period. The upper Vindhyan sandstones were probably formed of debris from these mountains, then at their maximum elevation. It would seem also that the more disturbed portions of the En Hills (Nallamalai and Velikonda Ranges) were elevated at the same time as this Vindhyan Aravalli folding. The Aravallis then suffered peneplanation, and were rejuvenated at the beginning of Gondwana times.

After this little or no compressional orogenic activity took place in the Peninsula, though other movements of a less tangential nature have had important effects, and peneplanation has probably been followed more than once by rejuvenation. Thus Wadia regards the highlands of Ceylon, and the Palni and Nilgiri Hills, not as merely "the residual stumps of an eroded plateau" but as great horsts produced by thermal expansion of the sima,[5] uplift taking place in post-Jurassic and in late Tertiary times. These periods are significantly close to those of intense mountain-building activity in the Himalayas, the Deccan Lava extrusions, and possibly the subsidence of the Arabian Sea area to form the Wn Ghats.

These latter are the most striking events in the later history of the Peninsula. The date of origin of the Ghats is one of the major unresolved problems of Indian geology. There is palaeontological evidence for the existence until late Jurassic times of a landbridge (Gondwanaland) separating the area N of the Arabian Sea from a sea which connected S Africa and Madagascar with the E coast of India. The long straight

[5] See Wadia's 1943 paper listed in Bibliographical Note.

edge of the Ghats, developed on practically horizontal Deccan Lavas and on ancient gneisses, itself strongly suggests faulting and subsidence on a very large scale; the Deccan Lavas extend down to at least 2000 ft below sea-level. The view that the Ghats have been formed by the subsidence of a land-mass to the W seems to be supported by the absence of any evidence for a simple Ewds tilting of the whole block. The main lines of the well-developed river-pattern are apparently of great age and carry no suggestion (such as a series of gaps through an old more or less central watershed) of the reversal or diversion of an original W-flowing drainage. The Palghat Gap hardly throws any light on the problem: it has been regarded as the ancient valley of a river flowing either from the E or, before the assumed Arabian Sea subsidence, from the W. Questions of isostasy and continental drift are obviously involved; it is difficult to see how, on the generally accepted view of isostasy, foundering on this scale could take place in a relatively immobile sector of the earth's crust; and on the other hand an appeal to splitting and drift can hardly take into account the relative youth of the phenomenon.

This youthfulness is indicated by the absence of river-capture on any significant scale, except in the S in the valleys of the Kalinadi, Gangavali-Bedti, and Sharavati: these are developed on the gneisses. The wide mature, or even senile, valleys of the E-flowing rivers are on the whole graded almost to their heads, nearly in sight of the Arabian Sea; the contrast with the youthful gorge-like forms of the W-flowing streams is very striking. These latter have only 50 miles or less in which to fall 2000 ft or more to base-level, as against 300–600 miles (straight-line distance) for those flowing to the Bay of Bengal; and they are further favoured by a rainfall of 80–100 ins. or more, as against 25–40 ins. in the lee of the Ghats. Yet, on the Deccan Lavas at least, there has not apparently been time for large-scale capture, and the deep canyons suggest that the streams are still eroding vertically faster than they cut back the valley-sides. It seems unlikely, therefore, that the origin of the Arabian Sea could be much before the Pliocene, possibly as late as early Pleistocene.

On the E coast the lithology and stratigraphy of the marine deposits seem to indicate that since the latter part of the Palaeozoic the general run of the coastline has never been very far, one way or the other, from its present position.

The anomalous E-W direction of the Narbada and Tapti Rivers is another problem. The most favoured explanation is that they occupy two rifts, formed by sag-faulting in the N of the Peninsula at the time of stress implied by the Himalayan folding. The long scarps of the Vindhya/Kaimur and Satpura/Mahadeo Hills and the trend of the S coast of Kathiawar might be taken as supporting this view.

Mention should be made of the considerable deposits of alluvium in

the Narbada and Tapti troughs (Fig. 4). In the former at least they are
500 ft or more thick, and occupy a definite rock-basin, another indication
of faulting. The straightness and relative steepness (with two waterfalls)
of the lower 300 miles of the Narbada, from Handia to the sea, indicates
a recent origin; below Handia the fall is 900 ft in 300 miles, above only
450 ft in 300 miles. Possibly the Narbada once flowed out by the gap
between Burhanpur and Khandwa, into the present lower Tapti. Warping
on either side of a line approximately NNE/SSW between Handia and
Paithan (on the upper Godavari) would probably account for interruptions
of profile producing this aggradation, as Vredenburg suggests, and this

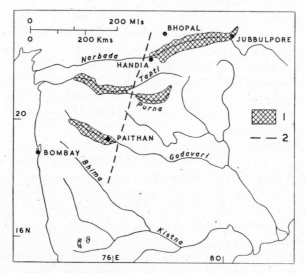

Fig. 4.—DECCAN ALLUVIUM. 1, alluvial basins; 2, line of
probable warp. After E. Vredenburg, courtesy GSI.

might in turn be connected with the presumed faulting of the Wn Ghats.
The irregularities are slight, but in view of the high degree of grading shown
by the major Peninsular rivers they are significant, even though the warping
is hardly strong enough to be detectable in the massive layers of the
Deccan Lavas. "All these changes agree in showing that a very extensive,
though moderate, disturbance has affected the Peninsula at a late period
previous to recent times." The Marble Rocks falls on the upper Narbada,
near Jubbulpore, may also be due to recent movement, or alternatively
to superimposition.

It should be noted also that there are numerous falls where rivers
leave the plateau, especially in the higher S, and even the greater rivers
cut through the En Hills in relatively constricted valleys with rapids.
Together with raised beaches at 100–150 ft and the general character

of the outer En lowland (a raised marine erosion surface) these features point to a relatively recent negative movement of considerable extent. At one time the Wn Ghats were even regarded as due to recent elevation of a cliffed coast; the lowland beneath them is undulating, but Deccan Lavas occur at and below sea-level and the steep sides of some of the hills, rising sharply from a bevelled floor of solid rock, certainly look like marine erosion forms. But the suggestion raises far more difficulties than it avoids: apart from the hydrographic problems of the crest the general effect of the great scarps and the lowland hardly agrees with that to be expected from wave action, though local features may be due to it. Detailed geomorphological studies are lacking, and it is perhaps unfortunate that the spectacular attractions of the Himalayas have led to many Peninsular problems being left to the future agenda of Indian geology.

Summing up, the main elements of Peninsular geomorphology are the great plateau of granite and gneiss (with higher bosses such as the Nilgiris) occupying nearly all the S and E; the mesa-like country of the Deccan Lavas in the W centre; the old shallow troughs of the Kistna, Godavari, and Mahanadi Valleys; the much-worn Aravalli Range; and the Vindhyan scarplands of the N, with the Narbada-Son and Tapti troughs or rifts. Even this brief and incomplete generalisation indicates that Peninsular India has much more geomorphological variety than is often credited to it. The general aspect, however, is one of senility or very advanced maturity, except along the escarpment of the Wn Ghats and in a few hillier areas; but there are erosion surfaces of more than one cycle, and evidences of important and relatively recent changes of level, mostly negative.[6] In many places the current cycle is only beginning to attack earlier peneplanation surfaces.

Present Relief

The Peninsula thus consists of a great tabular block with a general slope to the E, whether it has been tilted or is simply the remnant of a land-mass the Wn half of which has subsided to form the Arabian Sea. Its bold outlines are less simple on the N, owing to the very ancient Aravalli folding and the strain on the block of the tangential forces which produced the Himalayas.

The Aravallis themselves are now no more than the stumps of a once lofty range: they reach their maximum height at Mount Abu (5650 ft) in the SW, sink to low hills in the Jodhpur-Jaipur saddle, and rise again to the NE before petering out in a series of little echelonned ridges, half buried in the Indo-Gangetic alluvium and reaching as far as the Delhi Ridge. Wn Rajputana is a debateable land, peneplaned and largely

---

[6] Mostly, but not entirely, as is shown e.g. by the presence of a submerged forest at Bombay and of lignite 240 ft below ground-level at Pondicherry.

covered by the dunes of the Thar Desert but with little hills of Vindhyan lavas and of marine Jurassic and Tertiary beds. E of the Aravallis, the lower Chambal may be regarded as occupying a strike valley in the Vindhyan scarplands, but above Kotah it is probably superimposed, cutting across the scarps, and its uppermost course is more nearly consequent on the Deccan Lavas. The Chambal and Betwa Valleys are of great human and historical importance, providing a broad belt of relatively favourable country (Malwa) between the arid Aravallis and the scarp-rimmed Bundelkhand Gneiss terrain around Jhansi; the Malwa scarps of Vindhyan rocks face S and E at heights of 1500–1800 ft. The Vindhya (Deccan Lava) and Kaimur (Vindhyan sandstone) Hills form a great scarp overlooking the Narbada Valley and that of the subsequent Son; their drainage is practically all Nwds, to the Jumna and the Ganges, and the Narbada and the Son have no important N-bank tributaries. There is definite evidence in the Son Valley of a drainage pattern superimposed from a higher plateau level, the main outlines of which, however, were not dissimilar from those which now exist. This Vindhya-Kaimur scarp exceeds 2000 ft in only a few places but is remarkably regular and free from gaps.

Beyond the Son the gneissic plateau of Chota Nagpur reaches 3500 ft in the Hazaribagh Range, but most of it (the Ranchi Plateau) is a peneplane at rather more than 2000 ft with a few higher monadnocks. The Peninsula itself may be said to terminate in the Rajmahal Hills (largely basalts of Gondwana age), but it is probable that a sill of old rock relatively near the surface of the Gangetic alluvium connects it with the outlying Shillong Plateau. S of the Rajmahal Hills lie the economically very important coal-bearing Gondwana basins of the Damodar Valley, with sandstone ridges striking E/W in a synclinal trough; and S of the Ranchi Plateau is a corridor at just over 1000 ft leading from the Ganges Delta to the Brahmani and Mahanadi basins, between the plateau and the broken forested hills of Orissa—the most Nly section of the En Hills at 3000–3800 ft.

Between the Narbada and the Tapti lie the Satpura/Mahadeo Hills; there are some suggestions of folding and upheaval, so that they may represent an ancient tectonic range, but their present aspect is that of scarped blocks (on the whole steeper towards the Tapti), largely covered with Deccan Lavas but with some inliers of gneissic plateau country. From their En continuation in the Amarkantak Plateau (Maikal Hills), a mixed Deccan Lava and gneissic upland, radiate the headwaters of the Narbada, Son, and Mahanadi, as well as those of the Wainganga, an important tributary of the Godavari. The Burhanpur-Khandwa gap, possibly once occupied by the Narbada, and the saddle used by the railway between Nagpur and Jubbulpore should be noted.

All this Nn section of the Peninsula (except for the NE/SW trending Aravalli-lower Chambal area) is dominated by strong E/W trends (with some NE-SW strikes, e.g. in the Maikal and Hazaribagh Hills), themselves probably influenced by buckling and sagging of the Nn flanks of the old block under the stress of the Himalayan orogeny.

To the W, Kathiawar is mainly Deccan Lava, with a fringe of marine Jurassic and Tertiary rocks, which predominate in Cutch: these two areas form a country of small dissected plateaus and scarplands, linked to the Peninsula by the great alluvial plain of Gujarat. The subsidence which has formed the salt-marshes and bare mud-flats of the Rann is in part of very recent date, the Cutch earthquake of 1819 being responsible for much of the flooding.

S of the Tapti estuary the Wn Ghats (also known as the Sahyadri Range[7]) begin, and almost at once reach a height of 3000–4000 ft; this, with many interruptions but few of much significance, they retain for some 250–300 miles, with some culminations of 4500–5000 ft. There is a very steep and wildly dissected fall to the undulating and narrow coastal lowland of the Konkan, but once over the crest the broad mature or even senile valleys of the plateau begin almost immediately. The Deccan Lavas form the Ghats to a little N of Goa, and here the steep seaward face is like a great wall, dissected however by deep canyon-like valleys into spectacular mesas, buttes, and pinnacles. S of Goa the old gneisses and granites come in, and here more rounded forms prevail; for about 200 miles the crest sinks below 3000 ft (it is in this area that the only significant river-capture has taken place), but then rises again to the great gneissic boss of the Nilgiri Hills (summit 8760 ft). This culmination is essentially a much-worn massif, elevated and re-dissected, so that it forms bold swelling hills and downlands, with very steep drops on all sides. Swds, across the Palghat Gap, the wilder and more forested Cardamom, Anaimalai, and Palni Hills are similar in origin; Anaimudi in the Anaimalais is the highest point in the Peninsula, 8840 ft. The falls on the rejuvenated rivers of these Sn massifs are among the most important sources of hydro-electric power in India.

The Palghat Gap is apparently of tectonic origin; its summit is a

---

[7] "Sahyadri Range" has the disadvantage of attaching the idea of a mountain range to what is really only the crest of a scarp. The term Wn Ghats is of all but universal use, and this is one of those cases, not a few, in which an attempt to assert a more "correct" nomenclature leads only to confusion—particularly as the name Sahyadriparvat is sometimes given to the Ajanta Hills. The term 'Ghat' "really implies a place of access. The Western Ghats were the places at which roads from the westward led up to the plateau . . . the 'Eastern Ghats' are a figment of the imagination, the name belonging to the roads that lead to the Mysore plateau having been loosely applied to sundry groups of hills that have no connection . . . with each other." (W. T. Blanford on Oldham's paper, GJ III (1894), 193.) But the primary idea seems to be that of a step or terrace, and it is thus particularly appropriate to the mesa-like Deccan Lava topography of the Wn Ghats, though less so to the En.

broad tableland not much over 1000 ft. Except for the little Shencottah gap right in the S (where the width of the Peninsula is too restricted for sea-to-sea communication to be of much importance) this is the only really easy passage across the Ghats from the Tapti to Cape Comorin, some 880 miles. The Malabar coastal lowland W of Palghat widens out and has more definitely the aspect of a raised sea-floor than has the Konkan; it is fringed by a long series of lagoons and bars.

The "Eastern Ghats" are much less strongly marked than the Wn; indeed for about 100 miles between the Godavari and the Kistna they practically disappear. There is no structural continuity: dissected massifs of some of the older Peninsular rocks in the N; relics of ancient mountains such as the Nallamalais, Velikondas, and Palkondas in the centre (S of the Kistna); gneissic bosses, the Shevaroys, Pachamalais, and so on in the S. In view of this heterogeneity the term "Eastern Ghats" is avoided in this book, being replaced by 'Eastern Hills' for the Nn, 'Cuddapah Ranges' for the central, and 'Tamilnad Hills' for the Sn groups; if less handy than the old name, this is also less misleading. Except in the wild forested country of the Orissa hinterland—the most jungly and backward part of *India*—these border groups rarely exceed 3000 ft, but are often very difficult dissected country.

The coastal plain of Coromandel and the Circars is a typical uplifted plain of marine erosion, with the usual inland-facing cuestas, isolated granite or gneiss hills (old offshore islands), and coastal lagoons. At the mouths of greater rivers these features are masked by deltaic formations.

Within the frame of the En Hills, the Cuddapahs, the Wn Ghats, and the Satpura/Maikal/Hazaribagh Hills lies the true Deccan. In the N the main Bombay–Calcutta railway, once it has climbed over the Ghats into the Tapti Valley, meets no serious obstacles: the watersheds between the upper Tapti, Godavari, and Mahanadi Valleys are often mere swells, with perhaps some small serrated relict hills on the crest. In the NW, the most typical Deccan Lava country, such "ranges" as the Ajanta and Balaghat Hills are no more than maturely-dissected flat-topped ridges, often enough, it is true, with steep flanks. But so geometrical are the lines of the lava-flows that the landscape looks like nothing so much as an over-simplified block diagram. On much of the vast expanse of gneiss in the E and S the aspect is even more monotonous: great, often arid, plains separated by thin worn-down ridges, the disjointed vertebrae of watersheds. In places bosses or dykes of harder granite, gneiss, or quartzite give a more rugged relief, low but very steep and fantastically cragged tors and serrated ridges; in Mysore and the Sn Mahratta country the Dharwar quartzites, preserved in narrow synclines, crop out in belts of steep-sided little hills. But in comparison with the vast monotonous plains, these more accidented areas are but small.

The Peninsular rivers find their way from these broad well-graded upper basins to the sea by relatively narrow corridors through the En Hills; the correspondence of the lower Godavari and the gap shared by the Mahanadi and Brahmani with belts of Gondwana rocks has been noted as suggesting a tectonic trough origin. The passage is generally marked by rapids. It is noteworthy that none of these rivers is directly followed by an important route to gain access to the plateau; thus the main railway from Madras to Bombay crosses the En Hills diagonally, by a strike corridor between the Velikondas and the Palkondas, reaching the Penner River above the point at which it begins to break through these ranges.

II. THE HIMALAYAN OROGENY (Figs. 5–8)

Introductory

The vast scale of the mountains which form the continental borders of India may be appreciated from Fig. 4, from which it will be seen that the main Himalaya alone, which stretches over 22° of longitude (some 1500 miles) between the Indus and the Brahmaputra, could be wrapped round the Alps. Of the 94 Asiatic peaks which exceed 24,000 ft all but two are in the Himalaya and the Karakoram; and no other continent has peaks of this height.

The unravelling of Himalayan structure is only beginning, but already great nappes, less complicated perhaps than those of the Alps but much thicker and deeper-rooted, have been traced. Much of the area is still very imperfectly known geologically, especially in the E, and many phases of the history are still very controversial. There has of course been intense metamorphism and in many cases no dating of the rocks is as yet possible: "a large number of apparently independent rock groups have been established, each under a purely local name, thus giving rise to a confusing variety of sub-divisions, no two of which can be definitely correlated." In some parts uplift has been considerable since the mid-Pleistocene, in others are great stretches of high but subdued topography, the relics of old peneplains; elsewhere the deepest gorges on earth alternate with the terraces of old lakes and the undulating hills of inter-mont basins. It is impossible in the space available to give a comprehensive account of the geological and geomorphological complexities; but this is perhaps the less serious in that the Himalayas have attracted a disproportionate amount of attention and given rise to a voluminous and rapidly growing literature.

During Mesozoic times the Himalayan area was occupied by the great geosynclinal Tethys Sea; there is a marked contrast in facies between the sediments of the Tibetan area, laid down in this sea, and the rocks of the Himalayan core, which include ancient and relatively recent crystalline intrusives and sediments allied to those of the Peninsula. The orogenic activity which transformed the Tethys geosyncline appears to have taken place in three main phases:

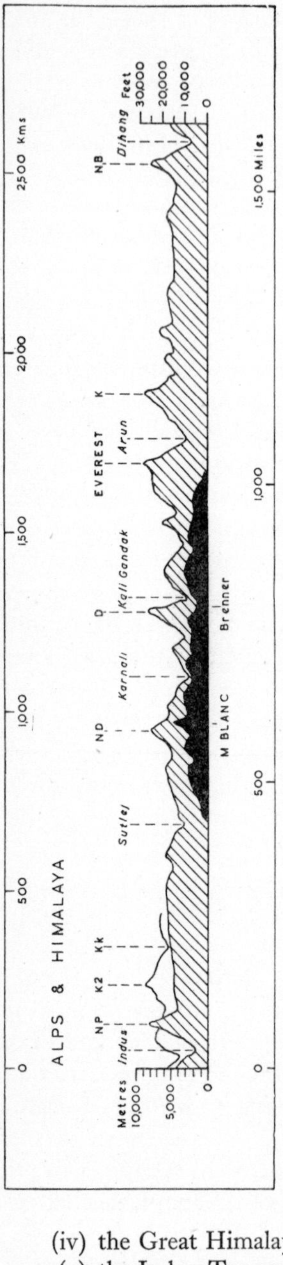

Fig. 5.—ALPS AND HIMALAYAS. Vertical exaggeration about 20 times. K2, 28,250 ft; Kk, Karakoram Pass, 18,550; NP, Nanga Parbat, 26,660; ND, Nanda Devi, 25,645; D, Dhaulagiri, 26,795; Everest, 29,141; K, Kangchenjunga, 28,146; NB, Namcha Barwa, 25,445. Cf. Mt Blanc, 15,780 ft; Matterhorn, 15,217; St Gotthard Pass, 6930; Brenner Pass, 4495.

(i) the elevation of the central axis of ancient crystalline and sedimentary rocks in Oligocene times; during this phase the important Nummulitic limestones were deposited in a series of basins, especially in Ladakh;

(ii) a Miocene movement, which folded the Murree sediments of the Potwar basin;

(iii) a post-Pliocene phase, which affected the Mio-Pleistocene Siwalik sediments and which, apparently, has not yet entirely ceased.

Initial disturbances probably preceded the first of these, and the Karakoram region, which has no marine Tertiary, may have been uplifted in the Cretaceous; there has been a definite Swd shift of orogenic activity, welding successive belts of geosynclinal sediments onto the Central Asiatic core. There is naturally a considerable variety of structures and of types of orogenesis.

Geographically the Himalayas have been divided into five longitudinal zones:

(i) the outer zone of the Siwalik Hills and the *Duns* or longitudinal valleys behind them;

(ii) the Lesser Himalaya, including a great number of minor ranges at 6000–10,000 ft;

(iii) the zone of spurs from the main ranges, presenting the aspect of a very highly dissected peneplain at about 15,000 ft;

(iv) the Great Himalaya itself, with many peaks of over 20,000 ft;

(v) the Indus-Tsangpo furrow at about 12,000–14,000 ft; this is succeeded by the old worn-down mountains of the edge of the Tibetan Plateau, up to 19,000 ft high.

To the N again are the Karakoram-Muztagh Ranges, which connect the Himalaya via the great Pamir knot with the Kun Lun and other ranges on the N of the Tibetan median mass.

The geological and tectonic zoning does not quite correspond to this purely topographical division. There are of course great local variations, but in general the old Gondwana foreland (masked by the Tertiary Murree and Siwalik sediments) is succeeded by an autochthonous fold zone—"recumbent folds of the Eocene with cores of Carbon-Trias rocks"; and this again by a nappe zone which includes the Purana slates of Hazara and the Kashmir basin; the axial crystallines, "a geanticline within a geosyncline", consisting of very ancient gneisses with many later gneiss and granite intrusions; and finally by fossiliferous Tethys or Tibetan sediments, ranging from Cambrian to Tertiary in age.

The direction of folding in the Central Asian mountain-masses is generally from N to S, but this is locally reversed in the Pamir area. This is probably connected with the presumed Nly extension of the old Peninsular block, which also accounts for the anomalous N/S trend of the Sulaiman and Kirthar Ranges, an exception to the general E/W run of Central Asia. This is a useful reminder of the intimate connection between the old Gondwana foreland and the Tertiary folding, of which more later.

The Himalayas: Lay-out

The following concise account of the main components of the mountain system is not intended as a detailed regional description but simply as a framework for reference.

From the great Pamir complex the ranges fan out E and W in two vast virgations: the Tien Shan-Kun Lun-Karakoram and the Alai-Hindu Kush respectively. The Alai and Hindu Kush are succeeded on the S by the lower ranges of Afghanistan and Baluchistan, which in turn are looped around the Sibi re-entrant. N of this the Sulaiman presents a steep face to the Indus Plains, while to the S the hills fan out again, the Kalat country between the N/S Kirthar Range (on the Sind-Baluchistan border) and the E/W Chagai Range being a mass of echelonned ridges sinking to the Seistan depression and swinging round E-W, parallel to the coast, in Makran: "each arc is in reality a series of concentric arcs connected at their extremities, leaving between them arid depressions." These mountains are of simple anticlinal structure and developed for the most part in relatively soft Cretaceous and Tertiary sandstones and limestones, with a flysch facies in the N. The parallelism between the

Sibi re-entrant and the greater re-entrant N of the Punjab is striking; it is no accident that, just as the NW syntaxial area culminates in the giant peaks of the Karakoram and Nanga Parbat, the highest summits between the Safed Koh (34° N) and the sea are found in the angle around Quetta. It seems probable that, as in the case of the NW syntaxis, a concealed projection of the Gondwana block is responsible.

The structure of the NW syntaxis has been educed by Wadia: put briefly, the Tertiary folding has wrapped itself round a projection of Gondwanaland, indicated e.g. by the outcrop of old rock in the Kirana Hills (Fig. 6). Fronting the Punjab plains is the great monoclinal scarp, largely due to thrusting, of the Salt Range; behind it, between the Indus and the Jhelum, is the Potwar Plateau or basin, a peneplain formed on folded Murree and Siwalik beds which are largely masked by a loess-like silt.

From Bunji to Hazara the Indus flows in a great gorge at about 3000–4500 ft with sides up to 15,000 ft high; E of it are the wild N/S or NE/SW ranges of Chitral and Kohistan. NE of the great bend at Bunji the country rises to the Karakoram, which in K2 (28,250 ft) has the second highest peak in the world; altogether there are 33 peaks over 24,000 ft in an area comparable to that of the Swiss Alps. The ranges here are certainly older than those to the S, perhaps even initially Hercynian, but they have been much affected by rejuvenation and faulting. The Karakoram and Muztagh merge Ewds into the Kailas Range, which is simply the rather higher edge of the Tibetan Plateau overlooking the Indus-Tsangpo furrow; the relationships and nomenclature of the ranges here are a matter of some dispute.[8] Mention should be made of the Ladakh Range lying along and cut through by the Indus; in the E it separates that river from its important tributary the Shyok, which leads up to the Karakoram Pass (18,270 ft).

The Great Himalaya Range begins at the culmination of Nanga Parbat (26,629 ft) in the angle of the Indus. To the N it is flanked by the Zaskar Range, overlooking the Indus, and by the high dissected peneplains of Rupshu and Deosai; to the S by a series of more or less continuous or echelonned ranges known collectively as the Lesser Himalayas. The famous Vale of Kashmir lies between the Great Himalaya and the most Wly of the Lesser Himalayas, the Pir Panjal; uplift here has been considerable (some 6000 ft) since the mid-Pleistocene. The Pir Panjal crest is merely a residual ridge on a broad plateau-like surface, and its accidented relief is due mainly to glaciation. The origin of the Vale itself is obscure; Wadia speaks of it as "an exaggerated instance of a dun" or longitudinal

---

[8] It is almost as dangerous for the uninitiate to venture into Karakoram and Himalayan nomenclature as it is to penetrate the mountains themselves. See the numerous papers in the *GJ* for 1936–38, ending with the report on "Karakoram Nomenclature" (*GJ* XCI (1938), 125–52). For the relations of the Indus and the Ladakh Range, cf. below, 384.

valley, and his section shows it as occupying a synclinal on the back of the great Kashmir Nappe; while de Terra holds that it is a recently depressed intermont basin, pointing to marked evidence of faulting on the Himalayan flank.[9] Most interest, however, attaches to terraces of the Karewas beds, deposits of a Pleistocene lake. The longitudinal depression of the upper Jhelum in Kashmir is continued by the upper Chenab; Pascoe thinks that the upper Chenab flowed into the Jhelum and was captured by a stream working back from the plains, but the apparently greater stability of the NW margin of the Vale and the directions of the upper Jhelum tributaries seem to point to an opposite direction of flow. It should be noted that the longitudinal section of the upper Sutlej and its tributary the Spiti is not a continuation of the upper Jhelum-upper Chenab depression; the Sutlej cuts right across the Great Himalaya in the Shipki area.

The Tertiaries of the Potwar geosynclinal basin narrow out Ewds into the Siwalik Hills, which extend as far as the Kosi River (87° E) and less continuously even farther E: the gaps in the Siwalik deposits around the Tista River have been attributed to the greater force of monsoon erosion opposite the passage-way formed by the Ganges Delta, but the recent work of Heim and Gansser suggests that they may have been over-ridden by Himalayan nappes. The Siwaliks are formed of great thick-nesses (15,000–20,000 ft) of Mio-Pleistocene sands, gravels, and con-glomerates, obviously the erosion products of the Himalayas themselves, and although not very high (rarely over 3000 ft) bear striking witness to the extreme youth of the mountain-building. They are backed by a discon-tinuous series of longitudinal vales—the *duns*—behind which are a number of Swd thrusts, the Boundary Faults thought to represent successive boundaries between sedimentation and mountain-building; they are now interpreted, at least in part, as the soles of nappes. The front to the plains is remarkably even and regular, and here again faulting may play a part—in Hoshiarpur Dt (Punjab) there is evidence for sub-recent thrusting of the Upper Siwaliks over older alluvium.

The Great Himalaya extend in a vast S-facing arc from the Indus to the Brahmaputra; most of the peaks over 25,000 ft (though not Everest itself) are formed of granites and gneisses, but much of the area is made up of old metamorphics which have definite affinities with the Peninsular rocks. After their great extent and height, the most striking feature is the contrast between the relatively gentle and rounded forms of the slope to the Indus-Tsangpo furrow and the wildly fretted Sn face. Apart from the great gorges of the Indus, Sutlej, and Dihang (Brahmaputra), the range is deeply cut into by the headwaters of the Ganges (Bhagirathi and Alaknanda Rivers), Sarda (Kali), Gogra (Seti, Karnali, and Bheri),

[9]Cf. below, Ch. XIV.

Gandak, and Arun; the last-named has a considerable plateau-section behind Everest. On the whole the rivers tend to cut through the range in its culminating massifs, and the trunk streams seem to have reached a later stage of development than their tributaries. To a large extent these features seem due to river-capture and the pushing back of the watershed by the much greater precipitation on the Sn face, but the detailed work of Wager on the Arun Valley strongly supports antecedence. There can be no doubt, however, that in many cases cutting back is more likely than antecedence. Everywhere the Sn ascents are far steeper than the Nn; the N-flowing streams appear to have lost much of their catchment area, and their valleys have been choked with their own debris. Again, many of the streams which cut through the crest do not seem to have catchment areas big enough to support antecedent rivers, an important point. The process of headward recession and capture can be particularly well seen at the Zoji La (N of Kashmir), where the S-flowing stream ends in a deep gorge and a 2000-ft ascent, beyond which is an open well-graded valley; the Zoji La has been compared to the Maloja Pass.[10] The asymmetrical development of the two slopes is, however, much more pronounced E of the Sutlej, where the excess of precipitation on the Sn face is much greater than in the W. A compromise view is perhaps possible, looking to the fact that elevation clearly took place in stages, so that it may be that "capture has created and antecedence maintained" the transverse gorges.

Corresponding to Nanga Parbat in the W, the En culmination of the Great Himalaya is the 25,000-ft peak of Namcha Barwa, overlooking the gorges of the Tsangpo-Brahmaputra (here known as the Dihang). The continuation of the axis farther E is very uncertain; Mason and Wadia incline to think that it swings round to a N/S alignment under the influence of the Shillong Plateau and the old block of Yunnan; but Kingdon Ward adduces cogent arguments (largely based on a floristic divide) to suggest that the real continuation is still Ewds and is cut across by the great antecedent trenches of the upper Salween, Mekong, and Yangtse.

This En area is very little known geologically and even geographically; but there seems to be at least a suggestive parallelism with the NW syntaxis. "The post-Archaean rocks of the Assam Plateau are unfolded and horizontal, as is so generally the case with the Peninsular formations, though on either side of the plateau . . . the Tertiary rocks are plicated, overturned, and overthrust, both in the Himalayan foothills and their strike continuations, the Patkai and Naga ranges." On this view the Brahmaputra Valley in Assam is a ramp-valley forced down between the

[10] R. D. Oldham, *GJ* III (1894), 187–90; but cf. L. M. Davies, *Geological Magazine* LXXVII (1940), 410–12.

Shillong Plateau and the Himalayan folding. At any rate the Assam-Burma mountains seem to correspond with those of Baluchistan, and their N/S direction is doubtless associated with the NE wedge of the Peninsula and the resistance of the old Yunnan block; they also are developed in relatively soft Cretaceous and Tertiary sandstones and shales, and have a marked Jura structure of quite simple anticlines and synclines, with some shallow thrusting.

The North-Western Syntaxis (Fig. 6)

The NW syntaxis of the Himalaya, already briefly noted, is of much more than local significance: it forms a great knee-bend some 300 miles deep and affects the strike of the ranges probably as far as the foot of the Pamirs; a very striking expression of it is the wedge of Murree and Siwalik deposits at the sharp angle of the Jhelum near Domel. The extension of the old Gondwana block is evidenced by the Kirana outcrop (32° N), far to the N of the Aravallis and only 60–70 miles from the Salt Range; its rigidity is shown by the occurrence of horst structures. The Salt Range itself, with its steep front to the plains and the long dip behind it, its thrusts showing a horizontal movement of some 20 miles, and its curiously twisted alignment, is very largely controlled by the resistance of the Archaean mass hidden beneath the Punjab. The stability and competence of the basement rocks of the foreland, underlying the Tertiary sediments of the Potwar trough, is shown by the fact that the mantle of Murrees and Siwaliks is merely wrinkled up on the basement, not metamorphosed nor even indurated; they are in fact only *plis de couverture* with no depth. Again, the Murree sediments are strikingly different petrologically from those of the Siwalik Hills, being probably derived from iron-bearing Peninsular rocks rather than from the rising Himalayas.

The influence of Gondwanaland on the alignment of the Himalayas has thus been profound: round the great salient the ranges are wrapped in loops, the strike of the rock systems paralleled by that of the planes of thrusting onto the foreland. The Great Himalaya represents the original axis of uplift of the Tethys geosyncline, bending sharply Swds at each end (into the Baluchistan and Assam-Arakan Ranges) where the pressure of the old block suddenly ceases. As we have seen, Kingdon Ward's views on the Ewd extension of the Himalayas are opposed to this interpretation; but it would seem the more logical one if, as is possible, the Himalayan compression is not merely the expression of an outward creep from Central Asia but largely due to underthrusting from the ocean floors and a definite Nwd drive of the old block; such a view is probably more in accordance with modern views of isostasy and orogenesis.

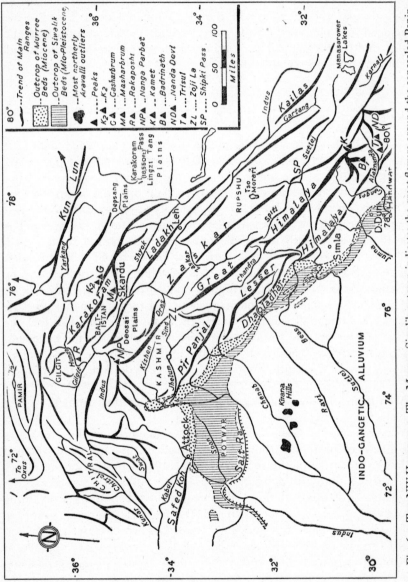

Fig. 6.—The NW Himalayas. The Murree-Siwalik outcrop indicates the great flexure around the concealed Peninsular Block; courtesy *Chambers's Encyclopaedia.*

Himalayan Thrusts and Uplifts (Fig. 7)

Older views of the rise of the Himalayas—which involved "special elevatory processes", such as great batholiths, in the higher areas—have been much modified by recent detailed work; in particular the concept of "blocks of mainly pre-Cambrian formations minutely crumpled and divided off by steeply inclined faults" has been largely replaced by interpretations analogous to the nappe theory in the Alps. So far, however, such detailed analysis has been confined to a few areas—Kashmir (Wadia), Simla (Pilgrim and West), Garhwal (Auden), and Kumaon (Heim and Gansser).

The "Boundary Faults" of the older geologists, which were regarded as steeply-dipping reversed faults marking successive Sn limits of mountain-building and Nn limits of Tertiary sedimentation, are now interpreted as great thrust-planes. Heim and Gansser look on this border zone as "an old surface of erosion, over which the older Himalayan formations were thrust, and through the gaps of which they advanced in huge arch-shaped waves", as on the Nn border of the Alps. The deposition of the 15,000–20,000 ft of the Siwalik beds is regarded as made possible by tectonic downwarp; conditions were similar to those of the present-day Gangetic alluviation but the foredeep was farther to the N, having been pushed Swds by tectonic advances involving successive detrital accumulations.

The general concept is perhaps best shown by Heim and Gansser's scheme, which harmonises very well with that of Auden in Garhwal:

(i) imbricated marginal thrusts, Simla-Kumaon;

(ii) interior secondary thrust-sheets;

(iii) the Main Central Thrust Mass, with deep-rooted injected crystallines, 10–20 km thick covered with 10–15 km of Algonkian-Mesozoic sediments; this is a *pli de fond*, produced by thrusting at depth succeeded by vertical uplift;

(iv) Palaeozoic and Mesozoic sediments thrust and recumbently folded onto the back of the main root;

(v) the "exotic" Tibetan thrust (the Kiogar *Klippen*)—one of the most baffling problems of Himalayan geology, no solution to which is yet in sight;

(vi) Flysch zone S of the Trans-Himalaya, with a possible weak counter-thrust Nwds.

Everest and Kangchenjunga are also carved out of the back of a vast nappe—probably the largest in the world—which *may* be a continuation of the Main Central Thrust Mass. The total shortening in Kumaon is possibly of the order of 180 miles, as compared with 120–180 in the Alps. The major thrust marks the contrast between the unfossiliferous undated

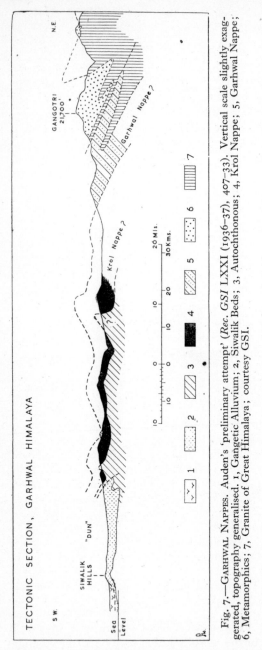

Fig. 7.—GARHWAL NAPPES. Auden's 'preliminary attempt' (*Rec. GSI* LXXI (1936–37), 407–33). Vertical scale slightly exaggerated, topography generalised. 1, Gangetic Alluvium; 2, Siwalik Beds; 3, Autochthonous; 4, Krol Nappe; 5, Garhwal Nappe; 6, Metamorphics; 7, Granite of Great Himalaya; courtesy GSI.

rocks of the Lesser Himalayas and the pre-Cambrian-Cretaceous fossiliferous sequence of the "Tethys Himalaya."

The general nappe concept is fairly straightforward but the relations of the central crystalline core are very obscure. E. B. Bailey draws attention to the occurrence of submarine volcanic flows (ophiolites) in this zone, and suggests that the earlier nappes passed over a line of active submarine volcanoes, so that the magma was extruded along the thrust-planes; he illustrates this idea by the analogy of a hypothetical thrust-mass on the Pacific floor meeting and over-riding a volcanic system of Hawaiian type.[11]

Thrusting, however, is far from being the only type of orogenic activity in the Himalayas, and in the latest phases at least a very important role has been played by isostatic uplift. The question of Himalayan compensation is obviously bound up with that of the origin of the Indo-Gangetic trough. According to de Terra there has been uplift of some 6000 ft in the Pir Panjal since the middle of the Pleistocene, and "young uplifts must have affected the entire Himalayan and Karakoram ranges." Garwood has suggested isostatic uplift consequent on the relief from load afforded

[11] *Bulletin Geological Soc. of America* XLVII (1936), 1713–25.

by shrinkage of the Himalayan glaciers, while Wager stresses that due to the removal of vast quantities of erosion products by the extremely active S-flowing rivers. His conclusion is noteworthy: "The Eastern Himalaya . . . have been produced in two distinct stages and by two different processes. The first stage was the production by horizontal compression of an elevated plateau in approximate isostatic equilibrium. This plateau is essentially the present plateau of Tibet, but when formed it extended farther south over the region which is now the Himalaya. The second stage, which is presumably still going on, is one of vertical upwarping of the edge of the plateau to maintain approximate isostatic balance as the rivers cut deeper and deeper into its edges. The second stage is the one which has produced the extra height of the Himalaya mountains above the plateau of Tibet. In the Eastern Himalaya, without the deep valleys and gorges, it is probable that there would have been no peaks towering 10,000 feet above the plateau of Tibet."[12]

In view of the evidence for considerable tangential movements persisting until geologically late times, one cannot help feeling that this conclusion unduly minimises the role of the horizontal compressional forces. It receives, however, some support from Heim and Gansser: "if the highest mountains, Kangchenjunga, Everest, and Dhaulagiri, are opposite the greatest foredeep of the Gangetic Plain, this may be the expression of a balance movement" in regions of the greatest exchange of load. The solution may well be a compromise: thrusting may still be going on in the border regions and vertical uplift both there (e.g. the Pir Panjal) and in the inner (Tethys) Himalaya.

The Tibetan Plateaus

There is a marked difference in facies between the deposits of the Tibetan Plateaus and those of the folded Himalaya. Marine Eocene sediments are found only S of the Ladakh Range and N of the Kun Lun, and during Upper Cretaceous times (when the Himalayas were still beneath the Tethys waters) there seems to have been a highland in the Karakoram-Kun Lun region, onto which the Himalayan ranges were welded in succession from N to S. Erosion was more active in these areas before the rise of the Himalayas shut out the rain-bearing winds from the S, and de Terra has worked out several erosion-levels. His work on the whole stresses the importance of epeirogenetic uplift, at least during the later phases. An interesting approach is provided by the ecological work of G. E. Hutchinson; the fauna of Pangong and other W Tibetan lakes has an older appearance than that of Kashmir and Ladakh and is related to Central Asian rather than to Indian associations.[13]

[12] *GJ* LXXXIX (1937), 249–50.
[13] "Limnological Studies at High Altitudes in Ladakh", *Nature* (New Series) LXXVII (1933), 497–500.

Relics of the old levels occur in the form of high rolling plains such as the Aksai Chin, Depsang, and Lingzi Tang N of the Muztagh Range, and these appear to be on the site of the oldest (late Cretaceous) uplift and to have extended Swds into the Karakoram region, where the spurs have high accordant levels and have been truncated by the former extension of the Karakoram glaciers. There are at least three old erosion surfaces in the Karakoram-Muztagh area: the high peaks of the Muztagh (24,000 ft) and peneplains at about 20,000 and 15,000–16,000 ft. Another level is represented by the Deosai Plains E of Nanga Parbat and by the high spurs of the Kashmir and Ladakh Mountains. According to Hayden the heights of the transverse ranges of the Lesser Himalayas are so uniform that it is impossible to resist the impression that they form parts of a dissected peneplain, and this is confirmed by Heim and Gansser.

De Terra's general conclusion is that the wide extension of mature or old forms points to a late uplift—certainly not earlier than late Tertiary. The first level represents an early Tertiary mature or old relief, with a few monadnocks, which was uplifted and dissected to form the second series of mature forms. This phase was succeeded by the first Pleistocene glaciation and the formation of the third level during an interglacial. After the maximum glaciation the fourth level was established in the Riss-Wurm interglacial, at which time much of the plateau was occupied by large freshwater lakes. The final retreat of the Wurm ice was succeeded by "recent uplift and post-Pleistocene rejuvenation, particularly effective along the Indus drainage", with local tilting of terraces and lake deposits in Rupshu, between the Indus and the Zaskar Range.

Himalayan Glaciation, Recent and Pleistocene

The glaciers of the Himalayas and Tibet, although much shrunken, nevertheless include in the Karakoram the largest glaciers remaining in the world outside sub-Polar regions: the Fedchenko (in the Pamir) and Siachen are 48 and 45 miles long respectively, the Biafo, Batura, Báltoro, and Hispar from 36 to 39 miles. Elsewhere the glaciers are not so spectacular, but there are several on Nanga Parbat, while in Sikkim and Kumaon those of the Kangchenjunga and Badrinath massifs reach 16 miles. The Wn glaciers are not only of greater size than those of Kumaon and Sikkim, but they descend to lower levels—in Kashmir as low as 7000–8000 ft, against 12,000 in Kumaon and 13,000 on Kangchenjunga. This is attributable partly to higher latitudes (36° in the Karakoram as against 28° for Kangchenjunga) and partly to the more direct exposure of the E to the monsoon: the total precipitation is much greater in the E, but the air masses are warmer, while in the W some of the scantier precipitation falls in winter and a much higher proportion as snow. The snow-line on the Sn face varies from about 14,000 ft in the En

Himalayas to 19,000 in the W; on the drier Tibetan side it is some 3000 ft higher, though this does not hold farther N, where precipitation conditions are more uniform; in Ladakh it is about 18,000 ft.

Mention may be made of the small glaciers of the Pir Panjal, which are exceptional (for the Sn ranges) in being better developed on the Nn face: the Pir Panjal is a much less decisive climatic divide than the Himalaya proper, and the firns are largely fed by *winter* precipitation, so that aspect can have its usual value instead of being largely counter-balanced by greater precipitation on the Sn slopes.

A distinction must be made between the longitudinal glaciers of the Karakoram, and the transverse. The latter are naturally shorter and more fluctuating, variations being dependent more on local topography than on climate; and owing to their steeper grade they generally descend lower. The Yengutsa glacier is believed to have advanced 3 miles in 8 days in 1903, "coming out of its side valley and covering up the fields of Hispar village. . . . Such abnormally rapid movements may be due to earthquake shocks or to the sudden release of masses of ice that have accumulated to such a size and shape that they are no longer stable on the floor upon which they rest. Possibly accumulations of wind-swept snow would also cause instability."[14]

The longitudinal glacier movements are very complex; at times they are more rapid than those of the Alps—up to 5 ft 10 ins. in 24 hours on the Báltoro in 1909, while the Biafo snout retreated by ablation no less than 400 yards in the month of August 1892. But in general they are "either stationary or in very slight secular retreat owing to excess of ablation." Thus the *net* movement of the Báltoro is practically nil as the contributions and deductions of its 50 transverse branches cancel out. The possible permutations due to aspect, shape, surrounding topography, gradient, climatic and seismic influences are endless, and variations in snout movement "may be due to causes which are in distinct cases secular, periodic, seasonal, or accidental." Even in the transverse glaciers there seems to be little evidence, save in a few cases, of any regular periodicity dependent on Brucknerian weather-cycles. Particular interest has been excited by the oscillations of the Chong Kumdan (Fig. 63), which intermittently advances across the upper Shyok, causing serious floods as far away as the Punjab when the ponded waters eventually break through the ice-dam. The great flood of 1841, however, which swept away a Sikh army on the dry bed of the Indus at Attock, was probably caused by the release of water dammed by a landslide from the Hattu Pir cliff on the slopes of Nanga Parbat.[15]

[14] J. B. Auden, "Glaciers", *CGR* I No. 2 (1937), 46–52.
[15] The recent history and possible future behaviour of the Chong Kumdan are discussed in a number of papers in *The Himalayan Journal*, of which those by Professor K. Mason in I (1929), 10–29, and XII (1940), 52–65, are particularly important.

An important general factor bearing on glacier movement is stressed by de Terra, who points out that "the crustal mobility of the Kashmir basin locally determined the extension of glaciers" in the Pleistocene, and thinks that similar processes may be responsible for the rapid glacier movements of the Nubra/Shyok watershed. These Wn glaciers frequently appear almost smothered under morainic debris, especially in summer, when excessive ablation leads to a great development of fantastic ice-pinnacles.

Obviously in the Pleistocene the ice was far more extensive than it is now, but the amount of extension is a matter of dispute and the evidence is of course complicated by the considerable recent uplift. The maximalist view is that of Trinkler: "it is highly probable that during the Ice-Age the whole mountainous region, from the Kun-lun mountains in the north to the Himalaya in the south, was buried under ice." This view is not generally accepted. Dainelli worked out a sequence of four main glaciations corresponding to the Alpine Mindel, Riss, Würm, and post-Würm I; de Terra, who has studied the glaciation of Kashmir in considerable detail, agrees with the sequence but would put it rather earlier.

Many of the Lesser Himalayan ranges which do not now carry permanent snow have clear traces of glacial erosion and moraines; terminal moraines are found at about 8000 ft below Laching in Sikkim, where the modern glaciers are at 13,000 ft. Coulson, who thinks that in Kangra glaciers descended as low as 3000 ft, emphasises the elevation of the Pir Panjal since the mid-Pleistocene: "after the boulder beds of the Karewas (in the Vale of Kashmir) were deposited, which happened in one or other of the Pleistocene glacial phases, the Pir Panjal range was elevated some thousands of feet. At one time during the Pleistocene glaciation of the Vale of Kashmir, glaciers extended down to a level lower than 5500 feet, the present level of the Kashmir valley. . . . the general statement that there is no evidence of glaciation in the Himalaya and Sub-Himalaya below 5000 feet must be discounted in view of the fact that elevation of these ranges has occurred after the main glaciation." The extreme view must be regarded as not proven, as is the case also with the attribution of certain boulder beds in Siwalik rocks to the melting of ice-tongues from the Waziristan highlands. A minor problem is the existence on the Potwar Plateau between Attock and Campbellpur of erratic blocks, some of which apparently derive from the high central Himalaya; these may have been transported by floods consequent on the breaking of ice-dams, or by icebergs floating down a lake along the line of the present Indus.

Evolution of the Himalayan River-System (Fig. 8)

At an early stage in the exploration of the Himalayas the remarkable lay-out of its rivers attracted attention; in particular the longitudinal

courses of the Indus, Sutlej, and Tsangpo on the Tibetan Plateau, and
the great gorges of these and other rivers cutting right across the Great
Himalaya in the vicinity of its highest peaks, challenged explanation.
The earlier theories, except those of simple antecedence, have little
scientific value, but in 1919 E. H. Pascoe and G. E. Pilgrim independently
worked out a comprehensive hypothesis which, although criticised in
detail and probably liable to much modification, provides the best starting-
point to any consideration of the problem.

Fundamental to the discussion is the great thickness of sands, gravels,
and boulder beds which make up the Siwalik Hills. These have been
attributed to fan deposition on a vast scale, the alluvial fans of the streams
debouching from the Himalayas coalescing to form a great piedmont
apron; the local variations in thickness and lithology and the generally
conformable grading into recent fluviatile deposits being taken as evidence
that through all Siwalik times the main drainage lines were substantially
the same as those of to-day.

The view of Pascoe and Pilgrim is that the deposits were laid down in
the valley of a great river—Pascoe's "Indobrahm", Pilgrim's "Siwalik
River"—which flowed to the NW between the rising Himalayas and a
Gondwanaland which was then continuous from the Aravallis right across
to upper Assam. The general line would of course have been to the N
of the present Ganges, the whole system having been pushed S at a later
stage by the advancing outer Himalayan foothills and the very active
deposition of the tributaries from the N—which have clearly forced the
lower Jumna and Ganges against the Nn flank of the Peninsula. The
river flowed out to the Arabian Sea more or less along the line of the
lower Indus, but presumably more to the W; Siwalik deposits border
the Sulaiman and Kirthar Ranges, but our authors pay relatively little
attention to this area and they do not clarify the relationships of the
Siwaliks in the Sibi re-entrant to the old estuary, which would need a
good deal of explanation. In Eocene times, however, the lower Indus
region was occupied by a Sind Gulf which has been filled in by the river
deposits (as in the parallel case of the lower Irrawaddy). Pilgrim points
out that the Upper Siwalik boulder beds are 5000 ft thick in Kangra and
disappear quite suddenly to the NW, while to the E they thin out more
gradually, not disappearing before Bhutan; this indicates a flow to the NW.
This view is not altogether incompatible with the interpretation of the
Siwaliks as fans from the Himalayan slope, since the rich Siwalik mamma-
lian fauna gives no evidence of desert conditions and, this being so, as
Pilgrim puts it "the mountain streams must have had an outlet to the sea
in one direction or another, and must have joined a main river in the
plains."

The continuity of the Sn flank of the great valley is indicated by the

thin alluvial cover on the sill between the Rajmahal Hills and the Shillong
Plateau. Pilgrim thinks that the Peninsula then extended over much of
the Bay of Bengal; he points to the "complicated drainage system and
breadth of the Mahanadi, so disproportionate to its length, as well as
the entire absence of any fluviatile deposits older than Sub-Recent" as
evidence that it is really only a betrunked relic. The dislocation which
has produced the present river lay-out he ascribes to earth movements

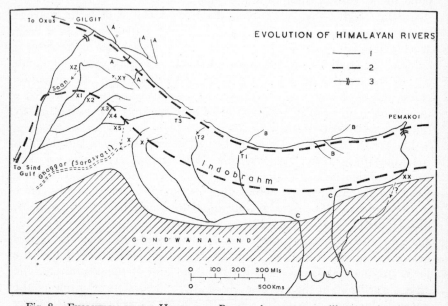

Fig. 8.—EVOLUTION OF THE HIMALAYAN RIVERS. An attempt to illustrate the views of
Pascoe and Pilgrim. 1, existing rivers; 2, Indobrahm and Tibetan River at end of Tertiary;
3, captures of Tibetan R. by Attock Indus and Dihang; T1, T2, T3, possible outlets of
Tibetan R. by Photu Pass (Kali Gandak), Karnali, and Sutlej; A–A, N Shigar, Nubra,
Shyok, Sn Shigar, Zaskar, suggesting SE-flowing Indus (de Terra); B–B, tributaries
suggesting possible W-flowing Tsangpo; C, C, possible disruption of Indobrahm by
proto-Ganges and proto-Brahmaputra; X1–X5, successive captures of Indobrahm by
Punjab rivers; XX, possible capture of Meghna waters by Indobrahm after former had
captured headwaters of Tibetan R.; XY, XZ, possible captures of U. Jhelum by Chenab
and U. Soan by Jhelum; X, X, captures by Ganges (reversed Indobrahm) cutting back
Wwds. No attempt is made to indicate more recent changes in Bengal.

damming the Siwalik River NW of Kangra, assisted by the cutting-back
of powerful rivers flowing S from the Rajmahal-Shillong watershed and,
in alliance with the uplift in the NW, diverting the drainage out by the
present Ganges-Brahmaputra Delta. A difficulty arises here: though
Pilgrim does not mention it, subsidence of the Bay of Bengal area would
lead to rejuvenation and consequent increase in the cutting-back capacity
of such streams. So far this would support his theory, but these events
were after all quite recent and there should be clear traces of rejuvenation,

if not in the rapidly aggraded area of the Rajmahal-Shillong gap at least in the upper Mahanadi Basin; and it is doubtful if his contention can be squared with the evidence for the general persistence of the E coast and its character (farther S it is true) of a raised plain of marine erosion. Evans and Oldham, in the discussion on Pascoe's paper, pointed out that the alluvium in the gap, though relatively thin, is after all several hundreds of feet thick, and that headward erosion in really hard rocks is of doubtful efficiency without structural assistance; they held that earth movements were a more likely agent of the change.

A very important point is the occurrence in many of the rivers of the Nn flank of the Indo-Gangetic Plain of sharp Vs pointing to the NW, generally near the Siwalik/alluvium boundary. The Nn limbs of these Vs are regarded by Pascoe as the remnants of old right-bank tributaries of the Indobrahm, becoming more deeply impressed and permanent with the rise of the Siwalik Hills. Meanwhile the middle Indobrahm was being attacked from two directions: from the SW by left-bank tributaries of the lower Indobrahm itself, from the SE by the headstreams of a Ganges now diverted into the Bay of Bengal. The former streams may have been rejuvenated by earth movements associated with the uplift of the Potwar Plateau, and similar events taking place in the sub-Himalaya itself, where on this view a stream along the line of the upper Chenab-upper Jhelum-Soan was cut into sections; there is no doubt that the present small Soan is a misfit in its broad alluviated valley. While all this was happening on the Wn front the Rajmahal-Shillong watershed had been breached and the Ganges-Brahmaputra drainage diverted into the Bay of Bengal. This of course implies some rejuvenation, and the activated Wn headstreams gradually annexed the right-bank Indobrahm tributaries in the Gogra/Jumna area. The last phase was the annexation of the Jumna, which is thought to have flowed in the course now marked by the dry Ghaggar depression in Rajputana until well into historic times, and to be in fact the lost Sarasvati of Hindu legend. The upper Sutlej may also have debouched into the Ghaggar bed until a late capture by a tributary of the Beas-Sutlej.

Pascoe also envisages a great W-flowing "Tibetan River" from Pemakoi to Gilgit; the furrow marked by the Tsangpo-Manasarowar Lakes-Sutlej-Gartang-Indus line, partly occupied by Ladakh Nummulitics, certainly seems to have structural continuity, whether it be a geosynclinal zone, a belt of soft rocks, or faulted. In Tibet many of the larger Tsangpo feeders (e.g. the Kyi, Rong, Nyang, and Shabki) have a Wly trend which suggests reversal of the main stream; but on the other hand this line of argument would indicate reversal of the Indus in view of the SEly trend of the Shigar, Nubra, and upper Shyok. According to Pascoe the Tibetan River may have flowed to the Oxus, or may have reached the plains either by the Photu Pass (a remarkable gap only 250 ft higher than the Tsangpo Valley), by the Karnali, the upper Sutlej, or the upper Indus. The plateau section of the Indus is twice as steep as that of the Tsangpo, and at Bunji the Indus is 3400 ft lower than the Tsangpo at the point where the latter leaves the furrow, so that it is the more active of the two; on the other hand its transverse gorge has a relatively gentle gradient and is cut in hard rock so that it cannot be very young. Pascoe thinks that his original Tibetan River was broken up by the Irrawaddy-Chindwin, by the Meghna (the present Meghna is regarded as a beheaded remnant, the upper portions of which, NE of the Shillong Plateau, were in turn captured by Indobrahm headstreams), later perhaps by the Kali Gandak (leading up to the Photu Pass), by the Sutlej, and by the Indus.

Complicated as this orgy of river piracy and cannibalism appears, it must be remembered that the phenomena which the theory seeks to explain—some of the largest rivers of the world flowing in relatively mature longitudinal courses and then cutting across the loftiest mountains in the world—are themselves complicated and on a scale not paralleled elsewhere; and it is supported by a mass of detail which cannot be adequately summarised here. Some of the evidence adduced has been severely criticised—e.g. the similarity of Indus and Ganges dolphins; Annandale thinks this detail more easily accounted for on the hypothesis of a broad marine strait between Peninsular India and the rest of Asia, gradually narrowed and finally obliterated by the advance of the Himalayas and filling in by their erosion products, the penultimate stage being one of constantly shifting lagoons. More recently, in his papers of 1933-34, de Terra has literally re-orientated the problem by drawing attention to the longitudinal valleys of the Karakoram-Pangong area, by contrast to "the transverse drainage of the Central Himalaya. The ancient character of this pattern becomes clearer as we try to eliminate its secondary attributes such as transverse cutting or capture by the Indus." He agrees that the longitudinal valleys antedate the transverse sections—as seems obvious—but holds that in pre-glacial times the drainage of the Karakoram-Ladakh region flowed SE and E, along the great Tsangpo furrow and possibly into En Tibet and Szechwan; the Shigar-Nubra-upper Shyok trend supports this. The extremely curious course of the Ngagong (between the Tsangpo-Brahmaputra gorge and the Salween) does not seem to have attracted attention; from a cursory map examination it would seem to suggest capture of Irrawaddy drainage by a Tsangpo (and a Brahmaputra?) tributary, but this area is very little known.

On the main question of the Indobrahm de Terra is decidedly hostile. He holds that the Siwalik deposits are "local precipitates of an antecedent slope drainage", "successive fan and basin sediments. . . . their origin differs in no way from that of other foredeep fillings (Alps, Rocky Mountains)." His explanation of the dolphins point by intercommunication along coastal deltas is inadequate (there is no evidence for deltas along 1000 miles of the W coast)[16] and he admits the difficulty of the NW-pointing Vs, his own suggestion hardly explaining anything; but thinks that the successive overlaps of younger over older beds from the Ganges Delta to the NW Punjab point to a great tilted syncline along which any master stream originally flowed to the SE. This has its own difficulties; the Rajmahal-Shillong gap is unexplained and it is not clear how the graded lower Indus (even with a base-level nearer the Punjab) could annex the Wn headstreams and the Karakoram drainage, as seems to be implied.

Accepting the Indobrahm, it is true that an E-flowing Tibetan River could have been broken up in the manner envisaged by Pascoe for his W-flowing stream; but it is very difficult to conceive of two vast longitudinal streams on either side of the rising Himalayas and flowing in *opposite* directions; while the balance of evidence seems to be for a Wwds outlet for the Indo-Gangetic drainage, and an Ewds one for the Tibetan River. The opposition is direct and cannot as yet be reconciled.

The Sutlej provides a problem of its own. Its source is apparently fed by underground water from the Manasarowar Lakes and in its longitudinal section it flows in a deep canyon cut in the soft fluviatile beds of Nari Khorsum; this upper course is distinctly arid and the river itself appears to be a misfit. This could be explained if it were an old outlet for the Tibetan River; Pascoe thinks that the Sutlej captured part of the Tibetan River and then lost again to the rejuvenated Tsangpo after the Dihang had cut back into the furrow, but this is not very clear. Burrard points out that the Sutlej has a much deeper trough than its neighbours the Giri (a headstream of the Jumna) and the Beas and has no large cis-Himalayan tributaries, which suggests that it is younger than the others: "the question as to how the Giri and the Beas have confined their giant neighbour into a trough less than 20 miles wide remains worthy of consideration"; more worthy perhaps if it is put conversely, how the Sutlej has been inset between the other two. On this, Davies thinks that the Sutlej is the youngest of the great Himalayan rivers and has developed owing to the collapse of the main Himalayan axis along the line of an old Gondwana fault-trough; in support he cites the deep Shipki gorge and a break in the Ladakh Range NW of Gurla Mandhata.

III. THE INDO-GANGETIC PLAINS

Structure and Surface

The great crescent of alluvium from the delta of the Indus to that of the Ganges represents the infilling of a foredeep warped down between the

[16] We obviously cannot postulate anything about the coast before the presupposed faulting of the Wn Ghats.

stable (or Nwd-drifting) Gondwana block and the advancing Himalayas. Its relations with the mountains are obscure and involve the interpretation of difficult geodetic data; the older view that the sediments are some 15,000 or more feet thick, deposited in a great rift or a trough sinking beneath the weight of alluvium, has been challenged by Glennie on the basis of new gravity anomaly readings which indicate a maximum of 6500 ft or so. The Himalayas themselves appear to be largely though not entirely compensated at some distance within the mountains, but on the plains deflections are to the S and suggest an upwarp of denser sub-crustal material from Orissa to Baluchistan.

Be this as it may, it is clear that the filling is of very unequal depth and the Indo-Gangetic trough does not correspond to the full extent of the Indo-Gangetic Plains; its approximate limits are shown on Fig. 2. Occasional outcrops of older rock indicate that the alluvial cover is thinner in the Indus than in the Ganges Valley. There is evidence also for concealed ridges prolonging the Aravalli axis between Delhi and Hardwar and also NW from Delhi towards the Salt Range. The floor of the Ganges Delta appears to be still sinking.

The plains are remarkably homogeneous topographically; for hundreds of miles the only noticeable relief is that of floodplain bluffs and belts of ravines and badlands formed by gully erosion along some of the larger streams, e.g. the lower Chambal (Fig. 93); the slopes of the broad inter-fluves or *doabs* (*do* = two, *ab* = water) are barely if at all perceptible. On this vast aggradational surface the only marked topographical changes are those associated with the numerous shifts and diversions of the rivers. There are, however, important surface differences. Along the outer slopes of the Siwaliks there is commonly a fairly steep gravel talus slope— the *bhabar*—in which all but the larger streams lose themselves, seeping out lower down in the marshy and jungly *terai* strip. The older (Pleis-tocene) alluvium is known as *bhangar* and as a rule occupies higher ground than the Recent *khadar*, which grades into the most recent delta silts. Generally the alluvium is a fairly stiff clay, with more or less sand according as it is near to or far from the hills. In the bhangar there are irregular limy concretions (*kankar*); in some districts there may be as much as 30% of calcareous matter in the alluvium. In the drier areas of Uttar Pradesh, the Punjab, and Rajputana there are stretches of barren saline efflorescence known as *reh* or *kallar*.

Contrast between Himalayan and Peninsular Rivers

A factor of the greatest importance in the human geography of India is the strong contrast between the rivers of the Peninsula and those of the Himalayas. It is easy to overlook or underrate the very large proportions of the basins of the Indus and the Brahmaputra, and even of the Sutlej,

which are included within the mountain zone. The Himalayan section
of the Indus drainage alone (excluding the Kabul) is over 100,000 sq
mls, larger than the whole basins of most European rivers; the Sutlej
tributary itself drains 20,000 sq mls. Even those rivers which do not
penetrate behind the wall of the Great Himalaya have not inconsiderable mountain courses. Erosion is extremely active and vast quantities
of silt are brought down: the Ganges and the Indus have been estimated
to carry some 900,000 and 1,000,000 tons respectively of suspended
matter daily, and the Brahmaputra more than either. Most important of all,
the rivers from the Himalaya are not dependent on the monsoon rainfall
alone for their water-supply, but have also a supply from the melting of
the Himalayan snows. This is the more valuable as it comes in the height
of the hot weather—February to April—when the Peninsular rivers are
lowest. Even in the N the régimes are indeed very variable; the Indus
above the Panjnad confluence can vary from 10,000 to 1,000,000 cusecs.
But there is usually some water available for irrigation, and the Nn rivers
are locally useful for small craft, though except in the deltas inland water
transport is of very little account in India.

By contrast, the Peninsular rivers flow in broad shallow valleys maturely
graded almost to their heads and with only slight interruptions of profile,
already noted, at the passages through the En Hills. They are entirely
dependent on a rainfall concentrated in five or six months of the year,
flowing over a thin soil-cover, and therefore are almost dry in the hot
weather; a river like the Kistna, with a bed some half or three-quarters
of a mile across, may have a trickle of water only two or three yards wide
in March. The Peninsular rivers are therefore of much less use for irrigation than those of the N; and where irrigation is possible it needs a
proportionately much greater capital expenditure on barrages and
reservoirs, so that large-scale river irrigation in the Peninsula is almost
confined to the deltas of the E coast. Hydro-electric sites are also on the
whole rarer in the Peninsula, though this is compensated for by the
concentration in the rejuvenated S and the heavy rainfall along the
Wn Ghats.

IV. THE COASTS

The coasts of India are very little indented by large inlets, almost the
only significant ones being the Gulf of Cambay and the Rann of Cutch;
but the W coast has numerous small inlets, the E its delta creeks.

Beginning in the NW, the Baluchistan coast W of Sonmiani Bay is
markedly Pacific in type, the Makran Ranges trending parallel to the
coast; Sewell's researches indicate that this is definitely a fault coast.
It is succeeded by the Indus Delta, off which a great trough reaches a
depth of some 3700 ft at its mouth; this is thought to mark a former

extension of the Indus or Indobrahm during the glacial fall of sea-level. Cutch and Kathiawar have generally low alluvial coasts; the Rann embayment is, as we have seen, in part of very recent date and the S coast of Kathiawar may be controlled by E/W faulting associated with the Vindhya-Narbada line. The alluvial coast on the E of the Gulf of Cambay is actively prograding, but from Damão down to Goa the coast is a succession of little inlets and rocky points with, however, a general straight alignment strongly suggestive of recent faulting along the Ghats; but in detail the littoral is complicated in both plan and elevation. Here, at Bombay and Goa and a few smaller inlets, are almost the only good natural harbours of India—maritime activity has always been relatively great—and some features seem to indicate slight local submergence.[17]

From Karwar S to Cape Comorin the coastal lowland widens out and the bars and lagoons of Malabar suggest a young shoreline of emergence; the contrast with the coast N of Goa may warrant the very tentative suggestion that there has been a slight tilt, depression in the N under the weight of the Deccan Lavas and the pressure of the Himalayan folding, upheaval in the S; the pivot would be about Goa. On the E coast the steepness of the submarine contours (greater than on the W) has been taken to indicate subsidence of the Bay of Bengal area, but the most recent movements of any consequence have been elevatory and the littoral is definitely a raised sea-floor, with bars and lagoons, inland-facing cuestas, and some abrupt hills of old rock representing off-shore islands; there are also of course considerable stretches of prograding deltas. Off the Ganges is a submarine trough corresponding to that of the Indus—the "swatch of no ground." The E coast of the Bay of Bengal is again strongly longitudinal; changes of level here have probably been complex, as raised beaches are found on some of the off-shore Burmese islands, while the general pattern suggests some subsidence complicated by the formation of deltas, mangrove swamps, and large mud volcanoes.

BIBLIOGRAPHICAL NOTE

General

J. W. Gregory (ed.), *The Structure of Asia* (1929). The relations between India and the growth of Asia are dealt with incidentally in several chapters.

D. N. Wadia, *Geology of India* (2nd ed., 1939). Indispensable standard work.

M. S. Krishnan, *The Geology of India and Burma* (2nd ed., 1949). Rather lighter in weight than Wadia, but deals with tectonic and geomorphological matters more consecutively.

[17] See Ch. XXII for a fuller discussion.

R. D. Oldham, "The Making of Indian Geography", *GJ* III (1894). One of the most stimulating essays on Indian geography ever written.

R. B. S. Sewell, "The Oceans round India", in S. L. Hora (ed.), *An Outline of the Field Sciences of India* (Indian Science Congress Asstn, Calcutta, 1937), 17–42.

W. D. West, "Earthquakes in India", *CGR* I No. 2 (1937), 53–78.

D. N. Wadia, "An Outline of the Geological History of India", in S. L. Hora (as above, 1937), 43–69.

——, "Geology and Geography in India", in *The Progress of Science in India* (Indian Science Congress Asstn, Calcutta, 1937), 86–132.

——, "The Making of India", Presidential Address, 29th Indian Science Congress (1942).

M. S. Krishnan, "The Structure of India," *IGJ* XVIII (1943), 137–55.

The Peninsula

R. D. Oldham, "Notes on the Geology of the Son Valley", *Mem. GSI* XXXI (1901), 1–178. An amazingly "modern" geomorphological study for its date.

E. Vredenburg, "Pleistocene Movement as Indicated by Irregularities of Gradient of the Narbada", *Rec. GSI* XXXIII (1906), 33–45.

A. M. Heron, "The Physiography of Rajputana", *CGR* II No. 1 (1938), 1–13.

D. N. Wadia, "The Three Superposed Peneplains of Ceylon", *Rec. of Dept of Mineralogy, Ceylon*, Professional Paper No. 1 (1943), 25–32.

The Himalayan Orogeny

S. G. Burrard, H. H. Hayden, and A. M. Heron, *A Sketch of the Geography and Geology of the Himalaya Mountains and Tibet* (Govt of India, ND, 2nd ed., ?1933). Indispensable for a general view, but exceedingly badly arranged and in places much less than scientific. Detailed criticism would be presumptuous from one who has penetrated the Himalaya no farther than Simla, but the curious reader is referred to Professor K. Mason's review in *HJ* VII (1935), 113–24, a critique equally authoritative and amusing.

A. Heim and A. Gansser, *Central Himalaya: Geological Observations of the Swiss Expedition, 1936* (*Mem. Soc. Helvétique des Sciences Naturelles*, LXXIII, Zurich, 1939). Fullest and clearest general account of the newer nappe views.

—— and ——, *The Throne of the Gods* (1939). Travel book covering the same ground as preceding item; a delightful narrative and magnificent illustrations.

G. E. Hutchinson, *The Clear Mirror* (Cambridge, 1936). Travel, aesthetics, physiography, and biochemistry in a fascinating work of art.

D. N. Wadia, "The Syntaxis of the North-Western Himalaya", *Rec. GSI* LXV (1931), 189–220. A most important paper.

H. de Terra, "A Scientific Exploration of the Eastern Karakoram and Zanskar-Himalaya", *HJ* V (1933), 33–45.

——, "Physiographic Results of a Recent Survey in Little Tibet", *GR* XXIV (1934), 12–41. Most accessible presentation of extremely important work.

F. Kingdon Ward, "The Himalaya East of the Tsangpo", *GJ* LXXXIV (1934), 369–97.

K. Mason, "The Himalaya as a Barrier to Modern Communications", *GJ* LXXXVII (1936), 1–16.

E. B. Bailey, "Sedimentation in Relation to Tectonics", *Bulletin Geological Soc. of America* XLVII (1936), 1713–25.

J. B. Auden, "The Structure of the Himalayas in Garhwal", *Rec. GSI* LXXI (1936–37), 407–33.

L. R. Wager, "The Arun River Drainage Pattern and the Rise of the Himalayas", *GJ* LXXXIX (1937), 139–50.

A. Heim, "The Himalayan Border Compared with the Alps", *Rec. GSI* LXXI (1938), 413–21.

D. N. Wadia, "The Structure of the Himalayas and of the North Indian Foreland", *CGR* I No. 1 (1936), 38–49.

——, "The Support of the Himalaya Mountains", *CGR* II No. 2 (1939), 55–66.

Himalayan Glaciation

H. de Terra and T. T. Paterson, *Studies on the Ice Age in India* (Carnegie Inst. Pubtn No. 493, Washington, 1939). Exceedingly detailed studies on geomorphology and glacial history of Kashmir, Pir Panjal, and Potwar.

.   .   .   .   .

K. Mason, "Indus Floods and Shyok Glaciers", *HJ* I (1929), 10–29.

——, "The Glaciers of the Karakoram and Neighbourhood", *Rec. GSI* LXIII (1930), 214–78.

J. Gunn, "Report on the Chong Kumdan Dam and the Shyok Flood of 1929", (Govt of Punjab, Lahore, 1930).

E. Trinkler, "Notes on the Westernmost Plateaux of Tibet", *HJ* III (1931), 42–50.

K. Mason, "The Study of Threatening Glaciers", *GJ* LXXXV (1935), 28–41.

A. L. Coulson, "Pleistocene Glaciation in North-Western India", *Rec. GSI* LXXII (1938), 422–39.

K. Mason, "Upper Shyok Glaciers, 1939", *HJ* XII (1940), 52–65.

L. Krenek, "Recent and Past Glaciation of Lahoul", *IGJ* XX (1945), 93–102.

Numerous notes and papers on the Shyok and other glaciers by Professor Mason and others will be found in *The Himalayan Journal*.

Himalayan Rivers

E. H. Pascoe, "Early History of the Indus, Brahmaputra, and Ganges", *Quarterly Journal Geological Soc.* LXXV (1919), 138–59.

G. E. Pilgrim, ". . . History of the Drainage of Northern India . . .", *Journal Royal Asiatic Soc. of Bengal*, New Series XV (1919), 81–99.

H. de Terra, *loc. cit. GR* XXIV (1934); and cf. *Studies on the Ice Age in India*, 300–01.

L. M. Davies, "Geographical Changes in North-West India . . .", in *Proceedings 6th Pacific Science Congress* (1940).

——, "Note on Three Himalayan Rivers", *Geological Mag.* LXXVII (1940), 410–12.

The Indo-Gangetic Trough

H. H. Hayden, "Notes on the Relationship of the Himalayas to the Indo-Gangetic Plain", *Rec. GSI* XLIII (1913), 138–72.

R. D. Oldham, "The Structure of the Himalaya and of the Gangetic Plain", *Mem. GSI* XLII (1917), 1–153.

E. A. Glennie, "Gravity Anomalies and the Earth's Crust" (*Survey of India*, Professional Paper No. 27, Dehra Dun, 1932).

C. A. Longwell, "A Challenge to Isostasy", *GR* XXIII (1933), 682–83.

D. N. Wadia, *loc. cit.*, *CGR* II No. 2 (1939).

W. Arden Wood, "Rivers and Man in the Indus-Ganges Alluvial Plains", *Scottish Geographical Magazine* XL (1924), 1–15.

Coasts

S. W. Cushing, "The East Coast of India", *Bulletin American Geographical Society* XLV (1913), 81–92. Some exceedingly dubious interpretations; see below, Ch. XXV.

R. B. S. Sewell, "Geographic and Oceanographic Researches in Indian Waters", *Mem. Asiatic Soc. of Bengal* IX (1925–35); summarised in *GJ* LXXIII (1934), 135–39, and LXXIV (1934), 154–56.

—— and J. D. H. Wiseman, "The Floor of the Arabian Sea", *Geological Mag.* LXXIV (1937), 219–30.

CHAPTER II

CLIMATE

I. THE MONSOONAL RHYTHM

Dominance of the Monsoons; Terminology

ALTHOUGH half its area lies N of the Tropic of Cancer, India is pre-eminently the land of tropical monsoon climates. The great wall of the Himalayas effectively shuts off the sub-continent from the immediate influences of the air-masses generated in the Central Asian source-regions; these do indeed affect the upper air, but the monsoon is in a sense a surprisingly thin phenomenon, and the impressionistic view of the Himalaya as a vast wind-break is borne out by upper-air soundings.[1] The land is sufficiently massive to develop its own individual system of monsoons, and to display marked continentality in the N and especially the NW, where winter minima, even in the plains, may drop below freezing. But the daily as well as the annual ranges are highest in these same areas, and, although the NW is well outside the mathematical tropics, its summer temperatures are more than equatorial.

Differences of rainfall rather than of temperature are of primary significance, except in so far as temperature controls rain at a remove, through pressure. The regional contrasts in precipitation are most striking: from Cherrapunji's annual average of 428 ins. (with a record claim of 905, 500 of them in two months!) to Jacobabad's 4 in. and completely rainless years in Sind. Yet underlying this great diversity is almost everywhere the same rhythm of the seasons; in few areas is the summer rainfall less than 80% of the total. Rain governs life to a degree not easily realised in lands with a more evenly distributed precipitation, and rain in turn is governed by the alternations of the monsoon.

The word *monsoon* (Arabic *mausim*) originally meant simply 'season', and by transference the very marked seasonal winds of the Arabian Sea. In colloquial European speech in the E 'monsoon' by itself nearly always implies the rainy season, but usually in meteorological literature and always in nautical it refers to the great air-currents of winter and summer, the 'NE' and 'SW' monsoons respectively. These directions, however applicable to the winds over the Indian Ocean, are not too appropriate to those over India itself, as owing to the excentric position of the area of greatest pressure-reversal and the general lie of land and

---

[1] ". . . the intervention of the Himalayas increases the temperature of the Indo-Gangetic plain from 3° to 5° above what it would have been if a low-level plain had extended northwards to the Arctic regions." *Imperial Gaz.* (1909), I 107; cf. Garbell, 170.

sea, mountain and plain, the actual direction of the prevalent winds is SW or NE in relatively few areas (Fig. 11). The use of these directional terms is thus probably a hangover from sailing-ship days.

The Indian Meteorological Department recognises four seasons: the NE and SW monsoon seasons (December–March and June–September respectively), the transitional hot weather (April–May), and the transitional period of the retreating SW monsoon (October–November). Popularly, however, the year falls into the cold weather (November–February), the hot weather (March–May), and the rains (June–September), with October as a 'sticky' transitional month, the rains not quite over and the cold weather not set in. Though less correct theoretically, this division accords very well with the sensible weather conditions.

Before following the standard practice of describing the seasonal conditions, the independence of the Indian monsoon system must again be stressed. Small-scale atlas maps, with their great homogeneous areas of pressure reduced to sea-level, give a misleading picture. The independence of India is reflected in the marked contrast between the relative development of the two monsoons in India and in En Asia. The Himalayan wall protects India from bitterly cold winter winds like those of Nn China (it is significant that the Baluchistan Plateau does suffer such conditions), while—largely owing to lower latitude and greater insolation —the high pressure then formed over India is much weaker and produces much lighter winds than that of Mongolia. *Per contra*, the extremely intensive heating of NW India in the hot weather produces steep pressure gradients and the SW monsoon is generally much stronger than its Chinese counterpart.

The Cold Weather, January–February

By the end of December relatively high pressures prevail over NW India, and the general movement of air in the N is down the Indus and Ganges Valleys, making for the low pressures just S of the Equator. But over the Peninsula winds are Ely as low pressures run farther N over the Arabian Sea than over the Bay of Bengal. Gradients are not steep enough to produce strong winds, and in the N breezes are very light indeed.

This is the season of greatest temperature contrast, means ranging from under 80° in the S to 50–55° in the Punjab.[2] Humidity is generally quite low and skies almost cloudless over most of the country. Night radiation is active in the N, and the low temperatures of the NW are due primarily to this, the nights being very clear, and cold for the latitude, while during daylight there is little check on insolation. Thus the mean January maxima and minima at Lahore (700 ft) and Peshawar (1164 ft) are 68·9° and 40·2°, 63·4° and 40·8° respectively. The higher night tem-

---

[2] All temperatures in Fahrenheit.

perature at Peshawar is probably due to the greater cloudiness brought by the more frequent depressions. At these stations absolute minima of 24·7° and 23·9° have been recorded. In the N, and on the Deccan Plateaus, ground fogs due to temperature inversion are quite common for two or three hours before and after sunrise. The extreme S is naturally more humid and this, as well as lower latitude, accounts for the much smaller ranges: at Trivandrum (Travancore) January means are 84·0° and 72·3°,

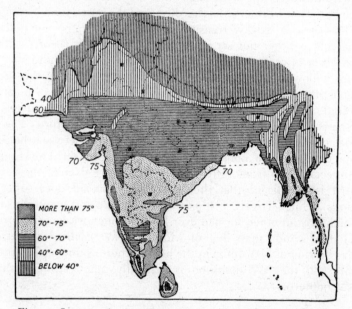

Fig. 9.—JANUARY ACTUAL TEMPERATURES; courtesy L. D. Stamp.

and the mean annual range is only about 5°, a fraction of the daily range in the N.

Over most of India the cold weather is almost rainless, except for occasional late monsoon storms; but the SE littoral has still some precipitation from the tail of the retreating SW monsoon, while in the NW the cold-weather rain, though not heavy, is extremely important as the winter crops, especially wheat and barley, depend largely upon it. This precipitation (at higher levels it is snow) is associated with depressions, mostly of "Mediterranean" origin but with some secondaries developed over Iran; the usual warm and cold fronts are observed. It must be admitted that the ascription of a Mediterranean origin to these depressions is rather an *a priori* conclusion, since adequate observed data in the lands W of the NW frontier are lacking. In the extreme NW this cold-weather rain is actually greater than that of usual rains period; thus in November-

April inclusive Peshawar has nearly 8 of its total 16 ins., and 14·5 of its 26 rainy days occur in January–April. Although the depressions bring some rain as far as Wn UP, it falls off very rapidly, and at Lahore, 230 miles SE of Peshawar, the November–April fall is 3·8 out of 19·6 ins., falling on 9 out of the annual 28 rainy days. The importance of the cold-weather snows to the sustenance of the Wn Himalayan glaciers has been noted.

The Hot Weather, March–May

From early in March temperatures rise rapidly and pressures decrease. The mean maximum is already over 100° in the Deccan in March; by May, the hottest month in most places, it is over 105°, with means of 85–95°, in the interior, except where modified by altitude. In Punjab the thermometer rises to over 110° and in Sind to over 120° in some places. Just before the SW monsoon breaks in June temperatures reach their maximum; Jacobabad has a June *mean* of 97·7° and has also the highest absolute recorded in India, 126°; even the nights have 75–80° over most of Nn India. The extreme S has a much more equable régime; Trivandrum's mean maxima and minima for April, here the hottest month, are 88·0° and 77·9° and the extremes recorded are 93·5° and 63·0°. Along the coast the heat is mitigated by sea-breezes, but this is offset by greater humidity; elsewhere humidities are low, very low indeed in the NW. By May the low pressure is fully developed, and along the coast light on-shore breezes prevail; but Nlies still hold over the Arabian Sea.

Precursors of the general rains, 'mango showers' occur in the S, along the E coast, and in Assam; in April and May respectively Trivandrum has 4·47 and 8·45 ins., Calcutta 1·89 and 5·75, Dacca 5·36 and 9·75. This rain is associated with local depressions and convectional movements and, especially in Bengal and Assam, with violent thundery squalls ('Nor'-Westers') which sometimes reach hurricane force; in Assam the rain is very important for the tea crop. In the interior, and especially in the Indo-Gangetic Plains, similar disturbances take the form of fierce dust-storms, driving sand and dust into the crevices of furniture and reducing visibility to a few yards; there is a strongly marked cold front, probably accompanied by condensation in the upper air, but no more than a trace of moisture, if so much, reaches the ground.

The Rains, June–September

The regularity of the date of arrival of the rains can be exaggerated, but hardly the dramatic abruptness of their onset in the coastal regions, especially in the W: strong winds from the sea, violent lashing rain, a sudden fall of temperature. Inland the change is less sharp, though as a rule still well marked. The SW monsoon breaks on the Bombay coast about

June 5th, in Bengal about June 15th, and by July has spread over nearly all India, advancing on a broad turbulent front aptly likened by Eliot to an estuarine bore.

Over the Peninsula winds are from W or S of W, stronger on the Bombay coast than elsewhere in India. Peninsular rainfall is therefore strongly orographical: the Wn Ghats have 80–100 ins. or more on their seaface, with a very well-marked rain-shadow to leeward: Mahabaleshwar, practically on the crest, has 261 ins., Panchgani, only 10 miles to the E, only 68; 10 miles farther on Wai has 29 ins. In Nn India conditions are rather different: the monsoon current over the Bay of Bengal is Sly and is deflected by the Himalayan wall so that it flows up the Ganges from the SE. Except on the Himalayan slopes and in Assam there are no pronounced relief features athwart its course, and hence there is a fairly steady diminution in amount of rain from Bengal to the Punjab:

Miles		Annual Rain	June–Sept. incl.	% June–Sept.
		ins.	ins.	
0	Calcutta	62·5	47·0	75
400	Patna	48·5	41·9	86
625	Allahabad	39·1	34·0	87
1000	Delhi	26·8	22·7	85
1275	Lahore	19·6	14·85	76
1500	Peshawar	15·9	7·2	45

The Himalayan slopes show a comparable decrease from E to W, but naturally with higher totals: Darjeeling, Simla, and Murree, the first two at about 7250 ft and the last 6350, and corresponding roughly with Calcutta, Lahore, and Peshawar in longitude, have 108, 48, and 35 ins. during the rains.

An important feature is the low pressure trough extending SW from the Indus low pressure centre along a line S of and roughly parallel to the Ganges into Orissa. Here converge the Arabian Sea and Bay of Bengal currents; it is thus an area of excessively unstable air and an avenue for depressions forming in the Bay and bringing local very heavy falls. This emphasises the fact that even in the wetter parts rain is not continuous after the first few days, but falls in frequent pulsatory downpours along the coast or in rainy spells inland. Thus at Calcutta 1 day out of 2 in the rains is a rainy day (0·1 in. or more), 62·6 out of the year's 85·2 rainy days coming in June–September: but at Delhi only 1 out of every 4 or 5 days in the rains is wet, June–September having 26·6 of the total 36. This 'pulsatory' activity of the monsoon is associated with the passage of depressions or the interlocking of new and old air-masses, and in the NW most of the 'rains' season is actually dry, except when cyclones press into the Punjab and Rajputana.

The opposite extremes of rainfall are of special interest. The Sn slopes of the Shillong Plateau, athwart the monsoon and immediately above the warm flood-waters of the Surma Valley, have up to or even over 400 ins. (Cherrapunji 428). This huge total is restricted to a small area, amounts

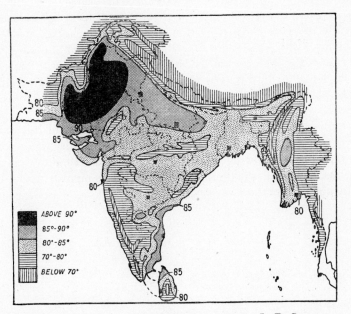

Fig. 10.—JULY ACTUAL TEMPERATURES; courtesy L. D. Stamp.

falling off very rapidly in the rain-shadow to the N (Shillong 55, Gauhati 43 ins.), but to the NE the upper Assam Valley is a funnel into which moist air is driven up the Brahmaputra itself and across the relatively low Cachar gap to the S, and has again a high total (90–100 ins. or more).

The Sn Punjab, Wn Rajputana, and Sind receive under 10 ins. (Jacobabad 4), and this often in violent downpours from either exceptionally strong depressions or local convection; on such occasions disastrous floods may result. As this area of intensest low pressure adjoins the Arabian Sea, with no relief barriers, the extreme aridity calls for explanation. On the N and W the region is shut in by the Himalayas and the Afghan-Baluchi ranges; any air from the continental interior will be warmed in the descent. Very obviously not much moisture is left in Bay of Bengal air by the time it has traversed 1200 miles of thirsty land. There remains the Arabian Sea branch. The area of maximum temperature and minimum pressure is naturally some way inland; air from the Arabian Sea current is largely deflected around the low pressure centre, bringing some rain to the Aravallis but not to the Thar. Some air does enter directly across the Sind coast, but this is largely derived from originally dry currents trending from the NW across Makran and swinging NE towards the pressure centre; they pick up a little moisture during their short sea passage, and humidity is high at Karachi, diminishing rapidly inland. Convectional ascension naturally occurs, but before condensation can take place the rising air usually meets a very strong and dry anti-monsoonal upper current from Baluchistan. This effectually prevents cloud-formation, permitting unchecked insolation at ground level, with consequent super-heating and loss of humidity. Thus it is only in exceptional circumstances, such as the occasional displacing of the continental air by Ely (Bay of Bengal) monsoon air, that precipitation can take place at all, and when it does it is often of a violent convectional type.[3]

Except in the NW, where June is the hottest month and July only 2–4° lower, mean temperatures in the rains are nearly everywhere distinctly lower than in May. Owing to humidity and cloudiness, however, there is much less nocturnal radiation, and in many places night temperatures are actually higher than those of May:

	Mean		Mean Minimum		Mean Range	
	May	July	May	July	May	July
Calcutta .	85·7	83·0	77·6	78·7	17·0	9·9
Patna . .	88·0	83·5	77·7	79·8	22·0	10·7
Delhi .	91·7	86·4	80·2	81·1	23·8	13·8

(All in ° F.)

Even where there is little rain, there is generally a good deal of cloud, and the loss of insolation brings day temperatures down. But the lower means are offset by higher humidities and lower ranges and the muggy overcast weather; but on the coast the rain itself vivifies the atmosphere and the actual physiological conditions are often quite pleasant, though psychologically long spells with not a gleam of sun become rather depressing. But a steamy break in the rains is worse; and in areas intermediate between the very rainy and the arid the 'rains' are as much break as rain.

[3] G. C. Simpson, 157–59; W. G. Kendrew, 132–33. For a good analysis of the air movements involved in an actual case of heavy rainfall in Gujarat and at Karachi, see Sur, 47–8. (For full references see Bibliographical Note at end of chapter.)

The Retreating SW Monsoon, October–December

By October the Indian low pressure is breaking or broken up, and thence-forward the low pressure centre shifts back to equatorial latitudes. Over India as a whole depressions become weaker and less frequent; there is no such abrupt change as marks the onset of the rains, but over most of Nn India drier conditions with Wly winds begin in September.

Pressure remains low over the Bay, however, forming cyclones which

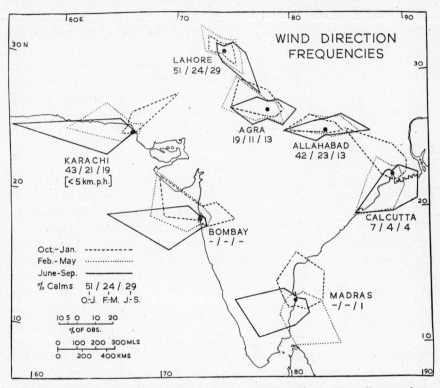

Fig. 11.—WIND DIRECTION FREQUENCIES, 1939. Angles of polygons at distances from station proportionate to number of observations of winds from each quarter. It should be noted that (i) the SE winds at Madras come mainly in January–April; (ii) the Arabian Sea current was relatively weak in 1939.
Source: Indian Meteorological Dept., *Scientific Notes VII*, No. 80.

curve round to the N of the central low and approach the E coast of India from the W; not infrequently they attain typhoon intensity. This spasmodic activity brings rain to the Nn coastal districts of Madras in October–November, to the Sn in November–December. The latter are rain-shadow areas in respect of the Arabian Sea branch and are largely by-passed by the Bay current earlier in the year, so that they receive most of their rain in this season:

	Lat. N	Annual, ins.	July–Sept. incl.	%	Oct.–Dec. incl.	%
Vizagapatam .	17° 42'	37·1	21·22	57·2	11·55	31·1
Madras .	13° 04'	50·7	15·46	30·5	31·78	62·5
Tuticorin .	8° 48'	21·9	1·2	5·5	15·6	71·2

This 'cold weather' rainfall of the SE is thus due to the retreating SW monsoon and not (as is still often stated) to the NE, which has not yet properly set in.

Temperatures are remarkably uniform in October—77–81° over most of India—and generally show a slight rise after the rainier months; together with the high humidity this makes the close of the rains perhaps the most uncomfortable season of the year. In Nn India November shows a sharp drop of 6–10° on the October figures, despite the generally clearer skies.

The Mechanism of the Monsoons (Figs. 11–13)

"It has been well said that although every schoolboy understands the Indian monsoon, the official meteorological department is still in doubt as its origin." [4] The vital importance of accurate forecasting to the prosperity and even the lives of the people of the sub-continent has led to a search for correlations, ranging as far afield as Alaska and the South Orkneys. Some seem established, e.g. excessive rains in Zanzibar and Java seem to portend a general deficiency in India (except the NE), while a lack of rain in the Seychelles in May is often followed by a good monsoon in NE India. But on the whole no large measure of success has been attained along these lines.

In view of the steady march of temperature and pressure in the earlier months of the year, the sudden 'burst' and its delay until June call for explanation; pressure in June is much the same as in May, and the lower June temperature is itself due to cooling by the rains. The explanation lies, apparently, in pressure conditions over the Indian Ocean as a whole. The SW monsoon when fully deployed is of course fed by the moist SE trades, and their normal goal is the equatorial low; in April, and even into May, a tract of *relatively* high pressure, or at least of slight gradients, persists over the Arabian Sea. This is shown, *inter alia*, by the 29·70 May isobar, which runs from Oman to Cutch and then bends S and SE over the Peninsula to the Cauvery Delta. The Arabian Sea in fact lies between two great lows, one over the Punjab and the other over the En Sudan, and winds round the Indian low trend mostly from the NW. Air currents do indeed cross the W coast in May, but their relative humidity is much less than that of similar

[4] G. B. Cressey, *Asia's Lands and Peoples* (1944), 420.

currents in July—at Karachi 76 against 80%, at Bombay 74 against
86%.[5]

With the continuous heating of May and early June the Indian low
intensifies and pressure gradients steepen, but the change from anticyclonic
to cyclonic conditions "takes place without any large alteration in the upper
circulation above 2 km." and up to 8 km., W of 70° E, "it appears probable
that on the aggregate the net transport of air is from north to south." [6] The
rising air thus probably flows Swds to settle in the equatorial low; once
that fills up, the moisture-filled SE trades sweep on unchecked towards the
Indian low. For reasons already given the NW remains an area of very little
rain and intense insolation; the surface low is thus perpetuated, gradients

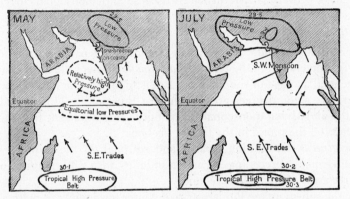

Fig. 12.—THE EVOLUTION OF THE MONSOON; courtesy L. D. Stamp.

over India itself are much steeper in July than in May, and strong winds and
depressions can penetrate the interior.

The 'pulsatory' nature of monsoon rainfall is due to the interaction
along local fronts of three distinct types of air-masses: old monsoon air,
fresh monsoon air, and old continental air from NW India. Old monsoon
air has a lesser relative humidity at the surface than fresh, but it is warmer
owing to contact with the land and has a higher absolute humidity. It may
simply act as a warm air-mass rising above fresh monsoon air, or a wedge
of continental air may persist between old and fresh monsoon masses, acting
at heights of 2–4 km. as cold air.[7] With these complex and ever-changing
conditions there is naturally considerable instability of humid air-masses.
Thus in Wn UP and Nn Rajputana rainfall can be caused by obstruction of
the Ely fresh monsoon air by continental air from the NW, which "may
either spread close to the ground or extend as a wedge between the south-
westerly branch of the monsoon and its deflected eastern branch coming

    [5] Simpson, 164.
    [6] *Meteorology for Airmen*, 11; Ramanathan and Ramakrishnan (1939), 204–06.
    [7] Ramanathan and Ramakrishnan (1933), 33–35; *cf.* Garbell, 87–88.

over the Gangetic valley"; or condensation may take place by direct ascent of the new over the old air.[8]

The intensity of these phenomena is greatly accentuated by the Himalayan wall, which influences the whole wind system up to a height of 6 km. (19,700 ft): "This is seen alike in the mean movement of air parallel to the Himalayas during the winter and hot season, and in the existence during this period of a region of maximum wind strength up to 6 km. in the east of UP and Bihar and also in the localisation of the monsoon low to within the confines of India."[9] Relatively little of the immense mass of air poured into India during the SW monsoon trickles, as it were, through the notches in the mountain rim; most of it probably joins complex circulations in the upper air or is eventually returned Swds as an anti-monsoonal current.

Climatic Regions

"In all that depends upon climate, the different parts of India exhibit very great diversity . . . the term *Indian climate* means little more than that, on a general average of the year, the sun is higher in the heavens, and the temperature some degrees greater, than in Europe." [10] This indeed overlooks the underlying monsoonal unity, but is ample warrant for Blanford's insistence on the plural in the title of his book.

The *general* distribution, spatial and seasonal, of the rainfall will be apparent from the preceding discussion and Figs. 13–14. We may recapitulate the three areas of anomalous régime:

  (i) the sub-montane Punjab strip of winter (cyclonic) rain with a feeble extension across the Jumna; slight as the January fall of 0·5–2 ins. is, this is nearly as much as that of an English January;

  (ii) Assam and Bengal, with 10–20 plus ins. in April–May from the Nor'-Westers;

  (iii) the SE littoral, where the normal rainy months are actually among the driest.

To these may be added the extreme SW littoral with its short dry season. All else within the mountain girdle, if it has rain at all, has it in the normal SW monsoon months.

Nevertheless this dealing with things in the gross oversimplifies a complicated picture. Nor, although temperature variations on the whole are less than those of rainfall, and of less human significance, are they by any means negligible. Altitude and exposure produce some remarkable extremes: minus 49° at Dras (Kashmir), 126° at Jacobabad, at Quetta reported ranges of 80° within 24 hours. Leaving aside these freaks, if the normal annual range on the Malabar coast is taken as unity, that of Bombay is 2, Karachi 4, N and central India 6–8.[11] These differences, of course, are

[8] Sur, 44.
[9] Ramanathan and Ramakrishnan (1939), 205.
[10] Blanford, 96–97.
[11] Normand, 10.

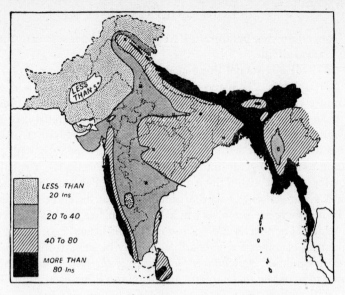

Fig. 13.—ANNUAL RAINFALL; courtesy L. D. Stamp.

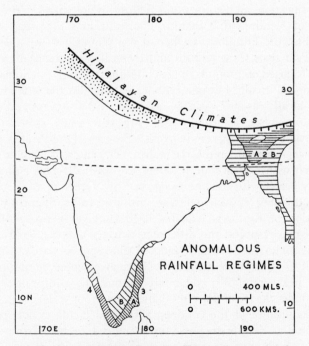

Fig. 14.—ANOMALOUS RAINFALL RÉGIMES. 1, 1–5 ins. in
cold weather (Jan.–Feb.); 2A, over 20 ins., 2B, 10–20 ins.,
in hot weather (March–May) from Nor'-Westers; 3A, over
10 ins., 3B, 5–10 ins., in retreating monsoon (Nov.–Dec.);
4, dry season only 3 or 4 months.

due to low winter temperatures as we go N, and correspond to the continental/tropical divide.

The over-all monsoonal dominance, then, masks a mosaic of regional differentiation which is made apparent by juxtaposing these significant temperature variations with even more significant, and more subtle, variations in amount, seasonal distribution, intensity, and reliability of rain. The pattern of monthly distributions varies considerably even over short distances in accordance with local topography and especially with position in relation to the two great branches of the monsoon. In the Wn half of the Deccan, for example, either the Arabian Sea or the Bay branch may be dominant at a given station, or at the same station at different periods of the rains. Hence there are some very puzzling anomalies, such as the régime at Salem which is neither of SW monsoon nor SE littoral type. Considerable refinement of classification is possible, as may be seen in the climatic discussions in Simkins' *Agricultural Geography of the Deccan* or Deshpande's *Western India*, or the maps (9 and 10) of month of greatest rainfall and of months with under 50 cm. in Krebs' *Vorder Indien und Ceylon*.

It is interesting to compare India as it appears on the standard worldwide classifications of Köppen and Thornthwaite with the more empiric divisions of Kendrew and Stamp. Thornthwaite's 1933 map [12] is almost inexplicable: the lumping together of everything between the Himalaya and the Penner as Ca'w (sub-humid tropical, with deficient winter rain) might be excused on grounds of generalisation, though it ignores the continental/tropical divide; but one cannot imagine how the letter *r*—"rainfall adequate at all seasons"—can be attached to the Ganges and Irrawaddy Deltas. Köppen's classification (Fig. 15) comes much closer to the facts, with its major boundary, running across the root of the Peninsula, between Aw (tropical savannah) and CWg (warm, dry winter, "Gangetic" temperature march with hottest month before the solstice). This boundary coincides very nearly with the line recognised by Normand, Kazi Ahmad, and Stamp as dividing 'continental' from 'tropical' India. Stamp's well-known modification of Kendrew explains itself; it gives a reasonable picture, except in two respects: the difference between the Nagpur/Raipur area, with 50 ins. or less, and the mid-Ganges Delta, with 60–80 ins., is perhaps too significant to warrant the inclusion of both areas under an undifferentiated label of "heavy rainfall"; and, more serious, the aridity of the Bombay Deccan, under the lee of the Wn Ghats, is not brought out at all.

The significance of the continental/tropical divide is not, perhaps, so fundamental as Stamp suggests; unless indeed we take extreme cases, as Blanford does: "when we compare the most northerly province, the Pun-

[12] C. W. Thornthwaite, "The Climates of the Earth", *GR* XXIII (1933), 433–40. But t would be of great interest and value to apply to India his new evapotranspiration formulae in "An Approach towards a Rational Classification of Climate", *ibid.*, XXXVIII (1948), 55–94.

jab, with the most southerly, such as Travancore or Tenasserim, we have in
the former a continental climate of the most extreme character, extreme
summer heat alternating with winter cold that sometimes sinks to the
freezing-point, and in the latter that almost unvarying warmth in conjunc-

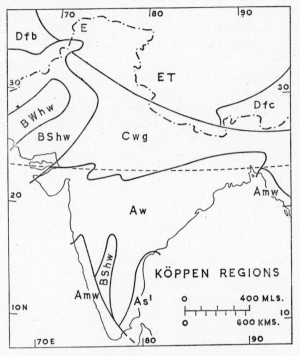

Fig. 15.—KÖPPEN CLIMATIC REGIONS.

Aw, tropical savannah (at least 1 month under 2·4 ins.);
Amw, monsoon with short dry season (rainforest); As¹, dry
season in high sun period.

BShw, semi-arid steppe, hot, winter drought (wettest
month 10 times rainfall of driest); BWhw, hot desert.

CWg, dry winter (wettest month 10 times rainfall of
driest), 'Gangetic' temperature régime) hottest month before
solstice and rains).

Dfb, cold humid winters, cool summers; Dfc, as Dfb with
shorter summer (over 4 months below 50° F.).

E, 'Polar'—warmest month under 50° F.; ET, 'Tundra',
warmest month between 32 and 50° F.

tion with a uniformly moist atmosphere, that is especially characteristic
of the shores of a tropical sea." [13] But examination of crop distribution, the
most fundamental fact in the life of India, suggests that at bottom this
continentality is of less human significance than is the E–W falling off of
rainfall; the pattern of most crops has more of a meridional than a latitudinal

[13] Blanford, *loc. cit.*; quoted (without acknowledgement) in Normand, 10.

aspect. In fact Pierre Gourou emphasises (perhaps too strongly) "a meridional axis of aridity . . . which has produced affinities between Rajputana and the extreme south of India and has played, in my opinion, a primary rôle in the evolution of the cultural landscape of India . . . there is always an element of aridity in the climates of the peninsular interior." [14] While farming practices and agricultural rhythms vary considerably between N and S, the transitional zones seem to bear little relation to this divide. Nor does it correspond meteorologically, except in part, to the important Arabian Sea/Bay of Bengal division. It is, in short, of mainly academic interest; as has been suggested, the boxing-in by the Himalaya really makes all India monsoonal and tropical, with the injection of a strong continental component in the NW. Far more significant is Blanford's other differentiation within "extra-tropical" India: "Northern or extra-tropical India alone, in its most easterly and most westerly provinces, in Assam on the one hand and Sind on the other, presents us with the greatest possible contrast of dampness and dryness, a contrast greater than that of the British Isles and Egypt." It must be admitted, however, that 4 inches of snow at Rawalpindi (only 1650 ft) does not look very tropical! [15]

II. CLIMATE AND MAN

Weather

The 'sensible climate' of India is largely a matter of humidity and of local and ephemeral phenomena—in fact, of weather as distinct from climate. To summarise the vast mass of material by writers from Blanford onwards would be impossible, but we may note some of the features which most directly affect human comfort.[16]

The regularity of the rhythm has at least the advantage that one knows what to expect, and adjustment both physiological and social is in consequence fairly easy. It is true that, despite the fact that rain falleth upon the just and unjust alike, the weather is not really the same to all men: however invigorating the Nn winter may be to Europeans, "the thinly clad native, inured to heat and living in a draughty hut, with perhaps a single meal a day of less stimulating food, is less enraptured with the delights of the cold weather . . . which he endeavours to meet by swathing his head and mouth in a fold of his body cloth, and cowering over the embers of his little fire . . ."; in the morning fogs of the NE at this season the shivering coolies make a picture of wraith-like misery not easy to forget.

On the whole it is true to say that for most people "it isn't the heat, it's the humidity" that counts, up to 100° or so at least. In the NW hot weather

[14] P. Gourou, "Quelques observations de géographie tropicale dans l'Inde", *Revue de l'Univ. de Bruxelles* (1950–51), *ad. fin.*

[15] Blanford, 204–05; the snow was associated with a winter depression (January 1883).

[16] Quotations in this section from Blanford, unless otherwise stated.

relative humidities are very low indeed—down to 1% in Sind, according to Kendrew; average annual humidities range from about 50 in the NW to 80 or more in the NE, where in August Darjeeling has 95%.[17] Even in the hot weather Calcutta has about 75%; this figure is of course affected by the 'Nor'-Westers,' and the driest months are November and December. A dry 105° is generally preferred to a humid 90–95°. It is in fact quite possible to work efficiently at over 100° with a low humidity,[18] though it is more sensible to work at night, when the temperature may be a bare 75–80°. In the daytime houses are kept shut (the blank-walled SW Asia type is obviously better than European styles) and a variety of cooling devices are employed, from modern air-conditioning and electric fans to the *punkah*, a fringed hanging curtain oscillated (when he is awake) by a servant, or, where there is a breeze, the *tatti*, a grass screen kept constantly wet. Water is kept cool by the use of porous pots which allow evaporation from all surfaces.

The hot weather has its breaks *of* rain, the pleasant mango showers and, in the NE, the 'Nor'-Westers'. These tropical cyclones, though destructive, are less frequent and as a rule less violent than those of the retreating SW monsoon season. Some of the latter are real typhoons which have moved across from the China Sea or even the Pacific, generally along the inter-tropical front "between the humid monsoon current and the comparatively drier winds from the north." They can be devastating: in the Bakarganj cyclone of 1876 "about 100,000 people were drowned in half an hour on the alluvial flats of the Meghna." [19] In the NW hot weather depressions generally take the form of violent dust-storms. In these visibility at ground-level may be only four or five yards, though this dense stratum may be quite shallow. These storms are local cold fronts, and associated turbulence may lead to some condensation in the upper layers, but only a few drops of rain, if any, reach the ground. The sharp drop in temperature is stimulating, if short-lived. Such dust-storms are distinct from the *loo*, a very hot dust-laden wind which may blow for days on end.

In the rains temperatures are lower, and feel lower than they really are. Gratifying as this initial coolness is, however, after a few weeks of eternally cloud-sealed skies the absence of sun has a very depressing psychological effect. Breaks are welcome enough at first, but in a day or two the steamy atmosphere becomes all but intolerable: this is good riot weather. The inconveniences of the rains are for the most part indirect: the insects, the difficulty of drying anything (whence the 'dhobi smell' on laundry dried

[17] The admirable suite of humidity maps in the *Climatological Atlas* should be consulted for diurnal and monthly variations.

[18] The writer has worked with verve and enjoyment for 8–10 hours a day with minima of 80–90° and maxima of 100–105°; at this time it was impossible to hold one's hand, for the first minute or so, under a "cold" tap fed by an exposed pipe. How long, and for how many seasons, this can be kept up is another matter.

[19] Normand, 10; cf. V. D. A. Iyer, *passim*.

over a cow-dung fire), the mould on books and all leather articles, the sogginess of cigarettes, the deliquescence of salt, sugar, and sweets. For the office worker there are the disagreeable alternatives of sweating profusely over his papers, or having them wildly blown about by a fan. The worst month from most points of view is usually October, when the air is still heavily laden with moisture but not cooled by much actual rain.

The cold weather, as has been noted, is delightful . . . for Europeans. From the weather point of view the most striking feature is the prevalence, especially in the NE, of morning ground-fogs. These may be very heavy and persist for a couple of hours after sunrise; even at sea-level in 16° N 'first light' can be, or seem, bitterly cold and raw.

The direct effects of climate on health fall roughly into the obvious and the obscure; the seasonal incidence of pulmonary diseases on the one hand, or the prevalence of trachoma in arid dusty regions; on the other the doubtful relationships of the numerous fevers and gastro-intestinal diseases of unknown origin and difficult diagnosis. It is clear, for instance, that climate by itself has little to do with the distribution of malaria: the map in the 1941 Census Report shows hyperendemic conditions in all the humid jungle tracts, but much of wet E Bengal is one of the few plains areas with an enlarged spleen rate of under 10%, while a large area in the NW (the Potwar Plateau, Loralai-Zhob country, etc.) has moderate to high endemicity. Still more obscure is the possible correlation of 'relaxing' or 'bracing' climates with local human traits; it is tempting enough to contrast Punjabis and Bengalis, but there are a host of other factors overlooked by the useless impressionism which usually marks such evaluations.[20]

One climatic phenomenon is not indeed peculiar to India but reaches perhaps its highest development there: the hill station.[21] The motivation is obvious, and yet in part at least social; men (and women) with serious work to do can do it in the plains through the hot weather for years on end, though there is probably a cumulative psycho-physiological effect.[22] Simla, as typical a hill station as could be found, is discussed below (Ch. VII). Nearly all hill stations lie at about 6000–7500 ft, except for the minor ones at 3000–5000 ft in central India, such as Pachmarhi. Places intermediate between hills and plain may be cooler than the latter but, unless they occupy an isolated prominence, may be more oppressive, as they are often in valleys without much air movement; such are Dehra Dun (UP) and Peradeniya (Ceylon), both in basins at about 1800 ft. Many people find these more

---

[20] Cf. the original note struck by A. Geddes, "The Social and Psychological Significance of Variability in Population Change", *Human Relations*, I (1947), 181–205.

[21] Blanford, 96–126; Kendrew, 148–49 (Simla); J. E. Spencer and W. L. Thomas, "The Hill Stations and Summer Resorts of the Orient", *GR* XXXVIII (1948), 637–51.

[22] To cite personal experience again, the writer in 8 years spent altogether some 10–11 weeks in the hills, with only one hot-weather spell of 5 weeks. He did not begin to feel really tired until the last year (1945), when hours of work would have accounted for this without any climatic intervention.

trying than Delhi or Colombo. Blanford draws attention to the difference
between hills stations on the Himalaya and on the Nilgiris and Palnis:
"while those in the North-west Himalaya are subject to great vicissitudes
of heat and cold, dryness and dampness in the course of the year, those of
Southern India and Ceylon are comparatively uniform in these respects,
and their fine dry season is shorter than at the northern stations, and by no
means so dry." Some of the Himalayan stations are developing towards an
all-year season with winter sports.

Agriculture and Rainfall: Reliability and Efficiency of Rain

There remains the all-important question of the efficiency and variability
of rain. It is obvious, to begin with, that the usefulness of the rainfall for
agriculture and for hydro-electric development is greatly limited by the
normal concentration into five months of the twelve. In the N this is to
some extent offset by the Himalayan snow-melt, which floods the rivers
two months or so before the onset of the rains. But the Peninsular rivers,
fed only by the monsoon, show much more extreme contrasts in stage.
Streams half a mile wide or more in high flood shrink to a trickle a yard or
so across, and their beds are great ribbons of sand across which the cattle
move in clouds of dust to the water-holes. Clearly this involves large costs
in reservoir construction both for large-scale irrigation and for hydro-
electricity. On some rivers, the Chambal for instance, the great difference
in stage amounts to a significant seasonal change in local base-level, and in
conjunction with violent but localised rainstorms this may be a contributory factor in the intense gullying displayed on their banks.

The general rule that reliability is inverse to total amount holds. Fig. 16
indicates those areas most liable to disastrous drought, and sometimes to
more local but still destructive floods, as in Rajputana. Floods, however, are
more serious in the Orissa Delta and the lower Gangetic Plain, where the
problem is made much worse by the construction of roads and railways
athwart the natural drainage lines.

Taken as a whole it is safe to say that agriculture in areas with under
15–20 ins. is practically entirely dependent on irrigation, and large-scale
cultivation demands very expensive major works. It is only areas with over
45–50 ins. that are normally secure from dearth due to failure of the rains.
Moreover the total amount received in a given year may equal or even
exceed the average, and yet if the monthly distribution goes awry—especially
if the rains are late—the results may be nearly as bad as those of a complete
failure. The areas on the flanks of the main monsoon branches are particularly liable to such risks: Gujarat (cf. below, 603), the Sn margins of the
upper Gangetic Plains.

Areas with, say, 25–35 ins. are worse off than the really arid NW, since the
rainfall is usually, but only precariously, adequate for crops. In such mar-

ginal regions agriculture is indeed balanced on a knife-edge; there may be more good years than bad, but a run of two or three deficit seasons may spell complete disaster, and even a well-to-do peasant may have to sell his draught bullocks. This is another aspect of seasonality; the almost complete absence of fodder over much of central and Nn India means that it is very difficult to keep cattle through the hot weather, and poorer peasants accept

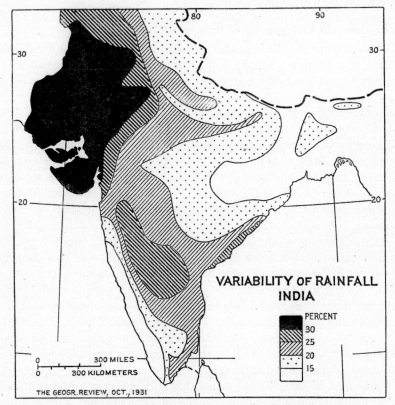

VARIABILITY OF RAINFALL
INDIA

PERCENT
30
25
20
15

300 MILES
300 KILOMETERS

THE GEOGR. REVIEW, OCT., 1931

Fig. 16.—VARIABILITY OF RAINFALL; courtesy L. D. Stamp and *G. R.*

the necessity of selling their bullocks as a normal event; the expense of buying again at the beginning of the rains is crippling, one of the strongest links in the chain which binds the cultivator to the moneylender. It is also in these marginal areas that soil factors take on the greatest significance for farming in general as well as for crop specialisation; a premium is placed upon moisture-retentive soils, such as the black earth (regur) of the Deccan Lavas. Unfortunately it is in these tracts of poor to moderate rainfall—notably the inner margins of Gujarat and the Bombay Karnatak (Wn

Deccan) that irrigation of any type is on the whole most difficult topo-graphically, and most costly in relation to area commanded and to possible returns. Here indeed it is not so much a capital investment as an insurance, at a very high premium, against disaster.

Intensity of rainfall is also a factor of the greatest significance. A rainy day in India, as in England, is one with 0·1 in. in 24 hours, but 10–20 ins. is not rare, and Purnea (Bihar) has recorded 25; and when 20 ins. fell in one day at Doorbaji (Sind), where the annual rainfall is about 6 in., the intensity of erosion may be imagined rather than described. At times very large falls may be recorded over great stretches of country, as for example the *average* of 5 ins. in two days for 30,000 sq mls of Madhya Pradesh (CP) in July 1882. "In consequence of this character of Indian, in common with tropical, rainfall generally, it is less penetrating in proportion to its quantity than in countries where much of it falls in a state of fine division, allowing time for its absorption by the ground. Instead of feeding perennial springs, and nourishing an absorbent cushion of green herbage, the greater part flows off the surface and fills the dry beds of drains and watercourses with temporary torrents." The results in flooding and erosion are widespread and serious.[23]

BIBLIOGRAPHICAL NOTE

H. F. Blanford, *The Climates and Weather of India, Ceylon, and Burmah* (1889). The enduring value of this work is attested by the often un-acknowledged use of it made by contemporary writers.

Sir J. Eliot (ed.), *Climatological Atlas of India* (1906). A splendid collection of 120 large coloured plates.

[Sir J. Eliot], *Meteorology* (Ch. III (104–56) in *Imperial Gaz.*, Vol. I, Oxford, 1909).

W. G. Kendrew, *The Climates of the Continents* (3rd ed., 1937). Ch. XIX (112–51) is a full account of Indian climate.

C. W. B. Normand, "The Weather of India", in *An Outline of the Field Sciences in India* (ed. S. L. Hora for Indian Science Congress Asstn., Calcutta, 1937, 1–16). Useful short summary.

Meteorology for Airmen in India, Pt I (Indian Meteorological Dept., 1936; 2nd ed., 1950).

Memoirs of Indian Meteorological Dept:

Vol. XXIV:

Sir G. T. Walker, "Correlations in Seasonal Variations of Weather (VIII, A Preliminary Study of World-Weather)", Pt IV (1923), 75–132.

W. A. Harwood, "The Free Atmosphere in India", Pt VI (1923), 167–216.

---

[23] Blanford, 64, 76, 259–76; cf. Vageler's views (below, 87). More modern discussion, with quantitative statements, will be found in the books by Glover and Gorrie cited in the bibliographical note to the next chapter.

Sir G. T. Walker and J. C. K. Rao, "Rainfall Types in India in the Cold Weather Period", XXIV, Pt XI (1924), 347–54.

Vol. XXVI:

K. R. Ramanathan and K. P. Ramakrishnan, "The Indian Southwest Monsoon and the Structure of Depressions Associated with it", Pt II (1933), 1–36.

N. K. Sur, "On the Physical Characteristics of Fronts during the Indian Southwest Monsoon", Pt III (1933), 37–50.

V. D. A. Iyer, "Typhoons and Indian Weather", Pt VI (1936), 94–130.

K. R. Ramanathan and K. P. Ramakrishnan, "The General Circulation of the Atmosphere over India and its Neighbourhood", Pt X (1939), 189–245.

Other articles:

G. C. Simpson, "The South-West Monsoon", *Quarterly Journal Royal Meteorological Society*, XLVII (1921), 151–72.

A. V. Williamson and K. G. T. Clark, "The Variability of the Annual Rainfall of India", *ibid.*, LVII (1931), 43–56.

K. G. T. Clark, "The Vicissitudes of the Summer Rainfall of the Indo-Gangetic Plain and the Assam Valley", *Geography*, XVII (1932), 286–92.

N. A. Holdaway, "A Note on Indian Rainfall Intensity", *ibid.*, XVIII (1933), 132–34.

H. A. Matthews, "A New View of some familiar Indian Rainfalls", *Scottish Geographical Magazine*, LII (1936), 84–97.

N. Carruthers, "An Analysis of the Variations in Rainfall at Akola", *Geography*, XXX (1945), 69–79 (diagrams by T. C. Warrington).

Additional Reference:

M. A. Garbell, *Tropical and Equatorial Meteorology* (1947). Ch. 12 contains perhaps the most readily accessible account of Indian weather in modern air-mass terms.

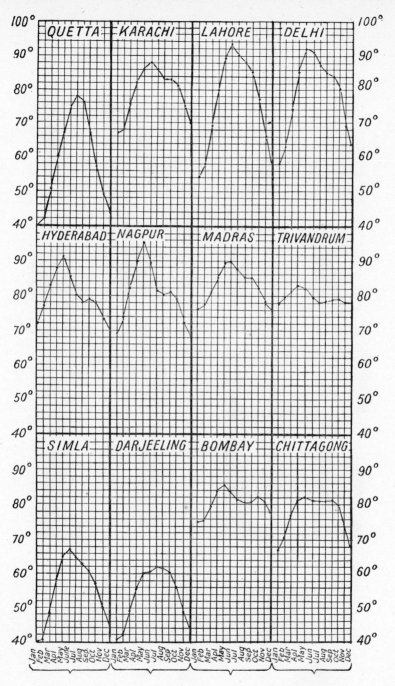

Fig. 17A.—Temperature Graphs; courtesy L. D. Stamp.

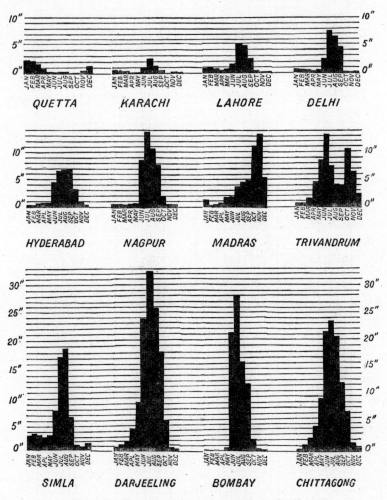

Fig. 17B.—RAINFALL GRAPHS; courtesy L. D. Stamp.

CHAPTER III

VEGETATION AND SOILS

I. VEGETATION

Original Forest Dominance

THE natural vegetation of India, except on the higher mountains and in the more arid parts of the Thar and Baluchistan, is essentially arboreal. Some 105,000 sq mls, or 12% of the total area, of British India is under forest; these figures refer to Reserved and Protected Forests, many of which consist of very open or stunted scrub and are essentially fuel or fodder reserves. But on the other hand large areas of jungle are outside the official forest area, so that the figure given is probably under rather than over the mark. Even in the central Punjab there is literary evidence of large forests in Alexander the Great's day, and the Gangetic Plain was probably originally covered with vast forests, largely of sal.[1]

This original cover has been profoundly modified. Three millennia of clearing for agriculture and of unregulated grazing (both often promoted by burning the jungle) have stripped the forest from nearly all of the plains and much of the lower hills and plateaus, or turned it into scrub. (Figs. 18–19.) In the Indo-Gangetic Plains as a whole woodland is almost confined to riverine strips and village groves of mangoes and tamarinds, while over vast areas of the less cultivated Deccan men and animals have produced the *aspect* of a short-grass savannah with scattered trees. From a strictly botanic point of view a map showing these areas as savannah would be inaccurate, but geographically it would not be nearly so misleading as one which showed them as forests. "Thin grass cover and scattered acacias . . . rough pasture, scattered acacias . . . thin cover of acacias, euphorbias"—such phrases occur time and again in field-notes of Peninsular journeys. But "it seems very doubtful if there are any examples of tropical climax grassland, though grassland is common enough as a secondary seral stage and it may be a very stable preclimax under the influence of fire and grazing. The typical savannah type of other countries is also apparently absent as a true climatic climax, closed deciduous forest grading into thorn forest without any open grassy park-like stage, in the absence of biotic influences", though there are small natural savannahs, especially on occasionally flooded alluvium.[2] With these qualifications, the forest classification must be taken as

---

[1] Calder, 83 (for full references, see bibliographical note at end of chapter).

[2] Champion, 14; for the role of fires, see Troup (1926), 307–10. Much of the terai is a savannah of tall (10–15 ft) grasses; and see Calder, Plate III, 2, for savannah on the river-terraces of a sub-Himalayan dun. Important grasses are *sabai*, a paper raw material, and *khas-khas*, used for the mats which, kept constantly wet, are a valuable hot-weather cooling device.

the basis of any vegetation study, the more so as, apart from the forest
literature, botanical work in India has been predominantly systematic
rather than ecological.

The lack of gregariousness in tropical forests is well known; on the whole
the floral landscape is rarely marked by an absolute preponderance of one
species or even an assemblage of species. The nearest approaches to this
condition are the Himalayan rhododendron belts, the semi-desert vegeta-

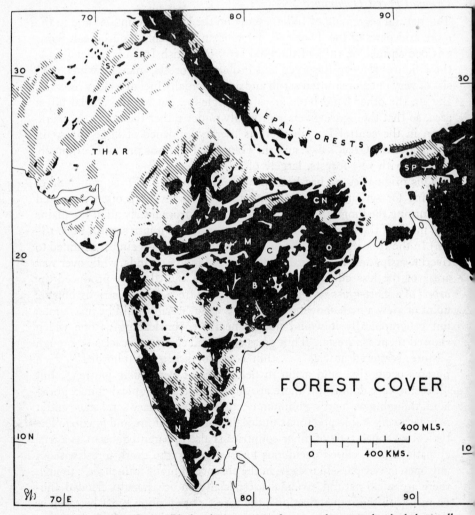

Fig. 18.—FOREST COVER. Black—dense or open forest or dense scrub; shaded—small
trees or open scrub. B, Bastar; C, Chhattisgarh; CN, Chota Nagpur; CR, Cuddapah
Ranges; J, Javadis, etc.; M, Maikal; N, Nilgiris; O, Orissa Hills; S, Sind Sagar Doab;
SP, Shillong Plateau; SR, Salt Range; V, Vindhyan Hills. Based on map in Census of
India, 1941; courtesy SOI.

tion of the NW, and bamboos locally in the S and (on old clearing) in the NE. Palms, acacias, and sal "give a mark to the vegetation over considerable areas, but they are far from taking the place of assemblages. They are at best conspicuous features of the landscape." The floristic affinities of India are in the main with the Malayan realm; European and even American

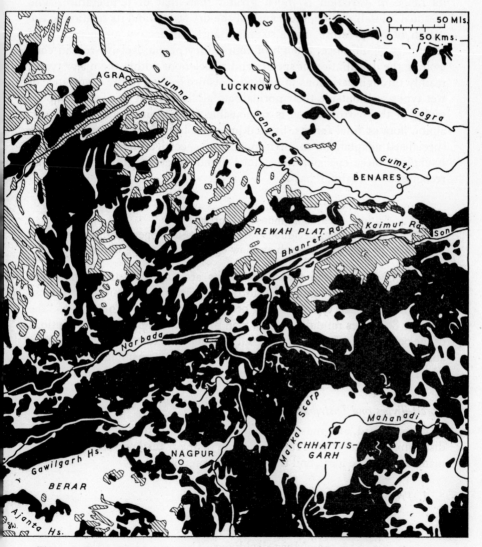

Fig. 19.—Forest Cover, Detail. Area 76–84° E, 20–28° N, illustrating complexity of patterns generalised on Fig. 18 (same key). Amongst the physical features picked out by the forest pattern note: terai edge in NE; badlands of Jumna/Chambal; Bundelkhand scarps; Vindhya–Bhanrer–Kaimur Hills; Chhattisgarh; Berar regur tract in SW; courtesy SOI.

elements are well represented, probably by unrecorded importations of the last four centuries. In the W, of course, there are strong affinities with SW Asia; and in the Himalayan temperate belt Chinese forms are not few.[3]

Climate is the major determinant of forest types, and on a broad view rainfall is more significant than temperature except in the Himalayas, since its range of variation is much greater than that of temperature. The seasonal rainfall régime, the length of the dry season and its relation to the march of temperature, are also important. Soil factors are generally of secondary significance, though of course they play a decisive role in controlling the distribution of species and associations within the major types, mainly through variations in ground moisture leading to the occurrence of wet types well outside their normal rainfall limits, and vice versa. Topography in the narrow sense is responsible for certain minor types, e.g. alpine flora or tidal forests, limited in extent but of interest as displaying specialised adaptations to environment or special economic significance. Excluding these specialisations, four grand vegetation divisions may be recognised on a rainfall basis:

over 80 ins., evergreen (rain) forest.
40–80 ins., deciduous (monsoon) forest.
20–40 ins., drier deciduous forest grading into open thorny scrub.
under 20 ins., thorny scrub and low open bush merging into semi-desert.

It must be emphasised that these limits are approximations only, that transitions are usually gradual, and that there are numerous anomalies in detail, half-a-dozen types possibly occurring within 50 sq mls. Thus "the familiar 80 inches rainfall limit for rain forest . . . is open to the exceptions of the occurrence of the type with only 50 inches of rain under very favourable conditions, and its absence with even 200 inches unsuitably distributed when it is associated with either a very porous or an impervious soil."[4]

Forest Types and Distribution (Fig. 20)[5]

The standard, and most detailed, classification is that of Champion; he distinguishes altogether 116 types, some of them further subdivided. But many of these are local, and there are 15 main types:

A. Tropical Forests

1. Wet evergreen (rain).
2. Semi-evergreen.
3. Moist deciduous.

[3] Calder, 74.   [4] Champion, 13.
[5] This section is based on Champion by courtesy of the Director, Forest Research Institute, Dehra Dun.

4. Dry deciduous.
5. Thorn.
6. Dry evergreen.

B. Montane Sub-tropical Forests.
      7. Sub-tropical wet hill.
      8. Sub-tropical moist hill (pine).
      9. Sub-tropical dry evergreen.

C. Montane Temperate Forests
      10. Wet temperate.
      11. (Himalayan) moist temperate.
      12. (Himalayan) dry temperate.

D. Alpine Forest
      13. Alpine.
      14. Moist Alpine scrub.
      15. Dry Alpine scrub.

To these must be added four highly specialised and very local types: tidal, beach, freshwater swamp, and riverain forests.

1 and 2. Tropical wet evergreen and semi-evergreen. These are the typical rain-forests. The true evergreen is found in a strip along the Wn Ghats (at 1500–4500 ft) S of Bombay, and up to 3500 ft on the Assam Hills, and is naturally best developed in areas with over 120 ins. rain, and a relatively short dry season; on the drier side it is bordered by the semi-evergreen which in turn merges with moist deciduous. Bengal and the Orissa littoral were probably once covered with semi-evergreen. The rain-forest is very dense and lofty, the upper storey reaching 120–150 ft with individuals of 200 ft. Owing to the deep shade the floor is relatively bare, but on the edges of breaks in the canopy (such as stream-margins) undergrowth of bamboos and palms may be extremely dense. Buttressed trunks are common and epiphytes highly developed. The number of species is very large indeed, especially on the Ghats; the Assam forests and still more the semi-evergreen tend to be more gregarious, and erect bamboos are more common, representing a transition to moist deciduous.

3 and 4. Tropical deciduous. The monsoon forests form the natural cover over nearly all of India between the Himalayas, the Thar, and the Wn Ghats; areas with a moderate (40–80 ins.) rainfall. But they are, of course, less resistant to fire and other man-induced interference than the evergreen, and vast areas have been destroyed. The moist forest forms a long strip on the E of the Wn Ghats, and the economically very important sal type covers the NE of the Peninsula (Chota Nagpur, Orissa, En Madhya

Pradesh (CP)) and a great strip along the Siwaliks, the bhabar, and the
terai from 77 to 88° E. The rest of the area is of the drier type, shading off
into thorn forest.

Although most trees lose their leaves for some 6 or 8 weeks in the hot
weather, the actual leaf-fall periods vary somewhat from species to species,[6]
so that the forest is rarely absolutely leafless, and undergrowth in moister

[6] For a detailed account see A. Geddes, *Au Pays de Tagore* (Paris, n.d., ?1927), 24–25.

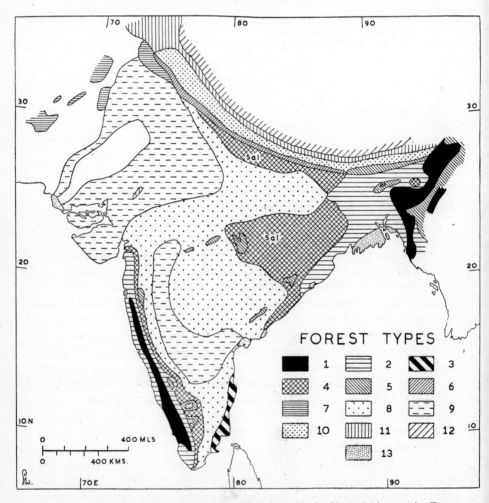

Fig. 20.—FOREST TYPES. Slightly simplified from H. S. Champion's map in *Forest
Types of India*; courtesy of Forest Research Institute, Dehra Dun.

1, tropical wet evergreen; 2, trop. semi-evergreen; 3, trop. dry evergreen; 4, trop.
moist deciduous; 5, sub-trop. wet; 6, sub-trop. pine; 7, sub-trop. dry; 8, trop. dry deciduous; 9, trop. thorn; 10, moist temperate (strip of wet temperate E of 88° E); 11, dry
temperate; 12, alpine; 13, tidal (*sundri*, mangrove, *nipa*).

areas is often evergreen. Nevertheless the general aspect is decidedly burnt-up and bare in April–May. The moist phase is naturally rather higher (80–120 ft against 50–75) and also denser than the drier, which indeed breaks down into thorn and scrub in climatically or edaphically arid areas. Under-growth is usually denser than in the rain-forest; climbers and bamboos are very common, especially perhaps in the moister types.

Economically these are the most important forests of India; the number of useful species is greater than in the evergreen, and they are on the whole more gregarious. This is so more particularly of sal (*Shorea robusta*), which "is very generally more aggressive than any of its associates and competitors in natural gregarious habit, coppicing power, resistance to burning, re-generation under burning and grazing, adaptability to soil and site condi-tions, and longevity; though it suffers from frost, it survives it where few other species could."[7] These traits have been strengthened by selective forest management. It often forms nearly pure stands of close and high (80–120 ft) forest, with a shrubby undergrowth replaced by grass in areas liable to burning; bamboos are absent. Edaphically it avoids purer sands and clays, too dry or too wet. The hard durable timber is in great demand, especially for railway sleepers and constructional work. Teak (*Tectona grandis*) is characteristic of the monsoon forest in the W; its distribution is to some extent complementary to that of sal in the Peninsula, though except where artificially aided it is not nearly so gregarious. Indian teak production (mainly from Sn Bombay) is much less than that of Burma (in normal times), and despite its greater fame the tree is on the whole less important in India than is sal, though valuable for its termite-resistant qualities. The evergreen sandalwood (*Santalum album*) is valuable in and around Mysore; a very hard and close-grained yellow wood with a fragrant scent, it is used for carved boxes and ornaments and for incense. Other important trees are sissoo or shisham (*Dalbergia sissoo*), very common along the En sub-Himalayan zone, producing a hard timber used for building, furniture, cart-frames and wheels; hurra (*Terminalia chebula*), less important for its timber (which is nevertheless hard and suitable for furniture, carts, and turnery) than for its fruit, the myrobalans which provide a valuable tan-stuff and are also used for dyes and mordaunts; mahua (*Bassia latifolia*), the flowers of which are eaten as a sweetmeat and are a potentially impor-tant source of alcohol; and *Acacia catechu*, common on the more arid margins.

5. *Thorn forest*. In areas with under 30 ins. (the NW and the lee of the Wn Ghats) the natural vegetation is open stunted forest breaking down into xerophytic bush and in the NW grading into practically complete desert. Trees are low (20–30 ft maximum) and may be widely scattered; acacias are very prominent, widely and pretty evenly spaced in consequence

[7] Champion, 76.

of the wide spread of their roots, which ensures to each tree its own little territory. Euphorbias are also conspicuous, sometimes indeed almost dominant and attaining the size of small trees. The Indian wild date (*Phoenix sylvestris*) is common, especially in damper depressions; its fruit is far inferior to that of the true date-palm (*P. dactylifera*) and is rarely used directly for food, though *gur*, a sort of thick molasses, can be got from it.

There are patches of taller and fairly close woodland in locally favourable conditions, but the general effect is depressing, and well depicted by Aldous Huxley:

> Once in every ten or twenty yards, some grey-green plant, deep-rooted, and too thorny for even camels to eat, tenaciously and with a kind of desperate vegetable ferocity struggles for life. And at longer intervals, draining the moisture of a rood of land, there rise, here and there, the little stunted trees of the desert. From close at hand the sparseness of their distantly scattered growth is manifest. But seen in depth down the long perspective of receding distance, they seem—like the in fact remotely scattered stars of the Milky Way— numerous and densely packed. Close at hand the desert is only rarely flecked by shade; but the further distances seem closed with a dense dark growth of trees. The foreground is always desert, but on every horizon there is the semblance of shadowy forests. The train rolls on, and the forests remain for ever on the horizon; around one is always and only the desert.[8]

This admirable passage was written of Rajputana, but it applies to much of the Indus Plains, and, with larger trees and a less dead foreground, to vast areas of the Gangetic and the Peninsula.

In many areas the originally poor forest has deteriorated yet further owing to grazing by cattle and browsing by goats, and this type is more important as a source of small fuel and of fodder than for timber. Khair (*Acacia catechu*), however, which sometimes covers considerable areas with fairly dense closed stands, is used for carts, tool handles, and so on and, more importantly, as the source of tan-stuff and of *cutch*, a brown or yellow-orange dye used for sails, cordage and nets, canvas bags, and in Burma for the robes of the Buddhist monks. Another product of this tree is *kath*, mixed with lime, betel leaves, and areca nuts to form the red *pan* chewed all over India. Babul (*Acacia arabica*) is perhaps more common than *A. catechu* in the NW lowlands, and has similar uses.

6. *Tropical dry evergreen*. This type is limited to the coastal strip from Madras to Pt Calimere, with a rainfall around 40 ins. but received mostly in October–December, and with generally high humidity. It has a closed but low (30–40 ft) canopy with shrubby, often spiny, undergrowth; bamboos are rare. The existence of an evergreen forest with such low rainfall is botanically interesting, but most of it has been cleared for cultivation.

[8] *Jesting Pilate* (1927 ed.), 71–72; quoted by courtesy of Messrs Chatto & Windus.

The tropical formations cover almost all extra-Himalayan India where forests exist, apart from the specialised littoral types. The sub-tropical and temperate forests, however, occur in two widely separated areas, the Nilgiris and Anaimalai-Palni Hills in the extreme S, and the Himalayan and Assamese mountains in the N. Although the Nilgiri flora shows marked affinities, as yet unexplained, with that of Assam and Manipur,[9] it is simpler to depart from Champion's sequence and treat the two areas separately.

7A. (*Southern*) *sub-tropical wet hill*. Owing to the restricted area of the Sn hills, the sub-tropical zone is difficult to distinguish from the clearly differentiated tropical rain forest below and the temperate forest above. It occurs at 3500–5000 ft on the Nilgiris and Palnis, and is described as essentially a "stunted rain-forest", not so luxuriant as the true tropical evergreen. Subtypes occur on the higher parts of the Wn Ghats and the Satpura/Maikal summits, and perhaps as far away as Mt Abu in the Aravallis; but in these localities little that is recognisable remains.

10A. (*Southern*) *wet temperate*. This occurs above 5000 ft on the Nilgiris, Anaimalais, and Palnis, with rainfall of 60–250 ins. or more, and monthly mean minima of about 45–55° F, maxima of 60–75°. Wind is an important inhibitory factor, and the forests (*sholas*) are found as a rule in the lower or sheltered aspects of bold open downland; the effect is that of a rich savannah or park-land with occasional peat-bogs. It is a dense rather low (50–60 ft) forest with much undergrowth and many epiphytes, mosses, and ferns; both tropical and temperate elements occur, and laurels, magnolias, and rhododendrons are found. Exotics include chinchona and eucalypts (cf. below, 641–42).

In the N the great altitude range of the Himalaya and the higher latitudes (up to 36° N) introduce new climatic and topographic features; temperature and aspect (insolation) become of great importance. There is a general distinction between the wetter E and the drier W, the change occurring at about 86–88° E; the zoning is shown in the tabular statement on p. 72 (cf. Fig. 22, C).

7B. (*Northern*) *sub-tropical wet hill*. This is a fairly high (70–100 ft) and dense forest at 3000–6000 ft on the Himalayas E of 88° E and at rather higher levels in Assam. Evergreen oaks and chestnuts predominate, with some ash and beech. Sal may be found in suitable sites on the lower and pines on the higher margins; climbers and epiphytes are common.

8. *Sub-tropical moist hill* (*pine*). This occupies a long belt from 73 to 88° E on the Himalayan slopes, mostly at 3000–6000 ft; patches occur on the higher Khasi and Assam-Burma Hills. The dominant tree is chir or chil (*Pinus longifolia*), forming large pure stands; there is often a grassy floor

[9] Calder, 87; *Imperial Gaz.*, I. 188.

TABULAR STATEMENT OF HIMALAYAN FOREST ZONATION

W   40–80 ins. ←————————86–88° E————————→ 80–100 ins. + E

		Altitude		
		16,000		
		15,000	Rhododendrons plentiful / 2 Junipers	ALPINE
	Birch			
		14,000		
	Junipers	13,000		
ALPINE	Silver Fir			
	3 shrubby Rhododendrons	12,000		
		11,000	CHIEFLY CONIFERS	
	CONIFERS / *Abies pindrow* 7500–11,000		2 Junipers	UPPER TEMPERATE
		10,000	Rhododendrons, willows	
	Pinus excelsa 6000–10,000	9,000	Bamboo (*Arundinaria racemosa*)	
	Cedrus deodara 6000–8500			
TEMPERATE	*Pinus longifolia* 3000–7000	8,000	BROAD-LEAVED Oaks, chestnuts,	
	Yew, cypress / BROAD-LEAVED	7,000	maples, magnolias, laurels, alders, birches	LOWER TEMPERATE
	Oaks spp. 4000–12,000	6,000		
	Walnuts, elms,			
	poplars, maples,	5,000		
	horse-chestnut,			
		4,000	Mixed forests, often evergreen, with moist bamboo	
SUB-TROPICAL AND TROPICAL	*Rhodo. arboreum*	3,000		SUB-TROPICAL AND TROPICAL
	Mixed deciduous, sal, dry bamboo (Siwaliks)	2,000		
	Riverain, savannah (terai)	1,000	Sal, mixed deciduous, tropical evergreen, riverain, moist savannah (terai)	
	Dry thorn and scrub (extreme W)			

Adapted from Troup's Figs. 46 & 47 in Tansley and Chipp,
"Aims and Methods in the Study of Vegetation".

with bulbous plants and little undergrowth, except for stunted evergreen oaks in wetter areas. Chir is a useful timber for furniture, boxes, building, and railway sleepers, and the production of resin and turpentine is important.

9. *Sub-tropical dry evergreen.* Like the tropical dry evergreen, this occurs in a restricted area, but at the opposite corner of the sub-continent. It is found at 1500–5000 ft on the Himalayan foothills and the Salt Range in W Punjab, Kashmir, and the NWFP, with patches in Baluchistan: rainfall is 20–40 ins. (with 6 to 9 ins. in December–March inclusive), summers very hot and winters cold enough for frost to be fairly common. Wild olives (*Olea cuspidata*) and *Acacia modesta* are the commonest species; the forest is low and scrubby and has a general resemblance to Mediterranean maquis. Considerable tracts are covered by the dwarf creeping palm *Nannorhops*.

10B. (*Northern*) *wet temperate.* A closed forest mainly of evergreen oaks, laurels, and chestnuts, with undergrowth often dwarf bamboo, at 6000–9500 ft; it is confined to wetter areas (over 80 ins.) E of 88° E.

11. (*Himalayan*) *moist temperate.* This is the most wide-spread Himalayan type, extending over their whole length in the 40–100 ins. rainfall zone; in the wetter E it occupies the outer ranges and here broad-leaved evergreens are mixed with the dominant conifers, becoming fewer to the W. The forest ranges from 5000 to 11,000 ft, but aspect is of great importance: "the conifers tend to avoid hot southern exposures, being there replaced by oak forests."[10] Pines, cedars, silver firs, spruce are the most important trees, forming high but fairly open forest with shrubby undergrowth including oaks, rhododendrons, laurels, and some bamboos. The forests have suffered greatly from fires and from lopping to clear land for grazing. W of 80° E deodar (*Cedrus deodara*) forms large pure stands in the intermediate ranges of moderate (45–70 ins.) rainfall; its fine, durable wood is much used for construction timber and railway sleepers.

12. (*Himalayan*) *dry temperate.* A somewhat xerophytic forest, rather open, found in the inner Himalayan Ranges (Kashmir, Nn Sikkim) with under 40 ins. precipitation, much of it snow. Conifers, including deodars and junipers, predominate, with scattered oak and ash.

13, 14, 15. *Alpine forest and scrub.* The vegetation of the Himalayas from about 9500 to 11,500–12,000 ft is largely a dense shrubby forest of silver firs, junipers, pines, birches, and rhododendrons, the last growing to heights of 30 ft. Most of the trees are crooked and tend to branch low down on the bole. The forest grades into low evergreen scrub and this in turn, on the drier Tibetan side (under 15 ins.), into very open xerophytic bush, with willows along the streams.

This cursory review cannot do justice to the complex permutations of the Himalayan forests. Along ridge-tops in the Assam-Burma Ranges and on

---

[10] Champion, 225.

benches in the Himalayas there is also a considerable development of rough natural grassland.

Specialised littoral forests. The tidal forests are the most widely known of the specialised tropical types, but much confusion has been caused by the indiscriminate use of the word 'mangrove' and by vivid, or rather lurid, descriptions of the most luxuriant parts of mangrove forests as if they were standard. While the *Rhizophora* mangroves which border tidal channels do form high dark forests, much mangrove is low and light olive in colour, most disappointing to those who expect giant knee-roots and crocodiles behind every tree. The common feature of the numerous species of mangroves, and of many other trees of the tidal marshes, is the existence of pneumatophores or breathing-roots sticking out of the marsh surface like a field of tent-pegs driven in upside-down. In the early stages of colonisation of the mud-banks the plants are scattered, and in conditions of poor mud-supply (e.g. parts of the W coast) the mangrove 'forest' remains very open and the trees low, looking like olives growing out of the water. Just as the reputation of the rain-forest as impenetrable is based largely on its luxuriance along the streams, where the whole side of the forest is accessible to light, so the popular conception of mangrove-swamp is based on the gallery of high dense growth along the tidal channels, trapping the silt at every tide. Behind this rapidly accreting zone is usually an infilling of smaller species; both the ground surface and that of the vegetation canopy are saucer-like in section.

Mangroves fringe the seafaces of most of the Indian deltas. In the Bengal Delta they are backed by the great tidal Sundarbans, so called from the sundri tree (*Heritiera fomes*). This pneumatophore forms a closed forest which, in the higher areas where the water is fresh or brackish in the rains, is over 100 ft high. At still higher levels, in Bengal and elsewhere, are tangled brakes of screwpines (*Pandanus* spp.), canes, and palms such as *Phoenix paludosa*. The creeks are often lined by *Nipa fruticans*, a palm with dense masses of fronds springing directly from a low stump. These forests have considerable economic value. The mangroves themselves are a valuable source of fuel, sometimes deliberately managed as such; sundri is hard, durable, and tough, much used for constructional timber and boat-building; the fronds of *Nipa* are a common thatching material, its sap can be made into gur or toddy, the leaf-stalks are used for giving buoyancy to sundri logs, and for fishing floats.

On beaches and dunes fringes of casuarina are common; in Madras it is often planted on sandy soils as a quick-growing source of firewood, and it also helps to stabilise coastal dunes. The riverain and freshwater swamp forests vary greatly with local climatic and edaphic factors, and with interference by men or animals; they range from dense jungle and canebrakes through thin strips of open tamarisk woodland into swampy savannah.

Bamboos and Palms

Two groups of plants are of such peculiar importance in the life of India as to deserve a special note; these are the bamboos and the palms.

The bamboos are of course really grasses; they are found throughout India except in the extra-Peninsular mountains W of the Sutlej. The commonest and most gregarious of the hundred and more species is *Dendrocalamus strictus*, with stems 30–50 ft high and 1–3 ins. in diameter. This is an 'all-purpose' bamboo: huts and scaffolding, basketry and mats, sticks, furniture, household and agricultural implements; the leaves are used for fodder and the stems and rhizomes burnt. In wetter Bengal and Assam it is replaced by *D. Hamiltonii*, a larger plant used amongst other things for timber-rafting. Also in Assam is *Melocanna bambusoides*, forming immense thickets, "like a hay-field 40 or 60 feet high", on abandoned shifting cultivation: this secondary growth is practically impenetrable and vast areas of good forest on the Chittagong-Arakan Hills have been replaced by *Melocanna*, which is, however, exploited as a raw material for paper-making, or at least can be so exploited. In the S the thorny *Bambusa arundinacea* is common, often cultivated in magnificent clumps 80–100 ft high.

Although probably no part of India, except the Assam-Burma Hills, has such a well-developed 'pure' bamboo culture as exists in the Shan States and other parts of SE Asia, the high usefulness of the plant is attested by the frequency with which it is cultivated in village groves, especially in the NE. Its quick regrowth provides an immense resource for the expanding Indian paper industry, a resource, however, which is not inexhaustible and needs proper conservation. The output of bamboos from Indian forests must be reckoned in hundreds of millions of stems yearly.

Of the palms, there are eight wild species of the date (*Phoenix*), as well as the cultivated date which is grown especially in the Punjab and Sind, but has nothing like the importance it possesses in SW Asia. The common wild date (*P. sylvestris*) "is one of the most conspicuous trees in India. . . . In some regions it is almost the only tree visible . . . on salt lands and about springs in the Deccan it covers considerable areas, forming a gregarious forest growth." [11] The stems of the wild date have often an odd zigzag pattern, the result of tapping for the juice, turned into gur or toddy.

The coconut (*Cocos nucifera*) is found all round the coasts, but is especially important in Kerala and the Tamilnad littoral, as well as on the Maldive, Laccadive, and Nicobar Islands. Its uses are too many to enumerate in full; but we may note here that it is the coconut/paddy association, in which not even the village-site is unproductive, which has the densest population concentrations (cf. below, 633). The toddy or Palmyra palm (*Borassus flabellifer*) occurs both wild and cultivated in most

[11] Gamble, 731.

plains regions, especially perhaps in the drier SE coastlands, though it is also important in Bihar; on the sandy *teri* tracts of Tinnevelly in the extreme S (below, 737) it forms forests which, while primarily important for tapping, can be managed for timber. Palmyra sap is the chief source of toddy, though more is probably used for gur; at any rate, with tens of millions of trees scattered up and down the country, the problem of prohibition enforcement is likely to be difficult! An important cultivated palm is the areca (*Areca catechu*), grown in hot humid regions, e.g. Kerala and Kanara, Bengal and Assam. The nuts, which hang down in long strings and bunches, are used for necklaces and other ornaments; cut and polished their reticulate convolutions are very handsome. The most important use of the areca is for chewing with lime wrapped in the leaves of the betel-vine; this is the *pan* responsible for the great gouts of red saliva which disfigure so many streets and buildings in India.[12] Other palms which may be mentioned are *Nannorhops*, branched and with a half-creeping habit, which covers with matted thickets large areas on the Salt Range, in the Kurram Valley, and in Baluchistan. The leaf-buds and fruits are edible, the seeds used for rosaries which used to be exported from the Omani port of Gwadar to Mecca. In the jungles are many climbing palms (*Calamus* spp.), often thorny, supplying canes and rattans.

Nearly all the palms are important as sources of mat and thatching material; many can be used for light construction work, house-posts, water-troughs, and so on; and while coir (from the coconut) is the most famous palm fibre, it is far from being the only one. The sheaths of the leaves, like those of bamboo stems, are used as a packing material. In earlier cultures palm leaves were used as a writing surface, especially those of the areca and Palmyra. Most important for this purpose was the Talipot (*Corypha umbraculifera*), the largest of Indian palms (sometimes over 100 ft high), common in Kerala and the Kanaras, cultivated in Bengal. The leaves are used as mats, fans, and umbrellas, and are often 10 ft in diameter. This is indeed one of the most magnificent of tropical trees.

Importance of the Forest Cover: Climate and Erosion

Much has been written in India on the direct climatic influence of forests, not infrequently in language so exaggerated as to suggest that trees in themselves create rainfall almost irrespective of the major meteorological influences. There can be no doubt, however, of their vital importance in increasing the effectiveness of precipitation by checking run-off, maintaining the water-table, and increasing humidity by transpiration; and it is not without reason that Sir Herbert Howard's *Post-War Forest Policy for India*

[12] "Betel-nut" is a misnomer. *Pan* has astringent properties and its chewing, in moderation, is probably mildly beneficial. It is not unpalatable, rather like tooth-paste, but very salivatory, and may thus be a source of acute embarrassment to the polite Westerner, whether it is his own problem of disposal or someone else's.

gives first place to forests the preservation of which is essential as a safeguard against floods, erosion, and desiccation. The first (ineffectual) steps towards conservation were taken in 1855, and in 1878 a Forest Act set out the general policy of reservation and protection since pursued, in the interests of assuring the timber supply as well as of protecting the river catchments.

Much of the Reserved forest occupies more or less inaccessible mountain country; but near the plains and lower plateaus the old grazing and cutting rights of the villagers (and sometimes of local entrepreneurs), often recognised on a liberal scale, are difficult to reconcile with an effective forest policy. Almost everywhere within reach of the more populated areas the forest has disappeared or been badly damaged; the rate of destruction was perhaps greatest in the mid-19th century as the demand for building and fuel wood rose sharply with more settled conditions, while Government was simply unaware that a problem existed; there was obviously a great deal of jungle. . . . With the growth of population considerable areas under the Forest Department were thrown open to cultivation.[13]

Such ignorance was not, of course, confined to India; but its consequences have been serious. Erosion is severe in almost all States, and it has been conservatively calculated that some 150,000,000 acres are affected more or less seriously.[14] The most spectacular effects are seen in the Punjab Siwaliks, large areas of which were almost entirely stripped by indiscriminate felling, charcoal burning, firing to promote fresh grass-growth, and above all by the browsing of goats. Rainfall is low, but often torrential, and the unconsolidated Siwalik sands and gravels are extremely susceptible to erosion. Great ravines hundreds of feet deep were rapidly gouged out, and large areas in the plains were overwhelmed by sandy outwash or crumbled away by violent shifts in the detritus-clogged streams (Fig. 89), while the water-table also fell with the loss of seepage from the hills. Some measure of control (the exclusion of sheep and goats) was commenced as early as 1900, and recently good progress has been made both in checking erosion and in reclaiming devastated land.[15] Further E the Siwalik forests of Uttar Pradesh (UP) are less damaged, and, though timber exploitation has recently advanced in Nepal, the vast forests of that country are still largely intact and are likely to remain a protection for some considerable time.

In the wetter and less-populated En Himalayas and the Assam-Burma Hills erosion is not so spectacular as in the dry W, but a new factor is introduced by *jhuming*, the shifting agriculture of the hillmen, also widespread in the central highlands (e.g. Chota Nagpur, and among the Bhils) and the

[13] *Royal Commission on Indian Agriculture* (1928), 268.

[14] Glover (1944), 4. The cultivated area (including current fallows) of British India was about 260,000,000 ac.

[15] See the references to R. Maclagan Gorrie at the end of this chapter; and for further details Ch. XVII (471, 483–84).

hills bordering the Deccan, and indeed throughout SE Asia. The secondary growth on abandoned *jhums* is nearly always dense and useless even as grazing: the tangled bush *Eupatorium odoratum*, bracken, or poisonous *Lantana* which, originally a garden shrub, now covers considerable areas with its dense thorny thickets. The cultivator seldom returns to old ground: new forest is easier to clear, more fertile, with more ash. Naturally also the more valuable deciduous monsoon forests are more affected than the fire-resistant evergreen. Unchecked *jhuming* thus leads to serious erosion, or at best the destruction of valuable forest, and the problem may become more acute with increase of the tribal population. To some extent the hill people may adopt a more settled agriculture, but this merely shifts the incidence of the problem: they must have land and the result is a demand for dis-forestation of reserves.

Throughout central and Sn India forest control is rendered extremely difficult by shifting cultivation, the complex intermingling of forest, often poor and open, with village lands, and immemorial rights of grazing, lopping, collecting leaf-manure and minor produce, and so on. Much land once wooded has now become a mere waste of acacias, euphorbias, very poor grass, and even bare rock, while in the Sn Deccan the water-table has in places been dangerously lowered by deforestation and erosion; sheet-erosion is very prevalent. In the upper Indo-Gangetic Plain spectacular gully-erosion has formed belts of badlands (Fig. 93), in places 3 or 4 miles wide, along the Jumna, the Chambal, and the edges of the Punjab doabs; again the water-table falls. Contour-bunding against sheet-erosion, and in the ravine terrain afforestation, exclusion of grazing (leading to a dense grass cover, which can be *cut* for fodder) and the introduction of the excellent soil-binder and fodder bush *kudzu* in Wn Pakistan and central *India*, have already had some effect. The need for a more vigorous prosecution of such measures is recognised by those in authority; on the other hand the new State governments are in many ways more accessible to opinion than the British Raj, and this works for ill as well as for good if that opinion is not well-informed: it is sometimes difficult to resist demands for release of reserves.

The importance of the closely allied grazing, fuel, and manure problems cannot be over-emphasised: they lie at the very heart of India's rural crisis. There is a vicious circle: lack of firewood in the all but treeless plains enforces the use of cattle-dung as fuel instead of as manure; grazing areas are extremely limited and the pressure of cattle population on the scraps of village waste inhibits forest growth. The problems interlock inextricably.

Ecology of the Plains

As a coda to this account of the (more or less) natural cover still existing in the less-settled areas, we may take the Gangetic Plains in Uttar Pradesh

(UP) as a sample of the present ecology of a densely-settled area.[16] This area was originally forested; apart from floristic survivals, the literary evidence is abundant and decisive. To go no further back than the 16th–17th centuries, the Mogul Emperors hunted wild elephants and buffaloes, bison, rhinoceros, lions, and tigers in the Ganges-Jumna doab. Some of these animals have completely disappeared, such as the bison, the rhinoceros (which survives, legislatively protected, in the Bengal terai and Assam), and the lion, whose last Indian home is the Gir forest sanctuary in Kathiawar. Tigers, bears, and leopards have been enormously reduced in numbers, as also the larger ungulates; but wild pigs and the smaller deer survive, in lesser numbers than formerly, it is true. This shift in the wild animal population is not without effects on human geography. With fewer enemies and food-competitors wild pigs, rodents, and monkeys (the last with a certain religious sanction) have improved at least their relative position; all these are destructive to crops, and the rat in addition is a plague-carrier. So serious are its depredations that in the 1897 famine some of the victims were actually reduced to rifling the rats' underground hoards. Again, with the extinction of the tiger and the decrease in the leopard population, the more decrepit cattle are no longer so liable to a speedy end (they may meet a grimmer fate beneath a cloud of vultures), and this adds to the desperate problem of bovine over-population. And in default of their natural prey, such tigers as survive are more likely to attack village stock and to become man-killers.[17]

Away from the terai fringe and the riverain strips of tamarind and khair very little of the woodland survives. There are a few patches, partly relics and partly planted, of dhak (*Butea frondosa*)[18], mahua, and nim (*Melia indica*); but the commonest tree, at least in the W, is babul. This acacia is not palatable to cattle, though its pods are eaten by cattle, sheep, and goats, so that in effect it is more likely to spread than to decrease as a result of grazing. Another plant highly resistant to cattle is *Zizyphus* spp., forming "dense impenetrable masses" of thorn-bush. Along with deforestation there go lessened soil-humidity and, owing to loss of transpiration, even micro-climatological desiccation. Such secondary wild or waste vegetation as can exist is thus markedly xerophytic, such as the 'dry meadow' of Wn UP, which when intensively overgrazed breaks down to coarse tussocks or gives way to useless annual grasses and a few rosette-plants. Even in the terai and the wetter E (with over 80 ins.) pressure of population has led to clearing and the spread of a savannah-like cover, which is likely to extend

---

[16] The Gazetteers contain many thumb-nail sketches of plains ecology, but the fullest analysis of a large area is that of Mukerjee, on which this section is based.

[17] Mukerjee, 126–36, gives highly interesting details.

[18] Dhak timber is more durable in water than out of it, and is used for well-piling, water-scoops, and so on; a coarse fibre is obtained from the bark and it produces a medicinal gum: nim is a sacred tree, used for images as well as for more mundane furniture and tools, while its bark, leaves, seed, and fruit all have pharmacological uses.

more rapidly as a result of the settlement of refugees from Pakistan in such areas.

A different type of ecological change is the provision of a free field for indigenous plant pests, or the introduction of new ones. The coarse *kans* grass, particularly prolific on the UP/Madhyabharat borders, seizes upon fallow and may be so closely matted as to inhibit ploughing; but after a cycle of 10–15 years it dies away and the land can be reclaimed. In Bengal the water-hyacinth, originally introduced as an ornamental pond-plant, is a very serious menace; not only has it completely blocked scores or even hundreds of miles of minor streams to navigation, and dislocated the natural drainage, but it may actually overrun flooded paddy-fields; it is exceedingly difficult to combat, and even where it has taken hold but lightly, the eradication of its clumps causes serious loss of the peasant's time and energy.

We may sum up in Mukerjee's own words:

> The combined effect of all the activities of man has thus been gradually to depress the natural vegetation from the original climatic climax monsoon deciduous forest to the open, dry grassland making up the grazing areas of the present time, with here and there remnants of resistant woody plants—which led Schimper to call the Plains formation 'thorn-scrub'. . . . On the Plains the vegetation is now rather delicately balanced against man at about the dry grass-land or the thorn-scrub stage. The soil over most of the Indo-Gangetic Plain seems to be supporting about all the human and bovine life that is possible under existing methods of exploitation. . . . Relaxation of pressure immediately results in a movement of vegetation towards the climax. But no relaxation is possible under present conditions. Dry grass-land and thorn-scrub formations remain practically stationary.

It may indeed be doubted whether the change has not been so complete that natural regeneration of the climax is unlikely; more probable would seem to be a taller and denser scrub. And it may be added that if, as Mukerjee thought, the Indo-Gangetic Plains were demographically saturated when he wrote, they are super-saturated now. The picture is a depressing one.

II. SOILS

Methodological Difficulties

The most competent pedologist would probably find it impossible to present a general view of the soil-pattern of India which should be at once accurate, comprehensive, and reasonably detailed; and the writer's equipment for this task is modest indeed. Apart from his own deficiencies, much of the difficulty is inherent in the nature of the available information, which must be sought on at least four levels:

(i) the traditional broad division into alluvium, regur (black earth), red soils, and laterite;

(ii) the refinements introduced into (i) by (*a*) the multiplicity of local types recognised by the peasants and named by them primarily on a basis of texture and (*b*) the Land Revenue grading of soils on a basis of their productivity[19];

(iii) the numerous but scattered analyses produced by agricultural chemists, primarily for investigation of manurial needs;

(iv) the attempt by Z. J. Schokalsky to synthesise these data in the framework of Russian pedological principles.

As for (ii), it is obvious that the data here are empirical and of local validity only; on the other hand for much the greater part of the sub-continent these local names and grades, described in the District Gazetteers and Settlement Reports, are really the only available materials. Moreover, based as they are on the closest observation through centuries of intensive farming, they are the most revealing data at present available from an over-all geographical point of view. Bearing in mind also Vageler's warning of the prevalence of the anomalous over the 'normal' in tropical soils, we thus fall back on this empirical level in the regional sections of this book. Here, however, we shall try to reach at least some idea of the general nature of Indian soils.

At the outset we are faced by the difficulty that the traditional classification, while valid enough so far as it goes, is again empirical and does not take us very far on the genetic road. In 1935 the Geological Survey of India, following a request (1929) from the International Association of Soil Science, threw what light it could on the matter, but the resultant report (by Wadia, Krishnan, and Mukerjee) is very thin, though the maps present a useful shorthand view of the main *geological* bases. At present steps are being taken towards a general survey, more or less on Russian lines (just as these are becoming a little dated); but the work so far presented by Viswanath and Ukil is hardly amenable to generalisation. In any case only 17,000 sq mls (1·07% of all-India) had been subjected to modern sample surveys by 1947, and of this area 11,000 sq mls were in the Madras deltas.[20] Some work has been done by geographers, notably S. P. Chatterjee in Bengal, but this is too local (and as a rule not sufficiently genetical) for synthesis.

For a synthesis, then, we have really the old four-fold scheme and the probably premature but certainly gallant effort of Schokalsky to integrate the extremely spotty and unequal data available to her, while at the same time translating it into the language and spirit of Russian pedology. Concerning this attempt two things must be observed. The first is that it is

[19] For all too obvious reasons this often takes the form of concentric zoning around the village.

[20] Even here the analyses are limited in scope; cf. Schokalsky, 130. Only 100 sq mls had complete modern profile survey.

clear that this was an *ad hoc* 'assignment', and the lack of first-hand (or even of comprehensive second-hand) knowledge of Indian geography is painfully apparent. Nor were the materials supplied by British and Indian agencies beyond reproach; they included a vegetation map which, to put it mildly, was grossly over-simplified, and a disgraceful agricultural map showing large opium-growing tracts, and the whole of the Sn Blocks (Nilgiris, etc.) and most of the Arakan Yomas as devoted to tobacco.[21] In the circumstances it is not so surprising that many of Schokalsky's ideas appear naïve as that she managed to produce a workable regional division and some acute regional observations. Secondly, the soil analyses available were made upon principles entirely different from those of the Russians; from internal evidence it is clear that essential data were missing, and there are significant asides—"Indian soil scientists, or, to be more exact, agricultural chemists studying the soil. . . ."[22]

We shall, then, first give résumés of the traditional classification and of Schokalsky's findings, regarded as at least an approximation to the pattern which will eventually emerge; and finally discuss some of the general features of tropical soil-formation, with special reference to lateritisation.

The Traditional Scheme [23]

(a) The *Alluvial Soils*, which in the Indo-Gangetic Plains cover at least 300,000 sq mls, are agriculturally the most important: on this main mass, 19% of the sub-continent's area, live some 42% of its people, and if we add the Madras Deltas, Gujarat and Kerala, half or more of the total population is alluvial in habitat. The general physical conditions of the Indo-Gangetic Plains have been described in Ch. I. The soils grade from the coarse material of the piedmont bhabar to the fine silts of the Ganges Delta; internally the most striking distinction is between the older bhangar and the long fingers of recent khadar in the main floodplains, in many places annually refreshed by new silt. Apart from this, variations in fertility are due mainly to factors of water-table, and the presence or absence of cal-careous concretions in the subsoil; in Tirhut (N Bihar) some soils contain over 30% $CaCO_3$, while in adjacent tracts lime is practically absent. In general lime is about adequate, the nitrogenous and organic content low. "Potash is adequate and phosphoric acid, though not plentiful, is generally less deficient than in other Indian soils." In drier areas strongly alkaline soils and even saline efflorescences occur.

(b) *Regur* is most typically developed on the Deccan Lavas (cf. below, Ch. XXIII), but is not confined to them. Some is redeposited in the valleys

---

[21] This map long appeared in a standard British atlas.
[22] Schokalsky, 96.
[23] This classification is set out in many places, e.g. Sir T. Vijayaraghavacharya, *The Land and its Problems* (OPIA No. 9, 1943), 15–20; the *ur-quelle* seems to be RCAI 70–74, on which this section is based.

of streams flowing from the Lavas, but regur of varying quality is found on Archaean gneisses and other rocks, especially in the Madras Deccan and in the extreme SE (Tinnevelly), while the alluvium of Gujarat and of parts of the Coromandel coastal plain includes considerable areas of similar soils. Most of these regions are important cotton-growing tracts. The moisture-retentive qualities of regur and its aeration by deep hot-weather cracking are well known; it swells when wet and this alternation ensures thorough mixing of soil-particles. Unless tilled very soon after the onset of the rains it is extremely sticky and difficult to work. The black colour was formerly ascribed to humus, but is more probably due to finely-divided iron particles. There is usually a high proportion of $CaCO_3$ and $MgCO_3$. The Deccan Lava regur at its best development is very deep, but on higher ground is thinner and grades into reddish-brown or red soils; on Archaeans it is often underlain by a kanker horizon. In the black soils in general "phosphoric acid, nitrogen, and organic matter are deficient, but potash and lime are not."

(c) 'Red Soils' is an omnibus category; most of the soils developed on the Archaean crystallines are included, some of which are brown, grey, or black. There is naturally great variation with parent rock, climate, and local terrain factors. Very poor indeed on uplands, where they may be almost loose gravels, they include in depressions (soil-wash traps) some good loams, which respond well to irrigation. Mineral deficiencies are similar to those of regur.

(d) The *Laterite* problem deserves a section to itself; its literature is vast, highly technical, and perhaps even more highly controversial. We may note here that many 'laterite' soils are really only lateritic; indeed lateritisation has for the tropics the same wide significance which podsolisation has for temperate latitudes.[24] From an agricultural point of view the prevailing characteristics of laterite are extreme acidity with an almost complete lack of lime and organic material.

Schokalsky's Survey

The broad outlines of Schokalsky's survey are shown on Fig. 21, which represents a degree of generalisation intermediate between the original and the simplified version in *The Great Soviet Atlas*.

The map on the whole may be left to speak for itself. Apart from the details of the Himalayan tract, the most important contribution seems to be the allocation of large parts of the Indus and upper Gangetic Plains to steppe-like s(i)erozem. Schokalsky's interpretation here seems sound, but it is difficult to accept the great area of "sub-tropical steppe soils" in the NE Peninsula, much of which is and always has been densely forested; the relevant text (134-35) hardly seems to bear out the map. The distribution of

[24] Joffe, 488.

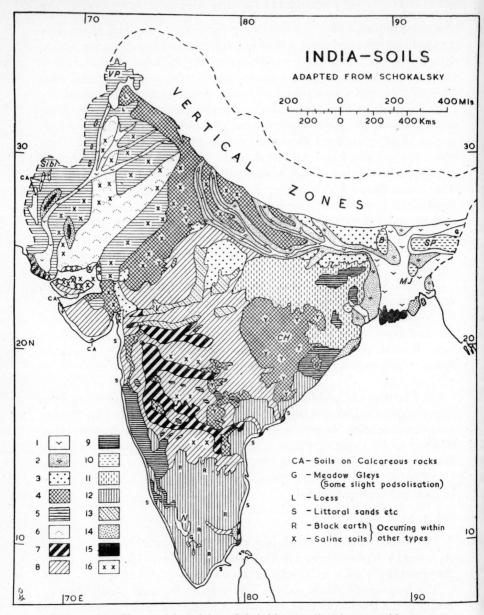

Fig. 21.—SOIL TYPES. Adapted from Schokalsky. 1, alluvial, traces of bog process, on newer alluvium; 2, meadow type on older alluvium; 3, prairie type; 4, tropical and sub-trop. dry steppe on older alluvium and hard rocks (Y = yellow soils); 5, serozems, often saline, some loess; 6, sandy semi-desert serozems; 7, deep regur; 8, medium-light black soils (incl. re-deposited regur in valleys); 9, laterite (high and low) and some higher lateritics; 10, lateritic; 11, sub-trop. red, less leached; 12, trop. red; 13, brown under deciduous forest, slightly or not leached; 14, swamp, peat-bog, and muck; 15, solonchaks; 16, solonets. B, Barind; CH, Chhattisgarh; MJ, Madhupur Jungle; N, Nilgiris; SP, Shillong Plateau; V, Vindhyan Hills; VP, Vale of Peshawar.

deep and medium black soils in Maharashtra should be compared with that of Simkins (Fig. 128, below). The red soil areas, even on the rather more detailed original map, do not represent much of a refinement on the old scheme; and although Schokalsky indicates the occurrence of medium and light black earths in the great red soil tract of the Sn Peninsula, the Tinnevelly occurrence is certainly large enough and precise enough to warrant separate insertion on a map of the original scale (1/10,000,000). The great alluvial area of the Nari Khorsum plains in Hundes on the upper Sutlej is also not shown. These omissions illustrate the dangers of extrapolation from scattered samples without the counter-check of a good knowledge of the general geographical background.

So far as a synthesis of the traditional and the Russian schemes is possible, we may give it in Schokalsky's own words.[25] Laterites were merely divided into high and low level (plus those of the Shillong Plateau), while in the black earths only medium-light soils taken together and true regur (deep black) were distinguished. But:

> Red soils are subdivided by us first of all into two main groups comprising the tropical soils, strongly affected by the leaching process, and subtropical soils less influenced by leaching; further soils on slopes frequently gritty and soils on calcareous rocks likewise form two separate groups. . . .
>
> To a most detailed subdivision are being subjected the soils known as 'alluvial', a term giving no indication on the character of the soil type . . . a special place is allotted to the subtropical steppe soils, the subtropical dry steppe soils, which occur also in complexes with salines, then the soils of the meadow type both revealing well-defined traces of processes of bog-formation and lacking in such, finally the soils of the serozem type in complex with salinised soils.

These are modifications of the traditional tetrad, but Schokalsky also recognised: various steppe-serozem-desert soils; meadow and bog soils; coastal sands, swamp-soils, and saline marshes; "finally the soils of the vertical zones of the Himalayas comprising most diversified soils varying from mountain-meadow soils to zheltozems (yellow soils) and krasnozems (red soils), supporting the evergreen forests of the Eastern Himalayas."

Finally, it should be mentioned that Schokalsky herself was "firmly convinced" that her work contained "many errors, many mistakes"; her appeal that Indian workers should approach their soils along genetic lines is only now beginning to bear fruit. The attempt well merits her own description of it as "daring"; it was put forward as a basis for discussion, since "it is well known that discussion originates knowledge": a sentiment which should have a bearing on more things than pedology.

[25] Schokalsky, 149–51.

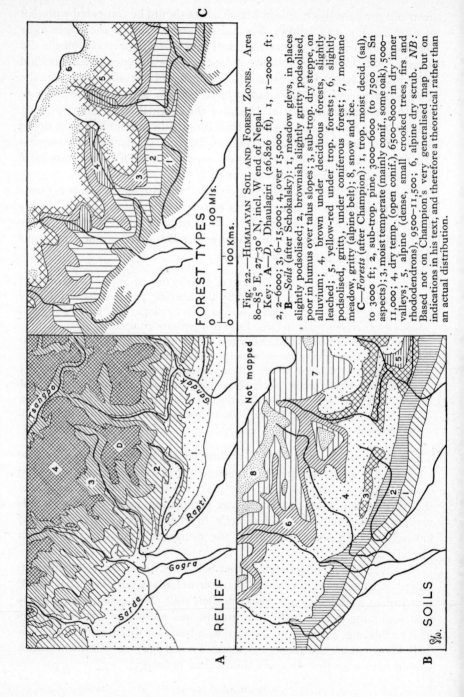

FOREST TYPES

100 Mls.

0   100 Kms.

Fig. 22.—Himalayan Soil and Forest Zones. Area 80–85° E, 27–30° N, incl. W end of Nepal. Key: A–D, Dhaulagiri (26,826 ft), 1, 1–2000 ft; 2, 2–6000; 3, 6–15,000; 4, over 15,000.

B—*Soils* (after Schokalsky): 1, meadow gleys, in places slightly podsolised; 2, brownish slightly gritty podsolised, poor in humus over talus slopes; 3, sub-trop. dry steppe, on alluvium; 4, brown under deciduous forests, slightly leached; 5, yellow-red under trop. forest; 6, slightly podsolised, gritty, under coniferous forest; 7, montane meadow, gritty (alpine belt); 8, snow and ice.

C—*Forests* (after Champion): 1, trop. moist decid. (sal), to 3000 ft; 2, sub-trop. pine, 3000–6000 (to 7500 on Sn aspects); 3, moist temperate (mainly conif., some oak), 5000–11,000; 4, dry temp. (open conif), 6500–8000 in dry inner valleys; 5, alpine (dense, small crooked trees, firs and rhododendrons), 9500–11,500; 6, alpine dry scrub. *NB*: Based not on Champion's very generalised map but on indications in his text, and therefore a theoretical rather than an actual distribution.

A RELIEF

Not mapped

Tsangpo

Gandak

Rapti

Gogra

Sarda

4

D

3

2

1

B ‰ SOILS

7

8

6

5

4

3

2

1

86

Tropical Weathering

Before discussing laterite itself it will perhaps be as well to consider some of the features of tropical, as distinct from temperate, weathering, and of the non-lateritic soils. On these matters Vageler is probably as safe a guide as any.

The most fundamental difference between tropical and temperate weathering is the stepping-up of tempo in the tropics: "In hot climates temperatures are higher by 10–20° C (50–70° F), and all chemical reactions proceed at two to four times the speed usual in temperate climates. . . . If one bears in mind that there is no interruption by winter, one will hardly err in estimating that over the whole year and in relation to temperate climates the intensity of weathering in the tropics is increased at least tenfold."[26] In strictly monsoonal humid regions the seasonal reversal of ground-water movement is of equal importance; such areas "may be described as subject for part of the year to equatorial soil processes where evaporation is nearly nil and for part to desertic soil processes in which soil evaporation is at a maximum."[27]

It is hardly necessary to combat the old ideas of the "inexhaustible richness" of tropical soils or the crude correlation of density of vegetation with fertility. According to Vageler, however, there is a tendency to understate the importance of humus in the tropics; for rain-forest he gives the annual production of organic matter as *c.* 100 tons per acre, for monsoon forest as 20 tons. But high soil temperatures mean very rapid decomposition, and except where the cover is dense enough to keep soil temperature below 75° F, or where waterlogging and consequent exclusion of oxygen inhibit bacterial activity, the rate of destruction of organic matter exceeds that of replacement. The humus layer even in 'primeval' forest is but a very few inches deep and is underlaid by bright red or yellow soils, which Vageler holds to have considerable humic component. This is strongly acid (*p*H 3–5·5).

A factor of great importance is the high intensity of tropical rainfall, resulting in a high proportion of run-off, in sheet-flow, gully erosion, and the great hill-foot fans of the arid regions. In humid regions slopes of any steepness are rarely able to absorb much of the precipitation, soil-creep is almost too rapid to be called creep, and the slopes are tracts of relative aridity. Conversely the hill-foot is a zone of deep soil, with a relatively high water-table and soil-humidity: these 'colluvial' belts are naturally agriculturally favoured and account for the lines of break-of-slope settlements to be noted so often in our regional chapters. But "while even the most gentle slope" is thus "withdrawn into more arid conditions of soil climate", deposition of fine impermeable soil-wash in hollows tends to maintain in

[26] Vageler, 4, 16.   [27] Dobby, 74.

them greater humidity than that of the regional soil-climate. Factors such as these, alternating fairly sharply, account in part for the occurrence in the Peninsula 'Red Soils' areas of grey- and black-soiled tracts; the dark colour is due to reduction by organic solutions of the iron oxides which provide the so prevalent red, and the two soil-colours are often sharply juxtaposed, with little transitional grading. In the tropics, then, we find:

> a mosaic of soil types which frequently exceeds all theoretical limits. Examples typical of what is expected of the locality on theoretical grounds are rarer than in any other region, even if one abandons systems of soil classification which are based chiefly on climate, and takes into consideration what Glinka calls endynamomorphic factors. . . . There are indeed broad lines of agreement between theory and fact, but a cursory enquiry into details very soon reveals more exceptional than 'normal' soils. . . . [28]

Minor factors mentioned by Vageler include the high nitric acid content of rainfall associated with frequent tropical thunderstorms, leading to rapid iron oxidisation; and the activity of termites. In India the latter is of some slight significance only in a few piedmont tracts of the extreme SE.

Non-lateritic Soils

Excluding the montane 'vertical zones', limestone soils such as rendzinas and terra rossa (important only in Baluchistan and Wn Sind), the red soils, and regur, non-lateritic soils in India lie mainly at the extremes of the humidity scale: swamp or forest soils, soils of steppe or sub-steppe affiliations. Many of the red soils also are at least allied to the lateritics.

(a) *The humid soils.* These are limited in extent. The rain-forest of India is mostly montane in location, and the largest areas are on the very permeable Cretaceous-Tertiary sandstones and limestones of the Assam-Burma Ranges: there is nothing really comparable to the vast poorly-drained tropical evergreen and swamp forests of Indonesia. According to Schokalsky's map, swamp, peat-bog, and muck soils are confined to the great deltas (especially, of course, the Sundarbans), the Sibi and Nara tracts of Sind (cf. below, 453–54), and small patches on the fans of streams debouching from the Sulaiman Range. Peat-bogs especially are rare in India; practically speaking they occur only on the Nilgiris and other Sn hills. The terai soils, which might be thought to come under this category, are shown as meadow greys, slightly podsolised (Fig. 22), the bhabar as "brownish sandy gritty slightly podsolised soils, poor in humus, on talus slopes"—which seems fair enough. The seaface and major tidal channels of the deltas are fringed with solonchaks.

---

[28] Vageler, 106. This underlines the dangers of extrapolation from scattered samples, interpreted in the light of the theoretically probable—the method perforce followed by Schokalsky.

The swamp soils, except where saline (solonchaks, etc.), are exceedingly fertile when first cleared, as for example on the Nn margin of the Sundar-bans; but the clearing of course involves a cessation of the supply of new humic material, and leaching sets in very rapidly.

(b) *The arid soils*. These occupy a far larger area than the humid, cover-ing most of the Indo-Gangetic alluvium W of Patna (85° E), or, if we include 'prairie' soils, W of the Bihar/Bengal boundary. They grade from the 'prairie' soils with a considerable calcareous element (kanker) into the sandy serozems of the central Thar and the Sind Sagar doab and a belt linking these two areas. The soils of central Punjab, Sind, and the Aravalli piedmont (where the water-table is far higher than in the Thar proper; cf. 567–71 below) are regarded by Schokalsky as somewhat saline serozems, with of course many patches of very saline solonets and solonchaks—the *usar*, *reh*, or *kallar* of the peasant. The serozems contain a good deal of organic matter; there is little doubt that very much of the area carried a heavier vegetation cover—including fairly dense forest—in the not very distant past, and the lack of replacement is offset by the little leaching the soils have undergone. This is an important factor in the success of Punjab irrigation; against it must be set water-logging and consequent development of strongly saline (alkaline) soils.

The large area of yellow "sub-tropical steppe" soils shown by Schokal-sky as extending from the upper Son to the lower Godavari—an area still densely forested for the most part (Fig. 18)—is inexplicable.

(c) *Regur and red soils*. An empirical description of these has already been given, and it seems unnecessary to add anything here.[29]

Laterites and Lateritic Formations

True laterites are more restricted, both in India and in the tropics at large, than many text-book references would suggest; on the other hand approaches, near or remote, to laterite are widespread.

The word "laterite" (from Latin *later* = brick) was applied in 1810 by Buchanan to a clayey rock, hardening on exposure, observed in Malabar. There seems now to be general expert agreement with Fermor's restriction of the term to soils formed as to 90–100% of iron, aluminium, titanium, and manganese oxides, while Pendleton confines it to "the more or less indurated, illuvial, quarryable horizon in the soil resulting from the accumu-lation of ferric oxides". But, as Joffe adds, the word is still often used merely "to designate the mature stage of the dominant soils in the tropics and sub-tropics."[30]

[29] Reference may be made to Joffe's review of the regur literature (507–18), but little emerges except the non-identity of regur and chernozem, Joffe's odd inclusion of it under "Laterites and Lateritic Type", and a belief in its hydrogenic origin, apparently based on similarity to the Moroccan *tirs*.
[30] Joffe, 460. One can hardly avoid dropping a brick or two in this section.

Formation. At all events, the essential feature of laterite is the virtual leaching-out of silica and the consequent concentration of the oxides mentioned. Of these iron (more usually) and aluminium are greatly preponderant, "often mutually excluding each other; hence we have numerous varieties of laterite which have bauxite at one end and an indefinite mixture of ferric oxides at the other".[31]

There are, of course, all stages of the process. Under monsoonal régimes leaching may be slow, being annually interrupted by the dry season, during which upward movements of ground-water bring up bases washed down during the rains; such soils are often agriculturally very productive. Nevertheless the bases are gradually leached out, and in the dry season the oxides tend to concentrate towards the surfaces where they form hard crusts and concretions. The probable process is well described by Vageler:

In the dry season these, together with bases and what is left of the silicic acid, rise to the surface, where, under the influence of heat and drying, they are irreversibly coagulated, that is, they are no longer able to pass into solution. This process is strongly assisted by capillary action. The following rains dissolve out what salts and bases are present, but can wash back into the subsoil only minute traces of the sesqui-oxides which reached the surface. . . . In this way the superficial layers of soil are enriched in sesqui-oxides by numerous repetitions of this process. The illuvial [32] horizon is thus caused to lie above the eluvial horizon. . . . The surface layers change to allite laterite, which finally contains up to 90–100% of hydrated sesqui-oxides. Owing to the tendency of iron hydroxide to pass into limonite, the surface of such soils is finally covered by an iron crust, often of wide extent and reaching to considerable depths.[33]

Naturally the process is at its best in more humid tropical conditions with free drainage. Laterite can apparently be formed on any rock, but pure quartzites are naturally very resistant, and in some areas the orange-tawny laterite is streaked with white quartz veins, their matrix long since destroyed. In a fully-developed laterite we may have:

(i) a few inches of soil retaining some organic constituents, or a surface crust of iron oxide, often forming extensive pavements of pebbly gravel or even a continuous carapace;

(ii) red and yellow, more or less crumbly and sticky, subsoil, with iron concretions around old roots;

(iii) deeper less-weathered red and yellow mottled clays; this is Buchanan's original laterite, and has often a reticulate structure, with vermiform iron nodules enclosing clay;

[31] Wadia, 294.

[32] Eluvial = A horizon, i.e. that from which leaching takes place; illuvial = B horizon, i.e. that in which accumulation takes place.

[33] Vageler, 173. Vageler's (coloured) Plate VIII (cf. Plate IX, Red Loam) and Dobby's Fig. 26 give an exceptionally clear idea of some aspects of laterite formation.

(iv) possibly more iron-pans along fracture-planes or quartz veins;

(v) a whitish decomposition zone (lithomarge) passing into the parent rock.

Occurrence and Origin. In India, laterite is formed at high and low levels: up to 3000–5000 ft on the Wn Ghats, and at 50–200 (or more) ft on the low dissected peneplains of the Konkan or the little cuestas of Tamilnad (Cuddalore sandstones, etc.). But, though it is found at all levels between these limits, it is found only on flat surfaces and does not cover the slopes between levels: it is essentially a capping, with at most a thin bevelled-off veneer reaching a little way down from the top of the slope.[34] In the Nummulitic series (Baluchistan, etc.) there are definite 'fossil' laterites, Eocene or earlier.[35]

Into the unspeakably dangerous question of the origins of laterite it is not proposed to go, further than to draw attention to the fact that it may not be a strictly tropical phenomenon only: Joffe regards Mediterranean terra rossa as "in the group of soils affected by the process of laterization" and thinks it possible that their parent rock may have been laterite.[36] According to Polynov lateritic soils may be "the end-products of weathering in any latitude given a sufficiently long time" [37]; Prescott in Australia ascribes it to extreme podsolisation with formation of deep pans (Fe and Al oxides); this would be a process of "great antiquity" on peneplains close to sea-level, since free drainage would inhibit it. Subsequent uplift would expose the indurated pans by erosion of their over-burden; this would also account for high-level laterites.

This may be applicable in Australia, but it seems very dubious in India, since (i) Palaeolithic artefacts are found *in situ* in the boulder conglomerate at the base of the Madras laterite,[38] which seems hardly compatible with "great antiquity"; and (ii) there are no signs of rejuvenation on a scale remotely commensurate with the uplift (or eustatic lowering of base) which would on this view be necessary to account for the high-level laterite of the Wn Ghats crest. Some reconciliation of the Polynov-Prescott view and the first objection is of course possible by an appeal to the accelerated tempo of tropical weathering.

The Human Importance of Laterite

As a soil laterite is obviously very poor. Yet even so it is not without a certain value, negative as it may seem, since in or adjoining intensively

---

[34] Apparent exceptions are probably re-deposited.   [35] Wadia, 298.

[36] Joffe, 498: "the author is inclined to believe that many areas of red soils in the Mediterranean region are relicts of an earlier geologic age when a humid tropical climate prevailed."

[37] Dobby, 81.

[38] V. D. Krishnaswami, "Environmental and Cultural Changes of Prehistoric Man near Madras", *JMGA* XIII (1938), 58–90: "Every item of evidence suggests that . . . man had come on the scene before the laterite was formed" (p. 70). This is a very careful paper based on good field-work.

cultivated paddy-plains the laterite (or strongly lateritic) 'islands' or fringing shelves may be valuable as grazing-grounds and sources of fuel from scrub forest. They form, as it were, 'neutral ground' between the waterlogged paddy-flats and the jungly dissected hinterland. Again, delta or floodplain may be too valuable as rice-land for much or any space to be spared for minor crops; hence the low uplands are favourite settlement sites, with an extraordinarily mixed land use: houses; gardens and orchards; rough grazing and even coarse grassland; scrub jungle for fuel, minor forest products, and small constructional timber; perhaps dry crops. If lateritic rather than laterite they may even carry small patches of sugar or (in Burma) rubber. These functions are perhaps best seen in the Irrawaddy Delta,[39] but the low-level peneplains of the Konkan are not dissimilar.

As a building material laterite is peculiarly valuable: it can be cut with a spade but hardens like iron on exposure to air, and, being an end-product of weathering, cannot be weathered much further and is indefinitely durable.[40] It is also used as road-surfacing; as such it is not very durable, the small pebbly ironstone nodules soon breaking down under traffic, but it is cheap and available in many areas otherwise devoid of road-metal, and the cloud of red dust which signifies a laterite road is a familiar feature of many Indian landscapes. Finally, its very obvious irony appearance (the pebbles actually look like polished cast-iron, or if broken like rust) led to its exploitation in the past by indigenous smelters; the Fe content may be as much as 30%.

BIBLIOGRAPHICAL NOTE

Forests

E. P. Stebbing, *The Forests of India* (1922). Standard history of forest development and administration.

H. H. Champion, *A Preliminary Survey of Forest Types of India and Burma* * (Indian Forest Records, New Series, Silviculture, Vol. I; ND 1936). Standard work on classification, a first-class survey.

R. S. Troup, *The Silviculture of Indian Trees* * (1921). Excellent descriptions of species and their habitats.

——, "Problems of Forest Ecology in India" (in A. G. Tansley and T. F. Chipp (eds.), *Aims and Methods in the Study of Vegetation* (1926), 283–313).

C. C. Calder, "An Outline of the Vegetation of India",* in S. L. Hora (ed.), *An Outline of the Field Sciences of India* (Calcutta, 1937), 71–90. Both these are very useful sketches of the ecology.

[39] Cf. O. H. K. Spate, "The Burmese Village", *G.R.* XXXV (1945), 523–43; and the brilliant description of the Konkan in P. Gourou, "Quelques observations de géographie tropicale dans l'Inde", *Revue de l'Univ. de Bruxelles* (1950–51).
[40] See Pendleton's paper cited in Bibliographical Note; Dobby draws attention to the laterite buildings at Angkor, "firm and square after centuries of exposure" to climatic and vegetational processes notoriously ruinous.

Sir J. Hooker, in *Imperial Gazetteer*, Vol. I (1909), still useful; the last contribution of a worker whose career began with *Himalayan Journals* in 1847–51.

Sir H. Howard, *Post-War Forest Policy for India* (ND, 1944). Survey of present position, effects of the war, and needs of development.

Uses

Sir G. Watt, *Dictionary of the Economic Products of India* (1889–93); abridged as *Commercial Products of India* (1908).

E. A. Smythies, *India's Forest Wealth* (2nd ed., 1925).

J. S. Gamble, *A Manual of Indian Timbers* (2nd ed., 1902).

Soil Erosion

Sir H. Glover, *Soil Erosion* (OPIA No. 23, 1944). An excellent outline of the problem.

——, *Erosion in the Punjab* (Lahore, 1946).

R. Maclagan Gorrie, *Soil and Water Conservation in the Punjab* (Lahore, 1946).

——, "Countering Desiccation in the Punjab",* *GR* XXXVIII (1948), 30–40.

A. P. F. Hamilton, "Siwalik Erosion", *HJ* VII (1935), 87–102. Excellent description of Siwalik topography and lithology, and of *cho* erosion.

G. S. Puri, "The Ecology of Erosion and Landslips", *IGJ* XXIV (1949), 12–27.

Works starred (*) contain important photographs. There are also many papers on all the above topics in *The Indian Forester*.

Plains Ecology

R. K. Mukerjee, *The Regional Balance of Man* (Madras, 1938). Especially Chs. VI, VII.

Soils—general

Royal Commission on Agriculture in India (1928), 70–79. The traditional classification.

Z. J. Schokalsky, *The Natural Conditions of Soil Formation in India* (in B. Polynov (ed.), *Contributions to the Knowledge of the Soils of Asia*, No. 2 (Leningrad, Dokuchaiev Institute, 1932), 53–155). Indispensable. Available from the library of the Rothamsted Experimental Station.

P. Vageler, *An Introduction to Tropical Soils* (1933). Readable and comprehensive, but criticised by Joffe as containing "interesting elements of scholasticism" (i.e. having some general ideas?).

D. N. Wadia, M. S. Krishnan, and P. N. Mukerjee, "Introductory Note on the Geological Foundations of the Soils of India" (*Rec. GSI*, LXVIII (1935), 363–91. Rather slight; full bibliography (excluding Schokalsky!).

B. Viswanath and A. C. Ukil, "Comparative Studies on Indian Soils: I. Regional and Environmental Factors" (*Indian Journal of Agricultural Science*, XIV (1944), 333–44.

S. P. Raychaudhuri and S. K. Mukherjee, "Present Position of Soil Survey in India", *Journal of Scientific and Industrial Research* (Calcutta), 6B (1947), 405–08.

Laterite

L. L. Fermor, "What is Laterite?" *Geological Magazine*, New Series VIII (1911), 454–62, 507–16, 554–66. A *locus classicus*.

D. N. Wadia, *Geology of India* (1939), Ch. XXIII.

E. H. G. Dobby, *Southeast Asia* (1950), Ch. 5. Contains some useful points.

R. S. Pendleton, "Laterite and its Structural Uses in Siam and Cambodia", *GR* XXXI (1941), 172–202. Comprehensive review, admirably illustrated.

J. S. Joffe, *Pedology* (New Brunswick, USA, 2nd ed., 1949), Ch. XIII. A very full and typically American survey and criticism of the literature; see especially 486–**88.**

J. A. Prescott and R. L. Pendleton, *Laterite and Lateritic Soils* (Commonwealth Bureau of Soil Science Tech. Communication No. 47, Farnham Royal (Bucks), 1952). An authoritative discussion, with plates and extensive bibliography.

PART 2

THE PEOPLE

CHAPTER IV

POPULATION AND ITS PROBLEMS

OF a total estimated world population of 2174 m. in 1940, no fewer than 1155 m. were in Asia, and the great bulk of Asia's millions were in four countries—India, China, Japan, Indonesia—which together have about 1000 m. people. By the Censuses of 1951, *India* has a population of 357 m. (plus 4 m. in Kashmir) and Pakistan 76 m.: the total for the sub-continent thus approximates to the conventional figure for China, and *India* alone equals the USSR and the USA put together.

Defective as Indian statistics are,[1] there is thus no other single group of comparable size for which such a wide range of demographic data is available, and in particular none in which, despite all changes, such great masses live in a pre-industrial environment. On the total area of 1,581,410 sq mls there was in 1941 an average density of 246 (1951:276), about five times the world average. Such a figure is striking enough in itself, but does not take us very far: actually densities vary from under 6 in large areas of Baluchistan, the Thar, and Kashmir, to **773** over the whole area of E Pakistan (more than 54,000 sq mls) and **1007** in Travancore-Cochin (9155 sq mls). In Cochin indeed there are small rural areas with a density of 2000–4000, and in E Pakistan the entire Dacca Division—15,498 sq mls, twice the area of Wales, had a density of 1077; of its population of 16,683,714 only 383,491 people were in the four towns of over 50,000. Such dense *rural* concentrations over large areas are approached only in China and Java.

---

[1] The 1941 Census is much less complete than the 1931, for which the excuse is economy and war conditions. "This is the falsest of false economies—an economy of knowledge"; war conditions were not acute in early 1941 and the value of occupational figures to India's future could hardly be over-estimated. These deficiencies are accompanied by much complacent window-dressing about the beautiful (and more expensive) new bindings of "India's ambassadors." Only incomplete figures for the 1951 Censuses are yet available, and these are inadequate for detailed discussion, though they have been cited where possible. Unfortunately (though not unexpectedly) the tabulations of the two Censuses are far from uniform, so that comparison is not easy; thus Pakistan gives literacy but not urban/rural figures, and conversely for *India*. The *Indian* Census has the interesting innovation of a regional grouping (not unlike that adopted in this book) and the welcome return of broad occupational ("Livelihood") figures broken down into Districts. See also p. 121.

In this chapter all figures unless otherwise stated refer to 1941, and "Census 1941" and "Census 1931" mean the general introductory volumes (Vol. I, Pt I (Report), and **1951** Pt II (Tables), of the whole Census), again unless otherwise stated.

French and Portuguese India, the Andaman and Nicobar Islands (3143 sq mls, poptn 33,768), and the ex-British 'Province' of Panth Piploda in central India (25 sq mls, 5267 people) are left out of account in the ensuing discussions.

Movement of Population

Increase over the last 60 years has been rapid:

Year	Population, 1000s	Increment, 1000s	% Increase [2]
1891	279,446		
1901	283,872	4,426	1·6
11	303,013	19,140	6·7
21	305,693	2,680	0·9
31	338,119	32,426	10·6
41	388,998	50,878	15·0
51	**436,948**	**47,950**	**12·3**

The total increase since 1891 is thus 157·5 m.—57% in 60 years—and the later increments of around 50 m. in a decade are startling. They must, however, be viewed with some proportion; the increase in England and Wales over the 60 years before 1941 was 44%, and this despite the fall in the birth-rate in this century. As Karve remarks, "If our population increased during the last census period [1921–31] by the size of whole nations in Europe, is it so strange when it is remembered that India is comparable not with a European country, many specimens of which are smaller in extent and population than some of our administrative districts, but with Europe as a whole?"[3] The rate of increase is indeed comparable with that of Wn Europe in the last hundred years or so; the alarming aspect is not so much the great absolute increases of 2·5 m. a year in this century as the fact that they have not been accompanied by an increase in industrialisation comparable to that of Europe, and thus indicate increasing pressure on the land in a dominantly agrarian country.

This point used to be brought out from another angle by the remarkable irregularity of the curve of increase, decades which add tens or even scores of millions alternating with others in which the net gain, viewed proportionately to the size of the Indian population, is almost negligible. This rhythm has been broken since 1921; but it is possible that in Bengal at least (with over one-seventh of the total population) the 1943 famine mortality, most marked among the young and amongst reproductive females, may have had some demographic effect. Bengal over 1901–41 showed a rate of increase markedly higher than that of All-India—43·1%

[2] Census 1941, Table II. Censuses before 1891 suffered from imperfect enumeration on a scale large enough to render further comparison pointless. Since 1891, no very material area has been added; for differences due to this factor see Census 1931, 5, and D. G. Karve, *Poverty and Population in India* (1936), 27.

[3] Karve, *op. cit.*, 32–33; cf. Gyan Chand, *India's Teeming Millions* (1939), 45–47, and P. M. Lad, in R. K. Mukerjee (ed.), *Economic Problems of Modern India* (1939), I. 89–90.

against 37·0, and in 1931–41 20·3% against 15·0. But in 1941–51 E and W Bengal together increased by only 10·9% against 12·3 for the whole sub-continent. This decreased rate has doubtless been affected by the post-Partition transfers, but it is unlikely that the number of refugees proceeding beyond W Bengal was large enough to affect this argument seriously. It should be remembered that the famine was as acute in the active En as in the stagnant Wn Delta, nor did Bengal stand alone, though it stood out by the spectacular scale of its suffering and its proximity to the military front. Very severe dearth was prevalent throughout Sn India, and actual famine in Orissa and the Bombay Deccan. A mere extension of the 1921–41 curve may therefore be misleading.

The fluctuating increase has been analysed by Arthur Geddes with acuteness and refinement of detail,[4] but the reason after all is not far to seek, even without the aid of the demographic analysis which rams it home: vast masses, perhaps the majority, of the Indian peoples live on such a low level of nutrition and so exposed to disease that their continued existence is 'marginal'. There are no reserves of human energy to meet the assaults of dearth and pestilence; hence the famines of the 1890s and the influenza of 1918–19 are reflected in the low decennial increases. On the other hand, despite apologetics, it seems broadly true that social customs practically place a premium on reproduction, so that when better times do come the flow of births is as overwhelming as is the mortality in bad years; there is thus a "close, direct correspondence between harvests and birth-rate and inverse correspondence between harvests and mortality."[5] This generalisation is fully corroborated by the rich detail of Geddes' studies, area by area; and, as he points out, the actual variations of rate are greater than appears from the bare statistics owing to the non-coincidence of famines and epidemics with Census years.

Some Socio-Demographic Factors

Among the factors most essential in the analysis of Indian population problems are those linked with social (in fact, religious) custom. Something must be said about these, though lack of space prevents any detailed discussion, and indeed most of them are not very susceptible of geographical analysis, their distribution being very general and bound up with complex religious and caste structures. Such spatial variations as they show are for the most part only very obscurely or indirectly related to geographical factors, and mapping them would be merely maps for the sake of maps.

[4] "The Population of Bengal, its Distribution and Changes", *GJ* LXXXIX (1937), 344–68; "Half a Century of Population Trends in India", *GJ* XCVIII (1941), 228–53; "The Population of India: Variability . . . as a Regional Demographic Index", *GR* XXXII (1942), 562–73.

[5] Mukerjee, *op. cit.*, p. ix. Davis thinks that the influenza epidemic probably killed nearer 20 m. Indians than the 'official' estimate of about 10 m.; cf. *The Population of India and Pakistan* (1951), 237.

They must, however, always be borne in mind; fuller discussions will be found in most of the works cited in this chapter.

First and foremost, probably, and *pace* disclaimers such as those of Gyan Chand, is the premium placed on marriage by practically all the religions of the sub-continent. Amongst Hindus this is associated with early marriage—as soon after puberty as possible—and often with early consummation; and with a general ban, except in some low castes, on widow re-marriage. Muslims on the whole do not attach so much importance to these customs, though the differences between the two communities are perhaps not so great as is often implied: there has been considerable cultural influence both ways, the seclusion of women (*purdah*), for example, has been widely adopted by Hindus from the Muslims, or as a result of conditions prevailing in the Muslim invasions, though it is not so strong as amongst Muslims and there was probably some antecedent tendency towards it amongst the highest social classes.

The prohibition of widow re-marriage obviously operates to limit births. It is, however, of less importance than it might be owing to the striking deficiency of females not only in towns (where it is to be expected and is in fact most marked) but in almost all regions and communities: practically all women are married sooner or later, generally sooner, and the spinster has no place in Indian society. The only States with more females than males are Madras (1009 : 1000) and Orissa (1069 : 1000), and the old states' territories in Assam, Chhattisgarh, and Cochin; in all the proportion of females in 1941 was slightly less than in 1931. Of the rest only Bihar, Madhya Pradesh (CP), Hyderabad, Travancore, and the old states now merged with Bombay have over 950 females to 1000 males. In ex-British Baluchistan the ratio falls as low as 703; here it might be ascribed to antagonism to enumeration of women in a tribal Muslim society but for the fact that the adjacent states (Kalat, etc.), where this might well be stronger, show a figure of 855.

Mukerjee [6] makes a rather ill-judged attempt to relate this to geographical factors, stating that the deficiency of females is greater in arid areas owing to their generally harsher conditions of life. But he also states that the deficiency is greater amongst higher castes—in which, on the whole, easier conditions would prevail. On his view the low female : 1000 male ratios for humid Bengal and Assam (899 and 896) would presumably be due to the influence of industrial Hooghlyside for Bengal and to the tea-gardens and generally 'pioneer' conditions of Assam; this is certainly correct for Bengal [7] and possibly for Assam. But the decided predominance of Madras and the Deccan cannot thus be explained away, and an examina-

---

[6] R. K. Mukerjee, *Food Planning for Four Hundred Millions* (1938), 230–34; and on the general question P. M. Lad in *Economic Problems*, I. 88–89.
[7] Female deficiency is general, but less marked on the whole in purely rural Districts.

tion of the figures for Madras by Districts lends the aridity hypothesis very little support: the areas with more women than men include, it is true, the wet NE and Malabar coasts, but also the dry SE (all Districts S of Trichinopoly, including the driest of the State). At all events, the apparent accentuation of an already well marked sex-disparity is obviously a factor of vital importance for the future rate of increase, which may slacken from this cause alone. In 1951 the ratio fell further, to 933 : 1000.

Early marriage works both ways: on the whole perhaps it may lengthen to some extent the effective reproduction period compared with that of the West, and it seems that fertility is greatest between the ages of 15 and 25. But there is some reason to believe that early consummation is associated with lower fecundity, and apart from that there is the notorious and terrible loss of life in childbirth and in infancy. With all this the birth-rate remains extremely high; Indian vital statistics, depending as they do on the lowest strata of village officialdom, are naturally grossly defective—childbirth has been returned as a male cause of death—but for obvious reasons their errors will be on the side of understatement, and it has been estimated that the deficiency in the records is on the average about 20%. This does not mean that they are valueless; sources of error are fairly constant and they are thus useful as indicating trends.[8]

Demographic Structure and Trends

The increase of the Indian population is accompanied by a tremendous toll of human life and by much suffering, especially for women. The expectation of life is almost incredibly low—in 1931 under 27 years at birth (only half the figure for Italy), and even at the best period (4–5 years) only 37 for females and 39 for males; and it showed no appreciable increase between 1891 and 1931.[9] The risks of early death are disproportionately higher for women owing to confinement in *purdah*, neglect of girl children (confined to a few areas and groups), above all the wear and tear of early and repeated childbirth, often in unspeakably insanitary surroundings and with hopelessly inadequate nutrition and care before and after parturition. Owing to lack of relevant figures it is impossible to calculate the Net Reproduction Rate for India, but this great female mortality can hardly fail to have an adverse effect on NRR. P. M. Lad, who presses this point,

[8] P. K. Wattal, *The Population Problem in India* (1934), 46–52; Census 1931, 91–92. The village statistics are not as bad as those of some municipalities. Wattal gives perhaps the most reasoned statement of the case that India is *not* over-populated. Since his work, however, nearly 100 m. souls have been added.

[9] Census 1931, 91 and footnote. By 1931–41, however, expectation at birth had risen to 32·1 years for males and 31·4 for females (Davis, 241). On the other hand there is no excuse for those writers who suggest that in ancient India, "100 years had been the normal span of life", and that "the public used to demand an explanation from the king for even a single case of premature death." G. Ghose, M.R.San.Inst., in *The Modern Review*, Calcutta, Dec. 1943, puts forward this delightful concept in an article which begins in the standard manner: "India had her past—her glorious ancient civilisation spread its bright lustre throughout the world. In sanitation, too . . ." etc., etc., etc.

admits, however, that 1931 shows some improvement over previous Censuses in the important proportion of females living through the reproductive period. It is one of the more damnable deficiencies of the 1941 Census that it contains no figures bearing directly upon this matter, though it does discuss, so far as is possible, some likely trends. Lad points out that on analysis fertility rates are much lower than many impressionistic writers would suggest, though the defects of the vital statistics must be remembered here.[10]

Lad draws attention to age-structure in 1931. Sundbärg's theoretical composition of an expanding population gives proportions of 40 : 50 : 10 for ages 0–15, 15–50, and over 50; for India, with its low expectation of life and premature senility for much of the population, 40 is perhaps a better lower limit for the upper group than 50. In 1931 the proportions on this basis were approximately 39 : 42 : 19; again it is unfortunately impossible to give figures for 1941, but the decrease in infantile mortality would give a more progressive aspect, unless this has been cancelled out by the famines of 1943. In 1931 there was a marked increase over previous Censuses in the proportion of females aged 15–24, probably the most important reproductive period. In 1911 this was 1756 per 10,000 females of all ages; in 1921 it was 1696, but in 1931 it had risen to 1923. This alone goes far to explain the great increase in 1931–41.[11]

But so far prognostications of a stationary population in some areas have not been borne out even in the most 'saturated'. The 1941 Census showed a break in the zigzag rhythm and the highest recorded rate of increase—explicable on Yeatts' cautious opinion that "there would be some ground for the view that in 1931 the reproductive position in India . . . may indeed have been at a peak." [12] Thus Karve's optimistic estimate of the population/food ratio; Mukerjee's pessimistic one that large areas of the Gangetic Plains were 'saturated' by 1931; and Lad's scouting of "the devastating deluge of babies"—all received a decisive answer in 1941, and according to estimates based on birth and death figures, checked by electoral rolls, increase has been maintained. The 1951 Census on the whole confirms the trend.

Moreover, there have been extensive inroads upon death-rates, especially of infants; it is more difficult to work out the trend of birth-rates. On the whole there seems little evidence of a general fall in the birth-rate as yet; but after oscillating between 32 and 36 per mille from 1920 to 1940, it fell sharply in 1943 to 25·6; in Bihar the rate stood at 28·6 for 1938–42, only 18·2 in 1943. In Bengal and adjacent regions this was doubtless due to

---

[10] Lad, *loc. cit.*, 86–94; Census 1941, 33–52.
[11] Lad, 92–99; Mukerjee, *Food Planning*, 12–14; Census 1941, 51. For errors in age figures owing to irrational attachment to or aversion from certain ages, or to avoid certain taxes, see Census 1931, 80–83.
[12] Census 1941, 52.

famine; elsewhere, e.g. in the Punjab and Maharashtra, to the transfer of males to the army and to war industries. These factors are of course only temporary, but the fall in births would amount to over 2 m. fewer babies in 1943 alone; followed by two more years of war this again might result in a markedly lower rate of increase from about 1960. Death-rates have fallen from 24–31 in 1920–24 to 22–24 in 1935–40; infantile mortality from 175–195 per 1000 live births to 156–64.[13] This still means that 1 out of every 6 children born alive failed to survive its first year; and it fails to take into account a high proportion of still-births (for which the reasons are too obvious); each of these 'vital'—or mortal—events represents acute physical and mental suffering. But the figures do witness to some increase in human welfare. On the other hand, as so often in India, we are confronted with a vicious circle: we must face the heartless question of whether, from a demographic point of view, this is a matter for unmixed congratulation. For the saving of new lives means a strengthening of the younger contingent, a more progressive age-structure, and consequently the prospect of increasing rate of increase; and it is not questioned, even by the most light-hearted optimists, that increase of population bears very hard upon food production.

The faintly optimistic views of Karve and Meek are based on the acceptance of figures the validity of which may be strongly doubted, and Karve himself admits that the situation is precarious. Salt, for example, is a necessity of life, on which the average annual expenditure per head is very small; yet an increase in salt excise by no more than a farthing a pound was followed by a decrease in consumption by a pound a head.[14] Mukerjee's generalised summary in 1938 seems fair for that period: "The excess of available food-supply index over population index was on the whole oscillating round about 20 till the end of the last decade. For the last four years there has been a gradual and significant decline, and the tendency appears to be for the margin to disappear altogether." [15] But in recent years the margin, if it exists at all, is quite probably the other way round; indeed, one might say that the most serious ground for mistrusting Indian food statistics is that if they were true there would be much more famine. Leaving aside indices and statistics and the evidence of 1943 in Bengal, there can be little doubt that in much of the more densely-settled areas there is over-population in the sense that the land available is insufficient, under current social and technical arrangements, to employ and feed the populations concerned on any decent standard; and it is difficult to see what social system could secure real welfare and prosperity for strictly rural densities of 800–1000 over thousands of square miles.

[13] For Indian "A" States in 1949, birth-, death-, and infantile death-rates were respectively 27, 16, 123 (all o/oo).
[14] Karve, op. cit., 77–78.
[15] Food Planning, 20–21. His specific figures are open to some question.

The decline in infantile mortality, then, may ultimately prove to have been purchased at the cost of such an excess of population over population-capacity that the initial saving of suffering may be negatived by increase of a poverty already so acute that any increase of it seems impossible. It does not look as if the improvement in welfare could be maintained, and we should be back where we started. Despite the manifold social and religious difficulties involved, the case for limitation of births is a strong one, as is stressed by most writers on Indian demography, British and Indian alike: "what is really wanted is fewer babies but better ones." Some observers think that it is the expense of contraceptives (were they available at all) rather than social repugnance which would prevent such limitation, and that the Indian masses—or at any rate their wives—would be more responsive than is generally assumed.[16] But it is beside the point to read lectures, whether from Malthus or from Gandhi, on the moral virtue of restraint; the simple human facts are too often overlooked, and it is difficult to see upon what principle of justice the poor should be expected to forgo the only pleasure in life which costs nothing at the time. Only by making life in general more worth living can its devaluation by an inflationary tide of births be avoided; but again we are caught in a vicious circle, since a slackening of the rate of increase is a prerequisite of such improvement. That is the tragic problem of India, and indeed of most of Asia.

Distribution of Population (Figs. 23, 30)

The distribution of population is perhaps best summarised as peripheral to the Deccan and to the great arid belt from Baluchistan to Rajputana. Thus areas with District densities equal to or greater than the All-India average of 246 extend right along the coast from Gujarat to Chittagong, with breaks only in the hilly forested country where the Wn Ghats approach the sea in N Kanara (111), and in Nellore (204) where the Peninsular area with under 40 ins. rainfall reaches the coast. In this littoral girdle densities of over 450 are found in small areas of the fertile alluvial plains of Gujarat, in Kerala, in Tamilnad (except for Ramnad Dt),[17] in the E coast deltas, and of course in Bengal. The entire extremity of the Peninsula, S of a line from Pulicat (N of Madras city) to S Kanara, has over 290, except for the hills of Coorg, the Nilgiris, and Hassan and Tumkur Dts in Mysore. This area of high density includes much poor gneissic country.

N of the Peninsula the entire Gangetic Plain (except for Pilibhit and Kheri Dts, UP) has District densities of over 450, with large areas of over

---

[16] A strong official committee (including Gyan Chand and Chandrasekhar) has supported birth control; see Notestein's paper cited on p. 121.

[17] This area lies in the lee of Ceylon in the summer monsoon and of the Cauvery bulge (Pt Calimere) in Oct.-Dec. Densities in this section by Districts; 1951 tables do not give District areas, though many have been changed, and for uniformity we must keep to 1941.

800. To the E, Assam has an average of only 186, but a strip with 200–330 extends along the Brahmaputra as far as Lakhimpur, separated from E Bengal by the Shillong Plateau (40–70). To the W, the Sutlej/Jumna Doab (largely the non-irrigated Ambala Division of E Punjab) has an average of 318, but beyond it in the sub-montane Punjab, with appreciable winter rain, densities rise above 450 in 8 Districts, while irrigation has produced densities of

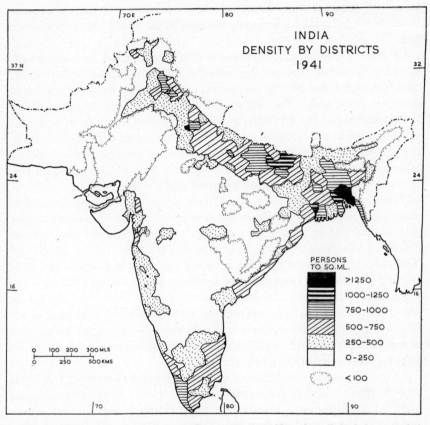

Fig. 23.—DENSITY OF POPULATION BY DISTRICTS, 1941. Note that *all* shaded or stippled areas are above the All-India average of 246. District areas for 1951 not yet available.

316 and 396 in Montgomery and Lyallpur (Rechna and Bari Doabs). The boundary of dense population lies roughly along the Chenab, and the scrub and sandy wastes of Sind Sagar Doab between Jhelum and Indus carry only 94 in Mianwali Dt; though this will soon by increased by the Thal irrigation. Beyond are a few favoured areas: Peshawar (551), Mardan (461), and Rawalpindi (388). In the Himalaya the Vale of Kashmir reaches 303 in Anantnag.

I.P.—4*

In the Deccan, apart from one or two tiny states, insignificant in the general pattern, the only areas of notable concentration are in the Tapti Valley (E Khandesh 289; cotton on alluvium and Deccan Lava), around the towns of Hyderabad, Nagpur, and Sholapur, and in the irrigated ricelands of the Chhattisgarh Plain.

The general control is obvious: high densities in areas of alluvial low-lands with either good rainfall or irrigation, while at the other extreme areas with densities under 40 are all either arid or mountainous or both. It is worth while looking a little more closely at the few Districts with over 800.

Of these Delhi, Lucknow, and Amritsar are inflated by those cities; Hooghly, Howrah, and 24 Parganas by the Hooghlyside conurbation; while Jullundur and Meerut represent perhaps merely local thickenings in generally dense areas. The really significant areas are the large spreads in E Pakistan and on the UP/Bihar borders. E Pakistan is an area of high and reliable rainfall, with active streams (hence a low malaria rate, in contrast to the stagnant Wn delta), and above all with a soil constantly renewed and revivified by the silt brought down in the monsoon floods. It is ideal rice country—in some Districts paddy is over 100% of *net* sown area—with in addition a valuable cash crop, jute. These factors are reflected not only in abnormally high rural densities, but also by a generally high and regular rate of increase, at least until 1943. Nine Districts, with a total area of 25,567 sq mls, have over 800, four of them over 1000, while Dacca and Tippera reach 1542 and 1525, on 2738 and 2531 sq mls respectively. Subtracting the towns of Dacca and Narayanganj, Dacca Dt has still over 1443 (1951: **1347**), and there are no towns of any size in Tippera. It should be noted that Dacca Division includes the lateritic Madhupur jungle, much of which is thinly populated scrub, clearly traceable on the dot-map; most of this lies in Mymensingh Dt which nevertheless has 6,023,758 people on 6156 sq mls—a density of 979 (1951: **934**).

In the UP-Bihar concentration again nine Districts have over 800 (total 21,778 sq mls), and of these four have over 1000—Benares 1114, Saran 1072, Muzaffarpur 1072, Dharbhanga 1033; Patna has 999. Towns are perhaps more important here than in E Pakistan; Benares and Patna together have 339,000 people, and there are three others of over 50,000. Rainfall, around 40 ins., is on the whole reliable; there is good paddy land in the khadar (new alluvium) of the valley-bottoms, and well irrigation ensures good rabi crops of wheat and barley on the interfluves; only in Patna is there much canal irrigation, while Champaran, with a good deal of canal irrigation but also of terai, falls to 675. All show big increases in 1951.

Finally Cochin owes its extraordinary densities (up to 2000–4000; for the whole state 953 on 1493 sq mls) to the combination of high equable temperature and high rainfall with a short dry season—allowing two paddy-crops a year—and highly productive non-paddy land in the coconut groves of its old beach-ridges. The villages are in the groves themselves and are thus productive of an important food and cash crop instead of being, as is usual, a deduction from the cultivated area. This combination is perhaps the most favourable of any to high density, and is also found in littoral Bengal.

A few points on the dot-map (Folder) may be noted. The summary given above is well brought out—concentration on the Indo-Gangetic Plains, the deltas, Kerala, and Gujarat. The sharpness of the break between paddy and forested hills is well seen in Kerala and in the little valleys extending from the Surma basin (Sylhet Dt, E Pakistan) into the Chin-Lushai Hills. In the Deccan the importance of the cotton soils in the Tapti/Wardha Valleys and of Chhattisgarh irrigation is clear. Less generally stressed are the relatively low densities for central Bengal, where Rajshahi Division minus Pabna and Bogra Dts (929 and 855) and Darjeeling (316) has about 580: this is the high-level Ganges/Brahmaputra doab with the poor soils of the Barind. Away from Hooghlyside the Rarh tract of W Bengal, with poor lateritic soils on the fringes of the Peninsula and stagnant malaria-breeding streams and marshes on the alluvium, is also an area of relatively low densities (Birbhum 601, Bankura 487, Nadia (deltaic) 611). The only areas where mining and industry give rise to significant concentrations (apart from Hooghlyside and Bombay) are the Damodar Valley and the Kolar Gold Fields of Mysore; in Bihar also the steel town of Jamshedpur stands out in a thinly populated area. In the NW the populations attracted by recent irrigation developments—the Sukkur Barrage in Sind and the extensions S of the Sutlej in Bahawalpur and Bikaner—cause pronounced thickening on the margins of the Thar; these areas have shown most change in the recent past and will do so in the near future. Finally the Vale of Kashmir and the minor Himalayan duns are notable.

Clearly this distribution implies great pressure on the land, to some extent irrespective of the absolute densities. This finds expression in the complicated miseries of Indian agriculture, discussed more fully in Ch. IX.

Recent Regional Trends

On the long view, 1891–1941, there are very few areas in India of stationary or declining population, and these are mostly in thinly-populated areas, e.g. a strip on the arid and rugged Sind/Baluchistan border, Cutch and Jaisalmer, a few scattered states in central India and Rajputana. The main exceptions are Coorg, where the coffee plantations have never really recovered from plant disease and Brazilian competition; Bhopal state and the adjacent Hoshangabad and Saugor Dts of Madhya Pradesh (CP), agriculturally rather marginal and with little prospect of relief by irrigation; N Kanara, malarial and with its small ports robbed of their hinterlands by the railways to Bombay and Marmagão; and finally Jessore in the centre

of the Ganges Delta, a region of stagnant *bhils* and decayed streams, part
of the zone of chronic agrarian depression, where the drain of population to
industrial Hooghlyside is not masked, as in some W Bengal Districts, by
the actual presence of urban agglomerations.

In general there are three zones of markedly high increase 1891–1941:
(i) an En tier of states and Districts from Assam to Travancore; (ii) the
lower Narbada/lower Tapti area; (iii) the Indus Plains. The first zone has
some areas of extremely rapid growth (over 149·9%)—the upper Assam
Valley (tea planting), parts of E Bengal, some small units in the Orissa
states (probably simply better enumeration in small and backward states),
Kolar in Mysore (gold mining). Assam (except the Shillong Plateau) and
E Bengal as a whole show very rapid increase, and other areas which stand
out are Chhattisgarh, the lower Godavari, the high (non-malarial) Nilgiris,

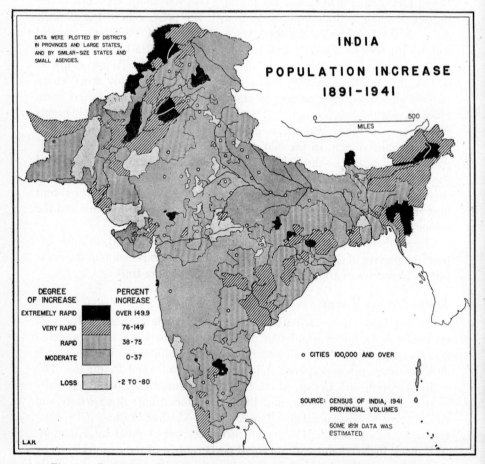

Fig. 24.—INCREASE OF POPULATION, 1891–1941; courtesy L. Hoffmann and *GJ*.

and Cochin-Travancore; while the belt is broken by areas of moderate
increase in W Bengal (apart from urbanised Districts), the Orissa Deltas,
Nellore, and Tanjore-Ramnad (above, 104, fn. 17). The second zone is
associated with the rise of cotton on the Deccan Lavas and the Gujarat
alluvium; while the last had originally but a small population (away from
the sub-montane Punjab) and is the scene of the greatest irrigation develop-

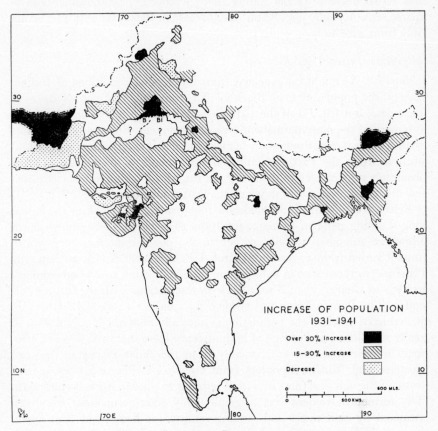

INCREASE OF POPULATION
1931–1941

Over 30% increase

15–30% increase

Decrease

Fig. 25.—INCREASE OF POPULATION, 1931–41.

ment. The extremely high increase of the NWFP is perhaps due to better
enumeration as well as to irrigation in the Vale of Peshawar, but irrigation
alone has transformed some W Punjab Districts—Lyallpur jumped from
60,300 in 1891 to 586,000 in 1901, and Montgomery and Lyallpur together
rose from 477,000 in 1891 to **3,971,000** in 1951 (753%), and of this increment nearly half came in 1931–51.

These trends are on the whole still operative, as may be seen from the
areas of high increase 1931–41 (Fig. 25); the effects of Partition are treated

separately. The very great increases in this decade in Bikaner and Bahawalpur (38·1 and 36·2% respectively) are due to extension of irrigation and are
confined to the N of these states. In the Balipara Frontier Tract, Assam,
better enumeration is probably responsible for the rate shown, actual numbers being negligible (6512 persons in 1941). In Baluchistan the juxtaposition of high increase (Chagai 32·9%, Bolan 28·2%, Karan 44·8%)
and actual decrease (Kalat minus 20·5%) reflects local movements in a
sparse semi-nomadic population; the increase in Bolan, for example, being
only from 4688 to 6009 souls.

Migration, Internal and External

Internal. As might be expected from the general conditions of Indian
society, the population is on the whole far from mobile. Again we have no
1941 data, but Ch. III of the 1931 Census Report provides an admirable
summary of the more permanent type of movement. But as a result of the
1939–45 war internal migration became more and external less significant,
until in 1947 the Partition enforced movements of people on a scale
absolutely unparalleled in the history of the world, taking into account the
few months or even weeks in which the shifts took place.

Before treating the Indo-Pakistani transfers we may look at the more
long-standing pattern. In 1931, for India as a whole, the numbers born
elsewhere amounted to only 21 per 10,000 population; for the political
units it varied from 57–120 in Madras, UP, and Bihar & Orissa (then one
Province) to 1000–2000 in Baluchistan, Baroda, Sikkim, and Assam, and up
to 2371 in Coorg—a small unit liable to fluctuations with the fortunes of
coffee. The Baroda figure was swollen by ephemeral political factors; in
Baluchistan much of the population is normally migratory; only Assam is
really significant, and indeed of high interest. Here there are, or were, two
main movements: labourers, mainly from the Bihar Plains, to the tea-
gardens, and Muslim squatters from crowded E Bengal taking up the
waste of the only real (non-irrigated) farming frontier in the sub-continent.
The former movement was originally only semi-permanent, labourers
attracted by cash wages and sending remittances home; but with much
improved labour conditions there is a tendency to more stable immigration
with wives and children. The Muslim movement of the two or three
decades up to 1947 was always on a family basis; it explains the Pakistani
claim to Assam in which Muslims were only about a third of the population: overcrowded E Bengal needed *lebensraum*. Before Partition the
movement led to friction between the governments of Bengal and Assam,
since communal motives led to measures restricting squatting or even dis-
possessing those in possession. More significant, there has even been some
Muslim entry since Partition—as clear evidence as could be found of the
over-populated condition of E Pakistan.

The numbers involved in 1931 were small as compared with Indian totals; the only units with movement in one direction of over 1 m. were: (immigrant) Assam, Bengal, and Bombay—in the latter two the attraction was the great cities; (emigrant) Madras, UP, Bihar & Orissa. The Provinces with greatest gross movement were Bengal with 1·73 m. immigrants and 0·94 m. emigrants and Bihar & Orissa with 0·47 m. inward and 1·76 m. outward. The only units with *net* loss or gain over 1 m. were Assam (1·24 m. gain) and UP and Bihar & Orissa with losses respectively of 1·01 and 1·29 m. Although these figures are so old, they reflect some fairly permanent geographical factors, and except where overlaid by the effects of Partition probably still indicate the main trends. These factors include the obvious pressure on the land in the Gangetic Plains and the Orissa Deltas (Madras also showed a large net outward movement, 0·89 m.) and the attraction of Assam; while in much of Bengal agrarian pressure leading to stagnation or even depopulation is masked by the urban pull of Hooghly-side.

There is of course a very marked flow to the great towns, which are unable to maintain themselves by natural increase; the reasons are too obvious: insanitary living conditions, very high infantile mortality, above all a great deficiency of females. Six towns taken at random had in 1941 the following numbers of males and females (in thousands): Madras, 408 males to 370 females; Ahmedabad, 345 : 247; Agra, 156 : 128; Lucknow, 223 : 164; Dacca, 123 : 90; Bhatpara, 78 : 39. Of the total urban population over 21 m. were males and 16·5 m. females, or 70 to 55 against 67 to 62 for All-India; the disparity in young adults would be even more striking. The extent to which the industrial labour-force is provided by villagers driven from the land in bad years, but still attached to their villages and returning as soon as possible, has perhaps been exaggerated and is certainly much less than it was two or three decades ago; nevertheless, as these sex-ratios suggest, much of the movement to the towns is still only semi-permanent.

There are naturally some groups much more mobile than the average. These are in the main traders and financiers, such as the Marwaris from Rajputana, adroit bankers and moneylenders, who number amongst them some of *India's* leading industrial families, such as the Birlas and Dalmias. In Pakistan the Pathans are mobile traders and moneylenders; some Himalayan groups, such as the Bhotiyas of high Kumaon, travel great distances, from Cawnpore or Amritsar to Tibet or even Sinkiang; and in the old days a great part of agricultural marketing in Hindustan was in the hands of itinerant grain-brokers, the Banjaras, who travelled about strongly armed, with great convoys of pack-bullocks resting in regular encampments.

It must be remembered that there is a not inconsiderable amount of purely local movement; in the fantastic *morcellement* of Wn and central India this inflated the figures of outsiders in tiny statelets, but on the other hand Madras is as big as Italy and there are a dozen individual units equal to England and Wales, so that it is possible to travel scores of miles without entering the statistics at all.

External. Until the great depression of the 1930s migration overseas was on a fairly large scale absolutely, though the numbers involved were inconsiderable in relation to the total population. Although there is hardly any emigration now there are important Indian colonies as far afield as Fiji (where Indians are 47% of the population) and the Caribbean, where "West Indian East Indians" form 44% of the population of British Guiana and 35% of that of Trinidad. But the main currents have naturally been to Indian Ocean shores: as labourers on the plantations of Malaya, Ceylon, and Mauritius; as traders and professional cadres to these countries and to East Africa; while in Burma, till 1937 an Indian Province, much if not most urban unskilled labour, a large proportion of the clerical classes in and out of government employ, and practically the whole independent (i.e. non-official) middle class were Indian—with peculiar and on the whole deplorable results on Burmese political life; not that this was anybody's fault. Some of these colonies began as indentured labour, notably the important group in South Africa, a fact which makes the present policy of that country appear particularly ungracious.

The largest groups abroad are as follows, according to 1949 estimates (in thousands)[18]:

Burma . 700	S Africa . 282	Indonesia 30
Ceylon . 700	E Africa . 184	Fiji 126
Malaya . 708	Mauritius . 271	West Indies and Guianas . 406

In Mauritius, Indians form 63% of the total population.

In most of these countries there is strong feeling against Indian immigrants, based essentially on their economic under-cutting of labour or their control of retail trade and petty finance, but in part also based on antagonism to the peculiarities of Indian, and especially Hindu, social customs. In Malaya the depression in tin and rubber led to a cessation of recruiting, and the Indian Government also objected to it on grounds of exploitation of Indian labour. The agricultural depression in Burma, forcing Burmese into occupations previously left to Indians, and the anti-Indian riots of 1931 and 1938, slackened and in some years reversed the flow. An Indo-Burmese agreement controlling immigration was reached in 1941, just in time to be rendered null by the Japanese invasion, during which some

[18] *IR* I/33 (18/8/49), 12–14.

400,000 Indians filtered across the Assam/Burma Ranges. Since the war Burmese nationalism has used its opportunity to break the hold obtained by Indian moneylenders on about a third of the land of Lower Burma. In Ceylon also an agreement was reached in time to be made irrelevant by the war; the situation is complicated here by the presence, in addition to some 700,000 plantation labourers, of a large Tamil community (about 800,000), the descendants of invaders who actually ruled much of the country for centuries. There is obviously not much hope for relieving over-population by emigration[19]; but these colonies provide excellent openings for Indian trade; the clove trade of Zanzibar, for example, is practically a monopoly of the Khoja Muslims of Bombay.

Immigration into India is of course almost negligible numerically: the standard of living is obviously not attractive. The only large exception is not a real one, since the territories involved, the fragments of French and Portuguese possessions, are strictly parts of India, and the movement is largely of the temporary remittance-home type. But immigrants from over-crowded Goa—clerks, teachers, doctors, musicians, hotel staffs—are found all along the W coast, and especially in and around Bombay, where they are socially a not unimportant (nor unattractive) element. An exception of a different sort is provided by the British, but their numbers are few and obviously likely to decline rather than increase. The Euro-American community, overwhelmingly British, is of course largely concentrated in Calcutta, Bombay, and a few other cities. Apart from technical officials of various types, and missionaries, the only considerable body up-country is the tea-planting community of Assam; the importance of the British is economic, to a less extent social, rather than numerical.

Urbanism (Figs. 26–29)

The phrase "a land of villages" is rather pointless, as it obviously applies to any agrarian country. There is some point, however, in the fact that of the 1941 total of 658,595 towns and villages no fewer than 450,902 had under 500 inhabitants, while those with over 5000 numbered only 4223. There has, however, been a steady rise in the urban percentage of the population, from 9·5 in 1891 to nearly 13 in 1941. The main features of urban development will be plain from Figs. 26–29 and the tabular statement below. The most striking points are the large areas over 50 miles from a large town; the practical absence of urban clusters—in effect only one,

[19] See R. K. Mukerjee, *Migrant Asia* (Rome, 1936) for a nationalist review of the whole situation. I cannot refrain from mentioning Professor Mukerjee's view (given twice) that Australia could "easily" support 450,000,000 people, "according to an acceptable estimate", which happens to be Japanese. He is of course fully entitled to be critical of the White Australia policy, and some of his points are telling; but in default of the slightest evidence as to the basis of the estimate, "acceptable" must be taken in a very psychological sense.

Hooghlyside; and above all the remarkable 1931–41 increase in cities of over 100,000 and especially of over 500,000 people. War conditions had relatively little effect in March 1941, but later undoubtedly greatly increased urban concentration, which has been still further accentuated by the migrations consequent upon Partition. The increase really reflects more widespread industrialisation, the beginnings at least of a true urban proletariat. This is perhaps most striking in Madras, where hydro-electricity has brought new life to such towns as Coimbatore and Madura.

The following figures are based upon the 1931 Census (p. 46) and Tables I, III, IV, and V of the 1941 Census; it should be noted that between 600 and 700 'towns' of under 5000 inhabitants are included.[20]

[20] According to the introduction to the 1941 Census (p. 26) such 'towns' were excluded from the urban calculations; but a careful check shows that they are in fact included as Class VI in Table V; see especially note 6 to Table I. The percentage of 12·8 above was worked out separately, including towns below 5000, and is the same as the general percentage given in the Census. Such small trials are inseparable from Indian demography.

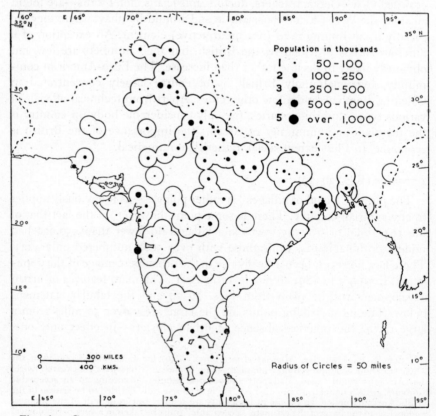

Population in thousands

1	·	50 – 100
2	•	100 – 250
3	●	250 – 500
4	●	500 – 1,000
5	●	over 1,000

Radius of Circles = 50 miles

Fig. 26A.—CITIES OF OVER 50,000 INHABITANTS, 1941; circles with radius of 50 miles.

Towns of	Number of Towns			Population, thousands			% of Urban Total		
	1921	1931	1941	1921	1931	1941	1921	1931	1941
over 500,000	3	3	7	2,749	2,972	6,900	8·4	7·6	13·6
250–500,000	3	6	10	957	2,094	3,372	3·0	5·4	6·7
100–250,000	29	29	40	4,506	4,608	6,261	13·9	11·8	12·5
50–100,000	54	65	95	3,518	4,572	6,173	10·8	11·7	12·3
under 50,000	2217	2472	2551	20,745	24,739	27,290	63·9	63·5	54·9
Totals .	2306	2575	2703	32,475	38,985	49,696	10·6	11·6	12·8
								% of whole poptn	

Although communal rivalry led to some inflation of the figures for the larger towns in 1941, this cannot account for an increase in 1931–41 of 81% (from 9·7 m. to 16·5 m.) in the population living in towns of over

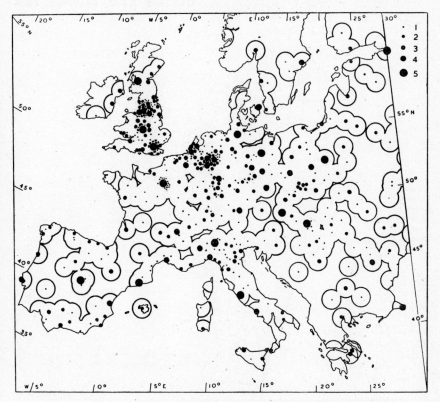

Fig. 26B.—CITIES OF OVER 50,000 INHABITANTS, EUROPE; scale as in Fig. 26A.
See Fig. 26A for key.

100,000. Between 1921 and 1941 the total urban population grew by 33·5% against the general increase of 15%. The seven towns with over 500,000 people in 1941 were Calcutta, Bombay, Madras, Hyderabad (Deccan), Lahore, Ahmebadad, and Delhi, in that order. By 1951 there were six "million" cities (against two in 1941): Bombay, Calcutta, Madras, Delhi (Old and New together), Hyderabad, Karachi, Lahore, Bangalore, Ahmedabad, and Cawnpore were around three-quarters of a million. In *India* urban population had risen to **17·3**% of total, and of the urban total **17·9**% were in cities of over 500,000. Clearly the urban trend is accelerating.

Pakistan is less urbanised than *India*; of the 152 towns with over 50,000 she had only 19, totalling 2·67 m. or less than 4% of the 1941 population, against 19·73 m. and over 6% for *India*. The figures for E Pakistan are extraordinarily low; in 1941 that area had only 5 towns of over 50,000

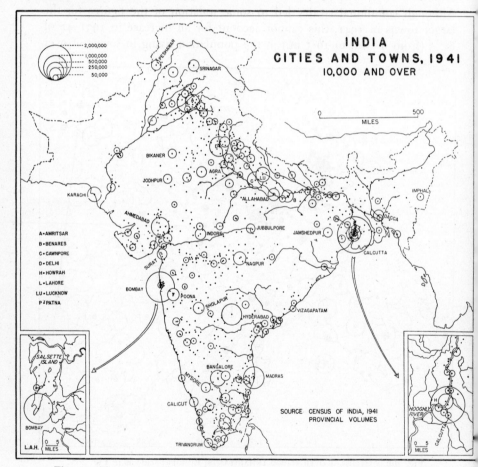

Fig. 27.—Towns of over 10,000 Inhabitants, 1941; courtesy L. Hoffmann and *GJ*.

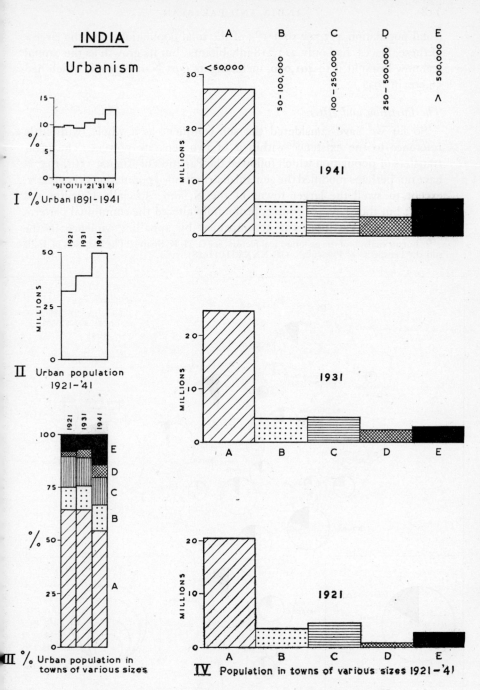

INDIA

Urbanism

A   B   C   D   E

< 50,000   50-100,000   100-250,000   250-500,000   500,000 ∧

1941

I % Urban 1891-1941

II Urban population 1921-'41

III % Urban population in towns of various sizes

1931

1921

IV Population in towns of various sizes 1921-'41

Fig. 28.—DIAGRAMS OF URBANISM, 1921–41. A–E in III as in IV.

117

(total population 475,792 or 1·1% of the total population), and the largest
of these, Dacca, had only 213,218 inhabitants; but its growth as the capital
has now brought it to **401,000**, including its port Narayanganj, which had
56,000 in 1941.

The Partition and After

So far we have considered the sub-continent as a whole, with little
reference to the existence within it of two separate powers. The great
transfers of population which followed the Partition of August 15th, 1947,[21]
have not perhaps modified the general distribution of population very greatly,
except to swell the larger towns of the N, and especially Calcutta and
Delhi; but they have, of course, profoundly altered the communal pattern.

The actual Partition was accompanied by appalling violence in the

[21] For an analysis of the geographical factors, see O. H. K. Spate, "The Partition of India
and the Prospects of Pakistan", *GR* XXXVIII (1948), 5–29.

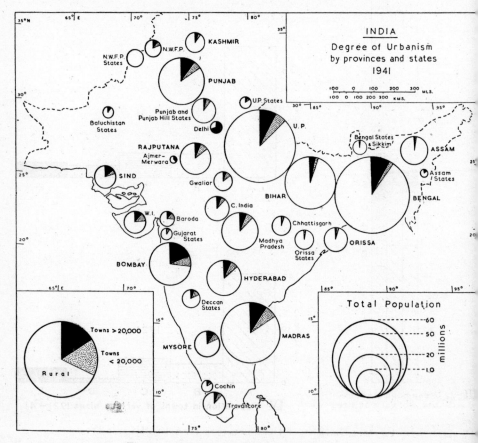

Fig. 29.—URBANISM BY POLITICAL UNITS, 1941.

Punjab, and within six weeks it was estimated that about 3·5 m. people had crossed the new border. The main movement in the W was over by the end of 1947, and by March 1948 about 6·5 m. Muslims had gone into W Pakistan, and some 6 m. Hindus and Sikhs had left it. During 1948 and 1950, however, disorders in Bengal led to further migration, amounting probably to 4 m. refugees leaving E Pakistan and 1 m. Muslims entering it. The total movement is thus of the order of 17 m., twice the population of Greater London or not far short of the combined peoples of Canada and Australia. No comparable event has ever been known. All means of transport were used, about 100,000 people being flown out, while in August–October 1947 the Punjab was traversed by immense convoys—the largest numbered 400,000 souls—of men, women, and children, with their beasts and such poor chattels as they could bring, making their way on foot and exposed to savage attacks from which they were very inadequately protected by the police and troops on either side of the border; several trains were stopped or derailed and the packed inmates systematically massacred. Most of the 5 or 6 m. who had crossed the Sutlej by the end of 1947 were utterly destitute; later refugees from Sind and E Pakistan were not in quite so desperate a case and some property could be salved or transferred.

The reception of these millions taxed the resources of both Governments to the utmost; at one time a single camp in E Punjab held 300,000 people. Rehabilitation is a long-term problem and is far from complete. Although the numbers moving from either country in the W were fairly balanced, the disparities in occupation, wealth, and status were immense; in Lahore, for example, a city two-thirds Muslim, the Muslim share in banking and insurance was almost ludicrously small, while non-Muslim traders paid eight times as much sales tax as Muslim traders. The greater landowners were often Sikhs or Hindus; land abandoned by them in W Punjab amounted to 6·7 m. ac., against 4·7 m. of Muslim land E of the border. As a result *India* was faced with the problem of assimilating large numbers of once well-to-do capitalists, landowners, or professional men, while conversely Pakistan lost a large proportion of essential administrators, technicians, entrepreneurs, and clerical workers. But in some *Indian* industries most of the more skilled employees were Muslims—the shoe-makers of Agra, for instance, or the drivers and firemen on some of the railways. In the E nearly 40% of the refugees from E Pakistan were traders or businessmen.

For a short time economic life in W Punjab came almost to a standstill; but the problem has probably been rather easier of solution in W Pakistan once the untried administration rallied from the shock. There were larger areas of abandoned irrigated land available for settlement, and a larger proportion of peasants to settle them; in fact there has been some return to the UP of peasants who could not adjust themselves to the very different irrigation methods of the Canal Colonies.

The *Indian* Government has made strenuous efforts to resettle its huge masses of displaced persons; 18 new townships are planned, to hold nearly 800,000 people, and by March 1950 over 4 m. acres of reclaimed or evacuee land were allotted to 390,000 families, representing, with village craftsmen and other services, nearly 2 m. persons. Some of these settlers are farming by co-operative methods; most of them are in E Punjab or in central India, where weed-infested land is being reclaimed by tractors. Others have extended jute cultivation into the terai of Bihar and UP, and a small group has even gone to the Andamans. But the fact that the refugees were so largely urban (as is natural with intrusive minorities) has given rise to great difficulties; they naturally tend to congregate in the great towns, accentuating always unsatisfactory conditions of overcrowding and insanitation; but this is the only life they know. It is not surprising that there has been much demoralisation; nor that in many areas the reception of refugees has been, to say the least, regrettably grudging.

The concentration in E Punjab and W Bengal is significant: [22]

	Area, sq mls	1950 esttd poptn, millions	Density		Density % change	Refugees, thousands	% of poptn
			1941	1950			
W Bengal .	29,000	24·3	751	840	+ 12	3,000	12·3
E Punjab .	37,000	12·6	408	341	− 16	2,465	19·5
Delhi .	564	1·5	932	2632	+ 190	377	24·0

E Punjab has lost more people than it has gained, and despite its precarious rainfall and general poverty, particularly in industry, its eventual prospects of adjustment are quite good if the great Bhakra-Nangal multi-purpose project is completed. The use of Sutlej water for this scheme has given rise to Pakistani apprehensions of undue diversion of water; it is perhaps fortunate that the great Thal and Rohri irrigation schemes depend on the Indus, which cannot be tapped by *India* whatever the fate of Kashmir. In W Bengal conditions are much more serious, even dangerous to social order. Apart from the Damodar coal and the over-concentration of industry on Hooghlyside, W Bengal is an exceedingly poor rump, with perhaps the most acute agrarian problems of *India*. The strain on its ill-found economy and faction-ridden polity has led to grave administrative difficulties and even scandals.

Partition was not, and was never expected to be, a complete "solution" of the communal problem. Even had Kashmir and all of the Punjab and

[22] Based on table in C. N. Vakil, *Economic Consequences of Divided India* (Bombay, 1950), 141.

Bengal been included in Pakistan from the start, about a third of the Muslim population would have remained in *India*. As it is there are still perhaps 30 m. Muslims in *India*, say 10% against the 24% of undivided India, and excluding Kashmir there is now not a single *Indian* District with a Muslim majority. Pakistan has still a large Hindu minority, perhaps a quarter of the total population; but this is mainly in E Pakistan, and the W is by now a solidly homogeneous block probably about 95% Muslim. Moreover, practically all the Sikhs of the sub-continent—about 6 m.—are now concentrated in Pepsu and the surrounding areas of E Punjab. As most of the Pepsu princes were Sikh, and as the community is much more noted for virility than for political tact, this obviously raises grave problems of assimilation, and renders more difficult the keeping of the peace on these troubled marches.

NOTE ON THE 1951 CENSUSES

Censuses were held both in *India* and Pakistan in 1951; but owing to the lack of comparability between the two countries and between 1941 and 1951, Figs. 25–30 and most of the text discussion must unfortunately be based on 1941, pending more complete tabulation.   Slight discrepancies between Table I and the text are due to new estimates or provisional figures; checks where possible do not suggest any serious modifications of the argument. There is an admirable critique, from the geographer's angle, in C. D. Deshpande, "Geography and the Indian Census, 1951," *IGJ* XXIV (1949), No. 4, 1–21.

BIBLIOGRAPHICAL NOTE

K. Davis, *The Population of India and Pakistan* (Princeton, 1950).   The most authoritative work; balanced and most comprehensive.

S. Chandrasekhar, *India's Population: Fact and Policy* (Annamalai Univ., Chidambaran, 2nd ed., 1950).

D. Ghosh, *Pressure of Population and Economic Efficiency in India* (ND, 1950).

Gyan Chand, *India's Teeming Millions* (1939).

All three of these analyses lean towards the necessity of family limitation; Ghosh is perhaps the most realistic in his attitude to "culturable waste" and industrialisation.

In the 1930s it was still possible to argue with some show of reason against the view that India was over-populated (P. K. Wattal, *The Population Problem in India*, 1934); yet even then B. T. Ranadive's conclusions in *Poverty and Population in India* (1930) were so gloomy that they led him to leadership in the Communist Party as the only way out. A very fair and brief review of the whole matter will be found in the concluding pages of G. Tagliacarne, *Demografia dell' India* (Roma, 1949). See also F. W. Notestein, "Policy of the Indian Govt. on Family Limitation", *Population Index* 17 (1951), 254–63.

CHAPTER V

THE PEOPLES OF THE SUB-CONTINENT

Generalities

THAT the diversity of the peoples of India baffles description is a common-place. Only less frequent is the observation that there is an underlying—or overlaying—cultural unity. This is undoubtedly true of the *Indian Union*: everywhere, except in some remote Himalayan and jungle areas, the structure of society and the architectural landscape bear the strong impress of Hinduism. If we think of caste rather than religion, the ambit of common cultural features is yet wider, since even groups whose origin was an avowed or implied rejection of caste still retain traces (sometimes more) of caste attitudes, or are influenced, in greater or less degree, by caste spirit: Indian Christians, Sikhs, some fractions at least of the Tribes and even the Muslims. In fact it is hardly an exaggeration to say that the only considerable groups with a culture not subsumed into or at least strongly influenced by Hinduism are the hillmen of Wn Pakistan, some of the Assam border tribes, and the Buddhists of Ladakh or 'Little Tibet'.

Despite the Pakistani 'Two Nations' theory, the main mass of Muslims have a culture which, if dominantly Islamic, is yet shot through with strands of "Indianism" (to avoid the word Hinduism). Only Islam has had sufficient strength to exert a reciprocal influence and that has been rather limited, perhaps most clearly seen in the extension of *purdah* (the seclusion of women); and here other sociological factors clearly have their part. In more recent times Christianity has compelled some re-assessment of Hindu ideals; like Islam, it had most to offer to those towards the bottom of the caste ladder. But the role of Christianity is difficult to disentangle from that of Westernisation in general; Western secular humanism does at least provide some neutral ground on which the adherents of various faiths can meet.[1] Finally it must always be remembered that the religion of the masses—Hindu, Muslim, and Christian—is pervaded by more primitive beliefs.

Ethnic and linguistic divisions do not, in general, correspond to any marked extent; and both are cut across by religion. The division of most practical significance is that of 'community' as used in the Census: this is for the most part a religious differentiation, but it has some ethnic linguistic and cultural connotations in the 'Tribes', and in the 'Scheduled Castes'

[1] It has been pointed out, for example, that some Indian leaders, whose final attitude is known to be essentially agnostic, would by that fact be almost certainly precluded from high political office in the United States. It is 'community' rather than actual belief which counts.

it recognises a cleavage within the main religious community. The minor religious communities—Sikhs, Parsees, Jains—may perhaps best be thought of as kiths as defined by Huntington: "A group of people relatively homogeneous in language and culture, and freely intermarrying with one another".[2]

Ethnic Stocks

Only the baldest summary of modern views, following B. S. Guha, can be given here; it would be the vainest of labours to attempt a description of the salient physical and cultural characteristics of even the main groups in the few available pages. The populations of the sub-continent exhibit in varying degree characteristics from the four major stocks of mankind: Negroid, Australoid, Mongoloid, and Caucasoid.

Of earlier peoples, almost the only known skeletal remains of much significance are those of the Indus Valley civilisation: these show very close affinities with those of pre-Sargonic Mesopotamia (Al-Ubaid and Kish). The numerous Megalithic remains of the Peninsula undoubtedly hold vital evidence on the peopling of India; their scientific exploration is but beginning.

The earliest of existing groups are the *Negritos* (Negroids of small stature), of whom the Andaman Islanders are good examples. The Kadars of Cochin, like the Andamanese still hunters and gatherers (except where contaminated by outside influence), also show some Negrito characteristics; and traces at least of Negrito physical types have been reported from the Rajmahal Hills.

Far more significant are the evidences of *Australoid* stock which appear in the tribal populations of the S and centre (e.g. Mundas, Santals). In varying mixtures, this is the underlying strain in very much of the Hindu population, especially of lower or 'exterior' castes, S of the Narbada-Chota Nagpur line. The Veddas of Ceylon seem to represent a more specialised development from this group, which is also often styled pre-Dravidian; but Dravidian, like Aryan, is better kept as a linguistic term.

The tribal peoples of the N are essentially dissimilar, and, as might be expected, show marked *Mongoloid* characters. They occupy a broad band of Himalayan and sub-Himalayan country from Kashmir to Bhután; in the hills on either side of the Assam Valley a long-headed Mongoloid type is dominant; the Burmese are more brachycephalic. The Assam Valley itself has an interesting fusion of Mongoloids (the Shan Ahoms, who were the mediaeval rulers) with Palae-Mediterraneans, the bearers of Hindu culture.

The populations which show the most marked evidences of these three major stocks (Negroid, Australoid, and Mongoloid) are mainly tribal, though of course these elements are not confined to the tribes, nor are they

[2] *Mainsprings of Civilisation* (1945), 102 fn.

represented in all tribes. The 'higher' populations are more complex still.

The largest *Caucasoid* element is *Mediterranean*; "moderate stature, long head, slightly built body, dark complexion". The Palae-Mediterraneans appear to have introduced a Megalithic culture, perhaps originally Neolithic; they form the main component of the Dravidian speakers. Another Mediterranean group, Guha's 'Large-brained Chalcolithic Type', represented by the numerous skeletons of the Indus Valley civilisation, is dominant in Nn India and forms a large proportion of the upper classes elsewhere. There is also an 'Oriental' type, mainly in the NW hills and the Punjab; it is intrusive elsewhere with upper-class Muslims, descendants of Pathan invaders, and has strong affinities with Anatolian and Arabian groups.

Somewhat later, apparently, than the 'Chalcolithic' type, there was a considerable penetration of *Western Brachycephalic* types—Alpines, Dinarics, and Armenoids. They entered probably via Makran, mingling with the Mediterraneans (they are represented among the Indus Valley skeletons), and thence moved as far as Ceylon, while another branch followed the Ganges to Bengal.

Finally, and in many respects more important, there were the great folk-wanderings which brought the *Proto-Nordic* Indo-Aryans. These steppe pastoralists, tall, fair, meat-eating, entered Nn India in the latter part of the 2nd millennium BC; together with Mediterraneans they are dominant in the country between the Indus and Bundelkhand, and in Maharashtra form an important element in fusion with Palae-Mediterraneans, Alpo-Dinarics, and Proto-Australoids. In the extreme NW almost blond types are found, and even in Maharashtra almost 10% of Chitpavan Brahmins have light eyes.

The ethnic history of India is thus complicated, in keeping with the general diversity of the sub-continent. The various stocks have brought diverse gifts, material and cultural, to the common store. The Vedic hymns and the treasury of Sanskrit literature are the obvious contributions of the Indo-Aryans; but the basic concepts of Hinduism seem rather Dravidian, stemming from the Mediterraneans of the Indus Valley and the Proto-Australoids.[3]

Language and Literacy

There is only a very rough correlation between ethnic stock and language. The Himalayan and Assam tribes speak mainly Tibeto-Burman languages, those of the central hills Dravidian or yet older Austric languages; the S is almost solidly Dravidian, the N mainly Indo-Aryan. That is about as far as one can go; both Indo-Aryan and Dravidian tongues are spoken by

[3] See B. S. Guha, *Racial Elements in the Population* (OPIA No. 22, 1944), 27–29, for a brilliant summary; and cf. G. Slater, *The Dravidian Element in Indian Culture* (1924).

representatives of almost all the main racial groups. And even so there are many outliers, of which perhaps the most interesting is the Dravidian Brahui of Baluchistan.

The 'racial' element has indeed its importance—a very great importance —in the cultural history of India; it is of little practical significance to-day. Few Indians (and for that matter few Englishmen) could speak with any degree of scientific accuracy as to their racial origins; everyone knows what language he speaks. Next to religion language is the greatest divisive force in *India* (and Pakistan) to-day.

The diversity of tongues was one of the standard imperialistic arguments against nationalist claims. Actually there is not a great deal in it. It is true that the 1931 Census showed 225 Indian and Burmese languages; but the great majority of these were mere tribal splinters spoken by a few hundred or at most a few thousand people: very interesting to philologists, but not insuperable obstacles to the unity of over 300,000,000 people. In any case 135 of the 225 were Tibeto-Burman, nearly all of which were confined to Burma; excluding Burmese itself and Shan, no language in this group was spoken by as many as 400,000 people. Indeed one language is solemnly recorded in the *Imperial Gazetteer* as spoken by one person: a lonely soul.[4] On the other hand, in 1931 six languages accounted for 220 m. of a total population of 338 m.—65%.

There are indeed only some 12 or 15 really major languages, and some of these are closely akin: hardly an alarming total for an area and population comparable to Europe. The most important distinction is that between the Dravidian tongues of the S and the Indo-Aryan of the N and centre. The chief Dravidian languages are Telugu and Tamil (Fig. 127) with over 26 and 20 m. speakers respectively in 1931, Kanarese or Kannada (11 m.), and Malayalam, the speech of Kerala (9 m.). The Indo-Aryan languages account for about three-quarters of the population of the sub-continent, and one of them, Hindi, with its branches ranks numerically as one of the greater languages of the world: in 1931 Wn Hindi was spoken by over 70 m. people, and it has been gaining rapidly by nationalist and (since 1947) official favour. Other important languages are Bengali (54 m.), leader in the literary renaissance in India; Bihari with 28 and Marathi with 21 m., and Gujarati, less important numerically (11 m.) but the main language of indigenous commerce in Wn India.[5]

Bi- and even tri-lingualism are widespread among all classes except the peasantry of linguistically homogeneous areas. It is probable that there are

[4] On which R. Palme Dutt remarks that "the philosophical conception of language as a means of communication between human beings will have to be revised in the light of Andro; Nora, with a grand total of two speakers, just scrapes through". (*India To-day* (1940), 264, citing *Imperial Gaz. of India*, Vol. I (1909), 390–94. The remainder of this section is based on pp. 133–34 of W. G. East and O. H. K. Spate (eds.), *The Changing Map of Asia* (1950).
[5] Figures for 1931: no data in 1941 Census.

not many market towns in which the traveller equipped with Hindustani, Tamil, and English could not be readily understood.

Yet the problem of a common language remains serious: the world has seen too much use of the linguistic weapon by forces making for disunity. So far English has been the language of most serious scholarship (outside theology) and has been a *lingua franca* for the intelligentsia; but only about 1–2% of the population is literate in English, though English of sorts is understood by many illiterates. Bazaar or camp English is a wasting asset (as well as an insult to Shakespeare's tongue), but the disappearance of academic English would be an intellectual catastrophe of the first order, gravely limiting contacts with the outside world. This is not likely to happen completely; but clearly English neither could nor should remain the language of instruction, even in universities,[6] where its exclusive use in the past has too often frustrated learning in other subjects without always imparting noticeable mastery in its own use.[7] Nor will English be the language of administration, central or provincial, after a limited transition period of a few years. It is regrettable, from the point of view of the 'projection' of India overseas, that the promising Indo-Anglian literary revival, which had some excellent fiction and verse to its credit, will also presumably wither away as did the Renaissance Latin culture of Europe. But these losses are in the nature of things, and must be set against internal gains.

The language areas are not coterminous with provinces, except for Bengal (itself now divided) and Orissa; the suggested linguistic provinces, a favourite hobby of some Congressmen, carry an obvious risk of sectionalism or even separatism at this stage of nation-building, and the Commission appointed to consider this matter has recommended that action be postponed indefinitely. However, in 1953 a beginning was made: 'Andhra Desa', a Telugu province, which would involve the splitting off of the Telangana section of Hyderabad and its union with the Nn Districts of Madras (below, 675, 682). This could hardly fail to lead to the establishment of Marathi, Kanarese, and Tamil provinces. There are the usual problems of mingling on the linguistic frontiers, and how far such a re-arrangement would be desirable may admit of large debate, though there are certainly great anomalies in the present lay-out of political units, especially Madras.

Nationalist opinion on the whole favours the spread of Hindi as a com-

---

[6] Concerning which see Ch. II of S. N. Chib's brilliant essay, *Languages, Universities, and Nationalism in India* (1936). Cf. G. Slater's remark (*Southern India* (1936), 33): "Ability to read and write . . . are the Indian census tests of literacy, and by these India makes a very bad showing. If ability to speak and understand a second language were also tested, Madras would show far better results than London. . . ."

[7] This is a disinterested opinion, coming from a man once faced with the terrifying prospect of lecturing on geomorphology in Burmese. The Osmania University in Hyderabad was the only one to use an Indian language as the medium of instruction before 1947; but as that language was Urdu, it was hardly less alien than English to the Marathi or Telugu speakers who made up about 75% (against Urdu's 10%) of the population of Hyderabad.

mon language, though it meets with considerable opposition in Tamilnad, conscious of its high literary tradition. With its Hindustani form it is undoubtedly the most widely known language; but Hindustani is often a debased *patois*: it has been said, with picturesque exaggeration, that the vocabulary of 'bazaar Hindustani' could be written on a postcard and its grammar under the stamp. High Hindi has a heavily Sanskritised vocabulary and uses the Sanskritic Nagari script. The attachment of the various linguistic groups to their scripts is a serious bar to intercourse, the more irrational in that languages orally more or less mutually intelligible become much more differentiated when written. Yet practically all the Indo-Aryan languages (with the major exception of Urdu) use scripts which stem from Sanskrit characters, and all the Dravidian from those of Pali. They all have the same ancient and very scientific syllabary, but the number of types necessary for printing is excessive (some 450 for Nagari) owing to special forms for joined characters; and they are difficult to write quickly, though aesthetically far superior to any *modern* European scripts. Romanisation would seem a feasible and an impartial solution, but for obvious reasons is not likely to be adopted.

The official language of Pakistan is, or shortly will be, Urdu; similar to Hindi in grammatical construction and basic vocabulary, it developed as the Court or camp language of the Moguls, uses Persian script and increasingly draws on Persian for its higher vocabulary: this increasing differentiation from Hindi was largely a deliberate political move. The script is also ill-adapted for printing, lithography being still important. It is being introduced into university teaching in W Pakistan, but in E Bengal the hold of Bengali is too strong for its supersession by Urdu to be lightly undertaken. The Urdu-Hindi controversy is now of less importance since it has been absorbed or resolved in the greater crisis of Partition.

The problems of literacy are obviously closely bound up with those of language. It is difficult to make a really objective assessment of the situation. In 1941 the percentage of literacy (taken as the ability to read and write a postcard) was 12·2 of total population, against 6·9 in 1931, an increase of about 75%—for males 60%, females 150%. But in 1931 literate males outnumbered literate females by five to one. Literacy, of course, is very unequally distributed geographically and communally, varying in 1931 from 79% for Parsees to 6·4% for Muslims and practically nil for wide masses of the tribes and peasantry. Since 1947, however, the Central and State governments have devoted much energy and money to combating illiteracy. Adult education is of course of much importance, and it may be that compulsory education, where enacted, is ahead of the means to carry it out: the danger of low standards may be worse than that of widespread analphabetism. But advance, though irregular, has on the whole been gratifying.

Education, however, remains badly balanced: the imposing concrete buildings of the universities rest on the timber and brick of the Government High Schools, they in turn on the mud or thatch hut of the primaries. The proportion of literates who have been to a university is higher than in the West (or at least was until the recent mass-literacy drive); but standards are very unequal and wastage appalling. The preference for arts and legal subjects led to the creation of a vast clerical and professional proletariat, too many for available openings and not infrequently driven to miserable shifts for existence; [8] but good technicians are too few for the country's needs. This ill-balance is perhaps due pretty equally to Indian traditions and the British demand for clerks, but its redress is essential, and happily there are some signs of change. Healthy progress will depend also on more serious attention than has generally been given to the elementary schools; the foundations of a building are after all its most vital part. And on a broader view the liquidation or mitigation of many social ills calls for education, particularly in the villages, in the widest and most liberal sense. There is no room for shallow enthusiasm about moral uplift and more literacy drives: their gains have all too frequently been dissipated by lack of *sustained* effort.

Religions and Communities

The 'communities' recognised by the Indian Census, in Indian politics, and in daily life [9] are primarily religious divisions, although race, language, caste, geographical localisation, and broad cultural distinctions also shape them in part. Thus the 'Aboriginal Tribes' include Hindus, Christians, and even Muslims, though the majority follow particularist religions in which emphasis is given to the worship of spirits. The great bulk of the population is of course either Hindu or Muslim; it is important to note that the Partition was not a 'solution' of the communal problem, and (except by a few extremists on both sides) was not intended to be so. Of the 92 m. Muslims in All-India in 1941, only 22 were in Wn and 29 in En Pakistan; some 5 of the remainder were in Kashmir and Hyderabad. This still left some 36 in *India*; but although the enforced migrations of the immediate post-Partition period (and after later outbreaks of communal violence) have greatly reduced the 'unredeemed' Muslims, and conversely rendered Wn Pakistan probably over 95% Muslim, it seems unlikely (allowing for natural increase since 1941) that there can be fewer than 30 m. Muslims in the *Indian Union*. This is, however, a bare 10% or less against the 24% of All-India, and there is now not a single Muslim majority District in *India*—excluding Kashmir.

The extent and nature of Muslim invasions and cultural influence are

---

[8] "WANTED: one clerk, Rupees 30 [45 shillings] per month; two trained teachers, Rs. 18 p.m." Advt in Bombay paper, 1943.

[9] Their significance will be diminished, but in practical affairs far from ended, by the abolition of separate communal electorates.

discussed in Ch. VI (Historical Outlines) and the relevant regional sections.

Hindus in 1941 numbered 251 m. or 66%, including 40 m. *Scheduled Castes*; but this cleavage will be discussed as part of the general question of caste. We may note, however, that most Muslims in the sub-continent are the descendants of converts from Hinduism, generally from lower castes, and though some caste attitudes were retained it is probable that the egalitarian elements in Islam formed a great part of its appeal. This is also the case with Christianity, though here too some compromise with caste has at times and places been considered expedient: perhaps more frequently by Roman Catholics, though Protestants have by no means been immune. Moreover, three Indian religions arose largely as reactions against the caste domination of the Brahmins. These are the faiths of *Buddhists*, *Sikhs*, and *Jains*, whose distribution is shown on Fig. 32.

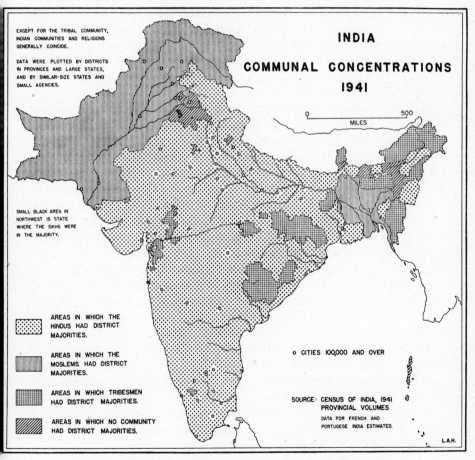

Fig. 31.—MAJOR COMMUNITIES, 1941; courtesy L. Hoffmann *GJ*.

I.P.—5

Incomparably the greatest of these is *Buddhism*, but it hardly survives in the land of its birth: only a few monks, mostly Nepalese and Sinhalese, are to be found in the holy places, Buddh Gaya where Gautama received Enlightenment, Sarnath where he began his mission. Early Buddhism had a simple and rational humanistic code, independent of theism and as far from the more pathological forms of asceticism as from hedonism, and with an emphasis on the fellowship, irrespective of caste or station, of men (and women) of good will. When Asoka, desolated by the horrors of his Kalinga war, devoted himself to 'the chiefest conquest'—of the hearts of men—he initiated the great missionary period which has resulted in the survival of the earlier and purer form (though shot through with Animism) in Ceylon, Burma, and Siam. The Graeco-Buddhist sculptures of Gandhara, the ruins of the great University at Taxila, and the colossal cliff-figures at Bamian in Afghanistan, attest the long vitality of Buddhism in the NW, whence it penetrated High Asia. Deterioration of the creed itself, Brahmin opposition and some persecution, gradually weakened it; by the time of the Muslim invasions it was strong only in its original home, Magadha. Of the 232,000 Buddhists of All-India,[10] 159,000 were in Sikkim and Himalayan Bengal, 41,000 in Baltistan or Little Tibet; but these are adherents of the Tibetan sects, far different from the earlier form.

Jainism antedated Buddhism, and may even represent a continuation of pre-Vedic opposition to Brahminism. It developed an exaggerated asceticism (particularly in the renunciation of clothing) and carried *ahimsa*—reverence for organic or rather animal life—to almost incredible extremes: the practice of wearing a cloth over the mouth to avoid accidentally swallowing insects probably gave rise to the report by the Greek Megasthenes (*c.* 302 BC) of a race which had no mouth and lived on delicate savours. Jainism hardly exists outside *India*, but its adherents numbered 1,449,000. They are strongest in Rajasthan (especially Marwar), Nn Bombay, and Saurashtra, which have over two-thirds of the Jains; their chief sanctuary is Mt Abu in the Aravallis. Many Jains are traders and financiers, Marwari Chambers of Commerce being powers in the land as far afield as Calcutta and Rangoon; nor, if common repute may be relied on, is their tenderness for physical life reflected in their business ethics: there are few more hard-headed forestallers and usurers than some Marwaris.

The *Sikhs* are much younger; their founder, Guru Nanak (1469–1538) was an eclectic drawing from Islam and Hinduism. Ironically, in view of their later reputation, the Sikhs were originally politically quietist, even pacifist; their military virtues were a response to Muslim persecution after the death (1605) of Akbar, himself the greatest of eclectics. Ideologically they are nearer Hinduism than Islam, but they reject caste; and, though diverse in origin, they have developed by inbreeding and strict discipline

[10] All figures 1941 Census and for All-India.

into a distinct people, recognisable as such even to the newcomer: their badges are the 'five K's'—*Kesh* (uncut hair and beard), *Kanga* (wooden comb), *Kachh* (shorts), *Kara* (an iron ring in the hair), and the short sword or *Kirpan* which they are (or were) legally entitled to carry—sometimes to the detriment of public order. Rulers of the Punjab under the great Ranjit Singh (1780–1839), they were the last country power of note to be sub-

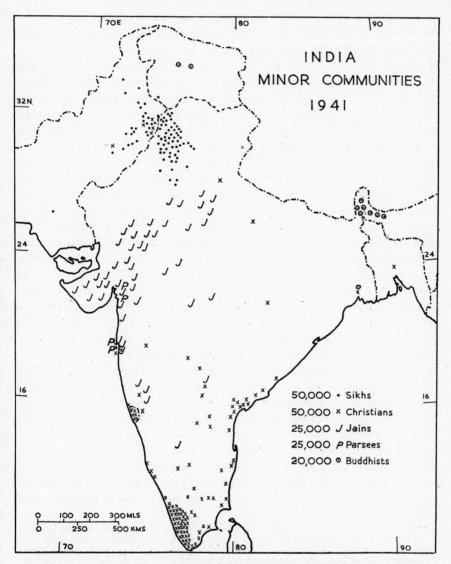

Fig. 32.—MINOR COMMUNITIES, 1941. Placings of symbols approximate, and the wide scatter of very small numbers (e.g. of Indian Christians or Jains) cannot be indicated.

jugated by the British; and there is little doubt that their feeling of being a chosen people played a major part in the disastrous violence which accompanied Partition. The great majority of the Sikhs (5,691,000) are now in E Punjab and especially Pepsu, where they probably form local majorities as a result of the expulsion of Muslims.[11] This concentration, and their rather assertive sense of mission, may present some problems to the State and Central governments.

By far the largest community neither Hindu nor Muslim is that comprehensively labelled '*Tribes*'; but it is very heterogeneous and very scattered, with two major zones of concentration: the Assam-Burma Hills and the jungles of central India (cf. Fig. 31).[12] In general they are spirit-worshippers and shifting cultivators, but Hinduism and Christianity have made progress among them, and the passage to a (*soi-disant*) higher civilisation has not infrequently been attended by the usual disastrous effects on social culture and individual well-being. It is shallow and imperceptive to write off these often balanced and integrated societies as totally 'savage' because they lack the tricks of technologically more advanced cultures; in the true decencies of life some at least (e.g. among the Nagas) yield to few peoples. We have already mentioned their general racial and linguistic affinities; to attempt to particularise would be hopeless, but special mention may be made of the Bhils, Gonds, and Santals. The Bhils (2,332,000) are found mainly in the marches of Rajasthan, Bombay, and Madhyabharat; very jungly and great shifting cultivators. More important are the Gonds (3,200,000, the largest group, of whom 2,500,000 are in Madhya Pradesh (CP)); once the rulers of much of central India, forced back into their jungles by stronger powers, they have left the name Gondwanaland as a symbol of their ancient domain. The Santals (2,733,000) live on the Bengal-Bihar borderland, and are best known for the rebellion of 1855, provoked by plainsmen taking unscrupulous advantage of legalistic land regulation.

Individuals amongst the tribal peoples have been able to make the best of both worlds: "the Gond Raja of Savangar lives in a palace which is equipped with every modern comfort; his well-stocked library includes the works of Aldous Huxley, Bernard Shaw, and [significantly] Malinowski; he is a brilliant cricketer and tennis-player. Yet he insists that he is a true Gond; his house is decorated with representations of his totem animal, the tortoise, and in the heart of the palace is a small thatched hut where the cult of the old tribal gods is maintained".[13] At the other extreme are such groups as the Kadar of Cochin, hardly out of the Stone Age. In between, most

---

[11] Most of the rulers of these states are Sikhs, but in 1941 they had an absolute majority in only one District (Ludhiana) and a relative one in only one small state (Faridkot).

[12] See in general V. Elwin, *The Aboriginals* (OPIA No. 14, 1943), and J. H. Hutton, "Primitive Tribes", in L. S. S. O'Malley (ed.), *Modern India and the West* (1941), 417–44; also Appx. II in 1931 Census, Vol. I, Pt. I, 502–08.

[13] Elwin, *loc. cit.*, 11.

tribesmen are economically exploited and increasingly morally degraded, admitted to become the lowest stratum of Hindu society, or rescued from that by a Christianity which too often consists largely in destroying all that remains of a once-integrated material and moral culture.[14]

The problem of ensuring reasonable conditions of life is sometimes complicated by wider economic issues: the legitimate interests of the forester and of the shifting cultivator may be hard to reconcile. The British policy of excluding tribal areas from the control of elected provincial legislators was naturally resented by nationalist opinion as another trick to divide and rule; even research was regarded with suspicion since, as Elwin remarks, the official ethnographic surveys were sometimes "too dependent on facts collected by [untrained] subordinates . . . collections of sensationally interesting but often somewhat discreditable superstitions and customs".[15]

It is of course true that the hills cannot be artificially fenced from the economic life of the country, to form scientific game-sanctuaries with a human fauna; but there is grave danger, if the barriers to exploitation go down too rapidly in the supposed interests of national unity and development, that the tragic histories of the Santals and the Mundas may be repeated.

Christians numbered 6,316,000, of whom 140,000 were Anglo-Indians and 135,000 'Others'—i.e. mainly Europeans. It is not, perhaps, a very impressive total after four and a half centuries of missionary effort, it is true discontinuous.[16] Most success has been obtained among the lower Hindu castes and the Tribes—especially, perhaps, those half-Hinduised and beginning to be aware of the disadvantages of coming in at the bottom. Christianity is strongest in the S, where in Cochin-Travancore it was professed by 2,369,000 or 31·5% of the population; Madras had over 2,900,000 Christians. Here they are largely the result of Portuguese mass-conversions and the assimilation to Rome of the Nestorian churches, which claimed continuity from St Thomas the Apostle and are certainly at least fifteen centuries old. Mylapore (San Thomé), just S of Madras, contains the Apostle's reputed tomb, and is still a centre of some Portuguese cultural influence, while some Nestorian or 'Syrian' Christians retain their ancient liturgies and usages. Of other provinces the Punjab had most Christians: 339,000, largely Protestants.

There are of course innumerable other sects, pure survivals of ancient

---

[14] For instance, by banning animal sacrifices among the Kachins of Burma; as the diviners proportioned the sacrifice to the known wealth of the individual, from a buffalo to a chicken, and as the victim was communally consumed, suppression of this custom cuts down the meat-ration and accentuates economic class-cleavage.

[15] *Loc. cit.*, 28.

[16] The EIC took so strict a view of the necessity of non-interference with established religions that in the early 19th century Baptist missionaries (American and British) had to work from Danish Serampore.

faiths such as the mysterious 'White Jews' of Cochin, or eclectic crossings of all known beliefs: one person in 1931 "described himself as 'spiritually universal', but manifestly could not be distributed to the various heads".[17] Three numerically minor groups must be discussed: *Parsees, Anglo-Indians, Europeans*.

The *Parsees* numbered only 115,000, of whom 86,000 were in Bombay Presidency, and about half of these in Bombay City. Zoroastrian fire-worshippers, they came, as their name implies, from Fars (Persia) about the 8th century AD, to avoid conversion to Islam. Socially they were regarded as hardly Indian and yet definitely not European; but they escaped the usual disabilities of an intermediate position by virtue of wealth and education, and were indeed a valuable lubricant, contributing greatly to the relative harmony of Indo-British relations in Bombay as compared with Calcutta. Like the Quakers, they have an altogether disproportionate share of economic activity and public spirit; the name of Tata bears witness to their energetic and diverse achievement. But their numbers appear to be kept low by inbreeding and a low birth-rate; proselytism is unknown, perhaps to avoid strain on their very complete internal social welfare arrangements and, again like the Quakers, they are essentially a professional and upper-middle class group.

The *Anglo-Indians* are unfortunately named; the effort to avoid the stigma of 'Eurasian' has deprived us of the useful original meaning of Anglo-Indian—an Englishman who had spent his working life in India. In any case many "Anglo-Indian" families, including some not the least in standing and social usefulness, are really Luso-Indian. Both Portuguese and British initially adopted deliberate miscegenation policies, to surround themselves as it were by a penumbra of subordinates bound by ties of feeling to the invaders. The history of British attitudes to Anglo-India is distressing; as Cox points out, the existence of caste enabled the British to be virtually a dominant caste, and so "able to make almost unlimited demands upon the mixed-bloods without necessarily making any concessions to them".[18] This has not always been so; in earlier days families such as the Skinners and the Hearseys were among the most valued servants and soldiers of the EIC.[19] The change is perhaps to be associated with the opening of the Suez Canal: home leaves became more frequent, and, more important, many more European wives (actual or potential—the cold weather saw the arrival of the 'fishing fleet') came out. It is to be feared that the prejudice against Anglo-Indians, always more common among

[17] 1931 Census, Vol. I, Pt. I, 391.
[18] O. C. Cox, *Caste, Class, and Race* (NY, 1948), 385.
[19] The heroic telegraph clerks at Delhi in the Mutiny were Anglo-Indians, a fact not often mentioned in patriotic school books. The most arduous portion of the writer's military service was beside (and under) Anglo-Indian Other Ranks and NCO's, and no words can be too high for their spirit when all the world they knew was breaking up round them.

women than men, was largely due to simple sexual jealousy, at times almost obsessional.

There were of course other factors: it is obvious that Eurasians would be by hypothesis outcaste, beyond the Hindu pale; and it is also true that many are the descendants of unions of rank-and-file European soldiers and traders with such Indian girls as they could find: very often poor ancestry on both sides. In the circumstances the Anglo-Indians naturally became mere clients of the British rulers; and the community was always liable to erosion at the top as its most successful members managed to 'pass' as Domiciled Europeans, while there was some—though decreasing—accretion at the bottom. Physically, of course, the Anglo-Indians include all shades from 'pure white' to almost black; judging by names and physique, the Portuguese element is more important than is usually allowed.[20]

That mixed ancestry in itself means 'the vices of both sides' it should not be necessary to refute; what matters is the social environment. It may be mentioned, as one example of many, that Amrita Sher-Gil, after Jamini Roy perhaps the outstanding modern Indian painter, was the daughter of a Magyar mother and a Punjabi father. But the social scales have been weighted heavily against the Eurasians; it is, though true, too facile to say that this was in large part their own fault. Their political fortunes were hitched only too obviously to the British star; and, as that set, their pleas that they were as Indian as anybody were not unnaturally discounted for the death-bed repentances they in fact were. Their legally privileged position in certain services (e.g. the railways) has gone, and it remains to be seen whether they will be able to adapt themselves to being Indian rather than Anglo in time to retain the not inconsiderable lead in technical education and aptitudes which they owe largely to the fact that English was, in a sense at least, their mother-tongue.

Now that the British army (to its own intense relief) has Quit India, *Europeans* are mainly businessmen in the towns. There are now very few officials (there were never very many), and those mostly technicians. The biggest groups are those in Calcutta (largely Scots) and Bombay; up-country there are a few missionaries and the planters of Assam. The total numbers (including troops) were never more than 120–150,000, except during the war years; and will now obviously decrease. It may be noted, however, that the Nazi persecution brought numbers of Jewish (and some Gentile) refugees from Central Europe, mainly doctors and other professional men; on the whole these have been assimilated into urban society and have brought some useful technical skills.

[20] Cox is, I think, misled on this point by reliance on the more articulate *Anglo*-Indian writers, for whom 'the call of [British] blood' was an article of faith. The Goanese cross is of course a different issue (below, 622). As for colour, I have seen a man with unimpeachably Saxon names who was better known to his Burmese neighbours as *Kala byu*—'the *black* black man'.

Hinduism and Caste

Hinduism and its symbiote, Caste, are entities so complex as to defy definition; as a counsel of despair Hinduism has been defined as "those beliefs held by Hindus", but this takes us too far and not far enough, as these include all possible metaphysical attitudes (not perhaps excluding solipsism, if that be a possible attitude) and on the theological side everything from virtual atheism in some of the Sankhya school (6th century BC) to pantheism and the spirit-worship of those tribes who have accepted a position in the Hindu scheme of things. Until recently it was roughly true to say that Hindus were those who accepted caste society and Brahminical hegemony; but there are now many who would consider themselves good Hindus but yet would condemn caste, even if they cannot always in practice repudiate it.

Into this maze of jarring sects (far more than Omar's two-and-seventy) and conflicting theogonies we cannot go, even were the author technically competent to do so. But Hinduism as a way of life impinges directly on the relations between men and the Indian environment in three important aspects: marriage; the special position accorded to the cow; caste. The first two are more appropriately considered in Ch. IV (Population) and Ch. VIII (Agriculture); the third must be discussed, with much diffidence, here. But many fundamental questions cannot even be touched upon, such as the movement of castes up and down the scale, *ahimsa*, and the linked concepts of rebirth and *dharma* with its peculiar connotation of both destiny and duty.

There are probably some 3,000 castes in India, and the literature on them is enormous; nor is there any general agreement on the origins and rationale of the system. Any definition can be effectively queried, unless it is so hedged about with qualifications as to fill a book. It would be folly for a novice to attempt even a rough working definition; but from a résumé of some admitted facts and of what appear to be the more tenable hypotheses it is hoped that some idea of the nature and workings of caste may emerge.

The salient features are clear enough. The caste system is the most intensely hierarchical organisation of society in existence; the accident of birth is the absolute determinant of a man's caste, and hence of his standing in society. Exclusivism is carried to an extreme; not only is marriage (with rare exceptions) strictly confined within the caste, but normally eating and drinking with members of other castes are banned. The idea of purity is indeed fundamental in the practice of caste. In some cases the cult of ceremonial purity was carried to pathological lengths—in Kerala Nayadis (quasi-aboriginals) could not approach within 72 feet of a Brahmin without occasioning defilement, and as late as 1932 the existence in the same region of an 'unseeable' group, emerging only at night, was reported:

these unfortunates washed the clothes of untouchables.[21] On the other hand, ceremonial purity has given rise to some undesignedly hygienic practices, such as the provision in Post Offices of stamp-moisteners to avoid licking, or the use as dishes of leaves or of cheap pottery subsequently discarded.

There are, or at least were, four great caste groupings: Brahmins (priests), Kshatriyas (warriors or, better, rulers), Vaisyas (traders), Sudras (cultivators); together with the lower groups known variously as Untouchables, Depressed Classes, Scheduled or Exterior Castes.[22] The 'Laws of Manu' (1st–5th centuries AD) represent the four as sprung from different parts of the body of Brahma; they have also been equated with *varna* or colour (from light Indo-Aryan to black Dravidian). These seem to be rationalisations; and as *varna* has wider connotations it does not seem that the racial theory of caste origins, so far as built on this equation, has very secure foundations.

Rigid as the system is, in course of time castes may improve their ranking, often by restricting intermarriage to a narrower group within a caste; or they may lose ground. In times of war and revolution energy and ability have carried men of lower castes to place and power, and the situation may then be legitimated by faking the pedigree, this adjustment being made by complaisant Brahmins. To-day individuals have obviously much greater facilities for breaking away, owing to the increased mobility and the increasingly economic values of modern society. Hence the *broad* occupational correlations suggested above have long been practically meaningless, except that only Brahmins can be priests. As Brahmins are essential to many necessary rituals they have an obvious key position, and as the educated class, the clergy, they tended (as the clergy of mediaeval Europe) to monopolise or at least dominate administration. Hindu rulers usually were Kshatriyas, or got Brahmins to say they were; trading castes are still largely Vaisya. But all groups include large numbers of cultivators. It is in individual castes, and still more in the innumerable sub-castes, that the usual Western concept of caste as occupational most nearly holds good. Many caste distinctions based on occupation appear very trifling: between those who yoke to the plough one bullock or two, who make white or black pots, and so on. But in towns at any rate occupational significance, while not unimportant, is of less and less account, except for definitely impure tasks such as those of Dhobis (washermen), Chamars (tanners), Doms (scavengers). In any case the cross-divisions are almost incredibly complex: "it suggests a division of the inhabitants of England into families of Nor-

---

[21] J. H. Hutton, *Caste in India* (1946), 70–71.

[22] *Not* 'outcastes': this means no more than those outside the pale (e.g. Englishmen), but carries with it the suggestion of 'outcast' or expulsion—a sanction which may be used on castemen, but these castes, unless by their own volition, are an integral part of the system. 'Pariahs' are but one group of the Scheduled Castes. Incidentally the progression from Untouchables to Scheduled Castes is not unlike that from Depressed to Special Areas: the implications are unflattering in both cases.

man descent, Clerks in Holy Orders, positivists, ironmongers, vegetarians, communists, and Scotchmen"[23]; except that the groups are mutually exclusive, and there are no classifications such as vegetarian ironmongers.

As to origins, it would appear obvious that no simple explanation can possibly suffice. Hutton lists 15 contributing factors, and does not regard this as exhaustive; he inclines to regard the geographical juxtaposition of many differing ethnic groups in India—the end of so many migrations—and beliefs in *mana* and taboo, especially associated with food, as among the most important. This can be supported by a wide range of anthropological evidence, from India and outside. Ethnic and occupational factors clearly play an important part, and the element of deliberate exploitation by Brahmins cannot well be evaded.

What is the objective function of caste? At first sight it appears to be (and indeed it is) a negation of democracy as known in the West: and after all, the values associated with the word 'democracy', while not the peculiar property of the West, are at least so much intertwined with Occidental views of the world as to give validity to Western judgments on the meaning of the word. To us, then, caste is alien and repellent. Yet it would be superficial to condemn out of hand a system which has met the social needs of so large a fraction of mankind for so many centuries. Loyalty to caste has inhibited the development of national patriotisms: but in the conditions of ancient and mediaeval India this was no unmixed evil, since it made adjustments to the constantly changing political pattern so much the easier. There was a place for everybody, for the intrusive conqueror and the aboriginal conquered; the structure was so integrated, so self-regarding, that few groups could long resist the temptation to find their assured niche, humble as it might be. At the same time Cox undoubtedly overstates his case when he claims that "its practice and theory are in complete synchronisation; it does not rationalise its position. . . . it has no shortcomings; it does not excuse itself; it is totally excellent. . . . Before the impingement of Western culture upon the system there was no 'caste question' in India". This is to forget Buddhists and Jains and Sikhs, the wide gains of Islam from the lower castes, and not a few Hindu thinkers, poets, and saints who taught that not birth but conduct was the ultimate determinant of a man's right rank in society. But the other phrases from the passage quoted sum up the situation as it was until recently: "The caste system does not represent a social order in unstable equilibrium; rather a powerful norm towards which social variations tend to gravitate. . . . Resting securely upon universal consensus, the system is taken for granted, and it cannot be legislated out of existence. . . ." [24]

[23] J. C. Molony, *A Book of South India* (1926), 106.
[24] *Op. cit.*, 22. Buddhism and Sikhism are relegated to a 4-line footnote (110); but even if they "did not seriously change the course of Hindu society", they certainly questioned it sufficiently to induce re-assessments.

This gift of stability to a highly plural society always in peril of being shaken to pieces by constant war, is perhaps the most positive argument in favour of caste. On a somewhat lower plane it fulfilled—and to some extent still fulfils—many of the functions of friendly societies and trade unions [25]; its conservatism has acted as a check on despotisms more capricious even than itself. But these are things of historical rather than contemporary significance; the price of stability is too high if it means ossification in a rapidly changing environment; resistance to new forces may indeed be more prolonged, but the ultimate wreck is more disastrous.

It is very difficult indeed to see how any really democratic society can co-exist with such an avowed, not to say violent, assertion of human inequality—not the natural inequality of individuals, but the automatic inferiority of whole classes of men, utterly irrespective of any individual talent or virtue. It may not be unfair to say that the Brahmin hegemony, by an intricate and half-consciously devised system of secular and eternal rewards and penalties, has secured acquiescence in this huge hierarchy of privilege in return for social stability, but at the price of physical and spiritual degradation for millions—and spiritually not alone for those of lower caste. It is beside the point—or rather an added condemnation—to say, what is true, that the lower castes have been conditioned through the centuries to accept servitude as privilege, and to insist among themselves on the most ludicrous refinements of exclusivism, "disputing the point of precedence between a louse and a flea". The suggestion of modern apologists such as Radhakrishnan that the lower castes are not in fact despised but have a role recognised as essential, and even honoured, is unconvincing—and not only to non-Hindus: one might cite Ambedkar, Panikkar, Ghurye, Paranjpye, not all of lower caste. To the philosopher indeed all men who fulfil their duty, in whatever station, may be equal in virtue and esteem, as in the sight of God; but the naked arrogance explicit in so much of caste teaching cannot fail to have a profoundly demoralising effect on average men, whether privileged or the reverse. In all other societies the proffer of a cup of water is the symbol of common humanity; in India alone is it an occasion of defilement, a symbol of division: a poor foundation for the brotherhood of man. Indeed the theory of caste, like all *Herrenvolk* theory, whether in Nazi Germany or contemporary S Africa, rests finally on the assumption that all of one group are superior in things of the mind and spirit to all of another. Quite apart from ethics, this is simply contrary to human experience.

To-day, therefore, caste faces what is probably the greatest crisis in its

[25] "Caste . . . amenities are rather those of an autocratic Trade Union administering an automatic Poor Law, from the aid of which those are excluded who need it most" (L. W. Lyde, *The Continent of Asia* (1933 ed.), 473)—overstated but not without point.

history. The new urbanism has greatly weakened it: without spending a prohibitive fraction of one's time and income on purificatory ceremonies, as a commuter it is simply not possible to escape contamination; and, with all the cultural loss implied in the rootlessness of modern city life, the gift of anonymity does enable the individual to break bonds which are unbearable but unbreakable in a village where all are known to all. Nor can an expansionist industrial economy submit to the occupational shackles of caste, shackles like those of mediaeval guilds but more rigorous.

On a different plane the influence of Western ideology and the ideals of secular humanism (probably more than those of Christianity), compel a revaluation of the old attitudes, on the part of the intelligentsia at least. Much of value may be lost in this process of adjustment, and the risk of disintegration and social schizophrenia is profound; but, short of some great and unforeseeable historic catastrophe, it has gone too far to be checked. And as a mere matter of expediency, the grosser forms of caste privilege, with what, despite all apologies, appear to outsiders as abhorrent violations of human dignity, obviously weaken the moral standing of *India* in issues like that of the grievances of Natal Indians.

These factors are clearly seen by most of those in whom leadership is now vested. Perhaps the most widespread attitude (at least among the educated) is that of Mahatma Gandhi: the salvation of caste itself by the elimination of untouchability. But it would seem likely that this will prove an untenable half-way house. Some of the earliest legislation of independent *India* was to enforce the right of untouchables to free access to temples and wells. Articulate opinion has welcomed this overwhelmingly. Yet it is a long way from the Council Chamber at New Delhi to the thousands of villages in the deep S, and the old ways may die hard; the gulf between legislation and enforcement in the face of social apathy or hostility is great in much less vital matters.

"Perhaps a sceptic whispers, 'Such revolutions are not brought about in the lethargic types of Indian climes'. Him we only remind . . . that the phenomenon of the conquering Indo-Aryans, who were passionate eaters of flesh and drinkers of intoxicating beverages, settling down as the upper castes of Hindu society and abjuring their food and drink for centuries, is a moral triumph of the people of India, for which there is hardly any parallel in human history. The same people, now called upon to throw off caste, would rise to the occasion and achieve a still greater triumph." [26] These are brave and sincere words; but the phenomenon was not a sudden one, and it is a long way back; nor are those conditioned by three millennia of caste "the same people". Yet, however long and hard the way, the essential first steps have been taken, and this is much.

[26] G. S. Ghurye, *Caste and Race in India* (1932), 188.

Some Social Tendencies

A description of the manners and customs of the Indian peoples, or even only those associated with caste, would itself fill an encyclopaedia. Such is their diversity that it has been justly remarked that the only valid generalisation about them is that any generalisation is both true and false according to *milieu*. The differences are extreme: from primitive tribesmen not far above a Stone Age level to the highly sophisticated urban intelligentsia, from rulers claiming descent from the sun to industrial families such as the Tatas and the Birlas forming economic dynasties in two or three generations. Yet, underlying this diversity, is an unmistakable cultural unity provided by the polymorphic complex of ideas and social and individual observances which is Hinduism, a culture which baffles definition but is everywhere recognisable.

A few leading tendencies may be briefly indicated. India is to-day the theatre of an indescribably complex interaction between the forces of modern technology (with its own metamorphosing mental outlook) and of an age-old metaphysical tradition. Although the general tendency of technological progress is undoubtedly to weaken the hold of caste and ancient beliefs, there are reverse eddies. Modern communications may contribute to the survival of dwindling groups, e.g. by widening the area within which endogamous marriage-partners can be found. Two examples, admittedly extreme, may illustrate the fantastic interdigitation—it cannot be called a synthesis—of East and West. The attainment of independence was accompanied by a campaign to prohibit cow-slaughter, even if need be under penalty of death; one of the leading self-made industrialists of India, the cement magnate Seth Dalmia, announced that he and his family would fast unto death if this prohibition were not legally enacted within twelve months. And in Kerala an unexpected result of Communist activity was the emergence of an embryonic sub-caste of Communist bridegrooms, more progressive and so better endowed economically than their fellows, and hence more eligible, and commanding higher dowries.

The love of metaphysic, so often noted, was ascribed by Buckle and other geographical determinists to the influence of the natural environment. It is perhaps more reasonable to regard it as the natural reaction to centuries, if not millennia, of political absolutism: in one sphere at least, that of cloudy imaginings, man was free. Since the suppression of Buddhism, Hinduism, however rigid in matters of ritual observance, has been extraordinarily tolerant doctrinally—hence its astonishing congeries of beliefs, practically from Animism to atheism. The result has been a metaphysical hang-over, shown in the constant tendency among intellectuals to accept an analogy as a demonstration. Moreover, even the most intellectual arguments are not infrequently betrayed into unregulated emotionalism; perhaps not more often than those of Western Europeans, but certainly in a more obvious way.

The hackneyed antithesis of Western materialism and Eastern spirituality, however, is as a rule grossly exaggerated, especially by Western neophytes. The trading castes have a religious sanction to gain almost for its own sake, resembling (but with greater intensity) the attitude of the Puritan bourgeosie in the West. The observer in India certainly does not see any widespread neglect of material advancement in the interests of salvation, and if "by their fruits ye shall know them" be true, the ethical advantage is not always conspicuously on the side of the East. In the long run it is not likely that the standard patterns of economic and political power-conflicts will differ fundamentally from those of the rest of the world, however exotic their forms of overt expression.

These remarks, of course, apply mainly to the educated and vocal classes of the towns. It must never be forgotten that the vast majority of Indians live in over half a million villages, most of them small and isolated. Here Custom is a king not yet and not easily dethroned (though increasingly tottering), and his laws are enshrined in a multitude of pithy proverbs which, with the religious songs, form a true and remarkable folk-culture. The ancient *panchayat* or village council, which through all the mutability of dynasties made the villages so many unfederated little republics, has, in general, been atrophied under British rule, in which administration was legal rather than customary and was far more all-embracing, impinging far more directly on all classes, than under any previous régime. It is doubtful whether, as some nationalists hope, the *panchayat* can be sufficiently resuscitated to play any very useful function in the epoch of change which has begun to penetrate (very unequally it is true) the Indian countryside.

In this excessively complex situation it is of course impossible to forecast what changes in the norms of society will take place under a Government modelled, in principle, on Western parliamentary democracy and relying for its administration on the inheritance of an immense bureaucratic machine. That there will be both loss and gain appears certain; there may be a loss of formal efficiency mitigated by more ready accessibility to public opinion. But for the latter to be constructive a new revolution of thought is needed, a break from the old traditions of community and caste to new groupings based primarily on economic function and with intelligible and coherent political and economic programmes. Paradoxically these seem as yet most clearly displayed by the big business of the Tata-Birla group and by the Communists. This struggle for the emergence of new groupings and new forms of political life is perhaps the true significance of the conflict between the forces of theocratic Hinduism, marshalled by the Hindu Mahasabha, and the more secular-minded wing of Congress which looks to Jawaharlal Nehru. So far as the future of *India* can be isolated from the great world-problem of peace or war, it depends upon the outcome of this conflict.

BIBLIOGRAPHICAL NOTE

To attempt to summarise the embarrassing riches of the great official surveys (ethnographic by Sir Herbert Risley, linguistic by Sir George Grierson) would invite the most fatal intellectual apoplexy; and some of their views have of course been outmoded by general advances in anthropology and linguistics. The leading modern authority on Indian races is B. S. Guha, who was responsible for the survey in the 1931 Census (Vol. I, Pt. III (1935)) and has conveniently summarised his views in pp. 125-40 of *An Outline of the Field Sciences of India* (ed. S. L. Hora for Indian Science Congress Association; Calcutta, 1937), and in *Racial Elements in the Population* (OPIA No. 22, 1944). A vivid and less technical, though not less scientific, survey of the main groups is given in the opening chapters of J. H. Hutton, *Caste in India* (1946). On the tribes there are valuable monographs by V. Elwin (Baiga and Maria Gonds), J. H. Hutton and J. P. Mills (Nagas), and C. von Fürer-Haimendorf (Hyderabad tribes).

On religion there is a superfluity of books. K. Saunders' *A Pageant of Asia* (1934) puts Indian religious evolution in its wider setting; Sir S. Radhakrishnan's *The Hindu Way of Life* (1927) is beautiful as well as authoritative; W. C. Smith, *Modern Islam in India* (1946) is an acute analysis; J. Farquhar, *Modern Religious Movements in India* (1924) gives some idea of the effervescent turmoil of faiths.

Hutton, Ghurye, Cox between them cover most aspects of caste; A. M. Hocart, *Caste* (1950) examines its manifestations in other lands; L. S. S. O'Malley's *Hindu Caste Customs* (1932) and *Popular Hinduism: The Religion of the Masses* (1935) present Hinduism in its aspect of everyday life as against that of its higher philosophies. The same author's opening and closing chapters in *Modern India and the West* (1941) are among the best analyses of social tendencies. The indispensable autobiographies of Mahatma Gandhi (*My Experiments with Truth*) and Nehru form a revealing contrast: the translation of the former by Mahadev Desai deserves to become one of the classics of autobiographical prose in English. Finally, P. K. Rao in *East and West: A Denial of Contrast* (1939) sweeps away, with much vigour, a great deal of semi-sociological junk (and possibly some useful furniture); and in Ch. 18 ("The Demography of Caste") of *The Population of India and Pakistan* (Princeton, 1951) a thoughtful discussion leads K. Davis to the conclusion that the caste system may essentially disappear within 50 years before the impact of industrialism.

CHAPTER VI

HISTORICAL OUTLINES

The Indus Civilisation

IT would be an exaggeration, but not a very great one, to say that little is certainly known of early man in India beyond the fact of his existence; the scientific study of prehistoric ethnology is very recent.[1] Palaeolithic implements, usually of quartzite, are widespread, and de Terra has correlated various Nn cultures (mainly in the Soan Valley) with the Kashmir glaciations; but while he and others have examined Peninsular sites, those scientifically studied are as yet too few and too far apart for any generalisations to be of much use. But attention is being increasingly directed to this field of archaeology, and the next few years may well see discoveries almost as revolutionary as was that of the Indus Civilisation.

Until 1922 the proto-history of India began with the coming of the Indo-Aryans, although finds of pictographic seals at Harappa in the Punjab had long hinted the existence of an unknown civilisation. The curtain was raised dramatically when excavations at Mohenjo-daro ('Mound of the Dead') in Sind disclosed an urban Bronze Age culture, of a general cast not entirely dissimilar to that of Sumeria in technical accomplishment and social organisation, though clearly independent in origin.

This culture is now known from some 40 sites, spread over all the Indus Plains and possibly (in its last phase of dispersal before barbarian inroads?) over the Indo-Gangetic divide and into Kathiawar.[2] It is of extraordinary homogeneity in both space and time, in this (as well as in its general level) contrasting strongly with the petty local cultures of the Baluchistan Valleys, which in their evolution show broad similarities with the Chalcolithic early Bronze Age communities of the Wn flanks of the Iranian Plateaus. The Indus Civilisation appears native to the soil, and so far nothing is known of its actual beginnings. There is definite evidence of trade (perhaps especially in cotton goods) with Sumeria around 2300–2000 BC, but by this time the Indus Civilisation was fully developed.

It was a trading empire of high technical accomplishment, but culturally, on the whole, it seems definitely poorer than Sumeria or Egypt. The great capitals, Mohenjo-daro and Harappa, are indeed impressively, if un-

---

[1] How recent can be judged by the fact that as late as 1943 the Madras Museum—one of the foremost in India—included in a series of skulls intended to illustrate racial types one labelled 'Muslim'! But see T. T. Paterson's review in *Chambers's Encyclopaedia* (1950), *s.v.* India.
[2] *India News* (London), II/22 (10/6/50); cf. Stuart Pigott, *Prehistoric India* (1950), 238–41.

imaginatively, planned; what seems to strike most observers, perhaps by reaction from the Indian present, is the high standard of the drains. But the art, for the most part, is gauche or slight, the architecture monotonous to dreariness, with a singular absence not only of *panache* but even of the monumental. The impression is of a utilitarian business culture with little of the civic, dynastic, or religious grandiosity of Sumeria or (*a fortiori*) Egypt; Pigott sums it up as "terrible efficiency which recalls all the worst of Rome", "a dead level of bourgeois mediocrity". There are exceptions: a delightful bronze dancing-girl, in which, however, Pigott detects the less sophisticated but more live spirit, and even the physical type, of the Baluchistan Kulli culture; above all the splendid stylised animals of the seals. These include tigers, rhinoceros, elephants, and water-buffaloes, which together with the architecture of kiln-burnt bricks (implying large supplies of fuel) are evidence of a distinctly more humid climate than now prevails. The seals carry an undeciphered script, and from their religious symbolism it appears almost certain that many important elements of Hinduism, especially the worship of Siva, were carried over from the Indus Civilisation through the Dravidian cultures. In this connection the survival of a Dravidian language, Brahui, in Baluchistan is perhaps significant, and also perhaps the system of weights in which "the unit was ratio 16, binary in the lower weights and decimal in the higher".[3] Conceptions of urbanism and urban polity may also be an Indus contribution to later India, though mercifully not the unspeakably standardised workers' housing, "evidently drawn out in the city architect's office", which marks the definite industrial quarter of Harappa, with its great granaries, grain-mortars massed in rows, and metal furnaces, antedating by a thousand years the similar lay-out at Tell-el-Amarna in Egypt, and by four thousand years the same deadly monotony in 19th century England.[4]

The end of the Indus Civilisation is obscure, but was not unattended by violence. It seems possible that it survived till about 1700 BC, but little before the generally accepted period for the arrival in India of the Aryan-speaking people from the steppe.

The Coming of the Aryans

The Aryan invasions, from their date, may well have been a part of the great folk-wanderings represented farther W by the Hyksos in Egypt and the overthrow of the Babylonian Dynasty by the Kassites. Be that as it may, the newcomers when settled in their original Indian territory— *Sapta Sindhu* or the Seven Rivers from the Kabul to the Jumna—retained many elements of a pastoral culture: a diet based largely on milk and meat, chariot-racing, the sacrifice of horses. Their religion, expressed in the often obscure but often noble hymns of the *Rig-Veda*, was essentially wor-

[3] Pigott, 181.
[4] *Ibid.*, 169–70. At least Harappa was not quite the Victorian back-to-back lay-out!

ship of personified natural phenomena—Sun, Moon, Fire, and so on—and at its height tended to monotheism. The Vedic hymns are the only sources of information: the impression is of an initially simple society based on the family and the village, with at least distinct classes of warriors, priests, and artisans; divided into monarchical or republican clans, gradually becoming more complex with the growth of towns, trade, and crafts.[5]

Larger kingdoms coalesced, and the frontiers of Aryandom were pushed outwards in struggles with the dark-skinned snub-nosed *Dasyus* or *Dasas*—struggles in which some have seen the prime origin of caste, though that is probably far more complex. By about the first millennium BC the Aryans had passed the Gogra, and later pushed through the Vindhyan barrier into the Nn Deccan. In Buddha's day (6th century BC) there were four major kingdoms in Madhyadesa, the 'middle country': Kosala (roughly Oudh), Avanti (Malwa), Vatsa (around Allahabad), Magadha (Sn Bihar). The last was the most powerful and exerted a certain ascendancy over much of Nn India; its later capital Pataliputra is represented by modern Patna, which may thus claim to be the oldest Indian city with a more or less continuous history.

So far the story has to be pieced out from religious texts and the great epics, *Ramayana* and *Mahabharata*: but the former do not profess to be history or even (until the Jain and Buddhist scriptures) biography, while the epics (especially the *Mahabharata*) are very composite collections of ballads and didactic verse (including the famous *Bhagavad Gita*) containing some material probably not added until the earliest Christian centuries. Socially their content is rich: this is the Heroic Age, an age of myths giving a vivid, if confused, picture of a culture in which cities and arts are increasingly important. The original clan society has developed the complex structure of caste, the austere beauty of the Vedic hymns gives way to elaborate metaphysics; and, by reaction to caste and excessive religiosity, Buddhism has arisen, in its origins simple and emotional, though in turn developing a refined and intellectual psychology and philosophy. But the patterns are shifting, splendid, and vague.

The Major Geographical Lineaments of Indian History

Already, however, we can see one of the major structure-lines of Indian historical geography: the Narbada-Chota Nagpur line which has been easily the most persistent internal boundary in India, rivalled only by the terai frontier zone between the mountains and the Indo-Gangetic Plain and the Bengal march between 'Hindustan' and alien Assam (Fig. 33). The Aryans infiltrated beyond the Narbada, but except on the Lavas of Maharashtra the 'Southland', *Dakshinapatha* or the Deccan, is still mainly Dravidian: in the E, Dravidian (and other non-Aryan) languages extend

[5] Pigott, Ch. VII, gives a brilliant interpretation.

farther N, and the Chota Nagpur-Orissa hill country is very mixed linguistically, while in the W the Marathi (Aryan) and Telugu (Dravidian)
boundary shows a remarkable correlation with that of the Deccan Lava
(below, 649). N of the Narbada-Chota Nagpur line, then, we have Hindu-

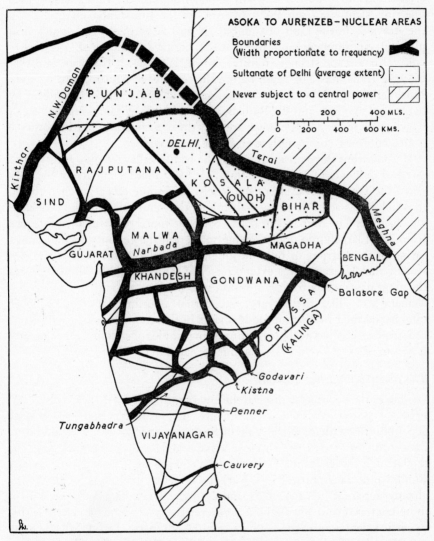

Fig. 33.—Asoka to Aurenzeb: an attempt to illustrate the relative permanence of
boundaries and the persistence of nuclear areas such as Malwa and Gujarat. The evidence
permits of rough approximations only, but it is believed that a fair representation is
attained. Based largely on maps in C. C. Davies, *An Historical Atlas of the Indian Peninsula*
(1949) and E. W. Green, *An Atlas of Indian History* (Bombay, 1937), and on standard
histories. Cf. map in W. M. Day, "Relative Permanence of Former Boundaries in
India", *Scottish Geog. Mag.* XLV (1949), 113–22.

stan, essentially the Gangetic Plain and its outworks in central India; S of it lies the Deccan, essentially Dravidian except on the lavas.

The other major structure-line is more clear-cut in the Muslim phase, but it is, perhaps, dimly foreshadowed in the limitation of the earliest civilisation and of Persian and Greek penetration to the Indus basin. This line runs slantwise from about Muttra, on the Jumna above Agra, along the Aravallis to the Gulf of Cambay. N and W of this the generally arid physical environment and the Islamic heritage combine to produce a cultural landscape strongly reminiscent of SW Asia: it has been said that the true India does not begin before the temples of Muttra, birthplace of Krishna.[6] In the NW, the mountain girdle of India narrows significantly between Turkestan and the Punjab, and is pierced by numerous passes, of which the Khyber and the Bolan are only the most famous. The importance of this entry is a commonplace and needs no stressing.

We have thus three great divisions: the Indus Valley, open to cultural and political influences from central and SW Asia; Hindustan, accessible only when the Delhi gateway has been forced, and more receptive than the S, to which it has acted as a shock-absorber; the Peninsula S of the Narbada, which, except in Maharashtra, has been far more resistant to influences from Asia: largely, no doubt, owing to mere distance, but to some extent owing to the barriers of hill and jungle, especially in the NE. It is noteworthy that Deccan Lavas extend far N of the Narbada in Malwa: this is the great passageway from Hindustan into the Deccan, and on its glacis in Maharashtra alike the Aryans, the earlier Muslims, and the Moguls established their first serious lodgements in the Southland. The pattern of the sub-continent as a whole—diminishing ripples of alien influence radiating from an entry in the NW—is thus repeated in the Deccan.

The Perennial Nuclear Regions

Thus early we can also discern the emergence of some nuclear regions or bases of power which are perennially significant in Indian historical geography: Gandhara in the Vale of Peshawar and Potwar; Sapta Sindhu narrowed down to the Punjab, seven rivers to five; Kurushetra or Sirhind, the Delhi or Sutlej/Jumna Doab; Panchala in the Jumna/Ganges Doab and Rohilkhand; Saurashtra (Kathiawar) and Gujarat; the four great kingdoms already apparent in Magadhan times. In the Dravidian S the pattern is more confused, but not without some relatively permanent pieces in the dynastic kaleidoscope: the Kalinga country or Orissa; Andhra, the Telugu country; the Chola (whence Coromandel) and Pandya kingdoms in the Tamil country; Kerala or Malabar, the isolated SW littoral. There are of

[6] Cf. S. Pigott, *Some Ancient Cities of India* (1945), 1, 42. Against this is the Hindu as well as Muslim past of Delhi; less seriously, a remark made to the author in Lahore: "Ah, *this* is the real India". As the speaker was a Muslim striving to get as much as possible into Pakistan, the remark has a delightful irony—dare I say characteristically Indian?

course many smaller areas which have preserved an historic individuality, e.g. Bundelkhand, Chhattisgarh, Konkan, Kanara. Some areas again have been debateable marches: such are Khandesh, between Narbada and Tapti, or the Raichur Doab between Tungabhadra and Kistna. It is noteworthy that many of the ancient names survive in the regional consciousness of the people, although not corresponding to any existing political unit, e.g. Andhra Matsya, Maharashtra; others have been used as the names of new sub-federations of the *Indian* Union, e.g. Saurashtra and Kerala, the union of Travancore and Cochin.

These nuclear regions clearly represent the major agricultural areas, for the most part alluvial; intersecting them are arid, broken, or jungly refuge areas such as Rajputana and the wild country of the Bhils between it and Maharashtra; the jungly Gondwana country between Son and Mahanadi; Bastar; the Rajmahal Hills in the angle of the Ganges between Bihar and Bengal. These are still the homes of most of the aboriginal tribes, and until the mergers of 1948 the great belt of country between Rajputana and Orissa was a major shatter-zone, a congeries of scores of semi-feudal states.

This pattern is perhaps more clearly grasped if we look at the Indo-Chinese peninsula, where its homologue persisted into our own century. Here we have the great rice-growing basins, deltas, or (as around Mandalay, the heart of ancient Burma) irrigated dry zones: these are the bases of organised kingdoms. Around these, on the more or less open plateaus of the Shan country (Burma), Korat (Siam), and the Laos country (Indo-China), was a penumbra of semi-feudal statelets, subject to Burma, Siam, or Annam, but with an allegiance the quality of which depended on distance from the centre and on the personality, vigorous or effete, of the reigning monarch. And in the wilder mountains, dissected and densely forest-clad, the hillmen lived their ancient and primitive tribal life. In India the Vale of Kashmir and Manipur corresponded to the larger plateau-states of the Shans, formed round an unusually large agricultural base in an old lake-floor silted into a rice-growing lowland.

Three regions have not been mentioned in this survey: the arid NW hills; Bengal; Assam. The first were generally dependencies of the dominant power in Iran—Medes, Persians, Macedonians, Parthians, Sassanids, and their Muslim successors. Often, indeed, the Wn Punjab and the Afghan basins were part of the same 'saddle-state', loosely straddling the hills and incapsulating rather than assimilating their tribesmen (below, Ch. XVI); power was sometimes based on the Kandahar-Ghazni-Kabul line, sometimes on the Punjab. This Afghan-Punjab relationship, foreshadowed by the Greek Bactrian Kingdoms and the Kushan Empire, naturally bulks larger in the Muslim period: but preoccupation with Hindustan inhibited effective power to the NW, and vice versa. Often the boundary has been the *daman-i-koh*—'the skirts of the hills'—the sharp break of slope at the detrital pediment. This was the boundary of the Punjab under the Sikhs, and is still that between Administered and Tribal territory in the NWFP. The India/Nepal boundary in the terai, the E Pakistan boundary with the Shillong Plateau and Tripura, and many internal boundaries (e.g. that of the Santal Parganas in the Rajmahal Hills) are essentially similar.

As for Bengal, until it became the base for British territorial aggrandisement in the NE, it was always something of a marchland: beyond lay the Ahom kings of Assam or the Arakanese. Assam itself in early days had something of the Kashmir or Manipur pattern: an agricultural lowland surrounded by hills and jungles, and though the Shan Ahoms were soon Hinduised, Assam remained *mlechha*—foreign, beyond the pale, unsubjugated even by the Moguls.

The Delhi-Agra Axis and the Cambay Node

One area stands out with peculiar importance: 'The Doab', a long fillet between Jumna and Ganges with Delhi and Agra as its poles. The reasons are clear: at the NW end is the gateway between the Aravallis and the Thar Desert on one hand, the Himalayas on the other; to the SE are the approaches to the great Malwa passageway.

The strategic significance of the Delhi gate is shown not only by the cities—more than the traditional seven—which have intervened between Aryan Indraprastha and British New Delhi, but by its role as the cockpit of Nn India. It is the theatre of the great warfare of the *Mahabharata* between the Kurus to the W and the Panchalas to the E of the Jumna; but at least seven less legendary and more decisive battles have taken place a few marches N of Delhi, where the great highway from the NW entry, along the well-watered sub-montane Punjab strip, approaches the Jumna.[7] The heart of Muslim rule in Nn India lay between Delhi and Agra, alike in the great days of the Tughluks and the Moguls and in the decadence under the Lodis (15th century) and the later Moguls. Agra shared with Delhi the prestige of being the Mogul capital, and near it, at Khanua, Babur consolidated his conquest by defeating a powerful Rajput attempt to take over from the discredited Lodis.

Only second in importance to the great highway through the Punjab was the ancient trade route from Agra through Ujjain to the Gulf of Cambay; earlier perhaps it lay farther E, from Prayag (Allahabad) and Pataliputra through Sanchi. Its main terminal was Broach, Ptolemy's Barygaza; and the importance of this great commercial entry persisted at least until the

---

[7] Muhammad Ghori's two battles with the Rajputs at Thanesar (1191 and 1192); Babur's victory at Panipat in 1526 and Akbar's 30 years later, the first putting the Moguls on the throne of Delhi and the second securing them there after a usurpation; the Persian Nadir Shah's defeat of the Moguls at Karnaul in 1739; the Afghan victories over the Marathas at Thanesar again in 1759 and at Panipat in 1761, which checked the Maratha flood at its highest tide. Outside Delhi itself Lord Lake defeated the Maratha Sindhia in 1803; and the significance of Delhi in 1857 needs no stress.

17th century, when the trade of Surat, the most flourishing port of the Mogul Empire, was fought for by Portuguese, Dutch, and English: the Portuguese enclaves of Diu and Damão, useless as they are, still attest their preoccupation with this entry to the Mogul realms. It will be noted that the two great structure-lines converge here.

Pre-Muslim Invasions and Empires

After the rich confusion of the Heroic Age, it is a relief to be able to resume the historical narrative with a definite date at last. In 326 BC Alexander the Great, after defeating various Punjab princes, reached his farthest east on the Beas.

The immediate results of Alexander's Indian campaigns were practically nil; not so the long-term effects. The Satrapies formed along the Indus soon reverted to Indian control; even Gandhara, which had been one of the richest provinces of the Achaemenid Persian Empire, was ceded by Alexander's successor Seleucus Nikator to Chandragupta Maurya. But it seems very probable that it was a reaction against the Yavana (= Ionian) invaders that enabled Chandragupta, the Sandrocottos of Greek historians, to seize the throne of Magadha from a decadent dynasty and so to found the first of the great empires which have endeavoured to bring all India under one sway. At its height, under Chandragupta's grandson Asoka (*fl. c.* 250 BC), the Mauryan dominion stretched from the Hindu Kush to the Brahmaputra, and well beyond the Kistna to the Penner. Not all of this area, of course, was directly under Asoka or his viceroys, but frontier kingdoms such as those of the Rashtrakutas (in the Konkan) and the Andhras were subordinate to him. The fragments of the account of India written by Megasthenes, the Seleucid ambassador to Chandragupta, and perhaps some of the traditions embedded in the manual of polity known as Kautilya's *Arthasastra*,[8] attest the high degree of fiscal and administrative organisation of the Empire, in which most of the familiar features of Hinduism were firmly established. From Asoka's time onwards brick and stone replace the earlier timber of Pataliputra and other towns.

The moral crisis which Asoka experienced as a result of the horrors of his Kalinga war brought him very close to Buddhism, probably actually within its fold; and the later years of his reign were devoted to a pacifist policy (even the royal hunt was abolished) and the fostering of Buddhist

---

[8] The *Arthasastra* is ascribed to Kautilya, adviser to Chandragupta, but in great part at least it is probably post-Christian date, since the elaborate rules for foreign policy (including alliance with the next state but one, and avoidance of alliance with a stronger state) point to a chaotic 'time of troubles'. Nevertheless it is a most remarkable work whether it is a guide to existing administration or (more probably) a blue-print of what ought to be; it strongly resembles Macchiavelli's *The Prince* in temper, though not in conciseness. It is indeed a sort of Gauleiter's Guide, with references i.a. to the inner ring of spies within and on the secret service and to the authoritarian control (through gilds) of trade and industry, down to the duties, rights, and fees of courtesans.

missionary activity: the inscriptions of the 'Asoka pillars' [9] and rock edicts scattered over India record missions to Tamilnad, Ceylon, and the Hellenistic World. The unique spectacle of a great Emperor publishing (in stone, for all time) his repentance for the sins of his imperialism, and doing all in his power in expiation, makes Asoka perhaps the most sympathetic monarch in all history: but, though the mission to Ceylon had results still important to-day, "the Greeks apparently were not much impressed by lessons in non-violence", and the wilful decay of the central military power led to provincial disintegration, not checked by Asoka's institution of touring officials analogous to Charlemagne's *Missi Dominici*. After his death disruption set in; the Dravidian S exerted its independence (or rather independences), and in the N the Greeks of Bactria (Nn Afghanistan) subjugated Gandhara once more. This Hellenistic domination lasted only a century or so, but to it belongs a fine coinage (a most important contribution to chronology) and the wealth of Gandharan or Graeco-Buddhist sculpture—much of which, it must be admitted, bears the mark of mass production.[10]

Renewed incursions from the NW—Sakas, Parthians, the Yueh-Chi or Kushans—make the centuries around the beginning of the Christian era a time of troubles. The most important of these 'Scythian' peoples were the Kushans, probably displaced from their homes by Chinese expansion under the imperialist Han dynasty. The Kushan Empire, centred on Purushapura (Peshawar), reached its height under Kanishka (1st or 2nd century AD), whose domains extended from Sinkiang to Benares; he carried on the Gandharan Buddhist traditions. During this generally chaotic period a strong Andhra power included most of the Deccan N of the Penner and disputed possession of Malwa—and the Ujjain trade route —with the Nn kingdoms.

In the middle of the 4th century AD the Gupta dynasty revived some at least of the Mauryan glories. Under Chandragupta II Vikramaditya (*c.* 385–413) the Empire extended, more or less loosely, from the Kirthar Range and the Chenab to Bengal, and S to the Narbada-Chota Nagpur line, with occasional penetrations along the Wn and En littorals. Vikramaditya's court was at Ujjain, centre of a cultural revival which marked the end of Hellenistic influence (except in coinage and astronomy) and the home of Kalidasa, whose delightful lyrical drama *Sakuntala* is perhaps the secular writing in Sanskrit best known to the West. Around 500 the Gupta Empire was shattered by the invasion of the White Huns, who destroyed the ancient Buddhist university at Taxila in Potwar. A long period of anarchy was only briefly mitigated by Harsha (mid-7th century), who seems to have ruled

[9] The three fine lions from the Sarnath pillar (near Benares) figure on *Indian* postage stamps.

[10] See R. E. Mortimer Wheeler, "Romano-Buddhist Art: an old problem re-stated", *Antiquity* XXIII (1949), 4–19.

(with considerable local variation in his real power) from the Sutlej to Bengal and the Narbada-Chota Nagpur line. The centre of his power, at all events, was in the Delhi-Agra region, where lay his capital Kanauj on the Ganges.

During these centuries the S was the seat of a bewildering array of dynasties. Between 800 and 1000 India was more than usually disunited, three major and a host of minor kingdoms locked in an indecisive struggle for power. The three were the Gurjara-Pratihara kingdom, within the old Aravalli-Himalaya-Narbada triangle; the Palas of Bengal, Kalinga, and the NE Deccan; the Rashtrakutas in Maharashtra. The country S of the Penner was, as usual, under its own ever-shifting dynasties, of whom the most generally successful were the Cholas, who in the 11th century held S Kalinga and sent armies as far as the Ganges; on the NW they were held, by the Chalukyas of Maharashtra, roughly on the Deccan Lava boundary in Hyderabad. The Cholas also took much of Ceylon from its native Buddhist rulers—whence a still existing minority problem—and at sea reached out as far as Sumatra.

But, as in Italy, wealth and disunity combined to attract invaders from beyond the mountains; and the newcomers were armed with ideological as well as material weapons. Already in the 8th century the Arabs had conquered Sind, later extending their power as far as Multan and raiding into Rajputana and Gujarat. The stage was set for the great Muslim invasions which

> Cast the Kingdoms old
> Into another mould.

But the changes were political and social rather than geographical: the nuclear regions of power, the great lines of advance, the refuges for the dispossessed, remain the same.

India between East and West

As we have seen, the earliest civilisation of India had commercial relations with Sumeria; and it is probable that Solomon's Tarshish and Ophir were S India and Ceylon. Herodotus knew of NW India as part of the Achaemenid Empire, and relates the exploration of the Indus and the Makran coast by Skylax on the orders of Darius (521–485 BC). But Alexander's campaigns, the scientifically organised exploration of the sea route to the Persian Gulf by his admiral Nearchus, and the reports of Megasthenes put classical knowledge of India on a firmer footing. Egypt under the Ptolemies had an active trade with India, which expanded greatly with the luxury demand of Rome. The Greek names for rice, ginger, and pepper are Indian, the Sanskrit for tin probably Greek [11]; the Byzantines had an

[11] K. de B. Codrington, "A Geographical Introduction to the History of Central Asia", GJ CIV (1944), 27–40 and 73–91.

official stationed at Clysma near Suez who visited India yearly to report on trade and political conditions; 'Roman' guards, 'the dumb *mlechhas*', were in demand by S Indian kings owing to their isolation from local faction. All-land routes were subject to interference by Parthia, often at war with Rome and always anxious to inflate transit profits; most trade was by sea, either via Palmyra or Petra and the Gulf, or by Berenice and other Red Sea ports. The chief Indian ports concerned were Barbarikon on the Indus Delta, Barygaza (Broach), Kalyan near Bombay, and Musiris (Cranganore). The drain of precious metal in exchange for such luxuries, including spices and sandalwood, is lamented by Roman publicists such as Pliny; recently evidence of Mediterranean exports has been found in the form of warehouses of Roman pottery at Arikamedu near Pondicherry.[12] Ceylon and the extreme S of India were the meeting-places of Graeco-Roman and Chinese traders.

Cultural exchanges, though often indirect, were also important: "Embassies were exchanged with the Hellenic powers by the sovereigns of Magadha and Malwa. Indian philosophers, traders and adventurers were to be found in the intellectual circles of Athens and the markets of Alexandria. The first of the Mauryas had entered into a marriage contract with a Greek potentate (Seleucus Nikator). His son was eager to secure the services of a Greek sophist. The third and greatest of the Mauryas (Asoka) entrusted the government of a wealthy province and the execution of important irrigation works to a Yavana chief. The services of Greek engineers seem to have been requisitioned by the greatest of the Kushans. Greek influence on Indian coinage and iconography is unmistakable".[13] Converse influences were those of Buddhism on the Graeco-Bactrians (their king Menander is the eponymous protagonist of the Buddhist *Milindapanho*); Indian thought may also have had some influence on Manicheism and hence on the early Christian Gnostic heresies. The early legend of St Thomas the Apostle (whose traditional tomb is to be seen in the Portuguese church at San Thomé, Madras) contains an indubitable reference to a Parthian king in the Indus borderland, and the Syrian Christian church of Malabar was possibly in existence in AD 200. Religion apart, the greatest gift of India to the West—and to the whole world—is the 'Arabic' numbers, without which it is difficult to conceive of modern scientific method.

The Western trade was largely in the hands of Asiatics, especially before the 'discovery' of the monsoon (long known to the Yemen Arabs) by Hippalus about AD 50. It is, naturally, much better known in Europe than the Indian expansion into SE Asia, which began in the 1st and 2nd Christian centuries. Yet this had in a sense a more positive effect, since the

---

[12] R. E. M. Wheeler *et al.*, "Arikamedu: an Indo-Roman Trading Station on the East Coast of India", *Ancient India*, No. 2 (ND, July 1946), 17–124.
[13] H. C. Raychaudhuri in *An Advanced History of India* (1946), 142.

beginnings of high civilisation in Burma, Malaya, Indonesia, and parts of Indo-China were due directly to Hindu and Buddhist traders, colonists, and missionaries. Indian dynasties ruled for over a millennium (2nd–15th centuries) in Champa (Annam); Kambuja (Cambodia) at times dominated the whole peninsula beyond Burma, then truly Further India; Sivaism has left its memorial in Angkor Vat, and the culture of Cambodia remains Indo-Buddhist to this day. In Indonesia the Sailendra or Sri Vijaya Empire, centred at Palembang in Sumatra, dominated the archipelago from the 8th to the 11th centuries. Sailendra was Buddhist, deriving its inspiration from Bengal and leaving in the 400-foot-square terraces of Borobudur (Java) perhaps the grandest material monument of any religion, alike in the superbly massive planning of the whole and in the richness and beauty of the innumerable sculptures. In the 9th century Java (a Hindu kingdom conquered by Sailendra) broke away; in the 13th and 14th the Javanese Majapahit dynasty gradually supplanted Sailendra and in turn controlled the archipelago, only to fall before the Islamic tide in the 15th century. Hinduism survived in Bali, the arts and customs of which reflect, if on a diminished scale, the golden days of classical Hinduism. The *Ramayana* and the *Mahabharata* are still the basis of much popular art—puppet- and stage-plays, poems and folk-tales—in Indonesia and even the Indo-Chinese peninsula.

Naturally the major part in the foundation of these distant sea-states was played by the kingdoms of the En littoral, especially Kalinga and the Chola Empire. How false is Lyde's still current concept of an almost solely inward looking India, with its sea-contacts those of alien traders, may be seen from the fact that the decline of Sailendra was due in large part to an attack by Rajendra Chola II (1012–44); the Cholas were driven out after a century of intermittent war, but in the 13th century a disastrous expedition against Ceylon fatally weakened the power of Sri Vijaya. These armadas presuppose high standards not only in navigation and seamanship, but in naval organisation, on both sides of the 1200-mile-wide waters between Coromandel and Sumatra. Certainly no European power of the day could have dreamt of such oceanic adventure: only the Viking voyages are as impressive, while the Crusading fleets were in comparison mere coastal forays. On the terraces of Borobudur the carved ships of Sri Vijaya still sail, immobile and endlessly, over their seas of stone.

Hindu expansion remained vigorous until about AD 1000–1100; but the declining fortunes of Hinduism in the homeland sapped its strength, and indigenous elements, seconded by Islam, reasserted themselves. Long before then an even greater work had been accomplished from India: by devious ways through mountain and jungle Buddhism had spread over the Far E and High Asia; the Chinese Buddhist pilgrims Fa Hien and Hiuen-Tsang (5th and 7th centuries) give us the first comprehensive

accounts of India by outside observers. Buddhism hardly recovered from
the devastation of the Huns in its NWn strongholds, and in succeeding
centuries it declined before a Brahmanic revival. By the time it was dead in
its birthplace its heirs had developed the strength to stand alone and to
evolve the complex cosmogony and psychology of later Buddhism in
China, Tibet, and Japan, the lands of the Mahayana or 'Greater Vehicle'
as opposed to the 'Lesser', the simpler Hinayana form which survives in
Ceylon, Burma, and Siam.

The Muslim Advance

Apart from the early occupation of Sind, never really followed up, the
first Muslim incursions of significance were the almost annual raids of
Mahmud of Ghazni, between 1000 and 1030. Mahmud, a first-class soldier
and a patron of the arts, was in India no more than a ruthless plunderer; he
penetrated as far as Muttra and Somnath (Kathiawar), but only the Punjab
—as far as Thanesar—was held, and that only as the frontier march of a
domain covering most of Persia and at times much of Turkestan. But the
ferocity of his devastations weakened the economy and morale of the Hindu
states, and though there was a respite of 160 years before the arrival of the
next great Muslim leader, Muhammad of Ghor in SW Afghanistan, Nn
India remained politically fragmented. Muhammad's victory over the
Rajput princes near Thanesar in 1192 was decisive: the Delhi gateway
was finally forced, the Rajputs split into the petty Pahari (= hill) chiefs of
the sub-Himalaya and the better-known princes of the Aravalli fortresses—
Rajputana or Rajasthan. Within 10 years the entire Gangetic Plain, as far
as Nadia in Bengal, had been overrun; and henceforth Islam was politically
dominant in Hindustan.

The Ghaznavid realm, and the new Empire in its first few years, had
straddled the NW hills. By dynastic accident this Afghan-Punjab relationship was broken in 1206, and the famous Sultanate of Delhi took form, to
survive in some sense until 1857, though in evil days the 'Ruler of the
World' sometimes ruled effectively 'from Delhi to Palam', 9 or 10 miles.
The Delhi Kingdom now formed a separate entity in the Muslim world, a
state at once Indian and Islamic. Under Iltutmish (1211–35), the greatest
ruler of the first ('Slave' or Turco-Afghan) dynasty, it corresponded
roughly with the perennial Nn triangle we have already seen as held by the
Guptas, by Harsha, and by the Gurjaras; with the difference of a firm hold
on the Indus Plains. The heart of Rajputana, and outlying regions such as
Kathiawar and Bengal, generally retained a quasi-independence under their
own princes or subordinate governors; and internal faction, wars of
succession, and at times Mongol raids were constant impediments to consolidation. Under the second dynasty, the Khaljis (1290–1320), forays
into the Deccan were frequent, and in 1311 reached Madura in the far S.

The rulers of these dynasties included some able if ruthless leaders, such as the astonishing megalomaniac Ala-ud-Din Khalji, a *soi-disant* 'Second Alexander', who ruled in the most totalitarian manner.[14] Nevertheless the general standards of society and government were probably not very different in degree from those of contemporary Europe, and at Delhi architecture around the Qutb Minar shows an extremely successful fusion of Hindu and Islamic tradition. The Qutb is the highest free-standing stone tower in the world (234 ft); it is characteristic of Ala-ud-Din that he began a minar designed to be twice as high.

The Tughluks (1320–1412) represent a sterner and more austere Islam, well shown by the stark cyclopean grandeur of Tughlukabad, only three miles from the Qutb complex but worlds away in spirit. The greatest of them, Muhammad bin Tughluk, was an energetic despot who would have been enlightened in the European 18th-century manner had any enlightenment been to hand. Like the Khaljis, he had a bad press, since he based his politics on the world as he saw it rather than on Quranic commentaries (again a parallel with mediaeval Europe, e.g. the Emperor Frederick II). Muhammad extended his power almost to the Sn extremity of India; it was in pursuance of a policy of definite conquest, rather than the mere depredations of preceding rulers, that he transferred the population of Delhi (or a large part of it) to Deogir in the Deccan, renamed Daulatabad and provided with spectacular fortifications. But although his domains were equalled in extent only by Asoka's before him and Aurenzeb's after, "it was impossible to control the Deccan from an external centre in Hindustan, just as it was equally impossible to rule Hindustan from Deogir" [15]—the same problem as faced the Hohenstaufen in Germany and Italy, or Ghaznavids and Moguls in their relations with their Iranian holdings; realisation of this probably accounts for so many invaders reaching Delhi and turning back, e.g. Timur, Nadir Shah, Ahmad Shah Durrani. Despite these and other aberrations Muhammad was a man of large ideas in many directions, not least in his conciliatory policy towards the Hindus. His successor Firoz Shah was more orthodox in this respect, taking piety indeed so far that he endeavoured to spare the blood of believers; an ineffective policy. He has at least the merit of initiating large-scale irrigation canals in the Punjab. Disintegration had set in before Muhammad's death—especially (as usual) in the S and Bengal, and after the death of Firoz (1388) the prestige of the Tughluks was irretrievably ruined in 1398 by the ferocious sack of Delhi by Timur (Tamburlaine). Centrifugal tendencies were scarcely checked by

[14] He actually succeeded in fixing prices for some years, a feat achieved but imperfectly by the British Raj in 1941–45. But then his espionage and policing were more efficient, and his fiscal administration so strict that "men looked upon revenue officers as something worse than fever. Clerkship was accounted a great crime and no man would give his daughter to a clerk".

[15] C. C. Davies, *An Historical Atlas of the Indian Peninsula* (1949), 34.

the weak successors of the Tughluks, the 15th-century Sayyids and Lodis.

In the S a strong new Hindu power, Vijayanagar, arose on the ruins of the older Dravidian dynasties, shattered by the Tughluk incursions, and made head against the Muslim princes, whose revolt had set into motion the disintegration of Muhammad bin Tughluk's Empire. In the Deccan, between Tapti and Tungabhadra, the Bahmani kingdom split off from the Tughluk dominions, and in turn split into five Deccani Sultanates: Ahmadnagar, Berar, Bidar, Golconda, and Bijapur; the broken country of the NE Peninsula was left to Gond tribal chieftains. Gujarat, at the height of its commercial importance, was an independent Muslim kingdom, as were Khandesh S and Malwa N of the Narbada, Sind and Multan in the W, Bengal in the W and for a few years even Jaunpur in the heart of Hindustan. All these were under Muslim rulers, but the Rajputs formed a confederacy under the leadership of Mewar, threatening the diminished Lodi realms, which at best formed a belt from the Punjab to Bihar, but were often not much more than the Delhi-Agra region.

Thus, after 300 years of Muslim conquest and attempted consolidation, all the old patterns of pre- and post-Mauryan India have once more emerged. Nothing better illustrates the perennial significance of the geographical factor in Indian history than this continual re-assertion of the nuclear regions as the power-bases of political entities. But two mighty forces were looming on the horizon of Indian politics: in 1526 Babur, who began his career as a boy of 12 dispossessed of his petty principality of Ferghana, utterly overthrew the Lodis at Panipat; and already in 1498 Vasco da Gama had reached Calicut, precursor of yet stronger and more alien powers who were to rule as much by economic chains as by the sword.[16]

The Mogul Synthesis

The key significance of the Delhi-Agra region is strikingly illustrated by the incidents of early Mogul rule. By 1529 Babur was in possession of Bengal; he died in the next year and his son Humayun, after an expedition as far as Cambay, was defeated at Kanauj in 1539 and expelled from Hindustan. His supplanter, Sher Shah, was a very capable ruler, who laid out the Grand Trunk Road from Bengal to the Indus, and whose principles of land revenue administration influenced, through the Moguls, British practice. Disputed successions enabled Humayun to return in 1555 after a victory at Sirhind; but in 1556 his son Akbar, on any reckoning one of the world's great men, succeeded at the age of 14 to a military situation in which Delhi and Agra had been lost. Once more the field of Panipat saw a

[16] See A. J. Toynbee, "The Unification of the World" (*Civilisation on Trial*, 1948, esp. 65–71). This is a very penetrating analysis of the situation; as always with Toynbee brilliantly written, and getting to the heart of the relations of geography, history, and technology much more effectively than usual.

Mogul triumph. The old significance of these sites—Kanauj, Sirhind, Panipat—will be remembered.

Before his death in 1605 Akbar had secured not only Hindustan and the NW, but had crossed the Narbada as far as the Godavari, and in the E held Orissa; between these salients the wild Gondwana country remained under independent or tributary chiefs. Territorial expansion, however, was the least of Akbar's achievements, nor, splendid as were his capitals at Agra and Fatehpur Sikri and his patronage of artists and scholars, were these his greatest. His administration was one of the best India had known, at least in its principles: but in all these vast empires, even-handed and accessible as might be the sovereign, he could not be accessible and effective everywhere, and there was much local tyranny. Nor were communications adequate to avert such natural disasters as the Gujarat famine of 1632; and the Empire was hardly so strong as it looked: in the later 17th century Tavernier estimated that 30,000 good European troops could march through it. Nevertheless it is impossible to visit Delhi, Agra, and above all Fatehpur Sikri without an involuntary comparison with the Versailles of Louis XIV—a comparison unfavourable to the latter. Man for man Akbar was immeasurably the greater of the two, and he was as well served by men as able and loyal as Colbert or Vauban. But with all this, social organisation was essentially semi-feudal, and India lacked the Enlightenment: when it came it was through the distorting prisms of an alien rule.

The grasp of Akbar's mind is the more astonishing when it is recalled that an excellent memory had to serve him in the place of formal literacy. He advanced from the tactical alliances of expediency with Rajput chiefs to a real tolerance and some degree of synthesis of the two great cultures, Hindu and Islamic: in his last years indeed he went so far as to foster an eclectic creed drawing from these and even from Christianity; but this artificial construct had only a temporary following of courtiers. Under his successors Jahangir and Shah Jahan the policy of toleration was still followed, with less conviction, and advances were made in the Deccan, as far as Bijapur and Golconda, though effective action here was hampered by preoccupations in Afghanistan.

With Aurenzeb (1658–1707) the Empire reached its greatest extent: from Kabul to the Cauvery. But the seeds of disruption, always latent, were fertilised by Aurenzeb's intolerance, which completely alienated the Rajputs, by this time probably the most valuable military elements in the Empire. More serious was the situation in the Deccan. Here, after long wars centring round the Raichur Doab, the allied Sultanates had in 1565 finally crushed Vijayanagar at Talikota, SE of Bijapur; only to fall in turn to the ceaseless Mogul attrition, advancing by the historic Malwa-Khandesh-Maharashtra route on the Deccan Lavas. But long before the definitive Mogul conquests of Bijapur and Golconda (1686–87) the Wn Ghats were overhung by a cloud, at first no bigger than a man's hand, but destined in the next century to sweep over nearly all India. And behind the Marathas another cloud was setting in from the sea.

The founder of Maratha power, Sivaji, son of a minor noble of the Ahmadnagar Kingdom, from his little fief of Poona had won fortress after fortress in the wild Ghats country; when he died in 1680 he held the Konkan less Bombay, the Portuguese towns, and Janjira—the last a holding of the Abyssinian Sidis, nominally the Bijapur and later the Mogul admirals. The core of Maratha power was a belt of country along the Ghats and as far E as the Bhima; and they had also various outliers in the S—Bellary, Bangalore, Tanjore. Sivaji's rise was of course aided by the extraordinary perfidy of Deccani politics, a tangle of ever-shifting alliances: war was generally triangular and might be polygonal. And the Moguls were long past their best: their Hindu subjects were sullen or in revolt; their armies were vast, cumbered with camp-followers, in a war of movement no match for the tough and mobile Maratha light horse; their leaders, no longer dominated by an Akbar or a Babur, but by a politician at once shifty and bigoted, more and more played their own hands. The stage is set for the chaos and anarchy of the 18th century; and by now the coasts from Diu to Chittagong were dotted with the trading stations and forts of Portuguese, Dutch, French, Danes, and English.

The Mogul Collapse

European expansion in India can be understood only against the background of 'country powers'. The successors of Aurangzeb were all ineffective, and the throne of Delhi became the plaything of internal and alien factions. Such morale as the Empire retained was shattered by the almost unopposed invasion of the Persian Nadir Shah and his savage sack of Delhi in 1739.

The Marathas represented the effervescence of a long-fermenting Hindu revival. Initially they kept tight discipline and were conscious of a mission as the liberators of Hinduism; but this element of idealism faded as they found their account in manoeuvres among the distracted factions of Muslim India. As their power expanded it became looser, a confederacy headed by the Poona Peshwas, ministers and supplanters of Sivaji's heirs; but the centre had influence rather than power. That was in the hands of the great war-lords: the Gaekwar in Baroda, Bhonslas in Nagpur and Berar, Holkar in Indore (Malwa), most powerful of all Sindhia in Gwalior. Even Calcutta had its 'Maratha Ditch'. At the same time Mogul and other Muslim warlords set up for themselves.

Thus by the 1750s Haidar Ali subverted the Hindu dynasty in Mysore; the Viceroy of the Deccan had become the Nizam of Hyderabad; Bengal and Oudh were but very nominally subject to the ghost of empire at Delhi.

Sind and the trans-Sutlej Punjab were under Afghan domination, and there was a separate Afghan state so near Delhi as Rohilkhand. So low had the Empire fallen that the Hindu Jats—little more than an armed peasantry —could dominate the Agra-Muttra region, plundering the Taj Mahal and Akbar's tomb near Agra.[17]

Already in 1719 the Marathas had marched to Delhi as allies of one of the king-making Mogul factions. Before the repeated invasions of Ahmad Shah Abdali, founder of the Durrani dynasty which still rules Afghanistan, the Muslim rulers of the Punjab, unsupported by their 'government' in Delhi, called in the Marathas, who as a mere incident took possession of capital and Emperor. But they alienated the Rajputs and the rising Sikh chieftains, while Ahmad Shah rallied the Rohillas and Oudh. In 1761 Panipat once more saw the climax of the drama, when the Marathas were utterly overthrown, losing thousands of their best men and nearly all their best leaders: "Two pearls have been dissolved, twenty-two gold Mohurs have been lost, and of the silver and copper the total cannot be cast up". This was a decisive check to Maratha expansion; although Afghan affairs prevented Ahmad Shah from consolidating his power, the Sikhs filled the gap. Originally a quietist, even pacifist, reforming Hindu sect, Mogul persecution forged them into a nation, and under the extraordinarily tough one-eyed Ranjit Singh (1780–1839) they rose to dominate the Punjab. The Marathas remained dominant at Delhi, the Emperor being merely Sindhia's puppet. But Muslims and Marathas virtually cancelled each other out; four years before Panipat, Plassey had been fought, and the future, for nearly two centuries, lay with its alien victors.

Europe in India: Portugal

The British Empire in India was only the latest phase of four and a half centuries of European intrusion. This long history falls into distinct periods: Portuguese monopoly (1500–1600); the age of conflict between the European powers (1600–1763); the rise to power of the East India Company and its Indian Summer before the Mutiny (1757–1857); the unchallenged hey-day of the British Raj (1858–*c.* 1900); and the struggle for independence.

It is important to remember that Vasco da Gama's voyage was not only the climax of decades of patient African discovery; it was also a part of the Iberian crusade against Islam. Once the road was known experience soon taught the value of the monsoons to Portuguese fleets, which developed regular sailing habits, leaving Lisbon in time to reach Delagoa Bay (where Lourenço Marques founded his colony in 1554) for the SW monsoon to take them across to Goa. But it was certainly not timidity which led da Gama to work up the E African coast as far as Malindi (N of Mombasa)

[17] Probably the only visitors to the Taj to get away without paying.

I.P.—6

before striking into the open ocean: the journey (*c.* 1486–90) of Pero da Covilhan by the Red Sea to Calicut and down the African coast to Sofala (20° S) had taught the Portuguese of the Arab hold on the Indian Ocean trade and something of navigation conditions; da Gama knew that on this coast he would find a pilot to bring him through.

The Portuguese fixation on Wn India was thus influenced by sailing conditions; but in large part also by their preoccupation with the 'Moors' as well as with the monsoon. This bias is suggested by the title adopted by the King of Portugal: Lord of the Conquest, Navigation, and Commerce of Ethiopia, Arabia, Persia and India. The 'Moors' fought tenaciously for their monopoly, with the support of the Muslim rulers of Bijapur and Gujarat, of Egypt and, after their capture (1518) of Alexandria, hitherto the great emporium of En trade, of the Turks. Afonso de Albuquerque, greatest of the Viceroys (1509–15), saw the key points for domination of the Indian Ocean: Goa, Malacca, Aden.[18] Goa was an island site, defensible behind its tidal creeks yet large enough to give a local agricultural base; it controlled the valuable trade in Arab horses for the armies of the Deccani kingdoms: it was taken in 1510. In the next year Albuquerque took Malacca, guarding the approach to the Spice Islands and the Far East. At Aden he failed, though the moral effect of his expedition beyond Bab-el-Mandeb was great; but he secured Socotra and Ormuz, the latter guarding the alternative seaway to the Levantine portages. With the fortification of Ormuz, Albuquerque's last act before he died in Goa harbour, Portuguese domination in the Indian Ocean was complete: it was only 17 years since da Gama's arrival at Calicut. The Portuguese achievement was secured against very heavy numerical odds, and with a much less margin of technical superiority than that enjoyed by later Europeans: by the time of the great sieges of Diu in 1538 and 1545 there was little that Europe could teach the 'Rumi' (Turkish) gunners in Indian service. But there have been few better geopoliticians than Albuquerque.

Besides Goa and a number of minor stations on the Konkan, Malabar, and Coromandel coasts, the Portuguese held by 1540 the flourishing ports of Chaul, Bassein, Damão, and Diu; in the E they were established—more precariously—at San Thomé (Madras), Hooghly, and Chittagong; they had forts in Ceylon and were beginning to dominate its politics; they were in official contact with China and free-lance adventurers reached Japan in 1542—

E se mais mundo houvera, lá chegára.[19]

But the royal trading monopoly was always cumbrous and usually corrupt; ill-paid officials made their fortunes where they could find them; the

[18] Four and a half centuries later these are the only important points on the Asian mainland shores of the Indian Ocean to remain in European hands.

[19] "And had there been more of the world, they would have reached it"—Camões, *Os Lusíadas* VII. 14.

bigotry of the ecclesiastics often wrecked promising political combinations; the administration, in theory tightly organised, was as a rule ramshackle in practice—to find money for the rebuilding of Diu after the second siege the Viceroy D. João de Castro had to pawn his beard as security for a loan from the citizens of Goa. On the other hand, the archaic theocratic outlook of the Portuguese fitted into the Asian scene better than the secular temper of their supplanters, and, together with their tolerance of miscegenation, accounts for the deep cultural impress of Portugal in Ceylon and parts of the Konkan.

Decay had set in before the catastrophe of 1580, when the crown passed to Philip II of Spain and Portuguese holdings were open to Dutch attacks, without any compensating aid from Spain. The Portuguese effective was locked up in too many scattered small garrisons; at Tuticorin 'the Captain-Major of the Fishery Coast' points to "what is little more than a hut: 'The fortress is that house in which I live. All the Portuguese consist of my-self'." [20] Yet the old Lusian spirit flared up in gallant last-ditch defences, as when Bassein fell to the Marathas in 1739; and indeed the *Novas Conquistas* of Goa were won in the 18th century.

Europe in India: The Age of Conflict

In 1600 the English East India Company was founded, in 1602 the Dutch: more efficient commercial mechanisms than the Portuguese monopoly, backed by the more modern ideology of energetic and youthful bourgeoisies rather than the inept control of a half-feudal state. In the struggle which ensued the English played a minor part, though they helped the Persians to capture Ormuz in 1622. But after this they and the Portuguese were as a rule on fairly friendly terms: after all, the Dutch might be Protestants but were obviously more dangerous trade rivals. As for the Dutch, they were greatly interested in the Spice Islands and not at all interested in warring with the enemies of Christendom: they based themselves well to the E, at Batavia, founded in 1619 to guard the Sunda Straits breach in the island barrier between the Indian Ocean and the Far East.[21] Malacca they took in 1641, Colombo in 1656, and Goa itself was blockaded in the open season for several years from 1639. Cochin was taken in 1653 and other Malabar forts in 1661–64. By this time Portugal was finished, and Bombay after it became English (1661–66) soon outstripped all other European bases on the W littoral.

Nevertheless the Portuguese had pre-empted this coast, and except at

[20] João Ribeiro, *The Historic Tragedy of Ceilão* (1685; trans. P. E. Pieris, Colombo, n.d.), 238. This simple, stout-hearted captain speaks much more sense on the decline than is found in either the modern Portuguese rhetorical historians, or in the traditional Popery-and-immorality English view of Portugal in the East.

[21] The Dutch normally sailed with the Wlies to about 100° E before turning N, which led them to the discovery of W Australia.

Surat, terminal of the Malwa trade-route, and the pepper coast of Malabar, it was hardly worth while turning them out. Dutch and English factories at Surat date from 1616 and 1612, and both fought the Portuguese in Swally Roads off the port. But the main interest turned to the E coast, where the 'country powers' were weak and disunited. The Dutch had stations at Pulicat (1610), Chinsura on the Hooghly (1653), Negapatam (1659); the English at Masulipatam (1611), Armagaon (1626), and above all Madras (Fort St George, 1639) and Calcutta (Fort William, 1691–98). In the 18th century the Dutch, weakened by the long struggle with Louis XIV and now definitely a junior partner to their British allies, gradually lost ground in India and concentrated on Indonesia, though Chinsura was not ceded to the EIC until 1825.

In the meantime a far more serious competitor had appeared. In 1668 the first French factory was established at Surat—then nearing its decline —followed in 1669 by one at Masulipatam; and while they were dispossessed of San Thomé by the Dutch in 1673, the same year saw their establishment at Pondicherry, and 1690–92 at Chandernagore. This initial development, largely due to Colbert, was not followed up, and the years of Marlborough's wars saw a general decline in French activity. In the 1720s, however, Mauritius, Mahé, and Karikal were occupied.

At this stage the French, like the Dutch and English, were content with 'factories': small extra-territorial holdings granted by the local ruler, and if possible further secured by a *firman* from the Mogul Emperor. Here, within a fortified *enceinte*, were offices, warehouses, official residences; and sometimes there were jurisdictional rights over native settlement attracted by the trade (and the security) afforded by the factory. All were managed by monopolistic chartered companies, an organisation adopted by other countries which took a hand: Sweden, Austria (the Ostend and Imperial Companies, 1722–44 and 1781–84), Prussia (the Emden Company), and Denmark. Only the last had any significance: Danish Serampore and Tranquebar were not sold to the EIC until 1845, and were important missionary centres when the EIC took its policy of non-interference in religion to the point of discouraging Christian zeal; Tranquebar has still a Lutheran Bishopric.

The Franco-British struggle for power was in appearance no more than a side-show to the War of the Austrian Succession (1744–48) and the Seven Years' War (1756–63). But it laid the foundations of an Empire which at its height included some 1,750,000 sq mls and 410,000,000 people (including Ceylon and Burma).

Ever since 1505, when the Captain of Colombo reported to the King of Kandy of the Portuguese strangers that "their guns were very good", European military aptitudes had been held in respect; but they had been mainly confined to the defence of fortifications. A chance clash in the open field between a small French and a large local force opened the eyes of all parties.[22] The Europeans were now courted for military assistance; and in the whirlpool of Sn Indian politics the possible gains were immense. Always liable to be cut off from France by superior British sea-power, the French under Dupleix and Bussy tended to fall back on this game, played with vigour and skill. There was a ding-dong struggle in which both Pondicherry and Madras changed hands, and at times it seemed that French influence would dominate the Deccan. But lack of steady metropolitan support ruined their chances. After 1763 there was never a serious French menace, though the British were long nervous of possible French-inspired coalitions, such as those suggested by Napoleon's intrigues with Tipu Sultan of Mysore.

Territorial Rise of 'John Company'

The serious beginnings of British territorial power were the acquisition of the Northern Circars (Madras-Orissa coast) and the 24 Parganas around Calcutta in 1757–59. There is truth in the traditional view that the subsequent advance was to some extent involuntary, since the anarchic turmoil of war and intrigue beyond the Company's borders made advance essential for security. Yet the appetite grew by what it fed on, and within 20 years of Plassey (1757) the Gangetic Plain as far as Cawnpore was either directly under Company rule, or under clients such as the Nawab of Oudh. In the W the Marathas were a more solid obstacle than the effete Mogul succession states of the NE; here even Salsette Island, immediately adjacent to Bombay, was not occupied until 1775–76. The great years, in which it became clear that no likely combination of 'country powers' could withstand British arms, were those of the Napoleonic Wars. Mysore, a serious menace under the vigorous and able soldiers Haidar Ali and Tipu Sultan, ceased to be so on the defeat and death of the latter in 1799; the Nizam of Hyderabad (one or two lapses apart) had been Our Most Faithful Ally almost from the beginning; the Marathas, rarely able to co-ordinate their powers, were finally defeated in 1818. By 1849 the last serious opponents (and perhaps the toughest of all), the Sikhs, had been subjugated, but the early disasters of the First Afghan War (1839–42) were a clear warning of the limits on this side. Apart from Baluchistan, annexed in part as a reaction to the Anglo-Russian crisis over the Balkans in 1878, Lower Burma (1852), and Upper Burma, annexed in 1885–86 to forestall French penetration from Indo-China, India was substantially as it stood in 1947, except for the separation of Burma in 1937.

"The actual distribution of British territory is too significant, in the broad, to be a mere absent-minded accident, although no other explanation will account for some of its fantastic local fragmentations and aberrations.

[22] See Sir J. Fortescue, *A History of the British Army* II (1910), 184–85.

The bases lay in the great Presidency provinces of Bengal, Madras, and Bombay, securing all the coasts with the unimportant exceptions of those of Travancore and Cochin in the south-west, one or two tiny States south of Bombay, and arid Cutch, Kathiawar, and Baluchistan (and the Oman outlier at Gwadar) in the north-west; apart of course from the Portuguese enclaves of Goa, Damão, and Diu, the French of Mahé, Karikal, Pondicherry, Yanaon, and Chandernagore, the total area of these amounting to under 1750 square miles. The entire alluvial crescent between the Ganges and the Indus deltas, a few enclaves apart, was British, and the three bases were linked by practically continuous bridges, with a wedge of the United Provinces reaching down to contact the Bombay-Calcutta corridor of the Central Provinces. The two great States of Mysore and Hyderabad were neatly cut off from the sea and from each other. From Kathiawar through Gujarat, Rajputana, and Central India, as far as the Orissa hinterland, stretched great but broken blocks of states' territory; but no single state in these groups exceeded 36,210 square miles or 3,050,000 inhabitants in 1941, and the political fragmentation (now largely swept away by the Union) was indescribable verbally and well-nigh unmappable: it was as if the feudal map of England in the anarchy of Stephen's reign had been frozen. In the northwest money, diplomacy, and arms, in adroit and ever-varying combinations, held a disjointed buffer-strip firmly under British control; and the key points, Peshawar and Quetta, were in British hands." [23]

The Indian Empire

"There have been in Asia, generally, from time immemorial, but three departments of Government: Finance, or the plunder of the interior; War, or the plunder of the exterior; and the department of public works . . . the British have neglected entirely that of public works." This indictment by Marx was ceasing to be true when he wrote it in 1853, as indeed he himself points out; but it is no unfair description of the India of Warren Hastings. In the next century came the economic catastrophe of the free entry of Manchester goods, ruining the old craft industries. Against this must be set an administration which at least set its face against corruption, and, in most times and places, a general peace which must have been unspeakably comforting after the atrocious warfare of the post-Mogul anarchy.

Yet revolutionary changes were afoot in 1853. Railway development had but begun—a few miles at Bombay. At least, according to Marx, the British were "laying down the material premises" for emancipation and social improvement: "They intend now drawing a net of railroads over India. And they will do it. The results are incalculable". This laying of the foun-

[23] W. G. East and O. H. K. Spate (eds.), *The Changing Map of Asia* (1950), 125.

dations of a modern state in India was the historic task of the British Raj, however blindly, and sometimes reluctantly, carried out.[24]

Nevertheless, after the EIC lost its trading function in 1833, it stagnated in a *laissez-faire* world, improving its administration, but doing little else: the heroic age was over with the defeat of the Sikhs. Into this Indian summer crashed the tremendous thunderstorm of the 1857 Mutiny.

Uniting, if imperfectly, the most diverse factions, it was complex in its proximate origins: resentment at Dalhousie's high-handed 'doctrine of lapse', whereby several states had passed to the Company in default of male heirs but in disregard of Hindu adoption law; the grievances of the landowners of Oudh, which had recently been annexed on account of the chronic misgovernment of its rulers; the famous scandal of the greased cartridges. Yet perhaps at bottom it was simply the last rally of the old indigenous India, a gigantic protest against a revolution from above and to the profit of an alien race. Delhi—significantly on historic and geographical grounds—was the major storm-centre. It ended in the death of one Empire and the birth of another. The last Mogul, Bahadur Shah, a blind old poet hardly understanding his proclamation by the mutineers, was taken to Rangoon to die; the discredited Company was superseded by the direct rule of the Crown when Queen Victoria was proclaimed Empress of India in 1858.

Nationalism

The first 50 years of the Empire saw much material change—the spread of railways and telegraphs, the initiation of great irrigation works; the cotton boom of the American Civil War years (1861–65) gave an impetus to commercial speculation; the Suez Canal (1869) brought England and India nearer [25]; large sectors of the peasantry were now tied to the world market. Yet it was possible to maintain that the fundamentals of Indian life and society had changed little, beneath the surface layer of public works, though in two directions forces of great significance were stirring. The necessity of staffing an enormous administrative machine led to the production of a vast clerical army trained (however inadequately) in Western techniques, and far too large to be profitably employed: hence the frustration of the unemployed intellectual, and the schizophrenia of those no longer believing in the old gods, yet with no secure place in the new world.[26] And by the turn

[24] See pp. 180–94 of *A Handbook of Marxism* (1935); a vigorous and astonishingly acute analysis. Lest Marx's attack should seem overdrawn, cf. the even more severe contemporary judgements of Sleeman and Lawrence (both British officials) cited in L. S. S. O'Malley (ed.), *Modern India and the West* (1941), 76–77.

[25] And, by facilitating the coming of English wives and the development of more exclusively English social life, contributed to detach the English in India yet further from their subjects. The old officials were not infrequently kept in good touch with Indian feeling by alliances, temporary or permanent, with Indian mistresses.

[26] On this, see G. Wint, *The British in India* (1947), (a most acute analysis); L. S. S. O'Malley, *op. cit.*, 763–97; East and Spate, *op. cit.*, 25–29.

of the century a vigorous capitalist class was growing, as yet industrially weak, almost confined to the cotton mills of Bombay and Ahmedabad, but conscious of potentialities and girding at fiscal restraint in the interests of Lancashire. These provided the sinews of war, the intellectuals the ideology, the young men of the urban middle-class (and increasingly the town workers) the rank and file; and at times sections of the peasantry gave massive weight to the attack. The Indian National Congress travelled fast from its innocuous beginnings in 1885; and in 1905 the Japanese victory over Russia ended the automatic acceptance of European invincibility.

This nationalism began in the 90s with Tilak's appeal to Maratha traditions and gained strength from the agitation against Curzon's partition of Bengal in 1905. It was thus largely Hindu in tone, and after the collapse of the Hindu-Muslim united front in defence of the Caliphate in 1921 this bias was on the whole strengthened by the ideology of Mahatma Gandhi. The distress and disturbances of the years after 1914–18, culminating in the appalling bloodshed at Amritsar in 1919, and the great mass Civil Disobedience movement of 1931, showed that the temper of articulate India was far ahead of the reforms which seemed doled out in niggardly instalments. In 1937, however, Congress decided to work, at least temporarily, within the 1935 Constitution, and Congress governments in 9 major provinces gained valuable experience and showed both the potentialities and the limitations of constitutionalism. The automatic entry of India into the war in 1939 without consultation with Congress led to a decisive breach; and the Japanese successes of 1941–42, bringing them to the very borders of India, gave point to the dictum (whether or not Gandhi uttered it) that the Cripps promise of Dominion status (with right of secession) was "a post-dated cheque on a failing bank". At the same time Congress blunders, the communal struggle for patronage, resentment of the fact that the numerical majority controlled an ever greater share of the economic life of the country, fed Muslim separatism.[27] At the end of the war two things were inescapably clear: British rule could by no possibility be said to retain or to be able to regain the consent of the governed, and could be maintained only at the cost, unthinkable morally and materially, of a 'super-Palestine'; and no settlement within a single state could meet the demands of the Muslim League, which now represented the political mass of Muslims. The Gordian knot was cut by the British Government, and on August 15th, 1947, the Dominions of *India* and Pakistan came into their inheritance. On January 26th, 1950, the *Indian Union* declared itself a Republic within the British Commonwealth. By one of history's oddest ironies the fragments of

---

[27] For a full discussion see O. H. K. Spate, "Geographical Aspects of the Pakistan Scheme", *GJ* CII (1943), 125–35; and "The Partition of India and the Prospects of Pakistan", *GR* XXXVIII (1948), 5–29.

Portuguese and French dominion survived their mighty supplanter the British Raj.

BIBLIOGRAPHICAL NOTE

General

The standard large work is *The Cambridge History of India*, which is incomplete and uneven: Vol. I *Ancient India* (1922) is comprehensive but out of date; Vols. III (*Turks and Afghans* (1928)) and IV (*The Mughal Empire* (1937)) disappointingly dynastic. Vols. V (*British India 1497–1858*) and VI (*The Indian Empire 1858–1918*) (which are also issued as Vols. IV and V of *The Cambridge History of the British Empire*) are full but naturally 'official' in temper. The first volume of a new and most comprehensive Indian work has appeared: R. C. Majumdar, *The Vedic Age* (1951). This is likely to supersede the older histories.

Of shorter works, *The Cambridge Shorter History of India* (1934) is compressed to dullness; J. Nehru, *The Discovery of India* (1946) is a highly stimulating nationalist corrective. But the best academic treatment, at once full and balanced, is R. C. Majumdar, H. Raychaudhuri, and K. Datta, *An Advanced History of India* (1946).

C. C. Davies, *An Historical Atlas of the Indian Peninsula* (1949) has useful maps and brief but acute notes.

Two admirable cultural surveys are H. G. Rawlinson, *India: A Short Cultural History* (1937) and G. T. Garratt (ed.), *The Legacy of India* (1937).

Special Topics

Early India. E. Mackay, *Early Indus Civilisations* (1948 ed.); but knowledge is advancing rapidly, and periodicals such as *Ancient India* (Govt. Publications, ND) and *Antiquity* are essential. S. Pigott's *Prehistoric India* (Pelican, 1950) is a most admirable survey.

Early External Contacts. H. G. Rawlinson, *Intercourse between India and the Western World* (1917); E. Warmington, *The Commerce between the Roman Empire and India* (1928); W. W. Tarn, *The Greeks in Bactria and India* (1936); K. M. Panikkar, *India and the Indian Ocean* (1945); J. Poujade, *La Route des Indes et ses Navires* (Paris, Payot, 1946).

The Discoveries and After. For the fascinating Portuguese phase, the biographies of Elaine Sanceau are lively as well as scholarly: *Indies Adventure* (1936; Albuquerque) and *Knight of the Renaissance* (n.d., ?1949; de Castro). In Portuguese J. Gonçalves, *Os Portugueses e o Mar das Indias* (Livraria Luso-Espanhola, Lisboa, 1947) has an even broader sweep than its title, including a stimulating survey of the earlier Indian history. For the early days of the EIC, see Sir John Foster, *England's Quest of Eastern Trade* (1933).

The 17th century travels and adventures of Bernier, Tavernier, and Manucci are exceedingly good reading in themselves and throw much light on social conditions. W. H. Moreland's books are essential economic history: *India at the Death of Akbar* (1920) and *From Akbar to Aurengzeb* (1923). The economic and social history of other periods is attracting much attention in India but is as yet unsynthesised.

I.P.—6*

The British Period. Works on this subject are often tendentious, and it is obviously too early for any standard view to be formed. G. T. Garratt and E. Thompson, *The Rise and Fulfilment of British Rule in India* (1934) is an illuminating account of the formative period; Nehru's *The Discovery of India* is probably the best strictly nationalist presentation.

On the states, J. Tod's classic *Annals and Antiquities of Rajasthan* (OUP ed., 1914) gives a lively picture of the whirl of war and intrigue, not without redeeming features, which characterises so much Indian history. More important is E. Thompson, *The Making of the Indian Princes* (1943), which brings out the relatively upstart origins of most of them.

For the origins of Pakistan, ideological and political, see W. C. Smith, *Modern Islam in India* (1946), and R. Symonds, *The Making of Pakistan* (1950).

For the general Asian background, R. Payne, *The Revolt of Asia* (1948), and G. Wint, *The British in Asia* (1947), should be read; the latter is the most thoughtful analysis I have seen.

CHAPTER VII

VILLAGE AND TOWN IN INDIA

I. THE INDIAN VILLAGE

OF the 658,595 inhabited localities of India in 1941, some 654,000 had under 5000 people and no fewer than 450,902 under 500. Settlements of under 5000 held 315,000,000 souls—81% of the All-India population. Some general remarks on the villages and their life seem desirable, although settlement patterns, house-types, and so on are treated in some detail in the regional chapters.

The Village in General

The great majority of the country folk live in small or large nucleated settlements, and areas of dispersed habitations are few: the Himalayan zone is perhaps the only extensive area of true dispersal, of the type found in European highlands; elsewhere, even in the hills, the normal unit is the small hamlet rather than the homestead. In the arid W this is enforced partly by the paucity of water-points, partly by the needs of defence—still visibly attested by the watch-towers of Pathan villages. In the Assam-Burma Ranges defence is also an important factor: villages are on hilltops or spurs, often stockaded; it must be remembered that in these jungly hills the valleys are extremely malarial, and that communication is easiest along relatively open ridgeways. Bengal—especially the En delta—is *sui generis*: there is indeed much settlement that is not nucleated, but "dispersal" appears an exceedingly inappropriate term for the dense stipple of separate homesteads, hardly isolated except in the most literal sense of the word when, during the rains, each is an island on its little earthen plinth.[1] Other more or less dispersed zones are found in the Konkan, in areas of recent or temporary reclamation by squatters in the Assam jungles, or in the great floodplains by farmers using the rich khadar for high-value crops after the rains. But in both groups the very small hamlet—say 6 to 12 huts—is the rule, rather than true dispersal; and in the latter case the huts are often only temporary, inhabited during the dry weather by people normally resident in big villages on the bluffs above.

These are anomalies: in the great homogeneous plains nucleation is almost invariable. In the past defence played its part, and in areas open to constant disturbance (e.g. the Sutlej/Jumna and Jumna/Ganges Doabs, Rohilkhand, the fringes of Central India, Khandesh, the Raichur Doab)

[1] See J. C. Jack, *The Economic Life of a Bengal District* (1916), 16–38; and below, Figs. 104 and 105.

villages are often grouped around a petty fort; and even to-day the close-packed houses, with blank outer walls and low doorways, massed into a ring with few entrances, present a defensive aspect. Often there is not much in the way of site selection; one place is as good as another, and the village rises are as often as not their own creation, the rubbish of generations. But any discontinuity, any break in the almost imperceptible slope, produces linear settlement patterns: especially notable are the bluffs above flood-plains and the margins of abandoned river courses. The bluff villages tend to be larger than those on the drier interfluves; they have the advantage of two types of terrain, the upland doab and the valley-bottom with its tamarisk brakes and the excellent soil of its *chars* or *diaras*—the floodplain islands—submerged in the rains and liable to disappear completely in floods, but cropping up again sooner or later. These alluviated areas are often given over to cash crops of high value; near large towns they are often used for market gardens, easily irrigated by wells taking advantage of the high water-table.

Settlement lines tend to occur also at the marked break of slope where steep residual hills grade into a fan, which has usually a fairly high water-table. Lateritic shelves along deltaic margins are also important building sites, poor in themselves but offering rough grazing, scrubby woodland (the source of a great range of minor necessities from timber to illicit alcohol), and providing space for dry crops, the flats below being entirely given over to paddy. They form as it were neutral ground between the jungly hills and the waterlogged paddy-plain. Here not only the general arrangement of settlements but also the village itself is often linear; islands of lateritic and older alluvium in the deltas are often completely ringed with houses. Linear settlement is also, of course, prominent in the deltas and wider floodplains themselves, strung out along levees or artificial embankments, and in places (e.g. Kerala and the Contai area of SW Bengal) along old beach ridges. Very often such sites are the only dry points in the rains and the only water-points in the hot weather.[2]

There is in general very little that looks like a "plan", other than that dictated by such site factors as alignment along bluffs or levees, grouping round a fort or a tank; but within the seemingly chaotic agglomeration there is, as a rule, a strong internal differentiation, that of the separate quarters for various castes.

A Village in Detail (Figs. 34 and 35)

These points are best brought out by a close view of a specific village, not indeed 'typical' (no single village could be that) but certainly the most

[2] For analogues cf. G. T. Trewartha, *Japan* (1945), Figs. 64 and 68; E. H. G. Dobby, "Settlement Patterns in Malaya", *GR* XXXII (1942); O. H. K. Spate, "The Burmese Village", *GR* XXXV (1945).

random of samples.[3] Our example is in the Deccan, more precisely in the Bombay Karnatak.

Aminbhavi lies seven miles NNE of Dharwar; an old settlement, going back at least thirteen centuries, originally walled and moated. Essentially its site is governed by the junction of the Dharwar rocks, forming poor red soils around the mosque-crowned hill to the W, with the crystallines which have weathered into deep black cotton soils in the E. It is a typical black soil agricultural village, with a rainfall of about 24 ins., devoted mainly to dry crops (cotton, jowar, wheat, pulses, safflower, in that order), tending to become a satellite of Dharwar, the market of its dairy and agricultural produce. On the poorer land to the W is rough grazing, supporting a few shepherds, and immediately W of the village the common or *gauthana*, an essential part of its economy, the centre of all harvesting.

Caste and community largely govern the layout. Of its 4106 inhabitants, Lingayats, the sturdy agricultural caste of the Karnatak, number some 2650. Next come 550 Muslims, an unusually high proportion, but the place was of some importance in the days of the Bijapur Kingdom, and the first element in its name is indeed that of some forgotten Muslim (Aminbhavi roughly = Amin's Well). But the culturally dominant groups are the Jains (250) and the Brahmins (75); this is an *Inam* (landlord) village, most of it belonging to the Desai (Jain) and Deshpande (Brahmin) families, whose *wadas* (more or less equivalent to manor houses) stand on the best sites, within large compounds. The Desais provide the village *patel* or headman. For the rest, each caste tends to occupy a solid block of contiguous houses in a lane named from the caste; where, as with the Lingayats, several lanes are occupied, each is named from the leading family residing in it. Besides those mentioned, there are 300 Talwars (domestic servants and agricultural labourers), 200 Harijans ("untouchables"), and smaller groups of other low castes: Wadars (quarrymen), Shikalgars (backward semi-nomadic casual labourers), washermen, and so on. These groups live on the circumference of the village, or even beyond the old moat. (Fig. 34.)

Occupations likewise are still mainly on a caste basis: the Lingayats provide the bulk of the tenant-farmers, Talwars and Harijans landless agricultural labour; carpenters, smiths, cobblers, washermen, barbers are all separate castes. Apart from these crafts and agriculture, there is some handloom cotton weaving, a subsidiary occupation of the Lingayats.

Houses are generally built on to each other, or at least the mud walls of the compounds are continuous. The house layout (Fig. 35) is as standard

[3] The coincidence of the writing of this chapter and a correspondence with Mr. C. D. Deshpande of Dharwar led me to appeal to him for a sample survey; the choice was left entirely to him. Nothing could be more random and free from preconceived choice. I am deeply indebted to Mr. Deshpande and his students for the very full and admirable maps, photographs and notes on which this section is entirely based. For the general setting, see 655–61 below.

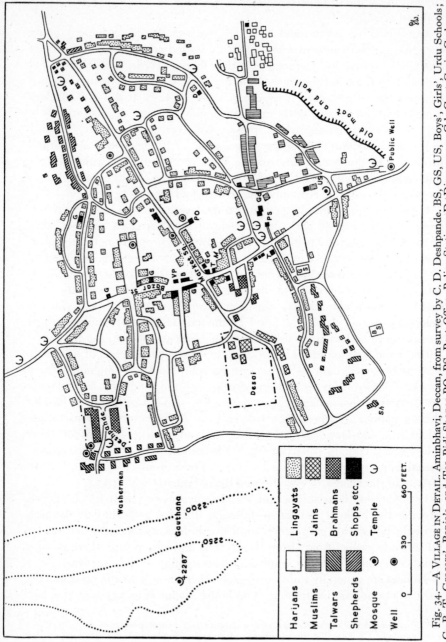

Fig. 34.—A Village in Detail. Aminbhavi, Deccan, from survey by C. D. Deshpande. BS, GS, US, Boys', Girls', Urdu Schools; G, B, T, Grocers', Bania's, and Tea-Bidi Shops; PO, PS, Post Office, Police Station; D, Dispensary; Gd, Govt Grain Godown; VP, Village Panchayat; M, Lingayat Math; Sh, Shikalgars.

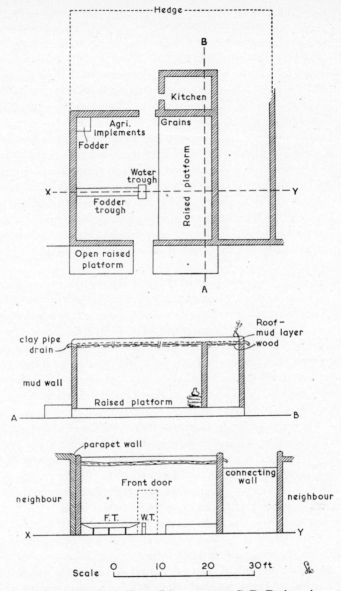

Scale

Fig. 35.—AMINBHAVI HOUSE PLAN; courtesy C. D. Deshpande.

as in any English working-class street. In front is a porch (*katte*), used for drying agricultural produce, as a formal reception room, as "a place of female gossip when the master of the house is out", and above all as a sleeping-room in the stifling summer nights. Behind this is the main room, some 25 ft square, part of which is a cattle pen, at threshold level; the remainder, raised some 2 or 3 ft, is the general living-room, for sleeping, eating, more intimate entertainment of guests, and perhaps handi-crafts. The most prominent object is the pile of grain stored in gunny bags and sadly depleted towards the end of the agricultural year. Behind is a separate kitchen (with a corner for the bath) and the backyard with manure-pit and haystacks. This is the standard pattern; construction is similar in all groups (except the lowest), differences in economic status being reflected merely in size, except that the well-to-do have more separate single-purpose rooms. Jains and Brahmins do not live so tightly packed as the rest, either in the spacing of the houses or within them.

The poorest castes live in wretched one-room wattle huts with thatched roofs. Apart from these all houses have walls 1 or 2 ft thick of mudbrick, with few (and high) or more likely no windows: Indians in general have a doubtless well-founded burglar-phobia. The flat roof is supported by wooden posts and made of mud on a framework of crude beams and babul (acacia) branches; they have rounded mud parapets and clay rain-water pipes.

As for services, these are mostly grouped around the main village lane: market-place for the weekly bazaar, eight shops (four grocery, two cloth, one tailor, one miscellaneous) and a number of booths selling tea and *bidis*, the cheap crude cigarettes of the Indian masses. Near the market-place is the room of the village *panchayat* or caste council, an ancient institution generally fallen into desuetude but now being fostered as the first step in local government. Associated with this tiny 'urban core' are the govern-ment establishments—Police Station, Post Office, grain warehouse. There are three mosques, one giving its name to the Idgah hill in the W, and eight temples, including that of the Deshpandes, as well as the Lingayat *math*, a centre of religious and charitable fellowship. The professions are repre-sented by an Ayurvedic (indigenous) dispensary, an Urdu school for the Muslims, and separate schools for boys and girls. The boys' school is the most modern building in Aminbhavi, its stone walls and red-tiled roof standing in sharp contrast to the monotony of mud walls.

Finally we may note the large masonry-lined public well, sunk in what was once the moat; it is no mean excavation, an apt reminder of the all-importance of water-supply in Indian life.

Once more, no one village can be typical of the whole sub-continent; but many of the features detailed above can be paralleled over and over again in most parts of India. Our random sample is at least very representa-tive.

The Village: its Aspect and Life

The aspect of the village varies not only with the general regional setting, with building materials and house-types, but with social factors. The generally greater emphasis on caste in the S takes social fragmentation allied with spatial separation to the extreme, segregating the untouchables in outlying *cheris* or sub-villages, sometimes located several hundred yards from the main villages of which they are service-components. This is indeed the climax of geographical differentiation; *apartheid*. A typical *cheri* may consist of two rows of huts with a narrow central "street"; in the middle this widens to make room for a tiny temple.[4] The huts have thick mud walls, roofed with palmyra thatch, and low mud porches scrupulously swept. To enter one must bend double; the only light comes from the door and from under the eaves, and the furniture consists of a few pots and pans, a couple of wooden chests, and the essential paddy-bin, 4 to 6 ft high and 3 to 4 in diameter, raised from the ground to escape the rats, and built up of hoops of mud. Poor as they are, these dwellings are yet homes, and obviously loved as such: their cleanliness, the surrounding mangoes, coconut and palmyra palms, redeem them from utter squalor. The nadir is reached in the bustees of Calcutta and the revolting camps of casual tribal labour found on the outskirts of the larger towns: shelters (they cannot be called even huts) of matting, of rags, of petrol tins beaten flat, on waste spaces open to the sun and reeking with filth.

A geographical study of Indian house-types (Fig. 36) would be a work vast in scope and rich in instruction; a few of the more striking instances are mentioned in the regional chapters.[5] Social factors are no less important than environmental, at least once we go beyond the fundamental antithesis of the NW (or SW Asia) type and the thatched gable of the more humid areas. Not only the site and layout of the village, but the 'geography of the house' often reflects age-old religious and magical traditions: the round huts of some lower castes in Telangana, with bold vertical stripes of white and rusty red, are clearly culturally rather than geographically influenced. At the other extreme from the rude massive huts of Bundelkhand we have the elaborate courtyard house of the richer UP farmer, with some pretensions to elegance—the survival of decayed traditions—in doorways and arcading. Some Indian domestic building indeed reaches a high standard of artistry: the carved timber of Kumaon or of the small towns of the Konkan, the restrained but excellent brick details and the very pleasant white bungalow-style houses, with low gables of semi-cylindrical tiles, found in small Maharashtra towns. Environmental influence is well seen in the flat-roofed blank-walled box standard in the Punjab and Wn UP—so strongly reminiscent of arid SW Asia, and fitting so well into the four-square planned villages of the Canal Colonies. Against these may be set the Bengal house, matting-walled, with thatched gables pitched high to shed

[4] Often put up by the pre-war Congress provincial governments as a concession: in 1943 one such had been decorated by the children with ARP signs.
[5] The most comprehensive survey for a large area I have seen is Enayat Ahmed's unpublished London Ph.D. thesis, "Settlement in the United Provinces" (1948).

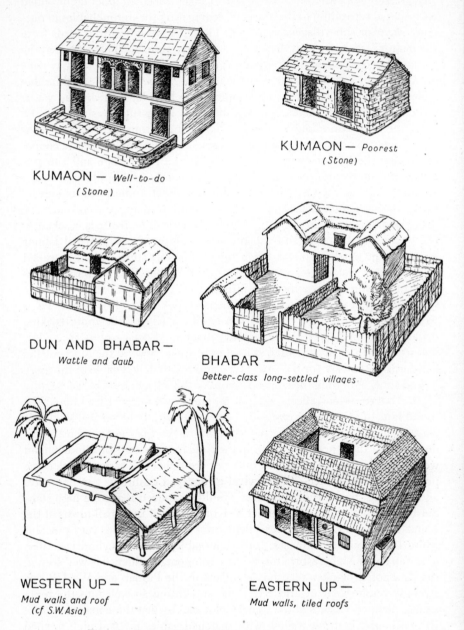

KUMAON — *Well-to-do*
(*Stone*)

KUMAON — *Poorest*
(*Stone*)

DUN AND BHABAR —
Wattle and daub

BHABAR —
Better-class long-settled villages

WESTERN UP —
Mud walls and roof
(*cf S.W. Asia*)

EASTERN UP —
Mud walls, tiled roofs

Fig. 36.—Some N Indian House Types. Redrawn by Marjory Fowler from

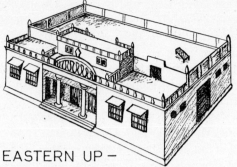

EASTERN UP —
Well-to-do, masonry

EASTERN UP —
Poorest, mud walls, tiles

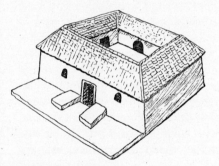

BUNDELKHAND —
Mud walls, tiled

BUNDELKHAND —
Stone, stone slab roofs

BENGAL (CONTAI) —
*Well-to-do, bamboo and thatch
on mud plinth. Double roof*

BENGAL — *Poorest,
Bamboo . thatch*

illustrations in theses by E. Ahmad and B. Mukerjee (see Bibliographical Note).

179

the rain and ingeniously designed to take the strain of cyclonic gales. In Madras "we see flat-roofed stone houses in the Ceded Districts (Deccan), so constructed as to protect the dwellers from the severe heat of the sun, the rocks and slabs locally available being used. In contrast we find in Malabar timber entering into the construction. Here the buildings are on high ground and have sloping roofs, both necessitated by the high rainfall. . . . In the Tamilnad we have tiled brick houses with open courtyards, reflecting an equable climate and moderate rainfall".[6]

As for what life in the Indian village is really like, who knows save the Indian villager? A few officials like M. L. Darling, whose Punjab rural rides compare with Cobbett's, a few devoted social workers, Indian and European, Christian and otherwise. But even then there is the difference between living in the village from cradle to grave (or burning-ghat), and living in the village with a territorial—and social and psychological—base outside. The alien may perhaps glean something from that rich harvest of salty rural proverbs (a comparative anthology of them would be fascinating) which are as vital a part of India's cultural heritage as the lyrical and metaphysical visions of her sages. Not that this latter strain of culture is absent from the village: the great epics *Ramayana* and *Mahabharata* pass from lip to lip in folk-versions, to some extent at least every man is his own poet, and not a few of the noblest figures in India's predominantly devotional literature sprang from the village rather than the schools: Kabir the Weaver, Tukaram. The things that strike the outsider, then, are not perhaps ultimately the most important: the flies and the sores, the shrill clamour of gaunt pi-dogs, the primitive implements, the utter lack of sanitation.[7]

At its worst the Indian village is infinitely depressing: in the plains where so much ground is cultivated that the scanty village site cannot grow with its growing population, or where a few miserable huts cling to shadeless stony rises in the drier parts of central India or the Archaean Deccan. Yet cheerfulness keeps breaking in, in the most unfavourable circumstances; fatalist as he is and must be, the peasant often displays an astonishing resilience and refuses to be broken by his often bitterly hard geographical and social environment. And over much of the land the villages have their amenities, even their beauties: in the plains and deltas they rise out of the sea of cultivation, emerald or gold or drab grey in the stubble season, like dark green islands, shaded in mango or orange trees, tamarinds, bamboos, palms. The tank or the well, the shade of the great banyan or the porch of

[6] K. M. Subrahmanyam, "Four Main House Types in South India", *JMGA* XIII (1938), 168–75.
[7] Whence the richer crops on fields immediately adjacent to the village; a difference officially recognised in land revenue assessment. In Burma the villagers arrange these things better, though the results of following a too well-trodden path into the jungle may be as embarrassing as the more casual ways of India.

the headman's hut, are essentially free clubs for the women and the menfolk respectively. Though the substratum of life—the gruelling round of the seasons—remains and will ever remain the same, though a miserable livelihood exacts an exorbitant price in endless toil, there have been great changes, material and psychological, since Edwin Montagu, Secretary of State for India, spoke in 1918 of the "pathetic contentment" of the Indian village. Pathetic it still too often is; contented, less and less; which is as it should be. "These idyllic village communities confined the human mind within the narrowest possible compass."[8] This is overstated; there *were* the epics and the proverbs; but the horizons were far too narrow for a full life. Now new motifs are changing the tempo of life in the large villages: perhaps a radio, perhaps a mobile film unit, more and more frequently a school. The mass movements launched by Congress have not always been amenable to a thus-far-and-no-farther policy: the peasant has other enemies than British imperialism, and Congress taught him organisation. All are helping to break down the isolation and lack of information which rendered the villager so helpless a prey to the moneylender, the retailer, and the grain-broker—often all three being one and the same person. Perhaps the most powerful agent of change is the battered, ramshackle motor-bus, packed to the running-board and coughing its way through clouds of dust along the unmetalled roads to the nearest town. There may be loss as well as gain in all this; but it is idle to bewail the break-up of integrated codes of life—too often integrated by religious, social, and economic sanctions which were a complete denial of human dignity. In any case the disintegration set in long ago, with the impact of the world market; and it is high time that new horizons should be opened, that the villager should see whence the forces that have subverted his old life have their origins, and what of good they may bring.

II. THE INDIAN TOWN

Some General Characteristics

Urbanisation is considered demographically in Ch. IV; the greater cities receive separate treatment in the regional chapters. There would be little point in classifying the towns of India and finding that after all they occupy similar positions and perform similar functions as do their compeers in the rest of the world. The fossil stronghold and the place of pilgrimage are perhaps commoner than in most countries: Carcassonne and Lourdes occur over and over again. The purely railway town is common, as in N

[8] K. Marx, cited in *A Handbook of Marxism* (1935), 186. The analysis here is remarkably vigorous and acute, and it is notable that—whatever motives he assigns—Marx pays full tribute to the potentialities of social change arising from British rule: "The question is [and remains], can mankind fulfil its destiny without a fundamental revolution in the social state of Asia? If not, whatever may have been the crimes of England, she was the unconscious tool of history in bringing about that revolution."

America. The most distinctive Indian contributions to modern urbanism are the hill station and the cantonment: but even these have their analogues elsewhere.

It would also be possible to describe the aspect, function, and morphology of a hypothetical generalised town: but its characterisation would certainly be inadequate to convey the real richness of the Indian urban scene. It seems more profitable and interesting to examine in some detail four scattered and very diverse towns which the writer knows at first hand. Before doing so, however, it may be as well to make some points of general application which are in fact largely specific to the towns of India.

1. **The Agrarian Setting.** It hardly needs stressing that the great majority of 'census towns' have still very strong agricultural elements within them; this holds, at the very least, for the 2329 towns (out of the total of 2703 in 1941) which have less than 20,000 inhabitants. The smaller ones are indeed little more than large market villages, with some very local administrative functions added; perhaps two or three central streets inadequately paved and lighted give the semblance of an urban *cachet*. Even in so large a city as Agra herds of dairy buffaloes are driven out in the morning, back in the evening 'hour of cow-dust'.

2. **Administrative Uniformity.** A large number of the towns are primarily administrative; they may have been local commercial centres and market villages picked as headquarters of Districts or their sub-divisions mainly on account of centrality. For the most part these have a strikingly uniform cast, owing to the alien and hierarchical character of the administration of British India: the artificiality of the territorial division can be seen from the fact that at least 192 of the 224 Districts of British India have been named from the chief town. The same official buildings occur; the architecture [9] of the Public Works Department is standard practically everywhere, and Economy has obviously been the watchword.

3. **Building Types.** These, of course, vary with local materials and traditions; but there are certain very widespread features, ancient and modern. Of the former the bazaar streets with open booths raised 2 or 3 ft above the pavement are typical. Middle-class Hindu town residences tend to have a verandah-plinth on the street, perhaps pillared, perhaps a mere recess between the party walls; there is usually room for a rope bedstead or two, used for daytime lounging and at night by the *durwan* or watchman. By the door is a little recess for a light; sometimes this is virtually a tiny shrine, but often it has degenerated into a vestigial niche, too shallow to perform its original function. On the modern side, new shopping areas are strikingly similar: box-like concrete shops-cum-houses, with cast concrete balustrades and so on. The glaring whiteness is often offset by pastel colours, very sensibly in view of the noonday dazzle. The monotonous

[9] Courtesy title.

architecture of the Public Works Department has been touched on; the railways are sometimes more imaginative, but with results often even more disastrous, until really ambitious efforts like Bombay's Victoria Terminus can hardly be described as other than Indo-Saracenic-Byzantine-Italo-Gothic-Baroque.

4. Incomplete Internal Differentiation. Most Indian cities (and large sections of even the greatest of them) have not separated residential and other functions to the same extent as Occidental towns. Well-to-do merchants still live over their shops and offices; and a large proportion of day-to-day consumer needs is still met by artisans living or working in tiny shops at street corners or in the bazaar area. Very often, as in mediaeval Europe, all of one trade will live in one or two adjoining streets [10]: this, of course, links up with caste segregation. But differentiation by class and wealth is also not so advanced—on the whole—as in the West: of course in the Civil Lines and similar areas there will be very few poor people other than domestic servants, and at the other extreme there are homogeneous slums; but in the older and more indigenous parts of the towns opulence and indigence often live cheek by jowl.

5. Community Quarters. Yet if the separation of work from residence often hardly exists, there is a very strong tendency (at all levels from village to metropolis) for members of each religious community, caste, or race to live together. This is only to be expected in the general social context of India. Notable examples are the *pols* of Ahmedabad (see below, 605) and the Parsee housing estates of Bombay; and where there are very large numbers of Chinese, as in Calcutta, there is a Chinatown—as indeed happens universally. In Rangoon (till 1937 technically, and in large part socially, an Indian city) one ward, Taroktan (which means literally Chinatown) had nearly all the Chinese, and was itself over 50% Chinese.

6. Western Elements: Cantonments, Civil Lines, Railway Colonies. The British in India as it were fused this communal separatism with their own emphasis on class. Large Indian cities generally consist of two entirely distinct areas [11]: the old Indian city, a squalid but picturesque confusion, and the monotonously planned open-developed town of European-style bungalows in large gardens along straight, broad roads, aloof and boring in a high degree, and absolutely dead in the heat of the day. These two are very often separated by the railway which—in some cases apparently by design—forms a broad barrier with few crossings: the motivation of 'internal security' is obvious. The 'Civil Lines' contain the official

[10] The sojourner in India is well advised to seek these out: prices are often about one-third of those for the same goods, made by the same men, but sold in European-style shops.

[11] Whence no small confusion in the Census figures: population may be for the Municipality, the Cantonment, or both together. The height of absurdity is reached when a town of say 10–12,000 people, of whom only 6 or 8 are Europeans, is described as having a "native quarter".

residences of the local bureaucracy and such hangers-on as the more flourishing lawyers; architecture is European, with an interesting climatically induced variation: absence of chimneys (except in the NW) and presence of a carriage-porch, essential in the rains. The European population is now generally very small indeed. The Railway Colony is generally planned on a far less generous scale, but on mathematically rectilinear lines. The Cantonments explain themselves; but they generally had a little Indian enclave, the bazaar to serve the needs, material and sometimes other, of the troops: this was necessary as for the most obvious reasons the Indian city was strictly Out of Bounds.

Generally the cultural divide made by the railway lines is sharp; but sometimes there is a transitional zone, as in the Mall and Anarkali Bazaar at Lahore: here are European and European-style shops, banks, offices, cinemas, some official buildings, and a variety of places of resort, from the first-class (in price at least) hotel to the seedy bar, in bounds to troops, but only just in.[12]

Four Representative Towns

We may now consider our four towns: in order of antiquity (which is approximately the order from S to N) Conjeeveram, Poona, Qadian, and Simla. They form a good sample from several points of view: the geographical scatter is wide, Tamilnad, Deccan, Punjab, sub-Himalaya; two are well-known and typically Indo-British, two of much less note and representing almost solid Hindu and Muslim communities. They include a minor commercial and religious town, Conjeeveram; a great military, administrative and educational centre, Poona; the queen of hill stations, Simla; and in Qadian the headquarters of a religious sect. Qadian is at once unique but typical, since the particular ruling group is unique, but the phenomenon itself is not uncommon: one interesting example is Chettinad in Madras, seat of the remarkable Chettiar banking caste whose children lisp in numbers and accounts, inheriting a tradition of business acumen which enabled them to dominate indigenous finance and actually secure control of about one-third of the ricelands in Lower Burma.

Conjeeveram (Fig. 37)

Conjeeveram, 40 miles SW of Madras on the Palar River, lies in a gently undulating countryside, paddy-floored bottoms and lateritic rises largely under poor grass and scrub. Agriculture is largely dependent on tanks; Conjeeveram lies in the heart of the Pallava kingdom (4th–9th centuries AD) and many of the larger masonry-bonded tanks were built by the Pallava kings, whose engineers had an uncanny flair for detecting the slightest usable drainage-line.

[12] Many of the points in this section are illustrated in O. H. K. Spate and Enayat Ahmad, "Five Cities of the Gangetic Plain", *GR* XL (1950), 260–78.

It is a fairly widespread town of 74,365 people; a market for the agricultural produce of its *umland*, with some hand industry, notably the weaving of silk saris; pottery, basketry, and bamboo crafts are also carried on. But it is far more famous as a religious centre, anciently Kanchipuram, the shining or golden city; popular tradition assigns it a thousand temples,

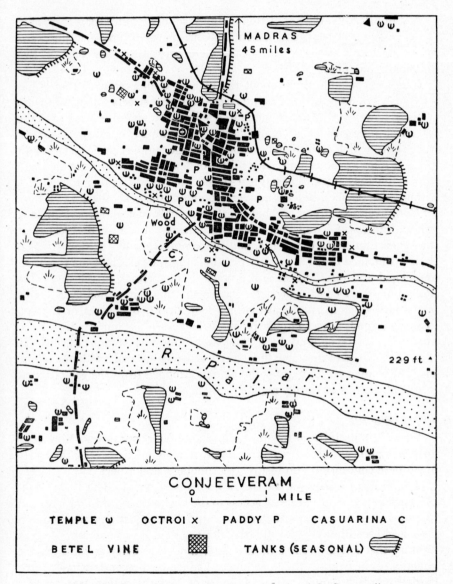

Fig. 37.—CONJEEVERAM. Heavy broken lines are main roads. Surrounding country mainly paddy; streams seasonal; courtesy SOI.

not without exaggeration: indeed the thousand pillars of the great hall in the Sivaite Ekambaranath temple are really only 540. But the great temples —largely dating from Vijayanagar times—are very impressive indeed, culminating in the lofty many-storeyed *gopurams* or gate-pyramids, covered with innumerable sculptured figures. There are also ancient Jain and Buddhist associations.

Not unnaturally, the population is almost solidly Hindu: there were only 3,452 Muslims in 1941, and 600 Indian Christians, with more in the *cheris* of surrounding villages; Europeans were represented by one or two missionary families.

The most notable thing about the plan of Conjeeveram is that it has obviously got one: the town is intersected by great streets some 60 ft wide. This is, however, due not so much to *a priori* town planning ideas as to the practical necessity of accommodating the crowds, numbering several thousands, which on festival days haul the huge temple cars. The largest of these is some 50–60 ft high, with solid wooden wheels 10 or 12 ft high and proportionately thick. These great streets are found in other towns with similar observances, but are not very common; the general aspect and life of Conjeeveram's streets are, however, thoroughly typical. Houses are low, with white-washed walls, roofs of several layers of semi-cylindrical tiles, the usual thin-pillared porches, and the lamp-niches by the doors: when well-maintained they have a very pleasing appearance. There are the usual municipal and *taluk* offices and schools, built of brick in the invariable Public Works Department style. Passenger transport is mainly by light carts with a semi-cylindrical matting roof, drawn by ponies or trotting bullocks; goods travel largely by pack-donkeys. The importance of the motor-bus is recognised by a large, well-built bus station; during the war, with its petrol shortage, the poverty of India was brought home by the sight of women scrabbling for the cinders dropped from the gas-charcoal plants of the buses. Hardly a golden city now.

Poona (Fig. 38)

Poona is in itself by far the most important of our four towns. As such its general significance is more appropriately treated in Ch. XXIII; the treatment here concentrates on history, morphology, and aspect.

The primary reason for the rise of Poona is historical. The Bhor Ghat, 48 miles to the NW, gives easy access to the lowlands around Bombay, and the town is now an important road centre. But almost any site between Poona and the Bhor Ghat would have done as well. It was not until the 17th century that Poona became of any note, though as early as the 13th the sanctity of the Mutha-Mula confluence had led to the construction of two fairly important temples. Sivaji, founder of Maratha power, was brought up in this poor *jagir* (fief) of his grandfather, an obscure Hindu noble in the service of the Ahmadnagar sultan; but his own capital was at Rajgarh, 30 miles to the S, a typical site on the saddle between the bases of Maratha power in the Konkan and the Deccan. Poona did not become the capital until 1735.[13] Thereafter for nearly a century it was the seat of whatever central authority the Maratha confederacy possessed; their decisive overthrow by the British took place across the river at Kirkee in 1817. The core of the city is the old Maratha capital; to it have been added the great Cantonments and the even more military suburb of Kirkee; these form three distinct units. Of the population (480,982 in 1951), about three-fifths were in the old city.

The general level is about 1800 ft; to the N extends a great plain broken by a few remarkably symmetrical buttes 2–300 ft high; the entire terrain is of course Deccan Lava. To the S the hills are closer and several mesas at about 2000 ft abut directly on to the town, such as the temple-crowned Parvati Hill. These dissected table-lands extend Swds until the horizon is closed by the steep scarps of the Singarh Hills (*c.* 3200 ft), carrying the great fortress of Singarh (= 'Lion Fort'), famous in Maratha history, clearly visible from Poona despite the distance of 15 miles.

The City proper lies along the Mutha, built fairly high along the E bank, which suggests indeed an old river-wall. The most striking monument of Maratha days is the citadel, Shanwar Peth, of which, however, only the simple but impressively solid *enceinte* remains, its gate studded with 9-inch iron spikes to discourage the use of elephants as battering rams. Around it lie the twisting streets of the old town, less irregular than those of many Indian cities. Here 18th-century timbered houses, with richly-carved balconies, produce a Jacobean effect, while others are of thin bricks set in herring-bone patterns or with a shallow false arcading of little 'Norman' arches; roofs are low gables of semi-cylindrical tiles. Altogether these represent two of the most pleasing domestic styles in India. The functions of the old town are mainly those of a commercial centre for the surrounding agricultural area; industry is mostly of artisan type, the few modern factories (including cotton mills) lying away from the town near the railway station, and the important Deccan Paper Mills 5 miles to the E. The City is remarkably homogeneous in community; it is in fact simply the regional centre of Maharashtra.

The Cantonments are not, as is so often the case, sealed off from the old City by the railway; but the cultural divide is sharp enough, the whole aspect changing in the width of one street. There is indeed some trace of a marginal or transitional fringe, largely Anglo-Indian; Eurasian would be a better adjective, since the most prominent outward and visible sign is the Portuguese Church.

---

[13] A vivid sketch of Sivaji's career will be found in Denis Kincaid's delightful book *The Grand Rebel*.

The Cantonments lie to the south of the Mutha-Mula, here bunded to form an elongated lake even in the dry weather. They are of course much more spaciously laid out than the City, with broad, clean, tree-lined avenues; but there does not appear to be any very intelligible general plan. Most of the official buildings, banks, clubs, hotels, and cinemas lie on the City side of the Cantonments, S of and close to the railway station; and Swds again lie the two main shopping streets. Farther out the cultural landscape becomes more and more military; even the Anglican Church seems standing to attention, and the very trees are numbered. This is the Poona of popular legend, of Colonel Sahibs and exclusive clubs; and (as again at Simla) the legend was nearly true. Across the river in Kirkee

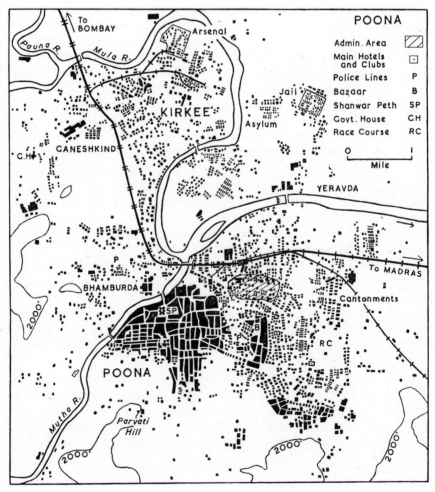

Fig. 38.—POONA; courtesy SOI.

militarism reigns supreme, but here it is the more workaday side of army life—sappers, gunners, ordnance, the great arsenal, and munitions factories.

The more important suburbs lie to the W; Yeravda in the E is notable only for the Aga Khan's remarkably hideous palace, honoured by the involuntary residence there of Mahatma Gandhi. Bhamburda, across the Mutha from the City, is more interesting: here are the engineering and agricultural colleges, the District Courts, and the headquarters of the Indian Meteorological Department. Nwds in Ganeshkind is Government House—Poona was the hot-weather capital of Bombay Province. The European buildings are not striking—the best is perhaps the Meteorological Office and Observatory—but they have at least the advantage of being built of Deccan Lava, a sombre material but one in which it is difficult to be undignified.[14]

To sum up, there were really three Poonas: the old regional capital of Maharashtra; the vast sprawl of military installations, individually tidily laid out but as a whole dumped down anyhow; and the educational and administrative suburbs in the W. Poona is thus in many respects a typical, if better than average, expression of the juxtaposition of Indian and British civilisations: for on the whole it is probably true to say that the two lived side by side, to some extent symbiotically, in a state of unconsummated matrimony. There were interdigitation, reciprocal reactions, but no fusion into a common culture; though materially, perhaps, there was an Indo-British civilisation.

Qadian (Fig. 39)

Qadian, like Poona, originated in a local *jagir*; there the resemblance ends. It was [15] the headquarters of a heretical and reformist Muslim sect, the Ahmadiyya, founded about 1908 by one Mirza Ahmad, the "Promised Messiah". This group numbers perhaps a million adherents and has missions not only in the more usual Muslim fields of Africa and Indonesia, but as far as Glasgow and Buenos Aires; it represents a remarkable combination of fundamentalism with a keen appreciation of modern technique. This is not the place to discuss its sociology, fascinating as it is to observe at first hand the growth of a new religious movement; but some points will emerge in the following pages.

According to the Ahmadis, the original land-grant was made by the first Mogul, Babur (1526–30). The Ahmadi family lived the usual life of local

[14] There is a detailed study: D. R. Gadgil, *Poona: A Socio-Economic Survey* (Gokhale Inst., Poona, 1945). Geography is limited to a page of gazetteer-stuff, but the description of trades and crafts is thorough and interesting.

[15] This section must unfortunately be written in the past tense; the material geography is doubtless still there, the spirit has fled. My visit was in August 1947; as a result of the Partition which left it in *India*, all but 3 or 400 of the Ahmadis have been forced to migrate to Pakistan. For the Ahmadi movement, see W. C. Smith, *Modern Islam in India* (1946), 298–302.

lords through all the vicissitudes of Mogul rule, Persian and Afghan incursions, Sikh and finally British power, until the great revelation to Mirza Ahmad.[16] For nearly 40 years (1908–47) Qadian was as it were a miniature Vatican; not sovereign, but something of a state within a state. Crime in Qadian, for instance, was invariably reported first to the Ahmadi office and then to the police.

Qadian lies in the Bari Doab (E Punjab), 35 miles NE of Amritsar. The old town, still called 'the Fort', and retaining traces of a town ditch, is like hundreds of others in SW Asia: some 12–15,000 people (the great majority were Ahmadis) living on the area of an English village of 2000; narrow twisting alleys, encroached on by stalls and swarming with children and donkeys; two bazaar streets, covered with rough awnings of sacking (poor relations of the Damascus *suqs*), and significantly a Hindu enclave; mud-walled houses, windowless, built round courts where spinning, milking of buffaloes, and all women's work is carried on; flat roofs littered with rope bedsteads, where the men smoke and gossip in the cool of the evening. A few large brick houses rise like monadnocks out of a peneplain. These include the Ahmadi offices, in a house once belonging to a wealthy Hindu, as is architecturally obvious from the details of the extremely beautiful brick façade and doorways, perhaps 18th century and certainly built when the now-decayed traditions of Hindu architecture were still vigorous; exterior windows are few and small—significantly—but within is a galleried court. Here was the vault containing the treasury, and the offices of a bureaucracy under seven 'Secretaries of State', including one for Entertainment of Guests, whose department was wonderfully efficient. An important feature was the guest-house, a caravanserai of courts and cubicles and cookhouses (more hygienic than many in the British Army), where disciples from all the Islamic lands endlessly commented the Quran and the writings of Promised Messiah.

From the 120-ft minar of the mosque all this warren lay at one's feet: to the N stretched the open modern development; to the S, on the rich fields of the Bari Doab, half a dozen large villages, darkly shrouded in mango-groves, seemed to enclose Qadian in a ring: all were Sikh.

In the new town, as in the old, women were in the strictest *purdah*; there were few other common features. Apart from an industrial fringe on the edge of the old town, this area was laid out in wide streets, with strict zoning and regulated densities. Architecture on the whole was poor, but sanitation superior to that in Lahore's best hotel. The most grandiose building was the big college, PWD Mogul in style, and well equipped

[16] "I tell the tale that I heard told," and have no means of checking it; it is inherently not improbable, though some of the embellishments certainly are so, e.g. that at one time during the Mogul decadence the Ahmadis were thought of for the throne of Delhi. But then, anything is credible of a family which speaks of an ancient quarrel with the House of Timur for all the world as if Tamburlaine the Great were a rather unfriendly uncle.

especially in physics and chemistry labs; the community had even secured the torso of a crashed plane for preliminary aeronautical instruction.[17] Between the town and the railway lay the industrial area, largely powered by Mandi hydro-electricity (below, 477-78). On the fringe of the old town factories were largely private enterprises, but in the more open areas the community was building more modern workshops for vegetable oil, paint

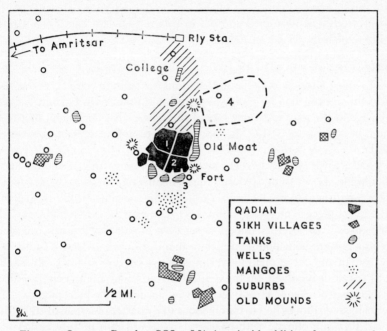

Fig. 39.—QADIAN. Based on SOI 44 M/5 (1913) with additions from personal observation. 1, Bazaar; 2, Ahmadi admin. and religious centre; 3, Ahmadi cemetery (guest-houses, etc., between 2 and 3); 4, modern planned area (villas, offices). The nearer suburbs are closer-built and more industrial than the Nn protrusion to the railway. Mounds (15–25 ft high) mark old settlements. The area lies midway between the Kasur and Sobraon branches of the Bari Doab Canal.

and varnish, and plastic industries—linked with research in the college labs. The most important activities actually existing were hosiery and knitwear, and all sorts of light electrical goods, all on a small scale (e.g. plastic presses electrically heated but hand-operated) and with apparently rather happy-go-lucky management; in which Qadian very faithfully reflected conditions in a large sector of Indian industry.

In a sense Qadian was a sociological freak, a combination of modern enterprise with fundamentalist theology; one might compare it with Salt Lake City. But the material expression of this duality was by no means un-

[17] To protect this treasure from the natural attentions of small boys, it was surrounded by a brick wall, irresistibly reminiscent of the cuckoo-retaining hedge at Gotham.

typical. The day-to-day life of the old town stood on the ancient ways, life as it has been lived in many Asian lands for centuries or millennia. The new, in its slapdash planning, in its architectural tawdriness or rawness (whether the "style" was traditional or modernistic), in its mixture of considerable drive and adroit improvisation with a certain lack of poise and stamina, can be paralleled over and over again on India's expanding industrial frontiers. But rarely are the contrasts of ancient and modern so sharply pointed within such narrow room; and yet in this too Qadian could stand for an epitome of India, if not of Asia.

Simla (Figs. 40 and 41)

The most famous of Indian hill stations lies at over 7000 ft, 175 miles N of Delhi, approached by motor road and mountain railway from Kalka on the edge of the plains. Nearly half of the railway has a gradient of 1 in 33, and it has 103 tunnels; Fig. 40 shows its necessarily roundabout entry into Simla.

That a town should be here at all is surprising; that it should have a population of over 18,000 (March 1941), mainly non-productive, is astonishing, a monument to the technical skill, and the social insensibility, of British rule. Every piece of metal had originally to come up the cart-road from Kalka; even to-day the internal transport services are mostly human, rickshaw-men or porters bent double under tremendous packs. Until recently both the Indian and the Punjab Governments migrated annually to Simla, and until 1912 this involved, for the Central Government, the 1115-mile journey from Calcutta. Army Headquarters was permanently located there. The clerks in some offices had to climb 800 ft in a quarter of a mile to reach their work: this in a climate with nearly 35 inches of rain in July and August together. Other services had a yet inferior situation: laundry-men had a pull of 1000 ft from their dhobi-ghats to their customers. There can be few places in the world where the upper ten was so literally upper; the Viceroy and the Commander-in-Chief had naturally the best peaks. But all these inconveniences were subordinated to mean summer maximum temperatures of 67–82° F. compared with 110–120 in the plains below.[18] And, if Englishmen (and women) set the fashion, beginning in 1819, well-to-do Indians soon found Simla essential to physical and still more to social health. Yet in a sense the whole place was a parasite.

The plan (Fig. 41), very typical of Indian hill stations, resembles nothing so much as a dissection of some invertebrate, an elongated tangle of guts and nerves with two or three ganglia. Roads tend to run sub-parallel to contours, and of course nearly all junctions are acute forks. Traffic would be a problem were it not nearly all banned (even bicycles, which

[18] In winter, indeed, it is inconveniently cold, with mean minima below freezing in December–February. Absolute maxima and minima are about 95 and 17° F. Communication with the plains is sometimes blocked for 3 or 4 days by snow.

could be used along the Mall) in the interests of rickshaw-men and porters —or their masters. The main axis lies along a saddle between Jakko (8040 ft) in the E and Observatory Hill (7050 ft) in the W; on the latter is what was the Viceregal Lodge. The hub of Simla lies under Jakko, on the broad Ridge between the Town Hall and Christ Church; here are the chief cinemas, libraries, and so on. The main road, the Mall, runs from end to end of Simla; the part of the Mall immediately below the Ridge is the only real shopping street, for all the world like the shopping street of some very minor English inland resort, say Crowborough. And indeed the whole atmosphere is like that of a watering-place without any waters.

Below the En Mall is the Bazaar, the only close-built area, approached by roads at each end but transversely by steps in narrow winding alleys, a good deal steeper than those of Clovelly. The Bazaar area is a mass of tin-roofed houses clinging to what seems an impossibly steep hillside. SW, towards the railway station, is the office quarter. Here the hill is so steep that many buildings can be entered by a short bridge on to the top-floor back, while the ground-floor front entrance is half a mile or so away by road.

Around this central belt is a great penumbra of villas and bungalows, for the most part on S-facing slopes but with two protrusions Nwds along the Kaithu and Elysium spurs. Villa-nomenclature (which descends to Trixie Cottage) would make an interesting social study, throwing a quaint light on the British (and Indian) holiday mind. Underneath Kaithu is the racecourse, sunk in a shadowed and gloomy combe.

Apart from its setting of forests and ravines, which is splendid, and its suitability as a centre for anthropological study of Indo-British tribal customs, there was not much of interest in Simla. Architecturally, besides the nondescript or Swiss-chalet bungalows, there were three main styles: baronial châteaux with corrugated-iron roofs (one or two, seen against the sunset, not so awful as it sounds); dull but relatively dignified Tudor-Gothic; and concrete and cast-iron boxes which did not even pretend to be 'modernistic'. The Bazaar was dull, apart from some good silversmiths and the Sikh woodworkers of Lakkar Bazaar N of the Ridge; itinerant Tibetans and Ladakhis sell various barbaric but effective ornaments, especially necklaces and bracelets of rough turquoise.

Simla has still some official functions under the new régime; the physical atmosphere is perhaps conducive to the efficient conduct of conferences. But the glory, such as it was, is departed; and that Holy of Holies, the United Services Club, has gone into nominally voluntary liquidation.

BIBLIOGRAPHICAL NOTE

The settlement geography of this land of 650,000 villages, far better mapped than any other large tropical country, has been strangely neglected. Almost the only comprehensive survey (both urban and rural) is Enayat Ahmad's excellent

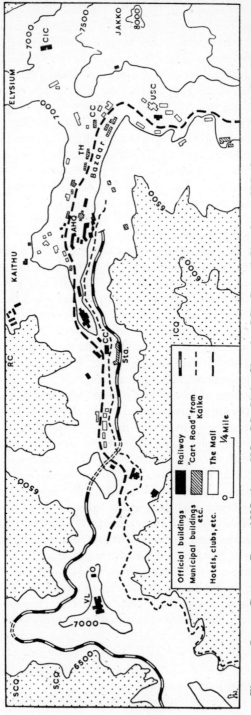

Fig. 40.—SIMLA: GENERAL PLAN. AHQ, Army HQ; CC, Christ Church; CC¹, Council Chambers; CIC, Commander-in-Chief's residence; I (S) CQ, inferior (superior) clerks' quarters; O, Observatory; RC, Racecourse; TH, Town Hall; VL, Viceroy's Lodge; USC, United Services Club. Based (as is Fig. 41) on SOI plan on scale 1/7920; courtesy SOI. Under 65,000 ft, stippled.

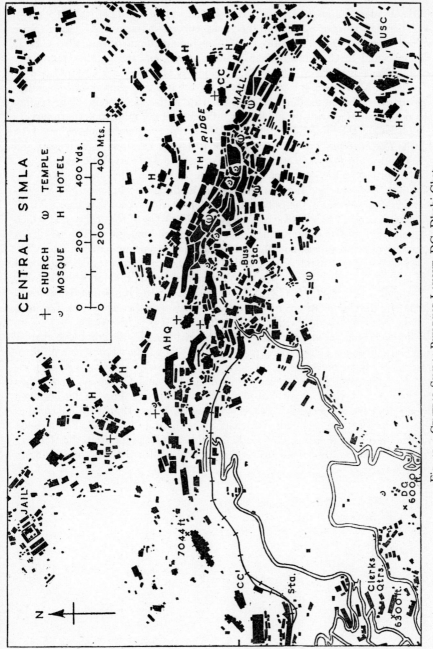

CENTRAL SIMLA

+ CHURCH   ω TEMPLE

ɔ MOSQUE   H HOTEL

0   200   400 Yds.

0   200   400 Mts.

Fig. 41.—Central Simla: Building Layout. DG, Dhobi Ghat.

study of the UP already mentioned; see his "Rural Settlement Types in the Uttar Pradesh", *Annals Asstn of American Geographers* XLII (1952), 223–46.

There is a mass of material in the village surveys initiated by G. Slater (*Some South Indian Villages* (Madras, 1918)), including the *Resurvey*, ed. by P. J. Thomas and K. C. Ramakrishnan (Madras, 1940), and the Bombay University publications of H. H. Mann and N. V. Kanitker (Deccan) and G. C. Mukhtyar (Gujarat). Many such surveys, however, have but a very skimpy and ill-under-stood geographical introduction, and such maps as they do contain might as often as not be omitted with profit. Rather different are the numerous short surveys published by the Punjab Board of Economic Enquiry. For Bengal we have J. C. Jack, *The Economic Life of a Bengal District* (1916; Faridpur in E Bengal), and A. Geddes, *Au Pays de Tagore* (Paris, n.d.; Santineketan in W Bengal).

Urban geography again has been neglected, though it has fascinating possi-bilities. There is a good London Ph.D. thesis by Binapani Mukerjee, *The Hooghly and its Region* (1948); the only other full-length study known to me is M. B. Pithawalla and P. Martin-Kaye, *Geology and Geography of Karachi* (1946), which despite its length and interesting detail has some odd omissions. The *IGJ* has a number of good studies, notably on Madras and Negapatam, cited in Ch. XXV; we may note here two interesting studies by C. D. Deshpande, "Cities and Towns of Bombay Province" and "Market Villages and Periodic Fairs of the Bombay Karnatak", both in *IGJ* XVI (1941), 268–86 and 327–39. Important recent town-planning developments are reviewed by O. H. Koenigsberger, "New Towns in India", *Town Planning Review* XXIII (1952), 94–131 (with maps).

There is much of value in non-geographic writing, e.g. the admirable chapter on "The Economic Transition" in Jathar and Beri's *Indian Economics*. W. Burn (ed.), *Sons of the Soil* (ND, 1941) is a collection of essays on the local peasantries. J. Tyrwhit (ed.), *Patrick Geddes in India* (1947), and C. Batley, *Architecture* (OPIA No. 35, 1946) are delightful as well as instructive. For the 'feel' of town and village life more creative writers are invaluable, e.g. Ahmed Ali for Delhi or R. K. Narayan for 'Malgudi', which is Somewhere in Tamilnad. Frieda Redi, *Behind the Mud Walls*, is a sympathetic study of village life from the woman's point of view. And there are always the unmatched 'Rural Rides' of Darling in the Punjab.

PART 3

THE ECONOMY

CHAPTER VIII

THE AGRARIAN BASE*

INDIA, and even more Pakistan, will remain predominantly agrarian countries for many years or decades. It is a commonplace, but also an important
truth, that their rural life and its problems are indescribably complex. The
Report of the Royal Commission on Agriculture in India (RCAI) runs to
700 closely printed pages, and yet contains hardly any detail on crops or
regional distributions, no statistical tables, and no discussion at all of the
vital but extremely intricate matter of land tenure—a subject barred by the
terms of reference. All that can be done in two chapters is to set out some
of the basic facts, to sketch rather than to discuss some agrarian maladies,
and finally to indicate some recent developments. The fundamental factors
of climate and soil should need no recapitulation.

The Nature of the Data

There is no lack of studies of Indian agriculture, though many consist of an
assiduous churning of the ocean of facts in the RCAI and other official reports,
while the more striking figures from such first-hand surveys as those of Darling
in the Punjab and Mann in the Deccan recur repeatedly. This is largely un-
avoidable, and certainly the present writer does not hope to avoid it. But it is as
well to cast a preliminary critical glance at the data available.[1]

Qualitative material is to be found in a vast mass of official papers on everything from lac to leather; these include (for areas not "permanently settled") the
District *Settlement Reports* on which the Land Revenue assessments are based.
Naturally such surveys are exceedingly minute; in fact far too detailed for use in
a general work. With these and with private studies one is on safe ground as
to descriptive facts; error here is a matter of personal equation, and internal
evidence usually gives a good idea of relative reliability.

It is otherwise with the statistics. It is true that one can rarely go behind the
great—and invaluable—mass of data contained in the *Agricultural Statistics*,
Season and Crop Reports, and so on; without them any serious study of Indian
agriculture would be impossible. But it is essential to recognise the limitations of
figures which profess to show the utilisation of land down to the last acre of
scores of millions. In the last resort much depends on the conscience and
efficiency of some half a million badly-paid and not very literate village officials;
there are of course checks, and the pious trust that errors cancel out. This may be
doubted: in Bengal, deprived by the Permanent Settlement of much of the Land
Revenue machinery, rice acreage by random sampling was 3·5 m. ac. more than

---

* A general Bibliographical Note for Part 3 (Chs. VIII–XII) will be found on pp. 327–
329, q.v. for full references to works cited by author or short title only.
[1] There is a good discussion in *The Food Statistics of India* (ND, 1946), 1–8 (cited as
Food Stats).

the official figure, by plot-to-plot enumeration 2 m. ac. more.[2] Such anomalies as the following defy comment: the *Season and Crop Reports* for Bihar returned for eight consecutive years the figures of 36,531 and 9752 ac. as the areas irrigated by tanks and by wells respectively in Bhagalpur Dt. In the ninth year the figures were respectively 200,000 and 100,000 ac.; in the tenth 100,000 and 500 (repeat 500).[3] Admittedly tanks and wells are variables, but this exceeds! Yet, in the gross, area figures are much less inaccurate than those which purport to show output and yield per acre.

It is on the face of it impossible for the most perfect bureaucracy to know the actual output; the surplus after deducting grain for home use is dissipated in millions of petty sales, and perhaps only about a third of total output is brought to market. Here again the village official is at the bottom of a shaky pyramid; his estimate of the season's crop is expressed in the crude impressionism of so many annas in the rupee (e.g. if all sown matured it would be a 16-anna crop) and obviously, if he cares for good feeling, he is susceptible to some influence from his fellows, who are not given to exaggerating their taxable capacity. His figure goes to the next in grade, the *kanungo* or circle officer, then through *tahsil*, District, and Division to the Director of Land Records or Agriculture, officials at each stage making "their own guesses at the figures reported by the lower officers". Various other subjective elements enter, and "there is at present no means of knowing the extent and direction of the bias".[4] But one feels that there *is* a certain bias by the time the figures reach New Delhi.

Moreover even the official estimates of "normal" yield per acre, made by responsible officers, are open to grave doubt. The crop-cutting samples are rarely random, and (despite a theoretical 5-yearly revision) some of these averages have persisted unchanged for 20 or 30 years. As a rule they are much above figures based on dividing outputs by acreages. To some extent the discrepancy is probably offset and accountable by the universal reluctance of farmers to admit their success, but the following statement of (i) "normal" yield in lbs per acre, based on crop-cutting samples, and (ii) "actual" averages for 1934–35/43–44 is a fair warning, especially when it is recalled that rice and wheat are the most important and perhaps the most accurately assessed of the cereals:

> *Rice:*   Madras (i) 1123 (ii) 1039; UP (i) 800 (ii) 619
> *Wheat:* Bihar   (i) 987 (ii) 864; CP (i) 561 (ii) 412.[5]

It will be seen that the maximum excess of "normal" over "actual" is no less than 36%! Such real random sampling as has been done gives results too inconclusive for any coefficient of correction to be possible. Yield figures, then, must be taken with the strictest reserve, though they probably give a fair *relative* picture of trends and intensities. But one suspects that maps of yield per acre are quite pointless.

Altogether just two-thirds of the approximately 1010 m. acres of All-India

[2] *Food Stats*, 4–5.

[3] P. Dayal, *The Agricultural Geography of Bihar* (London Ph.D. thesis, 1947), xii–xiii. See his introduction for a good general discussion.

[4] *Food Stats*, 5–6; there is an amusing account of the process in M. Brown, *India Need Not Starve* (Bombay, 1944), 76–77.

[5] *Food Stats*, 67–70; the provinces chosen are the best and the worst in yield for each crop.

were covered by the *Agricultural Statistics*—nearly all British India (the blanks, except in Baluchistan, being agriculturally of little account) and about a third of states' territory. The war-time Food Department obtained estimates from about 70% of the omitted area—estimates significantly described as "even more in the nature of guesswork than the statistics furnished by reporting areas". Increases in the cultivated area so obtained were from 2·6% for wheat to 28·8% for maize, altogether adding a probable 4·1 m. tons of foodgrains, or 8·4% of the estimated output of reporting areas.

Some of the states' figures are suspect, and changes in the number of those reporting renders long-term comparisons more laborious than they are worth. The figures which follow are usually for ex-British India, divided, where appropriate, to show the effects of Partition. The provinces are well enough distributed to give a reasonable general picture; inclusion of all states would probably scale up the proportion of forests and certainly that "not available for cultivation", as well as the proportion under lesser millets and pulses. It would decrease the proportion under irrigation, rice, and cash crops.

With all their limitations, the *Agricultural Statistics* do represent a big achievement. They are reliable enough for regional or crop comparisons, and as evidence of trends; and otherwise it is sufficient to bear in mind that they are indices rather than absolute statements. As with the Census, the wonder is not that there should be large errors, but that so large a mass of data should exist at all. But in view of the vital importance of forward planning for food, this does not absolve the Governments from making every effort to improve their statistical machinery.

I. GENERALITIES

Classification of Area

The primary division of the land is shown in Table II, which, however, can hardly be taken at face value. Thus "Forest" includes fuel and fodder reserves under the Forest Department, and these may be all but treeless, while conversely much land "Not Available for Cultivation" is well wooded. The definition of "Current Fallow" varies greatly from State to State, and it is very difficult to make out clearly what "Not Available" really means. It includes roads, buildings, and so on, but also scraps of roadside grazing, definite pasture areas, and village groves and gardens; much of it, however, is too broken, arid, or jungly to offer any hope of settlement, even to the optimistic publicist.

He has his field-day in "Other Uncultivated Land excluding Current Fallows." Formerly this was labelled "Culturable Waste"; the RCAI remarked that it was certain that much of it "could in no conceivable circumstances be brought under tillage", adding that the annual repetition in official documents that nearly a fifth of the land of British India could be tilled but in fact lay idle was "calculated to give rise to misconceptions".[6]

---

[6] RCAI, 605; figure adjusted for loss of Burma. The RCAI also mildly doubted whether all "Not Available" was in fact useless; this remark, on the same page, has been more popular than that on "Culturable Waste".

I.P.—7*

With no undue haste the Government met the RCAI's demand for reclassi-fication, which it achieved with elegant simplicity by re-naming it "Other Uncultivated Land. . . ." [7] But the old title and the old misconceptions re-main; 90 m. ghostly acres still haunt the literature, and many writers have paid no heed to these authoritative warnings, nor indeed to the witness of their own eyes. It is obvious that with populations nearly everywhere congested (even where not absolutely dense) and land-hungry, any land cultivable without prohibitive outlay would have been taken up long ago. Parts of this category might be useful for large-scale pastoralism—in a different society; we shall see some of the factors which inhibit such development. Against the marginal land must be set losses, not inconsider-able, of already cultivated land by soil erosion, waterlogging, and weed infestation.

Of these 90 m. acres, some 10 m. are definitely known to be culturable, nearly all in Madhya Pradesh (CP) and the Punjab, and accounting there for about a third of the waste. In E Punjab and Sind irrigation has still much new ground to take in, and in Assam, still a pioneer fringe, a higher proportion could probably be won. But on the whole it is probably safe to say that at most only about a quarter of "Other Uncultivated Land" could really be reclaimed [8]; and, except on the farming frontier of Assam, where much has been settled by squatter families from E Bengal, this is clearly, in view of the general land-hunger, very marginal, requiring a high outlay to break it in.

The essential fact of Table II, however, is that only 42% of even the more settled parts of *India* are cultivated; over-all between 28% and a guess (from hints in *Food Stats*) of some 33% for the whole sub-continent. Irrigation and multiple cropping (Table III) bring the proportion of cultivated land in British India to just half, and this is probably rather under-stated. Even on the impossible assumption of a stationary 1941 population, this amounts to under 0·9 acre of ploughed land for each member of a population of which two-thirds is *directly* dependent on farming for a living. The keynote of the whole agrarian problem is at once struck by this simple but terrifying fact.

Types of Farming; Kharif and Rabi

Farming practices are considered in some detail in the regional chapters; broadly speaking the types of cultivation in India may be grouped as follows:

1. shifting hill cultivation.
2. sedentary peasant agriculture:
    (*a*) food crops, dry or irrigated

[7] Perhaps on the analogy of the Scheduled Castes, ex-Depressed Classes, ex-Untouch-ables; or indeed the Special, *ci-devant* Distressed, Areas of Britain.

[8] This was written before seeing Vakil's estimate of 23–29%.

      (*b*) cash crops, dry or irrigated
      (*c*) arboriculture and gardening.
   3. capitalist farming:
      (*a*) estates
      (*b*) plantations.

The first and last may be briefly dismissed; the second is the norm of Indian farming, and forms the staple of these chapters.

Shifting agriculture—the *jhum* of Assam, the *kumri* or *podu* of the Peninsula—conforms to the standard pattern so widespread in tropical regions.[9] Dry rice, buckwheat, maize, poor millets, sometimes poor tobacco or sugarcane, are grown on burnt-over clearings; in, say, two to five years, when the ash-given fertility dwindles, new clearings are made, preferably in new forest as the dense twisted scrub of abandoned jhums is often less tractable than untouched high forest. Obviously this can usually support only a sparse population, but on all the borders of Assam and in the wilder parts of central India it is dominant, while on the Wn Ghats and the sub-Himalayan slopes both shifting and sedentary cultivation are carried on, as well as intermediate forms recalling 'run-rig' or the long fallowing (15–20 years) of the African *chitamene*.

Dry deciduous forest is obviously especially suited to jhuming, and as it is also the most generally valuable commercially, this devastating practice is frowned on by authority; moreover it may initiate severe soil erosion. But in some areas it is the only cultivation topographically possible, and in many there is at present no alternative to a considerable amount of controlled jhuming, sometimes turned to account by making the planting of commercial timber on abandoned fields a condition of licensing.

As for *capitalist farming*, there are a few large estates run on modern lines, though often cultivated by tenants; these include military dairy and vegetable farms, and some factory estates for sugar, cotton, and oilseeds. There is a strong factitious element about most of these estates, which often owe their success to initial high capitalisation by philanthropists or far-sighted businessmen. Perhaps the most notable is the Sir Daniel Hamilton Gosaba estate, 22,000 acres of reclaimed Sundarbans islands. Here co-operation is cherished, and for 30 years there was not a single serious civil or criminal case—a unique phenomenon in this litigious land. Interesting as these estates are, and useful as models, they are alien to the whole structure of Indian farming, and can hardly play a decisive role in agricultural advance.[10]

---

[9] E.g. *taungya* in Burma, *chena* in Ceylon, and so on; agreement on one name (or two, to cover the distinction between the 'nomadic' and the 'long fallow' types) is most desirable. For a general discussion, see P. Gourou, *Les Pays tropicaux* (Presses Universitaires de France, Paris, 1948), Chs. IV–V.

[10] See Nanavati and Anjaria, 147–50, 161–65, 259–61.

Plantations are almost entirely for tea, rubber, and coffee, and are therefore dealt with in Section II.E of this chapter.

Our second type is by far the most important. The overwhelming majority of Indians living by the land are small holders, usually very small indeed, or landless. It is clear from Table IV that their major activity is the growing of cereals (2*a*), though in some areas oilseeds, sugar, and fibres (2*b*) are nearly as important to the economy as are foodgrains, and locally minor branches (2*c*) are significant: market gardening, spices, sericulture, perhaps even lac collecting come under this head.

Two vitally important cross-divisions are those between (i) wet and dry crops and (ii) the autumn (*kharif*) and spring (*rabi*) harvests.

(i) Irrigation demands a separate place, but we may note here that 'wet' crops are not necessarily irrigated. While in much of W Pakistan crops of any sort are virtually impossible without irrigation, at the other extreme E Pakistan cultivation is wet enough but practically independent of irrigation.

(ii) Kharif is the monsoon crop, sown soon after the onset of the rains (June–July) and harvested in autumn: rice, jowar, bajra, sesamum, cotton (though this is long on the ground), jute. Rabi crops are sown after the rains and harvested in spring: wheat, barley, gram, linseed, rape, and mustard. Kharif and rabi may be, but as a rule are not, sown on the same ground; rabi is essentially the crop of doabs and uplands, kharif of flood-plains and the areas under tanks. A given crop need not fall exclusively into one category, and in the Sn half of the Peninsula, and particularly in Tamilnad with its October–December rain, the distinction is blurred; and sugar, which may be 10–18 months in the ground, clearly does not fit in. Locally, of course, there are minor harvests, especially in Bengal and Bihar, where the relations of the two (or even three) crops are exceedingly complicated.[11]

Irrigation (Figs. 42–46, Table III)

Altogether 7% of the surface of the sub-continent is irrigated—110,000 sq mls, an area 22% greater than the entirety of Great Britain. Irrigation of some sort has been practised from time immemorial—the Grand Anicut on the Cauvery, a million cubic feet of masonry, was built in the 11th century. But most canal development is the work of the last hundred years. The irrigation works of the sub-continent use about 7 billion cubic feet of water, nearly 20% of annual surface flow, and the great Punjab rivers are virtually drained dry by their canals. Roughly speaking 53% of the irrigated area is fed by canals, 11% by tanks, 25% by wells, 11% by other sources. The distribution of these types is shown on Fig. 42.

(i) *Canals* fall into two groups: inundation canals, mere cuts parallel to

[11] Mukerjee, *Economic Problems*, I. 7–15; table of harvest-times for different crops and areas in *Food Stats*, 12–14.

the rivers in the floodplains, and perennial canals fed by elaborate headworks, with regulated flow, and generally travelling along the doabs to
command a wider area. Many of the former date from Mogul times, a few
even earlier, but the perennial systems, a creation of the British period,
now cover a much wider area (cf. Fig. 85). Details of the layout and working of a modern canal system are given in Ch. XVII (Indus Plains).

Inundation canals merely fill with the rising river, and if it does not rise

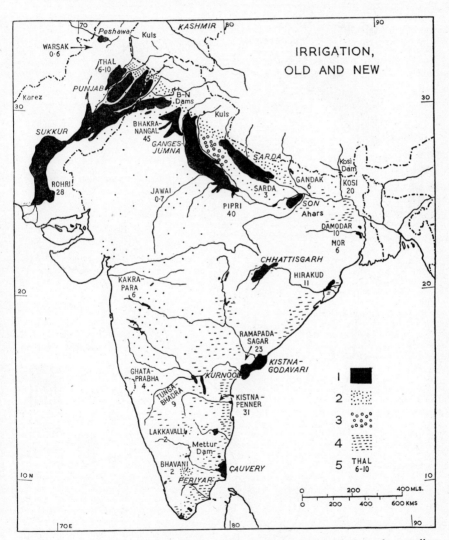

Fig. 42.—IRRIGATION, OLD AND NEW. 1, area commanded by modern canals; 2, wells;
3, UP tubewells; 4, tanks; 5, major projects with areas to be irrigated in 100,000 ac.
For *ahars*, *karez*, and *kuls*, see relevant regional chapters.

enough they remain empty. They are thus liable to fail precisely when most needed. Their offtakes silt readily. Perennial canals also have disadvantages, of which the most important is that their headworks may trap much of the silt so valuable to the ill-manured fields. Again "it is just as important to get the water off the land as to get it on, and few ryots still seem to know it. The water comes to the cultivator without much labour on

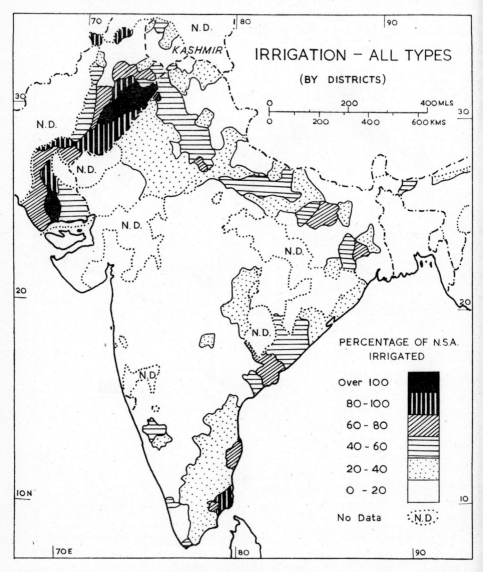

Fig. 43.—IRRIGATION—ALL TYPES. Keys for Figs. 43–46 identical; all courtesy G. Kuriyan.

his part, and the high esteem in which he holds it leads to over-irrigation without adequate drainage." [12] Hence waterlogging and the formation of alkali pans—menaces which have reached alarming proportions in parts of W Pakistan, leading to loss of cultivated land. A detailed analysis of the

[12] G. Kuriyan, "Irrigation in India" (*Journal of the Madras University*, XV, No. 1, Sec. A., 1943), 167; payment by volume has been suggested, instead of by area irrigated as at present; for objections to this, see RCAI, 336.

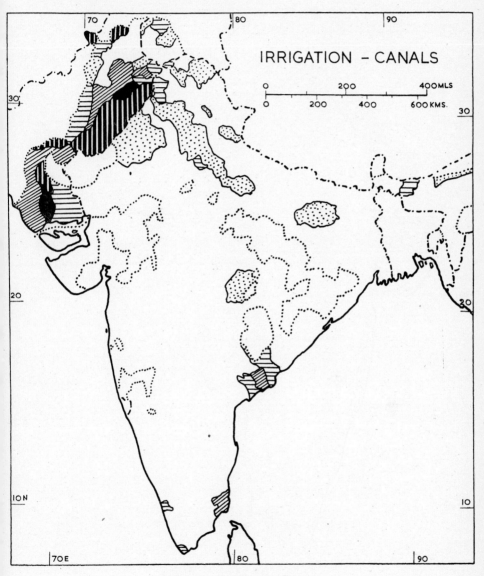

Fig. 44.—IRRIGATION—CANALS.

complex difficulties met with in the long-cultivated Cauvery Delta in consequence of changing from direct (inundation) to perennial irrigation will be found on pp. 719–22. When all is said, however, such great achievements as the Punjab Triple Project form a most impressive memorial of the British Raj.

(ii) *Tanks* are illustrated in some detail in Figs. 151 and 152. Their

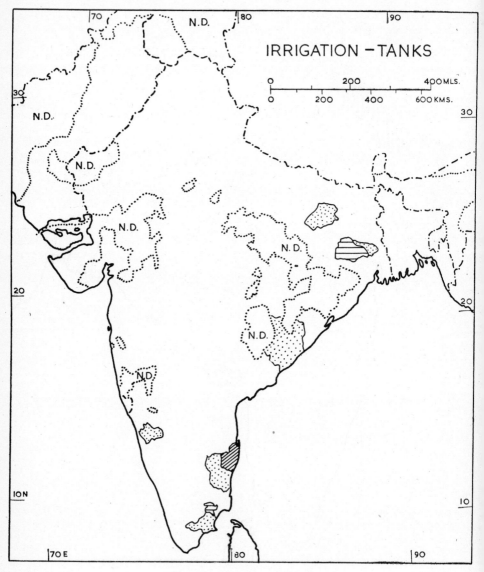

Fig. 45.—IRRIGATION—TANKS.

siting speaks to a wonderful flair for detecting the minutest variations in the terrain. A reliable tank needs a considerable catchment, which is usually waste; rice is the usual tank-fed crop, on gently falling terraces designed to secure an even flow of water over the fields. Often a whole stream is reduced to a string of tanks, the lower ones trapping the surplus water from those above. The high water-table below the tanks supplies good wells, used either for security in bad years or a second crop in good ones.

Nevertheless tanks are on the whole unsatisfactory. The water-surface is large in relation to volume, so that loss by evaporation is high, as is that by seepage; relatively few tanks hold water throughout the year (cf. Fig. 152). Sooner or later they silt up; the bed will retain some ground-water, held up by the bund, and for a while at least be very fertile; but the problem of a new supply remains.

Irrigation tanks must be distinguished from the small rectangular tanks for domestic water-supply. These are often built-up as much as excavated, rain and not stream fed, and except in wet areas like E Bengal (where they occur in tens of thousands) are obviously very likely to fail in the hot weather.

(iii) *Wells* of course command individually small areas; even in the Punjab, where they are large and permanent, the average area is only 12 acres. But in aggregate they are exceedingly important, and not only quantitatively.

A *pukka*—masonry or brick-lined—well is costly to construct, and the use of any well makes great demands on human and animal labour; well-irrigation is thus six or seven times as expensive as canal, and so tends to be reserved for high-value specialised crops—vegetables for urban markets, sugar, or, where soil is good, really first-class cereals. This is in fact garden cultivation; over-watering is obviously unlikely, and the well can be used exactly when needed, which is by no means always so with other methods. The small areas lend themselves to fencing and individual care, and are usually well weeded and manured.

Several types of lift are used. The simplest, for shallow wells, is the *picottah* (= Egyptian *shaduf*), merely a weighted pole pivoted on an upright; for lifts of over 15 ft bullocks are used. In the N, and especially in W Punjab, the 'Persian wheel' is common: an endless chain of pots on a vertical wheel geared to a horizontal and worked by bullocks endlessly circling the well. Also common is the *mhote*, a steep ramp up which the bullocks are backed to depress the bucket, raising it on the forward down-hill movement. In Tamilnad the *kabalai* is an ingenious variant (below, 707).

Oil-driven pumps have been used, but unless they can be worked for 4 hours a day—which would probably exhaust most wells rapidly—they are no more efficient than the *kabalai*, and to be economic they would demand large holdings of 10–15 acres.[13] This last argument, however, loses much of its force when put against the general high cost of well-irrigation, which means that only large holders could contemplate such methods anyhow. The introduction of cheap electricity is already causing major changes, and

[13] Kuriyan, *loc. cit.*, 56. Ch. VI of *Imperial Gaz.*, Vol. III (1908), is still valuable for a discussion of the indigenous types of irrigation.

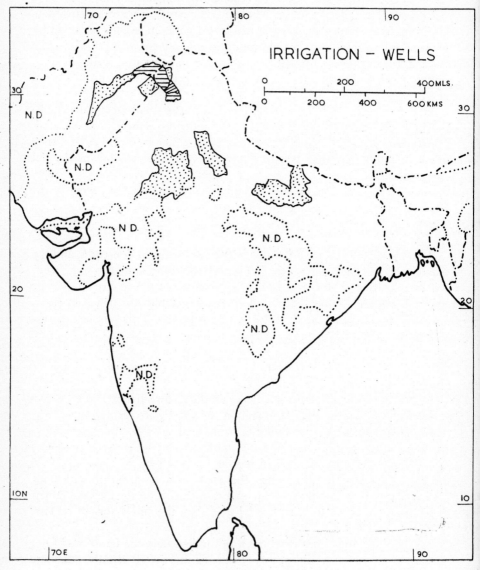

Fig. 46.—IRRIGATION—WELLS

there is an increasing demand for electric pumps in the areas served by Pykara and other S Indian hydro-electric plants. Another development of great promise is the introduction of tube-wells tapping the huge resources of water at depth beneath the Indo-Gangetic Plains; here the UP has led the way (below, 502–03).

(iv) *Other sources* consist for the most part of small temporary dams and channels (e.g. the *ahars* and *pynes* of S Bihar), the 'spring channels' of Tamilnad river-beds, mere water-holes in floodplains, direct lift from rivers, and so on. The most interesting type—Iranian rather than Indian—is the *karez* of Baluchistan (Fig. 74), tunnels constructed by connecting lines of shafts sunk in the detrital fans of the piedmont, which has a relatively high water-table. *Karez* may be a mile long, but most are much smaller, and the best probably do not discharge more than 9–10 cusec. In this semi-desert zone much of what little cultivation exists is by means of bunds across the drainage-lines of the hill-slopes (Fig. 83). This holds up the ground-water and is water-conservation if not irrigation.

The area under wells and other sources is capable of rapid, if temporary, expansion and fluctuates widely, being especially important in years of deficient rain.

II. MAJOR CROPS AND THEIR DISTRIBUTION
(*Figs. 47–55, Tables IV–XIII*)

A. FOOD AND FODDER

1. Cereals and Pulses: (i) *Rice*

Nearly a third of the cultivated area of *India* and half that of Pakistan is under rice; E Pakistan, indeed, would be practically monocultural but for the competition of jute, and here rice acreage often exceeds the NSA. The share of W Pakistan is only 8% of the Pakistan total area, but the W as a whole eats wheat and Sind has normally a sizeable export surplus—100–150,000 tons. The total sub-continental output of paddy (rice before any treatment) is around 30 m. tons, roughly equal to that of all other foodgrains combined. At 70 lbs per acre seed requirements are about 2·5 m. tons of paddy.[14]

The high temperature and water requirements of paddy—except the practically negligible dry hill rice—make it dominantly a crop of the deltas and floodplains, and the dominant crop there. It is at its best when the growing season has a mean temperature of 75° F. or more and, in non-irrigated areas, 60–80 in. of rain. The fact that rice is so pre-eminently a 'wet crop' is responsible for the not uncommon fallacy that it is grown almost entirely by irrigation. The plant certainly can mature satisfactorily

[14] The remainder of this section is largely based on G. Kuriyan, "Rice in India", *IGJ* XX (1945), 28–36, 76–84, 110–26—a very comprehensive account.

only if it grows in a few inches of water; a 5-month crop will need about 70
acre-inches. But in the great domains of paddy this is supplied by the rain
on the fields themselves or by natural flood, and is simply retained by the
low mud field-walls (bunds); whereas 'irrigation' surely implies an artificial supply. This is necessary wherever the rainfall is below 40–45 ins., and
at least very desirable at 50–55 ins. Paddy favours rather heavy soils—clays,
clayey loams, the clay-with-silt of the deltas.

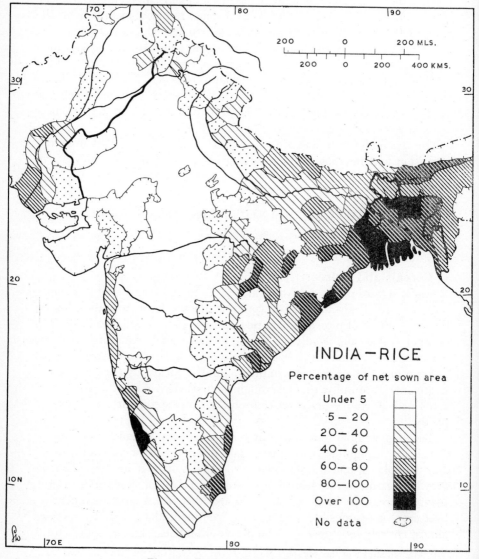

Fig. 47.—Rice; courtesy G. Kuriyan.

As a rule it is sown soon after the beginning of the rains and harvested in November–January, but in Bengal there are three crops: *aus* (harvested June–September), *aman* (November–January; *c.* 75% of acreage), and *boro* (February–May). This last is grown on the shrinking margins of lakes and swamps and has a very small acreage. Broadcasting is used, in Bengal for about half the crop, but more generally seedlings are raised in heavily manured beds and transplanted; this is back-breaking work, often done by the women. The soil is puddled and tends to become very heavy; organic and especially green manures are useful, but probably most paddy-fields get little fertilising except the burning of the stubble and sometimes of branches and twigs.

Of the complexities of paddy cultivation and the rice trade there is no end; in India alone some 4000 varieties are known, each with special requirements and qualities. Perhaps 5% of the area is under improved strains produced by the agricultural research institutes.

The grading of paddy for sale and milling is a fine art. Rice is not in itself a very good food, and it is made poorer by mechanical milling and polishing. Unfortunately the taste for polished rice—purely a matter of prestige—seems to be spreading, though of course village consumption is mostly home-ground or pounded in mortars and retains much of the valuable husk. Coolies often eat cheap parboiled rice, which is steamed before milling; this is valued as it keeps well when cooked, and the vitamins and minerals of the husk are not lost to such an extent as in ordinary milling. A diet based on milled rice, deprived of vitamin B, definitely predisposes to beri-beri, one of the most serious deficiency diseases of India, and not confined to the quantitatively under-fed. The famous experiment on rats fed on diets typical of provinces from the Punjab to Madras also shows the low dietetic value of rice.[15] But these qualitative failings are offset by heavy yields per acre—nearly twice those of jowar and bajra—and rice retains its place as the staple food of the wetter areas, and of the better-off classes nearly everywhere.

Paddy has developed a strikingly individual landscape, broadly similar from the Ganges to the Yangtse: myriads of tiny mud-walled fields, in the rains with only the bunds and the villages rising above the grey water through which the young paddy shows like thin flames of a most wonderful glowing emerald; in the hot weather a grey expanse of baked mud and thin stubble, dotted by the threshing-floors with their bamboo tripods whence swing open-meshed baskets into which the threshed grain is thrown to be winnowed by the wind. Here and there are the gaunt corrugated-iron roofs

[15] The average body-weights of the rats of each diet group (in grams) at the end of the experiment were: Sikh 235, Pathan 230, Maratha 225, Kanarese 185, Bengali 180, Madrassi 155. The Maratha/Kanarese drop is most significant, as these areas adjoin, the Marathas being practically confined to the wheat and jowar-bajra Deccan Lavas. See R. K. Mukerjee, *Food Planning*, 167–68.

and spindly chimneys of small rice mills. More significant are the social correlates of this landscape so intensively moulded by man. If intensive rice farming draws much energy from the soil, much energy must also be put in, and "the investment of effort required to develop paddy land immobilizes the population itself. . . . Industrial development may enable a people to levy on the produce of other lands and develop a denser popula-

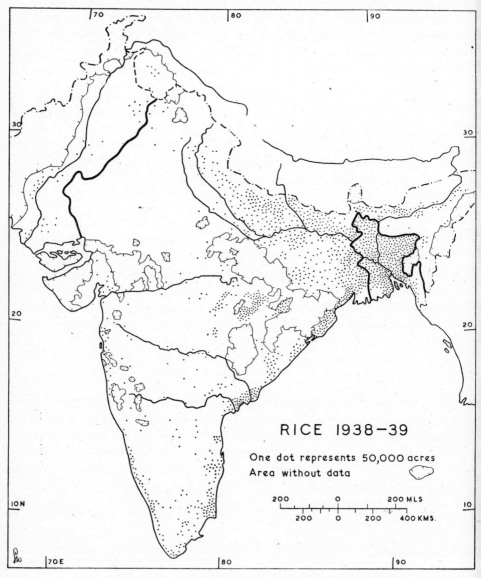

RICE 1938–39

One dot represents 50,000 acres
Area without data

Fig. 48.—RICE.   Figs. 48–52 and 54 compiled by W. T. W. Morgan.

tion than any agriculture will support", but no other way of life (except the not dissimilar economy of Egypt) has led to the evolution of a cultural system so stable and so permanent as that associated with the great paddy-plains of Monsoon Asia.[16]

(ii) *Wheat*

The distribution of wheat shows an even more marked climatic correlation than that of rice, but inverse to it. Of the total acreage (*c.* 35 m.) two-fifths are in arid W Pakistan, and about half of the rest in E Punjab and Wn UP. Wheat extends down the Ganges as far as W Bihar, and across Malwa into the drier NW quadrant of the Deccan; beyond these limits it is negligible. In the Peninsula, wheat is usually a dry crop on black soils; in the Indo-Gangetic Plains, irrigated on alluvial loams. The few inches of winter rain in the sub-montane strip of the Punjab enable good rabi crops to be grown. Most Indian wheats are hard.

The export of wheat through Karachi always fluctuated, falling off sharply in years succeeding a bad monsoon. The reason is obvious, and it is not likely that there will ever again be much significant export from the sub-continent.

(iii) *The Millets*

The total millet acreage perhaps equals that of rice, jowar and bajra alone having a combined acreage of 65 m. Yields, however, are on the whole low, the output of these two being only 10–12 m. tons. In location millets are intermediate between rice and wheat, jowar and bajra, for example, being usually rain-fed, in areas with *c.* 25–40 ins. Nothing displays more strikingly the contrast between the two Pakistans, wet in the E and dry in the W, than the fact that their acreage of these 'intermediate' crops is negligible. The concentration of jowar and bajra in the Deccan is also striking; ragi, the third of the more important millets, has a rather wider spread.

The idea, often held in the West, that the millets are spindly plants little better than grasses, and of inferior nutritive value, will hardly bear analysis. Jowar and bajra grow 6–8 ft high, or even more, and jowar indeed looks like a field of bulrushes. Table VIII shows clearly that in themselves even the lesser millets are better-balanced as food than is rice, and bajra ranks high indeed—level with wheat and oats in calcium content, between them in phosphorus, and with five and two times as much respectively of these minerals as even home-pounded rice. Yet there is a strong prejudice against them, and as they are generally grown on poorer soils and in the precarious 25–40-in. rainfall zone, yields are insecure.

[16] G. Kuriyan, *loc cit. ad fin.*

(a) *Jowar* (*Sorghum vulgare*),[17] known as cholam in the S, is both kharif and rabi. As kharif it needs 30–40 ins. of rain and is grown mainly on black soils, often rotated with cotton and usually mixed with pulses or sesamum.[18]

[17] The 'bread sorghum' of American writers, who apparently do not count it among the millets. American and British usages of the terms 'millet' and 'sorghum' are difficult to disentangle; here standard Indian usage is followed.

[18] Thus further, and indeed insolubly, complicating the statistics.

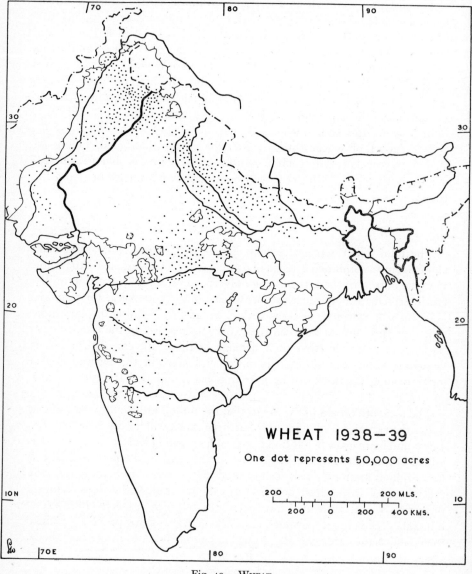

WHEAT 1938–39

One dot represents 50,000 acres

Fig. 49.—WHEAT.

Rabi jowar is less often mixed with other crops; it needs moisture-retaining soils which have received good rain in September–October, and is perhaps most notable in Tamilnad—where, of course, the 'rabi' is the monsoon crop. Jowar stalks form valuable fodder; the yield per acre may be 500 or more lbs of grain plus 100–200 lbs of inter-grown pulse and anything from 1000–3000 lbs of fodder. When grown specifically for fodder, as in Gujarat, parts

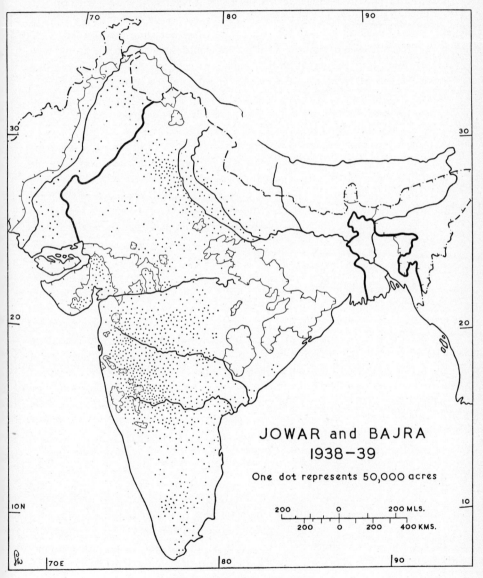

JOWAR and BAJRA
1938–39

One dot represents 50,000 acres

200   0   200 MLS.

200   0   200   400 KMS.

Fig. 50.—JOWAR AND BAJRA.

of the Deccan, and Coimbatore, jowar is sown very closely to make it run to stalk; in the Deccan a rude pit silage is practised.

(b) *Bajra* (or bajri, in the S cumbu or cambu, *Pennisetum typhoideum*) tolerates lighter soils than jowar, and is therefore grown extensively on the poorer Deccan Lava uplands, and on sandy or stony soils generally. It is nearly all kharif, but too much rain is harmful, and it is usually sown after the first force of the rains is spent. As a rule it is mixed, usually with pulses, so that rotation is not really necessary; but it may be 'rotated' with jowar in years of weak monsoon. Its nutritional value has been noted.

(c) *Ragi* (marua or madua, *Eleusine coracana*) ranges from the Himalayan slopes almost to the extreme S. Again it is a kharif crop, which may be transplanted; in the Archaean Deccan it is often grown under tanks. It is rarely intercropped. The highest yielder of the millets, with improved strains and careful culture it can give as much as 1500 lbs per acre or more; but as a rule only the nurseries receive much manure.

Ragi is perhaps the most important, though far from the most esteemed, food in such poor regions as Telangana. Although it is definitely a better food than rice, with a remarkably high calcium content (0·33%),"it is often regarded as food suitable for poor and ignorant villagers—also as the food of prisoners in the jails".[19] He who rises in the world exposes himself to beri-beri, while the diet and physique of the convict are generally better than those of his less enterprising fellows.

(iv) *Other Cereals; Pulses*

Apart from wheat, the only temperate cereals grown on any large scale are barley (6–7 m. ac.) and maize (8–9 m. ac., plus probably another 30% unrecorded). Well over half the barley and nearly a third of the recorded maize are in UP, largely in the sub-Himalaya; in the higher Himalaya ordinary and naked Tibetan barley (*grim*) are the staples. The pulses are of great importance; they are usually sown mixed, and the only one for which separate statistics are available is gram with 15–20 m. ac.: UP *c.* 6, E Punjab 3–4, W. Punjab 1·5 m. The pulses are useful as catch crops on poor soils or in bad years, and they are of course extremely valuable as 'nitrogenisers'; the extension of their use as green manure is desirable. As *dal*, a sort of lentil puree, pulses form an essential adjunct to most Indian curries.

2. Other Food Crops

Sugar and edible oilseeds demand separate treatment; no other crops cover a large area individually, the total area returned as under fruits and vegetables being 7 m. ac. and divided between plants far too numerous to be listed. Except on some specially favoured areas, such as floodplains near large cities, or around hill stations, horticulture is generally neglected: lack

---

[19] National Nutrition Research Laboratories, *Rice* (Bull. No. 28, Coonoor, 1940), 16.

of storage and transport facilities, and of purchasing power in potential markets, account for this dietetically deplorable situation. Mangoes, however, are all but universal, oranges—small and loose-skinned—and plantains (bananas) widespread; the Himalayan regions and the Wn border hills grow most temperate fruits, including grapes, and in the NW Himalaya apricots are an essential food. The fruit industry is best developed in Kashmir and around Peshawar, and there are possibilities of extension in Baluchistan. A dried and canned-fruit industry may develop in W Pakistan.

Condiments such as chillies, essential to give a specious appearance of variety to a rice diet, are grown almost everywhere; spices mainly along the Wn Ghats and the coast S of Goa; pepper is probably still the most important. Coconuts are officially oilseeds, but have too many uses to be easily categorised; other palms of value include dates in W Pakistan (the ubiquitous wild date has a practically useless fruit, but is tapped for toddy); Palmyra, widespread but especially important in the extreme SE, used for toddy, sugar, and thatching; and the areca palm with its associate the betel vine, sources of the red *pan* chewed by high and low, Hindu and Muslim. There is some export of cardamoms, pepper, and areca nuts.

3. Fodder Crops

Little, unfortunately, need be said about these: some 10–12 m. ac. only, nearly half in the Punjab and nearly a quarter in Bombay. This is exceedingly low for a country which contains nearly a third of the world's cattle, but the reason is distressingly simple: few peasants will devote land which might grow food for men to grow food for beasts, and indeed such are the demands on the scanty holdings that the ryot often cannot do so even if he would. The results, however, are directly deplorable for the bovine population, and ultimately for the human. To this problem we shall return.

B. Food/Cash Crops: Oilseeds and Sugar

These occupy an economic position intermediate between the cereals and the fibres; some oilseeds, such as castor and linseed, are exclusively for industrial use, while rape, mustard, and sesamum are mainly foods, and the internal consumption of groundnuts is rapidly increasing. Sugar is distinguished from the purely food crops by the strong industrial element in its development.

(i) Oilseeds

Pakistan's share of oilseeds is nearly negligible—*c.* 1·5 m. ac., almost all rape and mustard. In India oilseeds acreage for the decade before 1945 was fairly steady at 20–23 m. (*c.* 10% NSA), of which 16–18 m. were edible— sesamum, groundnut, rape—and the rest mainly linseed and castor. Within the group the most striking development is that of groundnuts, insignificant before 1913, under 2 m. ac. in 1918–19, and now nearly half the total.

    Groundnut is a crop of the Peninsula,[20] 90% being grown in Madras and the adjoining parts of Hyderabad and Bombay. Within Madras there are two major concentrations—in the Ceded Districts (the Madras Deccan)

[20] S. Velayudham, "Groundnuts in Madras", *IGJ* XXI (1946), 100–12 and 153–73.

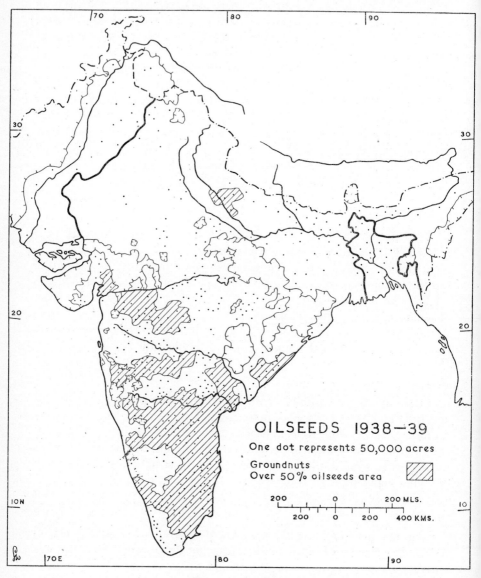

Fig. 51.—Oilseeds.

and on the coastal plain behind Pondicherry. Its export value has led to its receiving marked attention from the Agricultural Department, and a main factor in its spread has been its suitability to light sandy soils, of little use for cereals or cotton; it is a kharif crop. *Sesamum* (til or gingelly, *Sesamum indicum*) has rather more than a third of the area of groundnut, but is far more widely distributed, being significant everywhere except in Assam, W Punjab, and Sind; it is the source of the most widely used cooking oil. It can be grown as kharif (usually mixed) on light soils and as rabi, rotated with jowar and cotton, on heavy. Of the 1·5 m. ac. under *coconut*, at least 1·25 m. are in S Madras and Cochin-Travancore.[21]

(ii) *Sugar-cane*

Sugar is probably indigenous to India, the word itself apparently coming from Sanskrit through Hellenistic Greece. Again Pakistan's share is small: 573,000 ac. against *India's* 3,336,000 (averages 1936–46). About 250,000 ac. are grown in E Bengal and over 100,000 in the Vale of Peshawar, where the Mardan factory is one of the largest in the sub-continent. In *India* the UP has 55–60% of the area, followed by Bihar and E Punjab. The total production of raw sugar is about 5 m. tons, 85% in *India*.

The distribution shows some peculiarities. Nn India is the largest producer of cane-sugar in the world *outside* the tropics; and although in the S temperature régimes are closer to those of other cane-producing countries, and Sn canes produce 2·5 to 3 tons of sugar per acre against 0·6 (Punjab) to 1·5 (Bengal) in the N, yet 80–90% of total output comes from Indo-Gangetic regions, with thin, probably indigenous, canes in contrast to the thick varieties, perhaps Pacific in origin, of the S. One point in this low standing of the S is probably humidity: the really heavy producers—Java, Cuba, Hawaii, Mauritius—have all insular climates to which the nearest Indian homologue would probably be coastal Kerala, already entirely devoted to paddy and with no room for a cash crop. But for several physical reasons costs of production are much higher in the S than in the N. Outside the middle Ganges Plains (Bihar and En UP) sugar-cane must usually be irrigated, and irrigation is as a rule much easier and cheaper in the Indo-Gangetic plains than in the Peninsula; moreover the loamy alluvium, with sufficient lime and potash, does not need manuring to anything like the extent necessary in the S. The Godavari-Kistna deltas, indeed, approach optimum conditions, with ample cheap irrigation and rich alluvial soils; but here frequent cyclonic storms compel the use of some 5000 bamboos per acre to protect the canes, and the cost of this in 1942 was Rs.80–150 per acre, the latter figure being half the cost of cultivation. Further, although the main cane research station in India is at Coimbatore, work was originally

---

[21] The vegetable oil industry is discussed in Ch. XI, coconut culture in Kerala in Ch. XXII.

on the thin varieties, improved strains of which were in general use in the
N by 1938, when trials of new tropical canes were not complete. Finally
there are few other cash crops suitable to UP conditions, and hence cane is
grown in solid blocks; the more sporadic distribution in the S has inhibited
the growth of refineries, in turn restricting demand while the N was building up a great industry.

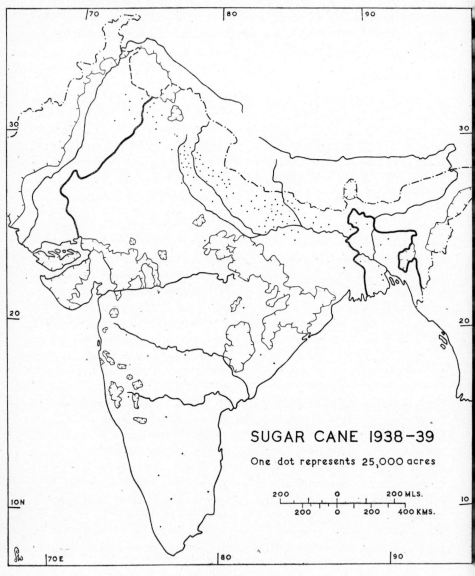

SUGAR CANE 1938–39

One dot represents 25,000 acres

Fig. 52.—Sugar Cane.

The main risk in the NW, as far as En UP, is frost; in Meerut losses of up to 20% are likely every five years or so, and in extreme cases losses of 50–80% have been reported. Frost is a menace as far S as Ahmadnagar and Nasik, at 1600–1800 ft in the upper Godavari basin; here also waterlogging and saline efflorescences have put over a third of some canal-irrigated areas out of cultivation.[22]

Indian yields are generally low, averaging about 3000 lbs of raw sugar per acre; this is less than a quarter of Javanese and Hawaiian yields, though not very far below those of Cuba and Brazil. This figure is not so likely to be understated as cereal yields.

C. FIBRES

Here at last Pakistan holds a strong, even a commanding, position. In 1947 she had *c.* 80–85% of the area and output of jute, and about one-fifth of the area but one-third of the output of cotton. Moreover while the raw cotton output of *India* has fallen almost catastrophically over the last ten years, that of Pakistan has been much less affected. (Fig. 53).[23] On the other

[22] This discussion is based on Chs. VIII and IX of Sharma, q.v. for much further detail. The sugar-refining industry is discussed in Ch. XI, Section II, below.

[23] The latest figures broken down to Districts and comparable for the whole sub-continent are pre-war; efforts to obtain more up-to-date detailed figures from both *Indian* and Pakistani sources were unavailing. Distributions for other crops have probably not changed significantly, so that it is legitimate to map the old distributions; but this is obviously not so for cotton and jute, and distribution maps of these have therefore perforce been omitted.

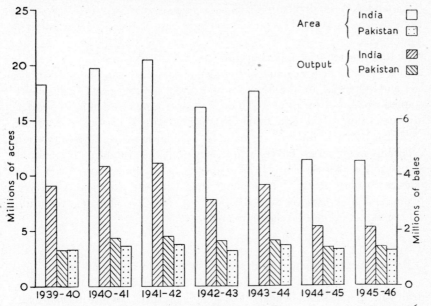

Fig. 53.—COTTON ACREAGE AND OUTPUT, *INDIA* AND PAKISTAN, 1939–40 TO 1945–46. Bales of 400 lbs. Source: *Estimates of Areas and Yields of Principal Crops in Undivided India, 1936–37 to 1945–46* (ND, 1949), Tables 109–12.

hand friction over fiscal policies relating to jute, and the abrupt price-rise consequent on Pakistan's refusal to devalue her rupee, have led to intensive efforts to increase the *Indian* jute area.

Both raw cotton and raw jute are now overshadowed as *Indian* exports by their manufactures, and there is a large import of raw cotton:

	Exports (*in* 1000 *tons*)	Imports
1946–47	162 (Bombay 63, Karachi 95)	99 (Bombay 92)
1947–48	209 (Bombay 140, Karachi 58)	113 (Bombay 99)

Before Partition about half the imports were from Egypt; in 1948–49 Pakistan provided 62,000 of the *Indian* import of 161,000 tons.

(i) *Cotton*

The cotton of W Pakistan is entirely an irrigated crop; in *India* only a little over 10% is irrigated, it being essentially a rains-sown crop in the 25–30-in. rainfall zone, usually grown on the deep, heavy, moisture-retentive black soils (regur) of the Deccan Lavas, the Gujarat alluvium, and pockets on the Archaeans. By far the greatest *Indian* concentration is in Maharashtra—the Deccan Lava area of Bombay, Madhya Pradesh (CP), and NW Hyderabad; secondary concentrations are in Gujarat, the Bombay Karnatak, and on the Coimbatore and Tinnevelly black soils in Tamilnad.

Cotton is again probably aboriginal to India, grown and woven from the earliest times. The indigenous (*desi*) cottons, of which the 'Tinnies' of the SE and 'Oomras' of the Deccan are perhaps best-known, are short-stapled—only $\frac{1}{2}$–$\frac{7}{8}$ in. Efforts to increase staple have resulted in a considerable extension of the area under improved strains (especially Cambodia, $\frac{7}{8}$–1 in.), but it is difficult to maintain standards owing to adulteration, especially in ginneries. On the whole, however, the proportion of medium-staple cotton is increasing. In W Pakistan development for export came later, with the Canal Colonies rather than with the American Civil War boom, and American varieties (staple 1–1$\frac{1}{16}$ in.) predominate, accounting for the higher output in relation to area.

(ii) *Jute*

Before Partition Bengal held practically a world monopoly of jute production: the nature and requirements of the crop are thus perhaps best dealt with in Ch. XIX (Bengal). The significant spread of jute in *India* since Partition is clearly a matter of nationalist rather than rationalist economics. It may be noted, however, that apart from the Orissa and Madras deltas and the W coast—all heavy rain areas—the main extension has been along the terai in Bihar and En UP. Here, on newly cleared land settled by refugees from E Pakistan, the claim that jute extension does not encroach upon the food area is doubtless justified; but it is difficult to think that this can be so in the other areas. But this is a part of the wider dilemma of food *versus* cash crops, to be discussed in the next chapter.

Experiments are being made in Bombay with an indigenous grass, *mesta*, as a substitute for or mixture with jute. It may be noted that the considerable linseed cultivation in *India*, as in other sub-tropical areas, is entirely for oil and not for fibre.

(iii) *Wool*

For the sake of a general view we may deal here with animal fibres. Of these wool is more important than silk. In 1948 *India* had about 37 m. sheep, over half in the states and over a quarter in Madras; at least 6 m. must be added for W Pakistan. Kashmir, Rajasthan, and W Pakistan produce nearly two-thirds of the annual clip of 90–100 m. lbs of raw wool, and it would seem that the Pakistani share would be fully 30%, and that again including most of the better grades from the hill sheep of Baluchistan and the NWFP. The Nn wools are usually white, those of the S anything from off-white through red to black, and also coarse and hairy.

About half the clip was exported for coarse manufactures such as carpets, felt, and rough blankets; for good woollens the *Indian* industry has to import most of its requirements from Australia.

(iv) *Silk*

It seems probable that the silkworms of ancient India were generally not mulberry-feeders (*Bombyx* spp.), though *Bombyx mori* from China is of old standing in Manipur. Mulberries are grown and the true silkworm reared along the Wn Himalayan slopes, especially in Kashmir, and on paddy-bunds in Bengal. In addition "India has three well-known purely indigenous silkworms: the *tasar*, the *muga*, and the *eri*. The first is widely distributed in the lower hills, more especially of the great central table-land, and feeds on several jungle trees. The second is confined to Assam and En Bengal, and feeds on a laurel. The third exists in a state of semi-domestication, being reared on the castor-oil plant." [24]

The EIC early took an interest in sericulture, exporting to England either fabrics or raw silk in accordance with changing economic or political circumstances. Despite considerable governmental support, Indian sericulture has long been in a decline. A small proportion of cottage-produced tussore is of high quality, but the worms are generally badly cared for, and indeed much of the cocoon production is wild, collected in the forests, and

[24] *Imperial Gaz.* (1908), III. 208.

"the reeling is so badly done in India that foreign countries prefer to take the cocoons." [25] Home production of raw silk accounts for only a small part of mill consumption.

D. Miscellaneous Peasant Crops

It would be hopeless to attempt even to enumerate the enormous variety of interesting special crops, from the saffron of Kashmir to the senna of Tinnevelly. It may be noted, however, that two of the most famous of Indian products are now all but extinct: *indigo* and *opium*. In 1897 synthetic indigo became commercially practicable, and in 15 years the area under the crop fell by 90% to 170,000 ac. It rallied to 700,000 in the 1914–18 war, but in 1939–40 only 40,000 ac. were cultivated, mainly in Bihar. Opium had in 1939–40 about 7000 ac., against over 600,000 before export to China was stopped in 1907. The destruction of the industry was thus a deliberate, though not immoral, political act. Opium is consumed in India, especially in the Himalayas and the Assam Hills, but is rigorously controlled, though there is probably sporadic illicit cultivation in the hills. The social effects of opium smoking in Himalayan India, however, are hardly serious. Indian hemp (*ganja*) is far more dangerous.

Tobacco shows if anything a slight tendency to increase in *India* (1945–46: 1,021,000 ac.), though in Pakistan there has been a marked decline in the last 10 or 12 years, from 350,000 to 200,000 ac., mainly in E Bengal. Probably there is a good deal of unrecorded cultivation. Tobacco is grown to some extent all over the country, and in the N is a favourite crop on the rich silts of temporary alluvial islands; but Madras has over a third of the *Indian* acreage. Smoking is universal—cheroots, hookahs, English and American cigarettes (some manufactured in India with imported tobacco), or the appalling *bidis*, the cheap smoke of the masses. By and large Indian tobacco is poor stuff, and the divine if financially deplorable habit is far from playing the part in the national life that it does in Burma. The main cheroot-making centres are Dindigul and Trichinopoly in S Madras, but even those brands which bear English (or Anglo-Indian) names are hardly as good as the humbler product of the petty shops of Burma, innocent of machinery or publicity. [26]

E. Plantation Crops

Plantations are almost confined to tea, coffee, and rubber, with a little—too little—chinchona in the Nilgiris and Darjeeling.

(i) Tea

The wetter Himalayan slopes and their gravelly piedmont fans, and the hills of the extreme S, offer admirable conditions for tea: indeed when the

[25] Jathar and Beri, II. 57.
[26] As a chain-cheroot-smoker (supplies permitting) the writer feels competent to judge.

EIC began planting with Chinese seed in 1834, a wild variety was found in the Assam Hills. Tea is grown in the S at elevations of over 4000 ft, and in Darjeeling to 7000, but generally speaking yields are smaller, though quality is better, on the higher plantations. Most of the larger plantations in Bengal and Assam are on the terai (here 'Duars') or its equivalent.

Of the total area of 840,000 ac. (40% of world area, excluding China) E Bengal (Pakistan) has 90,000, Assam and W Bengal 570,000, the Nilgiris and Travancore 165,000. Plantations in these areas are large, 450–550 ac.; but along the Himalayan slopes as far as E Punjab tea is grown on holdings

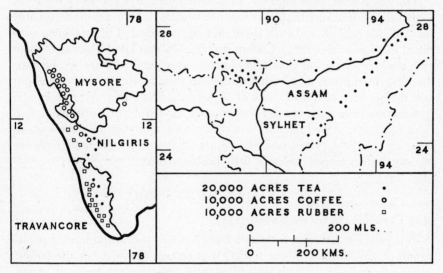

Fig. 54.—PLANTATION CROPS.

down to 4 ac., or less; but their share in output is insignificant. Labour is, or has been, a major difficulty in Assam.

Production is over 6 m. lbs, overwhelmingly *Indian*; from 1936 to 1947 the output of E Pakistan had increased more rapidly than that of *India*, but since Partition there has been a crisis in the Sylhet industry. Trade on a large scale began about 1850, and the sub-continent now provides over half the tea of world commerce; exports are usually 70–80% of output and in 1947–48 totalled 384 m. lbs.

(ii) *Coffee*

Coffee was introduced by a 17th-century Muslim saint returning from Mecca, who gave the plant and his name to the Baba Bhudan Hills in Mysore; but real development began in the 1830s. By 1885 there were 237,500 ac., but borers, leaf-blight, and Brazil brought catastrophe, and in 1877–87 no fewer than 273 plantations were abandoned. Coffee estates are usually small, only about 50 ac., and there are holdings of under 10 ac. which do not appear in the statistics. Area and output are irregular; the former was fairly steady at 180,000–200,000 ac. for the 10 years preceding 1946, but was reported at only 94,000 in 1946–47–48; output varied from 32 to 56 m. lbs 1936–46, but is now about 19 m. About 50% of the area is in Mysore, mostly on the Wynaad Plateau, and 45% in adjoining Coorg and the Nilgiris.

(iii) *Rubber*

Only in Kerala, with high but equable temperatures and a dry season of only three or four months (and those not rainless) are conditions reasonably suitable for rubber, and even there they are not ideal. The total area, confined to Travancore (72%), Cochin, and the Malabar Dt of Madras, is about 160,000–170,000 ac., of which *c.* 135,000 are bearing. Yields are low, perhaps less due to climatic disadvantages than to poor methods; they are about 280 lbs per acre, only half those of Malaya and Indonesia. Average annual production from 1940 to 1945—when only about 10% of world plantation area was left in Allied hands—was 16,600 tons. Costs are now too high in relation to world prices, and the future of these plantations, which are mostly Indian-owned, seems a little problematical.

III. ANIMAL HUSBANDRY

The Cattle Problem (see also p. 234)

It is possible that even truncated *India* has now the largest human population of any country in the world; it is certain that she has the largest bovine population. The Union alone (in this context 90% of states' territory reports) has 140 m. oxen and 40 m. buffaloes, and it is estimated that the whole sub-continent has around 213 m. head of horned cattle. That these figures, which are probably fairly accurate, represent excessive numbers cannot be denied by any reasonably unprejudiced student. Unfortunately the sanctity of the cow bedevils rational discussion, and even near-Communists to whom the cow is just an animal evade the issue behind a screen of historical apologetics, for no better reason than that most critics of the situation have been British.

The agriculture of India differs fundamentally from that of Japan and most of China in that it is firmly based on the use of draught animals. Sacred as the cow is, the bullock is of more mundane importance; there are about five bullocks to every four cows, and they do most ploughing and almost all carting. "The essential equipment of the peasant farmer includes a pair of bullocks or buffaloes to do the ploughing and draw the cart; a cow to propagate the species and quite secondarily to give milk." [27]

[27] L. D. Stamp, *Asia* (ed. 1944), 230.

Paradoxically enough, no branch of Indian agriculture is worse managed than animal husbandry. Except for the fundamental taboo against taking the life of the cow, this is not so much the peasant's original sin as the result of strictly geographical conditions. To take one example, Indian 'hay' is really dried grass which has lost its seeds and so is little better than straw, rather than hay in the European sense: it is too wet for hay-making when the grass (such as exists) is up towards the end of the rains, and after that the peasant is too busy with kharif harvest or rabi sowing. Where rainfall is too light to inhibit hay-making there is precious little to make hay with, and in any case—probably as a natural consequence of these conditions—the ryot "has been a grass-cutter, but a hay-maker never, and he finds it hard to begin." [28]

By and large the cattle, being essentially working rather than food animals, are where the men are, and in these areas pressure of population is so intense that often the village-site itself can hardly be squeezed into the sea of arable, and so obviously there is no meadow, no permanent pasture, no fodder crops: only the waste, which in the worst parts of the Ganges plains is reduced to mere wayside scraps. Elsewhere such fodder as there is —mainly paddy, wheat, and millet stalks—goes mainly to the working cattle, the bullocks; the cow must fend for herself. By April and May, the height of the hot weather, there is likely to be very little stalk left, the stubble has been grazed off, in many areas there is very little leafage on the trees, and finally the scanty vegetation of the waste, at best coarse, tussocky, and of little food value—or guarded by a fierce array of thorns—has been reduced in effect to a mass of dry cellulose. The general appearance of the cattle in most parts of India is then simply horrible—skeletons wrapped in hide, tottering to whatever patches of shade may be.

Some areas, it is true, look at first sight as if they could support more cattle, farmed on pastoral lines: such are the less arid parts of Rajasthan, in Malwa. But soils are thin, rainfall irregular, grass poor except after flushes of rain; any considerable stocking would probably result in heavy erosion. Moreover pastoralism as such is at a discount; the long distances to wretchedly poor urban markets render dairying uneconomic, and there is obviously no sale for beef.

Such a state of affairs would be bad enough even were the stock healthy. But the country is unenclosed, there is an almost complete lack of eugenic practices, and feeble bulls beget at will upon diseased cows. Veterinary services, despite recent expansion, are terribly inadequate, and epidemic disease such as rinderpest still takes a heavy toll.

The over-population, however, is not solely the result of an irrational apotheosis of the cow. Paradoxically there is often an actual deficiency in the cattle-power needed to work the land; the numbers are there, but the

[28] RCAI, 205–06; the whole of Ch. VII remains of fundamental value

bullocks are simply not strong enough for their work. Hence more are bred, which implies more cows and young stock—strictly speaking useless mouths—and the circle of starvation is complete. The disbalance within the cattle population is as bad as the actual excess of numbers: "It may be estimated that about 125 million cattle out of a total stock of 200 million are superfluous and uneconomical. There are as many as 67 cattle per 100 acres of sown land [the figures range from 35 in Bombay to 112 in Bengal] . . . while the total number of working cattle is only 60 million for about 300 million cropped acres (one pair of bullocks for every 10 acres), a number totally inadequate for intensive farming." [29]

However counter to average *Indian* opinion, the conclusion seems inescapable: the essential improvement of cattle cannot be attained without limitation and even actual reduction of numbers; but sentiment and policy act in a contrary direction. Even to a non-Hindu there may be something of a moral problem here; man has after all called into existence these millions of sentient beings for his convenience, to be liquidated when inconvenient. But on a different level we have the old dilemma of not being able to afford short-term what it is necessary to afford long-term: there are too many cattle in the gross, but most individual farmers may have too few to carry on with.

Better Breeds

As so often, these malpractices are virtually forced upon the husbandman, either by the weight of immemorial social pressures, or by sheer necessitous poverty; and they are not universal. Indian cattle in normal conditions are well adapted to their trying environment in that they have amazing powers of endurance and recuperation. "The finest stocks of tropical cattle now existing are probably to be found in India",[30] and the use of the zebu or humped ox for crossing as far afield as S America attests its inherent suitability to the leaner tropical grasslands.

When he is able to do so the ryot takes good care of his stock, and in some favoured localities really good strains have been evolved. These are mainly draught animals, such as the Kankrej of Gujarat, the Kangayam of Coimbatore, and the famous Amrit Mahal breed fostered by Haidar Ali of Mysore for military mobility. But they include milkers such as the Gir and Sindhi, and dual-purpose breeds such as the Hansi or Hariana of E Punjab. A few scattered groups are indeed pastoralists rather than cultivators: the few hundred primitive Todas of the Nilgiris, the Alambadi breeders of the Mysore-Madras border forests. In the extra-Peninsular mountains, of course, a different type of pastoralism, based on sheep and goats, is common.

[29] R. K. Mukerjee, *The Food Supply* (OPIA No. 8, 1942), 21–22; cf. RCAI, 190–92.
[30] RCAI, 222.

Dairying

Despite the enormous numbers of cows milk plays a pitifully small part in Indian diets; in Saurashtra daily consumption per head is about 19 oz., in the Punjab it is only 10, nowhere else consumes more than half as much, and in Madhya Pradesh (CP) the amount is under 1 ounce! The *Indian* average is 5·45 oz., against 40 (pre-war) in Britain. The urban milk supply is almost everywhere entirely deplorable in quantity and much worse in quality, even when (if ever) not deliberately adulterated. Much of it is produced in foul conditions within city limits, the herds being driven out each morning to the ragged fetid waste found around all large towns. Climatic conditions are at least partly responsible for the low direct milk consumption, since it is obviously impossible to keep milk for long; over 40% of it is in fact converted into *ghi*, butter clarified over a slow fire, for which cow-dung is the best fuel. Hence buffaloes are often preferred to cows as milch cattle, since their milk contains up to 50% more butterfat than that of the cow; buffaloes supply about 45% of total milk output. As might be expected, milk yields are almost incredibly low, except on a very few military or capitalist dairy-farms; in *India* they average 413 lbs a year for cows and 1100 for buffaloes; with 61 m. milch cattle, nearly twice as many as all Europe outside the USSR, *Indian* milk output is only about one-fifth the European total.[31]

Hides and Skins

Even though shielded from sacrilegious hands, the cow sooner or later dies and must be disposed of. This task is left to Muslims and the untouchable caste of Chamars or leather-workers. Something over 20 m. cow and 5 m. buffalo hides are produced annually, to which must be added 25 m. goat and sheep skins. Before 1939 some 40% of the hides and 50% of the skins were exported, about half the former as semi-tanned 'kips'. In the 11 years 1929–40 an annual average of 70,000 tons of hides, skins, and more or less tanned leather was exported; "for some time past India has been not only the most important exporting country for hides and leather but has constituted the only reservoir for the drawing of the large supplies of light hides by the world markets." [32]

Exports of bones and bone-meal were also very large, and here, as in the case of oilseeds (below, 296) the arguments of the RCAI against their processing and retention for fertiliser in India might be reconsidered.

Other Livestock

These need not detain us long. In addition to the 45 m. or so *sheep* there are over 45 m. *goats* in *India* and 10 m. in Pakistan—nearly half the latter

---

[31] *IR* II/39 (22/11/50).
[32] Sharma, 168, citing *Report on the Marketing of Hides in India and Burma* (1943).

in E Bengal. Again Madras leads, followed closely by UP, Bengal, and the Punjab. Goat "mutton" is probably the most widely consumed flesh food.

Horses are scarcely used for agricultural traction or indeed for any cartage, but they draw the light traps (*tongas* or *ekkas*), the taxis of the lower middle class, largely replaced in the S by the bullock-drawn *jutka*. *Donkeys*, in the mountains *mules*, and in the higher Himalayas even sheep, are used as pack animals; pack bullocks are also seen. *Camels* are still important in W Pakistan and Rajasthan, but hardly known elsewhere; in Karachi they do a good deal of the port cartage, hauling large rubber-tyred floats. *Poultry*, small and tough, are ubiquitous, but the *pig*, so conspicuous in China, is conspicuous only by his absence in India. Universally common to both countries are the village scavengers, lean mongrels of repulsive aspect: the traveller's entry into the village is invariably signalised by a clamorous reception committee of pariah dogs.

IV. OTHER RURAL OCCUPATIONS

It remains to glance briefly at other ways of life in the countryside. First in numbers and importance are the village artisans who, despite factory competition, in many lines still provide very essential services (below, 272–74). Apart from these the most important rural occupations are those connected with the forests, sericulture (already discussed), and fishing.

Forests and Forest Products

Forestry proper is almost entirely a government monopoly, either by direct exploitation or by licenses. The most important timbers are noted in Ch. III. *Indian* outturn in 1949 was 394 m. cu ft (Bombay, Madhya Pradesh (CP), UP each over 60 m.). Bamboo and *sabai* grass are the main bases of the paper industry. More important in the day-to-day life of those villagers who live within reach of woodland is the enormous range of 'minor forest products'. Many of these can be directly used or collected on payment of small fees; sometimes they are free by immemorial custom. Such items include foliage for use as fodder or leaf-manure; materials for thatching, mat-making, and basketry; grass-cutting and grazing rights; fuel-wood; bamboos for individual use. The right to collect commercial products has naturally to be paid for, except in unreserved jungle: these include a multitude of dye- and tan-stuffs, drugs, and nuts. Among the more important, in which there is already some export, are acacia gum, artemisia (source of the vermicide santonin), beeswax, canes, cardamoms, cashew nuts, chaulmugra oil, cinnamon, cutch, Indian kapok, lac, lemongrass oil, myrobalans, nux vomica, resins, sandalwood, senna, and tamarinds.[33] Sugar and alcohol are obtained from the toddy and nipa palms and

[33] S. Krishna and R. L. Badhwar, "Exploitation of Minor Forest Products" (5th British Empire Forestry Conference, Dehra Dun, 1947), 2.

from the edible flowers of *mahua* (*Bassia latifolia*); this tree is so common and so luxuriously florescent in the NE Peninsula that it has been suggested as a source of power alcohol.

By far the most important of these products, accounting indeed for nearly half their total value, is lac. This is a gummy excretion from the body of the lac-insect, which infests several species of trees, notably sal and dhak (*Butea frondosa*). The lac forms a crust on the twigs, which are collected and sold as 'stick-lac', and after processing shellac is produced. Shellac is an essential ingredient of some varnishes, of sealing-wax, and similar compositions, and has also a wide range of uses in indigenous arts and crafts.

Careless collection and processing, and rumoured progress in Siam, threaten the future of the industry, which before the war produced 90% of world supply and processed the remaining 10%, which came from Burma, Siam, and Indo-China. Lac collecting is particularly important in Chota Nagpur and adjacent areas, where it provides a useful subsidiary income to a very large number of villagers. Exports are around 500,000 cwts.[34]

Fishing

Even though the numbers of India's people are so great that it would seem that a large proportion of them would in any event be condemned to a poor life, the neglect of fisheries seems another striking example of what seems almost a masochistic tendency to make the worst of a bad world. Religious factors play a part: the caste status of fishermen, who automatically take animal life, is very low. Climate also is obviously unfavourable to marketing any but dried fish far away from coast or river-bank.

Although there are perhaps half a million fishermen, the total production in *India* is not much over 500,000 tons (two-thirds sea-fish), under $3\frac{1}{2}$ lbs per head of population. Obviously fish-foods can never attain the importance they have in truly maritime countries, but there is ample scope for expansion in both sea and inland fishing. The continental shelf in *Indian* waters is about 115,000 sq mls, and the coast is dotted with fishing villages; but sea-fishing is confined to five or six miles offshore, being carried on from craft which at best are hardly smacks and include the Madras catamarans, merely a few logs fitted together. Real deep-sea fishing scarcely exists, and there is a nearly complete lack of any but the most primitive shore facilities. Of the inland fisheries the most important and best-used are those of Bengal; many of the deltaic and estuarine fish are excellent, especially the *hilsa*.

Government assistance and co-operative marketing could probably lead to a great increase in the output of the inland fisheries by 'fish-farming', and this without undue difficulty. The improvement of sea-fishing is a

[34] Vakil, 311.

harder problem. The *Indian* Government is devoting considerable attention to fishery research and development, but given the poverty of the fishing communities the lines of advance open would seem to be (*a*) large-scale capitalist fishing or (*b*) state working thinly disguised as co-operation. The former is socially undesirable and in any case unlikely as returns are at present problematical, and there is no real interest in it; the latter would probably be 'improvement from above', and unduly costly in relation to the nutritional gain. There might, however, be possibilities in canning, using wastes as fertiliser, and extracting shark-liver oil.

Apart from the delta fisheries of E Bengal, the situation in Pakistan is much the same as in *India*, but even less developed.[35]

[35] There is a general discussion of fishery prospects—possibly too optimistic—in *A Food Plan for India* (RIIA, 1945), 40–43. For Pakistan, see M. Rahimullah (Qureshi), "Prospects of Marine Fisheries of Western Pakistan", *Bulletin of Karachi Geographical Society*, No. 2 (1950), 12–21.

ADDITIONAL NOTE ON THE CATTLE PROBLEM

The First Five Year Plan (1951) underlines the seriousness of the problem when it points out that *India* has to support nearly one-quarter of the world's bovine population, that there is probably roughage for only 78% of these numbers (and of course a far smaller proportion of concentrates), and that only about 750 good stud bulls are bred annually, against a total need of about 1 m. (pp. 109–10). The Plan's proposals include: diversion of area from foodgrains to fodder (to be compensated by more efficient bullocks and more milkfoods); rapid breeding of stud bulls in "key villages"; artificial insemination.

On the cow-slaughter issue, the Plan has the interesting suggestion (p. 111) that since "the wholesale slaughter of useless cattle is not a practical proposition", areas "where the fodder supply to-day is unutilised" should be used as camps for old and useless cattle, with arrangements for collecting manure, hides, etc. No such areas are indicated; they doubtless exist, but (as pointed out on p. 229 above) the risk of overstocking and serious erosion should be carefully considered.

CHAPTER IX

AGRARIAN PROBLEMS AND PROGRAMMES

MUCH more than in any Western country, the wealth of the sub-continent lies in its fields—fields often fragmented into mere rags of land, torn by erosion, tilled for so long without rest or fertilisation that over large areas they seem to have reached the ultimate base-level of infertility; and yet ultimately responsible for the sustenance of some 450 million souls. Advances in agricultural technique, while not entirely lacking, affect but a small fraction of the farming, and with increasing pressure on the land either sheer need or the seduction of cash crops has led, in some areas, to a lowering of standards in such matters as rotations, while increasingly the owner-cultivator has been forced into tenancy, the small tenant to become a landless man. The pressure of the cattle population is as bad or worse, with results ultimately disastrous to man and beast. There can be no possible doubt, then, that the rehabilitation of agriculture is by far the most pressing problem facing both *India* and Pakistan; more important even than industrialisation, which has a vital part to play in that rehabilitation, yet cannot be truly successful without the markets of a thriving countryside. This at once suggests what is indeed the fact, that every step forward seems enmeshed, as in 'concertina wire', by a tangle of interlocking vicious circles.

This interlocking of the problems renders the writing of a coherent account extremely difficult. But we can, perhaps, get a reasonably articulated picture by separating out (i) problems of technique, (ii) problems of social organisation, and (iii) the general problem, resuming all others, of the ratio between food output and mouths to feed. Finally we may survey recent developments and plans. But it must always be remembered that this breakdown is arbitrary, all specific problems having both technical and social aspects, as is obviously true, for example, of fragmentation and the cattle position.

I. PROBLEMS OF TECHNIQUE

1. *Sub-division and Fragmentation* [1]

The average Indian farm is very small, probably uneconomic if we admit any element of welfare into the economics. A general average would be pointless, and the position is complicated by the distinction (not always made) between ownership and cultivating holdings: the man who farms his

[1] Perhaps the best readily accessible discussion is in Jathar and Beri, I. Ch. VII.

own land, neither more nor less, is probably rare in the more settled regions. The following significant figures for the Punjab are given by the RCAI (and copied by practically everyone else):

% of Ownership Holdings	Area, acres	% of Cultivating Holdings
17·9	under 1	22·5
25·5	1–3 }	33·3
14·9	3–5 }	
18·0	5–10	20·5
23·7	over 10	23·7

To appreciate the full gravity of the situation it must be noted (i) that in the Punjab Canal Colonies and the Bombay cotton zone, holdings are unusually large; (ii) the figures are 25 years old, and the situation is probably worse to-day; (iii) as there are in India as a whole more cultivators than owners, the cultivating units are smaller than the ownership units. On the other side it is possible to support a family on a very small area indeed of good rice-land, and many of the tiniest cultivating holdings are worked by people whose main livelihood comes from some non-farming employment; are in fact allotments, not farms, tokens of attachment to the land rather than the main business of life.

Since overheads do not, of course, decrease proportionately as the size of holding goes down, the peasant with such an exiguous basis for his support is practically forced to overwork his land by neglecting fallows and by excessive double-cropping, until indeed returns diminish so markedly that even double-cropping no longer pays and the TSA itself shrinks.[2] Without venturing on the vexed and highly technical question of what an 'economic holding' might be, we may think it clear enough that the opening statement of this section errs if anything by moderation.

All this is the result of *sub-division* of property among all the sons, a practice sanctioned by both Hindu and Muslim laws of inheritance, but less invoked when the 'joint family' system was in full strength, or in old days when, in Jathar and Beri's phrase, "it was land that ran after tenants". Growing population and the substitution of the cash nexus for customary status have led to an insistence on individual rights which may reach fantastic extremes, and accentuates the allied, but distinct, *fragmentation* of one man's ground into scattered tiny parcels. In places this has reached almost incredible proportions; to cite again some often-cited figures, in one Punjab village 12,800 ac. were divided into 63,000 "fields"; in another

[2] Mukerjee, *Economic Problems*, I. 113.

28% of holdings had each over 30 separate fields; in a third 5 owners had over 100 plots each and one over 200; in Ratnagiri (Bombay) there are plots of $30\frac{1}{2}$ sq yds ($1/160$th or $0\cdot00625$ of an acre).[3] Even if physical division is impossible, partition between heirs has been insisted upon down to a half-share in a tree. To some extent this is understandable; he who has little must cling to what he has. But it is none the less deplorable, resulting, together with the multiplication of debt and tenancy suits, in a staggering burden of litigation. In 1939 nearly half the nearly $1\cdot9$ m. civil suits were directly concerned with the land, and over 1 m. were for Rs.50 ($£7$ $10s$.) or less. Unfortunately lawyers—and too often witnesses—must be paid, whence more debt.

Fragmentation does not, of course, arise solely as an incident of sub-division. It is deeply rooted in the old communal principle of fair shares, and has sometimes still some economic justification, as for example to secure to each holding a balance of kharif floodplain and rabi upland, to enable the farmer to plant two or more crops on different soils and so to insure against the weather, or to enable a better spread of working days than would be possible on a compact holding limited by soil and water factors to one or two crops in any one year. Nevertheless the general effects are most often evil: waste of time in journeying to and from the fields; of space in the boundaries; the prohibitive expense of fencing the small parcels, so that the cultivator is bound to follow the régime of his fellows or else see his standing crop destroyed by cattle grazing on the stubble; difficulties of water-supply. All these again give ample cause for dispute and litigation. At the worst agriculture becomes so unremunerative that land goes out of cultivation; in some areas of the Punjab "5% of the land which would normally be cultivated is lying useless owing to fragmentation being so excessive as to prevent any agricultural operations."[4]

Consolidation of holdings is the obvious answer; a little too obvious. Clearly it applies to fragmentation rather than to sub-division; it is one thing to exchange enclaves, another to surrender land, and in the absence of alternative employment compulsory formation of economic holdings could result only in an increase in the numbers of the most wretched rural class.[5] These are the landless labourers, condemned to work part of the year for minute wages and for the rest to exist in unemployment, from which the only "escape" may be the acceptance of an extra-legal and unavowed, but in effect real, state of serfdom, in return for a pittance from better-off peasants. In some States a fair beginning has been made in the task of con-

---

[3] See e.g. Nanavati and Anjaria, 46–47.
[4] RCAI, 134. But cf. S. M. Ali's important paper "Field Patterns on the Indo-Gangetic Divide", *Panjab Geographical Review* I. (1942), 26–35, for cases in which consolidation is either unfeasible or undesirable.
[5] Thus *The First Five Year Plan* admits (p. 102) that a main objection to rationalisation is that it would throw large numbers out of work, and that 'hasten slowly' must perforce be the motto.

solidation through co-operative societies; in the Punjab, where conditions are perhaps unusually favourable, 1·3 m. out of a TSA of 30 m. ac. were consolidated between 1920 and 1939. Pace is or was slow because until 1936 an intransigent minority, however small, could not be coerced—at least legally.

2. *The Fertiliser Problem*

Even if we follow the authority of Sir John Russell and add 25% to Indian yields, they remain pitifully low: rice 900–1000 lbs per ac. (Japan *c.* 2250); wheat 750–800 (*c.* 40% of Britain's, or equivalent to the yields of *extensive* farming in Australia); cotton 70–80 against 300 in USA. Moreover if the figures mean anything at all they show a marked fall in productivity in this century: the average rice yield was 982 lbs per ac. in 1909–13, about 840 in 1926–38. The main cause is simply failure to fertilise the fields; but again this is not mere stupidity or even ignorance. It is clear enough that the peasant with a tiny holding can hardly afford to grow a nitrogenous crop for the luxury of ploughing it in: the gain in output next year will not keep him alive in this. As a general rule he is far too poor to be able to buy artificials. Stubble may be burnt, but often it is needed for grazing. Where there is access to woodland, leaves and branches are burnt on the fields or leaf-mould collected; mud from tanks may be used; oilcake is sometimes applied. But in the areas of greatest population and greatest need such resources, if available at all, are hopelessly insufficient. For social reasons it is unlikely that India will ever emulate Chinese thoroughness in the use of human waste-products, though around some large towns night-soil, poudrette, and sewage have been exploited, and the universal use for natural purposes of the fields abutting upon the village-site has actually led to their up-grading in revenue assessments.

There seems little point in such picturesque impressionism as F. L. Brayne's remark that "if we could rescue the cow-dung from the house-wife" (whose duty it is to make it into flat fuel-cakes), then something like a third of India's agrarian poverty would be wiped out at a stroke.[6] As a matter of fact more cow-dung is actually used as manure than is generally realised; of a total of about 160 m. tons dry weight annually produced some 20% is simply lost, 40% burnt, and 40% spread on the fields.[7] Nevertheless a loss of 65 m. tons of organic fertiliser a year—though only equivalent, very roughly, to 6 cwt (8 maunds) per food-acre—is bad enough. One factor is the preference for a slow-burning fuel for making *ghi*; but, quite apart from this, over much of the Indo-Gangetic Plains there is hardly any alternative fuel. Such 'forest' as exists is needed for grazing and produces very little wood, and it may be added that the lack of decent fodder in itself

---

[6] Should we not rather wish to rescue the housewife from the cow-dung?
[7] *A Food Plan for India* (1945), 47 n. 19; hereafter cited as *A Food Plan*.

lessens the organic values of the cattle-manure. Sir Herbert Howard, in *A Post-War Forest Policy for India* (1944), pleads for the planting of thousands of small fuel and fodder forests to meet this situation; but without a numerous police these might not survive human and animal assault during infancy, though perhaps with intensive propaganda co-operatives or *panchayats* (village councils) could give some protection. It is precisely where additional grazing and alternative fuel are most needed—in the Gangetic plain —that there is least room to provide them; indeed barely room enough to expand the village-sites except at the expense of arable. And that expense can ill be afforded.

The conclusion seems inescapable that artificials must be supplied, and lavishly, even at financial loss to Government; a loss which might in time be recouped financially by increased taxable capacity, but which would certainly be worth while in terms of welfare. The steps taken in this direction seem, for once, all too timid.[8]

3. *Tools and Seeds; Roads and Markets*

The manifold inefficiencies of Indian agriculture are probably less the responsibility of the peasant than of nature and of society: of precarious seasons and poor soils, of the immemorial load of exploitation. Doubtless the Indian farmer is on the whole conservative, and on the whole he has had need to be so: for ages past his farming practices have been so closely adjusted to their environment that there could be little need or possibility of change—until the whole fabric of his myriad little closed societies was shaken by the impact of the tightly-administered British Raj and of the world market. "That in many places the system of agriculture followed has attained a very high standard is a matter of common knowledge; the cultivation of rice in the deltas, for example, has reached a marked degree of perfection, and the wisdom of many agricultural proverbs stands unchallenged by research." [9] Now that change is imperative sheer poverty too often inhibits it, and perhaps more often than mere conservatism; but it must be admitted that, especially in the harder or more precarious areas, apathy and fatalism have struck deep and sapped away the vitality of the people precisely where change is most needed.

It is essential to see that innovation is really improvement; condemnation of "the plough that merely scratches the soil", for instance, is too facile. The RCAI cites two widely held opinions to account for the cultivator's tenacious adherence to his ancient models: (i) a light plough is all that his bullocks can draw, and (ii) he prefers a plough which he can carry on his shoulders to and from his often scattered fields. These reasons are valid

---

[8] See section III below. It must be admitted, however, that *A Food Plan* rather glosses over the fodder-fuel-fertiliser tangle; see review in *GR* XXXVIII (1948), 158–59.

[9] RCAI, 14. A careful correlation of rural saws with the environmental conditions they reflect would be both fascinating and instructive.

and important; but the RCAI itself held that the main factor is a realisation of the importance of conserving moisture. Whether this is consciously felt may perhaps be doubted, but the RCAI's conclusion is noteworthy: while deep ploughing is essential for some crops and soils, "it has certainly not been established that it would pay the cultivator in all kharif conditions. Indeed, the contrary is more probable", as it might well lead to loss of moisture in areas of light rainfall, to the reverse in humid areas, in either case jeopardising germination.[10]

Nevertheless many implements could be much improved, and some new ones are desirable: seed-drills, cheap threshing and winnowing appliances, better water-lifts, more efficient cane-crushers and oil-expellers. Mechanisation in the normal sense is difficult, indeed probably impracticable while the farm unit, even if compact, is so small. The use of tractors is indeed increasing, and there are perhaps 10–12,000 in the sub-continent. These have been most successful on Government clearing schemes, or preparing the ground for tillage in new irrigation areas such as the Thal; they are obviously beyond the means of most individual farmers, but can perhaps be made available by co-operatives, while in W Pakistan a few progressive landlords use tractors to plough their estates thoroughly every three years or so, charging tenants for the fuel only. Except for actual tillage indeed there is not likely to be much need for mechanisation, since harvesting machinery does not itself increase production; it may save a crop threatened by weather, but this is too slight a risk to be insured against at so heavy a premium. Tractors might also be used for transporting pumps, small presses, and so on. But if tractors are wanted for a part only of their possibilities, the question arises whether it is economic to use them. Mechanisation, after all, is labour-saving, and in the sub-continent it is not so much a saving of labour that is needed as an improvement in its efficiency; by no means the same thing. And there is the problem of servicing: "of the villages in which manufacturers would normally establish the chain of dealers and sub-dealers . . . not one in a hundred (and according to some estimates, not one in a thousand) has anyone capable of undertaking the responsibilities involved." [11] Coming as it does in a generally optimistic survey, this admission has great weight. The application of cheap electric power to pumping (whether for irrigation or drainage), oil-pressing, and so on has great possibilities and has made a promising start. Great economies could be effected by improving bullock-carts; in some

---

[10] RCAI, 110–12; a discussion of great importance. Those who condemn the light plough are not often in the habit of carrying agricultural machinery on their shoulders.

[11] *Report of the UK Industrial Mission to Pakistan* (1950), 31–40 (refce at p. 35). It should be noted that the Mission included no representative of agriculture; and the words 'soil erosion' do not occur in this most interesting discussion. Cf. G. Slater, *Southern India* (1936), 57–58, on 'labour-saving'. But for an opposite view, see W. Klatt, "Agricultural Planning in East Pakistan", *Pacific Affairs* XXV (1952), 263–67.

areas wheels are still all but solid and the weight of the cart ridiculously large compared with its capacity. The increasing use of rubber tyres is a notable advance.

Much research has gone into the production of improved crops; the most notable achievements are probably in sugar-cane and the introduction of Cambodia cotton and the development of strains from it. But there is substance in the frequent criticism that activities have been too much devoted to cash crops; the percentages of area under improved varieties in 1937–38 were approximately: sugar 80, jute 60, cotton 25, wheat 20, rice 5, groundnuts 5, millets 0·5, gram 0·4.[12] The total for all crops in reporting areas (there is not likely to be much improvement outside them) was only 8%, rising to 25% in the Punjab and UP. A constant struggle against adulteration, especially by middlemen, must be waged.

A more vigorous attack on plant diseases, insects, fungi, wild pigs, rats, and monkeys is urgently needed. Crops such as sugar-cane, grown more or less homogeneously, are of course especially liable to diseases and pests. Total losses through these causes may amount to 1·5–2 m. tons of food annually.[13]

Rural communications are nearly everywhere inadequate: this is a major factor in the slight development of dairying and of fruit and vegetable crops, a large increase in which is exceedingly desirable to offset the excess of carbohydrates in Indian diets. Bad roads or rather tracks also impose a severe strain on bullocks, especially where kharif marketing coincides with rabi tillage.

Market facilities in India are in general poor. In some areas and for some crops (e.g. cotton in Bombay State) there is a good network of officially inspected markets, though even so malpractices are not unknown. Elsewhere the peasant is often at the mercy of unscrupulous traders, and there are too many brokers and middlemen. As the farmer has usually very slight storage facilities and so no holding power, and is often without access to reliable market information, efforts to by-pass the broker can easily be broken by rings and boycotts, though here and there co-operatives have scored notable successes. But as a rule the peasant is exploited by secret bidding between the buying and the selling brokers, arbitrary deductions for alleged deficiencies, false weights, unwarranted commissions, and so on. Local governments are increasingly publicising current prices, in part over village radios, in part by posters at markets; the importance of 'literacy drives' is obvious in this connection.

[12] Nanavati and Anjaria, 44, 109.   [13] Ibid., 99–100; A Food Plan, 13, 52.

II. PROBLEMS OF SOCIAL ORGANISATION

1. *Tenures and Taxes*

There was a fundamental distinction in British India between *ryotwari* areas, where the peasant held directly of the State, and *zamindari*, where the land was owned by landlords who were very often parasitic absentees.[14] This evil is in process of liquidation, though it must be paid for by liberal compensation to the expropriated zamindars. This will at least eliminate rack-renting and the grosser forms of exploitation, though there will remain ample scope for extortion by subordinate officials.

The situation is different in W Pakistan, where so far few serious efforts have been made to interfere with landlordism; this obviously stems from the fact that while Congress was essentially the aggressive organ of the urban middle-classes, the Muslim League was conservative and defensive in its fundamental *raison d'être*; however much the genius of Jinnah led it through a tactical offensive to a revolutionary outcome,[15] despite the important part played by the rising Muslim bourgeoisie, the revolution was strictly political rather than social. Thus while in both camps the spokesmen were lawyer-politicians, the weight behind Congress was largely that of big business, while the League rallied first of all the landlords. Something like a third of the land in W Pakistan is farmed on the *batai* or métayage system, the tenant (*hari*) keeping generally half the produce but providing cattle, seeds, implements and fertilisers: he is thus worse off than share-croppers in countries where capital equipment comes from the landlord. Together with the marked bias of the landed classes to Army and Government service, this obviously constitutes a policy fraught with social and political tensions, and despite a good start (based fundamentally on the old British training in administration) an evolution in the direction of Iranian standards cannot be altogether ruled out for W Pakistan; than which there could be few more dreadful prospects.

The abolition of *zamindari*, however, does not affect the innumerable petty tenancies which arise from fragmentation and sub-division. Millions of farmers let out part of their holdings and in turn rent fields more convenient for their own working. This is, of course, a major source of litigation, and on the whole can hardly fail to cause a good deal of waste and friction, only partially offset by more economic working. Only really large-scale consolidation could eliminate much of this, and so long as land is held individually some will persist for sound economic reasons.

[14] We are mercifully precluded from going into all the other varieties of tenure, and the eternal question as to whether Land Revenue is rent or tax; for once the author will plead "it isn't geography."

[15] This is another of the numerous similarities between the Pakistan campaign and the secession of the South in the American Civil War, likewise conservative in aim and revolutionary in tactic.

Much more serious is the problem of the landless labourer. The following figures from the 1931 Census are highly significant and deplorable (and cf. Table XV. B):[16]

	A. Labourers	B. Cultivators	Ratio A : 1000 B
1921	21,676,107	74,664,886	291
1931	24,925,357	61,180,004	407

It is not likely that the total agricultural population fell absolutely, and the classes labelled 'Labourers' and 'Cultivators' are not identical in the two years, but these figures represent the minimum increase in the ratio; on another computation the 1931 ratio would be 466. It is obviously only too probable that this trend was accelerated during the depression years, and it is not likely to have been reversed since; in Bombay between 1927 and 1937 nearly 5 m. acres passed to non-agriculturalists. It is likely that the land-less class now amounts to over 45 m.; their life is wretched in the extreme. This constitutes a social problem of the first magnitude, and it is clear that the 'industrialisation' panacea could not possibly take off this surplus population within any foreseeable time. Only, perhaps, a phenomenal revival of rural industry could be of much use, and this is more easily desired than attained.

Such problems have been appallingly complicated by the mass migra-tions arising from Partition. Some interesting experiments in co-operative colonies have been made in E Punjab, Rajasthan, and the terai, and it is often suggested that such collective or joint farming might be the solution. But clearly it is one thing to set up a collective of displaced persons on new land, backed up by a definite Government responsibility for rehabilitation; and quite another to reverse the trend to individualism which has been pro-ceeding, at an accelerating tempo, for the last 150 years in the territorially and socially tight-packed villages of, say, the Gangetic Plains or Tamilnad. Yet this may well be the only way out, the only way to render possible the application of those other necessities (which separately are but palliatives) such as improvements in technique and 'rural uplift'.

Taxation can hardly be said to be a very substantial addition to the peas-ant's burden, though it is sometimes the last back-breaking straw. The actual amounts levied were scarcely so onerous as the obligation to pay in cash at fixed times; as under the ancient kingdoms, remissions were of course made in times of famine or flood, but obviously this cannot be done lightly if the state is to maintain financial stability, and in general the British revenue system was more rigid, if less extortionate, than its predecessors.

[16] Census 1931, I. 287–88.

The long-agitated question of an Agricultural Income Tax is presumably of less importance now that *zamindari* is being abolished, and the anomalies in the incidence of Land Revenue assessment from State to State can hardly worry the individual peasant; some simplification of the complex procedures of assessment and revision, however, would probably be welcome. The broad overriding fact remains, that the main fiscal resource of *India*, and *a fortiori* of Pakistan, lies in the land and will do so for a long time to come. But if little can be done to lighten the load of taxation, much can (and indeed must) be done to ensure a greater return to the village in the shape of schools, hospitals, and roads; it is essential to social progress that the villager should be shown the connection between the taxes he pays and the amenities he receives. Hitherto the most obvious connection has been the police.

2. *Debt; Co-operation*

Nearly all agrarian societies developed beyond the subsistence level are debt-ridden, since (except for market gardeners, dairy farmers, and the like) the farmer's resources are liquid but once or twice a year, at harvest, while his outgoings recur more frequently: even in the American Middle West the spectre of the mortgage still walks. But nowhere is debt so crushing a burden as in the peasant societies of Asia and N Africa, and in India the situation has peculiarities arising from social attitudes and legal history.

In 1930 the Central Banking Enquiry Committee estimated the total rural debt at Rs.900 crores—about £675 m.—and unofficial estimates suggest that this figure had doubled by 1938, mainly as a result of the depression. These sums must of course be divided by millions to obtain the individual's indebtedness. The figure then looks low—about £8 in 1930—but was not far off the average annual income of the cultivator (debt Rs.106, income Rs. 133), and over twice the income per head of all the rural population. An official enquiry of 1930 put the debt of the Punjab (where agricultural expansion spells good credit) at 141% of the annual value of agricultural produce, or 25·5 times the whole Land Revenue of the Province. All these figures are of course very rough, the averages merely illustrative, but they do indicate the magnitude of the evil.[17]

The depression of the '30s not only swelled the actual total in cash, but the fall in prices greatly increased its ratio to the value of agricultural production. *Per contra*, the high agricultural prices of the 1939–45 war, together with the shortage of consumer goods on which agricultural profits might have been spent, undoubtedly resulted in a considerable liquidation of debt. On common-sense grounds, however, it seems probable that this advan-

[17] Figures mainly from Nanavati and Anjaria, 35–36, 50; estimate of income by V. K. R. V. Rao. Much doubt naturally attaches to all such figures; see the biting witticism of Jathar and Beri, II. 143–44.

tage accrued mainly to the middle and upper strata of rural society; the problem remains most serious and still carries the risk of real social catastrophe.

The causes of indebtedness are manifold. Fundamental, of course, are the facts already discussed: small holdings, the perversity of the weather, the peasant's lack of information and of storage which compel him to a quick and blindfold disposal of his harvest. Improvident as he so often is, it may fairly be said that improvidence is forced upon him by his necessarily hand-to-mouth existence. He has no reserves to meet sickness, drought, flood, cattle disease; his savings account is his wife's petty jewellery, a few rings and bangles, and when natural calamity comes and all are selling at once, these do not go very far. An unlucky slip may mean violation of caste rules, and the penalty (often a feast for all his caste-fellows in the village) may be ruinously expensive. Finally there is the undeniable extravagance with which he marries his daughter or celebrates the birth of his son, a failing much condemned by the unco' guid and the well-to-do. But seeing what a round of drudgery, monotony, and privation his life so generally is, who with any feeling shall blame him for seizing his few socially sanctioned opportunities for bringing into his home some colour and gaiety, a few days of uninhibited projection of his personality, of new clothes and good food?

The situation would be bad enough were the agents of credit impeccable: notoriously they are not. When it is considered that one party to the debt transaction is more often than not illiterate, and that the village money-lender may also be the village grainbroker and the village shopkeeper, has funds for retaining lawyers and bribing witnesses and police, and commands the services, as witnesses or strong-arm men, of numerous clients, it must be conceded that the balance is weighted a little against the borrower. On the other hand it must also be conceded that if interest is high so are risks. For a long time the legalism of British courts played into the hands of the rich and literate; but in the last few decades, since Thorburn's *Mussulmans and Moneylenders in the Punjab* (1886), many laws have been passed to curb the more notorious swindles, such as the giving of false accounts, to restrict the alienation of land for debt, and to fix legal rates of interest—rates which range from 9 to 15% for loans against security, and up to 25% for unsecured, Bengal having the highest rates. There is of course much evasion, but there has been some alleviation at least.

More positive is the fostering of co-operative credit societies.[18] The great majority of Indian co-operatives are concerned with rural finance, few with marketing, fewer with consumption. The success of the co-ops has not on the whole been commensurate with the energy put into them or the publicity they have received; they reach only a fraction of the rural

[18] Nanavati and Anjaria, Chs. XI and XIX; Jathar and Beri, I. Ch. X.

population; in 1940-41 about 4,300,000 members in nearly 124,000 societies, with a working capital of Rs.30·5 crores, about £23 m. This limited development is not surprising: they are always faced with the dilemma of too rigid management or too lax—if strict, they are unpopular with their public; if easy-going, with the government. They are less flexible than the moneylender, who is on the spot in the smallest village, knows all that is to be known about his clients, and is quite ready to prime the pump, since as a rule it is more to his advantage to receive interest to eternity than to foreclose. Co-ops, backed by government money or limited in funds, cannot—or at least should not!—lend simply to support more lending; their rates are lower than the moneylender's, but they are not nearly so obliging; or, if they are, they soon slide into insolvency. The depression indeed shook out many weak societies, but not all the survivors are beyond reproach.

Nevertheless the co-ops have performed a useful function. As they are usually located in larger villages only, it may be inconvenient to use them, but their mere existence suggests an alternative source of credit and so tends to hold down interest rates; and in some cases they have been able to mobilise funds for productive capital outlay.

3. *The Decay of Rural Society*

From all that has gone before it will be clear that the body social of the Indian countryside labours under a complication of ills, both acute and chronic. The most striking and alarming symptom is probably the increase in petty tenancies and landless labourers. Not less painful is the plight of the majority of those rural workers who are not primarily cultivators, the village servants and artisans. Those who merely follow population, provide personal service, or replace expendable trifles (such as pots) manage at least to carry on; but it is clear that many have little staying-power in face of competition of the machine, whether it is sited in Manchester or in Ahmedabad. There was a decline of 13% between 1911 and 1931 in the numbers engaged in "industry" (most of which would be better styled 'handicraft'), and this was most marked in the more skilled lines, workers in lace and embroidery, for instance, decreasing by 80% in 1921-31. Of course many craft workers were urban, and the remoter countryside fares least ill; nevertheless this has probably been a factor in the increase of the floating—or submerged—population in the towns. Added to this is seasonal unemployment in areas where rabi crops are limited.

Socially as well as economically the integrity of the village has been shaken. The general weakening of caste, however desirable on other grounds, implies a decline in mutual aid; we have noted the growth of an individualism rendered desperate by need. The old *panchayats*, the little councils of caste leaders which gave the village its social cohesion, were broken down by the massive impact of the rigid and far-reaching British administrative machine. Their revival is certainly very desirable, but it is not a panacea, as some seem to think, nor can it be done simply from on top.

There is obviously an appalling dead-weight to be lifted by 'rural uplift'; the agrarian problem is hydra-headed, and it is difficult to establish priorities. So many and so urgent are the tasks that there is always a danger of dissipating energy; "first things first", and yet how to tell which is first of education, sanitation, the revival of rural industry, the provision of fertilisers, dietetics, co-operative marketing, consolidation of holdings, eugenic animal husbandry? So obviously do they hang together that many deplore the concentration of the co-operatives on credit and demand multipurpose societies; a highly technical question, to which the governments seem now to be turning. Moreover the problems mentioned are not only merely a selection, but they vary in incidence from region to region; no standard pattern of advance is possible, and the attempt to provide one can lead only to bureaucratic paper plans and the comfortable feeling that an Act has been passed, an organisation set up, and all will be well. And, while it is a truism that reconstruction imposed from outside rests on the shakiest foundations, it must regretfully be admitted that leadership has rarely come from the peasants themselves, rarely even from the more educated and less poverty-crippled among them: perhaps only the Communists have had much success in tapping the reserves of energy and intelligence which must surely exist among so many millions, and this at the cost of some odd distortions, such as the emergence of a sub-caste of Communist bridegrooms.[19]

It is easy to rationalise this dearth of village Hampdens, or the way in which the initial impetus of an uplift project is followed by a quiet relapse into the ancient ways: physical vitality is sapped by disease and malnutrition; morale by the generations-old pressure of landlord, tax-gatherer, and an alien officialdom, well-intentioned undoubtedly but in essence restrictive. There is the further undermining by the ceaseless gnawing of the moneylender and the middleman, the incalculable vagaries of nature and the economic order, of the monsoon and the market price. Yet, all allowance made, the phenomenon is very ominous; nor does the change of régime seem as yet to have brought much, if any, change in this vital respect.

It is true that notable local successes have been attained by the enthusiasm of many, but too few, voluntary agencies; such were Brayne's Gurgaon experiment and Mahatma Gandhi's in Gujarat. But there is a tendency to

---

[19] This is explicable on good Marxist lines; the Communists, by using traditional modes of expression, song, and dance, inculcated all the precepts for better living put forward by official agencies in incomprehensible literature; and as the brighter young men responded most readily, they were soon on the road to becoming kulaks and were able to secure better dowries.

do too much at once, or alternatively to go all out for a spectacular but lop-sided improvement by concentrating on composts or anti-wife-beating or better wells. Most of these experiments have shown a lack of stamina: the departing servant of the people is garlanded, "he was a wonderful sahib, we shall not look upon his like again . . . now we can be ourselves once more." The Gurgaon experiment in particular has been the subject of serious criticism from M. L. Darling, than whom no one better knows or loves the Punjabi countryman.[20] This emphasises the need of clearer think-ing: but it is no excuse for passivity, nor should the devotion so freely spent be depreciated: *Say not the struggle nought availeth*, and at the very worst there is always some residuum of better living, some spark among the embers.

III. THE GENERAL PROBLEM AND POLICIES TO MEET IT

The Food/Man Ratio

The primary problem of the sub-continent may be succinctly put. While it is true that if the official yield figures were accurate the continued exis-tence of numbers of the people, not to mention their increase, would be hard to explain, yet there can be no reasonable doubt that the margin between food production and consumption, if it exists at all, is running out with extreme rapidity. The trend of Fig. 55 is unmistakably grim; no doubt it needs some qualification, but there is little in the post-Partition history of recurrent food crises to suggest that there has been any serious improvement in the population/food output ratio.

Strenuous efforts are being made to increase output; but even assuming that they are successful, the situation can be held in static equilibrium for only a few years unless (a) the rate of population growth can be checked and/or (b) much greater increases in food output than the $c.15\%$ now en-visaged can be secured—increases of the order of 30% or more.[21] Without one or both of these developments the chances of an advance in the standard of living do not even need to be discussed. But, while just before the war the daily food output (allowing for seed and wastage) was about 1 lb per head

[20] Brayne's methods are set forth in *The Remaking of Village India* (1929) and most amusingly in *Socrates in an Indian Village* (1929); but the latter book lends point to Dar-ling's criticism of his methods (*Rusticus Loquitur* (1930), 121–29, 153–59), for it is perhaps significant than Brayne shows no appreciation of the infuriating effects of Socratic dialectic on its (or his) victims. After reading his book one understands the hemlock. There is a review of 'rural uplift' in Nanavati and Anjaria, Ch. XI, but the best easily accessible all-round survey of these problems known to me is again in Jathar and Beri, I. Chs. IV, V, VII–XII.

[21] *A Food Plan* called for an increase of 25% by 1953, the 'Bombay Plan' for 130% by 1962—and this target is "deliberately fixed low" (p. 35). A short quantitative estimate of trends and needs will be found in A. V. Hill's discussion cited in G. C. L. Bertram, "Popu-lation Trends and the World's Food Resources", *GJ* CVII (1946), 191–210, refce at 197–98. But it is difficult to see how Professor Hill maintains even his much-qualified optimism in the face of his own terrible logic. (See also p. 256 below).

per day, it is certain that it is now appreciably less than that: total output of foodgrains in 1937–40 averaged 56·8 m. tons a year; the figure for 1947–48 was exactly the same, for 1948–49 a million more.[22] The Five Year Plan increases, if attained, will bring the per capita output to 14% below pre-war level; is this even running hard to stay in the same place?

Expansion of Area

(i) *Immediate Targets*. The most obvious course is simply a large-scale assault on such untilled land as is culturable. As far as E Pakistan is concerned the situation is clear-cut: practically speaking there is none.

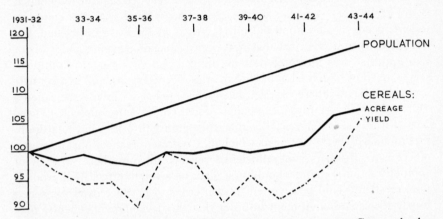

Fig. 55.—TRENDS OF POPULATION AND CEREAL PRODUCTION, 1931–44. Gram and pulse omitted (in any case practically stationary). Population for All-India, cereals for reporting areas only, but these include areas of most rapid increase of population. 1946 indices for cereals: acreage 106, output 87·3.

W Pakistan has much land which might be reclaimed, but only by modern irrigation; a good deal can be done to improve and extend the little oases of Baluchistan and NWFP, but the main hope lies in the two great schemes of the Thal and lower Sind (Kotri).

In *India* the problem is more complex. It is a revealing comment on the loose talk of "culturable waste" that the Government counts on only 10 m. ac. out of a total of 90 m. (in reporting areas only), and the current target is to reclaim 6 m. ac. by 1953–54; even of this only 2 m. ac. are *new* land, the rest being not clearance but rehabilitation of land recently driven out of cultivation by *kans* grass. Targets for the tractor teams are being reached, but the total envisaged is under 2·5% of TSA. Clearly this small beginning is almost insignificant in relation to the size of the problem, but even so not much more is possible along these lines.

[22] These figures of course neglect non-reporting areas and under-estimation, but they are comparable for both periods, and it is the ratio rather than the absolute which counts in this argument.

The per capita TSA is very small indeed, in 1941 ranging only from 0·5 ac. in Bengal to 1·25–1·6 in Sind, Bombay, and Madhya Pradesh (CP); even in the last State, with its large dependence on low-yielding millets, the per capita foodgrains area is only 1·2 ac., and this is the largest figure for the country. If we add to TSA all fallow and all "culturable waste" the result is not a great deal better: only in Sind and Assam, with a combined population of under 14 m. in 1951, does this total exceed 2 ac. per inhabitant. If the scope for extension is so slight even in these relatively empty regions, what are the prospects in the sub-continent as a whole?

(ii) *"Grow More Everything."* The Union Government can hardly be called pessimistic or defeatist; Nehru himself has stated that the food deficit is not really very serious, "only" 10%. The original goal was complete independence of food imports by 1951; 1950–51 might seem implied, but already in 1950 it was clear that 1951–52 was perforce meant, and by 1951 "no imports" was interpreted as meaning no imports except to build reserves, to allow of diversion of land to other needed crops, and to meet natural calamities.[23] There has also been what might not unfairly be called a "Grow More Everything" campaign—food, cotton, jute, oilseeds. On the face of it this seems unrealistic, and efforts to fix priorities have naturally to contend with vested interests which may represent real national interests. There is a subsidiary, but sufficiently serious, dilemma here: in view of competition for the land, should first place be given to direct food production, or should land be diverted to cash crops to produce exports needed to pay for capital equipment in order that the development schemes may enable more food to be grown later on? We have met this problem before; it is that of the individual peasant with too little land to be able at once to feed himself this year and to improve land for greater output next year. Only the scale differs.

(iii) *The Development Schemes.* The hopes of *India* and Pakistan are largely centred in the Development Schemes, which range from local plans for a comprehensive overhaul of tanks and wells to such titans as the Kosi project, which, if ever carried out in full, would irrigate 3 m. ac. and provide 1·8 m. kW of hydro-electricity. Many of the schemes, such as the best-known, the Damodar Valley, are multi-purpose projects on Tennessee Valley lines, power, irrigation, flood and erosion control, and navigation being all subserved.

Notes on the largest schemes will be found in the regional chapters, and the major ones are listed in Table XIV. Here we shall attempt a very general survey only.

(a) *India.* It is difficult to piece together a complete picture of *Indian* schemes, especially as the distinction between schemes initiated and those

---

[23] *IR* III/2 (10/1/51). It must be added that an unusual run of natural calamities is partly responsible for the current grave situation.

merely projected, or between the projected and the merely envisaged, is not always carefully drawn.

What may be a dangerous over-simplification is widespread, voiced even by *India's* Food Minister: that the main factor in low productivity is simply lack of irrigation.[24] This doubtless accounts for the Bombay Plan's call for an All-India increase of 200% in the irrigated area, which is fantastic.[25] The existing projects do not err on the side of pessimism, and those listed by the Central Board of Irrigation in 1948 would provide 5 m. kW and irrigation for some 22·5 m. ac., as well as improving over 3 m. ac. already irrigated. These figures exclude nearly 5 m. ac., which are obviously merely a distant vision, and a number of minor tank schemes, but on the other hand include many projects—including some of the largest—already postponed or scaled down; an official statement in 1951 gave a total of 18 m. ac. This would represent a 35% increase on the *Indian* irrigated total in 1945. Obviously the Bombay Plan has a symbolic value only.

At the very best—which is also the very unlikely—the schemes would add about 10% to the 1950 TSA; not an unimpressive advance, but not in itself enough to meet the increasing demand for food. Projects actually started—and except for Bhakra, Damodar, and Tungabhadra they are barely started—will command only 9 m. ac. Most of the larger projects are only in "an advanced stage of investigation": the Kosi has been split into several stages, of which only the first is likely to be put in hand in the reasonably near future; the Ramapadasagar project has been shelved; the Tungabhadra is the most advanced of major projects, and is expected to be complete in 1953, but it was started in 1945. Financial difficulties, of course, are mainly responsible for this slow progress, and they themselves are not unaffected by the armed peace which prevails between the sister-states of the sub-continent. And too much depends on the Colombo Plan.

(b) *Pakistan*. All 'development', as distinct from power, schemes are in W Pakistan: the Thal project is expected to irrigate about 0·7–1 m. ac. and the Lower Sind Barrage at Kotri 2·8 m.: the only multi-purpose scheme, at Warsak in NWFP, will add 60,000 ac. The total increase is proportionately of much the same order as *India's*. But it does nothing directly for over-crowded E Pakistan, at present barely able to maintain herself in food. Moreover in W Pakistan the problem of keeping irrigated land from ruin by waterlogging and salt impregnation is perhaps as urgent as that of

---

[24] *IR* III/6 (7/2/51). What follows is based in part on a personal communication from the Central Board of Irrigation.

[25] Considering that the Plan was signed by eight leading industrialists, including Tata and Birla men, it is strange to find that the capital cost for this 200% is obtained by simply doubling outlay on existing irrigation and adding one-third for new dams (p. 38). Apart from price-changes, it is obvious that the best projects were taken up long ago; and beyond these common-sense considerations the point is illustrated by the different attitude of the British Indian Government to 'productive' (i.e. profitable) and 'unproductive' (i.e. merely socially productive) schemes.

winning new ground; for instance, the entire power to be produced by the Rasul hydro-electric plant, 22,000 kW, will be needed not for irrigation but for undoing the effects of over-irrigation.

(iv) *Total Results of Expansion.* Necessary adjuncts as are reclamation and the development schemes, fundamentally there is no hope of retrieving the situation by this frontal assault. For, assuming that all schemes now more or less under way in the sub-continent could be productive by 1956 (which is out of the question), then a liberal estimate of the total increase in foodgrains would be of the order of 7·5 m. tons. But as we have seen, in 1937–40 the total annual output was estimated at 56·8 m. tons, brought down by wastage and seed requirements to 49·7 m. available, or rather over 1 lb per day per head.[26] Allowing for some increase already obtained by the Grow More Food campaigns, total increase cannot represent more than 13% on pre-war figures. But by 1953 the population in the sub-continent will be *c.* 18 % greater than that of 1941; and this is certainly against hypothesis. It seems obvious that more organic measures are required.

Intensification and Diversification

(i) *Fertiliser Policy.* Of first importance is the provision of adequate nutriment for the soil.[27] There is some, but not a great deal, of scope for increased use of green manure, urban compost, bone- and fish-meal, oil-cake, and so on; and there is the dung reserve, if it could be tapped. But the maximum use of compost would be equivalent to only about 50,000 tons of nitrogen a year, of oil-cake 75,000 tons, and practically all the oil-cake would be needed for cattle-feed and for specialised crops. For cereals, therefore, it seems that on the whole artificials must be the mainstay. Here the pre-war position was grotesque, and current plans seem timid. Before the war India used about 0·61 lb per ac. of fertilisers, against 233 lbs in Egypt; and half of this microscopic figure went to the million acres or so of plantations.

Nitrogen is the most serious deficiency of Indian soils, and ammonium sulphate the most suitable fertiliser. In 1938–39 total consumption was about 90,000 tons, 77,000 tons of which were imported, the rest coming from coke-ovens. As for its distribution, in 1943 tea took 28,000, sugar 25,000, potatoes and vegetables 11,000, out of a total consumption of 90,000 tons; most of the balance went to coffee and rubber. The share of food crops may be readily estimated.

As Thomas says, a requirement of 1 m. tons of sulphate a year for the 20 m. ac. of irrigated rice can scarcely be called ambitious; and his further suggestion of 5 m. tons of sulphate and 1 m. of superphosphate does not seem excessive; *A Food Plan* called for about 3·1 m. tons on 80–90 m. ac.

[26] *Food Stats*, 136.   [27] See *A Food Plan, passim*; Thomas, Ch. XXIV.

of the best-watered land. The present sulphate position in *India* is as follows: *c.* 30–40,000 tons from coke-ovens; 50,000 from Alwaye (Travancore) and 350,000 from Sindri; 6,000 from Belagula (Mysore); imports stepped up to 250,000 tons. There is also a vague suggestion for a unit to produce a further 100,000 tons, and imports may be increased to 400,000. All these together amount to less than a million tons; here for once targets seem pitched low, in comparison for instance with Japan's pre-war use of 4 m. tons on a cultivated area of about 16 m. ac., about $\frac{1}{19}$th *India's* TSA. It is true that half a dozen Sindris, which is the least that is really needed, appear insuperably costly; and there are difficulties such as the loss of the Salt Range gypsum to Pakistan and lack of raw materials for the technically easier production of superphosphate. But, considering the authoritative estimate of Burns that proper manuring would increase rice yields per acre by 20–40%, this seems by far the most likely line of advance towards a real solution. Shipping difficulties impede large-scale import, but to some extent the will seems lacking; Government directives stress the need for further exploitation of compost, which is excellent so far as it goes; but more is needed. India is probably particularly fertile soil for distrust of the "artificial" on principle; but it would be a pity if archaic sentiment in favour of nature and simplicity were to be pandered to, when the probable result is slow starvation.

In Pakistan also the fertiliser situation is most unsatisfactory, all potential (except for bone-meal phosphate) being in W and the serious, if not desperate, need being in E Pakistan. Yet current demand for ammonium sulphate in E Pakistan is about 20,000 tons—not met owing to congestion at Chittagong—and the estimated requirement for expansion of food output only is 50,000 tons—this for a rice area of 20 m. ac., giving the magnificent average of 6 lbs per ac.[28]

(ii) *New Foods.* The fertiliser problem is in a sense straightforward; there are serious difficulties of supply and finance to be overcome, but the actual dissemination of the technique raises no insuperable obstacles. It is otherwise with a second possible way from the impasse, the use of new foods. It is obvious that even when adequate in amount, Indian diets are very badly balanced, over-weighted with carbohydrate and deficient in nearly everything else: it is not only the poor who are ill-fed. In 1944 the authors of *A Food Plan for India* estimated that a balanced diet for the existing population would need the following percentage increases:

cereals 10, pulses 20, fruits 50, vegetables 100,
fats and oils 250, milk 300, fish and eggs 500.

Increased cereal yields would of course make it theoretically possible to release land for vegetables, groundnuts, and soya beans. The possibilities

[28] *Report of U.K. Industrial Mission* (1950), 41–42.

of the Japanese vine *kudzu*, for soil conservation and nitrogen fixation, as well as fodder, might be investigated.[29] But, apart from considerations of expense and marketing (where difficulties of transportation and preservation are important), the 'sales resistance' would probably be stronger than to an increased use of artificial fertilisers. Efforts are being made to popularise sweet potatoes and tapioca, the latter already a poor man's staple in Kerala; and groundnut cake, at present rarely fit for human consumption, could be a most valuable food.[30] But dietetic habits are notoriously difficult to change, and in the near future this attack on the problem appears theoretically desirable rather than practically feasible. The populace may be forced to it, of course, by the cereal shortage; but when the standard grain ration has been cut to 9 oz. a day (13 for heavy manual workers) [31] there seems a suggestion of the classic fatuity, "The people lack bread; let them eat cake".

(iii) *Seeds*. Other possibilities have already been mentioned in passing; that with the greatest potential net gain is probably an extension of the use of improved seeds; output of rice alone could probably be increased by 5–10% by this means alone. But, as ever, it comes back to the questions of educating the cultivator and keeping a tight watch over the middleman.

IV. THE APPROACH AND THE OUTLOOK

It will be apparent that very much depends on the approach to the cultivator; neither sentiment merely nor mere hardheadedness will suffice, and least of all a woolly mess of both of them. A less alien and more intimate approach than that of the old Agricultural Department is needed; its most successful efforts—agricultural fairs and the like—were apt to be regarded by the peasant and his family as agreeable places of holiday resort where one met one's friends and might, or might not, cast an indulgent eye on those sideshows illustrating odd European superstitions about farming. At the same time a more reasoned attitude than that of the sentimental rural uplifter, or the fanatic on one topic, is also essential.

These generalities may be supported by the experience of the 'Pilot Projects' in Etawah and Gorakhpur Dts (UP). These were initiated in 1948 and 1950 respectively, and cover together about 100 villages and 100,000 people. Results so far seem to have been strikingly successful; in Etawah, for instance, the wheat yield on the entire project area of 6000 ac. was increased by over 20%, largely by improved seed; and the area now supplies seed to a further 45,000 ac. On more restricted areas better tillage in general, including especially the use of legumes as green manures, resulted

[29] See V. S. Gananathan, "Soil Conservation and the Kudzu," *IGJ* XXII (1947), 46–50.
[30] See *IR* I/28 (14/7/49).
[31] What this means can be realised from the fact that Pattern Dietary Scales for the Far East call for 12 oz. rice as an emergency ration, 20 for moderate and 24 for heavy work; the full emergency calorie demand is 1700; the present Indian average 1600. (*A Food Plan*, 53; *Colombo Plan*, 14.)

in increases of 60%. From the published account [32] it is clear that success is due not only, or not so much, to the material techniques—important as these are—as to a psychological approach on the lines suggested in the preceding paragraph. It must be remembered that the extension of such projects will involve increased taxation, to be met by higher production; that even so there are financial limits on indefinite expansion; and that repetition is subject to a law of diminishing returns. For all that, these UP projects are perhaps the most encouraging experiments yet carried out.

For continual success the traditional suspicion of government—generally envisaged in the twin role of tax-collector and policeman [33]—has to be broken down. *A priori* this might be thought more likely now that an alien has given place to two indigenous Governments; unfortunately, however, many small and not so small signs suggest that the new régimes are if anything even more wedded to files and forms than was the old; with exceptions, of course. In one respect, and that probably disastrous, the *Indian* Government has shown itself more accessible to mass opinion; draft legislation for the guidance of the States would, if passed into law, make it penal to slaughter a cow without a certificate from the President of the local Municipality and the Veterinary Officer, agreeing that the animal is over 14 years old and permanently unfit for work or breeding. Yet a Central Food Minister can say, with truth, that half the cattle cannot pay for their keep, that charity keeps them alive, and that "if we share our limited food-supply with useless animals, we do so at our peril." [34]

The Salvaging of Rural Life; the Link with Industry

Finally there is the urgent need for reconstituting the bases of rural society, not only for those whose business is primarily their own farm, but for the artisans and the millions of the landless. To discuss this fully would take us even further into sociology than we have yet advanced; but some general considerations are relevant to the geographical picture. While the growth of rural industry is of the first importance, it cannot be fostered merely by lectures from above, nor is there much future in attempting to bolster up rural crafts whose products can be more efficiently and cheaply produced by machines. There remains, however, wide scope for an extension of agricultural processing and for the decentralisation of some factory industries into the countryside. In all this the availability of cheap hydro-electric power would be of prime importance. While there is little or no hope that factory industry could do more than take off the population at present surplus to the land (if indeed it can do that), cheap power might

[32] E. Converse, "Pilot Projects in India", *Far Eastern Survey* (Amer. Inst. of Pacific Relations, NY), XX (1951), 21–27.

[33] Neatly expressed by a Kumaoni settler in upper Burma, whose reply to a question as to his home area was, "Well, Almora is the place where they take us to hang us." This attitude is, of course, class rather than racial.

[34] See *IR* I/29 (21/8/49) and III/6 (7/2/51).

revitalise cottage industry in many branches and, however modest the financial returns, this would add immeasurably to the variety of country life, to its sense of dignity and security.

The prospect of rapid industrialisation is seductive and has better publicity-value than rural reconstruction; but, important as it is, it may be questioned whether industry is not getting more than its fair share of attention from planners and public: Vakil's excellent *Economic Consequences of Divided India*, for example, disposes of agriculture in about 35 out of 550 pages, while industry gets about 225. Industry is urban and articulate, to a large extent the driving-force of the struggle for independence. Undoubtedly it has a great part to play in the rehabilitation of agriculture, providing fertilisers and cheap power, for example, as well as a market. But its own development cannot be complete unless it is in turn based on a prosperous countryside; there is its primary market, but unless purchasing power is greatly increased the expansion of *Indian* industry to a degree commensurate with its great resources will be inhibited. And should the countryside remain a vast depressed area, it will be a reservoir of labour so over-cheap as to be a positive drag on the efficiency so badly needed in a competitive world. Once more the agrarian problem lies at dead centre to all the workings of man in this great sub-continent.

The picture drawn in this chapter is sombre; no one would be more glad than the writer were it proved false.[35] It is of course possible that some more hopeful factors have been overlooked; but on the most optimistic view the future of *India* and Pakistan depends on a complete reconstruction of their agrarian life, and this task will demand the highest effort and qualities from both leaders and peoples. Can the future be called really bright when the Colombo Plan itself envisages that, if and when it is successfully completed, the annual consumption of cloth in *India* will be 15 yds instead of 10, and the town worker will get 16 oz. of cereals a day instead of 9 or 12? The target itself is 20% below the standard estimate of the requirement for moderate work. It will be much if this is achieved; it will not be nearly enough.

[35] The argument of this chapter may fairly be called Neo-Malthusian; but I think it proper to make it clear that it owes nothing to W. Vogt's *The Road to Survival* (1949).

ADDITIONAL NOTE ON THE FOOD PROBLEM

The First Five Year Plan, admitting that a "lasting solution" would involve doubling the irrigated area in 15 years (p. 37), calls for 8 m. ac. of new irrigation (20% on 1950) which, with other reforms, could add *c.* 15% to the 1950 output of 45·5 m. tons foodgrains. This would keep consumption at the 1950 level of 13·67 oz. per adult per day. At this level and with no imports, the deficiency in 1956 due to increase of population would be no less than 6·9 m. tons; at a 16 oz. ration, 15·8 m. tons = 33% of present output (pp. 44–45, 68). Yet while area remained stable 1947–50, output apparently fell 4 m. tons (p. 76).

CHAPTER X

INDUSTRY: POWER AND MINERAL RESOURCES

THE agrarian problem undoubtedly lies at the centre of all things in the life of India to-day. Without a great increase—and a better distribution—of rural income industry cannot develop to the full, since agrarian poverty severely restricts the effective demand of the numerically huge internal market, and continually maintains, or indeed augments, the immense pool of landless or under-employed rural labour and thus keeps the worker's wages low, his living conditions often unspeakably bad, and his efficiency as a natural consequence very poor. Conversely the vital significance of the industrial contribution to agricultural reconstruction is patent: cement and steel for dams and power-houses; fertilisers; cheap machinery; and a market. Field and factory, then, are symbiotes.

This connection is not always clearly seen in an *India* which after all is in the full tide of a bourgeois nationalist revolution. To the makers of this revolution, the urban middle classes and the new business magnates or petty chiefs, it is the mills, the factories, the power-houses which fill the stage and nourish national pride. This is legitimate enough, provided it does not obscure the all-important fact that it is in the fields that *India's* destiny finally lies, and provided also that industrial advance is itself integrated and balanced, which at present it conspicuously is not. Its extreme unevenness of development is inherent partly in the natural endowment, but more largely in social history. Striking specific achievements and vague impressions of vast untapped resources have contributed to loose and uncritically optimistic estimates of potentialities.

Apart from the great industrial foci of N America, NW Europe, and the USSR, it does indeed seem possible, or even likely, that *India* has greater industrial potentialities than any other country except perhaps Brazil. Nevertheless it may be queried whether *India*, though certainly not poor, is in fact so rich *in relation to size and population* as her more cheerful publicists assume: our first task, therefore, is to survey the actual resources. The availability of raw materials, however, should be implicit in Ch. VIII. The differences between *India* and Pakistan in weight of resources, degree of development, and probable trends are so great that there is little point in comparing the two countries *seriatim* for each item; indeed for many Pakistan's entry would be nil. Her position, therefore, is reserved for separate treatment; Kashmir is touched upon as seems relevant when considering either country.

I. *INDIA*

A. POWER

1. *Coal*

India ranks about 7th among the coal-producers of the world, and her reserves are not inconsiderable. They are, however, limited in their distribution, and output is still more concentrated: some 90% is from the Damodar Valley, and over half from two fields, Raniganj and Jharia. This concentration imposes heavy transport charges on the long rail hauls to industrial centres, and Bombay has often found it cheaper to import from S Africa. Annual production since the war has stood at 28–32 m. tons, about $1\frac{3}{4}$ cwt per head of population.

Nearly all *Indian* coal is L. Gondwana in age, 98% of output coming from the Damuda coal measures which correspond to the Ecca series in S Africa and the Maitland in Australia. They are preserved in Peninsular fault-troughs flanking the lower Godavari and Mahanadi/Brahmani valleys and forming the series of basins along the Damodar. These last dominate Indian production, being followed at a long interval by the small and scattered fields of Madhya Pradesh (CP) (2–3 m. tons), of which those in the Pench valley are most important, and the Singareni and Tandur fields in NE Hyderabad (*c.* 1 m. tons). All these raise bituminous coals, often friable, with carbon content generally *c.* 55–60% and some sulphur and phosphorus. The Damodar fields are easily mined, seams often reaching 40–60 ft in thickness, sometimes 80 ft or more, and the Gondwana beds are rarely folded or faulted.

Outside the Peninsula the coal-bearing rocks are Eocene or later; the most important producer is Assam, with sub-bituminous coal of fair quality but of high sulphur content. Kashmir has largely anthracitic deposits in Riasi, with reserves of perhaps 100 m. tons, but seams are usually thin and broken. There is probably the same quantity of lignite in the lacustrine Karewas beds of the Vale of Kashmir, and large deposits of lignite have recently been reported as underlying the Madras coastal plain.

There is the usual doubt about reserves. Sir Cyril Fox's 1932 estimate of 60,000 m. tons is quoted again and again without qualification; but his figures for 'workable' coal—moisture-free, up to 25% ash, seams over 4 ft thick and within 1000 ft of surface—is 20,000 m. tons, and for 'good' coal down to 2000 ft only 5000 m. tons. More serious is the coking position: here Fox estimates 1500 m., but this has been progressively whittled down to 1426, 1185, and 700–750 m.—the last figure representing 65 years' consumption *at present rates*, which are clearly inadequate for large-scale industrialisation. All the coking coal is in the Damodar fields, largely controlled by the iron and steel companies; in 1932 it was calculated that coking supplies outside these preserves would be exhausted in 33 years. This may be too gloomy a view; in 1947 E. R. Gee put reserves of possible coking coal—including some deeper than 2000 ft—at 2290 m. tons, and suggested a probable life—with more careful exploitation—of 200 years.[1] It is clear that the most meticulous conservation is necessary; unfortunately methods are usually wasteful in the extreme, and unless they are reformed the probable life of good coking coal in India can be measured in a few decades.

A false start was made at Raniganj in 1774, but real exploitation waited on the railway demand. In 1868 output reached 500,000 tons, by 1900 it was 6 m. and the Madhya Pradesh and Hyderabad fields had been opened up. But, except in those collieries owned by the railways and the steel firms (which together in 1942 produced 17% of output), development has been

Vakil, 190–91.

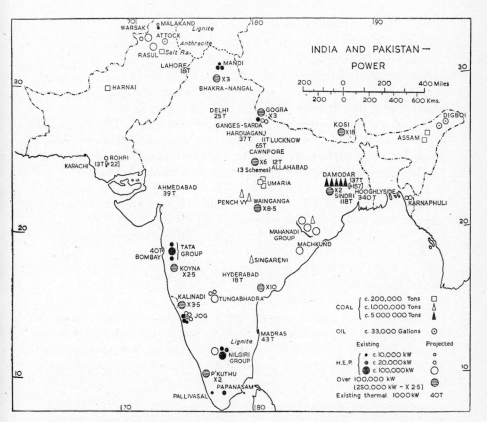

Fig. 56.—POWER: RESOURCES, DEVELOPMENT, AND MAJOR PROJECTS. Situation as in 1950; the more grandiose schemes shelved. Only major projects shown (cf. Table XIV). Figures in [ ] = thermal extensions in hand.

extremely haphazard; much of the area lay in the estates of zamindars who granted short leases to inadequately capitalised syndicates, and there was a 'fragmentation of holdings' problem: in 1942, 133 mines out of a total of 725 produced under 1000 tons each. It is to be expected that the new régime will tidy up this anarchic situation.

Collieries employ over half of *Indian* mine-workers, and labour problems are acute. Most of the workers are tribal, much exploited by gang-contractors, and naturally anxious to return to their fields at harvest: in some collieries monthly raisings vary by as much as 100% on this account. Living, working, and safety conditions are usually very poor, though the larger collieries are increasing the proportion of settled labour by providing better housing and smallholdings on the spot.

About a third of *India's* coal is used on the railways, 10% each in the steel and textile industries, 7% each for bunker and export and for electrical generation. Domestic consumption is naturally very slight.[2]

2. *Oil, Alcohol, Producer Gas*

Oil resources are very small; the only known fields of the slightest significance are those around Digboi in Assam, with an output of 65–70 m. gallons a year—less than 10% of current consumption of petroleum products. A large proportion of the crude oil goes to kerosene and wax, and the production of petrol, diesel oil, and lubricants is insignificant.

Nor are there likely to be any large finds in the future. There are small prospects on the Indo-Pakistani border in Sylhet, and much more dubious possibilities around the Gulf of Cambay, where there are natural gas strikes. But here, at least, Pakistan's prospects are better than *India's*.

There are, however, some alternative sources of liquid or gaseous fuel: ample low-grade coal for distillation, and the enormous quantities—*c.* 400,000 tons a year—of molasses produced by sugar factories and now largely wasted. These might well be transformed into industrial and power alcohol, and indeed the Government plans to produce some 20 m. gallons a year. Most of this would be from molasses, and the prohibition of alcoholic drinks, though no unmixed blessing,[3] has released some distilleries for industrial production. Installed capacity is already nearly 10 m. gallons, but production only 2–4 m., expansion being hindered by uncertain demand and high excise. These difficulties could be met by legislation, e.g. to enforce an 80% petrol/20% alcohol mixture for vehicles; some governments (notably Mysore, the pioneer in power alcohol) have already legislated to this effect.

---

[2] See the series of tables in Vakil, 186–95.

[3] In Madras alone loss of excise and cost of enforcement for five years would pay for the shelved Ramapadasagar scheme. While there is room for restriction of the liquor trade among the uprooted floating labour of the cities, it can hardly be said that drinking is a common vice in the villages.

Producer-gas units were introduced just before the war, and by 1945 over 23,000 vehicles (mostly in Madras) were running on this fuel—a monthly saving of about 2·7 m. gallons of petrol. Production from charcoal is easy, and there would seem to be some scope for the application of producer gas to small rural industries in areas where cheap electric power is not likely to be available.[4]

3. *Electricity*

To *India* to-day 'hydel' is a word of power which, if incanted often enough, will of itself produce an industrial revolution. And indeed the water-power resources of the sub-continent are vast, though not without limitations. The survey by J. W. Meares in 1918–24 arrived at an estimate of 12·68 m. kW as the potential at minimum flow; of this it was thought that 2·65 m. could be developed within 20 years. But by 1944 the total generating capacity was only 1·28 m. kW, and of this only 0·5 m. was hydro. Considering *India's* coal position, this laggard pace is difficult to explain and perhaps not easy to defend.

It is generally reckoned that Meares' estimate was less than half the real potential—current estimates range from the official figure of 25 to 40 m. kW—and indeed schemes projected or under investigation already exceed his total. Of course it is extremely unlikely that more than a fraction of these will be executed. Present total capacity is 2 m. and the current target is 4·85 m. kW by 1959—doubling the present thermal supply and quintupling the hydro.

Since electricity was introduced to Bombay and Calcutta in 1899, some 400 thermal stations, mostly very small, have been set up for town supplies. About 1943 Bombay and Calcutta alone used 42%, and adding Cawnpore and Ahmedabad, four cities with 1·5% of population accounted for over 50%, of the total electrical energy of India—which equalled a week's supply of the USA.[5] The concentration of coal in the Damodar kept costs high, on account of the long rail hauls, and it is not easy to generate centrally near the coal since there water supplies are inadequate.[6] Hydro-electricity started fairly early, beginning with a small plant at Darjeeling in 1907. In 1902 Mysore opened the Sivasamudram installation, powering the goldfields 90 miles away—a notable achievement in its day. By 1915 about 130,000 kW were generated, 45,000 at Sivasamudram and 60,000 in the Tata schemes behind Bombay. Subsequent development and the main projects are shown on Fig. 56.

The main zones of hydro-electric potential are: (i) a belt along the Himalayas from Malakand to Assam (with an outlier on the Shillong Plateau;

---

[4] For details on alcohol and producer gas, see Thomas, 155–60.
[5] Thomas, 134, 142.
[6] But half the electricity to be generated by the Damodar scheme will be thermal, using the great reservoirs of the project.

(ii) the Wn Ghats; (iii) the Sn hills, especially on the Nilgiris and the middle Cauvery. In 1947 the three Tata plants above Bombay accounted for 47% of the total hydro-electric capacity of India, the Cauvery basin for 29%.

The main, and most obvious, limitation is the very pronounced seasonal variation of the rivers. All along the flanks of the Peninsular plateaus there are many sharp falls, some several hundred feet high, with an immense volume of water in the rains; but in the dry weather they are mere dribbles. Thus the Ken, a right-bank tributary of the Jumna in Vindhya Pradesh, varies from 300,000 to 5 cusecs, while even in sub-Himalayan Kumaon the Tons, with a maximum of 400,000, has fallen to 45.[7] Reservoirs must be large, and, as a rule, allow for a high rate of silting. In the Himalayas the slippery contorted shales which form much of the terrain are liable to slipping, and this is also the great seismic zone of India: earthquakes can be guarded against, but only by expensive specialised construction.

Yet, when all is said, 'hydel' is in truth a main key to advance in industry, and so largely in agriculture; but a key more difficult to turn than many publicists are willing to realise: financial stringency has already held up many schemes (see Table XIV). At present industry accounts for about 80% of demand, and 60% of industrial use is in cotton. But there is an immense scope for electricity in a much-needed decentralisation of industry, and especially in the revivification of small-scale agriculturally-linked occupations: food-processing, cane and oilseed crushing, cottage weaving, and so on. It is gratifying also to note that the demand for direct agricultural uses—mainly for pumping water onto the fields (or, in Kerala, off them) is growing, especially in the S; in the N the deep UP tube-wells depend in part on thermal electricity but increasingly on that elegantly developed by concentrating the 130-ft drop of the Ganges Canal into little falls 8–12 ft high; a principle which could obviously be extended, at least on new canals. Nor should the gain to the villager in mere amenity be disregarded. Finally, railway electrification would greatly ease the coal situation, always rather tight and at times really critical.

B. MINERALS (Table XVI)

Apart from the shortage of coking coal, *India's* endowment for heavy metallurgy is rich indeed: not only reserves of high-grade iron ore hardly to be matched in the world, but good resources in alloy-minerals, fluxes, and refractories. In non-ferrous metals she is much weaker, though with some useful deposits as yet untouched, especially of bauxite; she has a quasi-monopoly of mica mining, and holds a strong position in some rare or strategic minerals and chemicals. We shall deal with her resources in that order.

[7] Sharma, 213.

As in coal, the dominance of the Peninsula, and especially of the Chota Nagpur-Orissa borderland, is marked: for fireclay, mica, chromite, coal, iron ore, kyanite, and copper the area within 200 miles of Jamshedpur accounts for 50–100% of total output. It seems unlikely that this hegemony of the NE Peninsula will ever be seriously challenged, or that any very striking discoveries are yet to be made there; but with more intensive prospecting and more hydro-electric power the share of the Himalayas in known resources and in production may well increase.

1. *Iron Ore*

The Dharwarian and Cuddapah rocks of the En half of the Peninsula contain some of the world's largest reserves of iron ore, mainly haematites

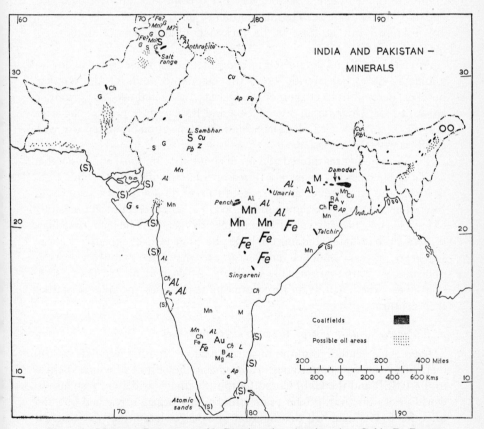

Fig. 57.—MINERAL RESOURCES. Al, Bauxite; Ap, Apatite; Au, Gold; B, Barytes; Ch, Chromite; Cu, Copper; Fe, Iron; G, Gypsum; L, Lignite; M, Mica; Mg, Magnesite; Mn, Manganese; O, Oil; Pb, Lead; RA, Refractories and Abrasives; S, Salt (in parentheses: by evaporation); V, Vanadium; Z, Zinc. Italics indicate unexploited reserves; size of letters very roughly proportional to importance. 'Atomic sands' are thoria-bearing ilmenite and monazite.

and magnetites of high iron content—60–70% Fe. The most important exploitation lies on the Nn flanks of the Orissa Hills, in what were the states of Keonjhar, Bonai, and Mayurbhanj and in Singbhum Dt, Bihar. Here "there is what appears to be a range of iron running almost continuously for 40 miles", and this alone is estimated to hold 2700–3000 m. tons of metallic iron—"thought to be the largest and richest deposits of iron perhaps in the world, surpassing in magnitude the Lake Superior ores." [8] This iron-field extends Swds into Chhattisgarh, Bastar (which jungly state has at least 600 m. tons), and Sn Madhya Pradesh (CP), where whole hills of haematite several hundred feet high are found; Madhya Pradesh has at least 1100 m. tons. On the Damodar Valley the ironstone shales of the Raniganj coalfield have reserves of about 400 m. tons of lower-grade ore (35–40% Fe). Mysore has 250–600 m. tons, all over 42% Fe, and 100 m. about 65%. The magnetite (35–40% Fe) resources of Salem are unknown but at least to be reckoned in hundreds of millions of tons.

After this it seems an anti-climax to note the vast quantities of lower-grade (25–40% Fe) lateritic ores; the magnetite sands of the Konkan beaches, derived from erosion of the Deccan Lavas and used for primitive smelting; the Dharwarian ores of Goa and Ratnagiri (Bombay); the large deposits of 40–60% Fe in Kumaon; and the association of poorer ores with the Tertiary coal of Assam.

The definite figures quoted add up to about 5000 m. tons, and altogether a total of 8–10,000 m. seems not unreasonable. So superfluous is this richness that the Jamshedpur and Asansol furnaces do not use ore below 60% Fe content, and some consignments are 69% Fe, "the theoretical composition of pure haematite being 70% iron and 30% oxygen." [9] The main drawback of *Indian* ore is that it contains too little phosphorus for the relatively cheap Bessemer process, though some Deccan ores may have as much as 0·15% phosphorus. Fluxes are usually available. At current output (*c.* 2·25 m. tons a year) the life of *India's* iron ore can be reckoned in millennia rather than centuries.

2. *Manganese, other Ferro-Alloys, and Refractories*

India is also endowed on no niggardly scale with other adjuncts of iron metallurgy. Of first importance is *manganese*, the output of which is third to the USSR and the Gold Coast. Output fluctuates widely in response to world prices: in 1907, fifteen years after mining began, it reached 900,000 tons, fell to less than half that figure in the depression of the '30s, reached the million mark in 1937, and fell again to a low of 210,000 tons in 1945. Reserves of good ore (*c.* 50% Mn) are estimated at 15–20 m. tons, mainly in Dharwarian rocks. Madhya Pradesh (CP) produces about two-thirds of the

---

[8] Jathar and Beri, I. 29–30; Wadia, 347.   [9] Heron, 13.

total; here development has been facilitated by the opening (1932) of the Raipur–Vizagapatam railway. Next come Keonjhar and Bonai, the hills of the Madras-Orissa border, and Singbhum: there is a steady production of *c.* 20,000 tons on the inland borders of Gujarat, and Udaipur (Rajasthan) is developing. There is also some production in Mysore. *Indian* ore is usually non-friable and so transports well; but much of it has too much phosphorus and iron to be suitable for the best ferro-manganese. Some 90% of output is exported, home production of ferro-manganese being only about 20,000 tons.

Chromite, as well as having chemical uses, is both an alloy and a refractory; *Indian* production, in 1944 rather below that of Baluchistan and in 1945 only half as much, now seems to have definitely outstripped Pakistan's. Again half to two-thirds comes from Singbhum and Keonjhar, the balance mostly from Mysore. There are small low-grade reserves in Salem and Ratnagiri, and rather better ones near Bezwada in the Kistna Delta; but the total is not impressive, and the increasing use of chromite in *India* may lead to restriction of exports. This is one of the few minerals in which Pakistan is better-found than *India*. There are unexploited reserves of 2–3 m. tons of *vanadium* in Singbhum and Mayurbhanj.

Singbhum produces the quartzite for *silica* bricks to line Jamshedpur's furnaces, and *fireclays* of good quality are found in the Damodar coalfields, in the Rajmahal Hills (W Bengal), and near Kolar (Mysore). Salem and Mysore have several hundred thousand tons of high-quality *magnesite* ore, and there are deposits on the Bombay-Rajasthan border. But production is entirely from the open workings of the Chalk Hills near Salem; three-quarters of the output (40–90,000 tons) is exported, the rest used for furnace-linings, the numerous uses of magnesium in light metallurgy being as yet not taken up.

Other refractories, not predominantly associated with heavy metallurgy, include *kyanite, sillimanite, zircon,* and *graphite.* The scattered deposits of the last are unimportant, but the Travancore beaches are one of the world's main sources of zirconia, while the total reserves of kyanite and sillimanite —valuable in glass and electrical industries—are estimated at 500,000 tons; production is confined to 13,000 tons of kyanite from Kharsawan near Jamshedpur, but this is a large proportion of world output.

Of abrasives *corundum* is the most important; most of it is found in Sn Madras and Mysore, but it is also found in Singbhum, Rewah, the Khasi Hills (Assam), and the Zaskar Range in Kashmir.

3. *Non-ferrous Metals*

Here *India* is distinctly poor, some metals being almost entirely lacking (e.g. tin, tungsten, cobalt, nickel), others inaccessible or hardly economic to work. Of these *lead* is perhaps the most widespread; there is a good deal of galena in the Vindhyan limestones and in Archaean schists, and this was once worked. Current shortages are leading to the re-opening of the great lead-zinc quarry at Zawar (Udaipur, Rajasthan), and perhaps to renewed interest in lead pockets in Chota Nagpur and the copper-lead of Sikkim. Lead and zinc are found, with antimony, in Lahul (E Punjab), but inaccessibly placed at the snout of the Shigra glacier. Perhaps the most likely lead deposits are in Riasi Dt (Kashmir). Small quantities of *silver* are associated with Chota Nagpur galena and Kolar gold.

The only non-ferrous minerals produced, or likely to be produced, in any quantity are gold, copper, and aluminium; the first two are strictly localised. *Gold* is mined solely from the Dharwarian quartz-reefs at Kolar in Mysore; peak output was 330,000 oz. in 1937, since when production has declined to 130–190,000 oz. as the mines are carried to deeper and less productive levels: some shafts are more than 9000 ft deep. Other untapped deposits in Mysore may soon be developed but could not produce more than a quarter of present output. *Copper* ores are found in the Himalayas (Sikkim, Garhwal (UP), Kulu (E Punjab)), and in N Rajasthan, but are worked only in the 80-mile copper belt along the Subarnarekha SE of Jamshedpur; these ores are low-grade (2–4% Cu), producing *c.* 10,000 tons of metal: reserves here are under 1 m. tons. The shortage of copper is the more felt as India's primacy in mica production has obviously great advantages for an electrical industry.

The outlook for *aluminium* is much more promising. Apart from the Eocene fossil laterites (60–80% Al_2O_3) of sub-Himalayan Kashmir, many of the laterites of the Peninsula contain 50–60% alumina; total reserves of bauxite may be as high as 250 m. tons, of which 35 m. are of really high quality. Nearly half of the best bauxite is in Madhya Pradesh (CP), where the present output (*c.* 15,000 tons) is concentrated; but the great new aluminium smelter at Muri, between the Damodar and Jamshedpur, will draw from Lohardaga in Chota Nagpur. The extensive deposits of the Wn Ghats in Kolhapur must wait for the postponed development of power on the Koyna River. There are ample supplies of the caustic soda, necessary to aluminium manufacture, from the alkaline efflorescences of Wn UP, but small but indispensable quantities of the catalyst cryolite must be imported from Greenland. The electricity at Muri is thermal and costs will be high.

4. *Mica*

Mica, mainly muscovite, is found and worked in Nellore (Madras; *c.* 15–20% of total) and Rajasthan, but about three-quarters comes from Hazaribagh Dt in Chota Nagpur. *India* produces 70–80% of the world's supply, Bihar alone supplying 75% of the higher qualities. Here some 60,000 workers are employed in mines and "factories", and a larger number of women and children split the leaves in their houses. Transport is difficult, labour conditions poor, and the industry as a whole is badly organised, though there is increasing concentration and capitalisation in both extracting and processing.[10] *India's* predominance may soon be affected by developments in Canada, Brazil, and Africa, and possibly by synthetics. Current exports (1949-50) are *c.* 350,000 cwt p.a.

5. *Salt*

About one-sixth of *India's* salt output comes from Lake Sambhar and the Pachbhadra pits in Rajasthan; the rest (mainly inferior) from evaporation of sea-water in the tidal flats of Cutch and on the drier coasts of Bombay and Madras; there are reserves of rock-salt in Mandi (Himachal Pradesh). The Cutch salts contain an appreciable proportion of magnesium chloride, which is exported. Bengal is a deficit area: the sea off the great deltas is relatively fresh, and the climate too humid, for successful evaporation. Normally this area imported from the Red Sea. "Salt thus represents another instance of the interdependence of both *India* and Pakistan. If *India* becomes self-sufficient in salt, Western Pakistan will lose a large market. But East Pakistan on the other hand will have to depend on *India* or transport salt at heavy cost from West Pakistan." [11]

6. *Miscellaneous Non-metallic Minerals*

To list the full range of *Indian* minerals would be tedious and useless; but a few of the more significant may be briefly noted.

(a) *Strategic Minerals.* Gaya Dt (Bihar) has pitchblendes which may prove an exploitable source of uranium; but at present the strategic minerals of *India* are the *beryls* of Rajasthan and the *monazite* of Travancore. In addition to being the source of beryllium (used for specially hard copper alloys), beryls are used in atomic fission, as is thorium, which is obtained from monazite. The exploitation of this mineral was originally for the gas-mantle industry, and as such it died a natural death about 1925, when production, which had been over 2000 tons, was 1 cwt. Its revival was due to new uses not only in atomic plants, but in benzine synthesis, for tracer bullets, and so on. With the monazite are associated *ilmenite* (source of titanium oxide for alloys, paints, electrodes, and smoke-screens) and *zircons*. Outputs of these minerals in 1944 were: monazite 2000 tons, ilmenite 200,000 (second to USA with 249,000), zircon sand 1600 tons. There are vast quantities of ilmenite ore—perhaps 250 m. tons—in the laterites, but it is of course too widely diffused to be of use except as concentrated by wave action along the beaches.[12]

(b) *Building Materials, Sands, and Clays.* The great majority of houses in *India* are probably built directly of mud (*terre pisé*) or of mud bricks, and

[10] Thomas, 95–104; cf. below, 588.   [11] Vakil, 204.   [12] Vakil, 211–13.

stones may be set in mud-mortar, or in lime derived either from the Kanker concretions in the alluvium, or from rock.

The most important large-scale exploitation is that of *limestone*—largely Vindhyan—for the cement industry, rapidly expanding to meet a demand in which dams, power-houses, and bridges form a significant fraction. In this connection the Partition has imposed some difficulties upon *India*, since the most important and readily workable *gypsum* deposits were in the Salt Range; production in what is now W Pakistan was over 45% of the All-Indian total. This also affects supplies to the ammonium sulphate plant at Sindri in the Damodar. There are, however, large reserves available in Rajasthan, Trichinopoly (Madras), and Kathiawar, which (in that order) account for most of the current *Indian* production of over 50,000 tons.

The *building-stones* of *India* are justly famous: good granites and slates (the latter mostly Himalayan), the Himalayan Permo-Carboniferous and the Vindhyan limestones, the peculiar freestone (miliolite) of Porbandar in Kathiawar (see below, 596), and many meretricious marbles. Deccan Lava is a sombre material, but it is difficult for even the PWD to be un-dignified in it, and it may be questioned whether any stone in the world is quite so beautiful as the Vindhyan sandstone of Akbar's rose-red palaces. Nor should the humble laterite be forgotten, whether squared to form the masonry of tanks and temples, or crushed to rubble and red dust on the local roads.

(c) *Odds and Ends.* Among minor minerals may be mentioned: alum, apatite, arsenic, asbestos, barytes, felspar, fuller's earth, garnets and other gem-stones, graphite, quartz, saltpetre, and steatite.[13] Many of these are worked locally on a very petty scale, and some—notably saltpetre and alum—were of great importance before the rise of modern chemical industries in the West. Others stand on the thresholds of their careers. Special mention may be made of apatite (rock-phosphate) in view of its possible use as fertiliser. There are deposits in Mussoorie (sub-Himalayan UP), Hazari-bagh, and Singbhum, but the source most likely to be workable is in Trichinopoly, where it occurs in septaria in Cretaceous clays: the quantity available is estimated at 8 m. tons, and exploitation might not be economic.

II. PAKISTAN

Apart from the fibres—jute, cotton, wool—it is no exaggeration to say that Pakistan's industrial endowment, alike in power and in minerals, is en-tirely dwarfed beside that of *India*. This is certainly one factor in Pakistan's anxiety to secure sub-Himalayan Kashmir, with its water-power, coal, iron, bauxite, and zinc; the area could hardly support much metallurgy in itself, but would be a significant asset to a country so deficient as Pakistan in the essentials of big industry.

[13] Details in Wadia, 355–78.

A. POWER

1. *Coal*

Coal in Pakistan is confined to the Salt Range and the country round the Harnai Pass, between Quetta and Sibi. Seams are thinner and more broken than in the Gondwana basins, and the coal itself has a high sulphur and ash content; indeed that of the Salt Range is little more than a lignite, with only 40% fixed carbon. Current production is about 500,000 tons, pretty equally divided between the areas mentioned. With improved transport, rationalisation, and better colliery techniques, it is hoped to double the present figure in 5 years and treble it in 10; but even this would be only two-fifths of current needs.[14] Coal supplies from *India* have been liable to constant interruption since the 'jute war' in the Bengals, yet another example of the disastrous effects of Indo-Pakistani friction; indeed taking the whole range of economic activity one might call this perpetual sabotage of trade relations a sub-continental suicide pact.

Discoveries in 1949 suggest that there may well be usable amounts of rather poor lignite near Bhairab Bazaar, on the Dacca-Chittagong railway.[15]

2. *Oil*

Pakistan's oil (*c.* 45 m. gallons) comes entirely from small fields in the sub-montane Indus region (Attock Dt). But clearly the old extension of the Tertiary 'Sind Gulf', and the great areas of folded Eocene rocks (with structural relations similar to those on the other flank of the Iranian Plateau) hold considerable promise. Prospecting has been active since the war, e.g. around Lake Manchar; so far no real success has been attained.

3. *Electricity*

Development in 1947 was extremely meagre; one hydro station of 9600 kW at Malakand (NWFP) and 40–50,000 kW of thermal power—in part diesel—mainly in the few large towns. Some power from Mandi still comes across the border to Lahore, but this is only 13–14,000 kW and is being diminished. As in *India*, however, 'hydel' is in danger of becoming merely a magic word. Resources, while not great, are probably sufficient for a moderate industrialisation, mainly linked with agriculture.[16]

In W Pakistan as an immediate programme Malakand is being doubled, the Rasul plant (22,000 kW) on the Jhelum and Dargai (15–20,000) were opened in 1952. It is hoped that by 1956 there will be available 20,000 kW

---

[14] *Pakistan News* (Karachi), IV/10 (5/3/50), 152–54.

[15] *Industry in Pakistan*, 20–21.

[16] It is impossible to see where the 5 m. kW potential given in the Colombo Plan comes from. Cf. O. H. K. Spate, "The Partition of the Punjab and of Bengal", *GJ* CX (1947). fn. at p. 216.

at Mianwali and 150,000 at Warsak—Pakistan's only multi-purpose scheme. But Rasul power will be mainly taken up by tube-wells for pumping over-irrigated areas. In addition the Kotri (Lower Sind) canals will produce 23,000 kW in four small units, and the thermal plant at Karachi is being expanded by a like amount. In E Pakistan the only scheme of significance is on the Karnaphuli River behind Chittagong—160,000 kW. The full programme represents an increase from c. 50,000 to c. 360,000 kW.

It will be seen that the bulk of the projected development is in the sub-montane Indus region; this will serve Pakistan's only "industrial" zone—if such it can be called—lying between Peshawar and Lahore. Sn Punjab and Sind are likely to remain backward in this respect.

B. Minerals

The only metallic ore definitely known to exist in really large quantities is *chromite*, of which there is a production of c. 20,000 tons in Zhob Dt (Baluchistan), while the considerable reserves probably extend N into Waziristan. *Antimony* is mined in Chitral, at a distance of 175 miles from the nearest railway: as it was processed in *India*, production has naturally declined. The only *iron* ores claimed are a few deposits in the NWFP and very low-grade lateritic haematite in the Madhupur Jungle (E Bengal); faced with Jamshedpur just across the delta, even the most ardent Pakistani can hardly be very enthusiastic about its exploitation—without any coal. The largest NWFP deposit is 40 m. tons of good *magnetite* at Drosh in Chitral; it is admitted in official publications that inaccessibility and lack of fuel render the reserves of no immediate importance.[17]

In non-metallic minerals the situation is rather better. The Salt Range produces c. 175,000 tons of *salt*, and across the Indus in Kohat are beds of nearly pure rock-salt 1000 ft thick and 8 miles long. At Khewra in the Salt Range, and also in Kohat, the saline beds are associated with large masses of *gypsum* (output 15–20,000 tons), and there are further reserves to the N in Hazara and to the S in Dera Ismail Khan. *Magnesium* and *potassium* salts are found in workable quantities in the Salt Range, and *alum* at Kalabagh. The *dhands* or alkaline lakes of Sind would also bear investigation. Pakistan has the sub-continent's only considerable supplies of *sulphur*, in the extinct volcanoes of the Baluchistan/Persia border: reserves of c. 500,000 tons and output (doubtless limited by distance from markets) of 10–12,000 tons. Salt (c. 125,000 tons) is also produced by evaporation around Karachi; but E Pakistan, of course, must import. The NWFP has many excellent building-stones; and the glass industry of Hyderabad has recently located large deposits of glass-sand near Tatta.

Nevertheless the general mineral endowment is extremely slight, though the Salt Range certainly seems to supply a firm basis for chemical industries,

---

[17] *Industry in Pakistan*, 20, 22.

given the power. It is of course possible, or even likely, that proper survey of the NW hills would bring further reserves to light; mica has been reported from Hazara, manganese from Chitral, which seems the most promising area. But it is not very probable that they would materially alter the situation.

CHAPTER XI

INDUSTRY: DEVELOPMENT, PROBLEMS, PROSPECTS

I. THE INDUSTRIAL REVOLUTION IN INDIA

The Historical Background

DURING those centuries when sailing-ships, water-mills, and handlooms were the most complicated machines in existence, India shared with China and Byzantium the leadership of the world in technical ingenuity, economic organisation, and volume of manufactures. Few finer textiles can ever have been produced than the "woven wind", the diaphanous muslin of Dacca, and the wrought-iron pillar at Delhi, dated at latest AD 415, would rank as an outstanding technical achievement in any century before our own. For about 150 years after 1600 Indian textiles were a main staple of Eastern trade, and quite capable of capturing Western markets from local producers; so at least thought the London calico-printers when they rioted against the EIC's imports in 1721, and so secured protective legislation.

The decline from this position was abrupt, and with the rise of Lancashire and the fall of the princely Courts India collapsed into industrial insignificance, complete but for the hard-hit village crafts. In its external relations the whole Indian economy was geared to that of Britain, whether as market or as source of raw materials. The first steps towards a modern industry were indeed taken a century ago, but on the whole progress has been irregular in time, space, and the internal structure of industry; if to-day *India* ranks about 5th among the industrial countries of the world, that is a function of size rather than of development: coal and steel outputs are a fraction of those of the great industrial powers, output per head of population a fraction of that of minor industrial countries.

Yet perhaps only Brazil and China offer such scope for industrialisation, and the technical bases have been laid. The main obstacles to advance are now probably social: low purchasing power, "cheap" labour inefficient to the point of dearness. These are clearly linked factors, though unfortunately urban enthusiasm still seems to regard industry and agriculture as autonomous sectors of the economy, except that agriculture can be milked for raw materials.[1]

The Crafts

It is hardly necessary to recount the dispossession of the artisan by the mill; in fact it is more to the point to indicate the limitations to this process. The town artisan, working for a market readily accessible to alien trade, suffered first and most; the village craftsman held out longer and in some areas, such as Assam, where communications are poor he has still a fairly strong position. Furthermore, distinctions must be made within the general category.

[1] How strong this view is may be seen from the very odd arguments against it in Agarwala, 34–41.

Those crafts with the highest survival value appear to be (*a*) services following population; (*b*) some luxury trades; (*c*) at the other extreme some crafts which have as it were a market sheltered by its poverty, or which deal in raw materials not worth processing by modern methods. Within all groups, in proportions varying with the technical cast of each trade, there is a wide range of organisation, from the true independent artisan owning both tools and raw materials, through all the variants of piece-work for entrepreneurs, putting-out, and so on, to workers in what is in effect an embryonic factory. The pages of Lipson or Cunningham take on visible flesh and blood in this paradise for the economic historian.

(*a*) The village servants include smiths, carpenters, tailors, potters. In the old days of self-sufficiency these were supported by a definite assignment of land or by a fixed annual payment in kind, in return for which they met all normal requirements through the year, but these customary arrangements have been largely superseded by payment for the job. Except where they do piece-work (knives, locks, etc.) for petty town entrepreneurs, the smiths are now less makers than fixers, and the same is true, to a less extent, of carpenters: they are the village repair and maintenance men, and "it is the smith and the carpenter who make the Persian wheels go round". The increasing use of simple machinery may actually improve their position, given some elementary technical education. Potters have to meet the demand for very cheap wares necessitated by the custom of smashing food-dishes after use (especially on ritual occasions) in order to obviate the risk of caste defilement; this is of course losing ground, but obviously no factory process could market at a sufficiently low price to meet the need. This custom is doubtless responsible for the striking lack of an important ceramic in Hindu civilisation, perhaps alone among the great cultures of the world.[2]

(*b*) The luxury crafts include the makers of the finest silk *saris*, of gold and silver-thread embroideries, really skilled jewellers, ivory-carvers, and so on. The old Court demand is all but dead, owing in part to the liquidation of the old aristocracies and in part to the aping of bad European taste by the survivors, and only in a few places are classic standards more or less maintained. There is a strong tendency for these crafts to turn to workshop organisation and the tourist market, with results more deplorable than describable.

(*c*) A vast demand at the lowest possible price-level is responsible for the survival of such trades as the making of *bidis*, the ersatz "cigarette" of the masses; the units of sale are so petty as to be not worth much capital equipment so long as there is a reserve of cheap labour. *Bidi*-making is essentially a sweatshop industry using female and child labour; it could of course be put-out, but the entrepreneurs prefer the adulteration to be done for their own profit. The factory leather industry has made notable advances, but the untouchable Chamars still produce millions of half-tanned 'kips' from their crude vats; the hides of diseased and half-starved cattle, riddled by sores and ticks, are hardly worth tanning by modern methods. "Like many other Indian handicraftsmen, the un-

---

[2] There is some attractive modern factory-made pottery, e.g. from Gwalior, but it is hardly equal aesthetically to the pots turned out in hundreds in any small Burmese town.

touchable tanners remain because of the presence of low-grade materials and a market for cheap products." [3]

The *charkha* or spinning-wheel and the handloom raise a number of difficult and much-canvassed questions: can they survive in the face of mill competition? if so, how? and is it really worthwhile to save them? The values involved are as much human as economic, and the answers therefore subjective; and the economic arguments are too technical to be discussed here. The whole question is studded with sociological man-traps, and the more sentimental devotees of the *charkha* simply ignore, or distort, the comparative costs of mill and home production. Nevertheless it would be socially very desirable to provide some relief to the seasonal un- and under-employment of the countryside. A compromise solution may be possible by decentralising the machine spinning industry to provide cheaper yarn, and fostering cottage or small workshop weaving with electric looms.

Other rural crafts and trades, at present strictly speaking uneconomic, might be salvaged and become economically worthwhile given a sufficiency of *cheap* power; and since the expansion of large-scale industry cannot hope to take in all the increasing surplus of rural population, some such development, if attainable, might provide a way out of the impasse of an increase of population at a rate disproportionate to the expansion of agricultural and factory output. But obviously there are no short-cuts on these roads, and no easy salvation for India's ancient crafts.

Phases of Industrialisation

Broadly speaking, India's industrial revolution falls into three phases:

(i) *c.* 1854–1914: the provision of a railway net, the usual initial concentration on textiles;

(ii) 1914–1921: (*a*) recognition of India's potential significance and actual insignificance to Imperial military economics; (*b*) political unrest and the attainment of fiscal autonomy;

(iii) 1921–1939: experiments in protection, rise of iron and steel and of sugar industry, considerable but uneven progress generally.

The years since 1939 might be considered the growing pains of a new industrial revolution; to this point we return later.

1854–1914: Cotton is King. In the 19th century the EIC itself did virtually nothing for Indian economic development, except to foster opium cultivation for the China trade, to introduce tea-planting from China, and to give some support to the long-drawn-out attempts at exploiting Salem iron ores (below, 708); it left the field clear for private enterprise to flood India with Manchester goods, to extend tea and indigo plantations, and to build up a great export trade in cotton, jute, hides, and oilseeds. Before 1850 a few steam-engines had been set up in docks, flour-mills, and so on, mainly around Calcutta.

But the decade 1854–64 was critical. Politically the Mutiny led to the end of Company rule; economically two distant wars led to the founding of Indian

[3] Buchanan, 94; his whole Ch. V is a very fair discussion of the craft *vs.* machine question.

factory industry: the Crimean War by cutting off hemp supplies to Dundee (which had been experimenting with power-woven jute since 1835) and so creating a great demand for raw jute; the American Civil War by producing an even more inflationary demand for raw cotton. With money pouring in and fibres pouring out it would have been strange indeed had nobody turned his mind to local manufacture. The major economic effect of the Mutiny was to render urgent— for military reasons—the extension of the two or three fragments of railway which existed in 1857, and this played a part in the general quickening of economic activity, not least by the establishment of railshops and collieries. But for 60 years at least railway rate policy favoured the export of cash crops and hampered industrial development away from the three great ports.

In 1854 a jute mill was opened at Calcutta, a cotton mill at Broach and another at Bombay [4]; the pioneers were respectively English, American, and—significantly—Parsee. By 1861 Bombay had 8 mills with nearly 200,000 spindles and a start had been made at Ahmedabad; the frenzied finance of the cotton boom was succeeded by merited catastrophe, but the Suez Canal (1869) was a stimulant and by 1877 there were 51 cotton mills with nearly 1·25 m. spindles, though only 10,385 looms. The jute manufacturing boom came later, with a jump from 5 to 18 mills in 1873–75. From the first, however, weaving was important in Bengal, while Bombay devoted itself primarily to spinning, largely for the hand-looms of China. Apart from the local raw cotton—offset by the necessity of importing coal from England—the major factor in the lead taken by the W coast was historical. The 60 years which intervened between Plassey and the overthrow of the Marathas were those of the most ruthless economic aggression by the commercial oligarchs of Calcutta, seated in the entry to Hindostan and with their attention fixed on the richest plains of India. The very active trade of Bombay had a stronger element local to the Arabian Sea, and was hence more largely shared by indigenous groups such as Parsees and Khoja Muslims; indigenous enterprise was never so stifled as in the E.[5] It is significant that the Managing Agency system is strongest in Bengal, where local capitalists—quite rightly— showed an entire lack of confidence in their own managerial capacity. Hence while, except for the great Sassoon interests, British participation in cotton was from the start very slight, it is only in the last few years that British interests in jute have been bought out, and the executives of the industry are still largely Scots.

Apart from the growth of coal mining and of the service industries (foundries, etc.) of the ports, the last quarter of the 19th century was marked mainly by the spread of cotton mills to inland centres—Ahmedabad, Nagpur, Sholapur. By 1900 factories employed some 500,000 workers, of whom 160,000 were in cotton.

By 1900 also there was a significant hardening of nationalist feeling; Congress was soon to change its tone from "we respectfully submit" to "we demand". A main part in this change was played by resentment against the Government's

---

[4] An unsuccessful cotton mill was set up at Bowreah, Calcutta, about 1818 (Buchanan, 128, 136). The Bombay mill is often dated 1851.

[5] Sharma, 13–16. The contrast in the attitudes to Indian business on the part of the British communities in Bombay and Calcutta remained striking, not to say shocking, as late as 1943.

adoption in 1883 of a virtually complete Free Trade policy; where the small revenue tariff applied to Indian manufactures (e.g. $3\frac{1}{2}\%$ on cotton goods) a countervailing excise was imposed. This certainly gave colour to suspicions that the whole policy was rigged in favour of Lancashire. The placing of India on the gold standard (1893–98) was a severe blow to the yarn trade with China, which adhered to silver; but this may have been a blessing in disguise since it impelled an increase of weaving and a better balance within the industry. There was neither disguise nor blessing in Lord Morley's doctrinaire refusal to sanction the Madras Government's industrial experiments. From the Indian point of view Free Trade was decidedly illiberal.

Yet despite all difficulties expansion continued: on the eve of the 1914 war coal output was over 12 m. tons, factories with over 50 hands employed some 900,000 workers, and few important towns had not been reached by a railway. And in 1911 the first pig iron had flowed into Jamshedpur moulds.

1914–21: the Empty Arsenal. World War I brought an abrupt fall in imports from the warring countries and a boom demand for Indian raw materials, while the important campaigns in Mesopotamia and Palestine cried out for stores which could have been supplied by an integrated Indian industry had it existed. The stage was set for large expansion, but the prime weakness of India's industrial structure was at once apparent: an almost complete lack of machines to make machines.

The growth of consumption industries had been favoured by untaxed machinery imports—some offset to "Lancashire interference"—but this inhibited the development of production goods. As a result purely extractive industries boomed, Jamshedpur was sheltered at a critical phase, and existing industries worked to capacity; but except for jute, for which Calcutta engineering firms managed to produce some plant, very little expansion was possible. Government now paid heavily for its policy (in bland disregard of its own rules) of purchasing stores in England even when, with little inconvenience, they could have been had in India; a policy at once discriminatory and lacking discrimination. As it was, Britain's loss in the Indian market was only in small part India's gain; the lion's share went to Japan. Exports also were affected: in the Chinese yarn trade the India : Japan proportions of 77 : 23 in 1906 were exactly reversed by 1924. No better justification could have been found for the thesis that fiscal control from London was indefensible.

The post-war boom-and-slump was aggravated in India by violent fluctuations of the rupee. Nevertheless in 1922 factory employment was 1·36 m., and it is significant that the share of cotton had fallen from a third in 1902 to a quarter. At this point India gained fiscal autonomy.

1922–39: "Discriminating Protection." The new powers were exercised with discretion, rather strict interpretation being given, for instance, to the principle that an industry to receive protection should have such natural advantages as adequate home supplies of raw materials; this ruled out the glass industry for lack of soda ash, though matches, dependent on imported splints, received protection. The following figures illustrate the progress of the chief protected industries: [6]

---

[6] J. Matthai, *Tariffs and Industry* (OPIA No. 20, 1944), 9–12.

	Steel	Sugar 1000 tons	Paper	Cotton Piecegoods 1 m. yards	Matches 100,000 gross
1922–23 .	131	24	24	1725	8
1939–40 .	1070	1242	70	4013	220
Increase % .	717	5075	192	132	2850

The depression of the early '30s slowed expansion, but there was little actual retrogression, in part doubtless because there was so much leeway to make up. Cotton, for instance, added to both spindles and looms in every year until 1937.

Progress, however, was on a very ragged front, the most serious laggard being perhaps heavy chemicals. The leading developments of the inter-war years were: (i) changes in the cotton industry—an increased proportion of higher counts, especially in Ahmedabad; a relative decline in the position of Bombay Province, with an actual fall in the number of mills in Bombay Island; a rapid expansion in Mysore and Madras, especially at Coimbatore, consequent on the use of Nilgiri and Cauvery power; [7] (ii) the expansion of Jamshedpur as a metallurgical centre; (iii) the rise of the sugar and cement industries; (iv) a proliferation of minor consumption industries. This last was in the nature of things, but was powerfully aided by the nationalist boycotts of British goods.

In 1939 coal output was 28 m. tons, steel had topped the million, and industrial employment (excluding Government ordnance and railshops, and seasonal gins and presses) was 1·8 m. Cotton again accounted for nearly 33%, probably owing to Tamilnad's entry into the 'first phase'. Allowing for the multiplied mechanisation of the second war, India was far better equipped in 1939 than in 1914. Developments since 1939 have been so manifold that they are best described under separate heads. Before summarising, as briefly as may be, the individual industries, it may be as well to glance at some features largely peculiar to Indian industrial life, but common to many branches.

Some General Features

(a) *Mistries and Managing Agents*. The old territorial patchwork, the *morcellement* of the fields, the ladder of sub-tenancies from ryot to zamindar, the vivisection of society by caste—all these suggest that 'fragmentation' is a main motif in the life of India. Nor is even modern industry altogether exempt, despite such great integrations as the House of Tata. There seems a curious tendency to depute and re-depute responsibility: at one end of the scale labour is recruited and controlled by contractors, at the other executive functions are farmed out to Managing Agents, and exchanges in between are in the sticky hands of multiple hordes of middlemen.

There was originally, doubtless, good reason for this fragmentation of functions, just as there was for caste, but it can hardly be doubted that it is now a burden on industry, with endless delays, frictions, and confusions, as well as the

[7] In 1921 Wn India had 68·6% and Sn India 9·3% of 280 mills; in 1937 the percentages were respectively 56·3 and 17·7 of 419 mills (Sharma, 28).

direct cash charge for services rendered. Thus the labour jobber or *mistry*—there are other names for him—who beats up a gang of labourers was useful enough in the earlier phases; he is now often an unscrupulous exploiter of both sides, at times even a strike-leader, more frequently a strike-breaker. He adds to legitimate commissions innumerable exactions from his workers, bound to him by initial advances, and thus secures his hold to the serious detriment of good and stable labour relations.

At the top is the curious Managing Agency system. This again was natural enough when Indian capitalists with no technical experience wished to start an industry; the importers who provided the plant would set it up and recruit technicians and managers; they would also buy stores and raw materials and market the product. This was, as it were, insurance against inexperience; but when in time one Agency came to run scores of firms, with perhaps a dozen of them in the same line, and was paid largely by commissions on both purchases and sales (or, much worse, on output sold or unsold) and took policy decisions for the "directors" to rubber-stamp, the possibilities of abuse became enormous.[8] There are now Indian Agents; the system is yielding as Indians gain experience, but none too quickly.

(b) *Industrial Psychology.* Indian industry has suffered from being initiated, as a rule, by men whose inherited aptitudes were commercial rather than industrial; hence a tendency to go all out for quick profits, often dissipated in speculative extensions. There is often a fantastic diffusion of energy and money into any number of petty unrelated projects—more fragmentation! Inflated optimism may be succeeded by as disastrous pessimism; in India one may really meet the snivelling bourgeois of Marxist satire, ruthless and timorous by turns. In actual management there is often very loose costing; allowance for depreciation is often minimal; and there is a reluctance to cut losses and scrap antique plant: in 1886 Jamshedji Tata bought a mill "which had a conglomerate mass of machinery operated by several steam engines and using 23 boilers. The mill's business had been wound up four times in twenty years. Tata literally threw the old machinery out of the windows."[9]

It must of course be emphasised that these attitudes are receding into the past, though too slowly in some industries; and there are plenty of businessmen of quick and solid ability.

(c) *Labour Problems.* While direct comparisons of output per man-hour are usually very unfavourable to India, they leave out too many factors to be worth much. Nonetheless it can hardly be doubted that much Indian labour is inefficient to an extent that goes far to offset its cash cheapness. The reasons are fairly obvious: bad physique, bad housing, bad food, bad working conditions, and as a corollary bad industrial and sometimes bad personal habits. Mills are often very insanitary—impure water has been used for humidifiers—and in any case the atmosphere is very exhausting in the hot weather. Overcrowding and bad water-supply, as in the great tenement *chawls* of Bombay or the *bustees* of Calcutta, negate the most elementary decencies. The worker is very often in debt, some-

---

[8] See Buchanan, 165–72, and especially the extraordinary balance-sheet at p. 171; Anstey, 112–15, 501–02. Cf. *First Five Year Plan*, 147.
[9] Buchanan, 206.

times to the tune of a quarter's pay, and there were few nastier sights in India than the factory gates on pay-day, with tough Pathan moneylenders armed with heavy staves waiting for their prey.

Serious efforts have been made, by both governments and the better employers, to improve conditions, but the general level remains deplorably low, and legislation is too often evaded or corrupted.

It is not surprising, then, that absenteeism is rife and that there is a large labour turnover, in part owing to the instigation of jobbers anxious for a new round of

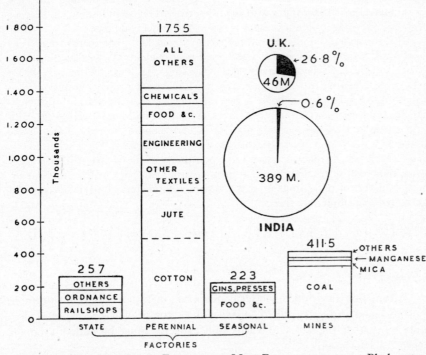

Fig. 58.—UNDIVIDED INDIA: FACTORY AND MINE EMPLOYMENT, 1947. Black sector in pi-graphs is percentage of industrial workers to total population. *India* had 2·4 m. industrial workers in 1949–50.

bribes and commissions. To check desertion to other mills, or to the villages, payment is often by the month, sometimes with a regular fortnight's arrear. But absenteeism and large turnovers will remain standard so long as a large proportion of industrial workers are really villagers supplementing their miserable incomes by a spell in the mills. Except where female labour is in demand, as in textiles, the worker is most properly unwilling to bring his wife; the urban sex-disparity is itself a social problem of the first magnitude. The worker's heart remains at home, whither he betakes himself at harvest or festival time. This constant interchange is a main factor in the sapping of the old village tradition, and owing to the large turnover a far higher proportion of the population is affected than would be indicated by the figures of factory employment at any one time. Only in a few places—notably Ahmedabad, perhaps Cawnpore—is the true urban proletariat more important than the migrant mass.

Trade unions are as rule extremist and effective (e.g. the Bombay Girni Kamgar—'Red Flag'—Union) or moderate and ineffective; often both extremist and inefficient; only in sheltered trades really stable. The illiteracy of the workers naturally makes them turn to outside organisers, often unemployed lawyers, some of whom have given devoted service while others have been amateurs in union methods but professionally skilled in exploiting their position, whether for politics or pay. While many unions are thus extremely irresponsible, little has been done to make easy the way of the properly-run registered union, and recent legislation seems retrograde, except perhaps for company unions.

All this is not to say that the workers are without fault, nor that there are not good trade unions, good workers, and good managements. Where labour is well provided for and has become a real settled working-class it can fill the most skilled jobs, as Jamshedpur experience has shown. Moreover at present various 'welfare state' measures seem to indicate a general improvement, though unfortunately largely at the expense (through sales taxes, etc.) of the middle clerical classes, who also are subject to extreme exploitation. Nevertheless on the whole the labour situation is one of the prime weaknesses of Indian industries. Those who call out most loudly on the inefficiency and irresponsibility of the Indian worker are too often those who place and keep him in an environment poor, nasty, and brutish, in the interest of mill profits of 40% or more. The moral responsibility and the social irresponsibility are theirs.

II. CURRENT INDUSTRIAL DEVELOPMENT IN *INDIA*

A. TEXTILES [10]

1. *Cotton*

Cotton, first of India's modern industries in time, retains its premier position, and India's installed capacity of *c.* 4500 m. yards a year is second only to that of the USA. To this mill capacity must be added 1300 m. yards for handlooms.

Its early location at Bombay was the result of the simplest geographical factors.[11] The raw material is 'non-localising', since it is not perishable and loses little weight in manufacture, but access to a wide range of grades is an advantage, and obviously most easily attained in the great export mart. Bombay was also favourably placed for the import of bulky machinery, stores, and coal, and for the yarn export to China, the initial *raison d'être* of the industry. The rise of cotton manufacturing in Japan and China, however, enforced changes which after about 1905 began to react unfavourably on the relative position of the original base. Weaving for the home market

[10] Recent figures for employment and output are given in Tables XVII–XIX, but changes are so rapid that such figures are so far as possible avoided in the text.
[11] The discussion of cotton milling distribution which follows is drawn from the admirably lucid and stimulating analysis in Sharma, Chs. II–III, q.v. for much further detail.

became more important, and later the *swadeshi* movement against buying British, largely backed by the urban middle-class, led to a demand for finer counts than those adequate for the China trade. Apart from the increasing overheads—higher wages and charges natural to a great metropolis, Weber's 'deglommerative factors'—in Bombay Island, this shift in emphasis from foreign yarn to internal piecegoods markets added to Bombay's costs the charges on long rail hauls. Despite a railway rates policy which worked strongly in favour of the great ports, mills at the many internal raw cotton marts could save freight on both raw material and finished product, while the growth of coal mining in the Damodar or even locally (as near Nagpur) provided power. Ahmedabad, with old textile and financing traditions, was off the mark very quickly, followed by Nagpur and Sholapur; outside the Peninsular cotton tracts Cawnpore, well placed between Punjab cotton and Bihar coal, led the way. Delhi shared slightly in this development, but beyond it even the great distributing market of Amritsar was handicapped by lack of power until the advent of Mandi hydro-electricity. Calcutta, "probably the largest single cotton piecegoods market in the world", nevertheless did not start until 1905, doubtless mainly because of the fixation on jute and the weakness of local indigenous entrepreneurs. In the S the Buckingham and Carnatic mills at Madras, established 1874–83, remained practically isolated until the sudden development in the early 1930s of centres served by Pykara power, most notably Coimbatore (below, 709–12, 716–17). Here spinning is still dominant, supplying the handlooms of Madura and Tamilnad generally.

Bombay State still has over half of *Indian* production, but the balance continues to shift away from it: in Bombay Island the number of mills has actually decreased, and in Ahmedabad seems stationary. But the spread has been accompanied by at least the beginnings of regional specialisation: spinning in Madras, light fabrics of cotton and rayon mixtures and so on in the Punjab, tent canvas and *durris* (rough rugs) at Cawnpore, where industry has always had a certain military bias owing to its start as the centre for Army saddlery. In face of the increasing competition Bombay and Ahmedabad, like New England, have found their account in specialising in finer products: the percentage of yarn output in counts above 31 increased at Bombay from 2 in 1921–22 to 17·9 in 1941–42, at Ahmedabad from 7·4 to 35·6. This turn to higher-priced goods, in which freight will be a lesser proportion of the final price, is the natural counter to the transport advantages of the inland centres. War restrictions have seriously interfered with this trend, but it is probably only suspended.

In general the industry suffers from a lack of well-integrated ancillaries. It is significant that Ahmedabad, which uses a far higher proportion of foreign (i.e. longer-stapled) cotton than any other centre, and has on the whole the most stable labour force, is also ahead in this respect: starch, reeds, and healds are made locally, and Tatas are now producing such essential chemicals as soda ash and bleaching powder at Port Okha, on the tip of the Kathiawar Peninsula.

The industry is at present in a difficult phase.[12] The raw material situation is not easy: the fall of nearly 50% since 1939 in cotton acreage has affected mainly the Deccan short-staple areas; there has been some recovery very recently, and cotton interests have presented plans for raising acreage to some 75% of pre-war. But, while not all the loss to cotton was taken up by foodcrops—some went fallow—it is difficult to see how this target could be attained without encroachment on the food area, which it would seem essential to avoid. Meanwhile the demand for foreign cotton is increased at a time of world shortage—and W Punjab, the only considerable source of the better staples, has become foreign. Pakistan's cotton industry is small, but it is one of the few she has, and she is determined to extend it; hence perhaps the imposition of an export duty of Rs.60 per bale, inadequately met by *Indian* exemption of all duty on raw cotton imported from Pakistan. In any case deliveries from Pakistan have been well below anticipation. All this has meant high prices, and while the annual per capita consumption of cloth is only about 10 or 12 yards, mill stocks are piling up for lack of purchasing power among the ill-clad masses.[13] No clearer illustration could be given of the thesis that industrial expansion and agricultural development are Siamese twins.

2. *Jute*

"In 1940, 95·5% of the jute looms in India . . . were situated in a small strip of land about 60 miles long and two broad", up and down the Hooghly from Calcutta; and the 70,000 looms of this tiny area were actually about 54% of all in the world.[14] But at Partition 80% of raw jute output was in E Pakistan, which yet had not a single jute-mill.

The reasons for this anomaly are in part historical: capital and management were largely supplied by the Scots oligarchy of Managing Agents, concentrated in the commercial metropolis of Gangetic India and the NE Peninsula. Calcutta in turn owed its trade hegemony to the physical character of the delta; poor as it is, the Hooghly is the best of the Ganges spillways until we reach the great conjoint Padma-Brahmaputra-Meghna estuary in the E, and this entry has a hinterland small in comparison with Hindustan, access to which is much more direct by the Hooghly-Bhagirathi or (for land routes) the Wn flanks of the delta.

Sharma's elegant analysis brings out a less obvious but beautifully geo-

---

[12] The remainder of this section is based on Vakil, 250–61.
[13] "The cause of his death you will soon understand,
    The thing that he lacked was *effective demand*."
[14] Sharma, 77, 89. This section based mainly on Sharma, Ch. V, and Vakil, 261–79.

graphical point. Calcutta, by its pull as the only port for seaborne trade,[15] was the hub of the internal waterways, and over half the jute arrivals were by water. Nevertheless 43% came by rail. But four Districts—Mymensingh, Dacca, Tippera, and Faridpur—supplied 70% of the Hooghlyside mill demand, and of these only the last and least lay W of the great unbridged barrier of the Meghna and its confluents. Transhipment was thus necessary; one ferry took loaded goods wagons, but on this route a break of gauge intervened. "Under these conditions of transport, involving a good deal of terminal charges, if the jute mills were located in the main jute belt in Eastern Bengal, the transhipment hurdles would have to be crossed twice —once in moving the coal, mill stores, labour, etc. to the mills and again in moving the finished goods to Calcutta for export. . . . But in the case of mills in the Hooghly area the transhipment ordeal has to be faced only once—in moving the raw jute to the mills." [16] In other words, the location of Calcutta was analogous to that of Bombay in the early days of cotton, not only for machinery from overseas, but also for Damodar coal which met the jute there just as if it had itself come oversea.

The splitting of the growing from the milling centres has largely disrupted jute movements. As we have seen (Ch. IX), strenuous efforts are being made to increase raw jute output in *India*, and not without success, though how far this is compatible with the policy of self-sufficiency in food is doubtful. It must be noted that Pakistan jute is usually of better quality than *Indian*; this again is largely a matter of the physical character of the delta, the more lively streams of the active E bringing their annual increments of silt to the fields, and providing much better conditions for retting than are found in the half-stagnant backwaters of W Bengal. It seems that however successful the jute drive in *India*, considerable amounts—perhaps two-thirds of consumption—will still be needed from Pakistan.[17]

On the other hand Pakistan's position is by no means impregnable, as Pakistanis seem to assume. Naturally enough Pakistan is determined to establish a jute industry, using Karnaphuli power. But the programme, in view of limited fiscal and power resources, is modest—only 6 mills. Nor can Chittagong, even with recent extensions, handle all the overseas export, much of which has still to go by Calcutta. As Vakil well puts it, the question "is not one of an absolute monopoly of Pakistan, but of a bilateral monopoly between Pakistan as the major producer and India as the major buyer." [18] It may be added that if E Pakistan has a quasi-monopoly of the

---

[15] Chittagong, at least until Partition, was too excentric, and is still too small, to count in this discussion.

[16] Sharma, 84–86. Theoretically of course another port might have been developed, but even were physical conditions more favourable, the self-reinforcing hegemony of Calcutta was hardly shakeable by the 1870s; and the difficulty of coal movements from the Damodar to Dacca would remain.

[17] Vakil, 264–65.   [18] Vakil, 272.

raw jute trade, the jute trade has a monopoly of E Pakistan: apart from tea there is no other significant cash crop. As for *India*, the importance of the commodity may be judged from the fact that in 1948 about one-third of all her foreign exchange earnings—and two-thirds of hard currency—came from jute.[19]

In these circumstances it is deplorable that jute should be the terrain of continual economic skirmishing, culminating in the major engagement of the devaluation crisis of 1949, which for six months brought the Indo-Pakistani jute trade to a stop—except for smuggling, said to have amounted to over 85,000 tons. This cut-throat attitude on both sides may well expose the jute trade to one of two opposite dangers: either dislocation of the manufacturing industry leading to prices so high as to accelerate the already menacing development of substitutes and bulk loading, and possibly planting in other tropical deltas; or frantic over-exporting of raw jute from Pakistan with a consequent collapse of prices. The economic cards are on the whole stacked against Pakistan; jute is a trump which is not to be recklessly thrown away to win some ephemeral political trick.

3. *Wool*

The woollens industry has also suffered from Partition: a third or more of the clip came from W Pakistan, and again this was the better third in quality. In the 'continental' NW are also the main markets for warm clothing; the Himalayas look after themselves with home-spun and sheepskin. Yet all but one of the factories were in *India*.

The distribution is very peculiar. In 1939 the total employment in the 17 fairly important factories was 8271; but Cawnpore, Dhariwal near Amritsar, and Amritsar itself, with one mill each, employed respectively 2311, 1960, and 701 workers—together about 60% of the total. These locations are significant. Cawnpore is on the border of the main wool-producing and wool-consuming zone, where it is nearest to Damodar coal. Here the first Indian mill was set up (1876), essentially for Army needs. Dhariwal and Amritsar are central to the main marts for the wools of the sub-continent and beyond—Peshawar, Multan, Fazilka, and a string of contact-zone markets, from Kumaon to Kashmir, collecting central Asian and Tibetan wool. Once hydro-electricity was available the industry almost followed.

Demand is seasonal, and except when Army contracts are available working also is seasonal: labour turnover is too high for efficiency. Again market requirements are exceedingly varied, specialisation almost impossible if mills are to work through the year, and administrative overheads (for supervisors, specialist technicians, etc.) correspondingly high.

Most of the more skilled workers at Dhariwal and Amritsar were Muslims

---

[19] *Report of Export Promotion Cttee* (1949), cited Vakil, 261 fn. 2.

who have gone to Pakistan. On the whole it seems that with some protection and Government assistance W Punjab might well replace E as the main woollens zone of the sub-continent, especially as imports of good Australian wools for worsteds, though necessary, should not be so great proportionately as for the *Indian* industry.

The handloom side is still strong, employment being estimated at anything from two to six times that in mills. It has, however, to meet the competition of cheap shoddies and mixtures from Japan, Italy, and Poland; the cessation of these imports during the war, and the all-out working of the mills for Army clothing, gave the craft industry a great impetus. At Srinagar (Kashmir) a centrally organised cottage industry employs about 9000 weavers; in the Himalayas spinning and weaving are family affairs, the producers owning everything from the sheep to the loom; but elsewhere, and especially in the carpet branch, the weavers are in debt-bondage to petty entrepreneurs. Apart from carpets the main products are coarse blankets, at once cheaper and more resistant to hard usage than mill products.

4. *Silk, Rayon, Hosiery* [20]

The *silk* industry suffers mainly from the inadequacy, both in quantity and quality, of the home raw material supply. The industry, located in Mysore, Madras, W Bengal, and Kashmir, is poorly organised, cottage production unequal and generally inferior in quality, and on the whole prospects do not seem bright. *Rayon* production is increasing rapidly: the main centres are Bombay, Ahmedabad, and Surat—an interesting location, reminiscent of the early days of cotton (the yarn is all imported). The chief inland centre is Amritsar, associated with the general development of light industry consequent on electrification, and linked with cotton-rayon mixtures and knitwear. There seems to be no reason, given the development of the necessary chemical industries (essential on other counts) why *India* should not produce her own rayon yarn: there is ample cellulose available in forests and bamboo groves, cotton waste, crushed sugar-canes, and so on. Once more, power and water may be the limiting factors. Normally most of *India's* rayon goes to Pakistan, but in the face of the constant interruptions of that market an Indian Ocean export is being built up.

Hosiery and *knitwear* works are found in the larger urban markets, but particularly at Rawalpindi and Lahore in W and Ludhiana in E Punjab. This seems to stem from the migration of a craft industry from Kashmir, but it is obviously particularly suited to electrification. Again Partition has led to some dislocation, and Pakistan might well take the lead could she develop her own yarn manufacture.

[20] Vakil, 281–85.

B Metal Industries

1. *Iron and Steel*

"The feature which stands out most prominently in a survey of the mineral industries of India is that practically nothing has been done to develop those minerals which are essential to modern metallurgical and chemical industries, while most striking progress has been made during recent years in opening out deposits from which products are obtained suitable for export, or for consumption by . . . direct processes." [21] This statement accurately sums up the position in the first decade of this century, when it was generally held by (British) authorities that not much more was possible, and in particular that experience had conclusively shown that India was never likely to possess a large-scale iron and steel industry. The magnificence of the endowment of the NE Peninsula was hardly recognised, or was thought of in extractive terms only, and Free Trade meant that import of machines, constructional material, and semi-manufactured goods was possible at prices with which an unprotected industry starting from scratch could hardly compete.

As far back as the 1830s attempts had been made to exploit Salem iron, and the furnaces at Porto Novo (S of Madras) and Beypur (Malabar) were intermittently productive until 1866–67 (cf. below, 708–09). In 1900 pig production from the iron-shales of Barakar in the Damodar was a mere 35,000 tons; the company concerned had just made the first profit since operations began in 1874, and was about to launch into a disastrous venture in steel. But in 1911 Jamshedpur's first blast-furnace was blown, in 1913 the first steel was made—and in 1914 the war provided a virtually protected market for the critical early years. *Indian* production is still small, especially in relation to population, but the Jamshedpur works are now the largest in the Commonwealth. Their history is a fascinating study in applied geography; Jamshedji Tata's success was due above all to three things: unflinching determination, adequate finance, and meticulous geographical planning which resulted in the selection of a site with positional advantages possibly unequalled anywhere in the world: between Damodar coking coal and the mountains of Orissa haematite; with ample moulding-sand and water from the Subarnarekha; with fluxes, refractories, and the major alloys within 50 or 60 miles; and with the biggest single market in India—the general engineering trades of Calcutta—only 150 miles away.[22] These advantages are unique; but except for the charcoal-smelted works in Mysore, the industry in general benefits from the fact that the cost of coke per ton of pig produced is less than that in UK, USA, or Germany,[23]

---

[21] *Imperial Gaz.* (1908), III. 128.
[22] See Sharma, 98–101, and below, 667–70. J. L. Keenan's *A Steel Man in India* (1945) gives an unorthodox but very lively view of a neglected aspect of Indian life.
[23] Thomas, 2–3.

and there is normally a considerable export of pig iron, especially to Japan.

The location and nominal capacity (in 1000 tons) of existing plants is as follows:

	Pig	Steel Ingots
Tata I & S Co., Jamshedpur, Bihar .	1533	1116
Indian I & S Co., Kulti, W Bengal .	913	—
Steel Corptn of Bengal, Burnpur, W Bengal	—	5–600
Mysore (State) I & S, Bhadravati . .	30	20–40

This would give a total capacity of around 2·5 m. tons pig and 1·75 m. steel; but the plants have suffered depreciation as a result of the unremitting production, with little replacement, of the war years, and recent estimates are 1·88 m. tons pig and 1·07 finished steel. This is roughly equivalent to inter-war demand.

The range of products is wide, and was notably increased by the demands of 1939–45. Around Jamshedpur and Asansol-Burnpur (on the Raniganj coalfield) cluster ancillary and associated industries: refractories, tubes and wires, heavy chemicals, and so on. One of the most important is tin-plate, in which India became almost self-supporting in 10 years, with a current output of over 80,000 tons. Considering the resources in alloys—manganese, chromium, silicon, titanium, and vanadium are all available, mostly between the Damodar and the Subarnarekha—very little high-speed or other special steel is produced.

This country on the Bihar-Bengal-Orissa border is really the only zone of primary heavy industry in the sub-continent, a concentration obviously due to the comparable concentration of resources, facilitating linked development, but hampering distribution by the long rail hauls necessary to any markets but those of Hooghlyside. Development elsewhere is of course hampered by lack of fuel, and it is unlikely that hydro-electricity can be produced cheaply enough for electro-smelting, though it has been suggested that the low-grade coal of Madhya Pradesh (CP) could be used for thermal generation.

At inter-war rates of consumption *Indian* industry could supply internal demand with a fair export surplus of pig iron and some of steel, though the W coast may still find it cheaper to import in view of high railway charges. But obviously development schemes and general industrialisation will mean a great increase in demand: c. 2 m. tons a year immediately, possibly 3 m. in the near future; demand for foundries and rolling mills is about 900,000 tons, two or three times current allocations. Projected extensions of existing plant would still leave a deficit of about 500,000 tons of steel. In 1949 two new steel works with initial capacity of 500,000 tons each were "shortly" to be set up. But by 1951 a single plant of 600,000 tons was merely envisaged, and the ominous note was struck that "the main consideration is finance"; [24] while the Five Year Plan target is only 1–3 m. tons in all.

2. *Aluminium and other Non-ferrous Metals* [25]

Apart from the alloy metals and bauxite, *India's* non-ferrous resources are poor. Aluminium prospects are good, the lack of cryolite is common to all countries except Greenland, and though there are possibilities in synthetic cryolite from fluorspar, this also would have to be imported. But the total amount needed of this catalyst is very small, and the bauxite reserves are immense and well distributed. Once more the limiting factor is power, since the very high temperatures necessary can best be obtained electrically.

The production of aluminium smallware was one of the Madras Government's initiatives, as early as 1912, and in the inter-war period raw metal imports of 4–5000 tons a year were the basis of a utensils industry located in the chief ports and exporting to Indian Ocean markets. In 1943 the production of aluminium ingots from imported alumina began near Alwaye (Travancore) and the actual production of alumina has begun at Muri (below, 590, 667) and Asansol; capacity is *c.* 10–15,000 tons, to be expanded to 20,000. Costs here are high as the electricity is thermal. Rolling into sheets (and foil for tea-chests) is mostly at Belur (Calcutta). Demand is estimated at 20,000 tons; in 1946 total consumption was 13,300 tons, of which 1800 were manufactured at Alwaye and 1200 from local bauxite at Asansol (1951 aluminium output: 3600 tons).

The situation in other non-ferrous metals is uneven and on the whole unsatisfactory, owing largely to the poor endowment in ores, aggravated by neglect of scrap-collection. Copper is by far the most important raw material, but even this is only a fraction of requirements and not being electrolytically smelted is not suitable for all uses. The war years saw a great expansion in miscellaneous light-metal trades—brass and copper wire and tubes, lead piping and sheeting, brass sheets, expanded metal, and so on. Significantly enough most firms are in Calcutta, with Bombay second; the few up-country outliers include one at Jaipur presumably located with reference to Rajasthan zinc and copper. A small but interesting industry is the manufacture of plumbago crucibles for non-ferrous metallurgy. This is carried on at Calcutta, Bombay, and Rajahmundry in the Godavari delta. Most Indian graphite is definitely inferior for this purpose, and imports from Ceylon are essential.

[24] Cf. *IR* I/11 (19/3/49), I/33 (18/8/49), III/2 (10/1/51).
[25] The best readily accessible survey of the metal and engineering industries is in Thomas, Chs. I–V and XIII–XX *passim*.

3. *Engineering: Heavy, Light, and Electrical*

The major concentrations in heavy engineering are, as we might expect, around Calcutta, at Jamshedpur, and on the Jharia-Raniganj coalfields, these areas accounting for 75% of output; lesser centres are Bombay, Madras, and Cawnpore. The 1939–45 war saw a great expansion: steel used in bridges, for example, was 1381 tons in 1940, 21,843 in 1943, and it is claimed that the largest floating dock in the world was constructed at Calcutta.[26] But such important lines as machine tools and textile engineering are in their infancy, the latter's capacity being only a fraction of the cotton industry's annual replacements of looms and spindles. While the war greatly increased demand for, and led to the introduction or expansion of the manufacture of, such things as jacks, road-making machinery, and hand pumps, the existing small production of centrifugal pumps and oil-engines, so important in connection with rural industry, was hampered or even reduced by the difficulty of importing essential tools and components, such as ball bearings. In 1945 demand for ball bearings was estimated at 400,000—but of 2500 different sorts and sizes—and "any economical unit would produce India's total demand in a week or so." [27] This illustrates the general lack of integration in Indian industry. The Swiss firm of Oerlikon is setting up a large Government plant at Bangalore, which is expected to be producing by 1955 high-speed lathes, ball and roller bearings, gears, drills, and so on. Before the war precision instruments were made chiefly by the Government Mathematical Instrument Office, established over a century ago at Calcutta; the war saw a proliferation of private firms, but their products were not always very precise. This important industry is also being overhauled by Government.

The production of most of the lighter types of electrical apparatus was either introduced or greatly increased during the war, and bulbs, fans, batteries, transformers, conduits, are now manufactured on a fairly large scale. Telephones are assembled, and many components made, in the Government-controlled factory at Bangalore, and it is expected that by 1953 complete instruments will be made from this plant, designed to meet ultimately all *India's* telecommunication needs. Radio receivers are produced (*c.* 25,000 a year, largely 'People's Sets' for communal village use), a pilot plant for valves is being developed, and a Government radio and radar factory is projected.

4. *Transport Engineering, Shipbuilding*

(a) *Land Transport.* Vehicle engineering is still largely in the assembly stage. Rail wagons and coaches are built mainly at Calcutta and Burnpur, and war-time difficulties should be overcome with the establishment of

---

[26] Thomas, 165.   [27] Thomas, 189.

wheel and axle works at Jamshedpur. Loco building, with imported components, began as early as 1896 in the BB & CI railshops at Ajmer, but despite Government's promise in 1921 to invite tenders and the consequent building of a plant at Jamshedpur, the Tariff Board refused protection—partly on the ground that electrification was pending!—and not a single engine was produced.[28] Since the war, however, Tatas have taken over the EI railshops at Singbhum, and together with the Government factory recently completed at Chittaranjan or Mihijam (near Asansol) it is expected that half of the 220 new locos needed annually will be Indian-made. So far about two-thirds of the components must be imported, but it is hoped to do away with this necessity.

Motor vehicles are assembled at Bombay (General Motors, Fords) and Baroda (Hindustan Motors), aircraft at Bangalore, but despite much planning and patriotic back-patting not a single motor or aircraft had actually been built in India by the end of 1952; by August 1950 only 20 aircraft had been assembled, though apparently some Indian-designed models were on the drawing-board. Bicycle demand is about 500,000 a year, including an unusually high proportion of tricycles, mainly for the 'trishaw' or pedal-bike-cum-sidecar which is replacing the man-pulled rickshaw in some towns. Current production is 70–80,000 units a year, and arrangements have been made, in association with British firms, to add 300,000 to this.

(b) *Shipbuilding*. Some of the 'wooden walls' of Nelson's day were built not of British oak but of Indian teak, and the Parsee shipwrights of Bombay enjoyed a high reputation throughout Eastern seas. With the change to iron, however, only country craft were launched, except for tugs, launches, and barges for the Bengal Delta, for which Calcutta was of course the main centre. Before the war a few sea-going tugs, up to 440 tons, were built there, and during the war a large number of motor-patrol boats and minesweepers were launched, though nearly all machinery had to be imported.

The only existing yards of any capacity are those of the Scindia Company —the premier Indian shipping line—at Vizagapatam, which can build vessels up to 8000 tons capacity. Though Vizag is the nearest open-ocean port to Jamshedpur, costs are so high (nearly twice those of UK yards) that in 1949 the company suspended operations after launching only three ships; negotiations for a sale to Government fell through, though orders have been placed for three large ships to keep the place alive. Meanwhile the Bombay Port Trust has put forward a scheme for a great yard with 10 slipways, capable of building ships of 15,000 tons, on Trombay Island. In view of the Vizag experience this proposition seems of more than doubtful wisdom.[29]

---

[28] Thomas, 205–06. There are at present 236 miles of electric railway.
[29] Thomas, 214–20; Vakil, 420–21; *IR* I/7 (19/2/49).

C. CEMENT

The cement industry is obviously of the greatest significance to the general programme. Good limestone is available in quantity in many parts of *India*; gypsum is less abundant and the loss of that of the Salt Range to Pakistan caused some temporary difficulty. More important is the necessity of using in the kilns coal of low ash-content: this means that while the central *Indian* factories can use Rewah, or Pench Valley coal for power, half their requirements must come from the Damodar.

In 1947 there were about 24 plants with a total capacity of 2·8 m. tons. A quarter of this was in Pakistan and at least a third in central *India*, notably based on the Vindhyan rocks forming the Nn flanks of the Son valley. Other important areas were Kathiawar, Telangana, and Pepsu, while the largest single unit (220,000 tons) was in Bundi state, Rajasthan. Most of these were located with direct reference to limestone, e.g. the Shahbad factory in Hyderabad is on the narrow strip of Vindhyans, long worked for building stone, which intervenes between the Archaeans and the overlying Deccan Lavas. Only in Saurashtra (Kathiawar) and Rajasthan are limestone and gypsum reasonably close together, and these areas seem likely to become major producers.

The industry is somewhat monopolistic, a good two-thirds of the 1947 capacity being controlled by Associated Cement Companies and two-thirds of the rest by Seth Dalmia, perhaps the leading self-made magnate of *India* to-day. Both these concerns controlled plants in what is now Pakistan, and there was some dislocation at Partition. Labour conditions are unusually good.

Altogether capacity in *India* increased from 2·1 m. tons in 1947 to 2·96 in 1949, output from 1·4 to 2·1 (1950 2·7 m.). As usual, early optimistic targets have been scaled down, but despite retrenchment on development schemes several plants are projected to bring production to 4·5 m. tons in 1955; these include Government plants at Mirzapur (UP) and Sindri, the latter to have a capacity of 250,000 tons. There is still some import, but also export to Ceylon and Burma, and altogether the industry is one of the most flourishing in *India*.

D. CHEMICALS AND ALLIED INDUSTRIES

1. *Acids and Alkalis*

The heavy chemical industry is one of the weakest sectors in *India's* industrial advance. Sulphuric acid, indeed, owing to the precautions needed in transporting it, and the fact that a ton of sulphur yields three of acid, must in general be made near its market, and this has favoured home production; and consumption industries based on chemicals are expanding rapidly. But the highly important alkali side, despite a notable increase in production since the war, is still under-developed. Although the possession of the Salt Range gives Pakistan the largest single source of chemicals in the sub-continent, *India's* resources are by no means poor, and their uneven development reflects the general lack of co-ordination and balance.[30]

Sulphuric acid (1950 target 130,000 tons, output 102,000) is produced in the larger textile centres and at Asansol, Jamshedpur, Belagula (Mysore), and Alwaye. Alkalis are mainly from Saurashtra, at Drangadhra and Mithapur (Port Okha), where Tatas have the largest soda-ash and caustic-soda plant in the country; the localising factor is the proximity of limestone and sea-salt. There is also some production at Mettur. Ammonium sulphate comes from Sindri and Alwaye, with a small contribution from Belagula and from coke-ovens. There are thus three main areas of heavy chemical production: Saurashtra, the NE Peninsula, and the electrified zone of the S.

2. *Lighter Chemical Industries*

The most important consumption industries based on chemicals are dye- and tan-stuffs, paints and varnishes, soap and cosmetics, matches, and drugs. For most of these natural resources, vegetable or mineral, are fair.

The indigenous production of vegetable *tan-stuffs* (avaram, babul, myrobalans, etc.) is supplemented by imports of wattle bark. Chrome alum (chromium/aluminium sulphate) is important in dyeing and photography as well as tanning; its manufacture is based on bauxite and sulphuric acid. Other alum salts are used for water purification, paper sizing, and as mordants. Production in this group more than doubled in 1939–45, despite difficulties in the transport of coal and bauxite and other demands on sulphuric acid, and there should be no difficulty in meeting requirements. *Dye-stuffs*, apart from primitive local production for use on the spot, are mostly imported. Output of *paints and varnishes* again more than doubled during the war; there is a fair resource base in the oilseeds, the resins of the Himalayan forests, barytes in the S, and various other pigments and vehicles. The industry has the usual Bombay/Calcutta localisation.

The *soap* industry has ample supplies of vegetable oils, tallow, and essential oils such as lemon-grass, citronella, and sandal, though these last are still generally exported as crude oil and re-imported as distilled. Imports of some alkalis and of coconut oil are still necessary. There is much room for expansion in the home market, annual consumption of factory-made soap being between 0·5 and 1 lb per head, and there would seem to be no reason why an Indian Ocean export should not be built up. The industry is again

---

[30] It is perhaps symptomatic that the figures for demand, capacity, and output given by Thomas and Vakil, both careful writers, are so hopelessly inconsistent that it seems best to avoid quantitative statements altogether. The situation may be improved by the Tata-ICI agreement.

located mostly around Calcutta and Bombay, with important units in Kerala; many of the products are of high quality. Other cosmetics are unimportant, except hair-oils which (to judge impressionistically) are produced and consumed in altogether excessive quantities.

Match-making is widespread as a cottage industry, but there are a fair number of factories, especially in Madras and W Bengal, though the largest concern, the West India Match Co., is linked with Swedish interests and has its main factory at Kalyan near Bombay. Imported splints are used, though it would seem that Indian wood could be used for these and for boxes; but resources are mainly in the N and most factories in the Peninsula. *Drugs* again fall into two sections: the remedies, largely herbal and with some elements of magic, used in the traditional medical systems and by village homeopathists; and factory-made pharmaceuticals. Resources are on the whole satisfactory, except that a much larger production of chinchona seems desirable. A Government penicillin and sulpha-drugs factory, Swedish-built, is being set up in Bombay. The production of *plastics* themselves, as distinct from plastic goods, is in its infancy.

E. Food Industries

1. *Generalities*

Food processing comes first of the major industrial groups in number of establishments, but third in employment. This is natural enough, since for the most part processes are relatively simple, needing little power or capital. Factories are often seasonal, and except for some concentration of larger units in ports and large cities their distribution follows that of the crop concerned. Rice mills, for example, can be worked by cheap oil-engines or by steam-engines of no great power and often of antiquated design; fuel for steam plants is no problem, since fires once started can be fed on paddy husks. Hence their rickety corrugated-iron sheds are scattered by rail or river-side through all the paddy-lands, with perhaps some tendency to thicken along the middle Ganges and the terai.[31] But flour mills are more urban in location, since the taste for wheaten bread instead of the unleavened *chupatti* (a tough but satisfying pancake) definitely goes with "Western sophistication." The most interesting recent development is the extension of fruit industries (jams, preserves, some canning), much of it in rather primitive and unhygienic conditions. With more care and adequate publicity there should be an overseas market for such delightful foods as pickled and even tinned mangoes.

Tobacco has been glanced at already (Ch. IX); three industries deserve special treatment—tea, sugar, and vegetable oils.

[31] For a general discussion of rice-milling, cf. O. H. K. Spate, "Beginnings of Industrialization in Burma", *Economic Geography* XVII (1941), 75–92.

2. *Tea Factories*

Tea for Western markets needs immediate and relatively elaborate processing; the industry has been more affected than most others by Partition.[32] Transport in particular was badly dislocated; the new railway into Assam has overcome the worst difficulties, though not without causing a temporary crisis by attracting labour from the estates. But much tea which used to go out by Chittagong has been diverted to Calcutta, where facilities are as yet inadequate; this is due partly to mere politics, but also because the development of Chittagong as the major outlet of E Bengal jute (the bulk of which formerly went through Calcutta) means that the lesser port can now handle only about half its previous tea trade of *c.* 70 m. lbs a year. Again about 225,000 tons of coal are annually used in *Indian* tea factories, and in 1947–48 supplies in the Assam Duars were so short that some deforestation took place. Even with the new railway transport costs are high; the situation may be eased if recently discovered coal in the Garo Hills can be exploited.

The supply of tea-chests also presents difficulties. Demand is high (4–6 m. a year) and quality important, especially for the more valuable markets. *Indian* plywood factories could probably meet the greater part of requirements, but their producers themselves admit the inferiority of *Indian* to imported chests, and bad packing has been an important factor in the fall of exports to the USA and Canada—dollar markets! however, Pakistan, with no home production, is spared a difficulty arising paradoxically from an internal industrial advance.

3. *Sugar*

The history of sugar production in India is one of marked vicissitude, dependent partly on imperial politics, as when British import duties were placed on E Indian sugar in W Indian interests. It culminates in a showy success which seems to have led to some complacency, concealing weaknesses which are now becoming apparent. Again it must be remembered that beside the modern industry is the village production of *gur* or *jaggery*, the coarse unrefined sugar (rather like fudge) produced by boiling in open pans. This is of course much cheaper, and recently the high controlled price of refined sugar has led to increased demand for gur and some diversion of cane from factories; and indeed gur normally took about half the cane supply. Other sugar, or at least sweetening, is obtained from the estuarine palms nipa and *Phoenix paludosa* and, more important, the palmyra (*Borassus flabellifer*); but this does not amount to much, and is mostly in the extreme S.[33]

[32] Vakil, 289–97.
[33] This section is based mainly on Sharma, Chs. VI–VII; Jathar and Beri, I. Ch. VI; Vakil, 297–303.

For most of the 19th century India was either self-sufficient or a net exporter, but in the 1890s the competition of European beet-sugar and of cane from Mauritius (where it is grown by Indian labour) and Java practically killed Indian sugar as an organised trade, though of course the petty local production of gur carried on. There was some revival from about 1911, but after 1931–32 the grant of protection led to a sharp increase in factories, from 32 in 1932 to 145 in 1939, and in refined output, from 100,000 to 1,230,000 tons. By 1940 "India was the largest sugar-producing country in the world, and her sugar industry the second largest industry, next in importance to only the cotton textile industry", and employing over 120,000 hands.[34] Under normal conditions there is an export surplus; the sugar industry of Burma, for instance, survived only on sufferance, and there were exports to the Indian colonies in Ceylon, Malaya, and Fiji, and more recently to SW Asia.[35] In the last two or three years, however, imports have been necessary.

As we have seen (Ch. IX), cane-growing is strongly localised in the N, and this is reflected in the concentration of the industry: in 1931–32/34–35 UP and Bihar produced 90·8% of total refined output, in 1935–36/38–39 still 84·1%; but by 1943–44 their share had fallen to 79·4%.[36] This trend is significant: there is a strong case for a more even spread of the industry.

In the first place, Indian cane as a whole is poor, output per acre being only a quarter of that in Java and Hawaii. But the disparity is much less for the thick tropical canes of the S, and greater reliance on these spells obvious economies, not to mention transport saving on the finished product. The extension of irrigation in the Deccan is likely to lead to an increase of cane-growing there, since the value of the crop renders it a favourite in irrigated areas; and the factories of the Deccan rely mainly on their own estates, instead of on 'gate cane' brought to the factory directly by independent growers, or on cane brought by rail. This has advantages—superior varieties are grown, and cutting takes place at a time to suit the refiner rather than the cultivator.

The hegemony of the N is thus threatened, though its vested interests are putting up a spirited defence. Point is given to the demand for breaking the quasi-monopoly of UP and Bihar by the internal situation of the industry, which has relied too much on the tariff. Cane prices are fixed by State governments, mainly in the interests of growers; the officially-recognised Sugar Syndicate has played its own hand without scruple, forcing up prices until in 1949 there was a scarcity panic, hoarding, and black marketing on a large scale, leading to a considerable increase of imports. At the same time

---

[34] Jathar and Beri, I. 172 (7th ed., 1942).
[35] *Indian* exports 1948–49: 26,268 tons (but 22,000 as molasses); of this 3377 to W Pakistan. Imports 10,576 tons.
[36] Sharma, 152.

smuggling into Pakistan was rife, although legitimate quotas to that country were not taken up because Brazilian sugar was available at not much more than half the *Indian* price.[37]

4. *Vegetable Oils*

Oilseeds account for about 5% of *India's* exports by value, and there is a considerable import of vegetable oils. It has often been suggested that home manufacture should be encouraged, if need be by legal restriction of raw exports. The RCAI pointed out that the *actual* demand for oil-cake as fertiliser and cattle-feed was so small as to render manufacture in India uneconomic. Since 1928, however, there has not only been a great increase in oil-using manufactures such as soaps and varnishes, but the whole economic climate has changed. The need for intensification of agriculture might well warrant state aid, even at a money loss, in order to improve the cattle-food situation; there is not likely to be much oil-cake to spare for fertiliser.

It is significant that there has been a marked fall in the exports of rape and mustard, of direct food value without any processing beyond the indigenous extraction in *ghanis*. The ghani is simply a great pestle-and-mortar worked by bullocks; sometimes a battery of ghanis may be driven by an oil-engine. The extraction rate is low, but this has at least the merit of leaving richer oil-cake. The loss of the European market in 1940 led to a marked increase in groundnut-crushing and the establishment of *vanaspati* or 'vegetable ghi' mills; while the increasing demand for coconut oil in the soap industry necessitates fairly large imports. On the other hand the active world demand and the need of foreign exchange to pay for capital equipment favours export.

However valid the RCAI's arguments in the days of economic orthodoxy, there is clearly a need for expansion in all branches of the oil industry, and it is anomalous that so large a proportion of the great resources should still be exported unprocessed and hence at the lowest rate of return.

F. MISCELLANEOUS CONSUMPTION INDUSTRIES

1. *Leather* [38]

The leather industry of *India* suffers from peculiar social disabilities. Before Partition three-quarters of the 25 m. hides produced annually came from animals which had died of disease, malnutrition, or mere old age; and the *Indian* proportion will be yet higher since it seems very likely that the religious sanction against cow-slaughter will receive some legislative support. Obviously this means a serious deterioration in the quality of hides,

---

[37] Vakil, 302–03.   [38] Sharma, Ch. X; Thomas, Ch. XXX; Vakil, 348–52.

and in fact good hides are in short supply. Moreover, those workers who were not Untouchables were mostly Muslims, and many—including the shoemakers of Agra—have migrated to Pakistan, which now has a superfluity of hides and of labour but a shortage of good tan-stuffs.

In *India* the raw material basis is obviously not quantitatively lacking, and there are plenty of vegetable tan-stuffs, especially in the S. "The dry north-west and the wet north-east (including Bengal) are the poorest regions in the supply of local tanning materials", and this is one factor in the importance of chrome tanning at Calcutta.[39] It will be noted that both these deficit areas are now largely in Pakistan. The N in general, however, has to rely on babul (*Acacia arabica*) bark, which has only 12–14% tannin against the 16–18% of avaram (*Cassia auriculata*) which is widespread in the drier Deccan. Myrobalans (35%) and divi-divi (40%) also grow mainly in the Peninsula. None of these, however, is as valuable as wattle bark, which has 35% tannin and loses it far more slowly than any of the others. Wattle is imported from S Africa, but it seems that it could be profitably grown in the Nilgiris.

Tanning and the production of leather goods are widely distributed, but show some interesting regional differentiation. Tanning is carried on at three levels: 'bag tanning', the production of kips, and modern factory tanning. In bag tanning the hide is sown up and, as it were, pickled from within; this is the standard method of the village tanner and accounts for 40–45% of the hides, but only the worst are used. Though any hides may be called kips, the word strictly applies to hides half-tanned in pits; no machinery is required, and little capital, but the scale of operations is larger than in bag-tanning. Over 40% of the hides are turned into kips, most of which are exported, especially to Britain. Madras is the leading centre, but kips are produced all over the Peninsula, and it is in this branch that wattle bark is most used. Modern methods account for about 15% of the hides; not all in large factories, since there is a considerable output of chrome-tanned leather around Calcutta, in small or even cottage units owned and mainly worked by Chinese. Most of the large modern tanneries are in the N, especially in UP where Cawnpore is the chief centre. Not only had this area a larger proportion of better hides than the S—perhaps in part owing to the stronger Muslim element—but here, for climatic reasons, are the main markets for solid footwear; the S can walk on sandals or bare feet. Hence too the N is far more important for finished leather goods, much of the demand being military. These regional specialisations may be summed up in the following statement, which refers to 1937–39 and to hides only (excluding goat and sheep skins):[40]

[39] Sharma, 164–67, 173.   [40] Sharma, 175–76.

(Main areas only)	% of Total Employees	% of Indian Kips	% of Finished Output	Process
Bombay . .	6·9	2·4	1·2	Mainly bark
Madras . .	37·0 ⎫	82·6 ⎫	29·4 ⎫	Bark, some chrome
Mysore . .	16·9 ⎬ 53·9	8·0 ⎬ 90·6	1·9 ⎬ 31·3	
UP . .	19·0	—	40·2	„ „ „
Bengal (West).	8·5	—	21·8	Mainly chrome

Apart from the Chinese craft industry at Calcutta, only a few tanneries—
a dozen or so—use the chrome method, and these are confined to Cawnpore, Calcutta, and Madras; but they handle 2–2·5 m. hides.

The production of finished goods is still mostly by hand, either by
individual shoemakers or in small shops; All-India production of footwear
has been estimated at 100 m. pairs of various indigenous types and 30 m. of
European shoes and boots; on the 1941 population this is one pair a year
for one person out of three. All sandals and 80–90% of European shoes are
handmade; Agra is, or was, the chief centre with nearly 150 small "factories". There are only nine modern factories—two each at Agra, Cawnpore,
and Calcutta (including Batanagar), one each at Madras, Bombay, and
Bangalore. But the enormous increase in Army demand, from c. 100,000
pairs a year pre-war to 6·6 m. in 1943, "involved a sudden expansion"; one
Cawnpore firm is said to have the largest self-contained footwear factory in
the world, and the Government Harness and Saddlery Factory, also at
Cawnpore, took on ten times its pre-war number of workers.[41] The localisation at Cawnpore stems largely from its old importance as a depot for military stores of all kinds.

2. Rubber

The rise of rubber industries in India was due to the international
restriction scheme of 1934, which meant that much India-grown rubber
could not be exported and so was available at prices well below the artificial
world level. W Bengal and Bombay have the great majority of the factories.
Pre-war demand for tyres was met mainly by plants owned by Dunlops and
Firestone, which by 1942 together produced 390,000 car and nearly 1·9 m.
cycle tyres; the war as usual intensified production, which by 1949 had
risen to 1·4 m. motor and 7·7 m. cycle tyres, together with nearly 18 m.
pairs of rubber shoes. It seems likely that capacity exceeds demand.

3. Glass

Of the 232 glass factories in *India* in 1947, no fewer than 92 were entirely
devoted to the making of bangles, which was also a cottage industry. The

[41] Vakil, 350; Thomas, 305. Batas have also a factory at Lahore.

great centre for the factory production of bangles is Firozabad (UP), with hundreds of small workshops to which finishing and decorating is put out by the factories. Japanese competition nearly ruined the cottage industry, to the benefit of Firozabad.

Of the remaining 141 factories, UP, W Bengal, and Bombay had respectively 58, 31, and 21, but the value of output was in reverse order, though not differing greatly. The localisation in UP is mainly along the flanks of the Vindhyan sandstone plateaus, mostly in Agra Dt and near Allahabad; the UP accounts for nearly half and Agra Dt for nearly a third of *Indian* employment. About two-thirds of the cost of raw materials is on account of soda ash, formerly obtained from Khewra (W Punjab) but now from *Indian* sources. About half the output, by value, is contributed by bottles. The war saw a marked expansion in range as well as output, and thermos refills, electric bulbs, and a small amount of scientific glassware are now produced. The industry, till recently using mainly crude pot-furnaces, has made much technical progress since 1939, but has suffered from a tendency to plunge into any line which looked lucrative: as a result the sheet-glass capacity of over 20 m. sq ft is three to six times actual output in 1946–49.

4. *Paper and other Wood-based Industries* [42]

(a) *Paper.* The classics of Sanskrit literature were usually written on palm-leaves, in the N sometimes on birch-bark; paper-making seems to have come from China via the central Asian Muslims, and the indigenous hand-workers were mainly Muslims. Paper-making by hand, usually from fibrous plants, lingers on in a few places but is of no importance. A few mills were set up in 1870–90, on the Hooghly and at Lucknow, Poona, and Raniganj; but supplies of softwood are limited to the Himalayas, and no mills were added until bamboo pulping became commercially practicable, about 1922; a protective duty was placed on imported pulp in 1931, and in five years the utilisation of bamboo pulp rose by 280%. The war once more checked imports and increased demand.

Bamboos supply about 55% of the raw material, grasses 22%, waste paper 10–12%, wood pulp only 1–2%. *Sabai* grass is better than bamboo, but yields are lower and more erratic. Obviously regeneration of cut-over bamboo areas is essential, but growth is rapid (only 4–5 years) and supplies at the rate of 600,000 tons of canes a year can be maintained indefinitely given proper conservation. Capacity is 135–150,000 tons of paper a year, but hitches in the supply of chemicals keep current production down to about 100,000 tons, a third of it boards. This is about half the demand; the bureaucracy naturally gets priority, and supplies to schools are short.

[42] Thomas, 290–302; Vakil, 306–10; M. P. Bhargava, "Review of the Pulp and Paper Industry in India" (*5th British Empire Forestry Confce*, Dehra Dun, 1947).

The increasing official mania for *papierasserie* will tax the industry to the utmost.

As usual W Bengal and Bombay lead with 4 and 3 of the 12 larger mills; but W Bengal, which produced over 50%, drew largely from the Chittagong Hill Tracts and Sylhet (E Pakistan) and must now go farther afield, into the Orissa Hills, for a product bulky in proportion to weight. This may lead to a shift to the areas with the most ample bamboo forests, roughly the hill borders of the Peninsula. The industry in UP and E Punjab relies largely on *sabai* grass from the Siwaliks.

Targets of the Five Year Plan are 165,000 tons of paper and boards, and 24,000 of newsprint, which is at present imported. The possibility of rayon pulp production, either from Himalayan softwoods or (more probably) from bamboo, is also being considered.

(b) *Plywood*. Madras and Assam lead in the production of plywood, which rose during the war (when Japanese and European imports were cut off) from 13 m. to 50 m. sq ft in 1944. The latter figure is much less than capacity, another example of plunging after quick returns, which will probably lead to a shaking-out of many small units, e.g. those around Calcutta. The following figures (million sq ft) are significant; they refer to 1946, when the war peak was passed and output was 29 m. sq ft against capacity of 61 m.[43]:

	Units	Capacity			Production			
		1. Amount	2. % of Indian total	3. Avge p/unit	4. Amount	5. % of Indian total	6. Avge p/unit	4 as % of 1
Assam .	3	14·75	24	4·92	10·83	38	3·61	73
Bengal .	9	6·75	11	0·75	2·79	10	0·31	41
Madras .	12	15·0	24·5	1·25	4·89	17	0·41	32

Timber supplies are adequate, and *India* usually produces sufficient casein and protein glues. But it is significant that the tea demand, which pre-war took over 80% of output, fell to less than half the 1944 figure as soon as imports were resumed. Plywood production is highly skilled, and get-rich-quick expansionism resulted in very poor chests being put on the market; some of them did not even survive to leave India. The industry is potentially very important, with a wide range of uses apart from tea-chests; plywood is especially useful in Indian conditions of temperature and

[43] Adapted from table in Thomas, 295; cf. Vakil, 292–93.

humidity in which ordinary woodwork soon cracks or swells. Only a start has been made in production of a quality suitable for aircraft construction.

(c) *Distillation, etc.* The 'collier' of the European Middle Ages survives in the person of the Indian charcoal-burner, whose primitive kilns, dotted about the vast scrub-forests, produce about 9 m. tons of charcoal a year. But all the valuable distillation products are wasted. There is so far only one wood-distillation plant, part of the charcoal-smelted iron and steel industry at Bhadravati (Mysore). This indeed is one of the biggest in Asia, producing daily 30,000 gallons of distillate, from which calcium acetate (main source of acetic acid), methyl alcohol, and formaldehyde are extracted. As Bhadravati's output of charcoal is under 20,000 tons a year, it is obvious that the recovery of distillates from even a fraction of the indigenous kilns would provide a most valuable contribution to the chemical industry, especially for plastics, rayon, and so on.[44]

Rosin and turps were formerly made chiefly at Jalo (W Punjab), but there is little industrial demand in Pakistan as yet, and as all the Punjab coniferous forests have gone to *India* production is now concentrated at Hoshiarpur (E Punjab). Output here is about 2100 tons, and there is another factory in UP; demand, chiefly in soap and paper, is about 6400 tons.

III. INDUSTRIAL LOCATION AND POLICY

The foregoing survey of *Indian* industries brings out the following main points:

(i) over most of the field there is a very strong tendency to concentration in four main areas: Hooghlyside, Bombay and its textile outliers (Ahmedabad, Sholapur); Jamshedpur-Asansol (the only zone of basic heavy industry); the Tamilnad towns (especially Coimbatore and Madura) powered mainly from the Cauvery;

(ii) the 1939–45 war saw a great expansion in range and output, but

(iii) this affected chiefly consumption and lighter production lines, and connected with this

(iv) too much development has been motivated merely by quick returns and there is a general lack of co-ordination.

Some decentralisation seems very desirable, if only to cut transport costs; and the unbalanced nature of the advance has led the new Government to undertake a considerable measure of initiative and control.

Location [45]

The extent of concentration for any area and industry may be gauged by the 'location factor'—i.e. the percentage of the area's workers in the indus-

44 Thomas, 300–02.
45 *Location of Industry in India* (Govt of India, Economic Adviser, ND (1944); B. C. Ghose, *Industrial Location* (OPIA, No. 32, 1945); above all the admirable analysis in Sharma, Chs. XIV–XV.

try divided by its percentage of total population; thus with 93% of Indian jute workers and 15·5% of population undivided Bengal had a l.f. for jute of 6·0. The salient points in Ghose's tables are these:

Bengal: 1st in jute, general engineering, paper; 2nd in chemicals; 3rd in iron and steel;

Bombay: 1st in non-jute textiles (l.f. 9·2, highest of all); 2nd in engineering; 3rd in glass;

UP: 1st in sugar and glass;

Bihar: 1st in iron and steel (l.f. 5·6);

Baroda: 1st in chemicals (l.f. 4·5); 2nd in non-jute textiles (l.f. 5·0);

Mysore: 2nd in iron and steel and glass; 3rd in chemicals.

The sporadic nature of industrial development is brought home by these figures if we recall that Baroda and Mysore owe much of their high rank to the possession of a single plant each, Tata chemicals at Port Okha in Baroda, Bhadravati in Mysore; in Baroda, of course, the small size of the state also affects the figure. Taking the simple ratio of percentage population (1941) to percentage all industrial workers (1939), Bombay led with 4·26, followed by Baroda (2·71), and Bengal (1·85); but W Bengal alone would have between 4 and 4·5.

The factors tending to concentration in the Jamshedpur-Asansol zone are obvious enough, and in the S the power of the Cauvery basin is a sufficient attraction in a land completely barren of coal. Calcutta, Bombay, and to a much less extent Madras, were metropolitan cities, accumulators of capital, of European economic activity (with the Parsees also at Bombay), and of demand. Until the 1920s, moreover, railway rates and facilities were adjusted in favour of the ports, in keeping with the view of India as providentially destined to be a British market and raw material store. This naturally acted to concentrate industrial activity in the ports, and later in a few inland rail centres such as Cawnpore and Nagpur. But such concentration is in its nature self-reinforcing, owing to the accumulation of financial and material facilities such as specialised brokerage, warehousing, repair services, and so on. Perhaps only in the cramped island site of Bombay have 'deglommerative' factors begun to produce any marked effect.

In the inter-war years there was a general spread of industries not fixed by bulky raw materials, fuel, or products, and this was facilitated in the S and between Lahore and Amritsar by hydro-electric development. Textile, soap, match, and cement industries showed marked dispersion, the UP-Bihar supremacy in sugar was weakened, and there was some scatter in leather, paper, and glass. But in some of these (as cement, glass, chemicals) this was perhaps not so much real dispersion as simple expansion located with reference to raw materials—in fact the beginnings of new concentrations. The war, with its get-rich-quick opportunities for the man on the

spot, accentuated the concentration in larger cities, especially Calcutta and
Bombay; new industries for Army contracts or in response to the cessation
of imports naturally clustered where contacts, 'know-how', and money
were most plentiful, and some older industries, such as Cawnpore leather,
merely multiplied *in situ*.

In 1947, apart from the few industries of Gwalior, Indore, and the Punjab, some cotton in Madhya Pradesh (CP), and the very small miscellaneous

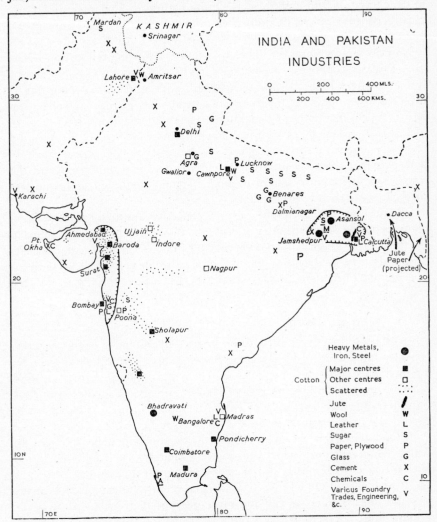

Fig. 59.—INDUSTRIAL LOCATION. The Ahmedabad-Bombay and Jamshedpur-Calcutta
areas enclosed within the heavy ticked line probably produce at least two-thirds of *India's*
industrial output. Towns marked by heavy dots have important craft or minor consumption industries. Sugar (except for Mardan) and glass represent numerous scattered
factories. *A*, Alwaye (aluminium); *M*, Muri (alumina); *S*, Sindri (fertiliser).

development of the Godavari/Kistna delta, there was no significant industry outside two zones: the Ganges valley and its Sn flanks from Delhi to
Calcutta, and the country S and W of a line Ahmedabad/Madras. The most
industrialised tracts, hardly even excepting Hooghlyside and the Raniganj/
Jharia coalfields, are much looser in texture than the industrial regions of the
W; *India* has her Manchesters, even perhaps her Birmingham (Alabama),
but no Lancashire and *a fortiori* no Ruhr. As Sharma remarks, this pattern
of concentration and emptiness is "quite natural in a country possessing
mostly consumers' goods industries oriented to labour and consumers'
markets".

Natural, but deplorable. There was always a floating population in the
great towns, sleeping on pavements or in ghastly camps of matting tents or
huts of flattened tins; the war expansion added greatly to these street-
dwellers, who numbered nearly 200,000 in Bombay in 1944; the effects on
health, not to mention morals and decency, are perhaps best undescribed.
The social consequences of unrestrained industrial urbanism, its negation
of family and cultural values, need not be stressed. What is often overlooked is that this concentration of employment and opportunity in the
towns robs the countryside of economic stamina and contributes no less
surely to rural than to urban slums.

The need for decentralisation is now generally admitted but, as with so
many desirable social attitudes, it is always the next man who should make
the first move. There is much talk, sensible or half-baked, of regional planning and of 'rurban' development based on cheap electricity, that philosopher's stone of modern India. Actual experience since the war is not very
encouraging.

Recent Trends and Policies

Apart from the effects of Partition, treated in Section V of this chapter,
the most immediate problems facing *Indian* industry after the war were the
simultaneous cessation of war demand and resumption (if on a reduced
scale) of imports, and the necessity of tooling-up after five years of work at
high pressure with few replacements. Machinery formed 15 and 18% of
the value of imports in 1948–49 and 1949–50 respectively.

Beyond these was the great debate on the fundamental principles on
which *Indian* economy should be based. Congress was committed to the
Welfare State, its less responsible spokesmen to the millennium so soon as
the British should Quit India. Over against them were capitalists as ruthless and unscrupulous as any and more nervous than most; in the background (and not very far back) whole armies of speculators and black
marketeers. These camps indeed interpenetrated,[46] since in Marxist terms

---

[46] As an example, the author of a nationalist pamphlet on "India's Year of Struggle"
(1942) solemnly thanked the local patriot who supplied paper *at the legal price*.

Congress before Independence was a Popular Front to carry through a bourgeois nationalist revolution. Of course there were also magnates of vision and humanity, and on the whole Congress intellectuals had given more solid thought to economic reconstruction than most leaders of nationalist movements.

Independence once attained, Congress in and out of the National Government spoke with two voices, not to mention Gandhian "back to the spinning-wheel" whispers; the more strident proclaimed nationalisation and restriction of profits—the latter not very unreasonably, since in the "recession" year 1947 cotton profits stood at 490·9 compared with 100 in 1928.[47] Together with the troubles of Partition, this propaganda led to something like panic and a marked fall in production.

If, indeed, the British Raj normally did too little too late, the National Government attempted too much too soon, or at least talked too much late and soon. The situation was complicated by federalism, State governments launching expensive schemes in happy anticipation of Central finance. Priorities were hardly considered and much proposed development was sketchily planned; thus, as Vakil points out, no surveys were made to ascertain what market would absorb the 1·8 m. kW from the Kosi project, while Bombay was short of power and the Ghats schemes were shelved for lack of funds. In fact, in 1949 the multi-purpose projects were cut, restored, cut again, and finally (in early 1950) more or less restored.

There has been some retreat from the early optimism, and certainly from the all-embracing collectivism of the Congress Left. The present programme is for a mixed economy, and it seems that 'mixed' is only too appropriate. Industries nationalised in the ordinary sense of the word are arms, atomic energy, and railways, but any new developments in coal-mining, iron and steel, aircraft, ship-building, mineral oils, and telecommunications manufactures will be primarily by the state; existing undertakings in these lines were given security of tenure, as it were, for 10 years from 1948. In addition the Central Government is to regulate expansion and plan distribution for 18 industries, which with those already mentioned cover the greater part of the industrial field. Since 1948 there has been less uncertainty and considerable recovery has taken place. But much development is hampered by fiscal difficulties, the role of foreign capital has been recognised, and much—too much—depends on the finance to be made available under the Colombo Plan.

The confusions and false starts are perhaps no more than the growing pains of an industrial revolution which is accompanied by an attempt to strike a balance between planned and 'free' economy; in any country, and

[47] In 1948 they rose to 912·5, sugar's to 731·1; those in jute, however, were only half the 1948 level. This "recession" reminds one of the jute industry's propaganda that a 54-hour week, worked on 4 days, was short-time (Buchanan, 140).

a fortiori in one so complex as *India*, it would be difficult to see very far and very clearly in the midst of such an experiment. But the resources are there, the knowledge to use them is growing, and if the will to do so is not dissipated in bureaucratic confusion and individualist exploitation of the main chance, there is ample scope for achievement. To anyone but an *Indian* capitalist the chief deficiency in the programme would seem to be inadequate attention to agriculture. Its importance is indeed recognised verbally, but it cannot be too strongly stressed that the agrarian crisis cannot be isolated from the general economy. The industrial contribution is surely not by way of a mere extension of tillage, which in any case must be physically limited, but by aiding intensification. Two million new acres from a giant dam would be of less value than a 20% increase of output on even a quarter of the paddy-land; but there are many dams projected and only one Sindri. In the last resort the factories cannot work if the men in them starve. The Five Year Plan is refreshingly realistic in this respect.

IV. THE INDUSTRIAL SITUATION OF PAKISTAN

Generalities

Industrially Pakistan must virtually begin at the beginning. A careful study of Table XVIII reveals very clearly the extraordinary immaturity of Pakistan *vis-à-vis India* at Partition. There are really no foundations on which to build heavy basic industry; for some secondary industries—textiles, food processing, chemicals, leather, glass—resources are fair to ample; but, without Kashmir, power potential is probably insufficient for more than modest industrialisation. It seems likely that for *continuous* electricity generation thermal stations must supplement hydro installations, though both coal resources and hydro-electric sites are at least well-placed for the "industrial zone" from Peshawar to Lahore. The splitting of the country into two sections, with 1000 miles of *India* between them, inhibits unified development, and a certain amount of duplication must be faced—a serious matter in view of the limited financial resources. Yet as the two parts are in some matters complementary, there must be direct exchanges between them, which probably implies considerable expansion of the negligible merchant marine.

The reasons for Pakistan's negligible industrial development at Partition are both social and geographical. Historically British economic influence came first and was most intense in the great ports, all except Karachi in Hindu areas. Karachi is little over a century old, against 260–320 years for the other three; it was very much a mere transhipment port, not a focus of economic life like Bombay and Calcutta; until 1936 in a rather neglected administrative outlier of Bombay; and in any case even numerically, much more economically, Hindu and Parsee rather than Muslim. The mineral resources of the sub-continent are overwhelmingly in *Indian* territories, and we have seen the geographical reasons for the localisation of jute mills outside the jute-growing area. Add to this that on the whole Hindu groups were much more adroit in exploiting the opportunities by Western education and economic methods, and it will not seem surprising that not only were the Pakistani areas industrially backward, but that a disproportionate share of such activity as they possessed was Hindu: even in Muslim Lahore, culturally the heart of Islam in India, Muslim economic strength was but a fraction of Hindu.[48]

To some extent, indeed, despite the vast differences between Pakistan E and W, the two sections were alike in one respect: both were essentially primary producers for markets outside their borders, and as such their economic interests showed some genuine divergence from those of *Indian* areas: the whole picture, indeed, resembled that of the United States before the Civil War. This very fact of economic weakness, however, was one of the strongest factors in the rise of separatist sentiment; Pakistani patriotism was to a large extent the last refuge of a new bourgeoisie which found its growth stifled by a strongly entrenched and numerically superior rival. The reaction to 'Hindu imperialism' is understandable.

Industries, Present and Projected

1. *Textiles.* Pakistan's production of fibres was built up on an export basis, and actual manufacturing is very slightly developed: a few cotton mills in W Punjab and E Bengal; a medium-sized woollen mill at Lahore; a handful of silk "factories" the claim of which to the title may be judged from the fact that all 7 had a total labour force of 121 in 1947. There are of course a very large number of seasonal cotton presses, which indeed in 1947 employed over 31,000 workers, the largest single group (Table XVII).

Here there is real scope for expansion; in E Bengal, for example, some 25% of cotton cloth is still hand-woven, and the 10 small mills—mostly at Narayanganj—produced another 10% of demand. There has already been a considerable increase in cotton in W Pakistan, and three woollen mills are planned. Silk prospects are negligible unless Kashmir becomes a part of Pakistan; and the timber and power of that state are probably also essential to any development of artificials. For E Pakistan the immediate target is three large jute mills (1000 looms each) at Narayanganj. The jute baling industry suffers from a severe shortage of plant, which is of special importance in view of the turn from *Indian* to overseas markets.

2. *Metal Trades.* There are at present no prospects of producing pig iron or raw steel in Pakistan; metallurgical industries are confined to using

---

[48] For further discussion see O. H. K. Spate, "The Partition of India and the Prospects of Pakistan", *GR* XXXVIII (1948), 5–29.

melted scrap or imported raw or semi-finished metal. There are two small but modern (electric) steel-melting furnaces at Lahore and an oil-fired furnace is being set up at Karachi; when complete this will increase Pakistan's steel-from-scrap capacity by 50%, to 18,000 tons. Iron foundries and rolling mills have a capacity of 80,000 against a demand of *c.* 350,000 tons.[49] Non-ferrous mining is to all intents non-existent; the (Hindu-owned) antimony of Chitral *was* refined in Bombay.

But though the production of raw metal is thus about nil, the making of metal goods is fairly well advanced. Significantly the most important lines are agricultural: oil-expellers (in which capacity is about 5 times demand), centrifugal pumps, agricultural machinery in general; in addition a few simple machine tools (lathes, etc.) are turned out and there is a small scientific instrument industry at Lahore. Part of the industry at Batala (E Punjab, below 477–78) migrated to Lahore, Gujranwala, and Sialkot. The war saw an increase in the production of light diesel engines, which are of considerable importance to Pakistan's most tangible industrial prospect, that of agricultural processing. There are also some light metal industries at Karachi, and some small producers of light electrical gear (flashlights, bulbs, switches, etc.) have migrated from *India*.

But for all these, of course, raw materials must be imported.

3. *Food Industries.* Of these the most important (apart from the obvious rice- and flour-milling) are tea and sugar factories. Tea factories employed over 13,000 workers (with estate labourers, 150,000) in E Pakistan, but in 1948–50 the industry was in severe financial crisis, and the 171 factories of 1947 fell to 116 in the next year. Sugar production should be almost doubled by the new 50,000-ton factory at Mardan (near Peshawar), said to be the largest in Asia; a number of other units are planned. Vegetable-oil resources are small, except for cotton-seed, and production as yet inadequate; similarly for tobacco, in which Lahore and Sukkur are the chief cigarette centres, though the tobacco acreage is mainly in E Pakistan despite rather too humid conditions. For both these industries W Pakistan has probably the greater potentialities, and large increases are envisaged under the Colombo Plan, including a cigarette factory at Chittagong.

Fruit canning and preserving were better developed than in *India*, and Baluchistan and NWFP include some of the best fruit-growing areas of the sub-continent; great importance is attached to the development of the industry, if possible for export. The main difficulties have been shortages of sugar—which may be remedied by Mardan—and of bottles and tin-plate, which must be imported, the former in part and the latter altogether.

4. *Cement and Glass.* At Partition Pakistan had nearly a quarter of All-India cement capacity, and this was thrice her own demand. But nearly all this was in W Pakistan; the one factory in E (in Sylhet) drew its limestone

---

[49] Vakil, 332–33. Another estimate (*Industry in Pakistan*, 94) is 60,000 and 260,000 tons.

from Assam, and coal supply from the Damodar was difficult. Most of the Pakistan factories were owned by *Indian* combines. Since 1947 *India*, which in 1948 was importing cement from Pakistan, has greatly increased production. In these circumstances the proposed second factory at Wah (Attock Dt, W Punjab), with a capacity of 100,000 tons, seems dubious. E Pakistan is a deficit area, but transport costs from the W are probably prohibitive.

Glass was negligible in 1947; there were three small plants at Dacca, one of which migrated. But the market is fairly extensive, local production would greatly assist fruit preserving, and the supplies of soda ash and glass sand in W Punjab will probably not go to waste. Already Hyderabad (Sind) is meeting much of the demand.

5. *Chemicals*. The raw material basis for a Pakistani chemical industry is quite satisfactory, and the Khewra (Salt Range) soda-ash factory was one of the largest in the sub-continent, with a capacity of 20,000 tons p.a. Owing to the loss of the *Indian* market it ran at only half capacity in 1950. But light chemical industries were little developed, and for most manufactures, including soap, paint, and varnish, Pakistani areas depended on *Indian*. Matches, apart from a WIMCO factory at Lahore, were mainly a cottage industry. In some lines raw materials were inadequate, e.g. industrial alcohol (although this will improve with the expansion of sugar-refining) and all coke-oven by-products.

But other factors than raw materials have to be considered. To begin with, the lack of a large textile industry means that the demand for heavy chemicals, such as sulphuric acid (for which pyrites are available) is uneconomically low. More serious is the splitting of the market between E and W. In the Salt Range, with gypsum, salt, alum, and potassium salts, and some coal, chemicals such as ammonium sulphate could probably be produced more cheaply than at Sindri; but it does not follow that they would be more economic. A 100,000-ton ammonium sulphate plant is projected here, but the market is in E Pakistan, where there are no reasonable chances of production. Sea freights from Karachi to Chittagong are higher than from UK, and it is difficult to see how the W Pakistan product could be competitively marketed in the E, unless protected by so high a tariff that the object of having fertiliser is defeated. The UK Industrial Mission concludes that neither the expansion of caustic soda production (6000 tons planned) nor of sulphuric acid is economical, though the latter would be of value for superphosphate, if W Pakistan farmers could be stimulated to use it to the extent desirable.

6. *Paper*. Here the conditions just discussed are reversed: potential (there is no production as yet) is in E Pakistan, using bamboo from the Chittagong Hill Tracts and Karnaphuli power to produce 30,000 tons, approximately the demand of Pakistan as a whole. Transport costs to W Pakistan will be high. The development of rayon and allied industries has

been suggested; but against this (and hampering paper production) is the absence of chemical resources in E Pakistan.

7. *Leather*. The general superiority of Pakistani hides, from slaughtered rather than disease-killed cattle, and the long tradition of Muslim leather-workers, provide good bases for the development of an industry at present existing (apart from the Bata factory at Lahore) only as a craft. Muslim manufacturers from Cawnpore are establishing factories at Hyderabad (Sind); the tan-stuff supplies are not so good as those of *India*, but this should prove no insuperable difficulty.

8. *Sialkot*. It remains to deal with Pakistan's only really individual industry, the sports goods and allied manufactures of Sialkot, perhaps the one essentially industrial town of the country. Here four factories employed about 1000 workers directly, but co-ordinated the labour of some 70,000 cottage workers. The products, mainly cricket and tennis gear, had an All-India market and there was even some export. Associated were rubber goods and some surgical instruments.

Sialkot, however, is likely to be adversely affected by Partition. Willow and gut came mainly from Kashmir, rubber from S India, though mulberry wood was available from the Changa Manga irrigated forest. But Himalayan E Punjab may be able to develop willow and mulberry plantations, e.g. in the Kulu Valley, and is at present better placed than Sialkot for supplies of tanned leather. Many entrepreneurs have emigrated to E Punjab, and as far as Agra, and the *Indian* market is now nearly lost to Pakistan.[50]

Location and Policy

Apart from some 'metropolitan' industry—most of it very petty—in Karachi, the industries of Pakistan are nearly confined to the N of the Indus Plains: the sugar of Mardan, the cement and oil of Attock, the Salt Range chemicals, and the light industries of Lahore—developed on Mandi power, an asset wasting away. In E Pakistan such industry as existed, apart from tea factories, was mainly in Dacca and its port Narayanganj. This distribution is not likely to change greatly, except perhaps for a spread of small metal industries, ancillary to agriculture, into the Canal Colonies, and more cotton-milling there; in fact the development of hydro-electricity in the N may strengthen the supremacy of the Peshawar-Lahore zone. In E Pakistan Dacca lies at about the economic limit of power transmission from Karnaphuli, which in any case will develop only two-thirds of estimated *industrial* demand. Inadequate as Chittagong is as yet, it is still a port and close to the only non-alluvial area of E Pakistan, with perhaps some low-grade coal in the hills, and it may well rival Dacca industrially.

Policy and Problems. Whereas in *India* industrialists are wont to complain loudly, and not always unreasonably, of the Government's initiatives in all

[50] Vakil, 325–27.

directions, in Pakistan the demand is for more state enterprise. This is probably due largely to the fact that most Muslim capitalists have traditionally been traders, and enterprise still turns more readily to commerce than to industry. Concessions to foreign capital are perforce more liberal than in *India*, and it is significant that financing is mainly by a State Industrial Corporation which mobilises capital to be deployed either through individual entrepreneurs or directly by the State—which plans to control a larger segment of the economy than does the *Indian* Government—jute, paper, heavy engineering, ship-building, heavy chemicals, and fertiliser will all be developed by the Corporation.

The problems to be faced are immense; first, perhaps, the loss of managerial and technical enterprise by the emigration of non-Muslims. "Even in the problem of determining priorities, Pakistan faces a dilemma—whether she should first concentrate on industries producing essential consumer goods or on process industries which utilise the principal raw materials. . . . There is plenty of raw jute but [little] export is possible so long as there are few baling presses and the port capacity continues to be limited. Concentration on development of ports and of baling presses means less funds for other purposes." [51]

More serious still is the possible clash of interests between E Pakistan and W. E Pakistan is obviously far more closely bound up with *India* than W; she is, as it were, economically no less than geographically encircled. If she is to be supplied with a wide range of consumer goods from W Pakistan (where is most of the industrial potential, jute and paper excepted), instead of from *India*, it seems likely that the cost of living will be high indeed; and E Pakistan is an overcrowded area with miserably low standards already. W Pakistan makes the running, as indeed it made Pakistan, and in time this may place a severe strain on loyalties at Dacca.

The desire of Pakistan to develop industrially is natural and up to a point reasonable. But it seems that any attempt to build up heavy industry is highly premature—the whole resource structure is unsound for such development—and that for a long time the way of advance must be by industries either ancillary to agriculture or processing its products. This is likely to prove a hard saying. Meanwhile it seems that Pakistan is endeavouring to orient her trade away from that of *India* to a greater extent than is reasonable or desirable in the interests of her own economy. Doubtless *India* also has a grave responsibility in these matters; but it seems folly for Pakistan to deliberately seek distant markets simply to hamper a neighbour with a vast actual and potential market for Pakistani products; yet it is to be feared that this is being done.[52]

[51] Vakil, 389.
[52] This view is not based solely on *Indian* sources; it is implicit in much Pakistani official information. Cf., for example, the tone of the article from *Karachi Commerce* cited with apparent approval in *Weekly Pakistan News* II/33 (21/1/50).

V. THIS HOUSE AGAINST THIS HOUSE

The natural interdependence of *India* and Pakistan is well summed up by Vakil: they should normally supply each other with raw jute, raw cotton, raw wool, antimony, gypsum, coal, some limestone, soda ash and other chemicals, tobacco, hides, barley, rubber, metals crude and smelted, electricity; on the manufactured side sugar, vegetable oils, cigarettes, leather goods, textiles, metal goods from girders to pins, plywood, soap, matches, glassware, cement, agricultural machinery. Further, technical instruction, labour, capital, transport, were all interlocked: "There was no part of economic life in India which was not in one way or another interlinked with that in Pakistan and *vice versa*."[53]

Vakil's straightforward sentences achieve a tragic eloquence by the simple addition of fact to fact with the remorseless stroke of a steam-hammer. Already the economies of the sister-nations, which have so much to give each other, are widely divergent; and yet a year's real peace and co-operation could re-knit the threads. Without it neither country can possibly reach its full stature; nor, incidentally, can they well reproach the West for its materialism so long as they are locked in so inept, so ignoble a struggle. The accuracy and the desperate implications of Vakil's clinching sentence cannot be questioned: "Politics based on communal hatred and suspicion is systematically undoing the work of generations by defying the facts of economic geography and the laws of economic science."

There are of course men on both sides with wider and more responsible views, and the economic half-war has been called off. It is to be hoped that real co-operation will come, but this is doubtful until the Kashmir dispute is resolved and its resolution accepted without question by both parties.

[53] Vakil, 354–55.

CHAPTER XII

TRANSPORT AND TRADE

I. TRANSPORT

IN old India transport by land depended mainly on the bullock, as a pack rather than a draught animal; and, especially in the Indo-Gangetic Plains, rivers carried a large part of such bulk traffic as existed. Inland waterways, except in Bengal and Assam, are now almost negligible; the rail monopoly of long-distance bulk movements is as yet hardly challenged by the road, though for medium distances lorry traffic is rapidly increasing. Yet in the country, and even in the smaller towns, the bullock-cart is still indispensable, and by reason of its working economy not likely to be soon superseded for jobbing cartage of small consignments over short hauls. Undoubtedly, however, pride of place in the Indian transport system still remains with the railway.[1]

Railways

The first train in India ran in 1853 on the 21 miles between Bombay and Thana; by the Mutiny about 200 miles were open: Bombay–Kalyan (33 miles), Calcutta–Raniganj (120 miles), Madras–Arkonam (39 miles). The Mutiny forced on construction; by 1870 about 4250 miles were open, and nearly 8500 by 1880. The spread of the system is shown in Fig. 60; it will be noted that the Bombay–Calcutta route was originally via Jubbulpore and Allahabad, longer but less heavily graded than the direct Nagpur line. By 1900 the main outlines are nearly complete; since then development has been mainly in-filling. The most important railways constructed in the inter-war years were the Raipur–Vizagapatam line (1932), the Manmadurai–Trichinopoly chord on the route to Ceylon, and the Khyber railway. Since Partition a direct *Indian* link with Assam has been constructed through the 12-mile gap between Nepal and E Pakistan. This line of 142 miles (metre, half of it widening the Darjeeling Hill Rly) was begun in January 1948 and opened several months ahead of schedule in January 1950, although the monsoon cut actual working time to 11 months. It bridges the Tista, previously crossed by ferry in Pakistan territory.

Table XX shows route mileage by gauges and the Indo-Pakistan division. The BG of 5 ft 6 ins. is really the Indian standard, but it will be seen that half the total is metre or less: the narrow-gauge lines (2 ft or 2 ft 6 ins.) are

[1] General refces: Jathar and Beri, Vol. II Ch. V; Anstey, Ch. XIII; Vakil, Ch. X; K. G. Mitchell and L. H. Kirkness, *Report on the Present State of Road and Railway Competition* (Calcutta, 1933); F. P. Antia, *Transport* (OPIA No. 34, 1946).

mostly hill railways such as those to Simla, Darjeeling, and Ootacamund, and in W Pakistan the strategic lines in the NWFP. Also strategic, and almost a dead loss commercially, is the long BG arm from Quetta to the Persian border. The metre railway in W Pakistan is the part of the Jodhpur State Rly taken over; for the rest W Pakistan's share consists of the major portion of the NW Rly, which funnels all trade down to Karachi; the last 550 miles, S of Lodhran, is double-track. E Pakistan has most of the old E Bengal and part of the Bengal-Assam systems, mainly BG to the W of the Brahmaputra and entirely metre to the E. Since Partition a short BG line has been built, linking the isolated Jessore-Khulna fragment to the main system, and a metre line from the main N/S BG axis to the Brahmaputra has been widened to link the W bank to Chittagong with only one break of bulk, at the river itself. Despite these improvements the E Pakistan system is badly divided by the great rivers.

The densest nets will be obvious from Fig. 61. As regards the actual

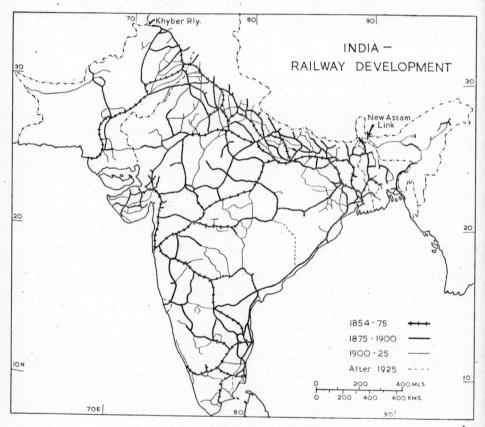

Fig. 60.—GROWTH OF THE RAILWAY SYSTEM.

area served it may be said that the more productive regions are fairly well covered. Construction and maintenance charges are heavy, owing to lack of ballast in the plains and to the innumerable bridges necessary nearly everywhere, and often spanning streams liable to sudden torrential floods. In many cases, e.g. along the flanks of the Ganges plains, the building of railways athwart the natural drainage lines has led to severe problems of flooding and repeated blowing of culverts.

There are now few missing links of any great importance, but, except in

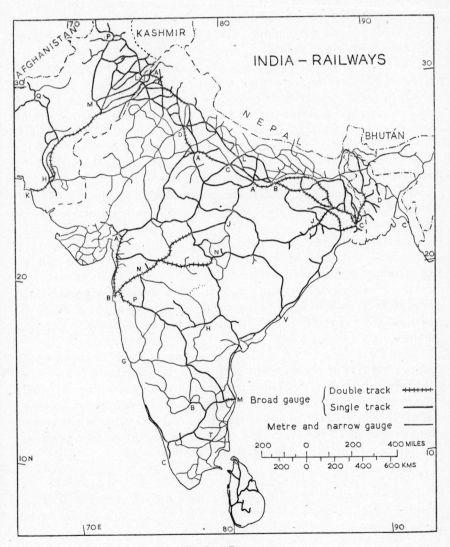

Fig. 61.—RAILWAYS.

the Punjab, mixture of gauges impedes smooth working. The great bulk of the system is single-track. This obviously increases the congestion and delays which are such a handicap to industry; Chittagong jute exports, for instance, are limited not only by inadequate port facilities but also by the long single-track into the main body of E Pakistan. Since Partition some double-tracking has been carried out in *India*, notably between Delhi and Muttra to facilitate the routeing of E Punjab traffic to Bombay rather than Karachi; and the line from the Raniganj coalfield to Calcutta is now four-tracked. An extension of electrification, if only to save coal in the S, seems also desirable; at present the only electric railways are some suburban lines in Bombay and Madras, and the lines from Bombay up the Thal and Bhor Ghats to Igatpuri and Poona.

The strain on the railways during the two wars was very great; by 1947 about a third of the locos were over-aged, and workshops are hardly adequate for all the servicing needed; it is hoped that the new loco factories at Tatanagar and Chittaranjan will rectify this within a few years. Partition worsened the situation for *India*, as the main shops on the NW and Bengal-Assam Rlys were in Pakistan. Partition also disrupted the staff: "On the East Indian Rly the shortage of drivers and firemen amounted to about 45% of total requirements. Goods train services had to be curtailed for some time by about one-third. Coal loadings were therefore reduced to half." [2] This in turn reacted on coal supplies to the Pakistan railways, a more permanent problem.

The railways were built and managed by a variety of methods—directly by central or state governments, by private companies with or without Government guarantees.[3] Since 1925 the Government has been resuming or taking over private lines, and the systems are now completely nationalised both in *India* and Pakistan. It is proposed to regroup all the *Indian* lines into six great regions; E and W Pakistan are each served by a single system.

In 1947–48 the railways carried 104 m. tons of goods (21,195 m. ton-miles), and 1131 m. passengers—over 90% of them third class. The hold of the railway on Indian social life can best be judged by watching the babbling turmoil of the great stations, the more leisurely reception of the daily through train at some provincial junction, and everywhere the crowded human comedy of the third class. But a new and even more pervasive solvent of rural isolation has appeared in the motor-bus.

Roads

Road development in India always has been and still is most inadequate; though for earlier times this statement begs the question "adequate for

[2] Vakil, 406; cf. *First Five Year Plan*, 171.
[3] For the interesting internal history, see Jathar and Beri, *loc. cit.*, and N. Sanyal, *Development of Indian Railways* (Calcutta, 1930).

what?" The Moguls kept up certain trunk roads for the movement of armies and merchant caravans, marking them out with distance stones and avenues of shade trees and providing police posts. The main route naturally followed the great ancient highway from Peshawar to Delhi, Agra, and Allahabad, the predecessor of the EIC's Grand Trunk Road which was the backbone of the British Raj in Hindustan. But wheeled traffic was rare, and for the most part "roads" were unbridged fair-weather tracks in the plains, bridle or even foot-paths in the hills; and for much of the country that is what they still are.

Setting aside town thoroughfares (c. 20,000 miles) the total mileage of made roads in the sub-continent is about 300,000, but of these under 100,000 are metalled, though a further 30–35,000 miles of the unmetalled (*kaccha*) roads are more or less motorable throughout the year. Total mileage in 1943 came to about 0·18 to the sq ml or 76 to 100,000 people, as compared with 2 and 392 for Great Britain and 1 and 2500 for USA; and in these countries practically all the roads considered are all-year motor roads.[4] Of these All-India mileages Pakistan's share is 9000 miles of metalled and 44,000 of unmetalled; of the unmetalled roads about a third are in W Punjab and—for obviously non-economic reasons!—no less than 26% in NWFP.

Large tracts of country are deplorably served. In so progressive a state as Bombay, some Districts have no real roads in 40 or even 75% of their area; in Guntur Dt (Madras) "some of the [locally] important trade centres in the interior are cut off for more than nine months of the year." In Bengal, for obvious physical reasons, even metalled roads are poor, and in some Districts "70–80% of the villages are totally cut off from outside communications during the monsoon." [5]

To improve this state of affairs the 'Nagpur Plan' of 1943 envisaged the construction or improvement of 400,000 miles in 20 years, of which 90,000 miles would be in Pakistan areas. 'National Highways' (largely the existing quadrilateral linking Delhi, Calcutta, Madras, and Bombay, remodelled) would account for 22,000 miles, the chief new road being a great artery from Benares to Cape Comorin. Proposed new village roads would amount to 150,000 miles; it seems likely that these are too few and that too small a share of the finance has been allotted to them; to bring all but the smallest villages within a mile or two of a road might take 700,000 miles, and there is probably good reason for the view of the 1946 President of the Indian Roads Congress, that "what India needed was a large number of all-weather roads, rather than a great increase in the mileage of roads of very superior types." The *Five Year Plan* (pp. 177–78) supports this view.

---

[4] Antia, 13–14; there has been little material change since 1943, except for the military roads (now probably decayed) of the Burma border.
[5] V. V. Ramanadham, *Road Transport in India* (Lucknow, 1948), 32–34.

The geographical difficulties confronting the Indian road engineer are serious. Very large areas, and those the most productive agriculturally, have no accessible road metal; in the Peninsula laterite is extensively used, but while its surface is initially quite good it is soon ground to powder, and traffic moves accompanied by great towers of red dust. As on the railways, bridging is a major cost. Besides these physical problems there is the question of the bullock-cart. When lightly and strongly built, as in Burma, the bullock-cart is a very flexible instrument, capable of taking amazing usage on tracks which are more rut and knobbly rock than surface; but its narrow iron tyres spell destruction to all but the best surfaces, and its deliberate pace is responsible for much frustration on the part of other users. It is not always possible to provide roughly-surfaced verges for the carts, and still less often possible to confine their drivers to verges when provided.[6] Yet there are about 6 m. bullock-carts in *India* against 250–300,000 motor-vehicles, and in many areas, of course, only cart traffic is feasible. One solution, initially costly but adding greatly to economic and efficient working (on made roads), is the use of rubber tyres, which is increasing especially near the larger towns.

But bullock-carts are "being eliminated from hauls of over 25 miles", at least in areas with decent roads.[7] For medium distances the motor is increasingly a serious competitor to the railway, for both passenger and goods traffic. This in itself raises problems, since bus and lorry working is mainly in the hands of small owners whose notions of management often exclude depreciation or even accounts, but give ample scope to virulent rate-cutting, gross over-working of popular routes, and even grosser over-loading, almost amounting to securing doubtful passengers by main force. Even if properly run there is obviously a good deal of economic wastage in these small concerns; in Madras in 1941 over 45% of public service and carrier vehicles were owned by "firms" possessing four or fewer motors. As Ramanadham remarks, "This is perhaps the limit to which democratic ownership can go, the most uneconomic limit." [8] On a longer view the dangers of *laissez-faire* in road-rail competition are obvious enough.

A solution is sought in nationalisation on a provincial basis. Hyderabad led the way in 1932 with an interesting and successful experiment in road-rail co-ordination, which provided a much improved service with lower fares. Similar measures elsewhere have not always had similar results.

Inland Water Transport

The rivers of the Peninsula are for the most part almost useless for navigation; the Indus was navigated by steamer as far as Dera Ismail Khan —800 miles from its mouth—and as late as the 1880s Ferozepore on the

---

[6] Personal experience.   [7] Antia, 17–20.
[8] Ramanadham, 43–45, 48–49, 80; and for a full account of the Hyderabad development, 82–93.

Sutlej was an important steamer station with repair services.[9] But its navigation was killed by the railway, by diversion of water to the canals and by barrages; and so also was that of the extra-deltaic Ganges, though there is still an unimportant service on the Gogra. Some of the Himalayan rivers are of use for timber-rafting. As for canals, although in the early days of irrigation some play was made with schemes for dual-purpose canals these proved impracticable, and outside Bengal the only navigation canal of significance is the Buckingham Canal N and S of Madras, and this is of limited use though it does bring some bulky traffic (fuel, lime) to Madras. The Malabar backwaters are also important, and there is some traffic in the Godavari delta. Of the total Indian mileage of 4300 in 1938–39, Madras and Bengal had each 1400.[10] The usual railway devices ensured the disuse of some canals and even coastal traffic.

In the Bengal deltas, however, river traffic is still of the greatest importance, and the Brahmaputra is an important highway as far as Dibrugarh. There are some 2800 miles of navigable waterways in E Pakistan; the larger rivers can take ships of 400–600 tons, while thousands of country boats move paddy and jute; their destruction or impounding (to secure them from the Japanese) was not the least factor in the 1943 famine. The orientation of traffic to Chittagong rather than to Calcutta, however, has to face a sea-passage, short but not infrequently dangerous during the monsoon. But perhaps 3–4 m. tons of cargo and 5–7 m. passengers moved annually by water in undivided Bengal.

Partition has deranged this traffic-flow, and it cannot be so easily reconstructed for *Indian* needs as the rail and road links: Assam water traffic must pass through Pakistan. But, as part of the Kosi and Damodar schemes, it is planned to make the latter river navigable to Asansol and to rehabilitate the Wn distributaries of the Ganges, giving Calcutta a direct water link with the middle Ganges.

Ocean Shipping

"In a total world tonnage of over 80 million [in 1948], India's share is just 0·04% [327,000 gross tons] while that of Pakistan is only 0·004% [33,000 tons]." [11] Considering *India's* position in the Indian Ocean, the volume of her trade with its shores, and the fact that the Peninsula is not so 'harbourless' as is often supposed, this position is quite absurd. Shipping has high priority in *Indian* plans and there has been some progress since Independence; but in 1949 *India* possessed under 100 ocean-going vessels totalling 400,000 gross tons. Pakistan, starting from scratch, had 100,000 tons in 1950.

[9] Reclus, *L'Inde* (1884), 213; faithfully followed by J. Sion, *Asie des Moussons* (*Géographie Universelle* T.IX, Partie I, 1929), 316.
[10] Antia, 24–26.
[11] Vakil, 419; for general discussion, *ibid.*, 418–24; Jathar and Beri, II. 157–65.

There can be little doubt that the miserable status of Indian shipping was largely due to the policy of the British 'Conference Lines', working through deferred rebates to shippers using their vessels only, or through rate-wars in which, with the weight of finance and experience behind them, they had far more staying-power than the struggling Indian lines. Legislation to end this discrimination was barred by the Government of India Act (1935) which forbade discrimination against British interests: after all, the coastal trade of Britain was open to any Indian vessel which could get there. It must unfortunately be added that neglect of safety measures and bad management contributed to the poor Indian development. The result was that the pre-war percentages of seaborne trade were: British 66, foreign 29, Indian 3·5–4, the balance being carried in sailing country craft.

The new régime plans to secure to *Indian* shipping all the coastal trade (this by legislation), 75% of the Burma and Ceylon, 50% of distant, and 30% of Far East trade. "This would amount to about 10 million tons of cargo and 3 million passengers every year, for which a shipping tonnage of about 2 million would be necessary." [12] These aims were to be entrusted to three corporations, but managerial and financial deficiencies have prevented much progress. *Indian* ships, however, now have regular services to UK and Australia.

Over 90% of the coastal trade is at ports between Kathiawar and Cochin; in 1942 it was estimated that the 4800 country craft of this littoral had a total cargo capacity of 200,000 tons. They move an appreciable proportion—1·25 to 1·5 m. tons—of a total coastal traffic of 7 m. Many of them are stout vessels of up to 400 tons, perhaps the nearest thing afloat to the Portuguese keels which first brought Europe to Asia; voyages are often made to the Persian Gulf and as far afield as Zanzibar. Here is a 'nursery for seamen' comparable to that of the old Geordie brigs from Newcastle, an asset not to be neglected.

Civil Aviation

Air services [13] have made rapid progress, as the following *Indian* figures (all in thousands) show:

	Miles Flown	Passengers	Freight (lbs)	Mail (lbs)
1945	3,320	24	852	481
1947	9,362	255	3,869	1405
1949	14,900	358	13,300	4900
1950	18,896	519	88,000	

[12] Vakil, 419.
[13] *Report of the Working of the Ministry of Communications 1949–50* (ND, 1950); Vakil, 426–30.

Here Partition and Kashmir at least provided valuable experience in emergency work.

There are about 12 *Indian* air lines, of which the most important are Air India (Tata's) and Indian National Airways (Birla's); 36 services link the greater cities. Air India International, in which the Government has some control, has a thrice-weekly service to UK, and there is also a service to Bangkok. High petrol costs and (owing to the lack of an aeronautical industry) high costs of replacement and maintenance are handicaps. The question of nationalisation—this year, in ten years, or never—is still under debate.

Air communications are obviously of the greatest importance to divided Pakistan; although she has only 2 lines and 9 services her route mileage in 1949 was 15,000 against *India's* 21,000. Of the four major airports in the sub-continent—Santa Cruz (Bombay), Dum Dum (Calcutta), Palam (New Delhi), and Karachi—only the last is as yet fully developed. The total number of operational civil aircraft in 1949 was 170 for *India* and 31 for Pakistan; a high proportion are of rather old-fashioned types.

II. TRADE

Internal, Coastal, and Land Frontier Trade

Any account of the trade of the sub-continent must deal mainly with overseas commerce, but brief mention may be made of other branches. Inadequate data and the complexity of such figures as are available render an analysis of the internal trade unprofitable, at least on the scale of this book; but it should not be forgotten that inter-State movements (not to mention those within the limits of each territorial unit) are probably two or three times as large as the foreign trade, and may involve rail hauls of hundreds of miles. With Partition, of course, much internal trade has become international.

Coastal trade is not insignificant in amount; in 1943 its volume was estimated at around 7 m. tons, mainly bulky commodities such as coal, rice, salt, tiles, timber; and with improvements in minor ports and some attention to such matters as insurance, coastal shipping could play a very useful part in relieving the load on the railways, as it already does on the W coast.

Trade across the land frontiers is highly interesting in its historical and human aspects, but economically of little significance. With Iran and Burma there is naturally very little; the trade to Afghanistan, Nepal, and Tibet is of great importance to those land-locked countries, but its loss would not materially affect the economy of the sub-continent except locally—i.e. in the Wn Borderland, Kashmir, Kumaon, and Darjeeling; some notes on this trade will be found in the relevant regional sections. The Afghan market is steadily growing with the general economic development of that country, but trade with central Asia has declined with political instability and the ever-increasing Soviet pull. At most it was only a very small fraction of the volume or value of sea-borne trade.

Sea-borne Trade: General Character

Something of the long trading history of India, from the times when it was the entrepôt between the Graeco-Roman world and the Land of the Seres to the days when it was an exporter of manufactures unrivalled in the West, has been hinted at in Chs. VI and XI; it would serve no purpose to recount the story, fascinating as it is. In the first half of the 19th century the great reversal was all but completed, and Indian manufactured exports became confined to ingenious trifles; the Suez Canal, the building of the railways, and Free Trade established a pattern of trade that to the Britain of the palmy days of imperialism appeared no more than the natural order of things: the Indian Empire was a providential market for manufactured consumption goods, a supplier of fibres, hides, and oilseeds. But the wheel has now shifted a good deal, if not full circle.[14]

Already in the last two decades of last century, however, signs of change were apparent, notably the yarn export to China; and in the first decade of this century the hegemony of Britain in Indian commerce was challenged by Germany and Japan, the latter country greatly strengthening her position during the 1914–18 war. The 33 years between 1914 and Independence saw many vicissitudes: wars, financial crises, political instability, the great depression of the 30s which seriously reduced both the volume and the value of trade. Through all these changes, however, there was a favourable visible balance of trade, one or two years only excepted.

This was in part offset by invisible imports—interest on capital invested in railways, docks, plantations, and so on; payments made in Britain for pensions, leave pay, Government stores, and other official expenditure. This latter group formed the 'Home Charges' of British economists, the 'drain' of Indian; regarded as disguised tribute, it was the subject of bitter controversy, now happily of historical interest only. Against the visible excess of exports had also to be set large imports of gold and silver, much of them destined to be hoarded by middlemen and the better-off peasants. This counter-drain of precious metals from the W had indeed been a perennial phenomenon, first deplored by Pliny in the 1st century AD.

There has been another great reversal: the export surplus, the 'drain', the gold imports, are now all things of the past. The 1939–45 war transformed India into a creditor country, and the field of Indo-British debate was shifted to the 'sterling balances' due to India for war-time purchases by the British Government. Two trends, however, have been persistent

---

[14] Some references to the earlier history are given in the Bibliographical Note to Ch. VI; for the later, see Jathar and Beri, Vol. II. Ch. VI.

through the present century: the declining share of Britain in Indian trade, and the increasing proportions of manufactured exports with their correlative raw material imports. These are illustrated in Tables XXI and XXII.

Finally, as might be expected in an area with so vast a population and so wide a range of resources, trade per head of population is exceedingly low: in 1940–41 it amounted to about Rs.9·2, or 14 shillings.

The War and Partition

We have already noted in Ch. XI many of the detailed changes in trade resulting from the two wars and from industrial development: in a wide range of consumption goods, and in some basic production goods (e.g. cement), *India* is now self-sufficient or nearly so; and imports of manufactures tend more and more to be either heavy material for further industrialisation (including the development projects) or else semi-manufactures for assembly. The 1939–45 war enforced important shifts in the direction of trade: the European continent and SE Asia were cut off, but there were better opportunities in SW Asia and E Africa. The Partition has meant that many commodities, such as Punjab wheat or Damodar coal for Pakistan, have as it were been transferred in the national book-keeping from the internal to the foreign side.

Trade at present is so much a matter of temporary bilateral agreements that an extended analysis would give a misleading impression of permanency, and would be long out of date by the time it was printed; industrialisation is no less dynamic, but at least it has, if not more permanent bases, more predictable trends. Values again may be highly misleading owing to price changes. A few tendencies may, however, be noted, and recent figures for *India* and Pakistan are given in Tables XXIII and XXIV.

(a) *Indo-Pakistani Trade*.[15] Despite a heavy falling-off due to the devaluation conflict and the breakdown in the working of the trade agreement eventually reached, Indo-Pakistani trade even in 1949–50 was of major importance to both countries: for both imports and exports it represented 16–17% of *Indian* and 30–35% of Pakistani totals. The disbalance between E and W Pakistan is met once more: *Indian* exports to W Pakistan are about twice those to E, but for imports the position is reversed; this is of course mainly due to the jute of E Pakistan, which accounts for nearly all *Indian* imports thence. This feature will possibly become less marked with the extension of jute growing in *India* and its manufacture in Pakistan, along with the development of Chittagong to handle jute now re-exported from Calcutta. After jute raw cotton is the leading *Indian* import, the two fibres together accounting for nearly 90% of the total imports from Pakistan in 1949–50. *India's* exports to Pakistan are much more diversified, though cotton manufactures are from a quarter to a third of the total. Though on

---

[15] This sub-section based on Vakil, 431–34.

the mere figures the trade between the two countries is twice as important to Pakistan as to *India*, the heavy concentration of *Indian* imports on the essential raw materials for what are still her two greatest industries (and much more her greatest exporting industries) suggests that in practice her position is on a par with Pakistan's, the more so as her exports to Pakistan are mainly consumer goods for which Pakistan might find other suppliers. Recognition of these facts may have played a part in the welcome rapidity with which a new trade agreement was reached in February 1950.

(b) *India*. (Tables XXI–XXIII.) *India's* total foreign trade in 1948–49 and 1949–50 stood at about Rs.1100 crores or £822 m., a figure well above any total for Undivided India. To some extent, however, this was due to price changes; exports in 1948–49 were £498 m. against £114 m. in 1938–39, but the actual volume was only two-thirds of that in the earlier year.

The most important recent changes have already been glanced at. The increase in raw material imports is likely to be permanent as a result of the loss of jute and cotton areas to Pakistan. The post-war feature of an excess of imports over exports is only in relatively small part due to the same cause; more important are:

(i) the necessity for large food imports;
(ii) the finance available from sterling balances to cover an adverse visible balance;
(iii) the great demand for capital goods for the development projects, rendering such a balance a calculated factor.

Of these (i), despite the self-sufficiency policy, may well become even more imperative; (ii) is obviously a variable, possibly a risky one; and (iii) may come to vary inversely with (i), unless it can be underwritten by the Colombo Plan. The export situation is complex; while on the one hand prospects for retaining Asian and African markets for manufactures, gained during the war, are quite fair, the real need is for exports to dollar countries to finance more rapid intake of capital goods. Here *Indian* manufactures will find it extremely difficult, if not impossible, to compete; diversion of production in UK and USA to armaments obviously does not have as a corollary larger imports of consumption goods, if anything the reverse. It seems, then, that recourse may be necessary to increased exports of manganese and other strategic minerals and of agricultural products such as oilseeds; but, as we have suggested in Ch. X (section III) this implies the great dilemma of food versus cash crops.

As for the direction of trade, the war saw the virtual disappearance of European suppliers to SW Asian and E African markets, and India moved in; SE Asian markets were of course lost owing to the Japanese invasion, but the temporary eclipse of Japan enabled India to secure a large share of this trade after the war, and much of this will probably be retained. SE

Asia is potentially a valuable supplier of food and mineral oil (SW Asian oil is of course largely directed to the West), but the post-war upheavals in the area have reduced its export capacity to a fraction of what it was,[16] except in Siam, and though their agrarian economies are resilient not much recovery is possible until conditions are settled—no very likely prospect. Setting aside Pakistan, the major share of *India's* foreign trade is divided between UK and USA, with respectively 22–25% and 15–17% of both imports and exports. Egypt has moved up to fourth place as a supplier —mainly, of course, of long-stapled cotton—and Australia has become the fourth export market.

(c) *Pakistan.* The total value of Pakistani foreign trade is only about 30% of that of *India*, and its structure is radically different: in 1948–49 some 90% of exports were raw materials and 70% of imports manufactures; and capital goods form a much smaller proportion of imports.[17] The favourable balance of 1948–49 was lost in 1949–50, largely owing to the steep fall in (legitimate) exports to *India*, which in April 1950 were only one-ninety-seventh of those in April 1949. The actual structure showed little change, jute and cotton between them making up 80% of exports and textiles 43% of imports (cf. Table XXIV).

Ports

An excessively large proportion of the sub-continent's ocean trade is concentrated in three or four major ports; Bombay and Calcutta between them handle no less than 75% of *India's* tonnage, Cochin and Madras the bulk of the remainder.[18] This is largely the result of historic accident accentuated by the earlier railway policy, and it naturally leads to congestion, delay, and unduly high internal transport charges.

Partition has meant some adjustment of hinterlands. The Peninsular ports, except for Bombay, have of course been little affected; nor, on the whole, has Karachi, the loss of some of its hinterland in E Punjab to Bombay being balanced by its generally enhanced significance as the great entrepôt for Pakistan. Admirably equipped as it is for bulk exporting, it needs further development to deal with the increased imports which will probably result from the erection of its hinterland into an independent political entity. A new port is planned at Pasni, 300 miles W in Makran, to open up Baluchistan and to act as a future relief for Karachi. Whether the poor hinterland can produce enough "wool, hides, bones, dates, fish,

---

[16] Rice exports in 1949 (million metric tons, cleaned): Burma 1·2, Indo-China 0·08, Siam 1·1; pre-war 2·5–3, 1·5, and 1–2 respectively. E. H. G. Dobby, *Southeast Asia* (1950), 356.

[17] Machinery formed only 6% of the value of Pakistani imports in 1948–49–50, against 15–18% in *India*. Vakil, 361 fn. 1.

[18] Details of the individual ports are given in the regional chapters. See also *Handbook of Commercial Information for India* (ND, 3rd ed., 1937), 62–109; Vakil, 421–24 and 460–61; V. Anstey, *The Trade of the Indian Ocean* (1929), 79–85.

and mineral products" to warrant expensive communications is perhaps doubtful.

In the E Chittagong's capacity has already been trebled, to 1·5 m. tons, and it is planned to double it again. But it is still very badly congested and cannot yet handle all the jute export, much of which still goes via Calcutta. The double-tracking of the long metre-rail link is perhaps the most urgent and practical proposition here. A new port has been opened at Chalna on the Pussur river, but this has only one berth for ocean steamers. Meanwhile Calcutta itself has been congested owing to the diversion of much of the Assam tea export from Chittagong. The new trade agreement may lead to a more rational use of the scarce port facilities of the Bengals.

In *India* a new port, to have an ultimate annual capacity of 3 m. tons, has been opened at Kandla in Cutch; this will divert some of the Gujarati trade from Bombay, overloaded by the addition of E Punjab to its hinterland. There are large plans for improvement at all major ports: more wharves and craneage at Cochin, electrification at Bombay, an extension of the harbour at Madras, and at Calcutta a ship canal from Diamond Harbour to Kidderpore, avoiding the Hooghly shoals. The long maritime tradition of the Wn littoral and the poor outlets of Wn Mysore warrant the new port to be located at one of the once-flourishing little harbours between Goa and Calicut.

NOTE ON THE NEW FIVE YEAR PLAN

In the avowedly modest Plan, agriculture, irrigation, and power account for 43% of expenditure, with target increases of 7·2 m. tons foodgrains, 690,000 tons sugar, 2 m. bales of jute, and 1 m. of cotton. Output 1950–51 and targets 1955–56 for major industries are: steel, 1·005/1·315 m. tons; cement, 2·613/4·600 m. tons; aluminium, 3,600/20,000 tons. Cotton cloth should be increased by 835 m. yards. Electricity should be 1 m. kW by 1955–56. In transport, railways and main roads receive most attention, with a 70% increase (260,000 tons) in shipping. All this is in Part I only, and *allowing for population increase would barely restore pre-war consumption.* Family limitation is therefore favoured.

It is a "middle way" Plan, with much scope for private investment and, for Part I at least, with very little recourse to long-term loans, "an orthodoxy worthy of Gladstonian finance". Part II, however, though costing only 20% of Part I, would depend very largely on external aid, or else of deficit budgets and inflation; and one may wonder whether 250,000,000 dollars a year will be readily forthcoming.

BIBLIOGRAPHICAL NOTE FOR PART 3

(Chs. VIII–XII)

General

Comprehensive works on Indian economic affairs discuss matters common to all the chapters of Part 3. The most generally useful is probably G. B. Jathar and S. G. Beri, *Indian Economics* (8th ed., 1949); an admirably balanced book in which the authors present the views of other writers fully and impartially, and add their own comments with modesty and eminently sound sense. It is supplemented by C. N. Vakil, *Economic Consequences of Divided India* (Bombay, 1950), with no fewer than 268 tables, which assembles an immense mass of facts and figures, conveniently divided for *India* and Pakistan, and also serves as a guide to the vast range of current official publications. B. B. Ghosh, *Indian Economics and Pakistani Economics* (Calcutta, 1949), follows Jathar and Beri too closely to be of much independent value. For Pakistan, S. M. Akhtar, *Economics of Pakistan* (Lahore, 1949, 1951), is a comprehensive survey.

Of earlier books, Vol III (Economic) of *The Imperial Gazetteer of India* (Oxford, 1908) is not only of value as a comparative historical study, but contains much useful permanent information, e.g. on crops and irrigation methods. Two admirable studies are V. Anstey, *The Economic Development of India* (3rd ed., 1948), and D. H. Buchanan, *The Development of Capitalistic Enterprise in India* (1934). The essays in R. K. Mukerjee (ed.), *Economic Problems of Modern India* (1939) are sometimes slight, but the book as a whole is a useful conspectus. There is a useful critique of war-time policies in A. R. Prest, *War Economics of Primary Producing Countries* (Cambridge, 1948), Ch. II.

The *Oxford Pamphlets on Indian Affairs* (1942–47) provide excellent introductions, among which may be mentioned: 3, *The Economic Background* (K. T. Shah *et al.*); 8, *The Food Supply* (R. K. Mukerjee); 9, *The Land and its Problems* (T. Vijayaraghavacharya); 10, *Industrialization* (P. S. Lokanathan); 20, *Tariffs and Industry* (J. Matthai); 21, *Nutrition* (W. R. Aykroyd); 28, *Mineral Resources* (A. M. Heron); 32, *Industrial Location* (B. C. Ghose); 34, *Transport* (F. P. Antia); 39, *Co-operation* (W. R. Satthianadhan and J. C. Ryan).

The three plans often referred to are published as follows:

A Food Plan for India (RIIA, 1945).

A Plan for the Economic Development of India (the 'Bombay Plan'; Penguins, 1945).

The Colombo Plan (HMSO, 1950).

Agriculture

The most fundamental source is the *Report of the Royal Commission on Agriculture in India* (1928), cited as RCAI, supplemented by Sir J. Russell, *Report on Crop Production in India* (1937) and W. Burns, *Technological Possibilities of Agricultural Development in India* (1944).

Official statistics will be found in *Agricultural Statistics of India*; the last complete issue with figures by Districts refers to 1938–39–40; more recent District figures must be sought from various Provincial publications such as *Season and Crop Reports*. Three very useful compilations are: *The Food Statistics of India* (1946 and 1949); *Estimates of Area and Yield of Principal Crops in Undivided India* (1949), which despite its title breaks down the figures into *Indian* and Pakistani totals; and *Abstract of Agricultural Statistics, 1936–37 to 1945–46* (1949) and *1950* (1952, with new and useful tables). All these ND.

Some of the many unofficial studies are noted in the relevant regional sections; for a general view Jathar and Beri, I. Chs. IV–XII, is admirable. Perhaps the best single book is M. B. Nanivati and J. J. Anjaria, *The Indian Rural Problem* (Bombay, 3rd ed., 1947). R. K. Mukerjee, *Food Planning for 400 Million* (1938) is an important study, though some of the arguments are perhaps dubious. M. Brown, *India Need Not Starve* (Bombay, 1944) is first-class journalism, packed with good sense and vivid illustration. An excellent and very full account of the conditions of production of all the chief crops is given in A. K. Y. N. Aiyer, *The Field Crops of India* (Bangalore, 3rd ed., 1950).

Power and Minerals

A useful survey is given in G. Kuriyan, *Hydro-Electric Power in India—A Geographical Analysis* (Indian Geog. Soc., Monograph No. 1, Madras, 1945); development schemes are detailed in *New Projects for Irrigation and Power in India* (Central Board of Irrigation; ?Simla, 2nd ed., 1948), and ample material may be obtained from the CBI, the Damodar Valley Corporation, and State governments. Vakil, Ch. VI, gives a connected account of the present position and the prospects in both *India* and Pakistan. For minerals, see Vakil again (Ch. V); D. N. Wadia, *Geology of India* (1939 ed.), Ch. XXVI; the GSI's *Bulletins of Economic Minerals* (in *Rec. GSI*) and its more popular journal *Indian Minerals*.

Industry

Buchanan provides an admirable historical introduction, Jathar and Beri a general survey; Vakil is especially valuable for estimates of demand as well as capacity, for his breakdown of figures for *India* and Pakistan, and for Government policy. There is a mass of detail in P. J. Thomas, *India's Basic Industries* (Bombay, 1948). T. R. Sharma, *Location of Industries in India* (Bombay, 2nd ed., 1949) is a first-class study with much more understanding of and emphasis upon geographical factors than is usual among Indian writers.

The Directorate of Industrial Statistics issues censuses of manufactures (Simla, 1946 and 1947) and *Monthly Statistics of the Production of Selected Industries*. *Indian Trade and Industry* and *India Record*, issued from India House, London, are useful.

The invaluable Vakil is particularly invaluable for Pakistani industry, and the *Report of the UK Industrial Mission to Pakistan* (HMSO, 1950) is an authoritative survey. There is a good deal of information in the official *Industry in Pakistan, 1947–1950* (Karachi, 1950), but it takes a little padding to run to 130 pages.

Otherwise estimates of Pakistan's industrial position and prospects must be gleaned from the scattered and repetitive notices in the official hand-outs.

Transport and Trade

Jathar and Beri, and Vakil, have excellent chapters on transport and trade (II. V–VI and X–XI respectively); other references for transport are cited in the text. V. Anstey, *The Trade of the Indian Ocean* (1929), and the official *Handbook of Commercial Information for India* (ND, 3rd ed., 1937) contain much of value. A. N. Agarwala (ed.), *Position and Prospects of India's Foreign Trade* (Allahabad, 1947) has some useful details and figures embedded in the generally poor essays of various Trade Commissioners. The Indian Council of World Affairs has published two interesting surveys: B. G. Ghate, *Asia's Trade* (?Bombay, n.d., ?1948) and N. V. Sovani, *Economic Relations of India with South-East Asia and the Far East* (?Bombay, n.d., ?1949).

Additional References

K. Davis, *The Population of India and Pakistan* (Princeton, 1951). Pt VI, Social Structure and Social Change, contains most admirable analyses of the agrarian/industrial/demographic situation.

Sir E. J. Russell, "India's Peoples and their Food", *Geography* XXXVII (1952), 125–41. The most comprehensive short survey I have seen.

The Indian and Pakistan Year Book ("Times of India", Bombay, annual) has useful, if poorly organised, surveys of the main industries and economic topics.

The First Five Year Plan: A Draft Outline (Planning Commission, ND, 1951). Far more realistic than any previous "Planning", with a refreshing emphasis on the primacy of agriculture—for which, indeed, it has been criticised. *The Draft Outline* provides a very good survey of the present economic position, in broad outline; it is admirably summarised by V. R. K. V. Rao in *Pacific Affairs*, XXV (1952), 3–23. See also above, 326.

STATISTICAL TABLES

THE INDIAN SUB-CONTINENT AND CEYLON:
AREA AND POPULATION, 1941 AND 1951

	Area, sq mls	Population, millions		Density to sq ml		Females to 1000 males	Increase per cent
		1941	1951	1941	1951	1951	1941–51
I. INDIA							
"A" States[1]							
Assam . . .	54,084	7·593	9·129	144	165	875	20·2
Bengal (W) . .	29,476	21·837	24·787	741	841	861	13·5
Bihar . . .	70,368	36·545	40·219	519	572	994	10·1
Bombay . .	115,570	29·507	35·943	255	311	929	21·8
Madhya Pradesh .	130,323	19·632	21·328	151	165	995	8·6
Madras . .	127,768	49·848	56·952	390	469	1004	14·3
Orissa . . .	59,869	13·768	14·644	230	245	1023	6·4
Punjab (E) . .	37,428	12·594	12·639	336	337	863	0·4
Uttar Pradesh .	112,523	56·517	63·254	502	562	909	11·9
Total . .	737,409	247·840	278·896	336	378	947	12·6
"B" States[2]							
Hyderabad .	82,313	16·339	18·653	198	227	971	14·2
Madhya Bharat .	46,710	7·152	7·942	153	170	924	11·1
Mysore . .	29,458	7·329	9·072	249	308	945	23·8
Pepsu . .	10,099	3·424	3·468	339	343	852	1·3
Rajasthan . .	128,424	13·282	15·298	104	119	920	15·2
Saurashtra . .	21,062	3·431	4·136	163	196	974	20·5
Travancore-Cochin .	9,155	7·493	9·265	820	1012	1007	23·6
Total . .	327,221	58·449	67·834	179	207	949	16·1
"C" States[3]							
Ajmer . . .	2,425	0·589	0·692	243	285	926	17·5
Bhopal . . .	6,921	0·785	0·838	113	121	910	6·8
Bilaspur . .	453	0·110	0·128	243	283	953	16·4
Coorg . . .	1,593	0·169	0·229	106	144	829	35·5
Delhi . . .	574	0·918	1·744	1599	3045	761	90·0
Himachal Pradesh	10,600	0·935	0·989	88	93	916	5·8
Cutch . . .	8,461	0·501	0·568	59	67	1077	13·4
Manipur . .	8,620	0·512	0·579	59	67	1034	13·1
Tripura . .	4,049	0·513	0·650	126	161	912	26·7
Vindhya Pradesh .	24,600	3·353	3·577	136	145	950	6·7
Total . .	68,296	8·386	9·995	123	146	912	19·2
"D" Territories							
Andamans and Nicobars . .	3,143	0·034	0·031	11	10	627	− 8·3
Sikkim . .	2,745	0·122	0·136	44	49	912	11·5
Misc. Tribes[4] .	?	no data	0·560*	—	—	?	—
Total *INDIA* .	1,138,814	314·830	357·462	276	314	946	13·4

TABLE I—(*Cont.*)

	Area, sq mls	Population, millions 1941	1951	Density to sq ml 1941	1951	Females to 1000 males 1951	Increase per cent 1941–51
II. DISPUTED TERRITORY							
JAMMU and KASHMIR	82,258	4·022	4·370*	49	53*	no data	8·4
III. PAKISTAN							
West Pakistan							
BALUCHISTAN	52,900	0·502	0·622	9·5	13	777	24·0
NWFP	13,815	3·038	3·239	220	234	888	6·6
PUNJAB (W)	62,987	15·802	18·814	251	299	874	19·7
SIND	50,443	4·535	4·619	87	92	829	26·5
KARACHI Fedl. Area	812	n.d.	1·118	n.d.	1377	747	n.d.
Total	180,957	23·877	28·412	133	159	824	19·0
BAHAWALPUR	15,918	1·341	1·820	84	114	842	35·0
BALUCHI Sts	82,239	0·356	0·556	4	7	880	56·2
KHAIRPUR	6,050	0·306	0·320	51	53	819	4·6
NW TRIBAL, etc.	27,242	2·378*	2·460*?	88*	90*?	901	3·4
Total	130,449	4·381	4·836	34	38	872	10·4
Total W. Pak.	311,406	28·258	33·248	90	107	865	17·7
East Pakistan							
E. BENGAL	}54,501{	39·112 }	42·119{	792 }	773	909·5	0·65
SYLHET		2·733 }		594 }			
Total E. Pak.	54,501	41·845	42·119	768	773	909·5	0·65
Total PAKISTAN	365,907	70·103	75·687	192	207	888	8·0
IV. FOREIGN POSSESSIONS							
PORTUGUESE	1,537	0·624 (1940) no		406	....no data	....
FRENCH	200	0·323	data	1592	....no data	....
Total I–IV	1,588,736	389·902	437·519	245·5	275·5		12·2
V. OTHER STATES							
NEPAL	54,000*	7·000*		130*		...... no data	
BHUTAN	18,000*	0·300*		17*		...... no data	
CEYLON (1946)	25,332	6·657		263		895	25·5†

Note.—1951 figures from provisional Censuses; areas in Pakistan from new estimate by Survey of Pakistan; 1941 densities have been calculated to these areas and hence differ slightly from those given in 1941 Census.

[1] Formerly Major Provinces of British India; but 1941 figures adjusted to include merged states.
[2] Hyderabad and Mysore old princely states, rest Unions of such states.
[3] Old 'Chief Commissioner's Provinces' (Ajmer, Coorg, Delhi) or minor states now directly under Centre: Bhopal as Muslim-ruled in generally Hindu area, Vindhya Pradesh as backward Union proving 'unviable'; rest probably strategic (for details see O. H. K. Spate, "A Year of Change: Territorial Reorganisation in the Indian Union", *GJ* CXI (1948), 288–92; H. Furber, "The Unification of India, 1947–51", *Pacific Affairs* XXIV (1951), 352–71.
[4] Tribal areas in Assam. * Estimate. † 1931–46.

GENERAL NOTE FOR TABLES II–XIII

For limitations, see "The Nature of the Data", Ch. VIII, pp. 199–201 above.

Owing to the difficulty of getting consistent and comparable data since Partition, these Tables have been based mainly on *Estimates of Area and Yield of the Principal Crops in Undivided India, 1936–37 to 1945–46*, and *Abstract of Agricultural Statistics, 1943–44 to 1946–47*, both published by the Ministry of Agriculture, New Delhi. For most crops this is safe enough, subject to some scaling-up which does not seem to affect distributions seriously; while for more detailed break-down for mapping we must go back to the *1938–39–40 Agricultural Statistics*, as explained in fn. 23 to Ch. VIII. But for jute and cotton this is obviously not true, and an effort has been made to bring Tables XI and XII nearer to date, although completeness has not been attainable.

All areas in 1000 acres and outputs in 1000 tons, unless otherwise stated. 'States' are old Indian (princely) states as opposed to old British Indian Provinces; chief reporting states were Baroda, Gwalior, Hyderabad, and parts of Kashmir and the Rajputana and Central India Agencies in *India*; in Pakistan, Bahawalpur and Khairpur only, the latter not completely. For distribution of non-reporting areas, see Fig. 43. Figures for Provinces as they stood *before* mergers of states, unless otherwise stated.

TABLE II

CLASSIFICATION OF AREA, 1948–49

		1. Total	2. Forest	%	3. Not Avail. for Cultn.	%	4. Other Uncultd., excl. 5	%	5. Current Fallows	%	6. NSA	%
INDIA	(a)	581·1	87·0	15	93·1	16	98·2	17	63·0	11	243·8	42
	(b)	810·8		11		11·5		12		8		30
PAKISTAN	(c)	123·0	5·2	4	30·6	25	21·9	18	11·8	10	46·6	38
	(d)	241·4		2		13		9		4	47·3*	20
Total (a + c)		704·1	92·2	13	123·7	18	120·1	17	74·8	11	290·4	41

In million acres: (a) by Village Papers; (b) and (d) total geogl. area; (c) Provinces excl. Baluchistan but plus Bahawalpur; *Allowance made for known cultn. in Baluchistan and Khairpur; total NSA is 27·6% of (b + d). Cf. p. 202.

TABLE III

IRRIGATED AREA

A. *Irrigation and Sown Area, 1948–49*

	1. Total	2. NSA	3. Irrigated	4. 3 as % of 1	5. 3 as % of 2	6. Sown more than once	7. Total Sown Area
INDIA	581,143	243,832	46,963	8·1	19·3	33,547	277,379
PAKISTAN	123,025	46,585	20,278	16·5	43·5	7,979	54,564
Total	704,168	290,417	67,241	9·5	23·2	41,526	331,943
Pakistan % of total	17·5	16·0	30·2			19·2	16·4

TABLE III—(*Cont.*)

B. *Types of Irrigation, old Provinces only, 1945–46*

	Canal	Tank	Well	Other	Total	% of Total	Total as % of: TSA	NSA
AJMER-MERWARA .	—	14	102	2	118	0·3	27·0	27·4
ASSAM . . .	661	31	—	524	1,216	3·1	19·7	22·6
BIHAR . . .	1,660	1,500	807	986	5,153	13·2	22·3	29·5
BOMBAY . .	425	102	628	36	1,191	3·0	4·2	4·3
COORG . .	3	2	—	1	6	0·0	3·8	3·8
DELHI . . .	28	2	22	—	52	0·1	17·2	23·4
E PUNJAB . .	3,236	7	1,954	21	5,218	13·4	31·6	40·4
MADHYA PRADESH .	1,366	?	190	51	1,607	4·1	5·9	6·6
MADRAS . .	4,420	2,874	1,629	312	9,235	23·7	26·2	30·2
ORISSA . .	461	459	36	708	1,664	4·3	22·9	23·3
UTTAR PRADESH .	4,205	10	5,322	2,206	11,743	30·1	24·9	31·4
W BENGAL . .	422	999	16	403	1,840	4·7	17·3	19·3
Total *INDIA* .	16,887	6,000	10,706	5,250	39,043	100·0	20·0	22·7
E BENGAL . . (with Sylhet)					424	2·2		2·1
BALUCHISTAN .	......no data, mainly canal and karez......							
NWFP . .					962	4·9		43·0
SIND . . .					5,495	28·1		100·0
W PUNJAB . .					12,687	64·8		74·5
Total PAKISTAN					19,568	100·0		43·8

TABLE IV

AREAS UNDER MAIN CROP GROUPS, 1936–39 AND 1948–49

	Average 1936–37 to '38–39			1948–49		
	INDIA	PAKISTAN	TOTAL	TOTAL	INDIA	PAKISTAN
Main Foodgrains .	158,844	34,408	193,252	214,475 + 11·0%	174,220	40,255
Sugar . . .	3,276	537	3,813	4,443 + 16·5%	3,729	714
Main Oilseeds .	21,343	1,679	23,022	19,672 − 17·0%	17,888	1,784
Cotton[1] . .	20,969	3,596	24,565	13,414 − 45·4%	10,710	2,704
Jute[2] . . .	862	2,118	2,980	2,748 − 7·8%	871	1,877
Tea[3] . . .	747	87	834	855 =	782	73
Coffee[3] . . .	185	—	185	201 + 8·5%	201	—
Tobacco . .	902	352	1,254	1,085 − 13·5%	910	175

[1], [2], [3] Cf. Tables XI, XII, and XIII respectively.

| | Total Area by Village Papers | Forest | Foodgrains | | | | | Sugar |
			Rice	Wheat	Jowar and Bajra	Gram	All Food-grains	
AJMER. . .	1,561	47	—	27	151	20	360	1
ASSAM. . .	33,462	4,056	3,967	2	—	—	4,221	55
BIHAR . . .	44,326	6,612	9,738	1,186	140	1,482	19,779	381
BOMBAY . .	48,662	7,933	2,093	1,707	12,720	534	21,023	125
COORG . .	1,012	331	87	—	—	—	91	
DELHI . . .	363	—	—	51	82	88	251	2
E PUNJAB . .	22,964	769	436	3,334	2,734	4,117	12,621	308
MADHYA PRADESH	63,083	15,829	6,071	2,679	5,154	1,307	21,171	41
MADRAS . .	79,934	13,515	10,204	12	6,467	67	24,628	161
ORISSA . .	20,142	2,606	5,208	7	44	146	6,448	35
UTTAR PRADESH .	67,623	6,963	7,045	8,056	5,401	6,140	40,765	1,819
W BENGAL . .	18,797	1,695	7,964	118	6	275	8,933	67
Total INDIA	405,927	60,356	58,013	24,480	61,383	15,180	160,291	3,201
E PAKISTAN . .	34,201	3,047	20,394	84	2	216	n.d.	257
NWFP . .	8,583	353	—	1,087	177	216	n.d.	95
SIND . . .	30,202	716	1,420	1,248	1,238	454	n.d.	5
W PUNJAB . .	37,239	1,150	395	7,259	1,644	2,037	n.d.	266
Total PAKISTAN	110,225	5,266	22,709	9,678	3,061	2,923	39,948	623

TABLE VI

SELECTED CROPS AS PERCENTAGE OF NET SOWN AREA,
1936–39 AND 1948–49
(Old Provinces only for 1936–39)

| | INDIA | | PAKISTAN | |
	Avge 1936–37 to 38–39	1948–49	Avge 1936–37 to 38–39	1948–49
Rice . .	29·4	26·1	46·1	46·2
Wheat . .	10·2	8·3	21·1	23·2
Jowar . .	12·1	14·1	2·2	2·3
Gram . .	6·8	8·1	4·6	6·3
All Main Foodgrains .	72·6	71·4*	82·1	86·4
Sugar-cane .	1·8	1·5	1·2	1·5
Groundnuts .	3·2	3·4	. . . . .no data.	
All Main Oilseeds .	9·3	7·3	4·1	3·8
Cotton . .	6·7	4·4	8·0	5·8

* For *all* foodgrains, 88% (78% of Total Sown Area).

V
MARY, 1945–46
(inces only)

Ground-nuts	Other Oilseeds	Cotton	Fodder	Irrigated	NSA	Sown more than once	TSA	
—	27	9	9	118	431	44	475	AJMER
—	344	36	5	1,216	5,372	790	6,163	ASSAM
—	1,458	39	64	5,153	17,506	5,587	23,093	BIHAR
1,418	812	1,165	3,074	1,191	27,558	834	28,391	BOMBAY
—	—	—	—	6	156	—	156	COORG
—	4	—	35	52	222	80	302	DELHI
61	500	385	2,398	5,218	12,904	3,621	16,524	E PUNJAB
585	1,665	2,956	456	1,607	24,302	2,970	27,272	MADHYA PRADESH
4,166	1,525	1,611	463	9,235	30,542	4,735	35,278	MADRAS
20	288	9	13	1,664	6,453	801	7,254	ORISSA
168	640	195	1,830	11,743	37,407	9,319	46,726	UTTAR PRADESH
—	249	—	26	1,840	9,552	1,126	10,678	W BENGAL
6,418	7,512	6,405	8,372	39,043	172,405	27,907	202,312	*INDIA*
n.d.		91	n.d.	424	19,932	5,679	25,611	E PAKISTAN
n.d.	1,427	9	n.d.	962	2,243	432	2,675	NWFP
n.d.		826	n.d.	5,495	5,495	773	6,268	SIND
n.d.		1,947	n.d.	12,687	17,028	2,522	19,550	W PUNJAB
n.d.	1,427	2,873	n.d.	19,568	44,698	9,406	54,104	PAKISTAN

TABLE VII

MAIN FOODGRAINS, 1948–49

	INDIA		PAKISTAN	
	Area	Output	Area	Output
Rice . .	63,528	22,597	21,545	8,429
Wheat .	20,350	5,650	10,824	4,103
Jowar .	34,334	5,022	1,092	213
Bajra .	16,572	2,171	2,299	373
Maize .	6,949	2,072	965	412
Ragi .	5,580	1,465	—	—
Barley .	7,605	2,206	611	179
Gram .	19,302	4,535	2,919	800
Total .	174,220*	45,718	40,255	14,509

* Excludes *c.* 41 m. ac. "other foodgrains and pulses".

TABLE VIII

NUTRITIONAL VALUES OF SELECTED FOODGRAINS

	Moisture %	Protein %	Fats %	Mineral Matter %	Carbo-hydrates %	Vitamins units/100 grams AA	B	Iron mgs/100 grams	Calories per 100 grams
Wheat .	12·8	11·8	1·45	1·5	71·3	108	230	5·3	345
Rice (1) .	12·2	8·5	0·35	0·7	78·3	—	100	2·75	350
Rice (2) .	13·0	6·85	0·55	0·5	79·1	—	26	1·0	349
Jowar .	11·9	10·4	1·9	1·8	74·0	136	—	6·2	353
Bajra .	12·4	11·6	5·0	2·65	67·1	220	110	8·8	360
Ragi .	13·05	7·1	1·3	2·2	76·3	70	140	5·4	345
Millets (minor)	11·75	9·55	2·75	3·5	64·9	trace	100–300	6·7	320
Maize . ("tender")	79·4	4·3	0·5	0·65	15·2	42	—	0·7	82
Oatmeal .	10·7	13·55	7·6	1·8	62·9	trace	325	3·8	374

Note.—Rice (1) home-pounded in mortar, (2) factory milled; minor millets average of six (low carbohydrate due to high fibre content, average 7·5%). Cf. especially bajra and oatmeal.

Source: *Health Bulletin No. 23*, Nutrition Research Laboratories, Coonoor, Madras (1937), 18–21.

TABLE IX

"NUTRITIONAL DENSITY", 1941–42

(Old Major Provinces only)

	Net Sown Area (nearest 100 sq mls) All crops	Foodgrains	Population to sq ml NSA All crops	Foodgrains	Area sown more than once (nearest 100 sq mls)
Assam . . .	7,900	5,700	946	1,241	1,000
Bihar . . .	28,100	23,500	1,286	1,551	7,200
Bombay . .	43,500	27,000	479	772	1,000
E Punjab .	18,200	15,000	692	841	3,400
Madhya Pradesh .	38,600	23,000	487	731	2,600
Madras . .	49,500	30,500	997	1,621	7,500
Orissa . .	9,200	8,200	949	1,065	1,000
Uttar Pradesh .	56,500	48,000	974	1,146	11,500
W Bengal .	13,200	12,500	1,606	1,616	1,700
Total *INDIA* .	266,100	193,400	858	1,171	37,100
E Bengal[1] . .	28,700	27,900	1,458	1,500	7,200
NWFP . .	3,500	3,300	868	921	700
Sind . . .	8,300	6,500	546 }621	698 }853	1,100
W Punjab .	25,500	17,600	620	895	3,400
Total PAKISTAN	66,000	55,300	985	1,179	12,400

[1] Including Pakistani Sylhet.

TABLE X

MAIN OILSEEDS, 1948–49

| | INDIA | | PAKISTAN | | |
	Area	Output	Area	Output	
Sesamum . .	3,197	335	177	29	⎫
Groundnut .	8,372	2,901*	....no data....		⎬ Edible
Rape and Mustard	2,064	735	1,530	265	⎭
Linseed . .	2,984	423	74	12	
Castor . .	1,271	108	3	under 500 tons	

* Nuts in shell.
  In addition there were in *India c.* 1,454,000 ac. of coconut palms and
2,719,000 of other oilseeds.

TABLE XI

COTTON AREA, YIELD, AND OUTPUT, 1945–46 and 1948–49

| | Area | | Yield per acre, lbs 45–46 | Output, 1000 bales of 392 lbs. | |
	45–46	48–49		45–46	48–49
BOMBAY . . .	1,165	2,122	62	180	280
MADHYA PRADESH .	2,956	3,053	72	535	346
MADRAS . . .	1,611	1,611	90	361	342
HYDERABAD .	2,155	2,048	48	261	234
BOMBAY STATES . .	904	*	70	159	*
BARODA . . .	452	*	80	90	*
OTHER AREAS .	2,117	1,854	102	538	565
Total *INDIA* .	11,360	10,710	75	2,124	1,767
SIND . . .	826	719	185	382	295
W PUNJAB . .	1,947	1,631	165	805	554
BAHAWALPUR . .	390	259	180	175	107
OTHER AREAS .	145	95	122	44	33
Total PAKISTAN	3,308	2,704	170	1,406	989
Pak. %ge of All-India .	22·5	18·5		39·8	35·9

* Included in Bombay.
  Note that 'other areas'—mainly E Bengal—pull down the Pakistani average yield; in *India*
the converse is the case, 'other areas' being mainly E Punjab and Madhya Bharat—i.e. at least
approaching W Pakistan conditions.

TABLE XII

JUTE AREA AND OUTPUT, 1939–40 TO 1951–52

	Avge 1939–40 to 1943–44	44–45	45–46	49–50	51–52
A. Area					
ASSAM . .	266	169	155	272	334
BIHAR . . .	245	163	159	288	487
ORISSA . .	25	24	20	47	161
MADRAS . .	?	19	33	?	?
UTTAR PRADESH .	?	4	4	60	68
W BENGAL[1] . .	341	224	233	492	900
Total *INDIA*	877	603	604	1,159	1,900
E PAKISTAN . .	2,517	1,524	1,855	1,599	1,799
ALL-INDIA	3,394	2,127	2,459	2,758	3,699
B. Output, 1000 bales of 400 lbs					
INDIA . .	1,877	1,164	1,459	3,117	
PAKISTAN .	7,005	5,025	6,332	3,332*	6,331
ALL-INDIA	8,882	6,189	7,791	6,449	

[1] Including Cooch Behar and Tripura.

* Abnormally low owing to floods. The general superiority of yields in E Pakistan is obvious.

The somewhat fragmentary nature of Table XII is due to the difficulty of extracting comparable and consistent figures from the official agencies; e.g. no information is available as to the results of announced jute programmes in Travancore-Cochin and even Bombay, and the *Indian* figures may be slightly understated in consequence.

TABLE XIII

TEA AND COFFEE, AREA AND OUTPUT, 1948–49

	TEA		*COFFEE*	
	Area	Output (1000 lbs)	Area	Output (1000 lbs.)
ASSAM . .	389	314,357	—	—
MADRAS . .	56	45,312	50	11,195
W BENGAL .	209	166,136	—	—
COORG . .	—	—	41	12,200
MYSORE . .	4	3,699	100	24,502
COCHIN ⎱ TRAVANCORE ⎰ .	91	41,790	9	1,195
TRIPURA . .	11	3,678	—	—
OTHER AREAS .	22	13,736	1	?
Total *INDIA*	782	585,030	201	490,920
E PAKISTAN .	73	45,000	—	—
ALL-INDIA	855	630,030	201	490,920

TABLE XIV

MAJOR DEVELOPMENT PROJECTS

		Power, 1000 kWs	Irrigation, 1000 ac.	Remarks
A. INDIA. (Only schemes for more than 100,000 kW or 200,000 ac. irrigation, and more or less definite, are included.)				
[1]Kosi	Bihar	1,800	2,000	Plus 1 m. ac. irrigation in Nepal
Gandak	,,	?	600	
Ghataprabha	Bombay	—	120	
Kakrapara	,,	?	560	Tapti valley
Kalinadi	,,	350	—	} Apparently in abeyance
[1]Koyna	,,	250	?	
Peringulkuthu	Cochin	200	—	
Bhakra-Nangal	E Punjab	400	3,915	In hand; 96,000 kW by 1956?
Tungabhadra	Hyderabad and Madras	140	900	Nearing completion
Wainganga	Madhya Pradesh	850	?	Shelved?
[1]Kistna-Penner	Madras	—	3,100	
[1]Ramapadasagar	,,	1,000	2,350	Shelved?
Bhavani	,,	—	200	
Pykara III	,,	212	—	
Machkund	Madras and Orissa	104	—	Completion Stage I (35,500 kW) expected in 1952–53
Mahatma Gandhi	Mysore	120	—	Jog Falls; 48,000 kW already installed
Hirakud	Orissa	259	1,095	Stage I of Mahanadi project; with Tikarpara and Naraj sites 353,000 kW
[1]Pipri	Uttar Pradesh	230	4,000	Power only envisaged as yet
Gogra	,, ,,	?	300	
Nayar	,, ,,	233	—	Abandonded?
Sarda Extension	,, ,,	—	300	
[1]Yamuna	,, ,,	257	—	
Damodar	Bihar and W Bengal	274	1,325	Advanced
Mor	W Bengal	—	600	
B. PAKISTAN. (All projects.)				
Dargai	NWFP	?	—	
Malakand Extension	,,	10	—	
Warsak	,,	125	60	
Mianwali	W Punjab	70	—	Started before Partition
Rasul	,,	22	—	Started before Partition; power will be used for reclaiming waterlogged irrigation
Thal	,,	—	693	Or 1 m. ac.?
Rohri, etc.	Sind	23	2,800	Advanced?
Karachi Extension	,,	22	—	Thermal
Karnaphuli	E Bengal	160	—	In hand
Chittagong Extension	,,	5	—	Diesel

[1] "In advanced stage of investigation" in November 1950, but omitted from Five Year Plan. This table has been compiled from information kindly supplied by the Central Board for Irrigation and (by permission) from Professor C. N. Vakil's *Economic Consequences of Divided India* (1950). It should be noted that policy in relation to any given scheme is subject to fluctuation, and quasi-official statistics vary a good deal: the figures above represent the order of things rather than precise absolutes.

TABLE XV

A. OCCUPATIONAL DISTRIBUTION OF POPULATION, 1931

(Per 10,000 total population)

		% of occupied population	
Earners and working dependants	4391	100	
Cultivation (incl. landlords and agents)	2766	63·0	
Plantation cultivation	47	1·07	
Forestry, etc.	9	—	65·39% agrarian
Stock-raising	100	2·3	
Raising of insects, etc. (silk worms, lac)	1	—	
Fishing and hunting	24	—	
Mining	10	—	
Industry (including crafts, etc.)	438	9·99	
Transport	67	1·53	
Trade	226	5·15	
Forces	24	—	
Administration	28	—	
Professions (including religion)	66	1·50	
Living on income	6	—	
Domestic service	311	7·06	
Insufficiently described (mainly traders, clerks, labourers)	222	5·05	
Unproductive (convicts, beggars, prostitutes, etc.)	46	1·07	
Non-working dependants	5609		
	10,000		

B. LIVELIHOOD CATEGORIES AND CLASSES, 1951 CENSUS

(*India* only)

	Millions	*% of category*	*% of total pop.*
Owner-cultivators*	167	67·1	46·8
Tenant-cultivators	32	⎱12·8	9·0
Labourers	45	18·1	12·6
Landlords, etc.	5	2·0	1·4
Total agricultural	249	100·0	69·8
Production other than cultivation	38	35·2	10·6
Commerce	21	19·5	5·9
Transport	6	5·5	1·7
All others	43	39·8	12·0
Total non-agricultural	108	100·0	30·2

* "Land is deemed to be 'owned' if it is held on any tenure which carries with it the right of permanent occupancy for purposes of cultivation."

TABLE XVI

MINERAL PRODUCTION

(1000 tons or other units stated)

	INDIA			PAKISTAN		
	1944	1949		1944	1949	
Antimony	nil	n.d.	D	1	0	A; Chitral 100%
Barytes	15	16(a)	A; Madras 90%	nil	nil	D
Bauxite	12	19	A; Madhya Pradesh[1]	nil	nil	D
Chromite	19		B; Bihar, Mysore	21	17	A; Baluchistan 100%
Coal	24,892	31,695	B; NE Peninsula 90%	204	338	C; Baluchistan 50%; Punjab 50%
Copper	326	326	C; Bihar 100%	nil	nil	D
Gold	188 (oz.)	164	?; Mysore 99%	nil	nil	D; (1938 4 oz.l)
Gypsum	66	51(b)	C; Rajasthan 50%	18	14	A; Salt Range 80%
Ilmenite	100	308	A; Travancore 100%	nil		D
Iron	2,364	2,809	A; NE Peninsula 98%	nil		D
Magnesite	41	91	A; Salem 100%	nil		D
Manganese	371	646	A; NE Peninsula 95%	nil		D
Mica (exports)	72 (cwt.)	326	A; Hazaribagh 55–60%	nil		D
Monazite	2	n.d.	A; Travancore 100% of world	nil		D
Oil	82,000 (gall.)	66,711	C; Assam 100%	15,000	34,589	C; Punjab 100%
Salt	n.d.	c. 2,600	C; Rajasthan; brine Bombay, Madras	n.d.	334(b)	A; Salt Range; brine Karachi[2]
Sulphur	nil	nil	D	12	10(a)	A; Baluchistan 100%

[1] But probably now outstripped by Lohardaga (Bihar).
[2] But E Pakistan = D.
(a)—1946, (b)—1948.
NE Peninsula—area between Hazaribagh Range and Orissa Hills.
A, normal export; B, adequate for consumption; C, import necessary; D, consumption (if any) all imported.

TABLE
INDUSTRIAL INSTALLATIONS AND EMPLOY-

	INDIA			
	Factories	*Workers (1000s)*	*Workers per Factory*	*Workers as % total Workers*[1]
I. TEXTILES . . .	1656	1193·9	719	·40·7
Clothing . . .	6	11·5	1919	1
Cotton . . .	926	782·4	849	65·5
Jute	89	307·4	3454	25·7
Silk	144	18·0	125	1·5
Wool (incl. carpets) .	70	39·0	571	3·3
II. ENGINEERING . .	1734	429·4	248	14·5
Railshops . .	175	129·6	740	30
III. METALLURGY . .	347	130·4	376	4·4
Foundries . .	122	9·4	77	7
Iron and Steel . .	38	94·3	2482	72
Oil Refineries . .	2	2·3	1150	1·8
IV. FOOD . . .	3749	360·4	96	12·2
Rice Mills . .	1276	50·4	40	14
Sugar . . .	170	97·3	572	27
Tea	868	64·1	74	18
Tobacco . . .	298	41·0	137	11
V. CHEMICALS . . .	1009	115·2	114	3·9
Bones, etc. . .	36	3·0	83	2·6
Chemicals . . .	105	22·0	2095	19
Dyeing, etc. . .	64	12·9	200	11·2
Matches . . .	127	17·5	138	15
Oil Mills . . .	467	35·0	75	30·4
Paint . . .	29	3·7	127	3·2
Soap . . .	4	4·4	1100	4
VI. PAPER, ETC. . . .	616	72·0	117	2·5
Paper . . .	35	22·2	634	30·8
Printing . . .	535	45·7	85	63·5
VII. WOOD, STONE, GLASS .	1035	142·0	137	5·0
Bricks, etc. . .	259	27·7	107	19·5
Cement . . .	87	33·5	385	23·5
Glass . . .	169	30·2	179	21·2
Stone Dressing .	207	16·2	78	11·4
Saw Mills . .	39	7·8	200	5·5
VIII. HIDES AND SKINS .	294	38·7	132	1·3
Shoes, etc. . .	34	21·2	625	54·8
Tanneries . .	220	14·8	67	38·2
IX. GINS AND PRESSES .	2123	141·5	67	5·0
Cotton . . .	1960	123·1	63	86·4
Jute	27	8·8	326	6·2
X. MISCELLANEOUS . .	600	312·1	520	10·5
Ordnance . .	60	164·7	2785	52·7
Rubber . . .	41	12·6	307	4

[1] For the major groups (Textiles, Engineering, etc.) this figure is the %age of total factory workers; for selected individual industries (clothing, cotton, etc.) it is the %age of workers in the major group. Both perennial and seasonal factories included in totals. Figures of numbers of factories and workers from Vakil, *op. cit.*, 286–87.

[2] Vakil gives no foundries to Pakistan, but 49 'miscellaneous' metal factories. It seems safe to assume that these are in fact mostly foundries and small metal shops.

XVII

MENT IN *INDIA* AND PAKISTAN, 1945

PAKISTAN

Factories	Workers (*1000s*)	Workers per Factory	Workers as % total Workers[1]	
46	32·1	675	15·5	TEXTILES
3	11·0	3673	34·4	Clothing
14	19·55	1325	61·1	Cotton
—	—	—	—	Jute
7	0·12	17	0·4	Silk
1	0·18	181	0·6	Wool (incl. carpets)
278	52·6	193	25·5	ENGINEERING
33	25·2	765	4·8	Railshops
51	4·1	80	2·0	METALLURGY
49	3·0	61	75·0	Foundries[2]
—	—	—	—	Iron and Steel
2	1·1	537	25·0	Oil Refineries
467	29·8	64	14·5	FOOD
166	3·7	22	12·4	Rice Mills
11	4·0	364	13·4	Sugar
171	13·6	79	45·6	Tea
—	—	—	—	Tobacco
56	4·8	86	2·3	CHEMICALS
3	0·65	215	13·5	Bones, etc.
10	1·1	111	20·8	Chemicals
—	—	—	—	Dyeing, etc.
6	0·43	72	9·0	Matches
26	1·8	71	38·5	Oil Mills
4	0·33	84	6·0	Paint
1	0·05	53	1·0	Soap
57	4·8	84	2·3	PAPER, ETC.
—	—	—	—	Paper
54	4·5	83	93·9	Printing
65	10·5	162	5·2	WOOD, STONE, GLASS
2	0·11	58	1·1	Bricks, etc.
8	3·3	408	31·5	Cement
2	0·6	238	5·5	Glass
19	3·9	207	37·1	Stone Dressing
1	0·04·	42	0·4	Saw Mills
8	2·2	278	1·1	HIDES AND SKINS
2	0·08	40	3·6	Shoes, etc.
3	1·95	651	87·9	Tanneries
353	39·0	110	19·0	GINS AND PRESSES
296	31·2	105	79·5	Cotton
51	7·4	189	19·0	Jute
33	26·2	793	12·6	MISCELLANEOUS
15	20·9	1395	80·4	Ordnance
5	0·6	119	2·3	Rubber

Significant points on this table are: (i) the general small scale of units, especially in Pakistan; (ii) the large size of Pakistani units in clothing, cotton milling, and tanning—industries which took on factory organisation early for Pakistan, but late for India as a whole, so that they profited by early experience; (iii) the large proportion of Pakistani workers in seasonal presses—19% against India's 5, another index of immaturity. Progress in Pakistan since Partition has been mainly in light-metal trades, glass, and leather.

TABLE XVIII

FACTORIES AND WORKERS IN *INDIA* AND PAKISTAN, 1945

A. Numbers

	FACTORIES			WORKERS (*1000s*)		
	Perennial	Seasonal	Total	Perennial	Seasonal	Total
INDIA . . .	9,734	3,529	13,263	2,645·3	290·4	2,935·7
PAKISTAN . .	832	582	1,414	148·1	58·0	206·1
ALL-INDIA .	10,566	4,111	14,677	2,793·4	348·4	3,141·8

B. Ratios

	INDIA	PAKISTAN		INDIA	PAKISTAN
% of all factories	90·4	9·6	*Average workers per unit:*		
% of all workers	93·1	6·9	All factories .	221	146
% of factories perennial .	74·4	58·9	Perennial factories .	272	178
% of workers perennial .	90·1	71·9	Seasonal factories .	82	99

Note.—Seasonal factories are mainly cotton and jute gins and presses, and some rice mills; a high proportion of seasonal factories is thus an index of industrial backwardness.

TABLE XIX

PRODUCTION IN SELECTED *INDIAN* INDUSTRIES

	1938–39	1944–45	1947	1948	1949	1950	% change 1938–39 to 1950
Cotton Yarn, million lbs. . .	1303	1651	1314	1445	1359	1168	− 10·5
Cotton Cloth, million yards	4494*	4726	3816	4319	3904	3642	− 18·9
Jute Manufactures . .	1221	1097	1052	1035	1040	836	− 31·5
Paper	59	100	93	98	104	110	86·4
Pig-iron. . . .	1576	1303	1320	1405	1517	1528	− 3·0
Steel . . .	977	1264	893	854	920	986	0·9
Sulphuric Acid . .	25·5	39	60	80	99·5	102	292·2
Cement	1512	2044	1441	1500	2100	2700	78·6
Sugar	668	1122†	925	1075	1000	976	46·1
Soda Ash . . .	. . no data . .		13·6	29·2	17·9	43·8	

All in 1000 tons except Cotton Yarn and Cloth. The increase in cement production is especially notable, as some large plants went to Pakistan.

* 1941–42.   † 1943–44.

TABLE XX
RAILWAYS AND ROADS IN *INDIA* AND PAKISTAN, 1947

A. *Route Miles of:*

	Broad	Metre	Narrow	Total Railway
INDIA	15,639·5	14,956·6	3,563·3	34,159·4
PAKISTAN	5,098·2	1,394·3	489·3	6,981·8
ALL-INDIA	20,737·7	16,350·9	4,052·6	41,141·2

B. Indian *Railway Working, 1948–49*

Passengers, millions	1,094	Freight tons, millions	.	78
Passenger miles, millions	38,765	Net ton-miles, millions	.	21,823
Average journey, miles	32	Average ton/haul, miles	.	280

C. *Road Mileage:*

	Metalled	Unmetalled	Total	Known unmotorable
INDIA	85,788	153,293	239,081	57,575
PAKISTAN	9,098	43,967	53,065	48,119
ALL-INDIA	94,886	197,260	292,146	105,694 (36%)

Source: Vakil, 402, 413, 414.

TABLE XXI
SHARE OF SELECTED COUNTRIES IN *INDIAN* TRADE
(Percentage of Value)

		United Kingdom	Burma	USA	Japan	Pakistan
Average 1909–10 to 1913–14	Imp.	62·8	—	3·1	2·5	—
	Exp.	25·1	—	7·5	7·5	—
Average 1914–15 to 1918–19	Imp.	56·5	—	7·0	10·4	—
	Exp.	31·1	—	11·9	11·2	—
Average 1919–20 to 1923–24	Imp.	57·6	—	8·5	6·9	—
	Exp.	24·2	—	12·0	13·3	—
1938–39	Imp.	30·5	16·0	6·4	10·1	—
	Exp.	34·3	6·6	8·4	7·5	—
1949–50	Imp.	24·9	2·1	14·7	?	7·2
	Exp.	34·1	6·3	9·1	?	8·3*

* In 1948–49 Pakistan supplied 15·8% of *India's* imports and took 16·4% of exports.

TABLE XXII
CHANGES IN EXPORT/IMPORT STRUCTURE
(Percentages)

EXPORTS	1920–21	28–29	36–37	44–45	48–49	49–50
Food	18	21	21	21	21	24·5
Raw Materials	45	52	53	26	23·5	22
Manufactures	36	27	26	51·5	55	53
IMPORTS						
Food	11	18	9	9	24	21
Raw Materials	5	9	16	58	31	30
Manufactures	84	73	75	32	44	49

Note.—Includes Burma to 1936–37; 1944–45, peak of war industry; 1948–50, *Indian Union* only.

TABLE XXIII

INDIA: MAJOR ITEMS OF FOREIGN TRADE, 1949–50

(In million rupees, excluding items of value under Rs.10 m.
Rs.1 m. = £75,000 approx., or more precisely £74,710.)

Imports		Exports	
Grain, pulses, flour	1338·5	Jute goods	1269·8
Machinery & millwork	1055·0	Cotton goods	743·1
Cotton, raw	632·4	Tea	724·4
Oils, mineral	583·9	Leather	209·6
Vehicles	234·6	Spices	191·8
Cotton goods	184·1	Cotton, raw	188·2
Metal goods, non-ferrous	181·6	Jute, raw	167·4
Drugs & chemicals	161·3	Oil seeds	148·0
Hardware, cutlery, etc.	159·0	Tobacco	119·6
Iron & steel goods	137·0	Hides & skins, raw	89·2
Electrical goods	130·2	Lac, etc.	89·2
Dyes, etc.	111·0	Oils, vegetable	87·9
Paper, incl. stationery	97·1	Fruits & vegetables	79·2
Provisions	72·5	Quarry products	73·3
Fruit & Vegetables	69·1	Ores, excl. Mn	71·6
Woollen goods	59·7	Coir goods	68·5
Spices	35·4	Manganese ore	58·5
Wool, raw	30·3	Coal	42·1
Wool & timber	28·3	Wool, raw	37·1
Quarry products	27·1	Woollen goods	36·6
Glass & earthenware	25·1	Drugs & chemicals	19·5
Tobacco	24·1	Fish	19·1
Seeds, incl. oil seeds	19·6	Hemp, raw	17·5
Gums & resins	12·9	Iron & steel goods	17·0
Arms & ammunition	12·5	Paraffin wax	15·7
Liquor	10·8	Dyes, etc.	14·9
		Coffee	13·0
		Hardware, cutlery	10·5

Total imports were Rs.5943·4 m., exports Rs.4720·7 m., excluding treasure in both cases. It will be seen that production goods account for about a quarter of the imports, textiles for over two-fifths of the exports.

TABLE XXIV

PAKISTAN: SEABORNE TRADE, 1949–50

(In million rupees. Note that Pakistani Rs.1 m. = £105,000 approx., or more precisely £104,166.)

Imports		Exports	
Cotton goods	252·0	Cotton, raw	355·0
Cotton twist & yarn	163·6	Jute, raw	297·7
Machinery & millwork	82·5	Tea	49·1
Vehicles	61·9	Wool, raw	31·6
Metals & ores	52·2	Hides & skins, raw	29·8
Drugs & chemicals	38·7	Seeds, cotton	4·0
Provisions	34·3	All other goods	51·8
Oils, mineral	30·8		
Tobacco	30·0	Total	819·1
Instruments, etc.	19·9		
Dye & Tan-stuffs	19·5		
Rubber goods	17·0		
All other goods	311·6		
Total	1114·0		

It will be seen that production goods (machinery and instruments) account for under 10% of imports, while no less than 83·5% of the value of Pakistan's exports consist of raw fibres.

PART 4

THE FACE OF THE LAND

CHAPTER XIII

THE REGIONS DIVISION OF THE SUB-CONTINENT

I. BASIS OF THE DIVISION

THE independent pioneer work of Baker and Stamp[1] resulted in a remarkably close agreement on a working regional division of India. Agreement on the main outlines is not perhaps surprising, the broad fundamentals are clear enough; but in detail the problem is by no means simple, especially if strict delimitation based on one master-principle is attempted. Indeed this ideal is unattainable. Structure is the most obvious guide, but it is clear that in an area like the Indo-Gangetic Plains it is of little help, since it is hardly too much to say that there is no real physical boundary in them from end to end, except local ones between *bet* and *doab*, *khadar* and *bhangar*, which may mark off sub-divisions but are in practice useless as a basis for regional description on the sub-continental scale. Yet the landscape and life of Bengal are obviously greatly different from those of Sind, imperceptible as may be the gradations between these extremes. Boundaries must be had, and in the absence of strong physical lines climate may be accepted as a guide, though obviously in an open plain climatic transitions are also inevitably gradual.

There are also difficult areas with strongly differentiated topography but with affinities far from clear, e.g. the whole great triangle between the Aravallis, the Vindhya-Kaimur scarp, and the Ganges alluvium. A mechanical but real difficulty lies in the fact that some definite regions, such as the Siwaliks and other sub-Himalayan zones, are ribbons hundreds of miles long and only a few miles wide. Some sort of arbitrary splitting-up is essential here, and in practice a semi-political grouping across the regional trend is as convenient as any: the avenues of human activity run transversely. The difficulties involved in trying to adhere closely to physical criteria may be instanced by Dehra Dun and Hardwar, obviously closely associated and yet separated by one of the primary divisions, that between the mountain wall and the plains.

The rather empirical divisions of Baker and Stamp were criticised by Pithawalla of Karachi, who in turn sacrificed too much on the altar of a rigid physiographical uniformity.[2] His accompanying map, however, was not always consistent with his text, and there were some bad anomalies, such as the treatment of the entire Irrawaddy basin as a single unit of the

---

[1] J. N. L. Baker, *Geography* XIV (1928), 447–55; L. D. Stamp, *ibid.*, 502–06.
[2] *JMGA* XIV (1939), 213–28.

Extra-Peninsular Mountains, while nearer home some of his boundaries in the plains between Indus and Ganges seem very confused. Pithawalla again was strongly criticised by Kazi S. Ahmad of Lahore, and others,[3] and later submitted a revised scheme meeting some of the objections.[4] Ahmad's own proposals seem in the broad quite sound, though Pithawalla rightly queries the lack of any hierarchical order, which results in the great un-differentiated mass of the Himalayas and the small sub-montane *chos* area in the Punjab ranking equally as regions—surely an example of local knowledge getting out of hand.

Typical of the rather verbalistic approach to the problem is the disagreement between Pithawalla and Ahmad on the Peninsular littorals. Ahmad objects to the standard three-fold division, claiming that it "may be geologically correct but is not desirable from the physiographic point of view as the peninsular area includes two quite different regions, Coastal lowlands and Deccan plateau." He states that "according to relief" there are four, not three, divisions, the coastal lowlands forming a division of the same value as the other three; but it is not really open to him to base this new division on relief alone since (apart from the fact that physiography and relief are not synonyms) he criticises Pithawalla from a structural point of view. Moreover if his argument be admitted there are not three or four grand divisions but five, since the En and the Wn littorals differ in almost every respect, including relief and structure. There is obviously no end to this sort of fission: Ahmad's view (as his omission of hierarchy suggests) appears not to consider sufficiently that the heavens themselves, and surely the earth as well, "observe degree, priority, and place." But it is perhaps less unrealistic than Pithawalla's curiously infelicitous description of the littorals as "shore-facies" of his Deccan Trap and Sn Plateau provinces—a distinct retrogression from his earlier views.

Physiography is certainly a criterion of first importance, but it is at least highly premature for Pithawalla to claim that "unscientific notions about the so-called 'natural' divisions of India have been discarded, and the idea of limiting the geographer, in a precise and specific manner, to geomorphological considerations in the first place, while producing the chief divisions, has found favour. Over such scientific and logical divisions of the country, all matters relating to climate, natural vegetation, and even human settlement must drape themselves completely and to the satisfaction of all other advocates of allied sciences." It is sufficient answer to this high-flown dogmatism to assert roundly that any *a priori* scheme (which is what the insistence on one-criterion precision amounts to—not that Pithawalla is always precise!) is not likely to be logical and scientific, that other factors

---

[3] *IGJ* XVI (1941), 257–67, and XVII (1942), 67–74.

[4] *Science and Culture* (Calcutta) VII, No. 11 (May 1942). I have not been able to procure this and Prof. Pithawalla was unable to send me a copy; but from other publications it seems unlikely that it could materially alter the views expressed above.

are not so obliging as to drape themselves in accordance with our preconceived desires, and that the *practising* regional geographer cannot bind himself in advance to so rigid a statute. Our study is far too rich, varied, and subtle to be tied down easily by rule and line.

Structure is the first factor to be consulted, but climatic and positional factors can never be ignored with impunity. We may discount the metaphysical dubiety which surrounds the concept of the region; for practical purposes regions exist, and if they did not they would have to be invented to obtain manageable units of study. But rigid definition is impossible, and even a modest precision will take years of detailed study.

Above all, it must ever be remembered that "in a large country like India, it would perhaps be impossible to choose factors which have a universal application, but understanding is more important than classification".[5] It is of course true that some preliminary cutting-out is necessary before a start can be made, but this can be only a first empirical approximation to facilitate the local spadework without which no precision can be gained. This is what has hitherto been lacking in Indian geography: the rough outlines are clear enough, but many more regional studies, and also studies of the sub-continental distribution of specific phenomena, will be needed before that division which satisfies the greatest number of criteria, and does least violence to any one of the fundamentals, can be drawn. We must delimit our regions before we study them, certainly; but after they have been studied in detail it will be suspicious if we find they have fitted with mechanical convenience into our preconceived scheme. Nor, considering the immense totality of the phenomena, distributed perhaps with correlation but hardly ever with coincidence, can we hope to escape doubtful affiliations and overlaps. After all, even in political geography there are frontier zones as well as boundary lines, and in this sphere the most meticulous efforts at precise definition are made. Nature will make no such concessions.

Any serious division at this stage, therefore, cannot be more than a reconnaissance, and this avowed empiricism may well shock purists. In fact some of the 'regions' listed below—e.g. the upper Mahanadi basin—are simply what is left over when more definite units have been sieved out: "though ... regions exist, it by no means follows that a whole continent can be divided up into well-marked areas." [6] Although the most constantly recurring factor will be structure, the division cannot be exclusively based on any one touchstone—"understanding is more important than classification". Moreover, while theoretically the three-fold division is paramount, as a matter of working convenience certain regional groupings—essentially positional or even political—are adopted in the following chapters, bringing

---

[5] G. Kuriyan, *IGJ* XVII (1942), 71.
[6] Ll. Rodwell Jones and P. W. Bryan, *North America* (9th ed., 1950), 41.

the treatment of regions belonging to two or even three of the primary regions into juxtaposition: thus the hills of Assam are treated with the plains, since the two cannot be intelligibly treated separately without much repetition and cross-reference. After all, regions *are* so juxtaposed in nature, on the map, and in human activity.

II. THE REGIONAL DIVISION

The regional scheme set forth below is empirical, having been arrived at in the actual process of writing the regional descriptions. The credentials of each region are set out in the text, and no attempt is made to justify the division here. Obviously many regions and sub-regions might be further divided, and some of the minor units listed are not treated in the text under separate heads. Hierarchy has been kept in mind, but can obviously be only approximate, since a ridge which might rank as a sub-region in the Peninsula would be hardly more than a feature in the Himalayas; variations in geomorphological texture and intensity of human activity compel variations of scale.

It would be fascinating and instructive to attempt a detailed division in Unstead's terms, but this is obviously a task for the regional monographer working in India. However, some of the more significant stows and features found within the minor regions (which correspond approximately to Unstead's 'tracts') are indicated.

The order of the list is not strictly adhered to in the text; thus the Wn Borderlands and the Indus Plains are juxtaposed, which has the advantage of bringing all W Pakistan in one place; and it would obviously be absurd to treat Assam in three places—as part of the Mountain Rim, of the Indo-Gangetic Plains, and (for the Shillong Plateau) of the Peninsular Block.

This scheme is tentative, but with 35 regions of the first order (under the three macro-regions, and excluding islands), 74 of the second order, and about 225 subdivisions of these, it may fairly claim to represent a refinement on previous divisions.

Abbreviations:

Hs	. Hills	Ss	. Stows	
P	. Pass	Fs	. Features	
pl	. plateau	@	. transitional	
rs	. ranges	Ø	. outlier	
vy	. valley	**Delhi**	. urban area receiving separate treatment	

A. The Mountain Rim

I. Baluchistan

   1. *Northern Ranges:*
      (a) Sulaiman r
      (b) Loralai-Zhob arcs
      (c) Toba-Khakar rs
   @ (d) Quetta node: Ss—Quetta basin, Harnai and Bolan Ps, Khalifat massif

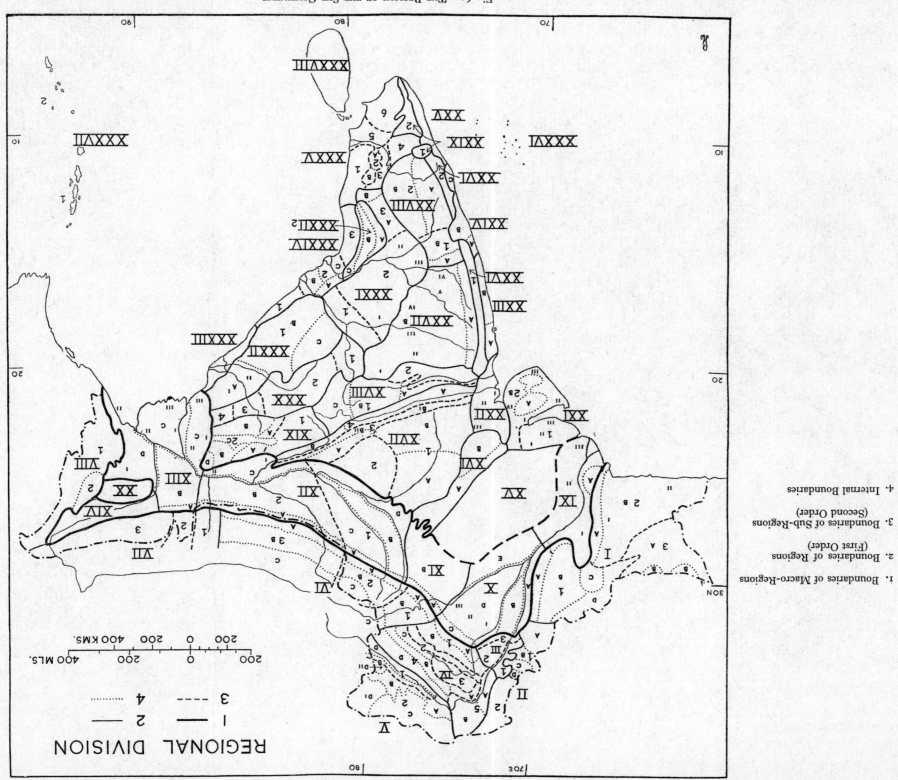

REGIONAL DIVISION

400 MLS. 200   0   200
400 KMS. 200   0   200

1 ─────
2 ─────
3 − − − −
4 ·······

1. Boundaries of Macro-Regions

2. Boundaries of Regions
   (First Order)

3. Boundaries of Sub-Regions
   (Second Order)

4. Internal Boundaries

Fig. 62.—The Regions of the Sub-Continent.

352]

2. *Southern Ranges:*
 (a) Kirthar: Ss—Kalat pl, Hab vy; Fs—*tangis*
 (b) Makran:
   (i) En limestone/lava folds and pls
   (ii) Wn flysch: Ss—Hingol, Dasht, &c. vys
3. *Interior Plateaus:*
 (a) desert basins:
   (i) Mashkel ⎫
   (ii) Lora ⎬ Fs—*hamuns* (playas), *dasht* (desert floors)
 (b) Chagai Hs: Ss—Koh-i-Sultan volcanoes

II. NORTH-WESTERN HILLS

1. *Southern Transverse Zone:*
 (a) Waziristan (@ from I.1b)
 (b) Kurram vy
 (c) Safed Koh
   (i) Safed Koh r
   (ii) Kabul vy: F—Khyber P
2. *Northern Longitudinal Zone:*
 (i–iii) Chitral, Panjkora, Swat vys (@ to IV.5)

III. SUB-MONTANE INDUS

1. *Trans-Indus Basins:*
 (a) Vale of Peshawar ⎫
 (b) (i) Kohat vy ⎬ Ss—*daman*; old lake floors
   (ii) Bannu ⎭
2. *Potwar Plateau:* Ss—Kala Chitta Dhar, &c.;
       Chach
              Fs—*khuddera* badlands;
3. *Salt Range:*   piedmont fans
   (i) Cis-Indus
   (ii) Trans-Indus: Fs—Kurram water-
    gap, Pezu windgap

[*Regions I–III = Western Borderlands (Ch. XVI)*]

IV. KASHMIR

1. *Punch and Jammu:*
 (a) Siwalik zone
 (b) sub-Himalayan zone:
   (i) foothills: Ss—Jhelum gorge, Tawi vy
   (ii) mid-Chenab vy
2. *Pir Panjal Range*
3. *Vale of Kashmir:*
   (i) border rs and vys
   (ii) Vale: Fs—*karewas* terraces, Jhelum marshes

4. *Main Himalayan Mass:*
    (a) Nanga Parbat massif
    (b) Great Himalaya
    (c) upper Chenab vy (@ to VI.1b)
    (d) Zaskar Range:
        (i) range proper
        (ii) Deosai Plains
        (iii) Rupshu

5. *Gilgit-Hunza:*
    (a)   (i) Astor vy
          (ii) Indus Kohistan: S—Indus gorge
    (b)   (i) Gilgit-Hunza vys
          (ii) Hindu Kush

V. KARAKORAM

1. *Ladakh:*
        (i) Indus furrow: Fs—fans
        (ii) Ladakh Range
2. *Karakoram:*
    (a) Baltistan (Nn Shigar vy)
    (b) Shyok-Nubra vys:
        (i) main vys; F—Shyok dam
        (ii) Chang-chenmo vy
        (iii) Harong vy
    (c) Karakoram massif: Fs—glaciers
    (d) Tibetan pls:
        (i) Depsang and Lingzi-tang Plains
        (ii) Pangong rift
      [*Regions IV–V = Kashmir and Karakoram (Ch. XIV)*]

VI. CENTRAL HIMALAYA

1. *Himachal Pradesh* (montane Punjab):
    (a) Siwalik zone: Ss—*duns*
    (b) sub-Himalayan zone:
        (i) main vys: Chandra (Kulu), Beas (Mandi and Lahul)
        (ii) main rs: En Pir Panjal, Dhaoladhar
        (iii) Sutlej vy
    (c) upper Sutlej
        (i) Spiti
        (ii) Hundes: Fs—Rakas and Manasarowar
2. *Kumaon* (montane UP):
    (a) Siwalik zone:
        (i) Siwaliks
        (ii) Dehra Dun
    (b) sub-Himalayan zone: Jumna, Ganges, Kali vys
    (c) high Bhotiya vys

3. *Nepal:*
   (a) Siwalik zone: Dundwa, Sumesar, Churia Ghati rs
   (b) Pahar: Ss—Katmandu vy, minor *duns*
   (c) high Himalaya

VII. Eastern Himalaya

1. *Kosi basin:*
   (i) Siwaliks and longitudinal vys
   (ii) Arun gorge
   (iii) Everest massif
2. *Darjeeling-Sikkim:*
   (i) Tista vy: Fs—Singaliya ridge, Darjeeling Hs, Tista vy proper, Dongkhya r
   (ii) Chumbi vy
3. *Bhután and Assam Himalayas*
   [*Regions VI–VII = Ch. XV*]

VIII. Assam-Burma Ranges

1. *Border Hills:*
   (i–v) Patkoi, Naga, Chin, Lushai, Chittagong Hs: Ss—Manipur basin, Kabaw vy (Burma)
2. *Barail Range:* S—Cachar gap (@ between XIII and XIV) (@ to XX)
   [*Region VIII grouped with XIV and XX as En Borderlands (Ch. XX)*]

B. The Indo-Gangetic Plains

IX. Sind

1. *Sind:*
   (a) Sindi Kohistan (@ to I.2a)
   (b) lower Indus Vy:
      (i) Sewistan (Sibi or Kacchi): S—Manchar
      (ii) Indus/Nara Doab: Ss—Rohri (Sukkur) and Hyderabad up-lands; Fs—*dhands*
      (iii) Indus Delta
   Karachi

X. Punjab

1. *Punjab Plains:*
   (a) Derajat: Ss—*daman*, Indus floodplain
   (b) Thal (Sind Sagar Doab)
   (c) Sub-Siwalik (winter rain) zone
   (d) central Doabs:
      (i) Jech
      (ii) Rechna } S—Kirana Hs (Ø of XVI); Fs—*bet* floodplains, *dhaya* bluffs, *bar* uplands
      (iii) Bari

(e) Bahawalpur (@ to XV)
　　　[Regions IX and X = Ch. XVII, Indus Plains]

XI. Indo-Gangetic Divide

1.　(a) sub-Siwalik zone: S—Bist Doab; Fs—*chos* torrents
　　(b) Sirhind (Hariana): S—Ghaggar *wadi*; F—Delhi Ridges (Ø of XVI)
　　Delhi

XII. Ganges Plains

1. *Upper Ganges Plains:*
　　(a) sub-Siwalik zone: Ss—bhabar, terai
　　(b) Jumna/Ganges Doab: Fs—Jumna badlands
　　(c) Rohilkhand-Oudh doabs: Fs—*bhur* sands
　　(d) trans-Jumna alluvial veneer (@ to XVII, XVIII)
2. *Middle Ganges Plains:*
　　(a) as for XII.1a
　　(b) Tirhut: S—Kosi floodplain
　　(c) trans-Ganges alluvial veneer:
　　　　(i) Son delta
　　　　(ii) S Bihar: Fs—Gaya Hs (Ø of XVI)
(The boundary between XII.1 and 2 is climatic. For IX–XII in general bhangar (old) and khadar (new) alluvium might be considered Ss.
　　　[Regions XI–XII = Ch. XVIII, Gangetic Plains]

XIII. Bengal

1.　(a) Duars (= terai)
　　(b) Nn Paradelta (Ganges/Brahmaputra Doab): Ss—Barind, Tista floodplain
　　(c) Wn Margins:
　　　　(i) Rarh (@ to XIX.2b): Fs—lateritic doabs, paddy floodplains
　　　　(ii) Damodar deltaic area
　　　　(iii) Contai coastal plain: Fs—old beach-ridges
　　(d) En Margins:
　　　　(i) Surma-Meghna vy: S—Madhupur Jungle
　　　　(ii) Chittagong coastal fans
　　(e) Delta proper:
　　　　(i) moribund: Fs—*jhils*, &c.
　　　　(ii) mature
　　　　(iii) active: S—Sundarbans; Fs—new islands
　　Calcutta and Hooghlyside
　　　[Region XIII = Ch. XIX]

XIV. Assam Valley

1. *Brahmaputra vy:* Ss—Kapili/Dhansiri re-entrants; Fs—detrital terraces, floodplains
　　[Grouped with Regions VIII and XX as En Borderlands, Ch. XX]

C. The Peninsula

XV. Thar Desert

1. (a) Pat
   (b) Thar proper: Ss—Bikaner irrigated area, Luni *wadi*, Aravalli *daman*;
      Fs—dunes, monadnocks

(The numerous hills of old rock protruding through the aeolian veneer indicate that the Thar is part of the Peninsular mass; but most of it is covered with superficial deposits, and the boundaries are hence ill-defined except where the desert is banked against XVI.1.)

XVI. Aravallis

1. *Aravalli Range:* Ss—Delhi Ridges (Ø), Jodhpur-Jaipur saddle; Godwar (*daman*); Fs—Mt Abu, Lake Sambhar
2. *Udaipur Hills:*
      (i) Mewar
      (ii) Bagar

XVII. Central Vindhyan Country

1. *Malwa:*
   (a) Vindhyan *rock* zone: Ss—scarplands, Dholpur-Karauli pl
   (b) Deccan Lava zone:
      (i) Malwa pl
      (ii) Vindhyan *Hills* scarp (overlap with XVII.3b(i))
2. *Gneissic Bundelkhand*
3. *Vindhyan "Ranges" and Plateaus:*
   (a) Rewa pl
   (b) scarps:
      (i) Vindhyan *Hills* (= XVII.1b.(ii))
      (ii) Bhanrer-Kaimur Hs
4. *Narbada-Son furrow:*
   (a) Narbada vy:
      (i) lower gorges
      (ii) rift floor
   (b) Son vy

XVIII. Satpura-Maikal

1. *Ranges:*
   (a) Satpura rs:
      (i) Satpuras proper
      (ii) Gawilgarh Hs
      } F—Burhanpur gap (@ to XVIII.2a(ii))
   (b) Mahadeo rs: Ss—intermont basins (Pench, &c.), Jubbulpore gap; F—Marble Rocks
   (c) Maikal dissected pl: Ss—upper Narbada vy, Maikal scarp; F—Amarkantak

2. *Khandesh* (@ to XXVII.1b):
    (a) Tapti-Purna vy:
        (i) lower Tapti gorges
        (ii) rift floor: S—Purna/Wardha watershed (@ to XXVII.1b(i))

XIX. CHOTA NAGPUR

1. *Upper Son-Deogarh uplands* (@ to XVII.4b and XVIII.1c)
2. *Chota Nagpur:*
    (a) Hazaribagh Range
    (b) peneplains:
        (i) Hazaribagh
        (ii) Ranchi
    (c) Gondwana trough (Koel-Damodar basins): F—Parasnath
    (d) Rajmahal Hs: Fs—*daman,* upper valleys
    [*Regions XV–XIX grouped as Aravallis and Central India* (*Ch. XXI*)]

XX. SHILLONG PLATEAU (Ø)

1. *Shillong Plateau* (Garo, Khasi, and Jaintia Hs)
    [*Grouped with Regions VIII and XIV as En Borderlands* (*Ch. XX*)]

XXI. CUTCH AND KATHIAWAR

1. *Cutch*
        (i) Rann mudflats
        (ii) lava/sandstone pls
        (iii) alluvial/aeolian margins
2. *Kathiawar:*
    (a) central platform:
        (i) Drangadhra-Wadhwan sandstone pl
        (ii) Nn and Sn lava pls: Fs—Gir Hs, Girnar (Ø)
    (b) lowland margins:
        (i) Halar coast: Fs—creeklands
        (ii) Dwarka foreland: F—Okha Rann
        (iii) Sorath coast: Ss—Bhadar-Ojat and Shetrunji vys (Fs—*gher* lands); miliolite zone; Cambay coast
        (iv) Gohilwad (@ to XXII.1): S—Nal depression

XXII. GUJARAT

1. *Gujarat Plains*:
        (i) Cambay coastal marshes
        (ii) central alluvial shelf: S—Charotar
        (iii) En alluvial veneer (@ to XVI.2(ii) and XVII.1b)

XXIII. KONKAN

1. *Konkan coastal lowland:*
    (a) N Konkan:
        (i) Nn lowland: Ss—longitudinal ridges and vys (Vaitarni, Amba); Fs—coastal alluvium and mangrove

  (ii) Ulhas basin (@ XXIII.1a and 1b, and to XXVI.1) Ss—foot-
       hills (@ to Ghats (F—Matheran mesa (Ø)), Kalyan low-
       land, Salsette Is. (Fs—dune and rock coast, alluvial lateritic
       shelf, central hills, creeklands)

Bombay
  (b) Kolaba-Ratnagiri:
      (i) indented coast: Fs—mangrove flats
     (ii) hilly lowland: Fs—paddy valley-floors, lateritic interfluves,
          Chiplun amphitheatres (@ to XXVI.1)
(The distinction between XXIII.1a and 1b is essentially that the trends of the
former are longitudinal to the coast, of the latter transverse.)

XXIV. Goa and Kanara

  1. *Konkan-Kerala transition:*
     (a) Goa:
              (i) Ilhas deltaic zone: S—Ilha de Goa
             (ii) lowland: Ss = Bardez, Marmagão peninsula
            (iii) foothills: F—Braganza Ghat (@ to XXVI.1–2)
     ((ii) and (iii) = approx. Velhas and Novas Conquistas respectively.)
     (b) N Kanara:
              (i) discordant coast: Fs—paddy valley-bottoms, lateritic inter-
                  fluves
             (ii) Ghats breaches zone (@ to XXVI.1–2): Fs—gorges (Shara-
                  vati, Kalinadi), high interfluves
     (c) S Kanara:
              (i) Netravati (Mangalore) lowland: Ss—alluvial coast, lateritic
                  shelves; Fs—Ghats outliers
(The whole Region is transitional between XXIII and XXV, and also displays
a marked softening of the contrast between the Wn Littoral and the Deccan.)

XXV. Kerala (Malabar)

  1. *Kerala coastal plain:*
              (i) littoral: Fs—dunes-and-lows, backwaters
             (ii) alluvium/laterite shelf
            (iii) gneissic lowlands (@ to XXVI.2): Ss—Palghat approaches
                  (@ to XXXV.4), Nagercoil valleys (@ to XXXV.6d(ii))
     [*Regions XXI–XXV grouped as Wn Littoral (Ch. XXII)*]

XXVI. Western Ghats

  1. *Deccan Lava Ghats, scarp and crest:* Ss—Dangs and Peint forests, Koyna
     and upper Kistna vys; Fs—Thal and Bhor Ghats (@ to XXVII.1a)
  2. *Archaean Ghats, scarp and crest:*
     (a) Ghats breaches zone (repeat of XXIV.1b(ii))
     (b) higher Sn zone:
              (i) contact zone along crest (@ between XXIV.1b and XXVIII.1)
             (ii) Coorg coulisses (@ to XXVIII.2a)
            (iii) Wynaad pl (@ to XXVIII.2a)

XXVII. Maharashtra

1. *Deccan Lava country:*
   (a) Maval (@ to XXVI.1)
   (b) plateau:
      (i) Wardha vy
      (ii) Ajanta Hs
      (iii) Godavari vy: S—Nasik basin
      (iv) Balaghat "Range"
      (v) Bhima vy
      (vi) Bijapur dry zone

(Nn limits ill-defined; culturally Khandesh (XVIII.2) is Maratha.)

XXVIII. Karnataka (South Deccan Plateaus)

1. *Bombay Karnatak:*
   (a) Belgaum marginal zone (@ to XXVII.1b(vi)): Fs—Kaladgi scarps
   (b) Dharwar peneplains: Fs—Dharwarian synclines
2. *Mysore Karnatak:*
   (a) Malnad: Ss—sub-Ghats strip (evergreen forest (@ to XXVI.2b);
       Fs—Babu Bhudan Hs
   (b) Maidan: Ss—peneplains, Mysore Ghat (@ to XXXV.3(i)); Fs—
       drugs (tors)

(Also Ss—longitudinal valleys of Tungra, Bhadra, Hagari, upper Penner in
both (a) and (b).)

XXIX. Southern Blocks

1. *Nilgiris:* Ss—Moyar trench, Nilgiri pl; Fs—*sholas*, downs
2. *Anaimalais, &c.:*
      (i) Anaimalai/Palni Hs
      (ii) Cardamom Hs: S—upper Periyar vy
      (iii) Varushanad/Andipatti Hs
      (iv) Comorin Hs: F—Shencottah gap (@ between XXV.1(iii) and
           XXXV.6d(i))

XXX. North-east Deccan (Mahanadi Basin and Annexes)

1. *Wainganga vy* (En flank, off Lavas) (@ between XXVII.1b(i) and XXX.2):
   S—Wainganga/Mahanadi watershed; Fs—haematite monadnocks of S
2. *Chhattisgarh:*
      (i) Nn (sub-Maikal) margins (@ to XVIII.1c)
      (ii) Seonath/Mahanadi doab
      (iii) Raigarh basin
           ((i) and (ii) should rank as Ss?)
3. *Sankh/S Koel/Brahmani basins* (@ in all directions)
4. *Jamshedpur basin:* Ss—Sanjai gap (@ to XXX.3), Subarnarekha vy (@ to
   XIII.1c(i))
   Jamshedpur

(Region XXX, except for its Chhattisgarh core, is the most ill-defined of the
whole sub-continent.)

XXXI. TELANGANA
 1. *lower Godavari trough* ((@ to XXX.1 and XXXIV.2(i))
 2. *Telangana proper:*
       (i) Hyderabad
       (ii) Bellary peneplains   } Fs—*drugs*
       (iii) Raichur (Kistna/Tungabhadra) Doab
 3. *Anantapur/Chittoor basins:*
    (a) interior basins:
       (i) Chatravati
       (ii) Papagni
       (iii) Cheyyur-Bahuda
    (b) transitional zone:
       (i) Suvarnamukhi vy (@ to XXXV.1(i))
       (ii) Nagari Hs: Ss—intermont basins
(XXXI.3 is shut in between XXVIII.2b (Mysore Maidan) and XXXII.2a
(Palkondas) and is really another left-over; all of it really transitional between
Telangana and Tamilnad.)

XXXII. EASTERN HILLS
 1. *Orissa/Bastar mass:*
    (a) Orissa Hs:
       (i) hill massifs
       (ii) Brahmani/Mahanadi trough (@ to XXXIII)
    (b) khondalite zone:
       (i) dissected peneplains
       (ii) Tel/Sileru trough
 2. *Cuddapah ranges and basins:*
    (a) Wn arcs (Erramalai-Seschalam-Palkonda Hs): Fs—Palkonda scarp,
       gorges (Cheyyur, Papagni)
    (b) central (Kunderu) basin:
       (i) Kurnool-Cuddapah plain
       (ii) Razampeta corridor: Fs—lateritic piedmont, Cheyyur shingle-
         spread
    (c) En ridges:
       (i) Nallamalais
       (ii) central (Sagileru) vy
       (iii) Velikondas
[*Regions XXVI–XXXII grouped as Peninsular Interior (Ch. XXIII)*]

XXXIII. ORISSA DELTAS
 1. *Mahanadi/Brahmani Deltas:* Ss—Baitarni vy; Fs—Balasore gap (@ to
     XIII.1c(iii), delta seaface, Lake Chilka, Mahendragiri gap (@ to
     XXXIV.1)

XXXIV. NORTHERN CIRCARS AND NELLORE
 1. *Vizag-Ganjam lowland:* Ss—Rushikulya, Languliya, Vamsadhara vys;
     lateritic foothill zone (@ to XXXII.1b (i)); F—Waltair Highlands.

2. *Godavari/Kistna Deltas:*
        (i) Godavari/Kistna breach (@ to XXXI.1 and 2(i))
        (ii) Godavari delta: Ss—sub-deltaic margins, delta proper; Fs—
            seaface, Colair Lake
        (iii) Kistna delta: Ss and Fs as for Godavari delta
3. *Nellore* (@ to XXXV.1)*:*
    (a) *Nellore lowlands:*
        (i) Archaean low peneplain
        (ii) coastal alluvium: Fs—cuestiform marine deposits, Pulicat
            lagoon
[*Regions XXXIII and XXXIV grouped as En Littoral* (*N*), *Ch. XXIV*]

XXXV. TAMILNAD

1. *Coromandel coastal plain:*
        (i) Archaean low peneplains: Fs—monadnocks, Cretaceous-
            Eocene inliers
        (ii) Cuddalore/laterite shelf: Fs—Red Hs, Capper Hs
        (iii) young alluvial zone: Ss—embayments, strandplain; Fs—
            Korteliyar, Cooum, Adyar, Palar vys

    Madras
2. *Tamilnad Hills* (Ø of Mysore Maidan)*:*
    (a) Javadis: Fs—Agaram—Cheyyur through vy, Yelagiri (Ø), Ponnaiyar
        gap (@ between 1(i) and 3(ii))
    (b) Sn group: Ss—Shevaroys, Kalroyans, Pachamalais, Salem monad-
        nocks (Ø)
3. *Palar/Ponnaiyar trough:*
        (i) lower shelf of Mysore Ghat (@ to XXVIII.2b)
        (ii) Baramahal
        (iii) Sn margins (Salem area, @ to 4): Fs—Chalk Hs, magnetite
            monadnocks
4. *Coimbatore plateau* (*Kongunad*)*:* Ss—Bhavani, Noyil, Amaravati vys,
    Palghat sill (@ to XXV.1(ii), Coimbatore Hs; F—Kangayam inter-
    fluve
5. *Cauvery delta:*
    (a) delta head (@ to 3 and 4)
    (b) delta proper:
        (i) Velar/Coleroon doab (@ to 1(iii))
        (ii) Coleroon/Cauvery doab:Fs—Srirangam Island, floodplains
        (iii) main delta plains: Ss—higher Wn margins (F—Vallam Table-
            land), older irrigated area
        (iv) seaface: Fs—marshy low, dune belt, Pt Calimere, Veddani-
            yam salt swamp
6. *Dry Southeast:*
    (a) upper Vaigai:
        (i) Varushanad vy
        (ii) Kambam vy
        (iii) Dindigul col (@ to 4)

(b) Madura/Ramnad shelf:
  (i) colluvial piedmont zone: Fs—monadnocks (Sirumalais, &c., Ø)
  (ii) laterite/old alluvium panfan (from Varshalei to Vaippar): Ss—
    tank country, coastal strip, Pamban Island (Fs—old reefs,
    Adam's Bridge)
(c) Black Soil area
(d) Tinnevelly:
  (i) colluvial zone
  (ii) red soil zone: Fs—*teris*, coastal dunes
  (iii) Tamprabarni basin: Ss—foothills (@ to XXIX.2(iv)), Chittar
    vy, Tamprabarni vy
    [*Region XXXV* = *Ch. XXV, Tamilnad*]

D. THE ISLANDS

XXXVI. MALDIVES AND LACCADIVES
    [*In Ch. XXII, Wn Littoral*]

XXXVII. ANDAMANS AND NICOBARS

 1. *Andamans*
 2. *Nicobars*
    [*In Ch. XXV, Tamilnad*]

XXXVIII. CEYLON

See separate division in Ch. XXVI; but it may be noted here that the main
divisions of Ceylon essentially reproduce those of the Sn Peninsula: central
massif (cf. XXIX, perhaps genetically connected), surrounding low gneissic
peneplains with alluvial embayments (cf. XXXV.1), dry zone (cf. XXXV.6);
the Jaffna area, despite lithological differences, is essentially a true coastal plain
(cf. XXXV.1(ii–iii) and 6b–d).

CHAPTER XIV

THE HIMALAYAS: KASHMIR AND KARAKORAM
(Regions IV and V)

Methodological Difficulties

THE vast system of ramparts and fosses which girdles India on the N presents all but insuperable difficulties to regional treatment on our sub-continental scale. Some of the regional units are, strictly speaking, narrow belts hundreds of miles long, and to work through and along these *seriatim* would be intolerably tedious and confusing to writer and reader. From another angle the whole area is a mosaic of small regions, similar but not merely standard repetitions; this is reflected in the richness of the *pays* nomenclature.[1] Even a simple topographic description of this multitude of little worlds, Gilgit, Rupshu, Spiti, and the rest, would fill a volume of Himalayan dimensions; while structure and genetics are known either in excessive detail (for our scale) for small areas, or in excessive vagueness for vast areas. Adequate climatic data are lacking over much of this huge area, where obviously micro-climates are of the highest importance; in ecology and pedology the site may be as important as the zone. Fragmentation, indeed, is the ruling theme. The human adjustments to a complex and difficult environment are nice and minute, and here, too, justice cannot be done within the limitations of our scale.

The compromise adopted is imperfect, but perhaps the most reasonable one available. In the W, where the width of the mountains proper is close on 300 miles, it is possible to discuss the main longitudinal units individu-ally and to synthesise in terms of the political unit, or rather problem, of Kashmir. Further E the true longitudinal regions will be broken up and re-assembled into transverse segments treated as far as possible as wholes. Convenience of handling dictates this allowance to locational, and even to political, factors of a weight to which they are not entitled on physiographic grounds; but this is not without justification since by and large the broader human divisions of the centre and E tend to run transverse to the physical. The whole Himalayan area may thus be divided as follows, premising that each 'unit' is in fact made up of longitudinal belts, except in the W where the more massive build renders treatment on longitudinal lines more feasible:

[1] "Nowhere in the world are the small natural regions more sharply separated than in the Himalayas." A. G. Ogilvie, "The Technique of Regional Geography", *JMGA* XII (1938), 109–24, refce at 123.

West		Central and East	
1. Sub-Himalayan Kashmir (Punch and Jammu)	IV	1. Himachal Pradesh (sub-Himalayan Punjab	VI
2. Pir Panjal		2. Dehra Dun and Kumaon	
3. Vale of Kashmir		3. Nepal	
4. Indus Kohistan and Gilgit		1. Kosi basin (E Nepal)	VII
5. Main Himalaya		2. Tista basin (Darjeeling and Sikkim)	
6. Ladakh and Baltistan (the Indus furrow)	V	3. Bhután and Assam Himalayas	
7. Karakoram			

The Himalayas in General

The general structural outlines have been set out in Ch. I, and as far as may be will be taken as read: there is no general account of the Siwaliks throughout their length, for instance. But we may recall:

(i) the great NW syntaxis, controlled by the concealed extension of the Peninsular Block and marked *inter alia* by the Murree/Siwalik strike;

(ii) the overthrust boundary faults on the inner edge of the younger (Eocene onwards) sub-Himalayan terrain;

(iii) the great development of nappes in the Himalayas proper;

(iv) the problem of the river gorges and the evolution of the drainage pattern.

The barrier function of the mountain wall is obvious. Climatically the monsoon as it were is banked up against the Great Himalaya, and but thin trickles of monsoon air lip over the few notches in this stupendous dyke: the Vale of Kashmir is intermediate in this respect, with a definite rain-shadow from the Pir Panjal, but with wet and cloudy weather in the monsoon months. The snow supply of the Himalaya, especially in the W, comes mainly from the "Mediterranean" depressions of the winter.

From the human point of view, the Himalayas are far from impenetrable, but on the whole there is not much point in penetrating them, at least in a military and political sense as against cultural and trade movements: the negative values concerned are as much a matter of what lies beyond as of the terrain difficulties, great as these are. Beyond the Vale of Kashmir transport is entirely human and animal, and not even draught animal: mules, yaks, even sheep carry the little trade that exists. Flying is theoretically possible over much of the area—except in the monsoon months; but difficulties in landing, and still more in taking off in the rarefied air, render it as yet impracticable for all but reconnaissance.[2]

[2] K. Mason, "The Himalayas as a Barrier to Modern Communications", *GJ* LXXXVII (1936), 1–16; cf. R. R. Rawson, in W. G. East and O. H. K. Spate (eds.), *The Changing Map of Asia* (1950), 377.

Yet the Himalayas have a high human interest. Where armies have rarely penetrated, Chinese pilgrims seeking the land of Buddha, Hindus the source of sacred Ganges and the hidden mountain Kailas, have left the impress of their faith in shrine and temple. Here indeed three mighty empires of the mind meet: Islam in the tangled valleys around the Indus and in the Vale; Hinduism in the Vale and the sub-Himalayan borders; the Mahayana Buddhism of Tibet and Ladakh spilling down the glacis to mingle with Hinduism in the peculiar culture of Nepal. Ethnically too, though ruling groups may be often Rajputs, most of the peoples of the Himalaya are probably Mongol or at least Mongoloid; and in Ladakh and Sikkim we are no more in an Indian nor an Islamic environment. Not only is the cultural landscape of monastery and prayer-wheel different, but the economy itself, though agriculturally based, is remarkable for the high development of transhumant pastoralism. So too the social world is different; the polyandry universal in Ladakh is rarely found south of the mountains. Over against the dwellers in the vast Indian plains these people are not even hill-men; they are mountaineers.

Finally, this land of difficulty and mystery has in all ages powerfully impressed the mind of India: around Kailas and the sources of Ganges cluster the beautiful legends of Siva and Parvati, and the eternal snows have always stood as symbols of an ideal serenity, attainable, if at all, only by indomitable patience and resolution. What the Himalayas have meant to India may be glimpsed from the lovely verse of Kalidasa[3]:

> God of the distant north, the Snowy Range
> O'er other mountains towers imperially;
> Earth's measuring-rod, being great and free from change
> Sinks to the eastern and the western sea. . . .

Kalidasa's view of the functions of Himalaya, "who steadies earth, so strong is he and broad", is not of course in accordance with the views of modern geomorphology:

Both from within and from without, the Himalayas are in a condition of extremely active change. . . . If we contemplate the Himalayas as a whole, we come to regard them as representing a mighty upward flow of the earth's crust. . . . Angara got the better of the thrust, so that the mobile mountain masses flowed over the sinking lowlands of Gondwana. Thus to the eyes of the geologist, who is used to thinking in great periods of time, the Himalayas seem a mobile organ of our planet—a planet which is not merely rolling on its course through the universe, but within its own framework is continually undergoing the throes of an active life.[4]

[3] A. W. Ryder, *Translations from Kalidasa* (Everyman ed., n.d.), 157.
[4] A. Heim and A. Gansser, *The Throne of the Gods* (1939), 220.

Sub-Himalayan Kashmir : Punch and Jammu

Very broadly speaking, Kashmir consists of two huge mountain masses —the Karakoram in the far N, the Himalaya/Zaskar to the S, with the Indus entrenched between them; and, on the Sn flanks of the main Himalaya, the famous Vale, walled in by the Pir Panjal which in turn breaks down into the lower but highly dissected Tertiary hills of the Punjab border (Figs. 63, 64). In actual fact the detail is exceedingly complex and the breakdown into seven units of study rather arbitrary, though not entirely so.

Kashmir includes a narrow strip, 5–15 miles wide, of the Punjab plains, here at 1100–1200 ft; this tract is badly ravined and of little significance except for the inclusion of the Mangla headworks of the Upper Jhelum Canal. N lies a belt of Siwalik terrain, hills up to 2000–4000 ft, largely anticlinal and overlooking a series of *duns*—longitudinal valleys—succeeded in turn by the Miocene Murree sandstones and Eocene Nummulitic limestone at 6000–8000 ft. The Siwalik zone, a "pile of rock waste" up to 20,000 ft thick, has undergone very recent folding and faulting, including early Pleistocene thrusting. In the earlier Tertiary zone strike-faults have disrupted anticlines and brought in massive Permo-Carboniferous limestones forming the higher ridges. The upper Murrees are preserved on the downthrow (Sn) side, while to the N the lower Murrees and the Nummulitics, resting with a great unconformity on the Permo-Carboniferous, are greatly disturbed and the terrain correspondingly confused; yet, "although dissection is intense, their heights display unmistakable signs of an older topography. Levelled spurs and plateau remnants, valley flats and abrupt terminations of high valley floors along master streams, indicate a mature relief which underwent rejuvenation".[5] This sub-Himalayan zone ends in the great boundary thrust-faults, beyond which the Pir Panjal rises steeply.

Rainfall varies with aspect, but in general lies between 35 ins. in the W and 28 in the E, with a fair contribution in January–March; temperatures are of course affected by altitude and aspect. The low outer ridges carry a sparse dry scrub, the inner rather better forest, largely of *chir* or *chil* (*Pinus longifolia*); but felling for rafting into the Punjab has made serious inroads.

The Siwalik and Murree terrain, with thin thirsty soils, very liable to erosion and often degenerating into pebble-spreads, is agriculturally poor, as are the limestone slopes. Here and there, in *duns* and in a piedmont belt at the foot of limestone scarps, conditions are better. Irrigation is limited, as the water-table is generally deep for wells, and channels are liable to be overwhelmed by spates from the numerous transverse gullies; while some lower areas are so fever-ridden that cultivation is largely carried on by a

[5] de Terra (1939), 8, 18. Until further notice, citations to de Terra are from this very admirable work.

seasonal immigration of hillmen. Wheat, barley, and rape are grown as rabi, maize and bajra as kharif. Higher up, in wider, better-watered valleys, bajra gives way completely to maize. Irrigation is difficult here also, as streams are incised, but it is not so necessary as in the lower valleys.

The unexploited mineral resources of the region are important. In Riasi Dt the Nummulitics contain three or four small fields with seams of anthracite (carbon 60–82%) up to 20 ft thick; farther W the coal is very friable and the thin seams too disturbed to be workable. The pisolitic limonites and ironstone of the same area and formation were exploited by indigenous methods in the past, and in view of the general mineral poverty of Pakistan might have some importance should she secure title to the area. The basal Eocene beds are fossil laterites, an old land-surface on the Permo-Carboniferous, and contain patches of pure bauxite forming a large reserve of aluminium ore.[6]

The region is fairly well peopled: densities range from 327 in Jammu and 238 in Mirpur to 144–174 in Riasi and Kathua, which contain definitely mountainous areas. All these showed decreases 1931–41, by as much as 15% in Jammu. The SE is strongly Hindu, 60–70% and locally over 80%, and should partition take place Jammu, Kathua, and Udhampur would be indisputably *Indian*: this is the home of the Dogras, the dominant minority in the state. Jammu (50,379) was the original base of the ruling house, whence the official title of the state is 'Jammu and Kashmir'; it is still the winter capital and the terminus of the only railway, a short line from Sialkot. To the W Punch is over 90% Muslim, a feudatory generally on bad terms with its Kashmiri overlord.

The whole region is of less significance in itself than in relation to W Punjab. The SE might well be detached, but the rest normally plays a very important part in the economy of W Pakistan. Its forests are the main supply for a country desperately short of timber,[7] while Riasi might at least mitigate the mineral deficiency. In addition the importance to the W Punjab of the Mangla headworks and of the hydro-electric potential can hardly be over-estimated.

Finally we may note the essentially similar, though rather higher, country across the Jhelum, which forms much of Rawalpindi and Hazara (NWFP). Murree, a hill station at the usual 6500–7500 ft, was chiefly noted for brewing; the high barley acreage of the region may have been significant.

The Pir Panjal

The Pir Panjal is in a sense a bifurcation from the main Himalaya farther E. Structurally and lithologically it is most complex; thrusting is important

---

[6] D. N. Wadia, *Geology of India* (1939), 339, 348, 431–2.

[7] The *Indian* counter-argument that the main customer was the railway system, three-quarters of which went to *India* on Partition, is transparent enough.

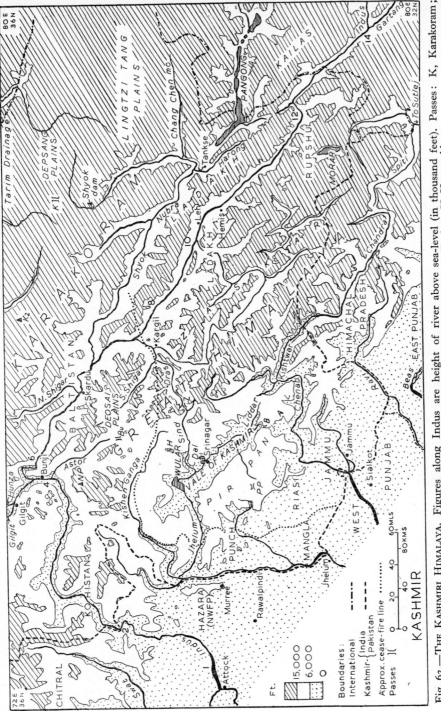

Fig. 63.—The Kashmiri Himalaya. Figures along Indus are height of river above sea-level (in thousand feet). Passes : K, Karakoram; Bu, Burzil; Z, Zoji La; PP, Pir Panjal; B, Banihal. NP, Nanga Parbat; H, Haramukh.

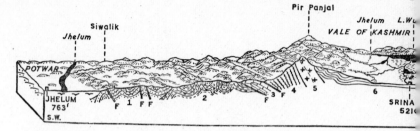

Fig. 64.—POTWAR TO LADAKH: BLOCK SECTION OF KASHMIRI HIMALAYAS. Line confluence; vertical exaggtn 8·3. Geology (based on de Terra) diagrammatic: 1, Siwa? Permian-Cretaceous) in NE; 4, older Palaeozoic; 5, younger Palaeozoic igneous

and Wadia considers it as the front of a great Kashmir nappe. The massive Permo-Carboniferous limestones, metamorphics, and intrusives form a broad swelling platform at about 13,000 ft, on which lies a serrated residual crest, the highest monadnocks reaching 15,500 ft. The passes lie as a rule at 11,000–12,000 ft.

The contemporary glaciation presents interesting features. Most of the thirty-odd small glaciers are on the Nn slope, in contrast to the Himalayas farther E where there is relatively little ice on the arid Tibetan side. The Pir Panjal snow, however, comes mostly in winter, from W or NW, and the Sn aspects are more exposed to warm air-currents from the plains. Only one or two of these glacierets have real valley tongues, the lowest at 11,600 ft; most of them are simply cakes of ice in wide cirques which form the collecting grounds. The river-pattern is very striking, with the great bends of Chenab and Jhelum (the latter controlled by the syntaxis), the tributaries at these bends carrying on the line of the lower main streams, and a general lay-out of feeders suggesting that the drainage was originally to the SE.

The Sn flank is wetter than the Nn, but slopes here are so often too steep for soil formation that the larger coniferous forests are mostly to the N. The SOI 1. 1/2,000,000 maps carry the Pir Panjal across the Chenab, the upper (Chandra Bhuga) Valley being closely inset in the angle of the Pir Panjal and the main Himalaya. The lower levels of this high basin (6000–12,000 ft) in the W carry a fair population; the density of Udhampur Dt is 58, and unlike the rest of Jammu it increased slightly from 1931 to 1941. The climate here is definitely cold, "the mango-tree gives place to the apple"; but terraced irrigation is not too difficult, and rice is important.

The region is, however, essentially negative, a barrier. Of the routes into the Vale the most direct is the old Mogul road by the Pir Panjal Pass (11,400 ft), which gives its name to the range. This is now of little importance, the main entry (in normal times) being by the motor road up the

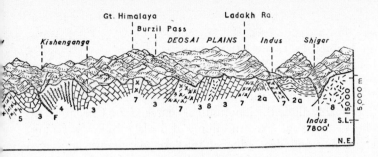

on on bearing 38° for 430 miles (690 km.) from Jhelum town to Indus below Shyok
Iurree; 2a, Flysch; 3, Permo-Carb. (thrust onto 2), and 'Tethys' formations (U.
ewas Beds; 7, Cret.-Eocene eruptives; 8, granites. F, major faults and thrusts.

Jhelum valley—excellent engineering but costly to maintain. At the other
end of the Vale access is had from Jammu and the Chenab via the Banihal
Pass (9290 ft), also motorable though with more interruption by snow than
the road from Rawalpindi. Military and political needs have led to the
hasty construction of a long projected direct link with *India* by the Banihal,
the last stage on the road from Gurdaspur through Kangra and Chamba
in the sub-Himalayan Punjab.

The Vale of Kashmir

The Physical Setting

Between the Pir Panjal and the main Himalaya lies the famous Vale of
Kashmir, a great basin about 85 miles by 25 with a floor which in the
Jhelum floodplain is only 5200 ft above sea-level. Wadia and de Terra agree
in regarding it as a great synclinal, which according to Wadia is seated on
the back of a vast nappe.[9] The Sn flanks fall relatively regularly and gently
from the Pir Panjal crest, but the Jhelum thalweg lies close to the Nn side
of the Vale, and here facetted spurs give a clear indication of faulting;
similar features on the Pir Panjal slope are as a rule masked by the Pleistocene deposits. The stream pattern is interesting. The Nn wall is dissected
by the Sind and other rivers which are antecedent to the immediately
bordering hills; but beyond the ridge crowned by Haramukh (15,999 ft) the
NW end of the valley shows a well-adjusted synclinal pattern, significantly
"rather suggestive of an ancient headwater portion of a master stream".[10]
On the Pir Panjal side the upper valleys are incised and dendritic, but
farther down the rivers have developed on parallel courses, consequent on
the uplift of the Karewas Beds and antecedent to the folds in them. As we
are about to see, the geomorphological evolution is extremely recent.

Among the most striking features of the Vale are the flat-topped ter-

[9] Cf. Fig. 34 in Wadia, *op. cit.* (1939), 315.   [10] de Terra, 23.

races known as *karewas*, which term is also applied to the Pleistocene sediments of which they are composed. These deposits consist of clays, sands, and silts of undoubted lacustrine origin, in which bands of marl and of loessic silt, together with lenticles of conglomerate from old deltaic fans, bear witness to many fluctuations of level. The sequence of events suggested by de Terra [11] is: (i) capture by the Jhelum of an original subsequent flowing to the SE, probably along the longitudinal course of the Chenab [12]; (ii) Pir Panjal uplift blocking this exit; (iii) filling of the lake and overspilling; (iv) alternate draining and deepening of the lake in response to glacial changes and changes in the ratio of uplift and erosion at the spill; (v) continued uplift accompanied by cutting-down of the Jhelum and complete drainage of the lake. It should be noted that the various existing lakes, of which Wular is the largest (area 12 to 100 sq mls, according to season and flood) are not strictly relics of the ancient lake, but rather enlarged old oxbows and abandoned courses of the Jhelum; in some cases ponding by detrital fans from the hills seems to be responsible.

In places the *karewas* have been eaten into great bluffs by the Jhelum, and the terrace lies at 450 ft above the river. On the S Karewas Beds extend from about 5400 up to 9000 ft, and are quite steeply tilted. With the Pir Panjal uplift the deposits were folded and in places faulted, another striking testimony to the persistence of orogenic process into recent, perhaps even contemporary, times. To summarise, we have [13]:

First interglacial	. .	Lower Karewas deposition (*c.* 2000 ft), lake beds, fluvial inwash and eolian drift
Second glaciation	. .	Karewas gravel (*c.* 400 ft), glaciofluvial outwash fans
Second interglacial	. .	Upper Karewas, *c.* 200 ft—"topmost beds of eolian and fluvial origin; lower beds lacustrine; also fluvial outwash (partly varved)."

The word *karewa* applies strictly to the level surface between the incised streams dissecting the terraces, the flanks of which are generally steep (Fig. 66). They are usually permeable and soils tend to be poor, though pressure of population enforces their cultivation. Lower down finer alluvium fills the marshy valley-floor, and where streams debouch from the hills fans of coarser material are formed. These relations are suggested by Fig. 65, which it should be noted does not represent any actual area, though all features shown are found on each of the several SOI 1/63,360 sheets.

[11] de Terra, 116–18. In this section, *karewas* = topographical, Karewas = geological.
[12] Note in this connection the directions of the Liddar and the tributaries joining the Chenab at the Kishtwar bend.
[13] de Terra, table at 224; for general glacial sequence see above, 27–28.

The climate is naturally continental, the severity of the winter being increased by drainage of cold air down the encircling slopes, and by radiation. Srinagar lies at 5200 ft and its climate is more extreme than that of hill stations lying 2000 ft higher on the outer Himalayan ridges:

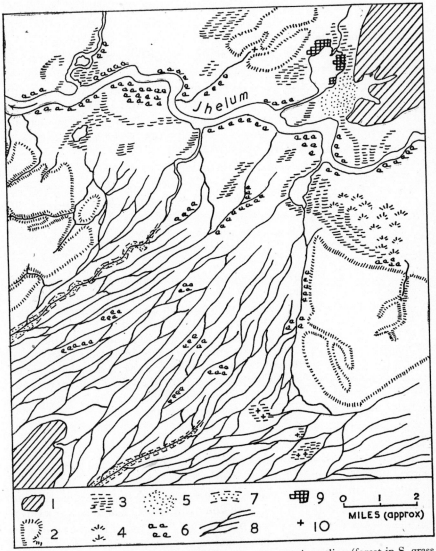

Fig. 65.—KAREWAS OF THE VALE OF KASHMIR. 1, mountain outliers (forest in S, grass or rock in N); 2, *karewas*; 3, marsh; 4, grass; 5, alluvial cone; 6, willows, poplars, orchards; 7, stream beds; 8, irrigation channels (*kuls*); 9, *demb* cultivation; 10, springs. All blank areas cultivated except ravines and flanks of *karewas* (cf. Fig. 66). Altitude about 5200 ft along Jhelum, 5800 on upper margins of *karewas*, 6000–7000 on hills. This map does not represent any specific area.

Temperature ° F.

J.	F.	M.	A.	M.	J.	J.	A.	S.	O.	N.	D.
30·7	33·0	45·1	55·7	63·9	69·9	73·0	70·8	64·0	53·2	44·0	36·3	Ra. 42·3

Precipitation, inches

2·7	2·8	3·6	3·8	2·3	1·5	2·2	2·3	1·6	1·2	0·4	1·5	Tot. 25·7

While the difference between the annual means at Simla (7200 ft) and Srinagar is less than 2° F. (55·1 at Simla, against 53·3), Simla temperatures for January, February, and March are 8·1, 7·6, and 6·4° above those of Srinagar, but those of July and August 8·7 and 8·0 less; the range at Simla is only 28·1°. Much of the precipitation is snow; the usual rains months (June–September) receive only 8·7 ins., January–March 9·1. It must be remembered that Srinagar is in the very bottom of the Vale, which as a whole receives 32–35 ins.

There is naturally a strong vertical zoning of climate and vegetation, and differences in exposure to insolation are most important. Immediately below the forests maize is the most important crop and walnut trees are numerous; at 7000 ft "hardy and stunted" types of paddy come in, to be succeeded by the better paddy of the lower terraces and the marshy tracts where the streams wind along through groves of willows.

> The side valleys . . . have certain features in common. At the mouth of the valley lies the wide delta of fertile soil on which rice, plane-trees, mulberries, and willows grow luxuriantly; a little higher up the land is terraced and rice still grows, while the slopes are ablaze with the wild indigo, till at about 6000 feet the plane-tree gives place to the walnut, and rice to millets. On the south bank of the river endless forests stretch from the bottom of the valley to the peaks; and on the north bank, wherever a nook or corner is sheltered from the sun . . . pines and firs establish themselves. Further up . . . millets are replaced by buckwheat and Tibetan barley. Soon after this the useful birch-tree appears, and then come grass and glaciers, the country of the shepherds. [14]

Agriculture

Kashmir as a whole contains some 52 m. ac., of which 44 m. are unsettled or have no agricultural returns. Of the balance of 8 m. ac. about a quarter is cultivated, and a third of this quarter is in the Vale. Rice at lower and maize at higher levels are dominant, nearly half and over a third of the TSA respectively. Wheat has 10–12%, and the only other crops of much areal significance are linseed and rape.

Farming methods are very distinctive. Not much care (except the use of a rough rotation) is given to crops other than rice and garden produce. Rice is intensively manured, sometimes by piling farmyard refuse at the irriga-

[14] *Kashmir Gaz.* (1909), 6.

tion entry, so that it is distributed over the field as liquid manure. The droppings of the animals in the winter, when they are kept indoors, are kept for the fields; in the spring sheep are folded on the fields, and turves cut from the marshy stream-banks are particularly useful. Near Srinagar the market gardeners use poudrette from the city's refuse. Rice seeds are pregerminated in water; the labour of transplanting rice is rendered even more arduous than usual by the necessity of weeding out various hill grasses which only an expert can distinguish from paddy seedlings; four weedings are needed in broadcast sowing. Maize is grown in association with grazing, high yields being obtained by folding buffaloes and cattle on the fields; at lower levels it is grown mainly on the heavy peaty soils along the Jhelum. Dry crops, including a little cotton, are grown on the *karewas*, rape or mustard on soft reclaimed swamp soils. Near the limit of cultivation buck-wheat and *grim*—the naked Tibetan barley—are the only reliable food-grains; the former is also a useful standby lower down, as it can be sown late on almost any soil if the season seems likely to be unfavourable.

Irrigation is almost essential, and over 400,000 of the 750,000 or so cultivated acres are irrigated. Practically all irrigation is by *kuls*, leats led off from the *karewas* streams, made and maintained by landowners or villagers; these are difficult to keep in good order where they run along the steep and erosion-liable *karewas* flanks or cross ravines in wooden aqueducts. Their numbers are astonishing (Figs. 65, 66). The mountain streams bring down good silt from the snow-melt, except where deforestation, as in the Sind Valley, has led to sand-spreads. Springs are sometimes used for irrigation, but they bring no silt and their waters may be cold enough to affect plant growth adversely.

Agricultural rhythms are, of course, differentiated from those of the sub-continent as a whole by the cold winters, which also affect tillage. "In March . . . the soil has perhaps been worked by the frosts and snow; but if, as is sometimes the case, no snow has fallen, it will be difficult work for the plough-bullocks, thin and poor after the long winter, to break up the soil." With this dependence on the spring melt the aspect of the

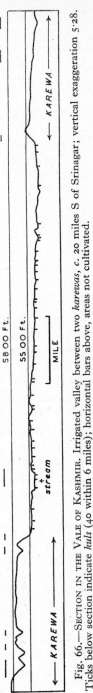

Fig. 66.—Section in the Vale of Kashmir. Irrigated valley between two *karewas*, *c.* 20 miles S of Srinagar; vertical exaggeration 5·28. Ticks below section indicate *kuls* (40 within 6 miles); horizontal bars above, areas not cultivated.

snow on the mountains is the cultivator's anxiously observed guide to the chances of the ensuing season. The agricultural calendar is roughly as follows:

March .	. ploughing, manuring with dung of winter
April .	. fertilising with turves from stream-banks; paddy, linseed, and sesamum sown (kharif)
May–June .	. rape harvest; *grim* sown (above 7000 ft)
June–July .	. paddy weeding; barley and wheat harvest (rabi)
July–Aug. .	. linseed harvest
Aug.–Sept.	. ploughing for rabi wheat and barley; *grim* harvest
Sept. .	. ploughing for rape; rape sown
Sept.–Oct.	. paddy and sesamum harvest; wheat sown
Oct.–Dec. .	. barley and later wheat sown.

January and February are dead months. The shortness of the *grim* growing season will be noted.

The lakes have a peculiar economy of their own. "They bear innumerable boats, from which fish are caught in skilfully manipulated throw-nets. Weeds are dredged up to provide fodder for the cattle, and water chestnuts and lotus roots for human food. And, as if such fertility were inadequate, sods of marshy earth are bound together into rafts heavy with manure, and these are moored in rows across the swamp to form floating gardens, so that the boundary between earth, air, and water is made fruitful and bears the fiery red fruits of tomato plants." [15]

More important, if less picturesque, is the formation of new land on the shallow lake-margins by planting willows in the water and filling up the compartments so formed with boatloads of lake-mud and weeds. These *demb* lands are used not only for fruit and vegetables, but even for rape, maize, and tobacco.

The orchards of Kashmir provide the most valuable of its exports after timber; most temperate and sub-tropical fruits and nuts are grown. The most important fruit is probably the apricot, and the walnut is a source of lighting and cooking oil as well as a food. One of the main attractions of Kashmir to hard-drinking Moguls like Babur and Jahangir was its wine, but the vine has no longer its ancient fame, despite the establishment of a state vineyard with Bordeaux stocks—one development which is not likely to appeal to the future rulers of Kashmir, be they *Indian* or Pakistani. Even hops have been introduced, doubtless to be withdrawn again now. Finally we may note the cultivation on one or two *karewas* of the saffron crocus, in demand as a condiment and as a pigment for Indian sect-marks. Minor crops include opium poppy and the recently introduced pyrethrum.[16]

[15] G. E. Hutchinson, *The Clear Mirror* (1936), 102.
[16] Most of the details in this section are drawn from the full and fascinating account in the *Gazetteer* (41–63).

Other Occupations

Supplementary to agriculture proper are sericulture and pastoralism. By 1900 the former activity was decrepit as well as ancient, but the introduction of modern filatures has led to a wide extension of mulberry culture, though not enough cocoons are produced to keep the filatures at Srinagar and Jammu and the weaving factory at Srinagar working to capacity. There is also, of course, a good deal of hand-loom weaving of silk, cotton, and wool; silk is a major export.

The main pastoral activity is sheep-rearing; this is transhumant, the sheep live in winter beneath the human dwellings—adding to their warmth—and in summer are taken by professional shepherds to the high pastures above the tree-line; this is the *marg* common in place-names and strictly equivalent to the Swiss *alp*. Winter feed is willow and dried flag (Iris) leaves. After agriculture, wool production is probably the chief means of livelihood in Kashmir, employing full- or part-time some 300,000 people. The famous Cashmere shawl industry died a languishing death in the 1870s, but there is naturally a large cottage production of woollen clothing, blankets, and rugs; felting is important also, and Srinagar has a large woollens factory. Mineral exploitation is insignificant, though a start has been made on the commercial exploitation of lignite from some of the karewas, which has been used locally by the villagers for years. A minor industry of interest is the manufacture of cricket bats and so on from the willows. But perhaps the most lucrative of all trades—in normal times—is the exploitation of tourists.

Srinagar

For this, of course, the capital Srinagar (207,787) is the centre: "quaint" in itself, with its carved wooden architecture, immediately surrounded by the beautiful Mogul gardens and magnificent lake and river scenery, central for hunting and mountaineering, it is—on the surface—one of the most attractive cities in all Asia. But it has always been liable to fire and to flood, at times to earthquake; its site obviously leaves much to be desired from a sanitary point of view.[17] Nor, if report be true, are its citizens any more virtuous, in any direction, than they need be.

The factories of Srinagar are largely due to state enterprise, and make it the only industrial centre of the slightest note in Kashmir. But craft industries are more important. Neglecting the obvious tourist lines—silver and copper work, wood-carving, papier-mâché and lacquer—the leading crafts are probably carpet-weaving and leather work: leather gear of various sorts is essential to transport in the mountains, and the products

[17] In the 1892 cholera epidemic 600 people died in one day "and the only shops which remained open were those of the sellers of white cloth for winding sheets." The total mortality was 5781 of a population around 120,000 (*Gazetteer*, 119).

have a high standard of durability. The supply of hides and skins was large, as the Hindu orthodoxy of the ruling house prohibited cow-slaughter and so inflated the numbers of cattle. The production of high-grade rag paper was once important, but has declined before the growth of the Indian mill industry. Finally we may note the importance of water-borne traffic: much of the provisioning of the city is done by flat-bottomed boats, 50–60 ft long and drawing 2 ft or so, which can carry up to 30 tons of cargo. The boat-men, particularly those who man the tourist house-boats, have a reputation for supplementing licit earnings by following the world's second oldest trade.

Much of the importance of the Vale, and hence of Srinagar, lies in its function as a staging-base on the Himalayan routes. The Sn entries have already been mentioned; to the NW the road to Gilgit and the Oxus lies across the Raj Diangan Pass (11,800 ft) into the Kishen Ganga Valley and then by the Burzil (13,755) into Astor; both these passes not without danger in winter. But the most important trade route, leading either up the Indus into Tibet or across the Karakoram into Sinkiang, is that to the NE by the Zoji La. At 11,578 ft this is the lowest col on the main W Himalayan axis, a pass of the Maloja type with the steep ascent on the S: this is due to the Sind cutting back into the headwaters of the Dras, which lies on the drier side of the mountains and has much farther to go before it reaches 5200 ft, the local base-level of the Sind.

If anywhere on earth presents the semblance of the Happy Valley of *Rasselas*, it is the Vale of Kashmir; but however pleasant the prospects, the human history of the region has been, on the whole, vile. To begin with, it is probably over-populated; density in Anantnag (Srinagar) Dt is 303 (and of course far higher in relation to cultivated area), and it is significant that sugar and grain come next to cotton goods in the Kashmiri import list. Beyond this it is hardly an exaggeration to say that the whole history of Kashmir for the last few centuries has been one of misgovernment and oppression, often deliberate, of the peasantry for the benefit of narrow Court cliques; nor was this tradition dead in this century. At this point it is probably appropriate to discuss the present Indo-Pakistani conflict.

THE KASHMIR DISPUTE

'The trouble in Kashmir' stems finally from the simple fact that a popu-lation 77% Muslim was ruled by a family of the strictest Hindu orthodoxy, descendants of a particularly able and ruthless *condottiere* under the Sikhs, Gulab Singh of Jammu, who 'mediated' between British and Sikhs to his own profit. It is safe to say that at no time in the century's existence of the state have relations between the dominant Dogra Rajputs of Jammu and the Muslim majority been other than those of exploiters and exploited, to such an extent that until quite recently agricultural progress was still inhibited by the peasant's simple reflection that, if any profit resulted, the tax-gatherer would seize it.

With the removal of British rule the throne of Kashmir became more than shaky; it is ironic to reflect that, while Congress had frequently proclaimed that only British bayonets kept the Princes on their thrones, *Indian* bayonets were not backward to support the least reputable of the major ruling houses.[18] Legally the ruler's right of adherence to *India* is unquestionable, and this is the basis of the *Indian* claim. Pakistan, of course, points to *Indian* inconsistency in apparently refusing the same right of option— or even of abstaining from option—to the Nizam of Hyderabad. It is not difficult, however, to put forward a reasonable justification of *India's* action in Hyderabad, and moreover Pakistanis are not really entitled to make this point, since shortly before the Kashmir crisis exploded they were seemingly prepared to accept the adherence of the Muslim ruler of Hindu Junagadh, which is not even contiguous with Pakistan.[19] The Pakistani case was still further weakened by complicity in the invasion of NWFP tribesmen; but the alternative might well have been an incursion into the Punjab, and they could only have been restrained by force of Muslim against Muslim: in the summer of 1947 this would have been beyond human nature. The respective proportion of looting and liberation in this tribal incursion cannot be evaluated, and the situation was worse confounded by the virtual war-within-a-war of the Punchis in support of their own ruler against the Dogras of Jammu. It seems that at first many 'Azad Kashmir' troops were genuine volunteers from the Pakistan army, returning on leave (rather freely granted) to their homes in Punch. Later, however, Pakistani intervention was avowed, and this has given *India* her strongest diplomatic weapon. On the *Indian* side much has been made of the democratic nature of Shaik Abdullah's 'People's Government' and its programme of reforms such as the expropriation of (mainly Hindu) landlords. It is impossible to reach any firm judgement. At present there is an uneasy truce along a cease-fire line which leaves *India* holding Jammu and part of Punch, all the Vale, and most of Ladakh W of the Burzil Pass. The charges of oppression from both sides of this line are too probably true, and again it is impossible to assess fairly the work of the rival governments; either territory is in the full swing of rehabilitation and social reform, or stagnant and starving, according to the source of information so liberally supplied by either party.

Leaving these legal and moral issues aside, as appearing to the candid outsider pretty fairly balanced, it would seem that if economic geography should count for anything, then Pakistan's case is stronger than

---

[18] It must be admitted, however, that His Highness has been relegated to an obscurity more decent than his previous fame. It is sad to reflect that this tragedy is in the last resort the result of the decision of one man placed in his position by the historic accident of a century ago.

[19] And the Junagadh question is still not entirely dropped.

India's. The importance of Kashmir water to W Punjab, for both irrigation and power, has been stressed already; Kashmiri timber was also very important to W Punjab, and conversely had its main outlet there, since exploitation depended largely on rafting down the rivers which all flowed into *W* Punjab. The Sialkot sports goods industry used Kashmir willow and resin. The import of salt for the Kashmir tanneries is also more costly from *India* than from the Salt Range mines, and Pakistan would obviously find it easier to supply the food deficit than would *India*. Oil is essential for transport into the Vale, and Pakistanis claim that the natural supply would be from Attock or SW Asia through Karachi.

The natural links of Kashmir are mainly with W Punjab. All roads are difficult to maintain, but the Jhelum route is really the only all-weather one. It is only 185 miles from Srinagar to Rawalpindi, 250 to Amritsar, and the *Indian* route is badly snow-bound (or at least impeded) for three months on the Banihal Pass, while its sub-Himalayan stretch lies athwart the drainage of an area notoriously liable to gullying and landslips. Fruit and timber were the largest exports from Kashmir, and while Pakistan has far more potential resources in temperate fruits than has *India*, the timber situation is the reverse.

Six years after the original outbreak no solution of this not so cold war was remotely in sight. At this stage Shaik Abdullah showed signs of playing his own hand and was obviously reluctant to enter the *Indian* union on the same terms as the other states; indeed he secured substantial constitutional concessions. His supersession further inflamed Pakistani feeling, fearful of a *fait accompli*; but at the same time the crisis held a clear warning that *India* also could overplay her hand *vis-à-vis* the Kashmiris. Hence the dramatic suddenness with which, in August, 1953, both countries agreed at last on a time limit—twelve months—for the ever-receding plebiscite.

But the organisation of it will raise difficulties. Is it to be a simple yes or no, *India* or Pakistan? If the Kashmiris are to decide, it might be that they should have the option of opting for neither, risky as that might be. *India* and Pakistan are likely to be at one in vetoing this, if in nothing else. Then again neither side, for internal political reasons, could well accept complete cession as a result of a possibly narrow adverse majority. However unsatisfactory, and however difficult it is to decide on the basic units, partition seems the only way out.

Indus Kohistan and Gilgit

Nanga Parbat and the Gorges

Nanga Parbat, the mighty NW pillar of the Great Himalaya, is almost separated from the main mass by the valleys of the Kishen Ganga and the

Astor, between which lies the Burzil Pass; and to the N and E it is moated by the deep gash of the Indus gorges. In several ways it differs from the main mass. "Located at a structural interference of two major geanticlines, both of which have undergone repeated uplift in the Quaternary", it consists of a core of granitoid gneiss with a "massive envelope" of sedimentary gneisses; the strike is N/S (probably the result of its situation on the syntaxis) instead of the normal NW/SE of the Kashmir Himalaya. There are no signs of nappes here, but to the N late Tertiary and even early Quaternary sandstones are folded in a steep syncline along the Indus Valley: "thus this very young folding appears here locally in the crystalline inner zone." [20]

The massif carries about 100 sq mls of snow-fields, draining into small glaciers descending nearly 8000 ft below the snow-line. Several erosion platforms can be traced, especially notable at just over 13,000 ft "where the rounded and flattened ridges and broad rudimentary valleys, cut short in front, resemble the old morphology of the Deosai plateau." [21] Nevertheless perhaps no mountain in the world is quite so impressive; certainly not Everest, perhaps not even K2. This is due to the intense erosion around it: the land falls to the N by 23,100 ft in 14½ miles, 20,600 in 17 to the W, 19,600 in 14 to the E; the relatively gentle Sn declivity is about 650 ft per mile. Vast moraines and talus slopes hardly soften a relief which includes precipices of 12,000–13,000 ft nicked by tiny hanging valleys and glaciers.

Round this massif the Indus flows in gorges 15,000–17,000 ft deep and only 12–16 miles wide. The floor itself is relatively wide and flattish, hot and arid, "a desert embedded between icy gravels". It was formerly fairly peopled, but ruined by the great flood of 1841 when the gorge was blocked by a landslide on the Hattu Pir cliff near the Astor confluence: the burst swept away a Sikh army on the river-bed at Attock. The Hattu Pir is "scarred with the remains of the many difficultly aligned and skilfully built paths, most of which have fallen hundreds of feet into the river below. . . . A heavy rock, stone shoot, or sharp shower of rain, any one of these is enough to destroy the tenderly cared-for road." [22] Round Bunji there are three to five gravel terraces lying on sands which seem to indicate a former lake—a point of some importance in connection with the Potwar erratics problem (below, 443).

This is Indus Kohistan—emphatically the 'land of mountains' in a mountainous land. In the tributary valleys are a few isolated villages, dependent on buckwheat and *grim*; in much of the gorge the walls are too steep to carry a track except at 4000–5000 ft or more above the river, and

[20] de Terra, 231; P. Misch and W. Raechl in "Scientific Work of the German Himalaya Expedition to Nanga Parbat, 1934", *HJ* VII (1935), 44–52.

[21] Raechl, *loc. cit.*, 47–48.

[22] R. C. F. Schomberg, *Between the Oxus and the Indus* (1935), 16–17; see pp. 29–30 for an amusing account of the difficulties of managing the swinging bridges—up to 100 yards long—made of birch- or willow-bark ropes.

communication—impossible in winter—is easier (*le mot juste?*) over the shoulders of the mountains.

The Astor Valley marks the transition from the vivid colours of rock, field, and wood in the Vale to the desolate outer marches of Kashmir. Agriculture in this dry valley is carried up to 9000 ft by little irrigation channels, but low temperatures render it precarious: wheat, barley, pulses, maize, buckwheat, lucerne, and other fodder crops are grown.

Gilgit

Beyond the Indus lies Gilgit, and around it the Frontier Illaqas, more or less feudatory to Kashmir. Although we have it on the high authority of Holdich that where small parties of Buddhist pilgrims "made their way with infinite pain and difficulty to the great monasteries of the Peshawar plains, no military force of any consequence ever has, or ever could, follow their footsteps",[23] nervousness about Russian intentions led to the preservation of the long panhandle of Afghan territory, 15–25 miles wide, in Wakhan, the valley of the Ab-i-Panja branch of the Oxus, and at no point did the two great Empires actually touch.

Outside Gilgit itself the area is held by a congeries of petty tribal republics and chieftaincies of which Hunza is the most important; Schomberg gives them all (except Hunza and Yasin) a bad name for turbulence, murder, intrigue, avarice, dishonesty, laziness, stupidity, and general backwardness. The population is very slight, in Gilgit and the frontier some 120,000 in all on 18,000 sq mls; the density in Astor is 10, Gilgit proper 15, Frontier Illaqas 4. But in relation to cultivated area it is a different story—in 1901 the Gilgit density was 1295.

Settlement is usually on little terraces in the better valleys; one such is occupied by Gilgit itself, a nodal centre near the junction of the Gilgit and Hunza Rivers, which between them drain nearly the whole area between the Indus and the 20,000–22,000 ft peaks of the Hindu Kush. At Gilgit rice and cotton are grown as well as the usual montane crops and fruits; higher up Yasin has even a tiny export of wheat and barley. Hunza is even better: 30–40 sq mls of tiny terraced fields, orchards and poplars, and "curling along the bleak stony hillsides" carefully engineered *kuls* provided with little tunnels for the escape of scree from the slopes above. "All are of dry masonry, all have been built without scientific aid, with nothing more than industry, common sense, and the usual tools of a peasant; ibex horns were chiefly used." Fruit culture is of the utmost importance to life in these valleys, and above all the apricot, according to Schomberg the sole diet for weeks on end.[24]

[23] *India* (1904), 105; but cf. Sir Aurel Stein, "A Chinese Expedition across the Pamirs and Hindukush, A.D. 747", *GJ* LIX (1922), 112–31. Lord Ronaldshay (*Lands of the Thunderbolt* (1923), 141) aptly calls Gilgit and Chitral "listening-posts in the vast system of natural defences which keep silent and eternal watch over the teeming plains of Hindustan."

[24] Schomberg, *op. cit.*, 59–60, 112–13.

The Great Himalaya and the Zaskar Range

The Great Himalaya may be taken as commencing in the Indus bend; across that river, in Swat, the strike is swung round by the syntaxis and is practically at right angles to the NW/SE trend of the main range. From the Zoji La to the Indus the really high ground (over 15,000 ft) is broken into a number of distinct massifs, of which Nanga Parbat is by far the most conspicuous; E of the Zoji La the passes are nowhere below 15,000 ft until the great break of the Sutlej/Spiti Valley—a distance of 250 miles, in which there are several peaks over 21,000 ft. To the S are the En continuation of the Pir Panjal (here 15,000–18,000 ft), beyond the Chandra-upper Chenab Valley, and S again the Dhaoladhar (10,000–15,000) with the upper Ravi between it and the Pir Panjal; the Beas itself as a whole cuts across the trend, with longitudinal stretches. Between the Great Himalaya and the Indus the same lines are well shown in the Zaskar Range [25] and its reticulate drainage pattern, e.g. the Sn Shigar, the headstreams of the Zaskar River, and the valleys of inland drainage in Rupshu.

"As a tectonic unit, the Great Himalaya is made up of the roots of the Kashmir nappe, the principal geanticline within the main Himalayan geosyncline, consisting of the Archaean and pre-Cambrian sedimentary rocks together with large bodies of intrusive granites and basic masses." [26] The granitic intrusions are post-Cretaceous, perhaps associated with the actual orogeny, and the thrusts of this area are not comparable with the great nappes of the central and En Himalaya, so far as is yet known.

The area N of the main axis is more interesting. The higher Zaskar peaks are seated upon a broad plateau-like range, much dissected, at about 19,500 ft. More definite erosion surfaces are found in Rupshu, round the enclosed basin of Tso Morari, at 16,600 ft, and in the NW the Deosai Plains lie at about 13,000. It is probable that these areas of rolling mature or late-mature terrain are merely the clearest expression of platforms of much greater extent—in Deosai the country intermediate between the deeper valleys and the 15,000 ft plus massifs from Nanga Parbat to the Zoji, and possibly connected with the Pir Panjal surface S of the Vale.[27]

The human geography is naturally almost nil. In the wide open valleys of Rupshu—the lowest are around 13,500 ft—some barley is grown, and here, above Tso Morari, is Korzok, at 15,000 ft claimed as the highest agricultural settlement in the world.[28] A little borax is produced from the saline lakes.

[25] Range nomenclature as on SOI 1/1M sheets 43 (Srinagar), 52 (Leh), 53 (Delhi); but Zaskar is often spelt Zanskar, Dhaoladhar Dhauladhar (both the latter in SOI).
[26] D. N. Wadia, op. cit. (1939), 312.
[27] de Terra, "Physiographic Results of a Recent Survey in Little Tibet", GR XXIV (1934), 12–41; refces at 21, 34. From now on citations from de Terra refer to this paper.
[28] According to S. D. Pant (The Social Economy of the Himalayans (1935), 9, 41) the highest settlement of any description is the pastoral steading of Lwan, N of the Kumaon Himalaya at 19,000 ft.

Zaskar also has its patches of cultivation, and is noted for its hardy ponies. The Deosai Plains "are mournful stretches of grass and stones, with many a bog difficult to cross, and uninhabited but for the marmots, an occasional bear, and swarms of big black gnats. The absence of wood for fuel, the distance from human habitations, and local superstitions regarding 'the devil's place' prevent the people from using the pastures." Such population as there is in the Himalaya/Zaskar region is largely nomadic, and the shepherds of Rupshu "complain bitterly of the heat of Leh"—average annual temperature 40·9° F.! [29]

Ladakh and Baltistan: The Indus Furrow

The Indus and the Ladakh Range: 'Little Tibet'

The Indus rises on the Nn flanks of the Kailas Range, and flows in a great Nly curve until it breaks through that range to the Gartang confluence; this tributary continues the line of the main river through Kashmir, occupying a narrow corridor between the Kailas and En Ladakh Ranges. Below the confluence the Indus holds on a generally straight SE–NW course until the Gilgit joins it at Bunji and it turns to round Nanga Parbat. S of Lake Pangong, however, it makes a sharp bend and cuts through the Ladakh Range,[30] which it pierces again above the Shyok confluence. This great furrow is on the whole fairly graded; from the Gartang confluence to Bunji (c. 450 miles) the fall is only from c. 13,800 to 4600 ft, or about 20 ft per mile. Alluvial flats are found in the extreme E of its Kashmir course, at about 13,800 ft. In the E—Ladakh proper—the whole catchment as well as the immediate valley is narrow, constricted between the closed basins of Pangong and Morari; but in Baltistan the catchment widens somewhat. At Skardu, where the Nn Shigar comes in a few miles below the Shyok, the Indus is often over 500 ft wide and 9–10 ft deep even in winter.

The Ladakh Range between the two Indus gaps forms a remarkably straight wall for some 190 miles: Indus and Shyok flow parallel 25–30 miles apart, and between them the range rises 10,000 ft or more to a rather even crest at 19,000 ft. Again the flanks, gentler on the N, carry evidences of a pre-glacial mature relief: "at 17,450 ft a rolling surface with valleys one to two miles in width separated by low divides . . . head-waters moving sluggishly around sand bars until they break through the terminal moraine walls and fall at a rate of 1600 ft per mile through boulder-choked gorges." The relations between the abrupt steps—often of 1000 ft—in the valley-floors and the moraines indicate that these are old erosion levels, independent of ice action, but affected by inter-glacial uplift. The pre-glacial Indus

---

[29] *Kashmir Gaz.*, 3, 105.
[30] de Terra, however, thinks that the Range bends sharply from NW/SE to W/E just here (18–19, 22, 40, and Fig. 6), and his arguments seem valid. But for convenience the accepted nomenclature of the SOI maps is retained.

valley-floor "must have been at the level of the flat spurs, which now are 3000 to 4000 ft above the valley." [31] The valley and foothills are largely formed of Eocene beds, dissected into sharp ridges which contrast strongly with the bolder granite forms of the mountain wall.

Climate

The climate of Ladakh may be illustrated by the figures for Leh, on a fan in the Indus Valley at 11,500 ft:

Temperature ° F.

J.	F.	M.	A.	M.	J.	J.	A.	S.	O.	N.	D.	
17·3	18·8	30·9	42·9	49·8	57·8	62·6	61·0	53·7	42·7	32·1	22·1	Ra. 45·3

Precipitation, inches

J.	F.	M.	A.	M.	J.	J.	A.	S.	O.	N.	D.	
0·4	0·3	0·3	0·2	0·2	0·2	0·5	0·5	0·3	0·2	0·0	0·2	Tot. 3·2

The absolute minimum is about minus 19° F.; mean annual pressure 20 ins.; mean relative humidity *c.* 40% from May to November, *c.* 70% in winter.[32] Farther W, around Skardu, conditions are a little less extreme. In the thin atmosphere insolation and radiation alike take place at an extreme tempo; mechanical disintegration of the rocks is rapid, and the saying that a bare-headed man with his feet in the shade can get sunstroke and frostbite simultaneously is hardly an exaggeration. Aspect and diurnal variation are of the greatest importance; many streams even in summer flow for only a few hours a day when the ice melts in their gravel beds. Vegetation is extremely thin: a few bushes, a kind of furze (*burtse*), stunted cedars, willows, alpine pasture: "timber and fuel are the most pressing wants of the people."

But it must be remembered that here climate, like nearly everything else, is 'vertical' and the mountains receive a fair precipitation: "the vertical diversity of the climate makes human life possible in Indian Tibet. To the east, where the mountain ranges die out, the country is too dry for any permanent settlement." [33] Without the glaciers and snow-fields even the W would be a desert; and even so the life of the region is in a sense an oasis and caravan life.

The Human Response

We are really neither in *India* nor in Pakistan, but in Tibet: Baltistan, it is true, is mainly Muslim, but in Ladakh proper are two-thirds of the sub-continent's 64,000 Buddhists, and Buddhist culture extends as far W as Kargil in the Dras valley.

---

[31] de Terra, 33–36.
[32] W. G. Kendrew, *The Climates of the Continents* (1937 ed.), 150–51.
[33] G. E. Hutchinson, *op. cit.*, 127–28.

The Indus furrow is in general broken, rocky, barren, and dry. But every snow-fed tributary builds its fan, and where there is enough water the stream is split into radiating channels: "the living greens of apricots, willow trees, and little fields of barley make the surrounding desert appear uniformly parched and brown." E of Leh the Indus flows for 20 miles along a fault which brings it against the softer Eocene rocks; here there is a little alluvial plain and the fans "end abruptly against swampy fields, so that a man can stand with one foot in a desert and the other on damp green grass". This is perhaps the best-peopled part of the region, which has an average density of 4. The plain is dominated by Hemis Gompa, the most important Buddhist monastery of Little Tibet.

Beardless *grim* barley is the dominant crop, and can be grown to nearly 15,000 ft; at lower altitudes two crops a year may be possible, as the plant matures very quickly. Wheat, buckwheat, pulses, roots, and lucerne are grown in sandy carefully-manured soils; new soil is brought to the fields from hill-side pockets, or sprinkled on the snow to melt it when it lies late. Ploughing and transport are mostly by the *dzo*, the offspring of the cow and the yak bull. The grain is ground by water-mills of rough but ingenious construction.[34]

The people are in part nomadic—the Champa herders of sheep and yaks —but the Ladakhis proper are for the most part settled agriculturalists. Although they are often in debt to the monasteries, these are apparently very amenable creditors, and the peasantry is on the whole much more prosperous than the Muslim Baltis down-river; there seems little doubt that this is mainly due to the check on population provided by polyandry and monasticism. The whole atmosphere is Mahayana Buddhist, and the most prominent features of the cultural landscape, after the irrigated fans, are the monasteries, the innumerable *chorten* shrines, prayer wheels, fluttering streamers to affright the demons, and the long piles of *mani* stones on the approaches to villages: "heaps of rubble, shaped like sheds, with a width of twenty feet, a height of five or six, and a length of from fifty to a thousand . . . covered with hundreds of flat stones on each one of which the lamas had inscribed the universal prayer" *om mani padme hum*.[35] Hard as life is, swayed by the most fantastic demonolatry, the people have their full share of the usual Buddhist—or Mongol—cheerful good-fellowship, and are not without amenities: festivals in the winter and, in the short slack season as the barley grows, a living and intricate religious art of painting and dance.

In normal times the transit trade was an important source of income: through Skardu lies the trail to the Muztagh Pass and Kashgar; at Leh, a

---

[34] Details and illustration in Hutchinson, *op. cit.*, 91–94.
[35] E. Huntington, *The Pulse of Asia* (1907), 58–60; cf. G. Dainelli, *Buddhists and Glaciers of Western Tibet* (1933), 41–90, an admirably vivid description.

pleasant little caravanserai town, converge the roads from the Zoji La and the high Himachal Pradesh passes, the Indus road into Tibet itself and eventually to Lhasa, and the route via the Saser and Karakoram Passes (17,480 and 18,290 ft) into Sinkiang. Leh owes its importance mainly to the unusual size of its fan—5 miles wide and 1000 ft thick; purely Tibetan in aspect, it is dominated by the palace of the old Ladakhi kings, a miniature of the Potala at Lhasa.[36] But the Sinkiang trade has been declining for years with the increasing pull of Soviet Asia, and the war in Kashmir has disrupted the external contacts of this remote and fascinating little world.[37]

The Karakoram

Here, rather than on the Pamirs, is the Roof of the World, a mass of rock and ice extending for 250 miles from the Shyok to the Hunza, with the greatest assemblage in the world of giant peaks—33 over 24,000 ft—culminating in the tremendous keeps of the three Gasherbrum summits, all over 26,000, and finally K2 itself (Fig. 67). K2 (Mt Godwin Austen) is an almost regular cone of ice and limestone on a granite/gneiss base; at 28,250 ft it is exceeded only by Everest, but the latter has no such spectacular company of high peaks around it, and "above all it does not display such an immensity of silence and desolation".[38] The very passes are rarely lower than the summit of Mt Blanc (15,782 ft) and several are over 18,000; though some of those shown on the map are probably topographical cols rather than passes in a real sense, the W Muztagh, at 19,030 ft, is certainly the highest trade route in the world. The name Karakoram means 'black gravel' and has been extended from the relatively subdued terrain—at 18,000–20,000 ft!—around the Karakoram Pass in the E.[39] Geomorphologically the region is intensely interesting; its human geography is obviously almost non-existent, but what there is may fairly be called heroic.

As we have seen (Ch. I, 16, 25–26), the Karakoram is probably much older than the Himalaya, as shown for example by the absence of Tertiary sediments between Ladakh and the Nn flank of the Kunlun. Its actual relations with the other ranges of the great orogeny remain obscure; to the NW the Karakoram Ranges abut onto the Pamir/Hindu Kush in a country of very confused topography, while their continuation to the SE is still debateable, but probably via the Pangong Range into the Kailas. The divergence of Himalayan and Karakoram trends is most clearly seen N of the Shyok, but de Terra, who regards the Ladakh Range as the first member of the Karakoram system, draws attention to the swing from NW/SE to W/E

[36] See plate at p. 74 of Dainelli, *op. cit.*
[37] This is dealt with in M. Geary, "Western Tibet" (London Ph.D. thesis, 1948)—a full and admirable study which I have regretfully refrained from using for reasons of space.
[38] F. Grenard, *Haute Asie (Géographie Universelle*, Paris (1939) T.VIII), 343.
[39] Heights and range-names in this section from the beautiful map of the Karakoram (1/750,000) published by the Royal Geographical Society.

about 78°35′ E in all four of his Karakoram Ranges—Ladakh, Pangong, Karakoram/Chang-chenmo, and Karakoram/Lingtzi-tang. This is in some degree paralleled by the Great Himalaya itself, and is shown very clearly in the outline of Pangong Lake, which apparently occupies a rift. The whole may well be controlled by the hidden margin of Gondwanaland.

Huntington noted that "the deep young inner gorge of the Shyok River grows shallower [to the N] and finally merges into the upland plain of Depsang",[40] and de Terra and others have refined on the earlier concept of

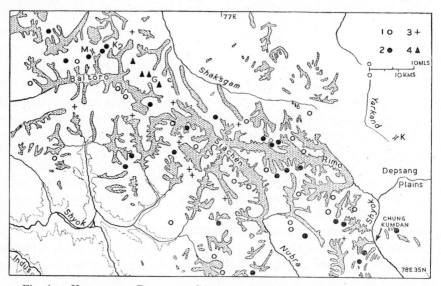

Fig. 67.—KARAKORAM: PEAKS AND GLACIERS. Glaciers dotted, dotted line 10,000 ft contour. M, Muztagh Pass; K, Karakoram Pass; G, Gasherbrum peaks. 1, peaks 20–22,000 ft; 2, 22–24,000; 3, 24–26,000; 4, 26–28,000; K2, 28,250 ft. Based on RGS map *The Karakoram* (1/750,000, 1939).

a vast peneplain dissected as a result of one major uplift; at least four erosion levels may be traced between the Muztagh peaks (*c.* 23,800 ft) and the Deosai/Pir Panjal platforms. The present drainage pattern is distinctly peculiar, especially in the Shyok, Nubra, Chang-chenmo, and Harong valleys; the Chang-chenmo in particular is a misfit, and there is also the through valley from Pangong to the Indus with its summit only 1600 ft above the lake at 13,900. Biological observations strongly support de Terra's view that all the valleys originally drained out to the SE; Hutchinson draws attention to the distribution of the hill barbel in the headwaters of Oxus, Indus, Tsang-po, Mekong, Yangtse, Hwang-ho, and the streams of the great enclosed basins of central Asia [41]:

[40] *Op. cit.*, 78; de Terra (1934), *passim.*
[41] G. E. Hutchinson, "Limnological Studies at High Altitudes in Ladakh", *Nature* (New Series) LXXVII (1933), 497–500; but less technically and more vividly in *The Clear Mirror* (148–52), from which I quote.

But a grander event than simple river-capture must be sought . . . to explain the similarity of the inhabitants of the Indus and the Tsang-po. The flat-edged shoulders of the Chang-chenmo mountains, where butterflies circle around pinnacles of rock, suggest the nature of this occurrence, though they lie aridly in the air, far above the homes of the few fishes that inhabit the stream below. Such flat ridges represent the levels of the valley floors before the last upward movements of the mountains. . . . The remains of such valley floors may be found throughout Indian Tibet. They all record the same history. All the rivers of the land ran toward the Tibetan plateau. . . . Not until quite recent times, when the mountains rose high enough to cut off the rain from the inner deserts of Central Asia, were the more northern of these streams dried up. Then, across the ever-growing Himalayas, gorges were cut . . . draining away the waters of the older rivers. In this manner erosion and earth movements have moulded the pattern of the present Indus, and have cut out the path by which the traveller enters the western confines of Tibet.

The physical characteristics of the Karakoram glaciers have already been discussed (above, 26–28); we may note further the contrast between the generally clear ice of the En Himalayan glaciers, girdled by forest and alp, and the Karakoram icestreams set in barren disintegrating rock and hidden beneath a mass of debris and wind-borne dust. The rivers emerging from their snouts flow over, or more often through and under, great ribbons of shingle. In winter, of course, the entire landscape is frozen, rigid, dead; in summer the streams wake only when the weather is clear. Cloudiness reduces evaporation, and the cold drizzly rain melts little snow; but with a few hours' sun the streams come down in sudden dangerous freshets. The Shyok itself, "a clear rushing stream thirty feet wide", is intermittent in this fashion: "We looked again, but there was no river. Yet even as we were talking about it, a new stream came pouring down a dry channel, a red muddy flood of freshly melted snow." [42]

There is, however, much evidence, morainic and other, of significant climatic change. Pangong at present consists of several lakes separated by deltaic fans, and for the most part is saline; there is no outlet. But beaches at various levels up to 200 ft bear witness to great oscillations, the most notable of which (in the Riss-Würm interglacial) must have allowed it to drain into the Shyok; the tendency has been to desiccation, not without fluctuations. Thus the patina on a palaeolithic artefact from Kargil speaks of aridity, while the representation of deer (with yaks and ibexes) on the sculptured rock at Tankse in the Harong valley suggests that within very recent times conditions have been more favourable to human activity; no deer are now found nearer than the Vale. There was a drier period at Pangong in the last century, but in other places there seems to have been no significant change, to judge from patches of dead ice which have not altered much since 1848. [43]

[42] Huntington, op. cit., 74.   [43] Cf. also T. Longstaff, This My Voyage (1950), 165.

Baltistan, the country between the Nn Shigar and the Nubra, is slightly more favoured than Ladakh, with *c.* 6 ins. precipitation and more glaciers; but it is still very harsh. The valleys at 8000–10,000 ft have a few patches of pine and deodar on the slopes, willow and poplar along the streams. Agriculture depends on the snow, which lies from mid-December to mid-March; in winter many villages are reached by the sun for barely an hour or two a day, but in summer the heat in the narrow rock-walled valleys— especially around Skardu—is intense. The usual crops, with ordinary and naked barley prominent, are grown, a spring and an autumn crop where water is sufficient. Lucerne, carefully tended, is important, but except for intensive manuring of the sandy soils farming is extremely primitive, and rotations unknown. The hot summer enables a wide variety of fruits— peaches, melons, grapes, above all apricots—and even a little tobacco to be grown. But the absence of the demographically restrictive social institutions of Ladakh keeps the Baltis miserably poor. Here and there washing for alluvial gold ekes out incomes a little, or at least enables revenue demands to be met.

To the E conditions get progressively worse. Around Pangong there are a few fields of barley and peas on the fans at 14,000 ft or a little more; at Tankse "the few houses that constitute the village seem to hide behind a little grove of willow trees planted on one side of a stream, as if these trees were the greatest treasure of a place that wished to put up a brave front, a green and damp façade, to the hostile dry world before it". But on the plateaus NE of Pangong even pastoralism is difficult. The Chang-chenmo Valley has some vegetation: tamarisks on the floodplain, *burtse* on the slopes, and just below the snow-line some flowering plants and patches of grass, shared by tame yaks and wild asses. Here and there hot springs "water the gravelly plains into producing a little green grass . . . so precious that each patch has a name." [44]

Yet this most negative of regions has its place in human history. The old trade to Yarkand and Kashgar is dead or dying, but at the hands of man himself: politics in Sinkiang and Kashmir are responsible for its decay, not the desolate leagues of rock and ice nor the murderous winds of the Karakoram. The passes are open for only five or six months of the twelve; but over them, carried on yaks or even sheep, travelled jade, hemp, and silk from China; from India goods from the bazaars of Srinagar and Amritsar, sugar and salt; borax from the dead lakes of Rupshu. Goods of less bulk, but to many of highest value, also traversed this, one of the strangest pilgrim routes of the world. Chinese disciples of the Enlightened One, seeking the shrines of Peshawar and Sarnath and Buddh Gaya or the libraries of Taxila, fought their bitter way over these savage gables of the world; and here too came Christian men, perhaps fleeing from the tide of Islam, per-

[44] Hutchinson, *op. cit.*, 106–07, 128–38. For the facts of the next paragraph, *ibid.*, 108–11.

haps couriers of long-forgotten churches. The great boulder of Tankse bears cryptic testimony to other changes than those of climate. A cross and a long inscription in Soghdian tell of the passage of a Nestorian Christian on the road to Tibet; two words, one unique and untranslateable, of Tokharian also carry the sign of the cross. On another face of the rock the name of Jesus lies among the symbols of Buddhism, dated in the Tibetan manner 'the year of the earth-tiger'; but what year, what century even, cannot be told. Can there be in the world a monument more moving than this rock, in solitude and mystery eternally spelling out its riddle of men who came this way on errands for ever unknown, and rested awhile, and are no more?

BIBLIOGRAPHICAL NOTE

The Himalayas have attracted a voluminous literature, and this is especially true of Kashmir, the Karakoram, and the greater peaks. Much even of the mountaineering narratives is of little geographical value; exception must be made for the records of the Italian expeditions, especially that of de Filippi on which Dainelli did his admirable glaciological work; but this I know only through de Terra. It is regrettable that, except for Heron's geological contributions, the official *Sketch of the Geography and Geology of the Himalaya Mountains and Tibet* (Hayden, Burrard, and Heron, ND, 2nd ed., 1933) shows a less than modest acquaintance with modern geographical ideas, and, while it contains an immense mass of facts, is perhaps the most incoherent scientific work ever put out by authorities of repute.

Of the travel books, those of Huntington and Dainelli are perhaps the most useful; mention may be made of E. O. Lorimer, *Language Hunting in the Karakoram* (1939) and F. Younghusband, *The Heart of a Continent* (1896). *The Geographical Journal* contains many papers, of which those dealing with the Karakoram are the most important (see note to Ch. I above). In the *Himalayan Journal* Professor Kenneth Mason's glaciological studies are especially valuable. Among papers not cited in the text are D. N. Wadia, "The Geology of Poonch" (*Mem. GSI* LI (1928), 185–370), and "Note on the Geology of Nanga Parbat" (*Rec. GSI* LXVI (1932–33), 212–34); and de Terra's important general paper "Himalayan and Alpine Orogenies" in *Report of the XVIth International Geological Congress*, Vol. II (1936), 859–72.

A special word is due to three remarkable books. H. de Terra and T. T. Paterson, *Studies on the Ice Age in India* (Carnegie Institution of Washington, 1939) is indispensable, not least for its splendid series of 56 plates and 193 text figures. In an unclassifiable class is G. E. Hutchinson, *The Clear Mirror: A Pattern of Life in Goa and in Indian Tibet* (Cambridge, 1936): a mannered but beautiful style, an extraordinary range of allusion, and careful scientific observation combine to form a strange but wholly satisfying work of art. Less mannered but as lively and ranging perhaps even wider is Tom Longstaff, *This My Voyage* (1950).

CHAPTER XV

THE HIMALAYAS: CENTRAL AND EASTERN
(Regions VI and VII)

FOR reasons discussed at the beginning of the previous chapter, any division of the Himalayas on a workable scale is likely to be to some extent arbitrary. Once the more massive zoning of Kashmir and the Karakoram is left behind, the arc of 1300 miles from the Ravi to the Brahmaputra gorges is built up of longitudinal belts, some very narrow, cut across by the human groupings: some compromise between the human and the physical is thus necessary, and it is convenient to use even political criteria, of course within the major frame of the mountain mass. Two excursions are necessary. The Tibetan boundary in the W cuts across the physical trends, in the E it often lies S of the crest; the Sutlej Valley, for example, cannot be understood if cut short at Spiti. In the S the terai/bhabar strip can by no stretch of the imagination be considered montane, yet it is genetically the creation of the mountains, the boundaries of the Himalayan political units generally lie within this formerly very negative tract, and its life has intimate links with both plain and mountain. It must thus receive consideration both as the glacis of the Siwaliks and the selvedge of the plains, and we must transgress in the N the political, in the S the physical boundary.

In strict theory these procedures may be only doubtfully legitimate, but the succeeding pages attempt, at least by implication, a pragmatic justification.

Before turning to our *ad hoc* divisions, we may note their place in the general human setting. Between the Buddhism of Ladakh and that, much modified, of Nepal is a broad salient of almost completely Hindu territory. Himachal Pradesh is a congeries of petty states, the holdings of Pahari (= hill) Rajput chiefs driven there when the Muslims forced the Delhi gate and so split the Rajput domain. In Kumaon the ethnic complex is more strongly tinged by Mongoloid strains, but except in the extremest N the whole texture of life is Hindu. In Nepal Buddhism still lives, whether surviving from the days when Asoka held sway there, or creeping down from Tibet; this is perhaps a function of the agricultural bases offered by large longitudinal valleys, together with the defensive curtain of the exceedingly malarial terai. In Sikkim and Bhután Buddhism is the ruling faith. Beyond, in the Himalayan fringe of Assam, the pattern of life is culturally tribal and animist, the ethnic stocks Mongol.

We may then divide the whole area as follows:

CENTRAL HIMALAYA

Himachal Pradesh

Himachal Pradesh, formed in 1948 from the 20-odd Punjab Hill States (less Tehri Garhwal), is controlled directly from Delhi, perhaps for strategic reasons. Bilaspur is separately controlled by Delhi, pending submergence by the Bhakradam. The region here considered also includes Kangra Dt between the main body of Himachal Pradesh and the Chamba exclave; the Siwalik parts of Hoshiarpur Dt, and the tiny enclaves of once-British territory around Simla. The total area is about 18,000 sq mls with 2,000,000 people.

Physical Features

There is the usual longitudinal arrangement: the Siwaliks, here with a remarkably even crest at 2000–3000 ft, but largely deforested and savagely eroded, forming the *chos* torrents which bring ruin to the plains below (Fig. 90); the tangled mass of intermediate spurs up to 7000–9000 ft; the 'Lesser Himalaya', here forming a definite range, the Dhaoladhar (12,000–15,000 ft) which separates the longitudinal sections of Beas and Ravi, the latter in turn walled off by the continuation of the Pir Panjal from the long NW/SE extension of the Chenab in the Chandra Valley; finally the Great Himalaya, which on the whole is lower and more broken here than in E Kashmir or Kumaon.

S of the crystalline core in the Great Himalaya the rocks are exceedingly varied: slates, phyllites, schists, quartzites, crystalline limestones, for the most part, probably, of Dharwarian and Vindhyan (Huronian and Torridonian) age. They are arranged in a great series of nappes: "Four overthrusts are noted which have trespassed over the 64 miles broad Upper Tertiary area of Kangra and restricted it to 16 miles at Solon" S of Simla. Simla itself lies on a klippe, with the Tertiaries exposed in a great window to the N, between Simla and the Sutlej.[1] Confused as the topography is in detail, old erosion levels are everywhere perceptible.

The layout of the Ravi and Beas valleys is similar to that of the Chenab, and, presumably, so is their genetic history, whatever it may be. At the head of the Beas, however, the Kulu Valley is nearly transverse to the main trends. The echelonning of these rivers, flowing roughly parallel at different levels,

---

[1] D. N. Wadia, *Geology of India* (1939 ed.) 312–13 and Fig. 35.

has suggested the tunnelling of irrigation water from Chenab to Ravi and Beas: proposals which have naturally given rise to considerable apprehension in Pakistan.[2]

The Sutlej

Very different from these rivers is the Sutlej, which breaks right through both the Great Himalaya and the Zaskar Ranges,[3] thus forming perhaps the

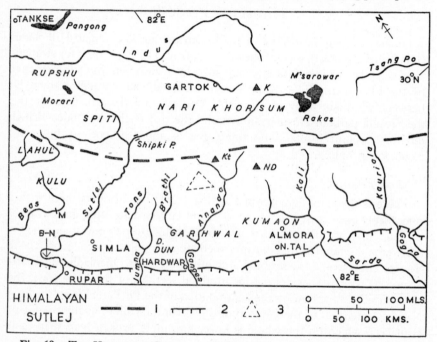

Fig. 68.—THE HIMALAYAN SUTLEJ. 1, Gt Himalaya; 2, Siwalik front; 3, Gangotri-Kedarnath-Badrinath peaks. K, Kailas; Kt, Kamet; ND, Nanda Devi; M, Mandi; B–N, Bhakra–Nangal dam sites.

most striking physical feature of the region (Fig. 68). As we have seen (Ch. I), Davies holds that the Sutlej is a young river, developed by collapse along a line of weakness—a Gondwana trough continued by the line of the Ghaggar (below, 484); and, doubtful as some of his arguments seem, the great cleft, 5000–7000 ft deep and 100 miles long in a straight line from N of Simla to Shipki, bears all the marks of youth, in strong contrast to its upper valley in Hundes or Nari Khorsum (Tibet). This is a broad arid basin at 14,000–16,000 ft, filled with detritus in which the glacier-fed river has cut a canyon said to be 3000 ft deep in places; at one point the Sutlej/

[2] See F. J. Fowler, "Some Problems of Water Distribution between East and West Punjab", *GR* XL (1950), 583–99. Tunnels 4 and 5 miles long, at 10,000 and 7700 ft, would be needed. It will be time enough for Pakistan to worry when *India* finds the money.

[3] And the Ladakh Range also, if Gurla Mandhata is taken as its SE culmination.

Karnali watershed is reported to be level "alluvium". The fall of the river itself is steep enough—5000 ft in about 200 miles from Rakas Tal to Shipki, and it has cut 600–700 ft deeper than its neighbours Beas and Giri (Jumna). Despite the fact that Heim and Gansser claim that "it has long been known that the Sutlej has ceased to derive any of its waters" from Rakas Tal and Manasarowar, owing to depression, it seems almost certain that the feeders of these lakes are in fact its sources. The upper lake, Manasarowar, has a water connection with Rakas Tal, at least in summer. According to some accounts the Sutlej course is dry for some 20 miles below Rakas, the suddenly emerging stream being presumably fed by underground channels through the gravelly detritus. But Swami Pranavananda states definitely that the "old bed" contains water in August. The large aggraded basin with the obvious youthful incision of the Sutlej itself certainly looks very much like capture of old Indus waters.[4]

Between the Zaskar and Great Himalaya crossings the Sutlej receives the Spiti from the NW, which leads us back to Rupshu. Here, too, the river is sunk deep between alluvial terraces; "the upper basin of the Spiti, in Rupshu, has been separated by local uplift combined with the accumulation of detritus: it has only enclosed lakes", of which the most important is Tso Morari.[5]

Climate

The montane climates are, of course, extremely diverse according to aspect and elevation. In Kangra the Dhaoladhar has over 100 ins., but a little to the N "two or three weeks of mist and drizzle represent the monsoon." Kulu has 30–40 ins., but the Sutlej gorges, transverse to the monsoon currents, are very dry, and in Spiti the scanty precipitation is almost entirely snow. Simla, at 7250 ft, represents fairly well the outer hills:

Temperature, ° *F.*

J.	F.	M.	A.	M.	J.	J.	A.	S.	O.	N.	D.	
38·8	40·6	51·5	59·3	66·0	66·9	64·3	62·8	60·9	56·7	50·1	43·4	Ra. 28·1

Precipitation, inches

J.	F.	M.	A.	M.	J.	J.	A.	S.	O.	N.	D.	
2·5	2·7	2·7	2·3	2·8	7·2	17·0	17·4	5·9	1·0	0·5	1·0	Tot. 63·7

Economy and Settlement

Most of the population consists of settled agriculturalists, with pastoralism and caravan trading becoming progressively more important to the

---

[4] On the Sutlej problem see: Burrard, Hayden, and Heron (1934), 227–32; L. M. Davies, "Geographical Changes in North-West India", *Proceedings 6th Pacific Science Congress* (1940); Heim and Gansser (1936 A) 96, 212; Swami Pranavanandra, "The Sources of the Brahmaputra, Indus, Sutlej and Karnali", *GJ* XCIII (1939), 126–35, an admirable paper full of good logic and convincingly circumstantial detail.

[5] Grenard, 349 (full references in note at end of chapter).

N.[6] Agricultural rhythms in the higher areas are largely controlled by snow-fall: in Lahul (the uppermost parts of the Chenab valley) and Spiti sowing takes place as soon as the ground is free from snow, about the end of April. Lower down, two crops are grown in some areas, such as the Kangra (Beas) valley: wheat, barley, and gram as rabi (sown September–December) and maize and rice as kharif (sown April–July). The 9979 sq mls of Kangra, nearly half the area of the region and straddling right across it, may be taken as typical. Of the total area of 5,644,000 ac. about 12% is returned as forest, but much of the 4 m. ac. uncultivable is presumably forested. The NSA is 480,000 ac., but multiple cropping adds another 255,000. Little but food is grown (596,000 ac. foodgrains of TSA 735,000), the chief crops being wheat, maize, and barley in that order.

Agricultural practices vary enormously, from precarious fields on tiny river-terraces in Spiti (where 2 sq mls, about 0·1% of the area, are culti-vated, solely to barley) to the fairly intensive cultivation of the Kangra valley, and the Kiarda and Jaswan *duns* behind the Siwaliks. In Kangra Dt the fields are

> generally unenclosed, but in some parts surrounded by hedges or stone walls. In the Kangra valley, where rice cultivation prevails, the fields descend in successive terraces levelled and embanked, and where the slope is rapid they are often no bigger than a billiard table. . . . where the country is less broken, the fields are larger in size, and the broad sloping fields, red soil, and thick green hedges are charmingly suggestive of a Devonshire landscape.[7]

Apart from subsistence crops, there are a few very small tea plantations (9000 ac. in Kangra) and, of growing importance, market-gardening both for hill stations and for the cities of the plain: potatoes are especially wide-spread.

Forestry is of great importance—indeed, it was disastrously so in the Siwaliks until conservation was enforced. Timber includes deodar from the higher forests, especially in Kulu, *chir* from the outer hills, with bamboo from the Siwaliks, where also *sabai* grass is cut for fodder and paper-making. Mineral resources are widely scattered and include lead, copper, antimony, and zinc. But it is not likely that they will ever be of much im-portance: the antimony and zinc, for example, are found in "deposits of considerable size," but the location at the end of a Lahul glacier at about 12,000 ft is rather against them.[8] The most important mineral output is slate from quarries at Kangra.

The major industrial resource of the region is not of local importance: this is hydro-electricity. So far the only development of any importance is

---

[6] See Y. D. Malhotra, "The Semi-Nomadic Gaddis of the Dhaula Dhar", *SGM* LI (1935), 14–21.

[7] *Punjab Gaz.* (1908), I. 363.　　　　　[8] Wadia, *op. cit.*, 354–55.

at Jogindernagar (Mandi state) on the Beas, where 48,000 kW of a potential 72,000 are generated. Power is—or has been—transmitted as far as Lyall-pur, and the recent development of a wide range of light industries in and around Lahore and Amritsar depends entirely on this source. At Partition *India* thus controlled the most important source of industrial power in the Pakistani Punjab: the significance of this needs no stressing.

The population is remarkably dense for so mountainous an area, although of course it is markedly concentrated in the *duns* of the S, and in Spiti and Lahul the density sinks to 4 or 5. But Kangra as a whole has 90 and Himachal Pradesh[9] 97. Sirmur, which includes the Kiarda *dun*, has 143, and even Bashahr, which lies astride the Sutlej below Shipki, 32. But settlement is hamletted rather than nucleated: two-thirds of the people live in groups of under 500 souls. Indeed, between Simla and the plains the unit is often an isolated farmstead, its fields occupying the sunnier sides of a little valley left hanging by the rapid erosion of the main stream, or a fragment of terrace, or the end of a little spur: below the centrally-placed square-built stone farmstead is contour-bunded paddy, with maize on un-irrigated slopes, and perhaps one or two field-huts. Building, while not reaching the massive solidity of Ladakh, reflects the rigours of winter and the availability of good timber and stone.

Apart from the hill stations of Simla (see Ch. VII) and Dalhousie, and petty state capitals, urbanisation is negligible: the 1941 figure was 2·6%, lower than that of any other units except the Bengal and Orissa states, and the rubric that a town is what the Census Superintendent likes to call a town must have been interpreted liberally, since the average town popula-tion was 3606—not much over half the figure for the other states men-tioned. There are, however, two mountain railways (2 ft 6 in. gauge), to Simla and to Jogindernagar; and the war in Kashmir has forced on the construction of the Kangra–Kashmir road. Apart from the economic strategy of power production, the region has a locational strategic value, athwart routes into Tibet, flanking those into Kashmir.

The Far North

To the N the cultural landscape of agriculture and Hinduism gradually gives way to that of pastoral Tibet: in NE Bashahr polyandry is prevalent, and religion and language are transitional. In Lahul January *means* are below freezing and most of the country is "entirely uninhabited, except for a few weeks in summer, when the Kangra shepherds bring up their flocks". Paradoxically this transhumance is made possible by the absence of any considerable local sheep population: the summer pastures are excellent, but deep snow from December to April (or even June) makes it impossible

[9] Less Kalsia, which is entirely on the plains. It is a good example of state fragmenta-tion: 188 sq mls, 67,393 people, in 20 enclaves from Ambala to Ferozepore.

to keep sheep and goats out of doors, in contrast to more arid Ladakh. The Lahulis are notable caravan traders.

Spiti is even poorer, and more purely Buddhist, a half-independent canton walled in by red and yellow cliffs; the mean elevation of the valley is 13,000 ft. In 1908 there were no schools, police, nor dispensaries; these services were no doubt adequately fulfilled by the three monasteries. The shortest route into Spiti, from Kulu, involves the traverse of a glacier and two passes at 14,200 and 14,900 ft, "so that this is beyond question the most inaccessible part of the British dominions in India".[10]

Hundes lies beyond the confines of India, "a vast little-articulated plateau" walled in by Ladakh and Kailas on the N, the great peaks from Badrinath to Gurla Mandhata on the S. There are a few half-bandit nomadic clans, a handful of monasteries and villages up to 14,500 ft. But around the remote lakes and desolate ravine-scored terraces "where'er we tread is haunted, holy ground". Due N is Kailas itself, which "seems to present the highest Tertiary conglomerate series of our globe still in the position of deposition. The accumulation must have been made possible during subsidence at low levels" followed by an uplift of at least 23,000 ft.[11] This is impressive enough; but the superbly symmetrical mountain is also the holiest of all the sacred places to both Tibet and Hindustan. Here Ganges divides, like the waters of Paradise, into four rivers: Indus, Sutlej, Brahmaputra, Karnali. The sacred way around Kailas is an avenue of cairns bearing the *mani* formula; the circuit is made clockwise,[12] and many pilgrims make it by repeatedly measuring their length on the craggy path; at the highest point, 18,000 ft, are votive piles of their hair and teeth. Yet, bizarre as these expressions of devotion are, it is no ignoble instinct which places 'the axis of the world' on this peak of serenest beauty.

Kumaon

The General Setting

Although the general culture of Kumaon is not dissimilar to that of Himachal Pradesh, it seems yet to have an individuality of its own. Perhaps this merely reflects the greater fame of an area which holds the sacred sources of Mother Ganges and so, despite a rather stronger Mongoloid ethnic infusion, is more deeply impregnated with Hindu tradition. Broadly speaking Kumaon is the country between the Tons feeder of the Jumna

[10] *Punjab Gaz.*, I. 378. These two paragraphs are based on *ibid.*, 371–78—the unacknowledged source of Grenard's account in the *Géographie Universelle.*
[11] Heim and Gansser (1939 B), 224.
[12] A heretical sect, maintaining pre-Buddhist animist traditions, perversely travels widdershins. See Grenard, 349, and the vivid description in Heim and Gansser (1939 A), 95–106.

and the (Maha) Kali feeder of the Sarda, which is the Wn boundary of Nepal. The region thus includes the Himalayan basins of the Jumna, Ganges, Ramganga, and Sarda.

Politically, it consists of the Kumaon Division (Almora, Garhwal, and Naini Tal Dts) of Uttar Pradesh, with Dehra Dun Dt and the state of Tehri Garhwal, now merged with UP. An area of about 19,500 sq mls with 2,250,000 people, the over-all density is 115, reaching 222 in Dehra Dun Dt. The whole area was wrested from the Gurkhas of Nepal after the war of 1814–15. Physically it rises from the sub-Siwalik bhabar to a magnificent series of glacier-garlanded peaks: the Kedarnath/Badrinath group (22,000–23,000 ft), of peculiar sanctity as feeding the Bhagirathi and Alaknanda headwaters of the Ganges; Kamet (25,447) across the Alaknanda; and farther E Trisul, Nanda Kot, and Nanda Devi, the last at 25,645 ft being the highest peak in *India* proper (excluding Kashmir).

Apart from the Dehra Dun and the deeper valleys, most of the region consists of highly dissected country at 6000–12,000 ft, formed of "an anti-clinorium consisting of several anticlines of normal and of fan-shaped type" with twisted strikes, and of great nappes.[13] The general pattern of relief and structure has been described in Ch. I. We may note once again, however, the extraordinarily late date which seems necessary for these movements, tangential as well as vertical. Ten miles NW of Dehra, Upper Siwalik boulders are "so shattered that it is impossible to obtain a hand-specimen of them". It is true that the *major* movements were earlier—probably in Helvetian times—and the upper nappes were then dissected to such an extent that they were "divided off into separated outliers, unable to trans-late the stresses as a unit". The Garhwal movement was at least 50 miles; later, intrusive granites were involved in a movement of several miles towards the SW.[14]

Superimposed, as it were, on this recently mobile and highly complex base are the effects of intense contemporary physiographic activity. It is true that the present glaciation is but the shadow of what it was: on the Alaknanda and Kali the outermost moraines are at 7050 and 6550 ft, while to-day the main valleys are ice-free and the lateral glaciers do not fall below 13,000 ft. "The glaciers in the larger valleys, such as . . . the Milam, are not only covered with detritus for several miles (three to ten), but float, so to speak, on their moraines, which they are no longer capable of sweeping away." But the intensity of water erosion is striking: Heim cites a hanging valley, filled with moraine, the floor of which is at least 160 ft above the present level of the Kali, and this post-glacial erosion is in micaceous schists and quartzites.[15] The reverse is seen in the tremendous detrital

[13] Heim and Gansser (1936), 221.
[14] J. B. Auden, "The Structure of the Himalayas in Garhwal", *Rec. GSI* LXXI (1936–37), 407–33; refce at 429–32.
[15] Heim and Gansser (1939 A), 219, 36–37.

terraces on the edge of Dehra Dun, which has been filled up to a height of 1000 ft above the plains.

The climate shows the usual montane variations. The lower valleys, and still more Dehra Dun, are climatically depressing: hot and sultry in summer, hung with heavy mist until nearly noon in the cold weather, when ranges are extreme. May–June maxima reach 110° F. in valleys below 5000 ft, ridges at 5000 ft or so going up to 94° F. At 6000–7000 ft. the winter mean is *c.* 40° F., at 9000 ft 32°. But at Almora and Ranikhet, on 6000-ft ridges, summer maxima are 85–90°. Precipitation is 40–50 ins. at these towns, rises to 80–100 on the outer 10,000-ft ranges, falls off to 35–40 behind them, but apparently rises again towards the snow-line, which as a rule is at 16,000–17,500 ft. Snow falls as low as 4000–5000 ft. The rainfall régime is normal, the rains beginning in the second half of June, with slight winter falls coming from the N and W. There seems to be some tendency to deterioration, Almora apparently now receiving over 25 ins. less than the 1892–1900 average. Run-off is of course extremely rapid wherever the ground is not blanketed by forest.

Much of the area below 12,500 ft is forested, largely on the Nn slopes with their less direct but more effective precipitation. In ascending sequence we have the sal forest of the terai/bhabar and the Siwaliks; at *c.* 3250 ft begins the evergreen oak/rhododendron forest, with ash, yew, ilex, and bamboo; then the coniferous belt from 10,000 to roughly 11,000–12,500 ft, succeeded by birch/rhododendron forest (up to 13,000 at the highest), and finally alpine scrub and steppe. Isolated rhododendrons are found at 15,400 and on the Tibetan border "adventurous grass-patches" up to 16,000–16,400.

In the region as a whole pastoralism and various trading activities are of less significance than agriculture, but in the higher N they may be said to predominate. Lower down the forests play an intimate part in the life of the people. Mineral deposits are patchy: iron, copper, alum, gypsum, lead, graphite, but none are of any economic significance at present.

It will be convenient to discuss the human geography by the subregions: the Dehra Dun, Kumaon proper, the Bhotiya Valleys.

Hardwar to Mussoorie: the Dehra Dun

Hardwar, where the Ganges breaks the Siwaliks,[16] is a typical contact mart, with the added attractions of the holy river: up to half a million pilgrims may attend the specially sacred twelve-yearly Kumbh Mela, presenting serious problems of police and sanitation. Behind the Siwaliks, as far as the Jumna breach 45 miles to the NW, stretches the great Dun, 15–20

---

[16] In some Hindu literature this water-gap appears as a mighty cleft in Himalayan fastnesses. Merit can be obtained with less exertion than by making the really strenuous pilgrimage to Badrinath—or Kailas.

miles wide and rising from 1200 ft along the two rivers to 2200 in the
middle. The Dun drains pretty equally to Jumna and Ganges, and Dehra
town lies on the low swelling interfluve. To the N the Mussoorie Hills rise
abruptly to 7000–7500 ft (Fig. 69).

With a rainfall of *c.* 90 ins. agriculture should be secure enough, but the
edaphic factors are not too favourable. The Dun is floored by gravelly
detritus with light, thin top-soils; erosion is very active indeed, and losses
by lateral shifting of the mountain torrents, by gullying, by sand and

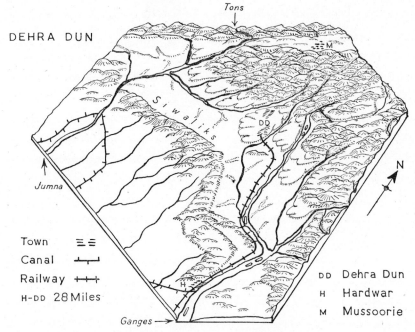

Fig. 69.—Dehra Dun—Block Diagram.

shingle spreads, are serious. The water-table is naturally low; irrigation is
by short canals. On the whole, also, farming methods are poor. The staple
crops are wheat, rice, ragi (locally known as marua or madua), and barley,
and there are fair acreages of maize, oilseeds, orchards (especially of mangoes), and rather poor tea plantations (5000 ac.).

Dehra itself (1951, with cantonments, **144,216**) is not an attractive
town: there is a small Anglicised core and around it a big straggle of loose
urbanism. Nor are the immediate surroundings any better—a tangle of
ravines, pebbly or ankle-deep in fine dust in the dry weather. The Survey
of India headquarters are at Dehra, and to the NW, on rather higher and
more solid ground, are the Indian Military Academy and the Forest
Research Institute; the first and last are among the most important scien-

tific centres of India. All around Dehra the most prominent features of the cultural landscape are connected with forestry: sawyards, piles of sleepers and fuel-wood, furniture shops, and charcoal kilns. Mussoorie (6000) is the usual hill station, less fashionable than Simla or Darjeeling, and much favoured by Anglo-Indians. It is of some importance as an educational centre.

Kumaon

The basis of life in Kumaon is an elaborately organised agriculture. It is impossible to summarise adequately the mass of detail in S. D. Pant's *The Social Economy of the Himalayans*, but the following tabular statement [17] gives some faint idea of its complexity and, though there are of course large local variations, is probably fairly representative of 'intermediate' Himalayan conditions as a whole; specialised sub-types are in parentheses.

KUMAON CULTIVATION TYPES

Local Name	Position	Nature	Crops (K = kharif, R = rabi)
1. *Katil*	Forest edge	"Intermittent" — 2–3 crops in 12 years to 3 in 5; first step to terracing	K: madua, horse gram, buckwheat, turmeric, potatoes; no R.
(a. *kharak*—intensive manuring on garden plots near temporary (pastoral) living-huts)			
2. *Upraon*	Hillsides	High stone terraces	K: madua, dry rice, millets, sugar cane, buckwheat, chillies, turmeric; R: wheat, barley, mustard.
(a. *talliya*—level, alluvial, unirrigated, "buffer" between 2 and 3)			
3. *Talaon*	Valleys	Irrigated, low mud terraces	K: paddy only (3 types of cultivation)*; R: wheat, barley, lentils, mustard, flax.

*(a. *sera*—fine alluvial clay, always plenty of water;
  b. *panchar*—coarser soil, water-supply may be precarious;
  c. *shimar*—waterlogged, only one crop yearly but best paddy.)

A few points may be expanded. The terracing is often most elaborate, covering entire hillsides with steps 5–8 ft high (occasionally up to 20 ft) and 10–20 ft wide: "in some places as many as five hundred of these terraces

[17] Based, with succeeding paragraphs, on Pant, Chs. VI–XIII *passim*. Madua is marua or ragi.

can be counted in continuous flights. In some villages there are more than six thousand terraces." Since it takes a day for one man (assisted by others to fetch the stones) to build a wall a foot thick, six long and three high, the cumulative labour involved is enormous. Maintenance also is arduous in a region where even properly built roads are often swept away by landslips; usually 25–40% of the cultivation terraces give way during each rains.

Rotations are elaborate and ingenious. On the *upraon* the village lands are divided into two compact blocks, the rice and the madua *sars*, and these have an alternating rotation; the sequence is the same on each *sar*, but they differ in phase:

Rice sar				*Madua sar*
paddy, chillies, oilseeds, or buckwheat	1	K	3	madua, pulses or buckwheat
wheat, pulses or mustard	2	R	4	fallow
madua, etc.	3	K	1	paddy, etc.
fallow	4	R	2	wheat, etc.

(K = kharif, R = rabi)

In *talaon* land the three very different systems of paddy cultivation enable the same area to grow kharif rice for years, rotating the type of tillage and introducing different rabi crops.

Soils are generally poor, shallow, and stony, and manuring is very important. Ample fuel-wood permits the storage of cattle dung, and during winter the litter of pine-needles in the cattle-sheds accumulates to form thick layers of compost. Folding of cattle and sheep is extensively practised, and when the Bhotiyas pass through with their flocks there "is sometimes a regular scramble to secure their services".

Irrigation is limited—*c.* 8% of cultivated area—and is mainly by leats (*guls*) from the smaller streams; the larger are too turbulent and too variable to be easily harnessed. Long flumes take the *guls* across ravines. Mills similar to those described in Ladakh are aligned along leats, and on some exceptionally favourable streams they may be stepped as closely as 12 in half a mile.

With the opening up of the outer ranges, as far as Almora and Ranikhet, to the motor-bus, the traditional transhumance is declining, while on the other hand there is a marked extension of market-garden and potato cultivation. But there is still a drift to the bhabar in the severe and agriculturally slack winter; petty trade and forestry work provide useful supplementary income, but a powerful motive is simply the desire of "eating sunshine". The importance of sunshine is also emphasised by the distinction between cultivated *tailo* slopes—the sunny or *adret* side of the valleys—and the forested *saylo* (= Alpine *ubac*).

Villages are usually along spurs low enough to avoid the bleakness of the ridge-tops, but well above the sultry valleys; the village lands often extend in 'strip-parish' fashion, from irrigated valley floor to forested or grassy ridge-top. There are traces of an original tribal settlement in the dialectal and cultural homogeneity of the chain of villages along a spur.

The towns are essentially petty marts: contact points of hill and plain in the bhabar, or nodes of valley- or ridge-ways. Almora (11,000) and Rani-khet (5000) are no longer isolated but retain considerable charm, largely owing to their high tradition of artistic wood-carving; Naini Tal (23,000) is again a favourite Anglo-Indian hill station.

The Bhotiya Valleys

At the highest level live the Bhotiyas,[18] among whom pastoralism and trading are more important than agriculture. Their alpine pastures lie at 10,000–13,000 ft, in valleys with little rain but much winter snow: here are the summer villages, of which Milam, with some 600 families, is the largest.[19] The fields are too small and irregular for ploughs to be much used, and hoe culture is far more common. The growing season is only about four months; wheat and barley are the chief crops, often irrigated by primitive methods on little outwash cones. The junipers and furze-like bushes of the hillsides are carefully preserved to check snow- and land-slips, and before flocks and goods can be moved up from the winter villages advance parties of pioneers are sent on to repair paths and bridges.

The highly mobile life of the Bhotiyas is summarised in Fig. 70: even in winter the Bhotiya men range far afield, generally making two trips to the bhabar market-towns and sometimes going as far as Cawnpore; to the N the range is as far as Gartok. During the long absences of their men-folk the women weave fine woollens, most of the yarn being produced by the men spinning as they walk. The trade into Tibet is mainly in grain, sugar, tea, small metal and general 'bazaar goods', imports thence are salt and borax (both declining), furs, ponies, yak-tails, and above all wool. The main baggage animals are sheep and goats, which can carry up to 40 lbs at 5 miles a day, mules, yaks, and various yak/cattle crosses: these can carry 2–3 maunds (160–240 lbs). The sturdy little Bhotiya ponies are also in much demand in the winter fairs at the upper series of contact marts (I, IV, and XI in Fig. 70). But man himself is the most reliable beast of burden on these all but impassable ways, where the local proverb has it that "it takes 10 goat-herds to drive 9 goats".

A notable contrast with the rest of Kumaon is provided by the higher and more independent status of the Bhotiya women, left for long spells in

---

[18] Bhotiya, Bhot, Bhoti, Bhutia, etc., all = Tibetan and are applied to different tribes from the Punjab to Bhután.

[19] See Heim and Gansser (1939 A), Chs. VI, IX, XI, XIV; Pant, Chs. II, III, XX–XXII.

charge of home and fields, with only the children and the aged to help them. Environmental factors in this situation are not far to seek, though Mongolian affinities are probably also responsible in part.

Nepal

Nepal "remains the last [independent] survivor of those Indian communities which stood for civilization, learning, and culture when Europe

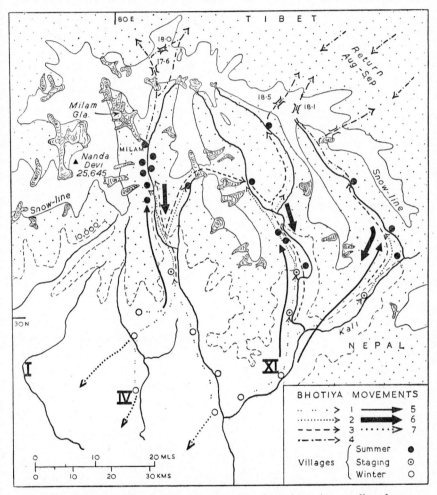

Fig. 70.—BHOTIYA MOVEMENTS. 1, movement of goods to intermediate bases; 2, advance pioneer parties to summer villages (both April–May); 3, goods to summer villages (May–June); 4, traders to Tibet (June–July); 5, families and flocks to upper valleys (June); 6, general descent (October); 7, trading trips to plains (usually 2 trips in Sept.–April). I, IV, XI—sites and months of fairs. Heights of passes in thousand feet. Based on text of S. D. Pant, *The Social Economy of the Himalayans* (1935), 50–60, 195–201, 240–42.

was still in the darkest period of her history. She alone among Asiatic Powers has never suffered either the galling triumph of the Moslem or the political and commercial results of Christian expansion." [20] This statement emphasises the strong cultural individuality of Nepal which in turn warrants its treatment as a separate region; though the extreme E (roughly the Kosi basin) is better taken with its Tibetan approaches by Sikkim and the Arun. Moreover, although Nepal has been mapped by the Survey of India, only Indian surveyors were employed, and, owing to the policy of seclusion, outside the Katmandu Valley little beyond the bare topographical outlines is known to Europeans. Treatment, therefore, must be on different lines from the usual regional pattern, and history and culture enter so intimately into any regional discussion that it seems better to deal with them first.

Generalities: Cultural

The heart of Nepal is the Valley around Katmandu; indeed this *is* Nepal to the Nepalese, the rest being either Terai or Pahar (= Hills). The earlier history is very obscure, but it is at least certain that in the Mauryan era the Valley was a centre of Buddhist culture: here, at Patan, Asoka built four great *stupas*, and at Rummindei, just inside the terai boundary, he erected a still surviving pillar to mark the exact site of the Buddha's birth. After the Muslim invasions and the final decay of Buddhism in Hindustan, Rajput infiltration weakened and overlaid, but did not completely supplant, Nepalese Buddhism, which by this time had taken on a pronounced Mahayana tinge.[21] In the 17th century the Valley was divided between three petty princedoms—their capitals are still the chief towns of the whole country, the centres of two of them, Katmandu and Patan, only two miles apart, and the third, Bhatgaon, a bare six miles away. To the W the Rajputs were consolidating around the little base of Gurkha—whence the name Gurkha loosely applied to all the fighting-men of Nepal. Around 1769 the Gurkha prince, Prithwi Narayan, subjugated the Valley, more perhaps by intrigue, terrorism, and a ruthless blockade [22] than by battle. This was the foundation of the present state, which at first was in an expansionist mood. By the 1780s Gurkha power extended to the Kangra valley, where it was turned back by the Sikh leader Ranjit Singh. On the NE expansion was checked by an unsuccessful war with Tibet, and infiltration into Oudh led to the Anglo-Nepali war of 1814–15.

This was decisive in the sense that neither side cared to try again—a unique phenomenon in British wars with the 'country powers'. Nepal lost Kumaon and some of the terai (later in part retroceded in return for effec-

---

[20] Landon, preface. For "Christian" read "European".
[21] A very clear account of the divergence of the two great Buddhist schools will be found in Lord Ronaldshay, *Lands of the Thunderbolt* (1923), Chs. VII and XII.
[22] There were only 7 feasible entries. Anyone attempting to use them was hanged—"man, woman, or child."

tive assistance in the Mutiny) and had to accept a Resident at Katmandu. In effect, however, the Resident was rather an Ambassador and Nepal remained independent.[23] Perhaps more important, the Court of Katmandu accurately assessed the probable effects of "peaceful penetration"—not perhaps a difficult assessment—and would have none of it. Europeans were admitted only by permission of both the Nepali and Indian governments in every individual case, and permission was not lightly given. The terai was gradually opened to commercial development, but only a favoured few could penetrate to the Valley, and beyond the Valley remained forbidden territory.

Behind the curtain of the malarial terai jungles, Nepal evolved an extraordinary polity, not without much palace intrigue and murder. As in pre-Meiji Japan or Merovingian France, the monarch became a virtual non-entity, all power being in the hands of the Rana family, shoguns or Mayors of the Palace, whose hereditary offices of Prime Minister, Marshal, and Supreme Commander-in-Chief descend in the agnatic manner—i.e. to all brothers of one generation in order of birth, then to the eldest surviving son of the eldest brother, and so on. On the whole the Ranas, if not progressive in the usual sense, were remarkably efficient; those who were not were deposed. A little economic development and social reform took place, but the former was more or less confined to the terai and the Valley, and social stability was preferred to rapid advance.

The resultant was apparently a well-knit state, combining the peasant and the military virtues, and until recently notably free from communal discord despite the fact that the rulers are Rajputs and the mass of the people more or less Mongoloid.

This is probably due in large part to the fact that Nepali Buddhism and Hinduism, while not fused, at least interpenetrate: most observers incline to think that Buddhism is declining, but it has certainly not left its rival unaffected. The pantheon consists of animist nature-spirits and demons, Buddhist boddhisatwas, and definitely Hindu gods; the most popular deity, Machendranath, the bringer of rain, appears to combine all three.[24] This unique culture is reflected in the mingling in Nepali architecture of Hindu and 'Chinese' elements, though there seems at least a possibility that some typical features of Chinese and Burmese building—the superimposed roofs, the bell-shaped pagoda—actually stem from Nepal, which has handed on the ancient traditions of Indian wooden building and of the *stupa*.[25]

The area of Nepal is about 54,000 sq mls; the constantly repeated population figure of 5,600,000 is that of 1920; perhaps by now it is about 7,000,000. The main tribes are Mongol: Gurungs, Magars, Bhotiyas; the

[23] What would have happened had Nepal at any time pursued an anti-British policy is perhaps different. But after 1858 there was no inducement. In 1934 the title of the British Resident was changed to Envoy and in 1947 to Ambassador.

[24] Landon, II. 216.   [25] See Landon, Appx. XX; S. Lévi, *Le Népale* (1906).

first two provide the bulk of the 'Gurkha' soldiery, though the Rajput
Gurkhas proper naturally preponderate among the officers. The terai, of
course, has a considerable Indian admixture, and the Valley is largely
Newar. The correlation of 'Newar' with the Nairs of Sn India is far-
fetched and unconvincing, but there do seem to be persistent and peculiar
links with the S in the earlier religious history. The official language—
Nepali (or Gurkhali or En Pahari)—is akin to Kumaoni and thus belongs
to the Hindi branch of Indo-Aryan speech; but much of the peasantry
speaks one or other of the Tibeto-Burman tribal tongues.

Generalities: Physical

Nepal lies along the Sn glacis of Tibet from the (Sarda) Kali to Kangchenjunga, 80° to 88° E., a distance of 550 miles; the breadth is 100–150
miles. The Sn boundary lies mainly in the terai, though in places it is formed
by the (Someshwar) Dundwa and Sumesar Hills. Beyond the Siwalik
ridges, of which the most important is the Churia Ghati barring the way to
Katmandu, is a broad zone at roughly 3000–9000 ft with strong WNW/ESE
trends, shown in the Mahabharat Lekh and in longitudinal vales, that of
the W Rapti/Kali Gandak/E Rapti being the most striking. The N is largely
occupied by NNE/SSW spurs from the Himalayan crest, such as the
Dhaulagiri (26,795 ft) massif and the Singalila ridge stemming from
Kangchenjunga, the world's third highest peak (28,146). Except for two
salients of Tibetan territory in the Kirong and Kuti Valleys, the Nn boundary lies along the Great Himalaya, from Api (23,397 ft) in the W through
Gosainthan (26,305) and the Everest group.

Not much is known about structures; Auden sums up accurately but in-
conclusively:

> The Siwaliks are probably the only ranges in which geological strike and
> geographical extension properly coincide. . . . The Mahabharat Lekh consists
> of ranges adjacent and roughly parallel to the Siwaliks and composed of a
> varied assemblage of rocks with strikes less constant. . . .
>
> The only definite structural feature which is known to follow through the
> further part of the Himalaya is the main boundary fault, a thrust which, east of
> about 78°, separates pre-Tertiaries from underlying Tertiaries. It is certain,
> however, that the units separated by this thrust are not everywhere geologically
> and geographically analogous. The geology of the lesser Himalaya is so com-
> plicated that more than one geographical feature may be represented by a
> single major tectonic unit. The converse also holds. . . . [26]

As for climate, all that can be said is that the general conditions can be
interpolated from those of the borders.[27] The vegetation sequence is as
follows:

[26] J. B. Auden, "Traverses in Nepal", *HJ* VII (1935), 76–82.
[27] This vagueness is literally all that can be said; Landon has nine references to climate
in his 668 pages, and not one figure.

under 4000 ft (terai
   and Siwaliks)   .   tropical deciduous (sal), riverain (sissoo), savannah
  4000–8500   .   .   oak, maple, pine
   8500   .   .   .   spruce, fir, cypress, larch
  10,000   .   .   .   alpine (rhododendron, juniper).

A point of some interest is the occurrence of deodar in the Karnali basin, an outlier 150 miles E of the normal limit of deodar in Garhwal.

The Terai

This, the least Nepali part of Nepal, is economically perhaps the most important; the policy of exclusion was not so rigorously enforced, and in any case did not apply, in general, to Asian peoples. Hence, despite its limited area—a discontinuous strip 10–20 miles broad—its notorious climate and malaria, and its large areas of savannah and sal forest, the terai holds over two-fifths of the population.[28]

The terai is still exceedingly unhealthy in the rains, when no traveller spends a night in the junglier parts if he can help it; only the Tharus, a tribe of carters, seem more or less immune from the dreaded *awal* fever. The dangers of the terai, including its wild animals, lost nothing in the telling, and have undoubtedly contributed to the seclusion and security of Nepal.

Much is still undeveloped, unless the organisation of vast battues for visiting royalty can be called development [29]; these include the large areas of 'elephant grass', often 15 ft high and so thick that elephants can hardly push through it. There is a good deal of timber exploitation, mainly sal, and much land has been cleared for crops—rice, rabi wheat on the paddy-fields, grain, some sugar and tobacco. Here also are the only railways (33 miles from the border to Bijulpara, 25 to Amlekhganj) and the only industrial development, a few rice mills at Birganj, rice and jute at Biratnagar in the E.

The little towns of the terai are places of trade and transit rather than of residence, with godowns and booths of brick and corrugated iron, almost empty in the hottest weather and the rains. The permanence of these marts is secured by their "position on the high road just where the under-features of the Himalayas burst up through the Terai, and further progress must be by one track alone." [30]

The Valley

The Valley of Nepal is now approached in three stages: rail to Amlekh-ganj, motor road across the Churia Ghati to Bimphedi, track by two steep

[28] 1920 Census (in thousands): Hills, 3032; Valley, 367; Terai 2176 (Landon, I. 256–58). *The Statesman's Year Book* (1950), however, gives 450,000 for the Valley (excluding Katmandu town), but retains the 'estimate' of 5,600,000 in all.

[29] It is typical that Landon's best description of terai topography occurs in the account of a shoot in which King George V secured 21 tigers and 10 rhinoceroses out of totals of 37 and 18 (II. 131–36).

[30] *Ibid.*, II. 7–10.

passes across the Mahabharat Lekh (*c.* 8500 ft) to the Valley; until about
1927 the track descended by rough centuries-worn steps at gradients of
30–45°, in one place 50°. Along this route come the external necessities of
what is in some respects a modern capital, and some luxuries hardly to be
described as 'high value low bulk'—e.g. 4-ton bronze equestrian statues of
the Ranas which were humped across by hand. An electric ropeway, rising
4500 ft above its lower terminal, can bring in loads up to 10 cwt.

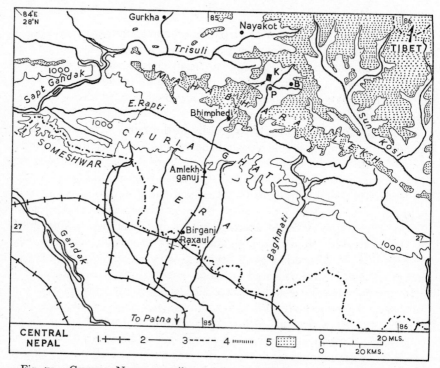

Fig. 71.—CENTRAL NEPAL. 1, railways (all metre ST); 2, motor road; 3, ropeway;
4, track (2–4 on Katmandu Road only); 5, over 5000 ft approx. K, Katmandu; P, Patan;
B, Bhatgaon.

The Valley itself, an amphitheatre about 15 miles across, around the headwaters of the Baghmati, appears to be an old lake-bed. The soils are said
to be fertile, and doubtless are; at all events this is the most intensively
cultivated of Nepali valleys, paddy apparently predominating.[31]

The Valley is concentrated history. The three old capitals are rich with
temples, pagodas, and a domestic architecture in which wood-carving has
been carried to the highest pitch. Katmandu (1920: 108,805) is naturally

---

[31] Neither Landon nor Northey gives any but the vaguest generalities, reserving details
for descriptions of the regalia and so on. But there is a good map (1/63,360) of the Valley in
Landon.

the most important, and has what little industry there is: the most advanced production seems to be that of the Arsenal, which can turn out light howitzers. Parade grounds are prominent in the cultural landscape, and the Ranas have a palace in a vaguely neo-classical style distinguished only by size: it suffered less in the 1933 earthquake than some of the less dispensable ancient architecture of the Darbar square. Patan (104,928) is chiefly notable for its Asokan *stupas*; Bhatgaon (93,176) is the least modernised and perhaps the most attractive of the three. Landon well sums up the charm of the Valley, "a world of varied interest, tradition, and beauty such as may be found nowhere among the history-coloured and majestic towns and ruins of India"—and there are no ruins in this land where Buddhism and Hinduism live friendly side by side, where the colour of life is still much as it was in the golden days of Indian culture.

The Pahar

Most of the hill country (Pahar) lies in three great basins: those of the Gogra headstreams (main rivers Karnali and Bheri), the Sapt (seven) Gandak (Kali, Trisul, Buri Gandak), and the Sapt Kosi (Sun Kosi and Arun). Here and there are fertile vales: Dumja on the Sun Kosi, growing rice and barley, Pokhara on the Seti Gandak, mainly rice; Jumla, high up on the Karnali, mainly barley. Maize is grown fairly generally. Around Palpa and Nayakot—the key by which the Gurkhas entered the valley—are extensive orchards; at Nayakot mangoes, pineapples, oranges, coconuts, areca and betel, cape gooseberries, and temperate fruits also are grown. Outside the terai and the Valley the only towns of any size are Palpa and Pokhara, each with only about a tenth of the population of any of the Valley towns.

N of the longitudinal belt the country rapidly becomes very wild; beyond Nayakot the Trisul Gandak and the Tadi descend some 8000 ft in 30 miles. Some trade goes over the passes to Tibet, but both the Kirong and Kuti routes are difficult—the latter passing through gorges where the path is in places built of stone slabs on iron pegs driven into the rock 1500 ft above the river: it is probably useless for animals. But these routes are of only the slightest significance since the development of the direct Darjeeling–Lhasa route after 1904.

Nepal: Present and Future

Nepal in the last hundred years has had a generally stable and efficient administration, not absolutely unmindful of progress (at least around the capital), but firmly convinced of the gradualness of the inevitable: thus domestic slavery was not abolished until 1924–26. Except perhaps in the terai, there have been no fundamental changes, though innovations were numerous enough in Katmandu itself. In many ways Nepali life seems to be well adjusted to social and physical environment. Yet the events of 1950 showed that the tradition of palace revolution was not dead, and that serious social tensions lay not far beneath the surface.

Thus increasing pressure on land has led to a considerable emigration of Nepalis as cultivators, especially to Darjeeling and Sikkim, while at home the potentialities of the sub-montane valleys are not fully exploited. Again mineral development is practically non-existent, although the Sapt Gandak basin alone is reported to hold deposits of corundum, graphite, mica, bismuth, cobalt, antimony, sulphur, semi-precious stones such as jasper and rock crystal, lignitic and possibly bituminous coal. Of these copper at least used to be worked, and lignite is dug for local use. Likely enough most of these deposits would not be economic propositions, but nothing whatever has been done to find out. Even Landon is moved to think that "more systematic development" would be worth while; mild as it is, this criticism is significant since, broadly speaking, his attitude is that in Nepal whatever is, is right.[32]

To an outside observer, not unappreciative of military virtue nor unsympathetic to the desire to fend off the disintegrating impact of the world market and world politics, it may yet seem that the Government has given too much of its energies to military organisation and to the conspicuous waste of 4-ton statues and neo-classical palaces. It is true, however, that the export of mercenaries[33] has meant a considerable addition to the national income in pay and pensions. At the lowest, the social contrast between the Valley of Katmandu and the Valley of Kashmir was all in favour of the former.

But clouds are forming on the horizons north and south, lipping over the Himalayan passes or beating up in great monsoon masses from the terai, and Nepal now faces a crisis more serious than any since Jang Bahadur Rana put an end to the anarchic factions which were tearing the state to pieces a century ago. Nepali traders have enjoyed special privileges in Tibet for nearly a century, but the diplomatic relations of the two countries have been marked by constant petty friction and bickering; the effects of an extension of Communist control to Lhasa can hardly be viewed with equanimity in Katmandu. On the other front, the opening up of the terai has meant a considerable Indian infiltration, probably with not a little of the baser element of contractors and the like. The 'Nepal National Congress' putsch of November 1949 was no more than serio-comic in itself, but the attitude of the *Indian* press (and of local officials) was ominously unambiguous, and in the event Delhi's interest in Nepalese affairs was and must remain decisive. The development of the great Kosi scheme

---

[32] II. 5–18.
[33] No slur is intended: 'the Swiss of India', like the Switzers themselves, have always given first-class value for their hire.

(Fig. 98, p. 520), even if delayed for financial reasons, remains an important objective of *Indian* planning; the main dam would be well within Nepal, and a million acres of the Nepalese terai would be irrigated. But such schemes may work for good will or enmity according to the general relations of the countries concerned; they may cement friendship, or foster discord. It would be sad should so mighty a work of peace water the seeds of conflict, but so it might be. For good or ill, 'the modern world' is knocking at the gate, and cannot be indefinitely denied.

THE EASTERN HIMALAYA

Between 86 and 88° E the general character of the Himalayas changes to such an extent that a new division is warranted. The NW/SE trend is replaced by an E/W line, and beyond 92° E the strike is more SW/NE. Further, for some 140 miles (87° 45′–90° E) the mountains are exposed to the direct impact of the monsoon across the open gap between the Rajmahal Hills and the Shillong Plateau. Rainfall is high and the dense, wet tropical jungle extends Ewds along the Assam Himalaya, where the funnel-shaped valley also acts as a rain-trap. Opposite the gap the Siwaliks, rocks and hills, simply disappear, whether overridden by thrust-masses or eroded out of existence by the intense rainfall; Siwalik rocks reappear again E of 90°, but hardly form so marked and persistent a topographic feature as they do from Jhelum to Kosi. Finally the drainage is now, in its main lines at least, directly transverse, as shown by the Arun-Kosi, the Tista, and the rivers of Bhután.

The bold lines and the human importance of the Tista basin, leading to the main gateway into Tibet, justify the treatment of Darjeeling and Sikkim as one unit. This leaves as the others En Nepal, and Bhután with the Assam Himalaya.

Eastern Nepal

Paradoxically enough, the only parts of this area which are at all well known are the mountain fastnesses of the N, mapped by the Everest expeditions, though the Kosi scheme must lead to fuller knowledge of the basin. The Kosi is an example of de Martonne's scheme of a mountain torrent with its "cone of deposition" on a vast scale: on the 3–5-mile wide Chatra gorge—site of the main dam of the project—converges the drainage of an area 150 miles wide, most of this being taken up by the longitudinal course of the Sun Kosi; while from the N the Arun rushes straight down to this narrow exit. Small wonder that in Bihar the Kosi is the most devastating of all the swinging rivers of the paradeltaic fans.

For much of the area Landon has to fall back on the traverses of Sir Joseph Hooker in 1848 and of Sarat Chandra Das—one of the admirable Indian explorers of the Survey—in 1881. But in any case interest attaches

chiefly to the mighty Nn ramparts, where five peaks exceed 26,000 ft:
Gosainthan (26,305), and Cho Uyo (26,867), Everest and Makalu (29,002 [34]
and 27,790), and, across the Arun, Kangchenjunga (28,146).

The Everest Massif

The world's highest point, known to the Tibetans as Chomo-Lungma,[35]
'Goddess-Mother of the Land', is in itself not so impressive as many less
famous peaks, including its neighbour Makalu with 11,000-ft sheer cliffs
and buttresses of black rock and dazzling ice. Everest is a "lumpy pyramid"
of calcareous gneisses and schists, probably Permo-Carboniferous, seated
on a plinth of originally sedimentary para-gneisses. These may well be
part of a great nappe, though Odell and Wager favour vertical uplift, at
least in the latest phases responsible for the present topography; and the
former distinctly repudiates large lateral movements.[36]

The glaciers of Everest and Kangchenjunga may once have spilled over
the cols of the 'Trans-Himalaya' along the S of the Tsang-po. Of the existing glaciers the most interesting is the Rongbuk, which descends to the N
from Everest itself. This is some 12 miles long, falling from 22,000 to
16,500 ft; transverse to the mountain axis, it is practically as long as the
longitudinal glaciers—a marked contrast to Karakoram conditions. Fusion
along the line of stress and compression caused by the confluence of tributaries seems responsible for its probably unique 'Trough', a fissure $3\frac{1}{2}$
miles long "up to 50 ft deep and 100 ft wide with steep sides buttressed and
pillared with fretted ice of exquisite tints of blue and white and green, and
paved at intervals with the ice-covering of innumerable charming glacier
lakelets, out of the surface of which grow here and there clusters of ice-
pinnacles, themselves sculptured into an infinity of forms". [37] Also,
apparently, peculiar to the higher Himalayas are the tremendous curtains
of nearly vertical and beautifully fluted ice encasing many peaks almost to
their summits, especially on N faces.

Between the Everest/Makalu and Kangchenjunga massifs lies the great
gash of the Arun, with two very remarkable gorges, ascribed by Heron to
cutting-back and by Wager to antecedence. In the lower gorge, below
Kharta, the river is over 100 yds wide and falls 4500 ft in 20 miles; the
trade-route abandons the 5,000-ft precipices of the valley for a switch-back
over the lateral spurs. On the Doji La, N of Kharta, is the Indo-Tibetan
climatic divide. In the arid open valleys and hollows above there is little
vegetation but sparse grass and dwarf junipers, and at the upper entrance of
the gorge "a sweet-smelling land of juniper and wild-rose thickets"; the

---

[34] Or 29,141 ft, after correction for gravity anomaly.
[35] 'Or words to that effect', Tibetan transliteration being notoriously one of the world's
major impossibilities (see Ronaldshay, *op. cit.*, 67–68, where 'Songa Chelling' = 'Gsang-
Sngags-Chlosgling'.
[36] Odell, 298; Wager, 248–50.   [37] Odell, 307

gorge itself has pine and birch woods. But the Arun lies directly facing the monsoon, and a little lower down the superlatively beautiful Kama tributary valley it is always raining, with forests to 12,000 ft, almost reaching the glacier snouts; forests of pines, rhododendrons, and giant junipers 60–100 ft high, covered with long streamers of grey lichens.

From a human point of view interest is concentrated on the Tibetan side, "characterised by somewhat soft sedimentary rocks, predominantly shales, with rolling, lumpy, rounded hills . . . alternating with open flat-bottomed valleys occupied by lakes or by swamps through which meander mud-laden rivers." [38] The sombre colours of the hills are relieved by multi-coloured lakes, blue, purple, green, yellow, even red. Some of these valleys have villages only a few miles apart, ringed with irrigated barley fields up to 15,500 ft, and groves, also irrigated, of poplar and willow. Sheep, goats, oxen, yaks, and horses are kept in the swampy meadows and moved to higher pastures in the summer. The staples of diet are barley meal (*tsamba*), mild sour beer, and the notorious tea mixed with salt and rancid butter, probably not much improved by being served (at wealthier monasteries) in agate and silver cups.

Over all is the peculiar impress of Tibetan Buddhism. The magic *mani* invocation is written on huge rolls of fine paper, encased in great prayer wheels at least 5 ft high and 3 across, so that with each revolution—and it takes only a second or two—several hundred thousand prayers are automatically registered. Elsewhere water-wheels and wind-mills provide mechanically for prayer without ceasing.[39] There is a far finer side: high in the sombre cliff-shadowed Rongbuk Valley are the cells of religious solitaries, women as well as men, spending years in devotion and protecting by their presence the birds and animals which have never learnt to fear man—or perhaps have learnt not to fear him *here*. It is fitting that such should be the last representatives of our race on these stairways to the stars. More lowly forms of life struggle higher: wild sheep, hares, foxes, and wolves at 17,000 ft [40]; "grasshoppers at 18,000, near the furthest limit of vegetable growth"; bees and butterflies at 21,000. Choughs have been seen at 27,000 ft, perhaps following up the Everest climbers for scraps of food; until the 1952 Swiss expedition the highest point certainly reached by men with their feet on the ground was between 28,100 and 28,200 ft, at which height Mallory and Irvine were last seen; when the mountain yielded in 1953 it was to the ninth assault in 32 years. The last permanent outposts of organic being are still the spiders which live on the mites of dead vegetation blown up to 22,000 ft, or on each other [41]: surely an ironic comment on existence. Beyond lie the elements: rock, ice, and wind.

[38] A. M. Heron, "The Everest Neighbourhood, Tibet", *CGR* I/1 (1936), 5–13.
[39] See Ronaldshay, 78–80, for comment on this mathematical piety.
[40] Their tracks have been reported at 21,000 ft.
[41] R. W. G. Hingston, "Animal Life at High Altitudes", *GJ* LXV (1925), 185–98.

The Tista Valley

Directly opposite the Ganges Delta, the Tista Valley, like the Kosi, reproduces on a vast scale de Martonne's scheme of a mountain torrent. The upper basin is 50 miles wide, and the river cuts through the Darjeeling ridge (7000–8000 ft) in a narrow gorge, to spill onto the plain in a vast fan seamed with old courses. With a rainfall of 120–180 ins. erosion is intense;

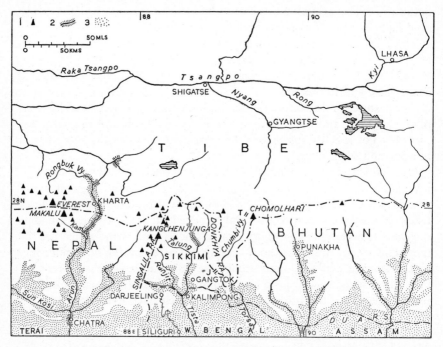

Fig. 72.—Everest and the Gateway to Lhasa. 1, peaks over 22,000 ft; 2, main Arun and Tista gorges; 3, below 6000 ft. J, Jelep La; T, Tang La. The Assam/Bhután boundary conforms much more closely to the plains/hill margin than the 6000-ft contour indicates.

the head of the gorge at the Ranjit confluence is only 750 ft. Sikkim is in effect the all but enclosed basin, the hills portion of Darjeeling Dt. the retaining wall; and the range of relief in Sikkim is 750–28,146 ft or over five miles.

To the W the little state is shut in by the Singalila ridge; to the E the Donkhya Range (15,000–17,000 ft) is the Tibetan boundary. But this is crossed by several easy passes at about 12,000 ft into the Chumbi (upper Torsa) valley, which forms a salient of Tibet between Sikkim and Bhután. This is by far the shortest and easiest route into Tibet, leading direct to Gyantse and Lhasa; the Tang La (15,200 ft) at the head of the Chumbi is two or three miles wide and the gradients on both sides are very gentle. The Chumbi carries as much trade as all the rest of the Indo-Tibetan routes put together; even Nepalese merchants, despite freedom from Tibetan tolls on the passes of Nepal itself, "have found it cheaper to send their goods down into India to be transferred by rail through Siliguri to the Tista". This is a recent development, since the grading of the road by the British expedition into Tibet in 1904–05.

Darjeeling, at 7376 ft, may be taken as typical of the climate of the outer hills:

Temperature, ° F.

J.	F.	M.	A.	M.	J.	J.	A.	S.	O.	N.	D.	
40·1	41·6	49·7	56·2	58·3	59·9	61·5	60·9	59·4	55·2	47·8	41·8	Ra. 21·4

Precipitation, inches

J.	F.	M.	A.	M.	J.	J.	A.	S.	O.	N.	D.	
0·6	1·1	1·8	3·8	8·7	24·9	32·3	26·1	18·4	4·5	0·8	0·2	Tot. 122·7

Higher up, Gangtok has 133 and Gnatong, on the Donkhya Range, 180 ins. Of course, aspect and exposure are main determinants of vegetation and cultivation.

(a) *Darjeeling* was secured from Sikkim in 1833, "a worthless uninhabited mountain"; the adjacent terai 11 years later. But by 1873 there were 15,000 ac. of tea; to-day Darjeeling and Jalpaiguri Dts have 190,000 ac., much of course in the Duars (= terai). Much of the labour is Nepali. Subsistence agriculture is marked by the dominance of rice—half the 120,000 ac. of foodgrains and 30% of TSA. Tea acreage is about equal to rice, and maize comes next with 50,000 ac. But the cultivated ground is barely a quarter of the total area, the rest being mainly magnificent forest with the whole range from sal to pine.

Already at Siliguri, in the terai 8 miles from the foot of the hills, we are in the contact zone: "Siliguri is palpably a place of meeting", evidenced by the appearance of Mongolian faces, the large iron-roofed tea godowns, different types of rolling stock, long lines of bullock-carts and lorries.[43] The metre railway is succeeded by two 2-ft lines, one up the Tista to a point opposite Kalimpong (12,000), the starting-point for the road to Tibet, the other a mountain railway to Darjeeling itself. Apart from its importance as a centre of the tea-trade, Darjeeling (25,873 (in March)) has obviously a most favourable site for a hill station serving the greatest conurbation of India; April–May mean temperatures are 27–29° F. below those of Calcutta. Like most hill stations, it has many schools, especially Anglo-Indian; mist-enshrouded for half the year, on clear days it boasts the magnificent view of Kangchenjunga 45 miles away.

[43] Ronaldshay, 6.

(b) *Sikkim* (2818 sq mls, poptn (1951) 135,646) consists of a mass of deeply-dissected highland. The state is to all intents an *Indian* protectorate; in the N it is practically Tibetan in culture, and indeed the state religion is Buddhist, though the Hindu proportion of the population is increasing with the immigration of Nepalis. The original inhabitants, the Mongolian Lepchas, are amiable but rather ineffective. Geoffrey Gorer's description[44] of Zongu, between the Tista and the Talung in the heart of the country, may be taken as representative of the more settled part. "Except for a few artificially levelled places, there is probably not a hundred square yards of flat ground", and tracks are too steep even for mules. Rain is "almost continuous" from June to September, at least on S-facing slopes; only October and November are dry. Above 8000 ft snow lies every year, and "there are often powderings of snow down to 4500 ft, the level of most of the towns", but oranges and peaches can be grown here; only once in the last 50 years has snow fallen by the rivers (2000 ft). Mean temperatures vary between about 40° and 86° F., and diurnal ranges are high:

> The river valleys are hot, steamy, and somewhat malarious, and consequently there are no houses right on the river, though the ground is used for growing sub-tropical plants; there are, however, occasional houses about 500 feet further up. Most of the houses and cultivated land are between 3,500 and 7,500 feet above sea level, a relatively narrow band between the two rivers, though occasionally fields are made at even higher altitudes. Above the cultivated land is the forest in which wild produce is gathered, a decreasing amount of hunting done, and to which the cattle are sent up to pasture in the winter months. Above the forest level comes first the rhododendron forest, and then the snows, rarely visited except by hunters searching either for ibex or musk-deer or for the wild aconite which forms the basis of their arrow poison.

Agriculture includes terraced wet paddy in the valleys, an innovation of the last 30 years and increasingly important. The main crops of dry rice, buckwheat, and millets are grown in clearings in secondary jungle, which then lie fallow for seven years; by the house is a more permanent field, the 'garden', planted in part to vegetables and condiments but mainly to mixed barley and wheat (sown October, reaped April) followed by a second crop of maize. There are usually a few fruit trees and a clump of bamboos, which are extensively used in building and for domestic utensils. Cardamoms, also a recent introduction, are the chief cash crop. Cattle are still the sign of wealth; known by name but left to wander freely round the common grazing- and wood-land, and (except for cows in milk) sent up to live untended in the forest from February to April.[45] It will be seen that this agriculture offers interesting points of resemblance to shifting cultivation and to

---

[44] *Himalayan Village* (1938), 51–54.
[45] Gorer, 75–6, 90–101, especially the agricultural calendar at p. 94.

'run-rig'. The diet is filled out with meat of almost all types; the Lepchas are fairly omnivorous and will eat even carcasses found in the jungle.

Settlement is essentially dispersed in hamlets of two to four homesteads; only those villages which have a monastery have any sort of focus. Even in Lingthem, the second biggest village in Zongu (poptn 176) and one of the most coherent, eight houses are the most that can be seen from any one point: "I should reckon that there were quite three miles and three thousand feet between the lowest house to the east and the highest house to the west in the village."

There are potentially useful deposits of copper, associated with bismuth, antimony, and galena; attempts have been made to exploit them but transport difficulties are so far insuperable. Except for the capital, Gangtok, with its little Court nucleus, the 'towns' of the map are simply staging-points on Tibetan routes, with a few trading and administrative functions. Across the Tista from Zongu the little settlement of Mangan has half a dozen Indian shops, belonging to Marwaris who exploit (in every sense) the cardamom trade; a dispensary, post office, and school, some liquor shops, and "a couple of Tibetan prostitutes for the use of the muleteers". In Lepcha society these last probably give Mangan an urban cachet.

In the far N and under Kangchenjunga even this thin film of life frays out into a tattered edge. Above the forests is a different world, not to be entered without charms and incantations: "Not far beyond the last of the thickets of rhododendrons stands a rough shed of stone, the home of two yak-herds who tend their charges in these high places during the summer months, a fact which entitles the spot to a definite location on the map under the name of Jongri. We had reached the threshold of the snows." [46]

Bhután and the Assam Himalaya

(a) *Bhután* is perhaps even less known than Nepal; it is just as exclusive and much less attractive: a country of the wildest mountain and forest, of drab rolling yak-pastures, of fantastic monasteries wedged into the clefts of huge precipices, of massive castles where life is as feudal as it looks. [47] In the NW it is dominated by the superb cone of Chomo Lhari, 'Divine Queen of Mountains' (23,930 ft), guarding the Tang La col on the Brahmaputra/ Tsang-po watershed.

From its conquest by Tibetan freebooters in the 16th century until 1907 Bhután was nominally governed by a temporal and a spiritual lord, the Deb and Dharma Rajas, and in fact misgoverned by the constantly warring Governors of E and W Bhután, working through their puppets the Deb Rajas, of whom there were normally two in play and half a dozen back in the box. Finally, the Dharma Raja having died and failed

[46] Ronaldshay, 171.   [47] See the plates in Ronaldshay.

to be reincarnated, and the current Deb Raja retiring to the contemplative life, one of the Governors established a stable monarchy. Since then the country has remained poor, remote, and aloof, but at least peaceful.

The valleys of Bhután open out normally to the S, the Nepal/Sikkim type of wide basin and narrow gorge reappearing, on a restricted scale, in Assam. Some of the valleys have ribbons of flat floor, given over to paddy-fields; elsewhere maize and millets are grown, some by semi-shifting methods; and forest products (lac, wax, musk) are collected. "Muzzle-loading guns and swords of highly tempered steel are manufactured." [48] The population is estimated at 300,000, on 18,000 sq mls; the culture is Mahayana Buddhist.

(b) *The Assam Himalayas* are the least known part of the whole sub-continent and have only recently been administered as the Balipara, Sadiya, and Tirap Frontier Tracts; the first two have a combined area of 3880 sq mls, poptn in 1941 66,630—not fully enumerated. Nor, indeed, does there seem much worth knowing, except by anthropologists. The people are splinter tribes of Mongoloid stock, Animists and shifting cultivators.

Beyond Namcha Barwa (25,445 ft) and the great hairpin bend of the Brahmaputra/Tsang-po lie the N–S furrows of the Salween, Mekong, and Yangtze, deep-cut into the wild mountains of the 'Hump'. At this blind end of the Assam funnel some rain is forced into the mountains through deep valleys such as those of the Dihang (the Tsangpo-Brahmaputra gorge reaches) and the Lohit, which seems to have captured some Irrawaddy drainage. Here, in a mild climate suitable for maize and millets, the Tibetans reach their lowest point—*c.* 3500 ft—at Rima.

We may note, finally, that it is possible that, instead of the Himalaya bending round into the great virgation between the Shillong and Yunnan blocks, as suggested by the parallel valleys from the Chindwin to the Yangtze, they actually carry on SE from the Dihang and cut across the Yangtze about 100° E 27° N. Kingdon Ward [49] claims that there is a line of culminating peaks seated on the N/S watersheds, suggesting that an origin-ally latitudinal range has been segmented by (? antecedent) rivers; this is backed up by floristic arguments. Here, then, on the marches of India, Tibet, and China we have one of the last unsolved strictly topographical problems of the globe. It seems unlikely that any scientific investigation will be possible for some little time. . . .

BIBLIOGRAPHICAL NOTE

The general references given at the end of Ch. XIV are relevant here also. There are two admirable books on Kumaon: S. D. Pant, *The Social Economy of*

---

[48] *Statesman's Year Book*, s.v. "Bhután".
[49] F. K. Ward, "The Himalaya East of the Tsangpo," *GJ* LXXXIV (1934), 369–97.

the Himalayans (1935), an excellent detailed study marred by exceedingly bad maps; and A. Heim and A. Gansser, *The Throne of the Gods* (1939 A), with 220 very fine plates of both human and physical interest. For the more technical papers by Heim and Gansser (1936 and 1939 B) and Auden (1936–37) see Biblio. Note to Ch. I.

On Nepal the standard work is P. Landon, *Nepal* (1928), lavish, enthusiastic, mainly archaic archaeology. Most of the geographical information is in Chs. XI and XII. It may seem ungracious to cavil at so fascinating a book, on which I have drawn so heavily, but even from a purely historical and social point of view some connected account of the geography would have been helpful, while the social values of the book can be gathered from the fact that there are 20 pages devoted to armorial bearings, titles, and regalia, and nowhere any account of the life of the people. W. B. Northey, *The Land of the Gurkhas* (Cambridge, n.d., ? 1937) is altogether slighter. S. Lévi, *Le Népale* (1906) is a minor classic but almost entirely devoted to cultural history.

On the Everest region, the most important papers are:

C. K. Howard-Bury, "The Mount Everest Expedition", *GJ* LIX (1922), 81–99.

A. M. Heron, "Geological Results of the Mount Everest Expedition," 1921, *ibid.*, 418–36.

N. E. Odell, "Observations on the Rocks and Glaciers of Mount Everest", *GJ* LXVI (1925), 289–315.

L. R. Wager, "The Arun River Drainage Pattern and the Rise of the Himalaya", *GJ* LXXXIX (1937), 139–50.

The official accounts of the earlier expeditions are summarised in Sir F. Younghusband, *The Epic of Mount Everest* (1926).

G. Gorer's *Himalayan Village* (1939) and C. R. Morris's *Living with Lepchas* (1939) give much detail on the social geography of Sikkim: once again the lack of maps is a drawback. Lord Ronaldshay's *Lands of the Thunderbolt* (1923) is largely devoted to admirable reflections on Lamaist Buddhism, but the author had a good geographical eye. On Sikkim see also *IGJ* XIX (1944), 41–48; on Himalayan Assam, C. von Fürer-Haimendorf, "Culture Types in Assam Himalayas", *IGJ* XXI (1946), 49–57.

CHAPTER XVI

THE WESTERN BORDERLANDS

(Regions I–III)

THIS chapter treats all the extra-Himalayan territory between the alluvial plains of the Indus and the Afghan and Iranian boundaries. These boundaries, except for short stretches in the extreme N and along the Safed Koh, pay little attention to physical features; there is little or no natural difference between the Kabul and Kunar Valleys E and W of the border, between the desert basins of NW Baluchistan and of Seistan, or between Iranian and Baluchi Makran; and for the most part the frontier peoples straddle the actual boundary. Yet, at least along the great routeways, decades of British administration have left a distinctive imprint on the land—the military symbol of the cantonment.

Regionally the whole area falls into three main divisions: the hills of the NW frontier; the sub-montane Indus region, including the Vale of Peshawar and the Bannu Plain, the Potwar Plateau, and the Salt Range; Baluchistan.

Baluchistan

The arid basins and hills of Baluchistan form the En portion of the great Iranian plateaus, sharply marked off from the Indus Plain by the Kirthar and Sulaiman ramparts. In the NE the Gomal River may be taken as a rational limit; beyond this the strongly trellised drainage patterns of Baluchistan are replaced by transverse valleys direct to the Indus, and the NWFP has distinct human—here strategic—values. The lowland of Kachhi (in the Sibi re-entrant) is treated as part of the Lower Indus region.

Relief and Structure (Fig. 73)

The mountain skeleton of Baluchistan consists of two great virgations, knotted together in the complex Quetta node, where Zarghun and Khalifat attain over 11,000 ft—a culmination probably associated with a concealed extension of the Peninsular block controlling the Sibi re-entrant (cf. Fig. 2).

Between the Kundar and the Zhob tributaries of the Gomal the 9000-ft Toba Kakar Range trends SW towards Chaman, with a slight convexity to the SE. S from the Gomal runs the great series of echelonned ridges, known collectively as the Sulaiman Range, which rise to over 11,000 ft in Takht-i-Sulaiman, only 30 miles from the Gomal, but have summits generally at 6000–7000 ft. At about 30° N the Sulaimans begin to swing Wwds, until finally their continuations in the Bugti Hills are pointing NW towards the Quetta node. Looped between the Toba Kakar and Sulaiman Ranges lie the trellis-patterned basins of the Zhob and the Beji: nested folds of Cretaceous and Eocene limestones and sandstones producing in Loralai an extraordinary landscape of innumerable scarps and hogsbacks, small plateaus and mesas, steep craggy outcrops with the talus-slopes littered with boulders half the size of the fields (very small fields, it is true); and set in these arid hills, grey and dun and ochre, a few greener patches in small alluvial or detrital basins.

SW of Quetta Baluchistan includes but a portion of the vaster Iranian loops; but something of the same pattern can be discerned, ranges trending N/S in the E and swinging round E/W in Makran. This pattern is broken across by the Arabian Sea, probably fairly recently subsided, and most of

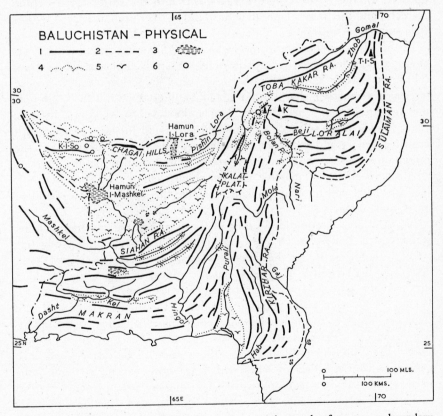

Fig. 73.—BALUCHISTAN, PHYSICAL OUTLINES. 1, main trends of ranges; 2, boundary of Indus alluvium; 3, *hamuns* (playas); 4, sand desert; 5, alluvial basins; 6, recent volcanoes. T-I-S, Takht-i-Sulaiman (11,100 ft); Z, Zarghun (11,730); K, Khalifat (11,430); K-I-S, Koh-i-Sultan (7654). Q, Quetta.

the coast is longitudinal, with many hammerhead peninsulas, one of which —Gwadar—belongs to the Arabian state of Oman; but in the E the ranges run out transversely in Ras Muari (Cape Monze).

There is a marked contrast between the ranges on either side of 66° 15′ E. To the E massive limestones, Cretaceous to Oligocene with some intrusions of Deccan Lava age, form great anticlinal bulges; erosion has opened up the anticlines, but in this arid climate and thirsty rock it has not progressed to the stage of inversion of relief: anticlines are still ridges and synclines valleys. The most striking feature is the Kirthar wall, rising from 4000 ft in the S to nearly 8000 in the N, and broken only by a few gorges such as those of the Mula and the Gaj, now useless for any but local traffic, though the former is relatively easy and was used by one division of Alexander's withdrawing army. The capping of the Kirthar is the massive Spitangi limestone (Eocene), which also forms the Kalat Plateau at 7000–8000 ft. In the S the ranges break down into the little scarps behind Karachi, and the triangular alluvial lowland of the Purali, occupied by Las Bela state, is set into them.

In the W the ranges are formed mainly of Oligocene flysch, weak sandstones and shales which (except in more massively built coastal Makran) fold more sharply. A rainfall rather less scanty, impermeable clays instead of calcareous masses, sharper folding, all combine to permit the more normal development of synclinal hills. The landscape of Sn Makran is bizarre: "that brazen coast washed by a molten sea", and inland "gigantic cap-crowned pillars and pedestals are balanced in fantastic array about the mountain slopes . . . with successive strata so well defined that they possess all the appearance of massive masonry construction . . . standing stiff, jagged, naked and uncompromising" [1] above the confused ravine-riddled lower hills of clay.

N of the great longitudinal valley of the Kej, in Pangjur, these parallel wall-sided or knife-edged ranges are higher than in coastal Makran, but beyond the Siahan Range they sink into the great desert depression (1500–3000 ft) of the Hamun-i-Mashkel (hamun = playa), flanked on the N, along the Afghan border, by the remarkable recent volcanoes of the Chagai Hills. Round this interior drainage basin, and that of the smaller Hamun-i-Lora, the hills are skirted by great coalescing talus-fans. The basins are floored by wide expanses of bare sun-cracked clay, spreads of black oxidised pebbles (dasht), and shifting reddish dunes; there seem to be terraces possibly indicating former levels of lakes which are now, except in flood-time, nothing but salt incrustations with a few marshy patches and fewer of more or less permanent water. Small wonder that the local proverb considers Baluchistan as the dump where Allah shot the rubbish of Creation.

[1] T. H. Holdich, The Gates of India (1910), 285, 289, 317.

Climate and Vegetation

Great aridity and great temperature ranges are the leading features of the climate. Quetta, in an intermont basin at 5500 ft, has mean temperatures of 39·6° F in January and 77·8 in July, and the mean diurnal ranges for these months are respectively some 20 and 28°; variations of 80° in 24 hours are said by Holdich to be not uncommon. The country is not sheltered by the Himalayan wall and winds are very strong, whether on the open desert plains of the NW or in the narrow corridors of the border valleys; prevailingly from the NW, they are scorchingly hot in summer, filling the air with dust from the Iranian deserts; in winter bitterly cold, "like a keen-edged blade, to the dividing asunder of bones and marrow." [2] Annual rainfall is hardly anywhere over 10 ins. (Shahrig has the maximum, 14·7), and it is of course extremely unreliable, falling when it does fall in intensely violent storms which send vast spills of detritus into the desert basins, or sudden spates, dangerous to travellers, through the *tangis* or transverse clefts, often only a few yards wide, by which the streams penetrate the longitudinal ranges; at other times most rivers are mere trickles and pools in their stony beds. Over most of the plateau precipitation (often snow) is brought mainly by shallow W-moving winter depressions, but in the lower highlands (Loralai-Zhob) it has the usual monsoon summer maximum, and Quetta is near enough to the En edge to show a slight secondary maximum then:

J.	F.	M.	A.	M.	J.	J.	A.	S.	O.	N.	D.	Total
2·1	2·1	1·8	1·1	0·3	0·2	0·5	0·6	0·1	0·1	0·3	0·8	10·0

Obviously vegetation will be everywhere xerophytic and in most areas scanty, though in the short spring many of the valleys are bright with flowering plants. Much of the hill country is covered with open scrub, and on the higher Nn Sulaimans there are forests of juniper and wild olive, with pistachio, laurel, and myrtle. Dwarf palms are common, and Makran has many date-groves, especially in the Kej valley. But the prevalent vegetation is thorny bush and coarse steppe grasses and bushes, and to the NW these grade into true desert, utterly barren but for the reedy wetter patches of the *hamuns* and thin lines of tamarisk along the bigger wadis or *loras*.

The desert pediments of the interior and the wild gorges of the bordering hills bear witness to the intermittent but intense spells of erosion, the natural consequence of the few downpours and the thin vegetation cover. Intense heat and cold, savage winds, rare but violent floods, in summer dust insidious everywhere; a surface largely rock, pebble, or sand; scanty and unreliable rainfall, earthquakes—a harsh environment, brightened

---

[2] Holdich, *The Indian Borderland* (2nd. ed., 1909), 112.

to brief beauty in the spring, and enclosing but few green islands of fertility.

The Peoples

The population of Baluchistan, excluding the lowland areas, was approximately 700,000 in 1941—barely 5 to the sq ml. Four main indigenous groups are generally recognised : the cultivating Jatti of Las Bela and Kachhi; Pathans, N of Quetta; Brahuis in the mountain border in Sarawan and Jhalawan, separating the Baluchis of the Marri-Bugti country from those of the W. All these are of course much intermingled both territorially and ethnically; all are tribal and there are a variety of kiths,[3] sometimes overlapping tribal and linguistic divisions; while in Makran some of the stocks, such as the Med fishermen and the Lori gypsies, seem to be very ancient. Perhaps the only common factor is Islam of no advanced kind, riddled with atavistic beliefs and customs. The Baluchi and Pathan languages are Iranian, but Brahui is definitely Dravidian, an outlier removed by 1700 miles from the main Dravidian mass : a fascinating riddle, yet perhaps not so strange as appears at first sight, since the Dravidians presumably entered India by the land-gates, perhaps picking their way Swds when the Indus was still joined by the Sarasvati and the Thar Desert was much more restricted. This conjecture of Holdich's is perhaps strengthened by the recognition of Dravidian elements in the Indus civilisation, and by the evidence of a more humid climate in Sind in Mohenjo-daro times.

Under Arab domination in the first centuries of Islam Makran seems to have reached a high pitch of prosperity; thereafter Baluchistan was a debatable land, constantly changing masters, between Moguls, Afghans, and Iranians. For obvious political and topographical reasons the N has a strong pull towards Afghanistan, Makran to Iran. In the 17th and 18th centuries the Khans of Kalat built up a strong Brahui confederacy, nominally (and perhaps sometimes really) subject to Delhi or Kandahar. They fell under British domination between 1840 and 1875—largely as an incident in relations with Afghanistan, whence the Nn districts were annexed by the Treaty of Gandamak after the Second Afghan War of 1879–81.

Economic Life

The economic activity of the great mass of the population remains primitive; as a rule no hard and fast line can be drawn between agriculturalist and pastoralist, and many add a variety of petty trading, carrying, or handicraft activities to their primary pursuits. Nomadism, both regular and enforced by bad seasons, largely accounts for the great fluctuations in rate of increase of population (e.g. in Chagai) and is still of importance, though declining:

[3] In the sense used in Huntington's *Mainsprings of Civilisation*.

	% Nomad	% Semi-Nomad	% Settled
1911.	33·1	12·6	54·3
1921.	22·4	17·7	59·9
1931.	25·3	12·0	62·7

Even among the settled groups the scanty amount of useful land enforces shifts of hamlets, and the dwellings themselves are often impermanent—matting or felt tents, summer shelters of reeds and branches. Among the Brahuis no less than 47% were returned as nomads in 1931.[4]

Much of this nomadism, indeed, is rather transhumance: Brahuis moving into Kachhi or Sind with their families and flocks, to escape the winter cold; Pathans and Baluchis, half farmers and half shepherds, moving on a restricted round between flocks and fields; influx into the fertile valleys of Kej and Pangjur for the date-harvest. True pastoral nomadism yet survives in the inhospitable NW. There is also the transit of the Afghan Powindahs who winter in the plains, trading in cloth and dried fruits for bazaar goods, or engaging in casual labour such as canal digging. Their numbers in 1931 amounted to some 20,000, about half of whom passed on into Sind and the Punjab. Even Quetta is not unaffected by this seasonal mobility: the population is perhaps 50% greater in summer than in winter, plains dwellers coming to escape the hot weather, families of quasi-permanent residents leaving to avoid the rigorous winter.

Pastoralism is obviously of great importance. Goats and fat-tailed sheep probably account for over 80% of the stock, and much of the petty local traffic is still carried on camels and donkeys, despite the rapid inroads of lorry and bus. Agriculture, equally obviously, is dependent on the most careful use of such water as exists. The canal irrigation of the province is mainly in the Sibi-Kachhi lowland, but about 5000 ac. are irrigated near Pishin, with wheat as the main rabi crop and lucerne and melons in the summer, and there is also some irrigation on the Zhob, though for much of its course its banks are too high and steep to permit its use.

The most remarkable indigenous irrigation method is the *karez*: shafts are sunk in the great fans skirting the hills, and these shafts are linked by galleries to form a tunnel, sometimes tapping a spring but more often collecting the sub-soil water (Fig. 74). The *karez* has the great advantage of avoiding loss by evaporation, and where hydrographic conditions are suitable it may remain productive a long time.[5] Elsewhere rough bunds on

---

[4] See the relevant chapters in the Census of India, Vol. IV, Pt. I, for 1911, 1921, and 1931, especially the text of 1911 and the diagrams of 1931. The 1941 Census, as on so many important matters, is completely silent, presumably in the sacred names of Economy and War Effort.

[5] See R. D. Oldham, *Rec. GSI* XXV (1892), 36–52.

hill-slopes and across valleys retain the soilwash of the rainstorms, forming a trap for the saturated soil; *karez* irrigation is mainly in the Quetta region, as in the S the *daman* is usually too gentle in slope to retain much water or give much head. Wheat, barley, and millet are the chief crops, with potatoes increasingly important in the En valleys. Apricots, peaches, apples, and grapes are grown in the valleys around Quetta, and the Harnai valley is thought suitable for citrus fruit. Makran has two distinctive occupations: date-growing in the relatively well-watered central valley; fishing along the coast. Future progress in Baluchistan probably depends on the

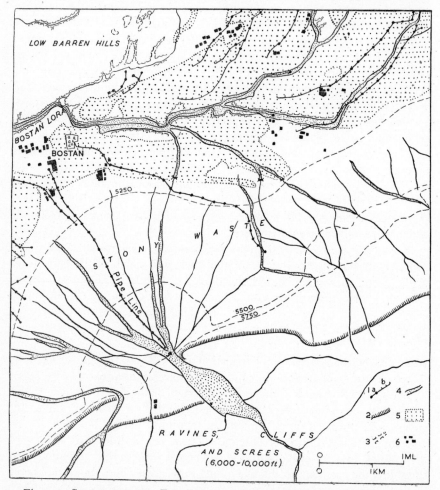

Fig. 74.—SETTLEMENT ON A FAN, BOSTAN. 15 miles N of Quetta (A on Fig. 76). 1a, *karez*; 1b, open irrig. channels; 2, abrupt edge of hills; 3, ravines; 4, stream beds (only permanent water channel shown in Bostan Lora); 5, cultivation; 6, settlement. Only *karez* in flow shown; numerous dry *karez* on fans omitted, as are Quetta–Zhob road (along 5250 ft contour) and railway just below it. SOP 34 N/3; courtesy SOP.

improvement of stock-breeding (e.g. by the introduction of Angora goats), the development of fruit culture and processing, and a more scientific development of indigenous irrigation methods and possibly of sub-artesian water.

Industrial development is almost nil. Good Tertiary steam coal is mined, mainly by adits at the railway colliery at Khost in the Harnai Pass, but also in primitive outcrop mines near Quetta and in the Bolan; these are the best coals in Pakistan (cf. Ch. X, p. 269). The chromite from ultra-basic Cretaceous intrusions at Hindubagh in Zhob Dt amounted to about half the All-India total. The high-grade sulphur deposits of Koh-i-Sultan volcano in the Chagai Hills may be better exploited now that adequate roads exist in the neighbourhood.

Communications and Towns (Fig. 75)

Alexander the Great's privations in Makran appear to have given Baluchistan an undeservedly bad name. The country has not been un-important as a passageway; but although access to the Indus is relatively easy by Quetta or Makran, the barrier of the Thar Desert blocked further advance, and the greater movements into India have generally been in the N. Ancient dams and cultivation terraces (perhaps early Arab) in widely separated areas suggest a more favourable climate; the Arab invasion of Sind in the 8th century, the first Muslim irruption into India, used the Makran route, where the long Kej corridor is less inhospitable than the coast, and in Arab times agricultural prosperity and town life seem to have been well diffused there. In the 19th century British interest in Baluchistan was motivated by the desire to control routes to Herat and Kandahar, the keys to W and S Afghanistan.

The En border hills are pierced by two BG railways, via the Bolan and the Harnai Passes; strategic lines reach out to New Chaman on the Afghan border, railhead for Kandahar (only 80 miles away), and for over 400 miles W to the Iranian border: obviously this latter line is hardly justified by local traffic. In any case motor transport has largely superseded even the strategic functions of this long finger of rail. On the other line, however, there is a fairly important transit trade with Afghanistan, likely to increase with the economic development of that country. The chief items to Afghanistan are bazaar goods, sugar, motor and lighting oils, with dried fruits, carpets, and wool (over 10,000 bales to America in 1940–41) as Afghan exports.

Quetta is really the only town of Baluchistan, and it is entirely extraneous —an administrative and strategic centre which, as the only concentration of population in the country, has added to itself some commercial and mar-ket functions. It is hardly necessary to emphasise its strategic value, commanding as it does both routes up from Sibi (Fig. 76). It was largely rebuilt after the very destructive 1935 earthquake, and in 1941 had a population of over 64,000: of these only 16,000 were females and over half the males were in the cantonment, while nearly half the Hindus of Baluchistan were in Quetta, forming 37·5% of the population of the town as against 6·3% of the Province—all evidence of the entirely alien nature of this intrusive town. Fort Sandeman had about 9000 people, while the local capitals of Kalat and Bela are mere bazaar villages of 2000–4000 souls grouped round the Khan's palace or fort. "In 1839 Quetta was described as a most miserable mud town with a small castle on a mound having one small gun on a ricketty carriage"—probably not an unfair description of the average Baluchistan "town" to-day.

STATISTICAL NOTE

The territorial structure of Baluchistan is excessively complex and confused even by Indian standards. The old 'British Baluchistan' proper was gained by

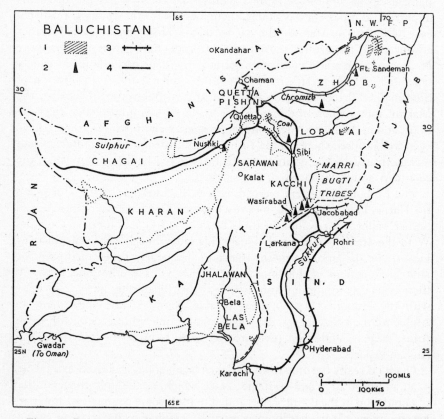

Fig. 75.—BALUCHISTAN, GENERAL. 1, forest (open); 2, irrigation; 3, BGDT; 4, BGST; E of the Indus only the main line to the Punjab is shown.

treaty from Afghanistan and covers about 9084 sq mls; certain territories (Quetta, Nushki, a strip along the Bolan railway, and Nasirabad in the S of Kachhi, adjoining Sind) were leased from the Khan of Kalat. To these leased territories and regular districts (including Zhob, Loralai, and Chagai) are added the Marri-Bugti Tribal Areas to form the 45,372 sq mls of administered area outside the original 'British Baluchistan'. The rest of the area is in the states of Kalat, Las Bela, Kharan, and Mekran, the last two recognised as separate from Kalat in 1940 and 1947. For statistics, see next page.

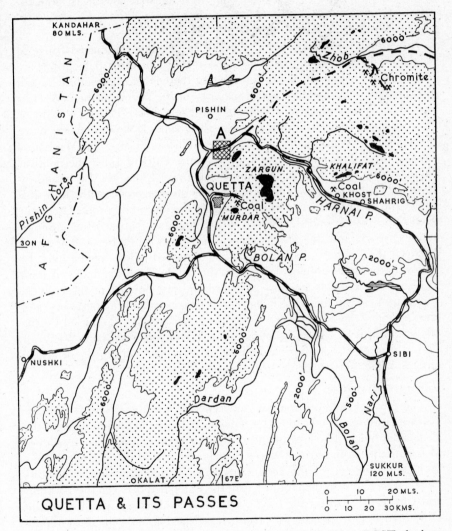

QUETTA & ITS PASSES

Fig. 76.—QUETTA AND ITS PASSES. Over 10,000 ft black. Railways BGST; broken line Zhob valley road. Note the great joint fan of the Dardan and Bolan Rivers. A = Fig. 74.

Provincial territory 52,900 sq mls; poptn (1951)		**622,000**
Kalat State		**283,000**
Kharan State	81,239	**54,000**
Las Bela State		**76,000**
Mekran State		**143,000**
134,139		**1,178,000**

The population was 868,617 in 1931 and 868,817 in 1941, the decrease being attributed to emigration of Kalatis to Sind. Areas above are now official estimates.

The North-western Hills

In a broad sense the hills of the NWFP are but the ragged fringe of Afghanistan. The clear trends and massive structures of Baluchistan are absent N of the Gomal, and to some extent there is a corresponding human fragmentation. Although the vast majority of the people of the NW Hills are of one ethnic stock, one language, and one faith—Pathan, Pakhtu or Pushtu, and Sunni Islam respectively—their political development is more amorphous, a congeries of petty tribal republics and clans. The Wn boundary of the region is of course arbitrary—the Durand Line, the political boundary between Afghanistan and (until 1947) India: the En boundary from the Vale of Peshawar Swds is taken as the *daman* where the hills sink under the basins along the Indus—roughly the old Sikh border. Except in Kohat this corresponds fairly well to the boundary between the administered Districts and the Tribal Agencies of the NWFP (Figs. 78 and 79), between the "settled" Pathans and their untamed fellows of the hills. In the N, in the spurs running down from the Hindu Kush/Pamir/Karakoram node, it is impossible to draw any hard and fast boundary: the political boundary between the NWFP and Kashmir is as suitable a line as any, and the 'no man's land' nature of this transitional area is emphasised by the doubtful status of Chitral, administratively grouped with the NWFP but with a shadow of Kashmiri suzerainty, imperceptibly dropped—or lost to sight in a larger crisis—with the formation of Pakistan.

The Physical Setting

The great change of direction between the Karakoram and the Hindu Kush is presumably controlled, at a distance, by the hidden outlines of the Peninsular block. The long tongue of Afghan territory in the Oxus Valley—Wakhan, the buffer-strip between Russia and the Indian Empire—runs W/E along the top of the arch. Here the Nn boundary lies at 16,000–24,000 ft, actually on the Hindu Kush, the watershed between the Yarkhun and Chitral Rivers and the Gilgit. Of the several passes which cross the Hindu Kush, here described by Holdich as "flat-backed", the most important is the Baroghil (only 12,460 ft) which can be used by laden animals for eight months of the year, a comparatively easy crossing.

S from this high watershed, as far as the Kabul River (220 miles), the general trend is NE–SW with a Nly component, falling from the 25,263 ft of Tirich Mir in the N of Chitral to 5000–6000 ft in the Mohmand hills and the Malakand ridge which separates the Swat Valley from the Vale of Peshawar. The far N is geologically Himalayan territory: the rocks of upper Chitral are Permo-Carboniferous and Jurassic with large areas of gneiss and granite; but all the human links are with the S. This mountain area is gashed by deep narrow valleys—the town of Chitral itself, only 30 miles from Tirich Mir, is under 5000 ft. The striking parallelism of the Yarkhun, Chitral-Kunar, Panjkora, and Swat Rivers to the middle Indus, and their relations to the Kabul River into which they flow, seem to call for a large-scale tectonic explanation.

S of the Kabul River the NE/SW trend is interrupted by the strong W/E line of the Safed Koh Range, which reaches 15,620 ft in its Wn culmination, Sikaram, falling to 3000–5000 ft in the Kohat Hills in the angle between the Kabul or Landai River and the Indus (Figs. 77, 78). This trend is perhaps a continuation of an outer Himalayan arc from the neighbourhood of

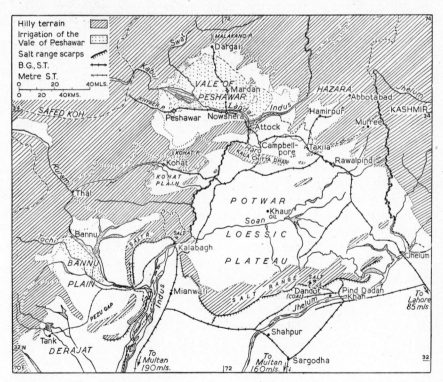

Fig. 77.—THE NW HILLS AND THE SUB-MONTANE INDUS REGION. Dotted line is boundary between administered and tribal areas of NWFP. Khewra (salt, gypsum) lies between Dandot and its rail junction.

the Jhelum gorges by the Kala Chitta Dhar S of Attock. The whole area between the Safed Koh and the Tochi River is a tangle of arid hills up to 5000 ft, largely Eocene nummulitic limestones and Siwalik sandstones, with a general W/E trend cut across from NW to SE by the more favoured upper Kurram Valley. In the Bhittanni country, between Bannu and Jandola, there seems to be an arcuate arrangement convex to the *W*; the spurs of the NW Hills and of the Salt Range nearly meet in the Pezu gap between Bannu and Dera Ismail Khan. In the extreme S, Waziristan, the N/S trends of the Sulaimans begin. The sinuous strikes of this area between the Kabul and Gomal Rivers express "the buckling caused by the meeting . . . of the Himalayan, Hindu Kush, and other more western systems of crust movement, setting in from three sides against the rigid peninsular mass", and are the habitat of the ever-warring tribes whose political fragmentation corresponds to the extremely broken terrain.

As on the Baluchistan Plateau, Wly climatic influences are important. On the whole the region is better watered than is Baluchistan, although the difference is naturally very little in the S. Rainfall is generally 12–25 ins., depending of course greatly on altitude, exposure, and aspect; in the N winter precipitation predominates, while farther S the Wly and the monsoonal influences are of approximately equal strength:

	J.	F.	M.	A.	M.	J.	J.	A.	S.	O.	N.	D.	Total
Chitral	1·2	1·6	3·2	3·9	0·7	0·3	0·1	0·2	0·2	0·7	0·3	0·9	13·3 ins.

2·2

	J.	F.	M.	A.	M.	J.	J.	A.	S.	O.	N.	D.	Total
Peshawar	1·7	1·5	2·0	1·5	0·7	0·5	2·2	3·3	1·2	0·3	0·4	0·6	15·9 ins.

8·2

Both sources are precarious and droughts are not infrequent either in winter or in summer.

Temperatures tend to extremes and are again much affected by topographical situation. Peshawar (in the plains, but very close to the hills) ranges from under 50° F in January to over 91 in June, and in the intermont valleys extremes are of course much more marked: Chitral, in its narrow wind-swept valley, has had temperatures as low as 5·4° F and as high as 108, and to the S in Waziristan the more or less enclosed plain between 4000 and 5000 ft at Wana has had *minus* 13° F.

There is naturally a considerable variation in the vegetation cover. The lower hills, as in Waziristan and the Mohmand country, do indeed conform to the usual impression of the Frontier: a land of bare jagged ridges carrying little but infrequent bushes, acacia, dwarf palms, coarse grasses. But in the higher W there are forests of pine, deodar, and ilex (evergreen oak), and those on the Sn flanks of Safed Koh form good tall stands of timber. On the Kurram River "more or less all along are cornfields and fruit gardens, mulberry groves and fertile glades, passing up to ridges crested by oak and olive, yew trees and pines". The Nn mountains have plane, poplar, and ilex, and great forests of pine and deodar, as well as extensive mountain grasslands; but in the far N altitude and exposure inhibit vegetation and many of the valley sides are rocky and barren.

The Peoples and their Life

The population of the hills is almost solidly tribal and Muslim. Strictly speaking, 'Pathan' implies tribal status rather than race, but in normal usage it is applied as a generic term to most of the tribes—Afridis, Mohmands, Mahsuds, Orakzais, Waziris, etc.—and the last few decades have seen the growth of something like a Pathan national sentiment. This is, however, complicated not only by the inherent particularism of the tribes and clans, but also by the political separation of the Pathans into three distinct groups: the settled tribes (over 1 m.) of the Administered Districts and so within the orbit of Indian self-government, with curious results; the hillmen between the administrative boundary and the Durand Line (2·4 m.) and their fellows in Afghanistan (estimated at 3–7 m.).[6] Nearly all speak dialects of Pushtu, an Iranian tongue, and culturally the region is in broad outline remarkably homogeneous.

For the most part the tribesmen are intensely democratic, eking out from scanty patches of arable land a hard living, supplemented by less licit but more exciting acquisitive processes; riddled with tribal, clan, and family vendettas; easily aroused to religious fanaticism, sometimes mitigated by susceptibility to hard cash. The cultivator goes to his fields with spade or plough on one shoulder and rifle on the other, and in some areas where village watch-towers are within range of each other cultivation is mutually inhibited by sniping. *Zar, zan, zamin*—gold, women, land—are at the root of most of the feuds, but politics and intra-Muslim sectarianism play their part. The Afridis "are so distracted by intestine quarrels that they have little time for carrying on feuds with the neighbouring tribes"; a truly appalling thought.

Anarchic as this tribal society appears at first sight, it is not without principles of conduct and rules of intercourse: the code of revenge enforces the wiping out of insult with blood, but it is to some extent offset by the obligations of hospitality and asylum. But on the whole Frontier life tends to be poor, nasty, brutish, and short; and, as the unkind critic remarked of Ireland, "its early history is myth and murder; its later, murder". This turbulent, not to say irresponsible, democracy is the root cause of the difference between border policy in Baluchistan and the NWFP, though the actual territorial layout is an important factor, in its turn affected, however, by the obvious difficulty of assimilating the wilder tribes. It seems

[6] All figures approximate.

possible that the difference is related to the physical background—more massive in Baluchistan, more fragmented in the NW Hills—and it is perhaps significant that in the N, which although higher is again rather bolder in its topographic outlines, the tribes are more oligarchic and something like feudal organisms—Chitral, Dir, Swat, Buner—have grown up. Other factors are involved, however, and the Chitralis at least are not Pathan, whatever their origin may be.

Agriculture is carried on throughout the hill country—mainly dry crops such as wheat, barley, and maize, with some rice in the valley-bottoms which are, however, generally malarial. In some areas the tribal lands are interchanged among the cultivators every few years. Large numbers of sheep and goats are kept, and winter transhumance to the plains is very important; the camel of Baluchistan is naturally replaced by the mule in this broken country. There is also a good deal of petty trading with the plains in wood, charcoal, fodder-grass, and mats and ropes made from the ubiquitous dwarf palm (*Nannorhops*). Some areas are particularly favoured: the upper Kurram has rich irrigated fields and excellent orchards—grapes, apples, apricots, peaches. Some spots in the Nn valleys are likewise noted for fruit, but despite their perennial streams, their groves of poplars and mountain forests, they are for the most part poor: in Chitral even the upper classes are said to have generally a hungry look. Mineral wealth is not likely to be great, though there may be deposits of iron and the antimony of Chitral—175 miles from railhead by mule-track and road—was worked before Partition. Building stones await demand; the only effective mineral exploitation is that of salt from the Kohat anticlines.

In fact the whole border from Chitral to Makran has been called a distressed area. There is a vicious circle of poverty, anarchy, and more poverty; even on low standards the region cannot support its relatively dense population by local resources alone.[7] Hence the necessity for outside income, in the past largely derived from raiding the plains or trading caravans. Under the British régime these activities were severely restricted, but to a large extent replaced by subsidies, military employment, road and mail contracts. There was also a considerable migration to Indian cities of Pathans as petty traders, mechanics, and labourers: their remittances home were a not unimportant contribution. As moneylenders and strikebreakers the Pathans had an evil reputation as far afield as Bombay and even Rangoon. It remains to be seen how far these resources will be available under the new dispensation.

The Evolution of the Frontier: a Study in Border Policy

The importance of this NW angle as the great entry into India is a commonplace of historical geography. Rhetorical reiteration and the

[7] Population in 1951 (including estimated) of the 27,242 sq mls of Agency territory was 2,460,000—over 90 to the sq ml.

notoriety of the disaster of the First Afghan War have put the limelight on the Khyber with a consequent overshadowing of past values. As a matter of fact the Khyber itself was often, perhaps generally, bypassed by a route up the Kunar and over the easy passes into the lower Swat Valley. This was the route which Alexander took in person, wherever he came out, and also that used by Babur, the first of the Mogul Emperors, in his decisive invasion. The earlier importance of Makran has been noted, and when the SW flanks of the Punjab were better watered than they are now, Multan and the Tochi and Gomal Valleys were correspondingly more important to the earlier Muslim invaders. Nevertheless the Vale of Peshawar has probably been the most usual first objective of invaders.

In such troubled times as those of the pre-Mogul Muslim dynasties and the 18th century anarchy, Pathans are of course found much farther E, at Delhi or in Rohilkhand. But their hold on the trans-Indus was firmer and it is sometimes said that the real frontier of India is on the Indus itself, both ethnically and geographically: the former is perhaps and the latter certainly an exaggerated view. The suggestion has its value, though the more ardent proponents of an ambitious Frontier policy opined that the "true" or "scientific" frontier lay along the Hindu Kush: together these extreme views emphasise the transitional nature of the whole frontier zone, within which a sharper divide—not corresponding to any ethnic, linguistic, or religious division—separates the plains from the hills.

Conditions have probably always been much the same along this shatter-zone, as is indeed suggested by the narrative of Alexander's invasion. This broken semi-arid country, inhabited by uncivilised hillmen, has probably been incapsulated rather than assimilated in the great empires which have reached down from the Iranian plateaus into Hindustan; taxable capacity (the real preoccupation of these states) was so obviously so far below the cost of effectively occupying and administering the whole area that, so long as caravans and official traffic were not too extortionately robbed, the tribes were left to misgovern themselves within the wide meshes of a net formed by firmly held roads and key strategic points. The obvious course is an opportunist policy of occasional punitive expeditions, protection of some tribes and licence to attack any particularly obnoxious element, economic blockade, the taking of hostages, and a judicious mixture of bribery, fêting, intimidation, and assassination of local chiefs. These (with exception of the last device) were essentially the methods used by the British Raj, the last-but-one inheritor of this intractable problem.

In the past state structures have not infrequently straddled the whole border, with bases on the Kabul/Kandahar line and in the Punjab; this was the case e.g. with the Ghaznavide and Ghori kingdoms (11–12th centuries AD), the Mogul Empire, and the Afghan Durrani kingdom of the 18th century. This facilitates border policing, as all the outlets of the hill country are

under one control—the absence of which was one of the great difficulties of
the British. But there are obvious elements of instability in such a territorial
structure, and with the exception of that of the Moguls such states tended
to be short-lived or else rather loose supremacies. The former was the case
with the Durranis, and the immediate predecessors of the British on the
Frontier were not Afghans but Sikhs. Their boundary was the *daman-i-koh*
—the 'skirt of the hills'—beyond which they made only occasional punitive
incursions; the tribute of their border tracts was not infrequently so many
Pathan heads. This 'close border' policy was that initially adopted by the
British.

During the 19th century, however, the problem became far more than
local. The first jealousies of Russia date back to the Franco-Russian
rapprochement after Tilsit; Napoleon's invasion of Egypt was thought of as
a mere starting-point for more grandiose Eastern designs,[8] and it was
feared that he had given Alexander a free hand in the East in return for a
quid pro quo in Europe. British seapower, which had checkmated the French
game in India in the 18th century, was obviously of no avail in these
changed conditions, and as early as 1809 a British mission visited Teheran
to stiffen up the Shah. The disaster of 1841–42, when a British-Indian
army of 16,000 retreating from Kabul through Jagdalak was reduced to a
single survivor,[9] was indeed avenged, but its memory doubtless inhibited
adventurism. Continuous Russian advance in central Asia and the Anglo-
Russian clash of 1878 in the Balkans, however, led directly to the Second
Afghan War of 1879–81.

Again the vital Kabul/Kandahar line was in British hands, but the costs
and risks of holding down a tough and desperately hostile population would
obviously be excessive, and the policy of maintaining Afghanistan as a
strong buffer-state, under definite and exclusive British influence, was
adopted. Nothing else was practicable, but the inevitable result was to
make policing more difficult as the outlets of the hills were once again
under two separate administrations. In Baluchistan this was not the case;
Kandahar was given up after some hesitation, but by the Treaty of Gandamak (1879) the Nn Districts of Baluchistan remained British and interposed
a belt of British-administered territory between Afghanistan and the tribes
of the mountainous Sind border. This, as well as the greater status and
power of the Baluchistan chiefs, greatly facilitated the policy of Sir Robert
Sandeman, who after 1880 successfully assimilated Baluchistan by what
was essentially indirect rule. In the N, however, the Administered Districts
lay back from the border (as yet ill defined) and the intervening 'Agency'
territory could hardly be said to be ruled at all by the British, except in so

[8] Cf. F. Rabelais, *Gargantua and Pantagruel*, Book I, Ch. XXIII.
[9] Despite traditional rhetoric, the army never reached the Khyber at all. The survivor,
Dr Brydon, came into the British-garrisoned town of Jalalabad, well on the Afghan side
of the Pass.

far as strategic centres were garrisoned and outrage outside tribal limits was liable to be visited by overwhelming force within them.

But although it was clear that actual occupation would mean an intolerable drain of life and money (not that the Agency policy was extremely economical of either), it was clear that the essentially negative 'closed

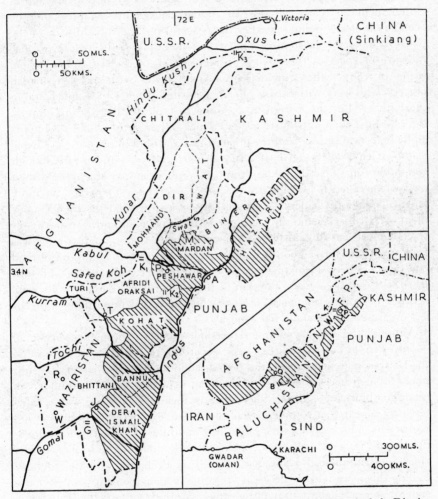

Fig. 78.—THE NW FRONTIER. Administered Districts of NWFP shaded; District, State, and important tribal names in capitals. Passes: M, Malakand; K1, Khyber; K2, Kohat; K3, Kankhun; G, Gomal. Military stations: P, Peshawar; A, Attock; T, Thal; R, Razmak; W, Wana; J, Jandola.

Inset: Makran to Chitral. Peshawar and the Khyber, Quetta and the Bolan, indicated by initials. The Districts of Baluchistan and NWFP are shaded: note how they lie on the border in Baluchistan, shutting off the tribes from direct contact with Afghanistan, while in NWFP a belt of unadministered tribal territory intervenes between the administrative boundary and the Afghan boundary (the 'Durand Line').

border' system was dead. It had been most successful under Jacob on the Upper Sind Frontier around 1848, and Jacob had relied on irregular cavalry and a mobility not easily obtainable in the NW, with its plains cut up into isolated basins by irregular hill salients. A policy of 'peaceful penetration' was therefore employed—direct subsidies to loyal leaders, the economic benefits of service in the regular Army or in local levies, and of employment on roads; all this, of course, backed up by force and the occupation of key points. Neither the peaceful nor the forceful side of the policy was very consistently applied, but it undoubtedly had a very fair measure of success; there were no recurrences of the widespread tribal rising of 1897—when, incidentally, Afridi levies without their British officers, who were withdrawn, put up a spirited defence of Landi Kotal in the Khyber. But the system, if anything so typically British and empiric can be called such, obviously needed a nice judgment of whom to support and whom to suppress, and the greatest tact and skill in handling the tribal *maliks* or chiefs, who, even if acting in perfect good faith (a rare enough commodity on all hands on the Frontier), were not always able to hold their own when called to account by the tribal assemblies (*jirgas*) or the more fanatical religious leaders. Moreover the levies received the high emolument of 25 rupees a month each, not to mention road and transport contracts, and it was obviously good business to see that enough trouble was kept afoot to ensure a good demand for their services. A falling-off of road contracts has been a proximate cause of outbreaks, e.g. that of the Mahsuds in 1921. Conditions were different in the far N, where better results were secured by supporting petty leaders who succeeded in forming more or less organised feudal states like Chitral.

Although the direct economic return of loot to the tribesmen is very small —only £10–12,000 in a normal year, according to Barton—the hills are in the last resort dependent on the plains economically—as markets, as suppliers of such necessities as salt, above all as winter grazing grounds. An economic blockade is thus a very effective means of pressure where tribal territory is nearly surrounded by administered, e.g. between Peshawar and Kohat Dts (Fig. 78). But on a large scale anything like successful assimilation would depend on a firm control of both sides of the broken border zone—on Kabul and Kandahar as well as Peshawar and the Derajat. Failing this it was clearly necessary to come to an agreement with Afghanistan for an exact delimitation of the spheres of the Amir and the British Raj. This was accomplished by Sir Mortimer Durand's negotiation in 1893 of the 'Durand Line', the present international boundary, which represents the balance reached, by waiting on events rather than by conscious policy, between the old concept of a tightly closed boundary on the *daman* and the 'forward school' which looked for a "scientific" frontier to include the Kabul/ Kandahar line in India. The Durand Line is demarcated S of the Safed Koh, between the Safed Koh and the Kabul River (i.e. across the Khyber), and for a section E of the Kunar. It bisects some tribes (notably the Mohmands —"as convenient neighbours as a nest of hornets") and there is thus constant opportunity for trans-border intrigue, but on the whole it has worked reasonably well. The separation of the NWFP in 1901 brought Frontier problems under the direct view of the Government of India without the intervention of the Punjab government, an intervention defended on the ground of the remoteness of the seat of the central Government (at that time Calcutta) from the Frontier. As the bureaucrats of both India and the Punjab crowded together in Simla for a third of the year, this argument ranks high among the picturesque absurdities peculiar to the Indian administrative machine.

The Afghan invasion of 1919 proved a mere incident and the introduction of aircraft outbalanced the gradual replacement of the antique *jezail* muskets of the tribesmen by modern rifles, in which a flourishing trade grew up in Persian Gulf ports before the 1914–18 war, while a primitive factory in the Kohat Pass turns out a passable imitation. But even with aircraft and motor-vehicles at call, and with the advantages of the Khyber Pass Railway (after 1925) and the earlier lines from Kohat to Thal and from Kalabagh to Bannu and Tank (Fig. 77), the Frontier has never been more than quiescent, and as recently as 1937 the Waziristan campaign against the Mahsuds and Bhittanis involved the use of nearly 40,000 troops and cost nearly 1000 casualties (not counting tribesmen) and some £1,500,000. The country is of course extremely favourable to guerilla fighting by tribal *lashkars* (rarely exceeding 700–800 men at any one time or place) and operations seem to have been rather like trying to hit a butterfly—or better a wasp—with a howitzer.

In recent years an additional complication was provided by the attainment of self-government in the administered part of the province and the consequent rise to power of the 'Red Shirt' party led by the able Khan brothers and attached, *mirabile dictu*, to Congress. A non-violent organisation of Pathans was a sufficiently bizarre phenomenon, even if the non-violence were entirely *soi disant* and tactical, which does not seem to have been altogether the case; but in the long run the Congress alliance was obviously factitious, being based merely on common enmity to the power in being, and it did not survive the wave of pan-Muslim solidarity evoked by the events of 1947 in the Punjab.

The weakness, fiscal and military, of Pakistan has compelled the evacuation of the military stations in the Agencies—the withdrawal from the recently and expensively fortified camp of Razmak had to be carried out with all the secrecy of a major operation—though subsidies are continued. Defence is now relegated to local levies. Although, in a country where a fighting psychology has been ingrained through immemorial generations of feud, it is clear enough that an economic policy is inadequate by itself—i.e. unless it has the sanction of force behind it—there can be little doubt that education, road building, medical services, and general economic betterment are essential factors in any possible solution. The topography of the plains makes the problem there vastly easier, but the experience of the 'settled' tribes in the Districts suggests that the Pathan can change some at least of his spots. Time alone can tell how far a general Islamic polity will help to ease the situation, and how far Pakistan can afford the not directly remunerative expenditure of a welfare policy. In another sense Pakistan cannot afford not to afford it.

Already the difficulty of controlling the tribes—and not improbably a certain lack of will to do so on the part of local officials—has played a major part in the explosion of the great Kashmir crisis. Nor are there wanting signs of an opportunist attitude on the part of Afghanistan, a solicitude for Pathan interests which might prove very inconvenient should the waters become sufficiently troubled for Kabul to fish in them; and there are still at least some links with Delhi. Of the many grave problems confronting Pakistan none is more pregnant with difficulty and danger than that of the Frontier, more especially should it not remain localised. The whole future of Pakistan may well depend on a viable solution of this *damnosa haereditas*.

The Sub-montane Indus Region

The area here described as the Sub-montane Indus Region consists of:

(a) the three plains of Peshawar, Kohat, and Bannu, all W of the Indus;
(b) the Potwar Plateau, E of the Indus;
(c) the Salt Range, marking off the southern boundary of the region both in Bannu and Potwar, and cut through by the Indus at the head of the remarkable Kalabagh re-entrant.

The Sn boundary is taken as the foot of the Salt Range scarp, the NEn as the edge of the foothills of Sub-Himalayan Kashmir.

This is not, it must be confessed, a very satisfactory division, and other arrangements are possible; the three plains might, for instance, be included within the NW Hills Region. But the Indus cuts across some of the most prominent structures and is in no sense a geographical division, and although the Salt Range has very different values from those of the other components, it is after all intimately connected with the Potwar Plateau behind it. To elevate each unit to the rank of a region, while theoretically tenable, would be practically difficult and distinctly out of scale with the regional scheme as a whole. Moreover the Indus does at least form a link in the complex structural history of the whole area.

Structural History

In Miocene times the whole region was an area of "foreland sedimentation" from the newly risen or rising Himalayas, whether this was by alluviation in the Indobrahm of Pilgrim and Pascoe or, as de Terra suggests, by the fans of transverse rivers—"such slope drainage, when repeatedly rejuvenated by intermittent uplift, is able to accumulate vast quantities of sediment." [10] At the end of the Pleistocene uplift took place, and by the Lower Pleistocene (Upper Siwalik) this foreland sedimentation was replaced by alluviation in basins and valleys formed by the increasing uplift and warping of the Potwar Plateau, now traversed by NE/SW or E/W ridges—generally limestone anticlinals, such as the Cretaceous-Eocene Kala Chitta Dhar and Khair-i-Murat.

On the Indobrahm view, the rejuvenation caused by this uplift contributed to dismemberment of the middle Indobrahm by its own tributaries cutting back from the SW. At any rate it is agreed by all that the present River Soan, the master stream of Potwar, is a complete misfit, far too small for the erosion of its great and very mature basin. A small stream entering the Jhelum very near its debouchment from the Sub-Himalayan foothills (Fig. 77), and pointing upstream, probably indicates the old course by which the Jhelum flowed SW on the present Soan line. This great, and doubtless braided, stream probably contributed to the extensive peneplanation of the break between the Middle (Mid-Pliocene) and Upper (Lower Pleistocene) Siwaliks. Relics of the peneplanation are found in the Kala Chitta Dhar and elsewhere, but the relief has been generally much altered by later erosion and deposition.

A strong erosive phase followed, during which the Jhelum was diverted, probably by a small anticlinal uplift N of Panjar, through a great boulder-fan of one of its own braided channels. Meanwhile, in the N, compression and faulting elevated yet further the Kala Chitta Dhar. The Indus abandoned its old course by the Haro River—a course along which it is probable that the much-controverted erratic blocks of Campbellpur were swept by immense glacial floods and mud-flows.[11] It now cut a channel across the En end of the Kohat Hills; it seems plausible that the erosive force needed was provided by the ponding-up of a great lake in the Vale of Peshawar. In late Pliocene times most of Wn Potwar drained direct to the Indus, until uplifts broke up the old drainage system; there is at least one clear case of antecedence, the Nandna Kas tributary of the Haro, which cuts right across the En Kala Chitta Dhar.[12]

[10] H. de Terra and T. T. Paterson, *Studies on the Ice Age in India* (1939), 300. The following, greatly foreshortened, summary is based mainly on de Terra.
[11] For the theory of their strictly glacial origin, see A. L. Coulson, "Pleistocene Glaciation in North-Western India", *Rec GSI* LXXII (1938), 422–39; for another view, de Terra, *op. cit.*, 266–68.
[12] de Terra, *op. cit.*, 259.

This erosive stage appears to correspond to the 2nd Interglacial in Kashmir, and was succeeded by the deposition of the Potwar loess or loessic silt, probably mainly in the 3rd Glacial of Kashmir. The later Pleistocene saw continuing deposition of loess, but probably more re-sorting of it by streams, with extensive terrace formation and gullying.

The Salt Range itself has an excessively complex history. The lowest—by no means necessarily the oldest—rocks are the Saline Series, which are overlain by several hundred feet of Cambrian sandstones and shales. From Cambrian to Upper Carboniferous times the area was apparently dry land; after this break deposition seems continuous in one part or another of the range except for gaps in Triassic-Jurassic and Oligocene times. The sequence begins again with the Carboniferous (Talchir) Boulder Bed, undoubtedly glacial and of great interest owing to the analogies with similar deposits in the Gondwana blocks of the Sn Hemisphere. The included boulders are largely rhyolites and granites of Vindhyan age from the Aravallis. The Carboniferous tillites and sandstones are succeeded by the massive *Productus* limestones, all together forming a Permo-Carboniferous (Lower Gondwana) sequence. The early Eocene Ranikot and Laki beds are of great importance, the Sakesar (Laki) nummulitic limestone forming the great upper cliff of the scarp from the En end of the range almost to Kalabagh. Near Kalabagh the limestone is altered to massive gypsum, and associated with important salt deposits; here the Saline Series seems definitely of Laki age. Overlying the Eocene beds is the Murree-Siwalik-Potwar loess sequence.

The whole of the Salt Range has been subjected to intense faulting, thrusting, and block-dislocation. The general structure would appear to be that of a monoclinal uplift overwhelmed by lateral pressure from the Himalayan orogeny, so that the Sn portion has been depressed under the Punjab Plains and overridden on low thrusts by the Nn part, leaving a truncated monocline with gentle rises from the Potwar Plateau and the great dissected scarp overlooking the plains. The striking horseshoe bend round the Indus at Kalabagh may be controlled in part at least by the underground topography of the Peninsular block and eaten out, as it were, by the Indus (Fig. 80).

The great stratigraphical problem concerns the Saline Series, which in places appears in a definitely Tertiary position, in places overlain in a complicated and irregular, but quite natural, manner by undoubted Cambrian. It contains organic dust—including remains of angiosperms, conifers, and insects—which, if not alien in origin, put a Cambrian age out of the question. The highly disturbed upper boundary has been variously interpreted as the result of buckling and yielding of the incompetent Saline Series beneath the massive sandstone overburden; of solution of the salts and consequent slumping and brecciation; and of great overthrusts bringing

Cambrian over Eocene. The evidence and arguments of the leading pro-tagonists, Gee and Sahni, are fascinating but almost indescribably intricate, and cannot be summarised here. The debate is far from concluded, and the Salt Range has the distinction of being probably the only place in the world where there can be serious and long-continued controversy as to whether a series with included organic remains should be placed in the pre-Cambrian or the Eocene.[13]

There is thus, if not an underlying structural unity, at least a unity of structural history for the whole region; the Salt Range cannot be separated from the Soan synclinal trough, "there is a gradual passage from the complex folding and overthrusting of the northern limestone ranges (Kala Chitta Dhar etc.) into the low-dipping Soan basin",[14] and the events which produced the great open synclinal of Potwar and the tightly-packed little anticlines of the Kala Chitta Dhar doubtless also played their part in the formation of the alluvial and detrital floors of the trans-Indus basins.

THE TRANS-INDUS PLAINS

(i) *The Vale of Peshawar* forms a great semi-circular lowland of some 2500 sq mls, hill-girt except along the Indus in the SE. The floor of the basin is formed of Attock slates (Vindhyan in age), but much of the area is covered by spreads of gravelly or clayey alluvial detritus with a general level of 1000–1200 ft. Some of this detritus may well have been deposited in a lacustrine phase; Coulson thinks that the weight of detritus may have been sufficient to depress the floor, or down-warping may have permitted deep accumulation. At all events there are several hundred feet of sediments, and in view of the liability of the Vale to earthquakes it is interesting to note that they show doming caused by very recent movements.

The hydrographic history of the Vale is also of interest. It is possible that Alexander the Great's approach from the N, skirting the Nn margin, may have been made to avoid the then marshy floor. But with a rainfall of 10–15 ins. irrigation is obviously necessary for secure cultivation, and so much water has been poured on to the land by canals that some streams, formerly dry for most of the year, now have a perennial flow from seepage or direct discharge. The most important work is the Upper Swat Canal, the headwaters of which are at Amandarra, five miles NE of Malakand. The water from the Swat is carried under the Malakand Pass by the Benton Tunnel, a branch tunnel from which takes off a supply for the Malakand hydro-electric scheme (installed capacity 9600 kW, potential being developed 20,000).

[13] The account in the text is based mainly in the scattered references in D. N. Wadia, *Geology of India* (2nd edition, 1939), especially 104–06 and 244–45. The controversy on the Saline Series is the subject of two symposia in the *Proceedings of the National Academy of Sciences of India*, Vols. 14 (1945) and 16 (1947), conveniently summarised by E. B. Bailey in *Nature*, February 21st, 1948, 265–66.

[14] E. S. Pinfold, *Rec. GSI* XLIX (1918), 140.

Some 750,000 ac. are cultivated in Peshawar and Mardan Dts, about 650,000 ac. of which are irrigated; with double-cropping the total sown area amounts to about 1 m. ac. Wheat is the chief crop, followed by maize; half the former and nearly all the latter are irrigated. Next come fodder crops and sugar, followed at a distance by jowar, rice, tobacco, and cotton. The Sn side of the Vale is naturally drier: in Peshawar the net cultivated area is only 42% of the total against Mardan's 62%, but two-thirds are irrigated in the former and only half in the latter; in both wheat covers about 40% of the TSA.

The Vale, then, with its irrigated fields and groves of mulberry, willow, and tamarisk, is a great oasis in the generally arid NW. The fans of the perennial streams on the Nn flank must always have attracted settlement —the area was one of the most flourishing centres of Graeco-Buddhist culture—and to-day the Vale has nearly half the population of the NWFP. In 1941 Peshawar City had 131,000 (in 1951 : **114,000**), the cantonments another 40,000; Mardan and Nowshera had about 40,000 each; the latter is mainly a cantonment town, but Mardan has now one of the greatest sugar factories of Asia. The site advantages of Peshawar are obvious (Figs. 77

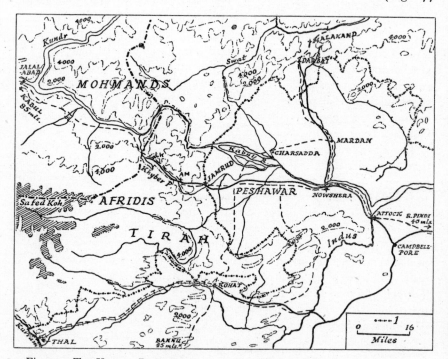

Fig. 79.—THE VALE OF PESHAWAR AND THE KHYBER PASS. Over 8000 ft shaded. Solid lines, BGST railways; thin ticked lines, metre ST; broken lines, more important roads. 1, administrative boundary; note its relation to the plains/hills margin (the *daman-i-koh*). LK, Landi Kotal; AM, Ali Masjid.

and 79); the major portion of the Afghan trade passes through it, and it has now power for light industry from Malakand. But its primary importance is strategic, and its characteristic urban landscape is that of the cantonment.

(ii) The *Kohat* valley lies higher than Peshawar and Bannu, around 1500 ft, and is much broken by W/E limestone ridges. The filling of the uneven limestone floor varies from lacustrine clays to gravel and boulder fans; there are many springs from the limestone, and the water-table is generally high. Damming the Kohat Toi might give security to agriculture in the lower valley, but at present the valley is little developed, and much remains scrub and poor grazing land. Rainfall is relatively high (16 ins.), and although some 300,000 ac. are sown, half to wheat, there is relatively little irrigation and that mainly by small tanks formed by bunding across the valleys, and by very minor privately-constructed canals.

(iii) The *Bannu* lowland (800–1500 ft) covers some 1700 sq mls and is entirely enclosed by hills except for the Kurram gorge through the Salt Range and the Pezu Gap in the S. Into this basin converge the Kurram, the Tochi, and numerous hill streams, all much braided and with broad boulder-strewn channels, dry for much or most of the year. Here again it is difficult not to postulate earlier lacustrine conditions, but soils are in general sandy or gravelly, except for the rich silts along the Kurram below Bannu town.

Nearly half the total area is cultivated at one time or another, but a very high proportion—about two-fifths—is under current fallows in any year. With a rainfall of only 11 ins. irrigation is obviously necessary for stable agriculture, and about half the 300,000 ac. sown each year is irrigated, mainly on the Tochi-Kurram doab; wheat accounts for half the cropped area, followed by fodder. The doab, like the Vale of Peshawar, is really an oasis in an arid scrub-covered country.

In both Kohat and Bannu fat-tailed sheep, camels, and donkeys are extensively reared, and wool is perhaps the most important commercial crop. But neither area is really of much significance; there are no real towns other than minor administrative or military centres, and the railways to Thal, Bannu, and Tank are primarily strategic.

The 1951 densities for Peshawar, Mardan, Kohat, and Bannu Dts were respectively about 582, 544, 112, and 180 to the sq ml. These densities seem remarkably high for the scanty resources, and any stability or prosperity must depend on a far more scientific use of the available water. Without this it would seem that cultivation has nearly reached the limit of extension, though not necessarily of intensity. Some security may be obtained by minor projects and tube-wells, but in Kohat and Bannu even these are probably beyond local resources. It is not without reason, therefore, that Pakistan's only multi-purpose scheme is on the flanks of the

Vale of Peshawar, at Warsak: this is planned to irrigate 60,000 ac. and develop 105,000 kW; a further 20,000 kW are planned at Dargai. Without such development the problem might become critical: the hills, as we have seen, are untamed and a large proportion of the plains population is not fundamentally different in racial stock and *mores*. An increase in population not accompanied by a very considerable increase in production might turn the valleys of Kohat and Bannu, if not Peshawar itself, from mere backward areas into active danger-spots.

POTWAR

The Potwar Plateau covers an area of 4–5000 sq mls at about 1200–1900 ft; there are a few outlying spurs of the Salt Range in the S, and in the N the Khair-i-Murat and the Kala Chitta Dhar with a very open cover of wild olives and bush. But in general it is open undulating country developed on the mainly sandstone Siwaliks and mantled by varying thicknesses of loessic silt which erodes easily into deep canyons; most of the hills and rivers are bordered by belts of intricately dissected ravine lands, locally *khuddera*. The streams are generally deep-set owing to rejuvenation, and of little or no use for irrigation: agriculture is thus almost entirely dependent on the rainfall of 15–25 ins., between a quarter and a third of which falls in January–March, especially in the less arid Nn strip near the hills; the SW is of course very arid at all seasons. Temperatures are extreme and snow, though rare, is not unknown. Soils are often sandy, or stony near the *daman*, and wind-blown sand from the stream-beds is a menace to agriculture. On the whole it is a hard land: symptomatic of the general poverty is the fact that donkeys are often used for ploughing instead of bullocks. Most of the area is insecure; in 1920–21 in one tehsil only 7% of the sown area matured and there was not even enough grain for seed.

The chief rabi crops are wheat (easily leading) and barley; kharif crops are jowar, bajri, and pulses; in more favoured areas onions, melons, and tobacco are grown. Irrigation is almost non-existent, but in many areas fields are carefully embanked to conserve soil-moisture. The most favoured area is the Chach, a strip some 20 miles by 10 along the Indus NE of Attock, and really perhaps a continuation of the Peshawar Vale. Here the soil is generally a rich loam and wells are numerous; wheat, maize, sugar-cane, and vegetables are grown, and snuff-tobacco is an extremely valuable cash crop. Farming is good and intensive, heavy manuring being the rule: unfortunately soil variety and tribal individualism have led to extreme fragmentation, the land being often divided into strips half a mile long and only 20 or 30 yds wide.[15]

Pressure on resources is severe and the population by no means sparse: deducting the urban centre of Rawalpindi, that District has still a density of

[15] M. L. Darling, *The Punjab Peasant in Prosperity and Debt* (1928), 89–91.

over 300. Cultivators readily take up alternative occupations: labour on canals or in towns, cartage on the roads to Kashmir or to hill-stations, and especially military service. Industrial development is very slight—the small Khaur-Dhulian oilfield in Attock Dt, a few factories in Rawalpindi town, most important the cement works at Wah based on Hazara limestone, with 1300 hands one of the largest in the N of the sub-continent. Capacity is 165,000 tons, and the proposed second plant of 100,000 tons seems superfluous. Rawalpindi is the only centre of any size (including cantonments, 243,000 in 1951) and is largely a cantonment town with an important arsenal and railway works, deriving its importance from controlling the main route into Kashmir by the Jhelum gorge. Attock is a site of great historical importance, the obvious crossing where the Indus narrows from a braided stream 2 to 4 miles wide to the gorge section across the En continuation of the Kohat Hills. The crossing is guarded by a hill-fort built by Akbar, and a mile below is one of the five bridges across the Indus between the Himalayas and the sea, but its strategic importance is largely superseded by those of Peshawar and Rawalpindi, and Attock itself is now only an insignificant village. Thirty miles from Rawalpindi are the ruins of Taxila, the greatest of the Buddhist universities of India: "Its medical school was specially famous, owing to the fusion of Greek and Oriental learning which its peculiar position rendered possible." [16]

THE SALT RANGE

The Salt Range ramparts, sinuous in outline and exceedingly complex in detail, sharply mark off the region from the Punjab Plains. They reach nearly 5000 ft at Sakesar, but in general the summits are at 2500–3500 ft. The Sn face is remarkably steep and dissected into great jagged spurs and crests separated by wild ravines: an intensely arid and unspeakably forbidding country. Nwds the hills sink more gently beneath the Potwar loess; between the great S-facing scarps and the indeterminate Nn edge is a belt 5–10 miles wide of isolated plateaus and valleys, some filled with alluvium and fertile enough near such streams as are perennial, though the lower courses of these are usually brackish. There are a few picturesque lakes in solution or aeolian hollows, often very saline. The N is diversified by scattered trees, but in the S vegetation is sparse, stunted, and xero- or halo-phytic. The Salt Range is flanked by the most intensely gullied *khud-dera* badlands.

Between the outermost Kashmiri foothills and the Salt Range is the convenient gap, guarded by Jhelum town (founded by Alexander?) at the river-crossing, followed by the main railway and the Grand Trunk Road which runs from Calcutta to Peshawar, the lineal descendant of the great military routeway from the NW into Hindustan. The Indus gorge at Kala-

[16] H. K. Trevaskis, *The Land of the Five Rivers* (Oxford, 1928), 43.

bagh is too narrow and wild even for a road, but a gap 5 or 6 miles to the SW is used by the Multan–Attock railway, and 18 miles farther SW the range narrows to a mile and Potwar and the plains are practically in contact (Fig. 80). W of the Indus the Kurram breach is also used by the metre railway from Kalabagh to Bannu and Tank.

There is some agriculture in the little intermont basins, but the human interest of the sub-region is centred on the enormous deposits of rock-salt —perhaps the most massive in the world—which are worked at several points, notably at Kalabagh at the Sn end of the Indus gorge, and at Khewra N of Pind Dadan Khan.

Kalabagh, built in close-packed hill-side tiers, the roofs of one tier forming the street of the next above, is probably the thirstiest place in the world;

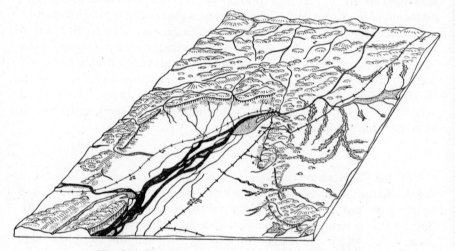

Fig. 80.—The Indus at Kalabagh—Block Diagram.

the air is salt-impregnated, roads cut through walls of salt, and the town is built on, one might almost say of, masses of rock-salt. Exploitation is in great open quarries; it has declined somewhat before the competition of the more scientifically run Government mines at Khewra, but the salt has a high reputation for purity and, together with Kohat, Kalabagh supplies the important trans-Indus (and trans-border) trade. The Khewra mines have better rail connections and are now the chief producers; there are five seams, totalling 275 ft in thickness, of practically pure salt. Some potash salts and large quantities of gypsum form the basis of one of the largest soda-ash factories of the sub-continent. Coal, mostly Tertiary and lignitic (carbon content only 40%), is widespread and is worked at Dandot N of Pind Dadan Khan. Mining is carried on in a 2–3-ft seam; this is the most important, though not the best, coalfield in Pakistan, and altogether the

Salt Range represents an area which may well be of vital importance in a country so poorly endowed in non-agricultural resources.

BIBLIOGRAPHICAL NOTE

The strategic interest of the NW has given rise to a large literature, much of it military and of very unequal value. The most useful books are Sir T. H. Holdich's:

India (Regions of the World series, 1904)—a general work but with very strong emphasis on this area.

The Indian Borderland (1909)—largely a personal record but full of information.

The Gates of India (1910)—a broad historical survey.

On Baluchistan the most valuable sources are the Census Reports of 1921 and especially of 1911; also

R. D. Oldham, "On the Recent and Sub-Recent Deposits of the valley plains of Quetta . . .", *Rec. GSI* XXV (1892)—(important for *karez*, etc.).

E. Vredenburg, "Geological Sketch of the Baluchistan Desert . . .", *Mem. GSI* XXXI (1904).

Ibid., "Report on Geology of Sarawan. . . ." *Rec. GSI* XXXVIII (1909)—much geomorphological information.

For the NW Frontier in a more limited sense see:

C. C. Davies, *The Problem of the N-W Frontier, 1890–1908* (1932), wider in scope than title suggests.

Sir W. Barton, *India's North-West Frontier*, 1939.

On the Sub-Montane Indus Region, the work of de Terra and Paterson already cited is the most important source for the physical side; see also:

D. N. Wadia: "Geology of Poonch State and Adjoining Portions of the Punjab," *Mem. GSI* LI (1928).

CHAPTER XVII

THE INDUS PLAINS
(Regions IX and X)

Sind

THE area treated here (*c.* 48,000 sq mls) corresponds nearly to the Province, but includes the Sibi lowland or Sewistan (i.e. the Kacchi area of Kalat) and part of Khairpur state, and excludes most of Thar Parkar Dt which, as its names implies, is better treated with the Thar Desert (Ch. XXI). The boundary here is taken as the sand-bluffs E of the E Nara River. Sind lives by the Indus, which has indeed given its name not only to the Province but also to the sub-continent.

The Physical Background; Hydrography

Pithawalla divides the Province into three major and seven minor divisions (Fig. 81):

1. Wn Highlands: (a) Kirthar, (b) Kohistan.
2. Lower Indus Valley: (a) Wn, (b) En, (c) Delta.
3. Desert: (a) Pat, (b) Thar.

Sewistan is included in the Wn Valley section, the boundary of which (on a bhangar/khadar basis) should not reach quite to the Indus, as it does on Pithawalla's maps.

The hydrographic history—really the history of the Indus—is extremely complex, and there have been many changes in historic times. In common with many great rivers of the Nn hemisphere, the Indus shows a strong tendency to work into its right bank, but from Sehwan to below Hyderabad its movements are to some extent limited by its impingement on to the more or less solid Tertiaries of Kohistan, and in the N the channel is as it were pinned down by the Sukkur/Rohri limestone outliers, forming a fixed point of the highest significance (Fig. 82). Between 1911 and 1930 the minimum discharge at Sukkur varied between 17,568 and 39,907 cusecs, the maximum between 430,445 and 885,165. High flood is usually in August or September, lowest stage between January and March; the time-lag as compared with the Punjab needs no explanation. The average annual discharge at Sukkur is over 5 m. million cu ft, carrying nearly 10,000 m. cu ft of silt; at Kotri the discharge is nearly 4·3 m. million cu ft. It has been estimated that in the 29 years 1902–30 the silt deposited between Sukkur

and Kotri amounted to about 1300 sq ml-ft.[1] Excessive levee-building
and many shifts of course are the inevitable consequence, and it is said that
hardly a square mile
of the En Valley sec-
tion has not been tra-
versed by an Indus
channel at some time.

From a point E of
Sukkur the E Nara
parallels the Indus at
a distance of 60–75
miles; now fed
mainly by a cut from
the Indus, this stream
possibly represents
the lower course of
the now dry Hakra
or Ghaggar (Ch.
XVIII). It effectively
divides the desert
from the sown, the
bulk of Sind's cultiva-
ted land lying on the
Indus/Nara doabs.

Kohistan ('moun-
tain country') con-
sists of an arcuate
mass of Tertiary
anticlinals, forming
low (1200–3300 ft)
scarps, hogsbacks,
and plateaus, of
which the most
prominent are asso-
ciated with the
massive Kirthar
Limestone. The only
permanent stream
is the Hab on the
Baluchistan border,

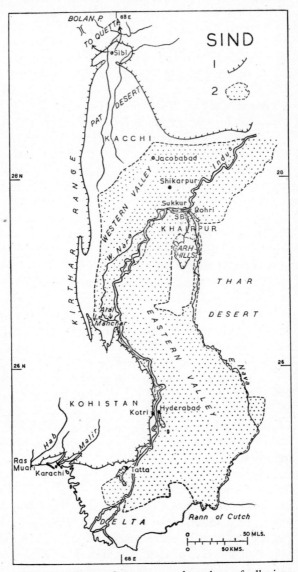

Fig. 81.—SIND: GENERAL. 1, boundary of alluvium;
2, areas commanded by irrigation works. SB, Sukkur
Barrage. Regional division after Pithawalla.

but in the S the large underground reservoir of the Malir supplies Karachi.

[1] M. B. Pithawalla, *A Geographical Analysis of the Lower Indus Basin* (*Sind*), Part I.
(Karachi, 1936), 329–35. I have drawn heavily on this work for physical details.

The *Wn Valley* section is mainly formed of older alluvium (bhangar). In the N, between Jacobabad and Sibi, is a clay *pat* desert; the S is sandy or loamy, with many small lakes, and the Indus/W Nara doab is one of the most fertile parts of Sind. The W Nara, now canalised for irrigation (and some local navigation), is probably an old Indus course; it expands in the S into the marshy Lake Manchar, which when full covers some 200 sq mls and is then the largest fresh-water lake in India. It is alternately fed and drained by the Aral, a stream reversible as the Indus is high or low. At low water Manchar covers only 14 sq mls, and it has been proposed to gain 20,000 ac, for rabi crops by draining it entirely during the winter.

The *En Valley* is in a sense the older delta, a great doab of recent alluvial sands and clays, falling from 250 to 50 ft in 200 miles and crossed by innumerable meander-scars and long narrow depressions (*dhoros*), apparently fragments of old drainage systems now disrupted by shifts of course, desiccation, and sand encroachments. Along the E Nara small alkaline lakes (*dhands*) are especially numerous. Very important features are the two Kirthar Limestone outliers, the larger in the N reaching 400 ft and providing the emplacement for the Sukkur Barrage, the smaller (250 ft) carrying at its Nn end the old capital, Hyderabad, and the sites of yet older cities.

The *Delta* merges Swds into the great mud and salt wastes of the Rann of Cutch (Ch. XXII). Changes in the distributaries have been numerous; according to Pithawalla they are facilitated in the N by a sandy micaceous surface. The coast is fringed with dead creeks and dead ports. When high tides and Indus floods coincide the littoral is flooded for 20 miles inland. In from the shore mangrove-flats are old sandy beach-ridges succeeded by clayey silts; the streams are fringed by tamarisk thickets. There are great stretches of tall grass and a few cultivable patches; but on the whole the Indus Delta is a savage waste: a marked contrast to that of the Ganges, unless indeed we equate the Sind Delta with the Gangetic Sundarbans, and even then the deltaic lands to the N would be a desert were it not for irrigation.

It is hardly necessary to stress the dominant features of Sind climate, heat and aridity. At Shikarpur "ice forms as late as February; yet in summer, for weeks together, the readings *at midnight* do not fall below 100° F.", and Jacobabad holds the Indian, and nearly the world, record with 126°.[2] As the local proverb well remarks, "O Allah, why, having created Sewistan, bother to conceive of Hell?" As for aridity and its concomitant variability, Drigh Road (Karachi), with an average annual fall of about 8 ins., recorded in five successive years 13·52, 0·69, 9·41, 20·82, and 6·97 ins. Almost it never rains but it pours; Karachi has recorded 12 ins. in 24 hours. The rivers of Kohistan, normally great trails of gravel and boulders, then come down in turbulent flood; even between Karachi and its marine airport it is

---

[2] *Bombay Gaz.* (1909), II. 176.

hardly worth while to build permanent bridges—they are likely to prove all too temporary—and roads cross the wadis on broad concrete aprons flush with the bed.

Vegetation, except in the Delta, is naturally mainly scattered acacia and thorny shrubs; along the Indus and some *dhands*, however, the jungle is thick enough to provide shelter for the Hurs, a Muslim sect whose turbulent criminality called for full-dress military operations as late as 1943–44.

Agriculture

Sind stood out among the old Indian Provinces by virtue of its high amount of cultivated ground per head of population—over one ac.—and of the very high proportion of fallow, actually more than the NSA (rather under 6 m. and 5·25–5·5 m. ac. respectively in 1941–42). The former peculiarity was a recent development dependent on the Sukkur (Lloyd) Barrage. Practically all cultivated land is irrigated, double-cropping raising the TSA to about 6 m. ac. Rice and wheat run neck and neck at about 1·25–1·5 m. ac. each; Sind has a sizeable export surplus of rice. Bajra covers about 0·75 m. ac., foodgrains totalling 75%, rice and wheat together 45%, of TSA. The only other important crops are cotton (1 m. ac.) and oilseeds, mainly rape. Dates are important.

Until the completion of the Suk-

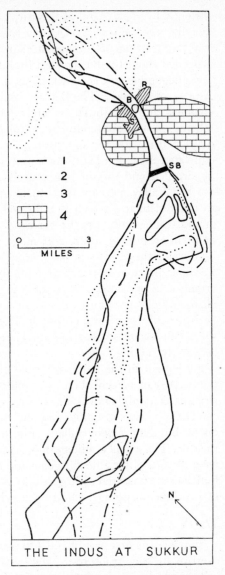

THE INDUS AT SUKKUR

Fig. 82.—THE INDUS AT SUKKUR. 1, course in 1900–01; 2, in 1908–09; 3, in 1916–17; 4, approx. limestone outcrop. S, Sukkur; B, Bukkur I.; R, Rohri; SB, site of Barrage. Adapted from M. B. Pithawalla.

kur Barrage in 1932 canals were mainly inundation. The Barrage takes advantage of the narrowing and fixing of the Indus by the limestone hills of Sukkur (right bank) and Rohri; between the two lies the anciently fortified island of Bukkur, a slab of limestone used by the bridge carrying the railway to Quetta. Even in the gap the Indus flows at a level higher than its immediate surroundings, and careful river-training is needed above the Barrage lest the stream should break away. That this is not a negligible risk is shown by an abandoned gorge in solid limestone at Aror, 4 miles away. The Barrage itself is about a mile long, and the main channels and distributaries total 36,000 miles; this is the largest single scheme in the sub-continent, probably in the world, and when fully developed is expected to irrigate nearly 5·5 m. ac.—more than the present cultivated area of Egypt. As a result of the Barrage the cotton acreage quadrupled and that of wheat nearly trebled. Waterlogging is serious in the Wn Valley, perhaps accentuated by a warp from Kohistan by Sukkur to the Sulaimans, which is indicated by gravity data and may hold up ground-water flow. The Lower Sind Barrage at Kotri is well advanced, and will eventually add *c.* 2·75 m. ac. to the cultivated area.

Most of the land is in large estates, farmed by share-croppers (*haris*). Farming practice is peculiar: "All the cotton land of an estate will be arranged in one compact block, all the wheat land in a second block, and all the fallow in a third. These blocks are then parcelled out among the haris for cultivation and cropping. They are rotated from year to year over the whole estate so that the areas cropped by individual tenants is [*sic*] constantly varying." [3]

Settlement in the better-irrigated areas is largely in nucleated villages, but in part of Kacchi there is a tendency for homesteads to be lined out along irrigation channels. Elsewhere, among the *dhands* of the E Nara, in the Delta patches of cultivation, or where precarious cultivation is carried on by bunding *daman* nullahs (Fig. 83), hamlets rather than villages are the rule. The camel is still an important transport animal, even in Karachi, where it draws long floats; goats and fat-tailed sheep are numerous, and buffaloes are pastured in large numbers in the Delta. Sea-fishing, at present in a rudimentary stage, could be largely increased.

The Province

Sind was the first part of India to come under Muslim domination, being overrun by the Arabs from Makran in the 8th century. Its subsequent history was mainly local and tumultuous until it was conquered by Napier in 1843 as a sort of by-blow of the First Afghan War; it was then administered as a part of Bombay until 1936, an historical accident which became an indefensible anomaly. The density was only 94 in 1941, and in 1951 was given as 92 on an area of 50,443 sq mls. Of the 1941 population of 4,535,000, 70·75% were Muslims, a marked decline from the figure of 76% in 1901. In the four largest towns, moreover, non-Muslims in 1941 numbered

[3] *Report of the UK Industrial Mission to Pakistan* (1950), 29.

392,000 against under 225,000 Muslims, and in Karachi itself Muslims
were only 42%. Non-Muslims in these four towns were 30% of the Hindu
minority, and as usual the intrusive element had most of the trade and

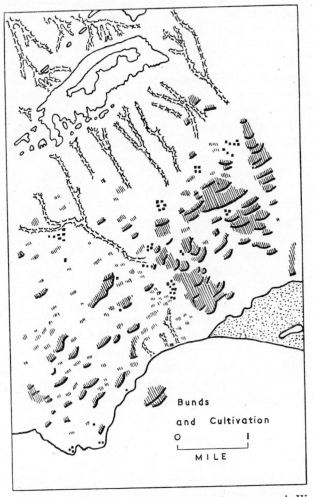

Fig. 83.—BUNDED CULTIVATION ON THE DAMAN. 10 mls W
of Karachi. Low scarp in N is last ridge of Kohistan, running
out to Ras Muari (C. Monze), 8 mls to W. Contours at 250
and 500 ft. Note settlement in hamlets. SOP 35 L/13; courtesy
SOP.

industry; the Parsees were particularly active. These facts doubtless
account for the rather lukewarm enthusiasm for Pakistan displayed in its
own capital in August 1947.

Apart from the Barrage, Sind is poor. There is some poor haematite and poorer lignite in Kohistan, neither of real significance; otherwise mineral wealth is confined to limestones (the Dalmia combine had a cement factory at Karachi), clays, and glass-sands. There are large deposits of salt in the Delta; current production (*c.* 200,000 tons a year) is by evaporation at Karachi. The geological situation would seem favourable for oil, and the fiscal position of Sind, and possibly of Pakistan, might be revolutionised by a good strike, but active prospecting (especially around Manchar) has not so far had any success, and indeed seems likely to be abandoned.

The committee which examined the question of separating Sind from Bombay summed up: "There is thus obviously no question of Sind standing surety for the Barrage—the problem is whether the Barrage can stand surety for Sind." [4] So far it has.

Industrialisation, until very recently at least, has been negligible and the degree of urbanisation small. But Muslim refugees from UP have set up glass and leather factories at Hyderabad which are already meeting a great part of the W Pakistan demand. In the old days ports and trade centres flourished or decayed by favour or disfavour of the shifts of the Indus; thus Tatta, on firm ground at an old head of the Delta, was said in 1742 to have no fewer than 40,000 weavers and 60,000 dealers; gross exaggeration, but symptomatic. Already in the 18th century decline began, and it is now an insignificant market village. Shikarpur (62,746) was long a trading centre with wide connections with SW and central Asia, but has now been largely superseded by Sukkur (66,466), with its more advantageous railway position and its increasing importance as the site and service-centre of the Barrage. The only pre-British town of real importance, Hyderabad (229,000 in 1951), dates only from 1768, though the site at the Nn end of the limestone outlier has had permanent significance. The Indus crossing and nodality ensure considerable commercial activity, and Hyderabad is once more the capital of Sind. But the only really important city is Karachi itself.

KARACHI

In a century Karachi (Fig. 84) has risen from a mere local port of 14,000 people to become the capital of the largest Muslim state (by population) in the world, with a 1941 population of 359,492. In 1951 the federal district (812 sq mls) had **1,118,800** people, of whom **1,005,000** were in Karachi city and cantonments and **899,000** in the municipal corporation area.

The set of the Arabian Sea currents is to the E: Karachi lies just off the En extremity of the Delta, sheltered from the Makran longshore drift by Ras Muari (Cape Monze). It occupies a peninsular site between the Kohistan rivers Lyari and Malir. The harbour is formed by the Lyari mouths, sheltered by the long Manora spit and the little island of Kiamari, which is

---

[4] *Report of Sind Financial Committee* (1931), 29.

connected to the mainland by the 3-mile-long Napier Mole with its railway; the whole area has of course been greatly altered by port development. The surrounding area is practically semi-desert, with a mangrove-fringed coast; the more densely populated areas towards the tip of the peninsula are subject to flooding, but to the E the usual open suburbs and cantonments extend along a 50–100-ft ridge, and to the S the raised beach at Clifton provides an attractive lung. Strong sea-breezes in the wide suburban avenues give exceptionally invigorating conditions for a town with mean summer minima a degree or two on either side of 80° F.

Sind was the favourite, if illegitimate, child of Sir Charles Napier, to whose energetic (though far from modest) initiative the early development

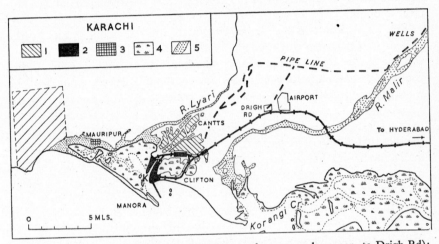

Fig. 84.—KARACHI. 1, built-up area (now extends, more or less open, to Drigh Rd); 2, port area (K = Kiamari); 3, salt pans; 4, marsh; 5, dry streambeds. Shaded rectangle = Fig. 83. SOP 1/253,440 35 L & P; courtesy SOP.

of Karachi owed much. It owed more to the boom when the American Civil War cut cotton supplies; by this time steamer navigation on the Indus was in full swing, and in 1863–64 the value of trade was about 28 times that of 1857–58. A 50% slump followed, but the railway tapping the Indus traffic at Kotri (one of the earliest in India, opened in the mid-1860s) was extended through to the Punjab in 1878, and by 1884 trade was nearly double the 1863–64 peak. Since then the development of the Punjab and the rise in Karachi trade have been symbiotic, while with the opening of the Barrage exports again rose by 40–50%. Exports formerly greatly exceeded imports, but this structure was altered as Karachi developed to be the entrepôt of a new political entity. Cotton, wheat and flour (declining), hides, skins and bones, oilseeds, and wool are the leading exports; the import structure is the usual one—piecegoods, mineral oil, construction goods, vehicles. The main wharves are on Kiamari; vessels drawing 27 ft can enter at low water, though constant dredging is necessary. Port facilities include 11,000 ft of wharfage, with the usual graving docks, oil storage, and so on.

Industrially Karachi is as yet of little importance: the enthusiastic Pithawalla can find only 46 establishments to list, and some of these (e.g. the perambulator works which produces wooden toys) are not exactly basic. The chief lines are salt evaporation at Mauripur, flour-milling, and cement; but consumption trades and light foundry and engineering works, appropriate to the new metropolitan functions of the city, are expanding.

Of recent years Karachi, with three aerodromes (including the best-equipped of the sub-continent) and the marine air base at Korangi, has become the most important airport of India; its positional advantages are clear enough.

The chief problems facing the city in its present boom phase are the difficulties of sewage and drainage in the overcrowded low-lying portion, and the search for an adequate water-supply. At present the main supply comes from elaborate modern wells tapping the underground stores of the Malir, but during the war a 90-mile-long conduit was constructed from the Indus.

The selection of Karachi as the Pakistani capital was logical enough, given the fact that all the drive came from the W. Lahore was at least technically in dispute before August 15th, 1947, and the event showed that it was fortunate that it was not chosen, since the urgent problems of setting up an administration for 70 m. people would have been excessively difficult to solve in a city almost wrecked by civil violence and for a time economically ruined. The only other entrants were Rawalpindi, too isolated, and Multan, too hot for any sensible bureaucracy. Karachi, if in a corner of Pakistan, is a window on the world, and especially the Islamic world of SW Asia. But the decision to shift the Sind capital from federal Karachi to Hyderabad met with the understandably heated (and unprecedentedly unanimous) opposition of Sindhi legislators.

Great plans exist for the development of the capital, which as yet must be confessed to have, in many ways, a decidedly provincial air. There are few good buildings; the best are the Cotton Exchange, the Assembly Building, and the main airport, all in good modern styles. Although Karachi had not even one Muslim English daily until Mr Jinnah's *Dawn* irradiated Independence Day (owing to an unfortunate hitch it was printed on its Hindu rivals' presses), much progress has been made in the fostering of a Pakistani metropolitan sentiment. But Karachi has still a long way to go before it can rival Lahore as a general, let alone an Islamic, cultural centre.[5]

[5] See M. B. Pithawalla and P. Martin-Kaye, *Guide to the Geology and Geography of Karachi* (Karachi, 1946) and M. B. Pithawalla, *An Introduction to Karachi* (Karachi, 1949), as well as the *Bulletin* of the Karachi Geographical Society, *passim*.

The Punjab

The area described here is smaller than the old Punjab Province; it covers about 55,000 sq mls, plus the 16,000 sq mls of Bahawalpur. The area NW of the Salt Range is obviously excluded, as is the montane part of the old Province. In the Wn, trans-Indus, area the boundary again lies on the *daman*. But for the rest it must lie in the Indo-Gangetic alluvium, and here there are no clear physiographical breaks. The climatic transitions are inevitably gradual and any boundaries must be arbitrary, at least until more detailed soil and crop mapping has been carried out, and then of course they will not be the boundaries of natural regions.

There is an obvious difference between the broad doabs of the Indus basin in the Punjab and its more Nilotic character in Sind. In Bahawalpur the region marches with the sandy wastes of the Thar—obviously an indefinite margin. The real difficulty is in the debatable marchland of Sirhind—the 'Delhi doab' or the Indo-Gangetic divide. The transition between the definite aridity of the central Punjab and the relatively humid mid-Ganges area is fairly rapid between Sutlej and Jumna; and hence the SE of the old Province, the area within the sphere of Delhi rather than that of Lahore, had a distinctive *nuance* and in the E was more closely akin to the UP than to the Punjab doabs. Drainage lines do not help as in this basin of the 'lost Sarasvati' drainage (where there is any water to drain) is indeterminate. The Sutlej was often traditionally considered the boundary of Hindustan, culturally, communally, and economically, and the Beas-Sutlej line would seem to be perhaps the most reasonable of a number of difficult choices for the division of the old Province, although E Punjab in fact takes in a portion of the Upper Bari Doab. The use of this line as the regional boundary has also the minor advantage of enabling us to regard the two major groupings of the Wn Borderland and the Indus Plains as practically coterminous with W Pakistan.

The old Province really consisted of a central core—the doabs of the Five Rivers—and two wings, of which the En, the Bist (Beas/Sutlej) Doab and Sirhind, has been separated, here and by the 1947 Partition. The Wn wing, more arid and for local physical reasons less easily irrigated, consists of the Sind Sagar Doab, between Jhelum-Chenab and Indus, and the trans-Indus Derajat (including the NWFP Dt of Dera Ismail Khan). Another extremely important differentiation is the sub-montane belt of greater rain, with an appreciable amount in winter, and a high water-table from seepage from the hills. These divisions are hardly clear-cut enough to be treated as sub-regions, but they will enter repeatedly into the discussion.

Topography (Fig. 85, inset)

The whole area forms an immense plain, some 350 mls NW/SE by 450 NE/SW. All of it (with a tiny exception to be noticed) is under 1200 ft, most of it under 600, while in the extreme SE, along the Indus, it falls to under 250. The fall is naturally steepest (about 15 ft per mile) in the submontane strip; over most of the area it is one foot and in the extreme SW only six inches. The region is a great mass of alluvium brought down by the Indus and the Five Rivers—from W to E Jhelum, Chenab, Ravi, Beas, and Sutlej—which give the province its name and unite in the SW to form the Panjnad or Five Streams.[6] The interfluves—doabs or 'two waters'— are given names compounded from those of their confining streams[7]—in the same order Jech or Chaj, Rechna, Bari, and Bist; the last is *the* doab in the Punjab, but in India as a whole 'the Doab' is that of Jumna and Ganges. Near the Kashmir foothills the country is to some extent undulating and diversified, and numerous smaller streams and torrents (mostly dry except in the rains) descend from the hills. Most of these are dissipated in the fields—it must be remembered that the natural drainage has been greatly interfered with by canal construction—but the Degh parallels the Ravi for 150 miles before entering it.

The only breaks in the alluvial monotony of the plains are the little groups of arid broken hills near Sangla and Kirana, on either side of the Chenab. These are very small in extent but rise in jagged pinnacles 1000 ft above the plains (their highest point is 1662 ft) and are geomorphologically of great interest, as they are Aravalli outliers of quartzites, slates, and rhyolites and indicate the concealed extension of the Peninsular block postulated by Wadia as controlling the NW Himalaya syntaxis: they lie within 40 miles of the Salt Range.[8]

For the rest, the sole topographical differentiation is that provided by existing or abandoned river-courses. Hydrographic changes have been complex and far-reaching: "The Chenab used to flow east of Multan. . . . Ancient Multan stood on two islands in the Ravi, and in Tamerlane's time the Ravi joined the Chenab below Multan." [9] The riverain belts are of course of great importance for human settlement, an importance reflected in their detailed local nomenclature. The great rivers are countersunk in broad floodplains of newer alluvium (the khadar, locally *khadir*) bounded

---

[6] The joint course of Jhelum, Chenab, and Ravi above the Panjnad is the Trimab—'Three Rivers'.

[7] A practice generally associated with the USSR, but in this case attributed to the Mogul Emperor Akbar.

[8] See A. M. Heron, "The Kirana and Other Hills in the Jech and Rechna Doabs", *Rec. GSI* XLII (1913), Pt. 3, 229–36.

[9] W. H. Arden Wood, "Rivers and Man in the Indus-Ganges Alluvial Plain," *Scottish Geographical Magazine* XL (1924), 1–15; reference on p. 13. The Sutlej problem is discussed below (484–86).

by steep bluffs (*dhaya*) which may be 20 or more ft high and are often intricately gullied. The actual banks of the rivers are naturally a little higher than the *khadir*, owing to silt-deposition in floods; the immediate riverain or *bet* lands are agriculturally valuable but exposed to flooding. Villages are generally perched on top of the *dhaya* or occupy minor terraces, the bluffs of old meander-scars, in the *khadir* itself. Away from the rivers the higher and more arid parts of the doabs—often mere waste where not irrigated—are known as *bar*; the most notable is perhaps the Ganji or 'bald' Bar (so called from its patches of bare hard clay) lying W of the well-marked old course of the Beas, which formerly extended as far as the Trimab-Sutlej confluence and gave more point to the name of the Panjnad.

The old unreclaimed Punjab still persists (not, perhaps, for much longer) in the dreary steppes of the Sind Sagar Doab and especially in its central section, the Thal, which at least approaches true desert conditions. Once past the Jhelum-Chenab *bet* there is an abrupt cessation of cultivation along the scalloped edge of the Thal, which from the air is a sea of sand with a remarkably even (and very light) stipple of bushes and low acacias and a very occasional village, alive or dead a mere pattern in the sand. In years of good rain there is a thin grass cover, and there are scattered patches of precarious cultivation in the lows. But "such is the absence of shelter that the removal of a telegraph line is said to have been objected to on the ground that the poles gave good shade in the hot weather"—perhaps the objection was not very serious, but, like so many Indian tales, *si non e vero e ben trovato* as a symbol. Wwds a strip of level ground, the Daggar, runs parallel to the Indus at a distance of 20–25 miles; its centre is a narrow level depression in which the water-table is high enough for well-irrigation; this probably represents an abandoned channel of the Indus. The broad and braided present river is bordered by the Powah, an upland strip some three miles broad and in places 40 ft above river-level, an obvious settlement-line for villages farming the *bet* below. W of the Indus, in much of Dera Ismail Khan, the *bet*, irrigable by inundation canals, is called *Sindhi* after the river, and is narrower or absent, the main channel often abutting directly onto a high bank. Beyond lies the *daman* of the Sulaiman Ranges. E of the Sutlej, Bahawalpur state borders the Thar, a greater Thal, with a fringe of irrigable khadar 5–25 miles wide between the desert and the river.

The soils of the area are for the most part sandy loams (brown or grey semi-steppe soils), with patches of clay and larger areas of almost pure sand. In places limestone concretions and useless expanses of alkaline efflorescence—*reh* or *kallar*—are found. Over most of the area precipitation is too small for leaching to have occurred, and the almost virgin soils respond generously to irrigation.

Climate and Vegetation

The influence of the Wly winter depressions extends right across the Punjab, dying out only around the Jumna: Lahore still gets 2·7 ins. in January–March, though this compares poorly with Peshawar's 5·2. But the sub-montane strip is narrow: while the immediate foot of the hills gets around 35 ins. this has fallen to about 20 at Lahore, only 25 miles from the hills, and the whole of the Sn half has under 10 ins. and that, of course, very unreliable. Its torrential nature is also important: Lahore has 5–6 ins. in both July and August, but the average number of rainy days is about six in each of these months.

Temperatures are extreme for Indian plains stations. Lahore ranges from under 55° F (January) to nearly 94 in June; and the mean of the lowest minima for January is only 34·7°; the corresponding maximum figure for June is 115·2°. Frosts are normal in January in the N and not uncommon even at Multan. Dust-storms are a prominent feature of the hot weather, less distressing than might be assumed since they are accompanied by a marked and very welcome drop in temperature (by as much as 20°) and rise in relative humidity.

The weight of modern opinion appears to be against desiccation in the true sense of an actual climatic change; but prolonged human interference with natural drainage, deforestation on the Siwaliks, and so on have undoubtedly led to marked deterioration in ground-water conditions and so in vegetation. The accounts of Alexander's campaigns and Mogul hunts bear witness to considerable forest growth; and to-day on the more arid margins strong winds and infrequent but torrential rains have led to a serious spread of shifting sands and more serious if less spectacular deterioration of good cultivated land.[10] It is probable also that Multan and the Sn routes from the Gomal Pass to Hindustan were of more importance in the later Middle Ages than they are to-day; here hydrographic changes in Sirhind may have been decisive (see below, 484–86). But away from the streams it does not appear likely that the S can ever have carried more than very open acacia scrub and bush, with scattered low trees, saltworts, much bare ground, and thin grass after rain; W and E, in the Thal and the Thar, this thorn "forest" shades off into what is to all intents desert country. It is interesting to note a strong 'European' element in the annual herbs of the W, which include poppies, vetches, thistles, chickweed, and so on.

The *bets* carry stretches of tall 'pampas' grass and streams are often lined with tamarisk: large areas of scrub, locally dense, remain in the unreclaimed Wn *bars*, but there is practically no real natural forest. Along the Lower Bari Doab Canal trees (mostly sissoo) are grown by irrigation: this

[10] See R. MacLagan Gorrie, "Countering Desiccation in the Punjab", *GR* XXXVIII (1948), 30–40.

Changa Manga Reserved Forest was originally planted to increase the rainfall, but has more undoubted value as conserving soil-water and supplying local fuel. The cultivated areas are by no means treeless: much of the submontane strip has almost a parkland appearance, and even in the Canal Colonies the scattered trees appear to close in towards the horizon.

The natural conditions over much of the Region have been vividly described by E. S. Lindley:

> A typical *Bar* of the western Punjab was a desolate place; the surface mostly bare, in places hard and smooth and almost impervious to water when rain fell, in places powdery with saltpetre, and in places growing some grass after rain. Belts of such open ground alternated with belts dotted with small hardy trees or shrubs, which tended to collect the moving sand and dust to form sandhills that in places formed a miniature Sahara. . . . Animal life is represented by snakes, lizards, and a few gazelles . . . a few pastoral and nomad tribes lived a free but hard life, living precariously by their camels which could eat anything, and their cattle that seem able to exist on the smell of grass roots, finding sport and occupation in stealing cattle from each other and from riverain neighbours. The water-table was 80 to 120 feet below the surface; in the shallow valleys of a plain that is perfectly level to any but a trained eye, the collection of the annual rainfall of less than 6 inches gave better grazing, and here these Janglis ('jungle folk') had their regular camping places, at wells they had made . . . holes, up to four feet in diameter and going into the bowels of the earth . . . the huts were made of reed screens. . . .[11]

Very much of this unpromising area has been transformed by the canals into one of the most prosperous agricultural areas in Asia, a feat of bold and imaginative planning which can have few parallels in the world.

Agriculture: the Development of Canal Irrigation (Fig. 85)

Agriculture is the mainstay of the Punjab, and before 1947 it was no exaggeration to regard the Indus Plains (including Sind) as the granary of India. This strong position has been temporarily weakened by the economic and social dislocations consequent on Partition; but there can be little doubt that the primary function of W Pakistan, of which W Punjab is by far the most important unit, will remain the provision of a grain and cotton surplus. It is true that the 1931 Census showed a larger proportion (17% of occupied population) engaged in "industry" than in any other Province, but this is largely illusory: much of it is small-scale craft production, and such organised industry as exists is closely based on agriculture, either as a supplier of materials for processing or as a market for agricultural necessities.

[11] From an unpublished paper on "The Canal System of the Punjab", kindly communicated by the author.

Agriculturally three main divisions may be recognised:

(i) the sub-montane strip with appreciable winter rain and a high water-table from seepage from the Siwaliks; well-irrigation supplements rainfed cultivation and is more important than canals;

(ii) the main mass of modern canal irrigation between Jhelum and Sutlej;

(iii) the arid margins: the W beyond Jhelum, in which such agriculture as is possible is dependent mainly on inundation canals, really modern irrigation being as yet little developed; and Bahawalpur, SE of Sutlej.

These three divisions are brought out on Fig. 86. The NSA is about 15 m. ac., the total being raised to 17 m. by irrigation. Altogether over $12\frac{1}{2}$ m. ac. are irrigated (counting double-cropping). Food growing accounts for over 10 m. ac. (wheat 6–6·25 m., rice about 700,000). Cotton is next to wheat, with c. 2·25 m. ac. Oilseeds account for over half a million ac. and sugar for a quarter of a million. Rice is grown mainly on the sub-montane strip or in the W by irrigation, sugar is predominantly a sub-montane crop under wells, although some is grown by canal irrigation in Lyallpur Dt. A feature of great importance is the relatively high acreage under fodder crops, some 4–5 m. ac. in the old undivided Province. Before discussing the divisions it is convenient to consider the development of canal irrigation.[12]

The régime of the Punjab rivers, though very irregular (the normal summer discharge is about 20 times the winter minimum) is more favourable to irrigation than that of the Peninsular rivers, since the spring snow-melt in the Himalayas makes the high-water stage begin earlier, and the winter precipitation in the sub-montane strip and the foothills gives a minor rise at the end of the year. The main rise usually begins about the middle of March (the Peninsular rivers are dry for a full three months after this date) and by July the monsoon rains bring a greater but more fluctuating volume; this discharge begins to fall off in September. Some idea of the scale of irrigation is given by the facts that the rivers take off about one-third the summer discharge and that for half the year the rivers would be dry were it not for the considerable seepage return from the irrigated land.

Small inundation canals have of course been made from time immemorial. Inundation irrigation is still very important immediately beneath the headworks of some of the major canals, and more especially in the W and Bahawalpur (cf. Figs. 85 and 86). In the SW many inundation canals were constructed by Diwan Sawan Mal, the remarkably able governor of Multan under the Sikhs. Inundation canals, however, are useless when most needed—in the dry weather—and of course, being dependent on the current river flow, are liable to run low in a bad rainfall year, again when irrigation is most vital. "The limit of irrigation under an inundation canal is

---

[12] For this section I have drawn very heavily on Mr Lindley's article, with his courteous permission.

restricted to the lower land and such canals reach their maximum development where the rivers of the Punjab converge to form the lower Indus and the khadir widens at the expense of the bhangar" or older alluvium of the doab.[13] The earlier canals were of inundation type, but all the greater

[13] G. Kuriyan, "Irrigation in India", *Journal of the Madras University*, XV (1943-44), 46-58 and 161-86; refce on p. 161.

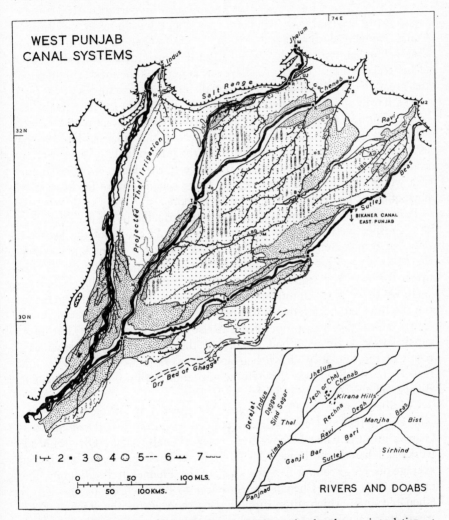

Fig. 85.—W PUNJAB: CANAL SYSTEMS. 1, canals; 2, headworks; 3, inundation, 4, perennial, canal areas; 5, projected canals; 6, alluvium/hill margin; 7, old river banks. *Canals:* C, Chenab; UC, Upper Chenab; U (L) J, Upper (Lower) Jhelum; U (L) BD, Upper (Lower) Bari Doab. *Headworks:* K, Kalabagh (Indus); M, Mangla; R, Rasul; T, Trimmu; P, Panjnad; M1, Marala; K, Khanki (Chenab); M2, Madhopur; B, Balloki Weir; F, Ferozepore; S, Sulemanke; I, Islamabad. Other initials are District headquarters, for which see Fig. 86.

schemes are now perennial, with headworks designed to give an assured supply throughout the year.

The first canal of any size to reach an upland, as distinct from the khadir, was constructed from the Jumna in AD 1351, extended and improved by the Moguls, and renovated, at first very ineffectually, by the early British administration. But modern canal development really began with the construction in 1859 of the Upper Bari Doab Canal (in part on a Mogul alignment) with headworks at Madhopur on the Ravi. In 1886 the Sidhnai Canal, from the lower Ravi in Multan Dt, was opened, and this was the first 'colony', although Sawan Mal had earlier introduced settlers into some of his reclamations. The Ravi, however, is perhaps the most unreliable of the great rivers (it has a relatively small mountain catchment) and these works hardly gave a full perennial service. The UBD (as its Mogul prehistory implies) served an already settled countryside, a fact reflected in its settlement and field patterns and the aspect of the villages. The Sidhnai irrigated only a small and not particularly inhospitable area, and topographically it was favoured in that the ridge of the doab, giving command of a wider area, was quickly reached. Later schemes were far bolder and have effected far more striking transformations.

Parts of the Rechna and Jech Doabs were irrigated in the early and later 1890s respectively. By 1900 the area E of the old course of the Beas was only partly irrigated by inundation canals, while the Ganji Bar was dry; the Multan area was irrigated by the Sidhnai and inundation canals. The upper Rechna Doab stood in great need of irrigation and so did much of the Jech. Of these as yet untouched areas the Ganji Bar was most promising; but the Ravi had been reduced to a relative trickle of water, the Chenab was fully utilised. The first proposal was to use the Sutlej and Beas; but major canals so far constructed had run Ewds, the W banks lying higher as a result of the tendency of Nn hemisphere rivers to work into their right banks; and the Sutlej water would be needed in Sirhind, Bahawalpur, and Bikaner. There remained the distant Jhelum.

Consideration of these facts inspired the great Triple Project (1905–17). The Upper Jhelum Canal irrigates 350,000 ac. in the Jech Doab and discharges into the Chenab above the Lower Chenab Canal (1887–92) headworks at Khanki: the Lower Chenab irrigates some 2·5 m. ac. and has an average discharge four or five times that of the Thames at Teddington. The upper waters of the Chenab are thus free to be taken off by the Upper Chenab Canal, which after supplying 650,000 ac. in the Rechna Doab passes its remaining water across the Ravi by a barrage 550 yds long. This feeds the Lower Bari Doab Canal on the Ganji Bar. In the great Canal Colonies of these three doabs the land was empty and everything could be, and was, planned in advance on a generous scale, even if the results on the map look a little inhuman. The land is divided into *chaks* or blocks fed by a single outlet, of about 2 cusecs, from a main distributary, and so far as possible villages conform to *chaks*; hence the repulsive numbers on the maps, though fortunately on the ground human nature softens the severe rectilinear patterns with some minor untidiness, and insists on giving the *chaks* a local, often personal name: the village in Fig. 87, for instance, officially Chak 73 G.B., is more humanely known as Kala Gaddi Thamman.

The colonisation of these areas was a remarkable phenomenon in itself. The allotments were high—as much as 55 ac., more to men of substance—and the attractions for cultivators and larger landholders obvious. Contingents came especially from the over-populated plains beneath the submontane strip; some selectivity was exercised, but they included, as well as the more enterprising spirits, not a few induced by pressure or reward to leave their village for that village's good. But on the whole the human material was good and amply demonstrated that, where uninhibited by age-old population pressure on scanty plots of soil, the Punjab peasant is no mean farmer. Early conditions were hard enough to weed out incompetents: scrub had to be cleared, fields banked and levelled; marketing was difficult, and the lack at first of accustomed village social amenities was not compensated by the attitude of the local *janglis*, who saw in the settlers' bullocks an admirable supplement to their own herds. But the reward came in crops far superior to those on the overworked soils of the N.

The increase in population has been phenomenal; in Lyallpur and Montgomery Dts from 60,306 and 416,669 respectively in 1891 to **2,157,000** and **1,814,000** in 1951; in terms of density from 17 to **612** and 99 to **432**.[14] Despite this, holdings (at least in the Colonies, covering over half the irrigated area) remain large and standards consequently high. Elsewhere the traveller's eye becomes wearily accustomed to the manifold distressing makeshifts or slacknesses which bespeak an unequal struggle with a too narrow environment, or a mere fatalistic apathy in the face of overwhelming difficulties, the whole vicious circle of agrarian poverty; here it is rejoiced by numerous evidences of good farming and, by Asian standards, very good living. To the community at large the gains have been immense: canal income (to which the Colonies contribute a share well in excess of their acreage) amounted to over 20% of Punjab revenues in 1946–47, *after* deducting working expenses, and contributed to what was probably the best provincial administration in India. These gains have unfortunately been gravely jeopardised by the emigration of many of the larger non-Muslim farmers and the problem of rehabilitating their largely destitute successors from the E. Many will eventually be accommodated in the new Thal irrigation (*c.* 0·75–1 m. ac.) on the Sind Sagar Doab.

---

[14] For all that, it remains mysteriously difficult to see where Professor Lyde derived his twice-mentioned figure of 7 to the square mile for the density of population in the Punjab in 1891 (*The Continent of Asia*, 1938 ed., 390). In 1891 the density was 190.

Other developments envisaged include an increase of storage capacity in the foothills and joint hydro-electric irrigation installations, as well as an *Indian* project for tunnels linking the headwaters of the Chenab in Chamba and Lahul with the Ravi and the Beas.[15] But in the past the proposal to use Wular Lake in the Vale of Kashmir as a storage reservoir for the Jhelum met with political difficulties—Kashmir objecting to Punjab control: political agreement between *India* and Pakistan seems a *sine qua non* of really well-found economic advance.

Technical difficulties remain to be overcome. There is great loss by percolation; on the UBD it was estimated that this accounted for nearly half the water entering the canal, of which total "28% would have sufficed for the irrigation actually done". The obvious course, lining with concrete, is practically prohibitive in cost, and it is almost impossible to take a reach temporarily out of a main canal for treatment. Associated with seepage is waterlogging with its consequent formation of pans and, in arid areas, *reh* efflorescences: this has meant the loss of thousands of acres of good ground, and the construction of extensive drainage works; pumping takes most of the 22,000 kW of power developed at Rasul. Finally the administration and maintenance of the canals, and the prevention of illicit abstraction of water, demand a high pitch of organisation: a typical Canal Division "is about 60 miles long and 20 miles broad, comprises 500 miles of Government channels, utilises a designed discharge of 1500 cusecs to be distributed to 1000 outlets, and directly employs 300 men above the status of labourer". Once again political stability is seen to be all-important.

Agriculture: Sub-regional Variation and Settlement Patterns

(i) *The Sub-montane Strip.* Rainfall varies from 25 to 35 ins., and its seasonal distribution permits wheat to be grown without irrigation. The total annual rainfall is, however, much more influenced by the monsoon than by the Wly depressions, so that aridity increases and wells become more necessary towards the W. Well-water is drawn either by the Persian wheel or by ramp (*mhote*). Both methods make great demands on the time of the cultivator and his animals, and well-irrigation is thus often associated with intensive market gardening, though its main use is to protect the rabi wheat. The cropped area is 70–80% under foodgrains, and wheat accounts for about two-thirds of the acreage under these. Bajra, maize, sugar-cane, and cotton follow wheat, at a great distance. Yields are relatively high.

A rich, smiling country-side, with many trees—especially the dark village groves of mangoes; but it has the defects of its qualities. The high water-table is partly responsible for the unhealthiness of the tract, especially during the rains. The fertile soil and the ample water-points have led to a great

---

[15] F. J. Fowler, "Some Problems of Water Distribution between East and West Punjab", *GR* XL (1950), 583–99; see above, 393–94.

proliferation of settlements: holdings are very small—2·5 to 5 ac.—and densities very high—in 1941 Sialkot, the most purely sub-montane District, had 755 to the sq ml, and by 1951 the figure had risen to 940. Fragmentation is extreme, and in such conditions the practice of grazing cattle on the stubble inhibits any attempts at new crops or rotations. Loss of land by sand-spreads and erosion in the streams debouching from deforested foothills, though perhaps not so critical as E of Beas, is nevertheless serious.

(ii) *The Canal Areas.* Within the great irrigated doabs a distinction must be made between a Nn zone, transitional from the sub-montane strip, and the zone of newer colonies to the S.[16] These in turn are succeeded by the inundation areas of the Sutlej khadar and the Multan/Muzaffargarh bor-

[16] These two zones correspond respectively to the Wn portions of K. S. Ahmad's "East Central Plain" and "West Central Plain or Colony Region" in "Agricultural Regions of the Punjab" (*Panjab Geographical Review*, I (1942), 21–26).

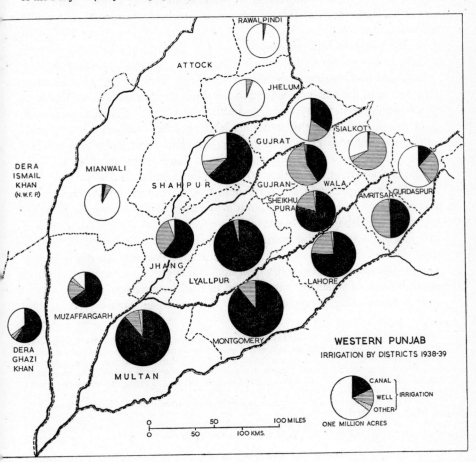

Fig. 86.—W PUNJAB: IRRIGATION BY DISTRICTS AND TYPES. Circles proportionate to NSA.

ders. The Nn zone was well-peopled before modern canal irrigation, though density has of course increased greatly. To the S, though population has increased with great rapidity, the evil effects of population pressure were scarcely felt. Since settlement was planned in a practically new land, the pattern of villages and farms is mathematically rectilinear, a very striking contrast to the irregular patchwork of the N, where irrigation was superimposed on existing close rural settlement (cf. Fig. 87).

Rainfall is 20–25 ins. along the Nn margin, but falls off very rapidly, in both amount and reliability, to the SW. The great staples—rabi wheat and kharif cotton, maize, and fodder—are the same for both areas; and there is also some rice and sugar-cane, the latter mainly for local consumption. The Colony areas have naturally a strong emphasis on cash crops, growing longer-stapled Punjab-American varieties primarily for export. In the N market gardening is of increasing importance to supply Lahore, Amritsar, and other large towns; this of course is specially associated with well-irrigation in the *bet*.

In the N, with District densities of **400–700** in 1951 (after deducting Lahore and Amritsar Cities, which inflate their Districts), pressure on land is high and holdings correspondingly small and fragmented, though rather larger than in the sub-montane strip. In the S the primary division of land is into squares of 25–27·5 ac., and although tenancy has increased with population, and ownership holdings have tended to decrease in size, the cultivating holdings are still large—perhaps half of them lie between 7·5 and 15 ac. There is thus some possibility of using more advanced farming methods; co-operation is fairly strong in the Colonies and some capital is available for implements and fertilisers. Fig. 87 brings out the contrast in village layout and holdings; it should be noted that the fragmented holding in Gaggar Bhana is only *one* of the worst in the village and has 32 plots; in Chak 73 G.B. the *most* fragmented holding is in 4 plots only, of which only one is really outlying. The great distance between isolated plots in Gaggar Bhana is an obvious drain on time and energy, and the inset suggests another form of wastage—that of land in field boundaries.

Fig. 88 is a highly typical section. The doab is canal-irrigated, but

---

Fig. 87.—A CONTRAST IN VILLAGES: Gaggar Bhana, 25 mls E of Amritsar, and Chak 73 G.B., 11 mls SE of Lyallpur, respectively in long-settled well-and-canal zone and new Canal Colony. A, Abadi (village site); CB, Canal Bungalow. Uncultivated land includes cemeteries, cremation grounds, cattle pounds, etc.; wells small circles. The most fragmented holding in Chak 73 (4 plots) and in Ghaggar Bhana (32 plots) in black—cultivating holdings show similar pattern.
Inset (twice scale of main map) shows field pattern for part of Gaggar Bhana; that of Chak 73 is severely rectangular.
Area, cultivated area, poptn (1921) and density of Gaggar Bhana and Chak 73 respectively: 1644 and 1856 ac.; 1386 and 1362 ac.; 1468 and 964 persons; 571 and 332 to sq. ml.
Based on maps in Punjab Board of Econ. Inquiry *Village Surveys* Nos. 1 (1928) and 4 (1932).

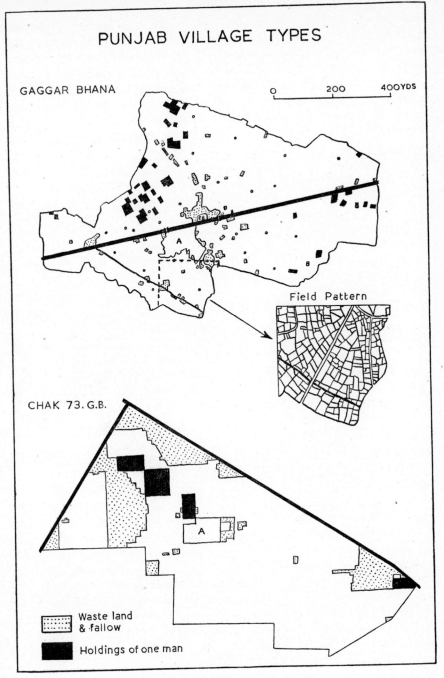

PUNJAB VILLAGE TYPES

GAGGAR BHANA

0   200   400 YDS

A

Field Pattern

CHAK 73. G.B.

A

B

:::::::: Waste land
:::::::: & fallow

▇ Holdings of one man

Fig. 87.—For caption see page 472.

below, in the Ravi *bet*, wells, almost absent on the doab, are very numerous. This suggests good soil and intensive culture; the braided course of the river, the patches of tall grass, suggest the persistence of marshy conditions and the liability to flood. In general the importance of the *dhaya* as a settlement-line is striking; the houses are mud-walled, flat-roofed, incredibly tight-packed, and the village generally occupies a slight rise—probably the debris of generations of settlement. In the *bet* most wells have a field-hut, in itself an indication of the intensity of well-cultivation.

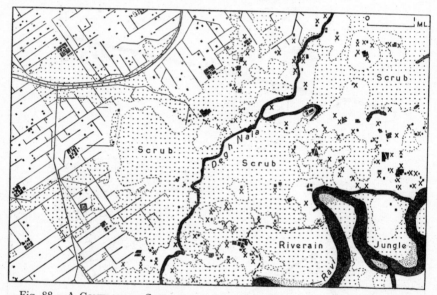

Fig. 88.—A Contrast in Settlement: Doab and Bet. Lyallpur Dt, 70 mls SW of Lahore. Continuous lines, canals; crosses, wells; stipple, land *not* cultivated. Contrast between planned settlement pattern of L. Chenab Canal Colony and amorphous settlement in Degh and Ravi *bets*, irrigated by wells. SOP 44 E/8 (1915—colonisation incomplete); courtesy SOP.

In the newer canal areas everything is rectangular or at least rectilinear: a Roman pattern. From the air a chequerboard of square fields, wheat and cotton, with much fallow and ominous patches of sand towards the arid margins, and neatly-planned rectangular villages like Roman *castra*, the major squares outlined by distributaries and roads; on the ground a thriving countryside, on the whole drier in aspect than the N. Except for those in the centre of the village (the social equivalent of the British housewife's queue) wells are virtually absent; the numerous dispersed huts are generally for cattle. It would be unfair to deny imagination to the Canal Colonies; after all the Triple Project has a boldness of scope which is aesthetic as well as scientific; but the Roman comparison is a good one, and there is a completely British lack of imagination in the detail planning of the villages. One feels the point of Darling's comment: "The canal colony with its rectangular fields, its straight roads, its interminable avenues of shisham trees, and its trim four-cornered villages speak of a new order of things. But this [in the N] was the old India—melodious, plaintive, prodigal, prickly, above all warm-hearted." [17] Also, it must be added, as a rule unspeakably squalid. Another reply to Darling is afforded by the Sandal Bar, named from a famous cattle lifter of *jangli* days. The waste of sandy scrub and actual dunes was hot as hell and certainly prickly, but hardly warm-hearted. But when all is said the Canal Colonies were a great achievement in civilisation and human welfare; no small part of Britain's legacy.

(iii) *The Arid Margins*. Conditions W of the Jhelum-Panjnad line are summed up by Darling in Zolaesque phrases: "This insecurity dominates everything. Out of every five years it is reckoned that at least two will be bad. . . . Half the country is burnt up by the sun and the other half drowned by the river, and the whole is waterlogged by debt." [18] Rainfall is under 10 ins. and extremely variable, a year of torrents followed by an almost rainless year. "So valuable, in fact, is water that property in it arose before property in land." Agriculture is dependent on natural floods, inundation canals, wells in floodplains, and abandoned river courses; and on the gamble on an inch or two of rain at the right time: ". . . where there is neither canal nor well, insecurity may be greater, but at least without rain nothing can be sown, and where nothing can be sown nothing can be lost. But in this area (outside the Thal) a crop can almost always be sown and almost always be lost." The inundation canals are unreliable: "the monsoon may abruptly end and the river sink before it has done its work. Then must the cultivator choose between losing what he has already sown and not sowing the winter wheat, the biggest crop of all, as there will not be enough water for both." In the trans-Indus, apart from the Sn riverain in Dera Ghazi Khan, cultivation is largely dependent on bunding across the wadis of the *daman* and so trapping the moisture in the soil after the infrequent rain-storms.

E of the Indus wheat accounts for half the sown area, followed by the lentil-like foodpulse gram: jowar and bajra are the kharif crops; there is some rice in the more inundable areas. Cotton is not important except in the better parts of Muzaffargarh; elsewhere the leading non-food crop is rapeseed. In the trans-Indus wheat still leads, but its predominance over the millets is much less marked. Dates are widely grown; in bad years the datestones are ground for flour.

Although in some Canal Colonies horse-breeding for the Army was

---

[17] M. L. Darling, *Wisdom and Waste in the Punjab Village* (1934), 55.
[18] Cf. the fascinating Ch. VI of Darling's *The Punjab Peasant in Prosperity and Debt* (2nd ed., 1928), from which all quotations in this paragraph are drawn. It is true that the conditions there described are over 20 years old, but the physical environment has changed not at all, the human response but little; though great changes are probably at hand with the Thal development.

fostered by the Government, and goats and long-eared sheep are kept as well as the draft bullocks and milk buffaloes, the open pastoralism once characteristic of the central doabs is now of real importance only in these arid steppes. Camels are still of some importance for transport.

Despite the low densities (c. 70–135 in 1951) pressure of population is acute; obviously areas such as the Thal and much of the Derajat are virtually empty and the restricted *oecumene* is seriously over-populated. The severity of the environment is reflected in the settlement pattern, largely semi-dispersed in wretched little hovels around the wells. Already in 1891 the economic holding was estimated at 13–40 ac. of cropped land, but 68% of holders cultivated one to five ac. and only 13% over 10. Land is often owned in different wells too widely scattered for one man to farm; the outliers must be leased out and more rented nearer home, a fruitful source of waste and friction. The keeping of sheep and goats and the scanty local opportunities for coolie labour eke out subsistence agriculture but are hardly adequate supplements to it. Along with this was the ever-present isolation and past exposure to incessant warfare in the days when the Sn route to Hindustan was more important. In many ways, indeed, this portion of the Punjab is among the most primitive of the settled parts of the sub-continent. But it will soon become a new farming frontier when the great Thal project is developed.

In the E, Bahawalpur state lies for some 300 miles between the Sutlej and the Thar. Not essentially dissimilar to the sandy wastes of the Sind Sagar Doab, it has been largely revivified by inundation and some perennial canals, though there are still stretches of scrub and bare sandy waste, and one is conscious of the fact that the desert margin is near at hand. Cotton, wheat, jowar are the leading crops. Away from the Sutlej the Desert Canal irrigates part of the dry bed of the old Ghaggar, though this is more important farther up in Bikaner.

Long before Partition there was dispute over the water of the Sutlej, Bahawalpur insisting on the completion of its works before any water was taken off for Bikaner. The undivided Punjab had large schemes for further irrigation in Sirhind; but the Sutlej is now an international river and the prospects of friction thereby much increased. In the W again the sandy hills of the Sind Sagar Doab offer greater physical obstacles to irrigation than were found in the central doabs; yet it is obvious that little social or economic progress can be made without the large-scale irrigation of the Thal, which should provide land for about 1,000,000 people. Here again there was some difficulty with Sind, apprehensive of the effects of any great abstraction of Indus water on the Sukkur Barrage.

It is clear that in the strictest sense the prosperity of the Punjab is artificial, dependent as it is on the efficient working of an extremely intricate man-made machine; and for this, political stability is the obvious first essential. Neither Pakistan nor *India* can afford to let this immense food-factory fall into slackness and disrepair.

Industry

W Punjab is as yet little industrialised, nor can it well be claimed that its potentialities for large-scale industrialisation are great, except possibly in textiles. On the other hand there is scope for increase in agricultural processing, and the development of Mandi power has led to the establishment of a number of light industries in the upper Bari Doab. Craft production is still considerable, and in some cases—e.g. small metal goods such as locks and cutlery—the craft tradition is adapting itself to small-scale factory methods.

There are no large power resources within the boundaries of W Punjab except the limited and inferior coal of the Salt Range and the small amount of electricity to be obtained from Rasul and Mianwali; Attock oil hardly enters the picture. Rail hauls from *Indian* coalfields are long and expensive, so that industrialisation, present and future, must rely very largely on hydro-electric power. Here again the really large power sites, developed as at Mandi or but projected as at Bhakra-Nangal, lie outside W Punjab —in montane Punjab or in the Kashmir foothills. The Mandi site, Jogindernagar on a tributary of the Beas, generates about 48,000 kW (potential 72,000 kW); it served a large area about equally divided between the two Punjabs, *Indian* and Pakistani, the chief consumers being Lahore, Amritsar, and Jullundur, though power is or was transmitted as far as Lyallpur, 262 miles.

The low humidity and the export demand for the longer-stapled Punjab cottons has hampered the development of cotton mills, though a few (not more than 15–20 in all) do exist at Lahore, Amritsar, Lyallpur, Montgomery, and one or two other Colony towns. Cotton ginneries number over 300, well in excess of demand except perhaps at the seasonal peak. The woollen and silk industries, though as yet in their infancy as factory industries, do to some extent represent an evolution from the old crafts for which Lahore, Amritsar, and Multan were famous. There are more factories in hosiery and knitwear than in any other single line, while Punjab *durris* (rugs), carpets, and blankets, still mainly craft productions, have an All-India reputation and even an overseas export. Owing to the severity of the cold season there is a considerable local demand for woollens, and the important Kashmir and Punjab production of raw wool is supplemented by the import of better qualities from Australia. Montane Punjab produces a fair amount of raw silk, and Amritsar is an important centre for the distribution of silk yarn to semi-domestic and craft weavers. Experiments have been made with sericulture in the Changa Manga Reserved Forest.

Heavy industry is conspicuous by its absence, except for the foundry and engineering trades essential to a great city like Lahore, railway workshops, and the like. More interesting is the agricultural machinery industry at Batala (between Amritsar and Gurdaspur), which is worth examining in a little detail as typical of the grafting of small-scale factory methods onto indigenous crafts in response to a local demand, a development which accounts for not a little of Indian manufacture. Batala is only a small market town, and the main factors in the growth of the industry appear to have been (i) the accident of a local magnate with initiative to import cane-crushers for hire and to expand his repair shop into a foundry as early as the 1880s; (ii) the presence of good moulding sand, of which there is an export to foundries in centres such as Lahore; (iii) the availability of semi-skilled labour, a blacksmith caste being locally numerous; and (iv) the strong local demand. There are—or were—between 20 and 30 small foundries and shops at Batala, employing altogether only a few hundred men in the busy season (July–December), but with a fairly considerable aggregate production of chaff-cutters, cane-crushers, rice-hullers, small milling and pressing units, pumps, ploughs, lathes and so on. Raw material is railway and other scrap supplemented by pig from Bengal, and Bihar coke is used in the cupolas. Most of the owners are illiterate and organisation is primitive—"in the smaller foundries the office is a mobile unit comprising the set of account books, etc., which the clerk uses sitting on a charpoy [rope bedstead], wooden board, or chair at the gate"[19]; but when hydro-electric power became available in 1933 it took only six months for the whole industry to abandon oil- and steam-engines. This development and the light industries (hosiery, flashlights, etc.) at Qadian near by provide perhaps the only instances in the entire Punjab of industrial initiative coming from Muslims rather than Hindus or Sikhs, and it is probable that, lying so close to the new frontier and the Sikh strongholds in Amritsar Dt, it has been wrecked in the post-Partition fighting; some of it has transferred to W Pakistan, and at least one firm has modernised itself in the process and now uses electric crucibles.

The only other Punjab industry of any individual note is the manufacture of sports goods, especially tennis rackets and cricket bats, at Sialkot, the products of which have a market beyond India. This again has been hit by Partition; much of the raw material came from Kashmir (above, 310). Near Sialkot also paper is made from gunny bags and paper waste as a cottage industry. For the rest, Mandi power has led to a considerable growth of light consumption industries—soap, paints, varnishes, matches, electrical fittings, sewing machines, hosiery, and so on—especially around Lahore and Amritsar.

Further possibilities are mainly in the direction of agricultural process-

[19] Punjab Board of Economic Inquiry Pub. No. 71, *Iron Foundry Industry at Batala* (1941), 8; and personal observation at Batala and Qadian.

ing, especially perhaps cottonseed oil and cake (at present ridiculously underdeveloped, except by wasteful processes in the villages), fruit and jam canning, and so on. The large production of hides and skins and the various salts of the Salt Range await better organised exploitation, and the woollen industry might well become more important than cotton.[20] A start has indeed been made with leather and woollens factories, again mainly in the Lahore-Amritsar area. Pakistan is of course reluctant to remain solely a primary producer and there is perhaps too much all-too-forward Planning and too little serious estimation of resources, which, although not great, nevertheless offer scope for industries mainly ancillary to agriculture. But everything is dependent on accessibility to credit and to the forests and power resources of Kashmir and the montane Punjab, and so again, in the last resort, on politics.

Communications and Towns

Until about 1880 the Punjab rivers were of importance for navigation, Pind Dadan Khan and Wazirabad, for example, having boat building and repair yards and steamboats ascending the Sutlej, at high water, as far as Ferozepore. But railway competition and the abstraction of water for irrigation killed this navigation (except for small craft on the lower Indus), and early projects for using the canals for country boats met too little demand to make the costs of special construction, and the interference with the primary object of irrigation, worth while. Only the upper reaches of the rivers and of canals above the first railway crossing are now used for rafting timber from the Kashmir foothills.

The railnet, except W of the Jhelum, is one of the best in India, and the Punjab is also fairly well supplied with roads. The main physical trends of the region—the NW/SE sub-montane strip and the NE/SW run of the doabs—are reflected in the orientation of the railways. The whole area is in the hinterland of Karachi, and all lines converge on Lodhran, between Multan and the Sutlej, whence there is only the one line Swards; and although, in contrast to the other lines, this is double-tracked, congestion at the height of the cotton harvest is serious.

The N, of course, has for centuries been the great highway for armies and peoples from central Asia into Hindustan: the Aryans, Alexander the Great (who reached the Beas), the earlier Muslim invaders, Babur the first of the Moguls, the Afghans and Persians in the post-Mogul anarchy, to mention but a few. The highway is marked by a string of towns commanding river crossings or central positions on doabs: Jhelum, Gujrat, Wazirabad, Gujranwala, Lahore, Amritsar. Away from this routeway the only really large town is Multan (1951: **190,000**), in the Middle Ages the commercial

[20] Cf. K. T. Shah, *Industrialisation of the Punjab* (Punjab Government, Lahore, 1941), *passim*.

and military key to the middle Indus and the Sn route into Hindustan. A centre of craft production—textiles, pottery, leather, enamel—it is also an exchange centre for the semi-nomadic Ghilzai traders from Afghanistan ; Muslim merchants in other parts of India are, or at least were, generally known as Multanis. The two Colony towns, Lyallpur and Montgomery, are, as their names imply, entirely new creations: Lyallpur rose from 13,483 inhabitants in 1906 to **180,000** in 1951. Primarily administrative and commercial centres, great cotton marts, they have the rigid rectangular plan of the Colonies, and the brand of newness sets them apart.

Of the three big Nn towns Sialkot (1951: **152,000**) is the least. Lying off the great route, nearer the hills, it was the capital of the Punjab under the White Huns (6th century AD) and lost some importance when Wazirabad, on the main route, was planned (on rectangular lines) by the Italian general Avitabile for Ranjit Singh; but as already noted it has a certain industrial individuality. Amritsar (391,010; **325,747**) grew up round the main centre of Sikh devotion, the Golden Temple (actually a copper-gilt dome of doubtful architectural merit), built on a site presented (by the Moguls!) to the fourth Sikh *guru*. It has important crafts, especially carpets, silks, and embroideries in silk, gold, and silver thread, and in normal times is a great mart for traders from Kashmir, Tibet, and Sinkiang, exchanging silk, wool, borax, tea, and so on for piecegoods and general 'bazaar goods'; but the more far-flung elements of this trade have of course greatly declined with the increasing gravitational pull of Soviet Asia. Despite its importance to the Sikhs, they were only 15% of the population in 1941, though they had a majority in the surrounding countryside.

But the queen of the Punjab is beyond all doubt Lahore. The 1941 Census population of 671,659 may have been somewhat inflated, but even with a large allowance for this it was the fifth city of India, the second excluding the great ports; and in 1951 was returned as having **849,000** people. The city lies on the En edge of the floodplain of the Ravi, which once washed the Fort walls; across the river is the magnificent tomb of Jehangir at Shahdara. Lahore was the capital of the Punjab from early Muslim times and, despite decay, retained that position under the Sikhs, while the tremendous development of the Province in the century of British rule gave it a new lease of life. There are the usual components of a great Indian city: the Fort, and under it the incredibly crowded and irregular walled town, a bazaar area (Anarkali) between the walls and the great spread of bungalows for the bureaucracy and lawyers [21] and their hangers-on, the Civil Lines and government offices and the Cantonments,

---

[21] No small contingent: in 1922 H. C. Calvert estimated that 2½ million persons—equivalent to 40% of the adult male population—annually attended the courts as parties or witnesses (*The Wealth and Welfare of the Punjab* (1922), 206.)

the railway suburb. Industrially, apart from the big Moghalpara railway shops, Lahore is not of great importance, though there is a considerable amount of craft production; its commercial hegemony was to some extent weakened by the rise of the Colony towns. But as the seat of government of an historic and proudly self-conscious Province and as an educational centre (incidentally with more and better bookshops than are to be found in comparable English cities) Lahore was supreme. With the loss of much of the area which formerly looked to it as a cultural and political centre, and with the far more serious loss of its non-Muslim traders and industrialists (who controlled the great bulk of its economic activity), it seems possible that Lahore may experience a new phase of decline. But it is not likely to lose its pre-eminence as the leading cultural centre of Islam in the sub-continent.

The new boundary runs down the Ujh and Ravi Rivers to a point NE of Lahore, then across the Upper Bari Doab to the Sutlej NE of Ferozepore: all of Amritsar Dt, most of Gurdaspur, and a corner of Lahore thus go to *India*. In the S a slight extension to the left bank of the Sutlej secures the Sulemanke headworks, on which Bahawalpur depends, to Pakistan. The bisection of the Upper Bari Doab Canal area and of the area supplied with Mandi power should not have raised insuperable problems, so obviously and inescapably is it to the interest of both countries to secure the efficient working of these enterprises; but Pakistan has already duplicated the Canal and the supply of electricity is being diminished. The mere physical amputation of E Punjab does not seem an irreparable loss to the parent Province; more serious is the economic disruption, the replacement of energetic entrepreneurs by a demoralised refugee peasantry. There is now a practically homogeneous Muslim population for W Punjab, and in the conditions of the sub-continent this is no small gain; but the task of rehabilitation and social adjustment will be hard.

One cannot escape a feeling of pity that a Province that had preserved an historic entity for centuries, that was so alive and vigorous, in fact a country and not a mere administrative unit, should be compelled, in part by its own internal stresses and in part by the all-Indian play of old sectarianisms and a new nationalism, to face if not disintegration, at least disruption.

BIBLIOGRAPHICAL NOTE

The Punjab has produced what is probably the best regional literature of the sub-continent, though much of it is naturally and properly concerned in the main with agrarian economics, following the cue of Thorburn's *Musulmans and Moneylenders in the Punjab* (1886). The more important books are:

H. C. Calvert, *The Wealth and Welfare of the Punjab* (Lahore, 1922). A very thorough if rather arid analysis of the basic economy.

H. K. Trevaskis, *The Land of the Five Rivers* (1928). Admirably written and most interesting economic history to 1890, with much incidental geography.

M. L. Darling, *The Punjab Peasant in Prosperity and Debt* (2nd ed., 1928). Crammed with important information; I have not been able to use a tenth of my notes on it.

——, *Rusticus Loquitur: The Old Light and the New in the Punjab Village* (1930).

——, *Wisdom and Waste in the Punjab Village* (1934). These two are the Rural Rides of a more humanist Cobbett, and I know nothing like them (except *Kim*) as a picture of the roadside and the well, the fields and the village, with an under-burden of acute thinking which is *not* like *Kim*.

The publications of the Board of Economic Enquiry (Lahore) are less lively but very valuable, especially the series of village surveys. There are many good articles in *The Panjab* (now *Pakistan*) *Geographical Review* (University of Lahore). An important thesis is K. S. Ahmad, *The Agricultural Geography of the Panjab* (London Ph.D., 1939); see also his paper "Economic Holding in the Panjab", *IGJ* XVIII (1943), 24–29, which brings out a number of very suggestive points.

CHAPTER XVIII

THE GANGETIC PLAINS
(Regions XI–XII)

The Indo-Gangetic Divide

(Bist Doab, Sirhind and the Ghaggar, Delhi)

IN a very real sense all the regions lying between the Indus and the Ganges Deltas are transitional, but the area between Sutlej and Jumna is peculiarly so, both physically and culturally; if the correspondence is not causal, it is at least significant. Primarily it is the actual divide between the two great river-systems, but it also includes two important climatic limits: in the N that of the sub-montane strip receiving really significant winter rain, in the S that between the area where any large agricultural development is possible only by irrigation, and the area where rainfed agriculture can precariously persist. Communally and culturally it is the great marchland between Islam and Hindustan: Muslim culture to-day probably finds its highest expression at Lahore, while on the other side of the region Muttra is rich in Hindu tradition; between them Delhi is (or was until very recently) a Muslim outpost, yet with deep roots in the remoter Hindu past: the history of the Nn part of the sub-continent is summed up and symbolised in Delhi to the highest degree.

The region is bounded on the N by the sharply-rising and straight Siwalik Hills, W by the Beas-Sutlej, E by the Jumna; on the S it grades into the Thar, and its limits here may be taken as the Ghaggar and, in the SE, the low broken Aravalli ridge which reaches out to Delhi. The area is of the order of 35,000 sq mls.

Topography and Hydrographic Changes: the 'Lost Sarasvati'

Apart from a few scattered and broken Aravalli outliers in the SE, and the topographic discontinuities of the river-courses, the terrain is simply the usual alluvial monotony. Most interest attaches to the sub-Siwalik strip in the N and to the hydrographic history of the Ghaggar. Between Beas and Sutlej the Siwaliks are on the whole more sharply defined than they are to the W, and for climatic and historical reasons more deforested than they are to the E. The result has been erosion on a spectacular scale. The Siwaliks in this area are formed for the most part of "barely coherent" sandrock, with occasional clays, gravels, and conglomerates, an ideal lithology for gullying. In the 80 miles of the Siwaliks in Hoshiarpur Dt nearly a hundred streams debouch onto the plains. These *chos* are dry except in

sudden spates, when they come down armed with masses of sand and are
agents of rapid erosion on the plain below, itself sandy and with a perceptible slope near the hills. The *chos* country is really an immense 'pan-fan',
in which individual detrital cones are hardly perceptible, while erosion is
so violent that the *chos* are graded from two to four miles back into the
hills—a marked contrast to the usual torrent profile (Fig. 89). On a vastly
greater scale the *chos* belt is not unlike a beach crossed by runnels, each *cho*
is a broad river of sand, with a shallow ever-shifting bed, and with banks
which, where defined at all, "are composed of unstable sand . . . or of
scarped cultivation liable to be washed away by any flood". [1] Except in the

Fig. 89.—Sub-Siwalik Chos Erosion. About 6 miles N of Hoshiarpur. SOI 44
M/14; courtesy SOI.

Salt Range *khuddera* and the great Jumna-Chambal ravines, nowhere in
India has erosion been so devastating as on this Siwalik front, where e.g.
Rupar town is islanded in a broken sea of troughs and ridges.

Except for a few streams at each end, the drainage of the 100-mile-long
Siwalik ridge between Sutlej and Jumna is either dissipated into the fields,
or converges into the Ghaggar. The identification of this stream with the
Sarasvati, the lost river of the Vedic hymns and other early Sanskrit
writings, seems secure enough, and the ancient name still appears on the
maps as that of a Ghaggar tributary. But the old records tell of a mighty
stream, "rich in lakes" and the mother of cities, and the Ghaggar of to-day,
although the only river actually piercing the Siwaliks between Sutlej and

[1] A. P. F. Hamilton, "Siwalik Erosion", *HJ* VII (1935), refce. p. 95; see also R. Maclagan
Gorrie, "Countering Desiccation in the Punjab", *GR* XXXVIII (1948), 30–40. There is a
large literature, summed up in Sir H. Glover, *Erosion in the Punjab*, and R. Maclagan
Gorrie, *Soil and Water Conservation in the Punjab* (both Lahore, 1946).

Jumna, is rainfed only, and at a short distance from the hills it becomes non-perennial, a monsoon river merely. Even its rainy season flow normally ceases at Hanumangarh, about 290 miles from its source and 15 miles within the Bikaner border; occasionally it extends for another 16 miles or so. Its dry course, the Hakra, in Bikaner and Bahawalpur, is impressive enough: for over 100 miles the flat bed is nowhere less than two miles wide, in places over four miles, bordered on either hand by steep and continuous lines of dunes. These are not true river banks but as it were aeolian levees, accumulations of windblown sand trapped by vegetation on the riverain strips once seasonally flooded: "The gradually rising accumulation of driftsand, usually protected by some growth of scrub, has prevented the onward march of the dunes and thus preserved the dry bed from being smothered." [2] But it is unlikely that this broad bed was ever completely filled with water; the fertility of its loamy levels when water can be brought to them, and its striking definition between the bordering sand-ridges, are responsible for the local belief in the existence of a river of the first magnitude. This is very unlikely, but that water once flowed well down into Bahawalpur is attested beyond doubt by numerous ancient settlement-mounds, and it is often held that the E Nara in Sind is the continuation of the Hakra, beheaded by the Sutlej.[3] The reality is unknown, but in all probability less dramatic. The confused evidence and exceedingly controversial interpretations of the ancient tradition, the magic of the name Sarasvati, a complete failure to discriminate between prehistoric and mediaeval sites (natural enough before any serious archaeological investigation was attempted)—all have fostered exaggeration of the changes in historic or pseudo-historic times. Theories of extensive climatic change have been generally succeeded by theories of sweeping recent river-diversions; the annexation of the Jumna drainage by the Ganges has been referred to historic or at least proto-historic times, while the line of the Sutlej above the Rupar elbow has been projected to the convergence of the present Ghaggar tributaries.[4] The balance of evidence seems to be against this. Stein, whose views are based on first-hand fieldwork rather than on dubious documentation, does indeed hold that a branch of the Sutlej along the line of the Desert Branch Canal (see Fig. 90) built a deltaic fan in the Hakra S of Bahawalpur town, and so made possible the extensive prehistoric settlement there, and according to the *Punjab States Gazetteer* some Sutlej water still enters the Hakra. "But it may be considered as certain that the riverine belt along the Hakra in this area knew no settled agricultural life

[2] Sir Aurel Stein, "A Survey . . . along the 'Lost' Sarasvati River", *GJ* XCIX (1942), p. 175; this interpretation, based on Tarim analogues, is now generally accepted but not always acknowledged as to source.

[3] See W. Arden Wood, "Rivers and Man in the Indus-Ganges Plains", *Scottish Geographical Magazine*, XL (1924), 1–15.

[4] So far as I understand him, Siddiqi appears to hold both views simultaneously.

during historical times. What small settlements existed near the Hakra before the modern canal system reached it were those of a very scanty pastoral population, maintaining itself partly by the supply of camel transport for caravan traffic following an old route . . . from Multan and Sind towards Delhi. . . ." [5]

In his very balanced review of the problem S. M. Ali holds that at least during historical times the Ghaggar has been an independent non-perennial river; he neatly turns the interpretation of Sarasvati as "rich in lakes" by pointing out that after the monsoon such streams naturally form large pools or "lakes". The diversion, natural or artificial, of some upper Ghaggar tributaries into Jumna and Sutlej is a contributory factor in the dwindling of the river. The Indo-Gangetic divide has been settled (fairly densely in the N) for three millennia, and main communication lines lie athwart the drainage: the cumulative effect of their interference with the drainage lines is probably not small. The destruction of the plains forests in the N, generations of cultivation and over-pasturing, irrigation diversion, not to mention the Siwalik deforestation (perhaps too recent to affect the main issue) have resulted in too-rapid run-off and the familiar alternation of "frequent floods during the rainy season and little or no water during the rest of the year". [6]

To sum up: it is certain that a larger stream penetrated more deeply to the SW, but it is very unlikely that this was the main Sutlej, and still less likely that the Jumna has followed this course since human occupance of the region began. River diversion has had some part, but according to Ali's view—which seems to be borne out by Stein's facts and general conclusion—the main action in the Ghaggar drama has not been by way of catastrophic changes in the river-pattern but by slow, unspectacular, but cumulatively decisive deterioration in ground-water conditions, largely aided by human activity. And·there is the menace of the spreading Thar.

Agriculture

Agriculturally the three-fold aspect of the Punjab proper is repeated: submontane strip, canal-irrigated area, arid margins. But there are significant differences: the Wly depressions are tailing off; canal irrigation is at once older and on the whole less well developed; and the arid margins, except along the Ghaggar, have not the topographic mitigations of the Indus riverain: there are no great streams to fill inundation canals, no *daman* to be bunded, and the water-table is very low.

By far the best-favoured area is the Bist Doab, as is shown by its District densities of **790** for Jullundur and **497** for Hoshiarpur (which

---

[5] Stein, *loc. cit.*, 180.
[6] S. M. Ali, "Population and Settlement in the Ghaggar Plain", *IGJ* XVII (1942), 157–82; cf. S. I. Siddiqi, "River Changes in the Ghaggar Plain", *IGJ* XIX (1944), 139–48, and "The Physiognomy of the Ghaggar Plain", *IGJ* XX (1945), 87–92.

includes parts of the sparsely populated Siwaliks). The Sutlej riverain is also densely populated (Ludhiana 577), but the arid S falls to 200 in Hissar.

In the sub-montane strip well irrigation is more important than canal; the water-table is high and this is a rich parkland country, except where waterlogged (as in the Beas bend in the NW corner) or where it has been torn to pieces by *chos*. Losses of good land by erosion and sand-spreads have been very serious. Before British rule the Siwaliks had been under petty feudal lords and the forests were on the whole preserved for hunting; this society was largely broken up by the conquest, and legal titles were secured virtually by squatting. No control was exercised over land use, and at the same time the general economic development of the plains called for much constructional timber. The forests were gutted by reckless timber-felling, charcoal burning, and the all too intensive grazing of goats. The results are shown in Fig. 89. Erosion has now been checked, to a considerable extent, by forest control and afforestation, contour bunding, and more systematic fodder exploitation, but it remains a serious problem. Settlement patterns and crops are similar to those in the sub-montane strip in W Punjab, but sugar-cane becomes more important as the great sugar belt of Wn UP is approached.

Sirhind or Hariana, the Sutlej/Jumna or 'Delhi Doab', is largely occupied by the mainly Sikh states of the Patiala and E Punjab Union. Soils are lighter than in the sub-montane strip—"a great wedge of light loam and sand which Rajputana pushes northwards almost to the Sutlej". In the N well-irrigation is still important in light fertile loams; in the Jangal Des—'jungle country'—to the SW the water-table is too low. Nevertheless the sandy loams are remarkably drought-resistant and crop failure is less frequent than might be expected considering the low rainfall (*c.* 12–17 ins.). Gram, wheat, and barley are the chief rabi, millets the chief kharif dry crops. Irrigation is mainly for wheat. Villages are fairly large, nucleated, evenly spaced.

The real S—especially Hissar—is in worse case, except in the Sutlej and Jumna riverains and where the Ghaggar brings a belt of irrigation across it (Fig. 90). The water-table is too deep for wells, rainfall is scanty (10–12 ins.) and unreliable, yet most of the crops must depend on it. Insecurity is the dominant note. Density is relatively low, though probably high enough in relation to resources, and holdings are of necessity large— 7·5 to 10 ac., and in places up to 60. Owing to the paucity of water-points villages also are definitely large and rely on tanks for their domestic supply; this is rare in Nn India. In a really good year—say one out of five—the large holdings provide large surpluses of wheat and barley; more normally kharif bajra and rabi gram are the chief crops. Stock-rearing is of great importance, the Hissar or Hariana cattle being among the best Indian breeds, and camels are used for transport and even for the plough. But here too a run of two or three bad years means ruin. "I remember a year in Hissar when we had less than four inches, and a man could ride for 50 miles and see nothing greener than the poisonous *akk*. . . . At such a time fodder is so scarce, that any bit of scrub that cattle will eat is guarded as jealously as if it were a crop of valuable sugar-cane. Every tree, too, is lopped to the bark, and there is no more desolate sight than the long roadside avenues raising flayed, twisted arms to a bare, pitiless sky. After a bad famine there are villages where not a cow, buffalo, or calf is to be seen." [7]

Partition, however, has forced on the long-projected Bhakra-Nangal scheme for irrigation (3·9 m. ac.) and power (400,000 kW) from the Sutlej; this has a high priority, while in the background are the projects already mentioned (394,470) for tunnelling in the upper valleys of Ravi and Beas. Little need be said about non-agricultural occupations. E Punjab possesses the Mandi hydro-electric installation (see above, 477) and potentially other sites in the montane area, as well as its timber; otherwise, except for hides and skins, its resources are even less than those of W Punjab: minerals, except for patches of *reh* salts of doubtful economic value, are non-existent in the plains, and cotton of little importance. Paper-making (using *sabai* grass) near Ambala, a few agricultural processing mills, a few foundries in the railway towns, practically exhaust the list of factories, though Ludhiana has some 35 hosiery and knitwear works; but their average number of employees is only 33. The availability of *kikar* (Acacia) bark, an important tan-stuff, the large supplies of hides and skins, and the large number of Chamars (untouchables who have no caste to lose by handling dead cattle) has led to a fairly marked concentration of petty village tanneries in the SE; although of course it is a question whether tanning is responsible for the numbers of Chamars or vice versa.

Since Partition the rosin and turpentine industry, and some firms from Sialkot, have migrated to E Punjab.

The Great Highway and its Towns

The cities of the region are mostly route centres, associated with the great highway from the NW into the gates of Hindustan at Delhi: four times has a great struggle for power been decided at Karnaul or at Panipat, respectively 75 and 55 miles NNE of Delhi. Of these battles the most far-reaching in their effects were Babur's victory at Panipat in 1526, which gave Hindustan to the Moguls, and the complete overthrow of the Marathas by the Afghans near the same town in 1761, which, although leaving the Marathas as the greatest power in central India, ended their hopes of complete dominion in the N and left the field open to the British power advancing up the Ganges. On this historic highway lie three important cities,

[7] M. L. Darling, *The Punjab Peasant in Prosperity and Debt* (1928 ed.), 92.

THE INDO–GANGETIC DIVIDE

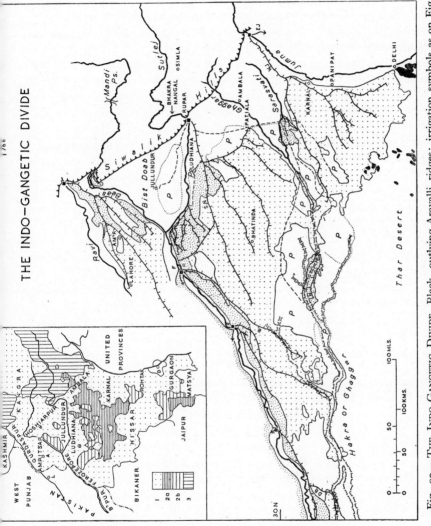

Fig. 90.—The Indo-Gangetic Divide. Black, outlying Aravalli ridges; irrigation symbols as on Fig. 85. *Canals:* B, Bikaner; DB, Desert Branch; H, Hariana; SN, Sutlej Navigation; W (E) J, West (East) Jumna. *Headworks:* F, Ferozepore; S, Sulemanke; I, Islamabad. P, projected irrigation areas. Inset: 1, E Punjab; 2a, Patiala, 2b, other states of Pepsu; 3, Himachal Pradesh.

Jullundur, Ludhiana, and Ambala, as well as Delhi itself, which deserves separate treatment.

Jullundur (**168,816**) lies in a central position on the Bist Doab; an important rail junction with a little local industry, for a short while after Partition it was the temporary capital of E Punjab. At present the capital is Simla, but a new one on the most modern lines is being planned at Chandigarh, at the foot of the hills close to Kalka. Ludhiana (**153,795**), commanding an important Sutlej crossing, and Ambala (62,419) are the leading industrial towns, but as we have seen this amounts to very little. Ambala is an 'economic border' town between plains and hills, and owes much of its importance to its early selection as a cantonment centre. Other towns—Ferozepore, Bhatinda (in Patiala state), Hissar—are merely railway towns and local administrative centres.

The states of the Sutlej/Jumna doab, mostly under Sikh rulers and including in Faridkot the only major administrative unit which had in 1941 an absolute Sikh majority, are grouped in the Patiala and E Punjab States Union (Pepsu). They represent the survivors of the cis-Sutlej British client states of the marchlands; before the Sikh Wars (1845–49) all E of Jumna was undisputed British territory, all W of Sutlej the domain of Ranjit Singh's Sikhs. The EIC was loath to extend its power much beyond Delhi, and Sirhind was the NW Frontier of the day; but the necessities of 'influence politics' led to local accretions of territory and extensions of British protection: hence the interlocking of provincial and State territory and the numerous ex- and en-claves. Patiala (area 5942 sq mls, poptn 1,936,259) is by far the most important state, and its capital, Patiala town (69,850), is also the capital of Pepsu.

DELHI

It is hardly necessary to emphasise the larger nodality of Delhi: the gateway between the Thar-Aravalli barrier and the Himalaya; the marchland position between the NW, ever accessible to new waves of invasion and cultural intrusion, and the shock-absorbing Gangetic Plains; the convergence of the routes from the ancient Cambay ports and the Deccan by Rajputana and Malwa. Few sites enjoy such advantages, and perhaps none save Rome and Istanbul have had such long-sustained significance: to the N lie the fields of Karnaul and Panipat where the fate of India has four times been decided. But not only is the general area thus marked out as the great crossroads of the sub-continent: the pattern is reproduced in detail by the famous Ridge, the worn and arid last spur of the Aravallis, pointing like a lean but wiry finger straight to the Jumna crossing.

A triangle of some 70 sq mls is strewn with the ruins of old capitals (Fig. 91): New Delhi is commonly reckoned the eighth. Delhi proper is Shahjahanabad, founded by the Mogul Emperor of that name (reigned 1628–

58), on the low bluff overlooking the Jumna floodplain; on the landward side its red sandstone walls extend for $3\frac{1}{4}$ miles, while on the river front the vast enceinte of the Red Fort encloses the Mogul palace, still magnificent despite barbarous usage by Persians, Afghans, Marathas, and British. W from the Fort runs the long, straight Chandni Chowk, 'Silver Street',

the bazaar of the goldsmiths and other craftsmen; and across the broad, open space surrounding the Fort walls lies the finely proportioned Jama Masjid or Friday Mosque. Beyond the city walls the nearer suburbs and the immense and ill-planned Civil Lines (the administrative headquarters of Delhi Division until 1911) sprawl across the Nn end of the Ridge. There are a few light industries (flourmilling, cotton textiles, printing, small metal goods), and such industry (mainly cotton-milling) and commercial importance as Delhi now possesses is to be found in the teeming tight-packed lanes of Shahjahanabad and in

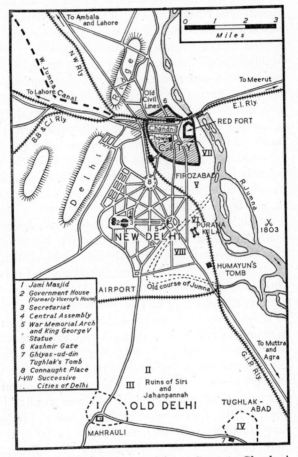

Fig. 91.—THE CITIES OF DELHI. Courtesy *Chambers's Encyclopædia* (1950).

its formless nearer suburbs. New Delhi is administrative and nothing else; perhaps no other city in the world—almost certainly no other of its size—is so bound up with the business of governing. In the old city the ancient arts carry on the Mogul inheritance, much degraded by pandering to tourist taste, real or alleged. Over all is, at least was until 1947, a Muslim imprint; Shahjahanabad is a town of the NW, and this was nowhere more apparent than in the shabby forecourts of the absurdly castellated railway station, where camels, pack donkeys, mules, and herds of sheep and goats give the air of a dusty market town.

S of Shahjahanabad lie both New Delhi and the ancient cities. The oldest site, going back perhaps to the beginning of the Christian era, is Indarpat, traditionally Indraprastha, one of the five cities of the epic Mahabharata War. But the visible remains, the Purana Qila of Humayun and his supplanter Sher Shah, are early 16th century. Beyond New Delhi the countryside is a litter of mouldering walls, the domes and cupolas of innumerable tombs, kiosks, enclosed tanks and gardens, culminating in mediaeval Mahrauli and Tughlukabad, capitals of the earlier Muslim dynasties. These two form an impressive contrast. At Mahrauli is the towering Qutb Minar (AD 1220), its 234 ft making it the highest free-standing stone tower in the world, and the richly beautiful tomb of Altamsh (c. 1230), the faces of its masonry a maze of interlacing calligraphic ornament. Near it stands the famous iron pillar, a Gupta monument of the 4th century AD and an astonishing metallurgical achievement, being in effect a single piece of wrought iron 23 ft long; and here too is the stump of the minaret which the megalomaniac Ala-ud-din began in 1311 and planned to be twice the height of the Qutb. Three miles away the massive sharply-battered walls of Tughlukabad crown a rocky outcrop, grim beyond expression; even the tomb of the first Tughluk ruler, austerely beautiful as it is, is simple to the point of severity. Mahrauli appears sophisticated, even decadent, beside this puritanic and cyclopean architecture, and it is difficult to realise that chronologically Tughlukabad is a century later.

So much for the past. The transfer of the capital of India from Calcutta to Delhi in 1911 was conscious historical imitation: the Moguls were to be matched on their own ground. A new Province was created, covering 574 sq mls, mostly from the Punjab but with a few trans-Jumna villages; since the Government of India Act (1935) and the achievement of Independence the Province has taken on the character of a federal district. Its population has more than quadrupled, rising from 413,851 in 1911 to 1,743,992 in 1951. Of the 1941 total, Shahjahanabad and its near suburbs accounted for 521,849, New Delhi (which did not exist in 1911) for 93,733; the rest were in outlying cantonments and the villages. Old and New Delhi together ranked as the sixth city of India in 1941, being outnumbered by Hyderabad (Deccan) and Lahore as well as by the three great ports; but the tremendous increase in Governmental activity since 1941, with the very rapid growth of New Delhi, nearly doubled the population in ten years, and have now put the double city near the 1,250,000 mark (Delhi, **914,790**; New Delhi, **276,314**), so that it is now the largest inland city of *India* and Pakistan.

New Delhi naturally affects the monumental, and not without success: at least the gulf between New Delhi and the barbarous generality of Indo-

British official architecture is far wider than that between New Delhi and its Mogul precursors. On the whole it is fine planning, though the distances are too magnificent: in the common Indian phrase, fitted For Princes and Rich Men Only. The main axis runs E–W, from the huge but dull 1914–18 War Memorial Arch (which carries in gigantic letters the single but superfluous word INDIA) to the rise on which stand the immense buildings of the Secretariat and the former Viceroy's House. This triple avenue, with its long canals and lines of trees, is flanked by the houses of the chief Princes; fortunately its mirror-symmetry is broken by two small ruined mosques. Splendid as it all is, the artifice is too apparent; the houses of high officials nicely proportioned to their several statuses, the side-avenues named after Hindu and Muslim rulers in strict communal balance, the oppressive symmetry—

> Grove nods at Grove, each Alley has a brother,
> And half the platform just reflects the other.

As for the architecture proper, it is perhaps no disgrace if it fails in the competition with its near-by rivals the Jama Masjid and Humayun's Tomb, since these are two of the noblest of Mogul buildings, which is as much as to say two of the really great architectural achievements of the world. . . . But although New Delhi does achieve its monumental ambitions it lacks as a rule the final touch of imagination needed for greatness, and in places it is positively inept—as for example in the unrelieved monotony of the exterior circular colonnades of the huge Assembly building, with a skyline broken only by the meanest of puny finials. The most modern-looking building in New Delhi—not excepting the modernistic All-India Radio building, with its clover-leaf plan—is the open-air observatory built by the astronomer-prince Jai Singh of Jaipur in the 18th century, immense dials and gnomons with beautifully clean lines which make the mean and shallow architecture of the shopping centre, Connaught Place, look even shoddier than it really is.

Yet with all its faults New Delhi has undeniably an imperial as well as a merely bureaucratic impress: a tribute to the Mogul tradition, a costly monument to the British Raj, but beyond that the always busy (if not perhaps always purposeful) governing centre of one of the world's greatest states; and that function remains to it under the new dispensation. Nor does it seem likely that this site, so rich in historic association and so magnificently placed in relation to the sub-continent, can easily be displaced as the central focus of *Indian* political life.

The Upper Ganges Plains

Regional Divisions

The rational regional division of the Gangetic Plains is extremely difficult; physiography is of no help, since there are no marked physical breaks other than river courses, and the surface variations that do exist, such as the *bhur* tracts, are only local. Climate would seem the obvious alternative principle, but the isohyets trend diagonally NW/SE across the lie of the land, cutting the rivers, the topographic master-features, at acute angles, and it seems absurd to put places a few miles apart into separate regions on the basis of a line which is strictly speaking hypothetical and does not correspond to any marked ecological change. J. N. L. Baker heroically treats the whole area from the Jumna to the deltaic margins as the Indo-Gangetic Plain East, which is reasonable physiographically but takes no account of the big difference between the dry Delhi-Agra country and the wet jute-growing E of Bihar, a difference big enough to enforce some division. It seems best to follow Stamp and make a rather imprecise division on a line running roughly from the Ganges-Jumna confluence at Allahabad across to the NNW-SSE section of the Gogra. This does not correspond very well to the 40-in. isohyet, as Stamp implies,[8] but it does conform quite closely to an area of more mixed main crops to the W—our Upper Ganges Plains—and the Middle Ganges Plains where rice predominates, with an acreage at least double that of wheat; and the former region also contains the great bulk of the irrigated area of the Gangetic Plains (Fig. 94 and inset).

An unsatisfactory solution, it must be confessed, but perhaps in as much accord with the intractable facts as is possible pending the production of more, and more detailed, local studies. The region includes three areas of some historic individuality:

(i) *The* Doab, that of the Jumna and Ganges, commanding the Nn approaches to the Malwa passage into the Deccan; this was the core of the pre-Mogul Delhi Sultanate;

(ii) the greater part of the Kingdom of Oudh, a successor-state set up by a governor nominally under the Moguls in their 18th-century decline, and later a British client-state until its overdue suppression in 1856—one of the proximate causes of the Mutiny;

(iii) between these two lies Rohilkhand, so named from the Rohilla Afghans who were dominant here in the post-Mogul anarchy. Rampur state (now merged into UP) was a survival of their power.

Politically the Upper Ganges Plains occupy the Wn two-thirds of the United Provinces of Agra and Oudh (renamed Uttar Pradesh), excluding in the N the montane Dts of Dehra Dun, Garhwal, Almora, and the hills portion of Naini Tal, and in the S most of Jhansi and those parts of Banda and Hamirpur Dts lying on the Peninsular foreland. Agra was the old 'North-Western Provinces', separated from Bengal in 1834–36, of which the Wn portions were acquired in 1801–03 when Rohillas, Marathas, and the Nawabs of Oudh had cancelled each other out. The distinction

[8] *Asia* (1944 ed.), 261, 295.

between Agra and Oudh has long ceased to have much but a formal administrative significance. As statistics by Districts are not always available the treatment of some topics below refers to the whole UP rather than to the restricted region, but where this is so it is clearly stated and the general argument is not greatly affected.

Land and Climate

The lie of the land is simple; a great plain built up of detritus from the Himalayas, and traversed by the great rivers Jumna, Ganges, and Gogra, which show a very marked parallelism, with the main drainage-line naturally pushed well over to the S. The Nn limit is marked by the very smooth curves of the Siwaliks (which E of the Sarda lie within independent Nepal); but on the S the boundary is very irregular, as the old rugged surface of the Peninsular Foreland has been smothered by the Gangetic alluvium and that of the Sn tributaries of the Jumna (Chambal, Betwa, and Ken), leaving, of course, much-broken peninsulas and islands of older rock rising out of the alluvial flatness. The main physiographical variation within the great mass of the plain is that between the upland bhangar alluvium of the doabs and the fingers of khadar along the main streams and their sub-parallel tributaries such as the Ramganga and Sarda and the Gumti, which last is wholly a plains river. There is of course a great development of dead arms, deferred junctions, and *jhils* in the broad floodplains, which on the greater rivers are several miles across and in the rains have almost the aspect of arms of the sea, with a great expanse of water extending right to the horizon up and down stream. The right banks are generally the higher, with bluffs and some ravining, though nothing comparable to the great belts of badlands which border the lower Chambal and the Jumna in the arid SW, where one knows by the gullies that one is coming to a river when still three or four miles away. (Cf. Figs. 92 and 93.)

In these all but featureless alluvial expanses there are, it is true, what may be called micro-regional differences of slope and aspect, in some areas undulations faintly perceptible to the eye. These are tracts or facets rather than sub-regions, though they may be associated with soil or water-table variations by no means without agricultural significance. But broadly speaking there are only three really important variations from the norm: *bhabar, terai, bhur*.

The first two may be treated together. The bhabar (= 'porous') is simply the great detrital piedmont skirting the Siwaliks, where the stream profiles suddenly flatten out and the coarser detritus—boulders and gravels—is deposited. In this tract, 20 miles wide in the W but narrowing Ewds, the smaller streams, except when in spate during the rains, are lost in the loose talus, to seep out again where the slope is still flatter and finer material is

deposited in the marshy and jungly terai below. Originally the terai
covered a great zone perhaps 50–60 miles wide and extending in Oudh as
far S as the middle Gogra.[9] But much of this has been so altered by settlement that the true terai is now confined to a relatively narrow strip parallel
to the bhabar. Its practical absence W of the Jumna (where the immediate
sub-montane belt is occupied by the *chos* country) may be due to the fact
that between Jumna and Sutlej the Siwaliks stand well away from the
Himalayas and so have developed their own purely rainfed drainage system
to a greater extent than is possible where the Siwaliks are as it were im-
pacted into the Lesser Himalaya and are cut through by snow-fed rivers;
the significance of the gap between Jumna and Sutlej has been discussed
above in connection with the Ghaggar problem. Farther W in the Punjab,
where the Siwaliks again abut onto Himalayan ranges, it is too dry for a
terai development and the daman corresponds to the bhabar; farther E in
turn, where the Siwaliks are again separated from the snow-mountains by
the longitudinal valleys of Nepal, the rainfall itself is much greater and

[9] M. H. Rahman, *L'Oudh: Étude de géographie économique* (Paris, 1940), 18–21.

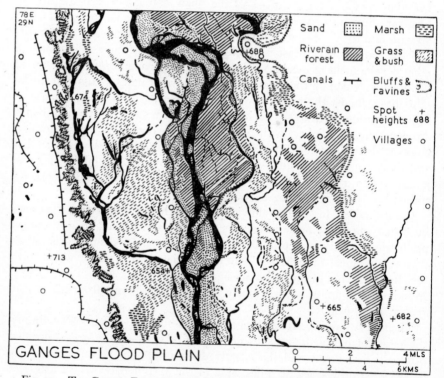

GANGES FLOOD PLAIN

Fig. 92.—THE GANGES FLOODPLAIN, *c.* 65 mls NE of Delhi. Black = perennial water;
all blank areas cultivated. 3 village-names in floodplain have 'khadar' as one component.
SOI 1/126,720 53 L/NW; courtesy SOI.

there is an ample water-supply for the terai.[10] Both terai and bhabar are jungly, except where colonisation has taken place along the Sn margins;

[10] I owe the original hint for this view to a remark of my former student Dr Enayat Ahmad.

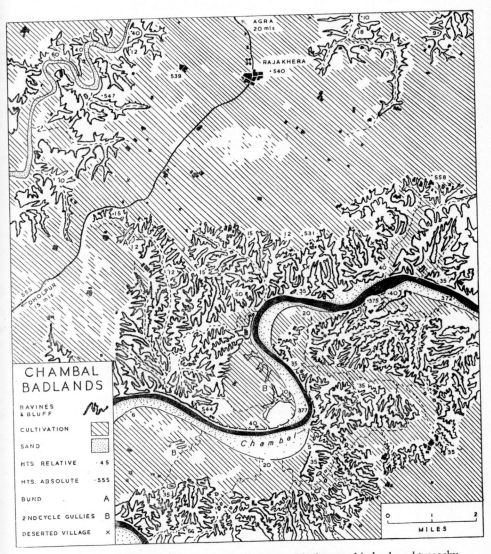

Fig. 93.—CHAMBAL BADLANDS, *c.* 30 mls S of Agra. Blank areas thin bush and tussocky grass, much bare ground in ravines; settlements black. Note unsuccessful attempt to protect road at A; cultivation on floors of larger ravines (probably enlarging laterally) and slip-off slopes, with suggestion of second-cycle gullying in latter. Since the date of original map (1922) some contour-bunding and afforestation have probably taken place; properly controlled the area might be a useful fodder reserve. SOI 54 J/1; courtesy SOI.

they carry dense sal forests and in places tall-grass savannah; and both are intensely malarial.

Bhur is a generic term for patches of sandy soil, in places sufficiently extensive to form low but undulating sandy uplands. The Bhur proper is a belt on the E bank of the Ganges in Moradabad and Bijnor Dts; generally rather arid but waterlogged in the depressions, especially in wet years, it was until recently a somewhat negative tract, but most of it has been reclaimed by tube-wells.

The general landscape is admirably described in the *United Provinces Gazetteer*,[11] although over much of the region irrigation has now somewhat softened the seasonal contrast:

> . . . a level plain, the monotony of which is broken only by the numerous village sites and groves of dark-olive mango-trees which meet the eye in every direction. The great plain is, however, highly cultivated, and the fields are never bare except during the hot months, after the spring harvest has been gathered, and before the rainy season has sufficiently advanced for the autumn crops to have appeared above the ground. The countryside then puts on its most desolate appearance; even the grass withers, and hardly a green thing is visible except a few patches of garden crops near village sites, and the carefully watered fields of sugar-cane. At this time the *dhak* trees burst forth with brilliant scarlet flowers. . . . With the breaking of the monsoon in the middle or end of June the scene changes as if by magic; the turf is renewed, and tall grasses begin to shoot in the small patches of jungle. Even the salt *usar* plains put on a green mantle, which lasts for a very short time after the close of the rains. A month later the autumn crops—rice, the millets, and maize—have begun to clothe the naked fields. These continue to clothe the ground till late in the year, and are succeeded by the spring crops—wheat, barley, and gram. In March they ripen and the great plain is then a rolling sea of golden corn, in which appear islands of trees and villages. . . .

The soils of the plain range from the very heavy *usar* clays—towards the W with alkaline *reh* efflorescences in the more arid areas—through the very generally distributed loams (*dumat*) to the sandy bhur; the reasonably heavy *matiyar* clays of the khadar are the best paddy-land.

Temperature is relatively unimportant—January means range from 55 to 64° F, May from 90 to 95° with extremes of 115° or more. In the NW, however, the cold season has special features of significance, approximating to the more extreme Punjab winter; night frosts in January, hail-storms in February and March, are not uncommon and are sometimes severe enough to damage the rabi crops, and especially sugar-cane.

Rainfall, as universally in India, is of prime significance. Only in the extreme NW is winter rain worthy of note, with one or two inches in

[11] Vol. I (Calcutta, 1908), 8.

January and February together—enough to account for the large proportion of unirrigated wheat in Saharanpur and Muzaffarnagar; unirrigated wheat is also associated with the high rainfall (over 45 ins.) of the Nn tier of Districts. The 40-in. isohyet slants across the region: N and E rainfalls of 50 ins. or so are attained in the immediate sub-montane strip, S and W they sink to 30, and in Agra and Muttra to under 25 ins. Some of the agricultural correlations will be immediately apparent from Fig. 94.

Along the Nn border there is still a strip of forest in the bhabar and terai; on the plains the natural vegetation has largely disappeared but survives in riverain strips, mainly of the khair/sissoo type which is an early coloniser of new detrital spreads. The trees named are the most important economically: sal (*Shorea robusta*) and sissoo (*Dalbergia sissoo*) for construction, khair (*Acacia catechu*) also for timber but perhaps more important as a source of tanstuffs. Much of the floodplains is occupied by tall coarse grasses or tamarisk brakes. "Two well-marked features are observed in the annual herbaceous species. Those appearing in the cold season on waste ground, or as weeds in cultivation, are mostly of European origin and are more abundant in the wheat-growing Districts of the north-west; while the annual herbage which springs up in the rains is composed mainly of species which have come from the east or from Central or Southern India"[12]—an interesting point emphasising the transitional nature of the Gangetic trough.

The Agricultural Foundations: Crops and Irrigation

The region is one of the most highly cultivated in India. Out of a total area of between 40 and 45 m. ac., nearly 27 m. are cultivated, or with double-cropping 32 m. Forests are under a million acres and current fallows, with 2 m. (nearly half in the dry SW), show a marked decline as compared with the Indus Plains; so also, unfortunately, do fodder crops, of which there are only about 1·5 m. ac.[13]

Foodcrops as usual predominate, wheat being easily first with over 6 m. ac., followed by rice ($3\frac{1}{2}$), barley ($2\frac{3}{4}$–3), jowar and bajra (together $5\frac{1}{2}$); gram ($3\frac{1}{2}$) and maize ($1\frac{1}{2}$) are also important. Of cash crops sugar-cane, especially in the moister N, is the most important, with $1\frac{1}{4}$–$1\frac{1}{2}$ m. ac., followed by oilseeds ($\frac{3}{4}$–1). Cotton is of declining importance before the competition of sugar; the half-million or so acres are mainly in the drier W. A considerable quantity of tobacco is grown, but opium and indigo are now practically negligible. On Fig. 94 we may note: (i) the high proportion of unirrigated wheat and *per contra* of irrigated rice in the NW, associated with the small but useful winter rainfall for rabi wheat and the relative falling off of mon-

---

[12] *UP Gaz.* I. 13.
[13] Owing to the difficulty of determining the precise limits of the region on the S and E these figures are more than usually approximate only. Reasonably broken down statistics are not readily available later than 1938–40, since when crop figures have probably increased slightly all round, except for cotton. This note is of general application.

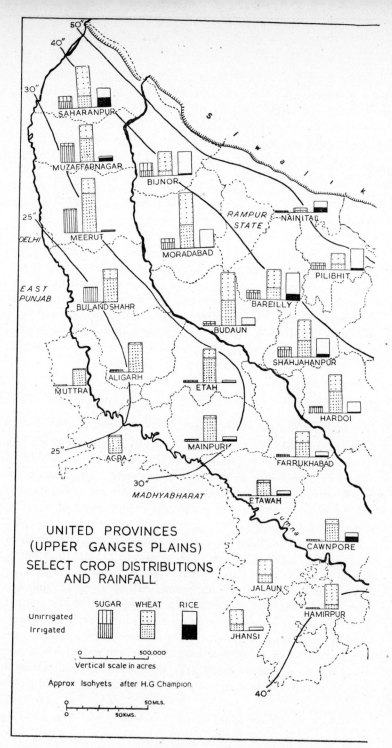

Fig. 94.—UTTAR PRADESH: SELECT CROP

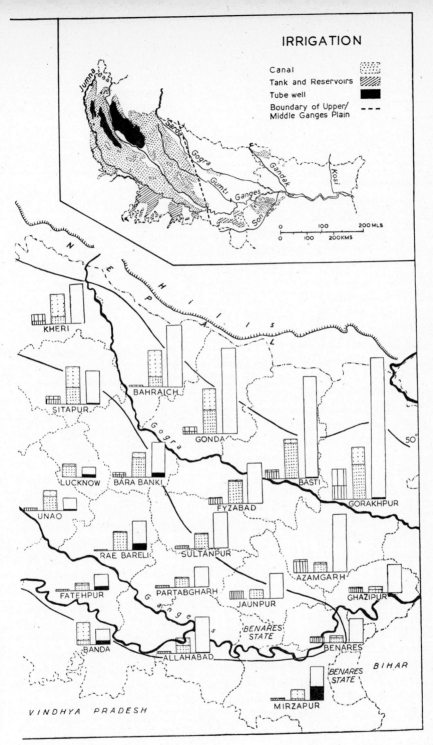

DISTRIBUTIONS, RAINFALL, AND IRRIGATION.

soon rainfall for rice; (ii) the virtual disappearance of sugar and rice in the arid or unreliably watered SW; (iii) the increasing importance of rice *vis-à-vis* wheat as we go Ewds and beyond the limits of the region. The high proportion of wheat irrigated is striking—some 60% against 15% for rice—and it must be remembered that wheat is a winter (rabi) crop and rice kharif, relying on the monsoon; of course this does not imply that paddy-fields are not flooded, but except in the khadar this is mostly by the local rain. Finally we may note the universal village mango-groves and the production of market-garden crops (especially melons, gourds, and the like) in the fertile floodplain silts near the greater towns.

Although irrigation is not such a *sine qua non* of agriculture as it is in most of the Indus Plains, the actual cultivated area, and still more the security of agriculture and the proportion under cash crops, has been greatly increased in the last few decades by irrigation. Of the 11·5 m. ac. irrigated in the UP, the great bulk is in this region (Fig. 94, inset).

The older canals are mainly in the Doab: the En Jumna (an improved version of an 18th century original), the Upper Ganges taking off at Hardwar, the sacred portal where the Ganges cuts through the Siwaliks, and the Lower Ganges. The major works for these were mostly constructed between 1850 and 1880, but there have been many improvements and a full perennial supply was not attained on the Upper Ganges Canal until 1926. The Ganges and Jumna have not such large mountain catchments as the Punjab rivers (except the Ravi) and occasionally shortages occur; these are being increasingly met by tube-well pumping into the more distant tails. The Lower Ganges headworks contains a special passage to allow sufficient water always to pass through for Hindu ritual bathing. These canals irrigate some 50% of the Doab; on the Jumna right bank is the smaller Agra Canal.

In Oudh the most important work is the Sarda Canal, first mooted in 1870 but held up for decades by the short-sighted opposition of local landlords. A proposal to take Sarda water right over to the Wn UP, however, not unnaturally produced a sudden change of front, and they then petitioned for the original project. The canal was opened in 1928, extended in 1941, and now irrigates over 1 m. ac.; an extension of the Sarda by 300,000 ac. is planned, and an additional 400,000 ac. from various small schemes.

Besides the canal systems a considerable area in the dry Sn margins is irrigated from large reservoirs in the valleys of the Peninsular foreland. But most interest attaches to the remarkable recent tube-well development, tapping the underground resources of the Gangetic alluvium. Experiments were made with oil-pumped tube-wells, but these proved on the whole uneconomic, and attention was turned to hydro-electric possibilities on the small artificial falls which adjust the slopes of the canals to those of the country they traverse and promote an even flow. The natural fall of the Upper Ganges Canal is about 146 ft, broken into 13 vertical falls of 6–12 ft each. Some of these have been utilised for small hydel stations, generating altogether about 20,000 kW. These are linked into a grid, with supplementary and stand-by thermal stations, and provide the power for about 2000 tube wells; a further 600 are projected. These are located on the higher parts of the doabs on each side of the Ganges, and have been especially valuable in the great *bhur* tract in Moradabad and Bijnor, which is unsuitable for canal irrigation. Each well commands an area of about two sq mls, with up to 1000 ac. of cultivable land; altogether 750,000 ac. were thus irrigated in 1941–42. The water-supply, held up in lenticular aquifers at depth, seems to be well in excess of any likely withdrawals and there is still great scope for extension of the method. In addition to working the wells the grid brings electric light—otherwise almost unknown in really rural India—to many villages, and there is an increasing demand for power for small agricultural processing industries such as sugar-cane crushing; the application of electricity to such purposes represents an important reduction in the usually exorbitant demands on the energies of underbred and underfed cattle. Power pumping also enables water to be lifted from the Ramganga, otherwise useless for irrigation owing to the enormous variation in its discharge (from 20 to 100,000 cusecs) which would make ordinary canal methods utterly uneconomic.[14]

It is hardly too much to say that the success of the tube-well scheme bids fair to revolutionise rural life in its area; not the least promising aspect is the supply of cheap power for badly needed light rural industries; and, perhaps most important of all, the scheme has led the way to the exploitation of the vast potential resource of underground water at depth.

Agricultural Life

In many ways the region provides a type-section of Indian agrarian life and problems. As usual cultivating holdings are small; they average 13 ac. in the arid SW, but for the UP as a whole over 80% are under 5 ac. This is too small for really efficient farming and the evil is made worse by fragmentation. The UP in general, and Oudh in particular, were largely the domain of big landlords, often absentees; but the Partition obviously weakened the Muslim *taluqdars* of Oudh, and the long-mooted legislation to abolish the *zamindari* (landlord) system is now being carried into effect; land is now vested in the State as in *ryotwari* provinces. Despite, or rather because of, the fertility and good rain of most of the region, population presses very hardly on resources; between the Jumna and the Gogra almost the entire area has District densities of **600–800**, reaching **948** in Meerut, and this without much urbanism. Farming methods, except in the NW, are primitive, debt is high, and the cattle problem is perhaps the most

[14] Most of these facts are drawn from P. K. Dutt, *Power Resources and Utilization in the UP* (London M.A. thesis, 1947); see also A. H. Siddiqi, "A Regional Study of the Budaun District", *IGJ* XXV (1950), 16–33.

serious in India. The cultivator has very inadequate storage and market facilities and is still the prey of the moneylender, retail seller, and grain-broker, often one and the same person.

The division between kharif and rabi is of great importance; the chief kharif crops, besides rice, are maize, millets, and cotton; wheat, barley, gram, and oilseeds are rabi. The agricultural year begins with the onset of the rains and has the following rhythm:

mid-June to mid-July . . .	kharif sowing
August through September .	tillage for rabi
early October to early November	kharif harvest, rabi sowing
December to mid-February	weeding and irrigation of rabi
March to mid-April . .	rabi harvest
mid-April to mid-May . .	threshing and sale of rabi
mid-May to June . . .	culture of cane in irrigated land.

The most striking development of recent years has been the supplanting of cotton by sugar-cane as the chief cash crop. The State has fully shared in the increasing production of sugar since protection was introduced in 1931 and normally has over half the *Indian* cane area. Cotton on the other hand has seriously decreased. The average acreages in the UP under cotton and cane from 1901–02 to 1930–31 were respectively 1,075,000 and 1,321,000, but in recent years the sugar acreage has been about ten or twenty times that of cotton.

The cattle population of the UP is very heavy—90 per 100 acres sown as compared with the All-India (including Pakistan) average of 67. Except in the extreme N and the extreme S, the terai and Peninsular margins, there is very little grazing—the human population is far too thick on the ground. Cattle are grazed on stubble fields after the harvest (in itself a practice inhibiting improved husbandry in hedgeless and fenceless fields); but otherwise they are as a rule left to pick up what they can get on road-side verges and meagre patches of waste, generally carrying more weeds than grass, and quite burnt up in the hot weather. By May most of the beasts look like tottering skeletons, and in the SW even in mid-rains the buffaloes present a shocking appearance to eyes accustomed to the sleekness of Burma. Eugenic practices are at a discount in the heart of Hindu India; there are about 6,000,000 cows to 26,000 bulls, and even allowing a million for old and useless cows this still leaves 200 cows for one overworked bull; a reasonable allowance is 50–60.[15] The cattle are thus individually weak in proportion to their excessive numbers, in many places not strong enough to draw a modern plough. The cultivator, looking for a tangible return, either in food or in cash, from his crops, is generally loath to "waste" time and space—still less irrigation water which has to be paid for—on fodder

[15] Rahman, *op. cit.*, 216.

crops. The large jowar stalks do provide fodder, but the use of oilcake is as yet neglected. Significantly enough, it is only in Saharanpur, Muzaffarnagar, and Meerut Dts, with winter rain and better farming (and perhaps Punjab influence), that fodder crops account for more than 10% of the TSA. Except near the terai and the riverain jungles there are few or no fuel reserves and little or no space in which to create them, and in consequence cattle dung has to be used for fuel rather than manure. The reclamation of some of the Jumna badlands with quick-growing grasses and bushes may do something to relieve this joint fodder-fuel problem locally. But on the whole the region is thoroughly typical of India in its interlocking vicious circles of agrarian poverty and inefficiency.

Settlement, Communications

Settlements are generally nucleated in large and remarkably evenly spaced villages, though there are of course interesting variations in detail, among them the common preference for new or old river-bluffs as settlement-lines; in some cases a large village on the *dhaya* will have an offshoot in the fertile but insecure silts of the floodplain below. The general characteristics of the villages are well described by Rahman, with specific reference to Sn Oudh:

> These villages form large enceintes of sun-dried brick huts. In the centre one sometimes finds a few masonry houses and the Pukka Haveli, a small burnt-brick house belonging to the landlord or moneylender. The huts of the lower castes are found on the outskirts of the village. There are generally two or three entrances to the village, but the absence of main roads shows that it is self-sufficing. Each village has one or two temples or shrines. Where water is sufficiently abundant, the village pond is surrounded by groves of neem, pipal, and plantains, a splash of green pleasantly breaking the monotony of the grey and drab houses.[16]

In the terai and the arid margins the villages are naturally smaller and poorer; in more intensively cultivated areas there is severe competition for space between fields and houses, and villages "reach the densities of industrial towns, sometimes 600 to the acre". In the extreme W and SW the flat roofs of SW Asia still predominate—here "the sun is more to be feared than the rains"; farther E brushwood covered with mud is used for roofing, and in the more humid extreme E huts are gabled and thatched; a very significant transition.[17]

True urbanism is slight, though there are a very large number of "towns" of the 5000–10,000 class; but as Rahman remarks, "all the towns, except the

---

[16] *Op. cit.*, 84–85. Unfortunately space does not permit even a summary of the important work of Enayat Ahmad: *Settlements in the UP* (London Ph.D. thesis, 1949). This fascinating study is the best and most detailed known to the writer on any large Indian area.
[17] Cf. J. Sion, *Asie des Moussons* (*Géographie Universelle*, T. IX Pt. I, Paris, 1929), 312.

largest, have something of the aspect of village life". There can be no more
striking testimony to the broad homogeneity of the plains than the approximation of the distribution of smaller towns and larger villages to Christaller's
hypothetical diagram of the service-centre and its region, although owing
to the very different conditions of Nn India and Sn Germany the analogy
must not be pressed too hard. Nevertheless in Fig. 95 Etah and Aligarh at

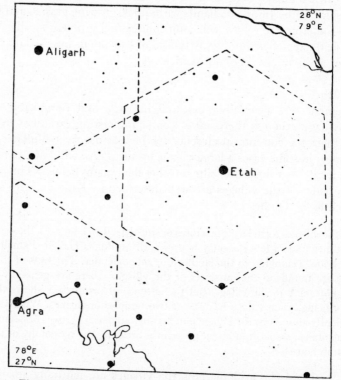

Fig. 95.—Settlement Spacing on the Jumna/Ganges Doab.
Whole area of SOI 54 I. Largest circles are District capitals, medium
tahsil headquarters, dots larger villages. Broken lines represent
Christaller 'service regions' for the 3 large towns; the distinct approximation of this theoretical construct to the actual spacing of
larger and smaller centres will be noted. Distance between centres
and angles of hexagons, 22·5 mls.

least correspond well in size and function to the county town of 30,000 to
100,000 inhabitants.[18] The five great cities of the UP, Cawnpore, Lucknow,
Agra, Benares, and Allahabad, have each a distinctive individuality; below
them come the more generalised bigger administrative and commercial
centres. Many of these grew up around the forts (*garh*) of petty magnates
playing their own hands in times of trouble, Rajputs, Rohillas, Marathas;

[18] Cf. R. E. Dickinson, *City, Region, and Regionalism* (1947), 30–35.

others are later creations, nodal points on road or rail, and the eponymous headquarters of Districts or tahsils. The larger have attracted some industry, generally in straight association with the agricultural milieu: such are the great wheat, sugar, or cotton commodity markets Meerut, Muzaffarnagar, Aligarh, Bareilly, all occupying central sites on their doabs. Such towns generally have populations between 50,000 and 100,000. Aligarh is of interest as the seat of the Muslim University, until 1947 at least probably the most important centre of geographical studies in India. The small town of Hapur (Meerut Dt) is the biggest wheat market of the UP.

There is a good railnet, but road development is very inadequate: for the whole of the UP only 8600 miles of metalled road in 1944, about one mile to 13 sq mls or 6400 people. Until the railways came, river traffic was of great importance and exercised a strong influence on the siting and layout of towns; but apart from the usual slowness of water transport, the frequent changes of course, fluctuating volumes and speeds, and numerous sandbanks of the rivers were unfavourable to steamer navigation. The Bengal and North-Western Rly still runs small steamboats on the Gogra during the rains, between Ayodhya (Fyzabad) and Lakarmandi,[19] and the Gogra and Ganges carry a certain amount of local traffic by country boats with a capacity of up to 70 tons avoirdupois. The Ganges is still navigated from Calcutta to Buxar in Bihar (1000 miles), and the navigation may be carried on another 200 miles to Allahabad. Animal transport is still of great importance—bullock and buffalo carts (generally of wastefully heavy construction, mechanically inefficient and ruinous to roads), pack donkeys, and in the SW even camels.

Industry

The region is devoid of significant mineral resources and power is as yet little developed, although four important schemes are proposed. These are (i) the reconstruction of the Sarda Main Canal to form one fall of 59 ft, generating 20–40,000 kW, to link with the Ganges grid and to serve Nn Oudh; (ii) a dam 650 ft high across the Nayar, a tributary of the Ganges 50 miles above Hardwar, to produce 233,000 kW besides irrigation water (this scheme is apparently shelved); (iii) another large dam near Pipri in Mirzapur District, planned to produce 230,000 kW; (iv) the Yamuna scheme, 257,000 kW. Besides these are a number of minor and thermal projects totalling *c.* 137,000 kW. By no means all of these are likely to mature.

Meanwhile, apart from the great industrial centre of Cawnpore (treated separately), industry is practically confined to (i) agricultural processing and textiles; (ii) small consumption goods (especially glass), whether survivals of old luxury trades or to meet modern urban needs; (iii) the usual village

[19] Rahman, *op. cit.*, 94–95.

maintenance crafts—tanning, carpentry, pottery, and the like—and hand-loom weaving, which still employs about 250,000 workers.

(i) The chief processing industries are naturally sugar-refining and oil-seed-pressing. The refineries have the advantage of producing their own fuel in the refuse of the cane, *bégasse*; there are about 70 modern vacuum-pan factories, but less advanced open-pan works are still numerous, and much *gur* (unrefined brown sugar) is produced by still more primitive methods in the villages. Nearly a quarter (40–50,000) of the industrial workers of the UP are employed in sugar-refineries, but many of these are seasonal. Cotton ginneries and presses employ only about 1000 hands, but cotton mills 56,000, naturally mostly in the W—Cawnpore, Aligarh, Meerut, Bareilly, Agra, Moradabad, and Hathras, with an outlier at Benares.

(ii) The chief centres for luxury trades and for arts such as brassware, ivories, silks and gold- and silver-thread embroideries, and jewellery, and for the finer craft-produced textiles such as shawls and printed calicoes, are Agra, Benares, and Lucknow. The associations are clear: the patronage of the extravagant Court of the Nawabs of Oudh at Lucknow, the tourist attractions of Agra, the great flow of pilgrims to Benares. More modern trades, mainly in the five great cities but with outliers in such towns as Meerut and Aligarh, include paper, matches, paints and chemicals, soaps and cosmetics, hosiery, and a variety of small metal goods. Perhaps the most individual and important is glass; excluding those devoted solely to bangles, UP has about two-fifths of the glass factories and half the workers of *India*, but as these fractions come to about 60 factories and under 5000 employees the total does not amount to much. A third of these factories are in Agra Dt alone. Glass works are mainly over towards the Vindhyan margins whence they get their sand; Firozabad is the centre of the important bangle trade, in part a cottage industry (cf. p. 299).

(iii) Village industries play a very important part in the life of the people but hardly enter into the wider trade currents. It is of course possible, and much to be desired, that the introduction of hydro-electric power will lead to an increasing development of light rural industries.

The Five Cities

The UP had the largest Muslim minority of any non-Muslim province of the Indian Empire—over 15% in 1941—and, as the intrusive commun-ity, an unusually high proportion (30·6%) of the Muslims were urban, while as landowners and officials they had a larger share of influence than their numbers would account for, again an inheritance from the Kingdom of Oudh. It is noteworthy that the Muslim University was in the UP and not in the more Muslim Punjab.

Of the five great cities of the UP one, Benares, is in the Middle Ganges

Plain region; but together they form a curious cross-section of Indian cultural history and for that reason it is more interesting, if admittedly not very logical, to treat Benares with the rest. Benares, then, and Allahabad represent the heroic and mediaeval ages of Hindu civilisation; Agra is a relic of the Mogul heyday, the apogee of Islam in India, Lucknow conversely of the post-Mogul Muslim decadence; while Cawnpore typifies Indo-British civilisation, in both its earlier John Company phase and that of the modern economic revolution.[20]

The origins of Benares or Kasi (**355,777**) are unknown but very ancient; at its old site, Sarnath, a few miles to the N, is the deer park where Buddha commenced his mission. But during the Muslim invasions so notorious a centre of idolatry fell on evil days, and most of the temples are relatively recent, many being built by Maratha princes in the 18th century. The city lies along the Ganges, on a *kankar* ridge, for about four miles; and the curving riverfront is lined by great flights of steps, the bathing ghats, and by massive temples, in turn tawdry and splendid. Behind these is a labyrinth of narrow fetid alleys, overhung by tall galleried houses, with innumerable shrines "ranging from a shapeless fragment of stone smeared with vermilion to magnificent temples". The streets are crowded with priests, mendicants, and touts, and their pilgrim prey, and through the turmoil the sacred bulls of Siva lounge arrogantly. In Christian countries the odour of excessive sanctity has not infrequently a commercial taint, but in Benares it is all-pervading. The resort of Hindu princes and rich men, either on pilgrimage or to end their days, brings much trade, and Benares is noted for fine silks and embroideries and for cheap brassware, which last is largely intended for the tourist trade and of suitably atrocious design. There is also a certain amount of modern industry; but essentially Benares lives parasitically on its past and on the exploitation both of genuine piety and of superstition. It is also, appropriately, the seat of the Hindu University.[21]

Allahabad (**332,295**), the ancient Prayag, is at the junction of Jumna and Ganges—obviously a sacred site, and made more so by the legendary underground confluence of the Sarasvati; at Benares the lack of a confluence (other than that of the insignificant Barna) is compensated by the meeting of five rivers at the Panchganga Ghat, of which "the Ganges alone is visible to the gross material eyes" of geographers. The great Fort in the angle of the rivers was built by Akbar; beneath it, on the dry sandbanks, is

---

[20] For fuller treatment, see O. H. K. Spate and E. Ahmad, "Five Cities of the Gangetic Plain: A Cross-Section of Indian Cultural History", *GR* XL (1950), 260–78. All quotations in this section are from *UP Gaz.*

[21] Lest these remarks be ascribed to Western materialism (the great Aunt Sally of Indian publicists) and offensive British insularity, I may mention that they are largely based on, and a faint reflection of, Mahatma Gandhi's disgusted description of the greed with which the pious are despoiled and of the revolting fakes—such as five-legged cows—produced by the allegedly religious for their edification. See his admirable autobiography, *My Experiments with Truth* (Ahmedabad, 1927, and other eds.; Pt III, Ch. XX, and Pt V, Ch. VII). I trust that this is an untainted source.

held the annual Magh Mela fair, which attracts about 250,000 people; every twelfth year the Kumbh Mela gathers together perhaps the greatest known assemblies of human beings on one site, over a million people sometimes attending. The old city lies along the Jumna; to the N, on a long terrace-like tongue of higher ground between the rivers, extend the rectilinear Civil Lines and the Cantonments. There is some industry, but Allahabad is more important as an administrative and legal centre.

Agra (**375,665**) lay originally on the left bank of the Jumna, but Akbar moved it to the strategically better Wn side, where the route into Malwa and the Deccan diverges from the great arc of the Jumna. Much of the city is filthy, squalid, and ruinous, and even the Civil Lines are shabby and ill-planned; the suburbs are in places made hideous by ravines used as refuse dumps. But central Agra contains some of the glories of Mogul architecture: the serene strength of Akbar's Fort, the exquisite Pearl Mosque and the little kiosks looking from the Fort walls to the Taj; less successful is the Jama Masjid with its bizarre zigzag striped domes. For thousands the Taj Mahal symbolises India; by the time (1631–48) that Shah Jahan was building this sumptuous mausoleum for his favourite wife Mumtaz Mahal there was some decline from the strength of Akbar's building, and the dazzling white marble is less beautiful than the rich reds of the Vindhyan sandstone favoured in the preceding century; but despite serious defects the Taj remains a beautiful building, not least in its setting, a great red-walled formal garden, by the river. Few visitors go on to Akbar's soon-deserted capital at Fatehpur Sikri, 22 miles away; those who do are the richer by an unforgettable aesthetic experience. In its originality and daring ingenuity, in the combination of the towering magnificence of the great Gate of Victory with the charming fantasy of the smaller buildings, Fatehpur undoubtedly represents the peak of Mogul architecture, at its best perhaps the most satisfying style in the world. Looking out over the populated and yet in appearance lonely landscape, it is a far cry to the squalor of modern Agra, with its crafts degenerated to supplying shoddy alabaster models of the Taj to the tourist trade. Agra has some cotton mills, a considerable craft production of woollen carpets and *durris*, and great hide and wool markets.

If in Agra and Fatehpur we are in a rich dreamland, in Lucknow we have entered the realm of lunatic fantasy. Like the Mogul centres, Lucknow was built on the sordid exploitation of the peasant masses; but at least the Mogul dignity and splendour show tangibly their imperial standards of culture and catholicity of interests; the clumsy and garish provincialism of Lucknow, the bastard progeny of debased Oriental and debased European models, reflects an appalling decadence. There are a few solid and relatively restrained buildings, and it must be admitted that the Nawabs of Oudh have had a bad press; but all allowance made, their private morals, their public administration, and their taste seem to have been all on one

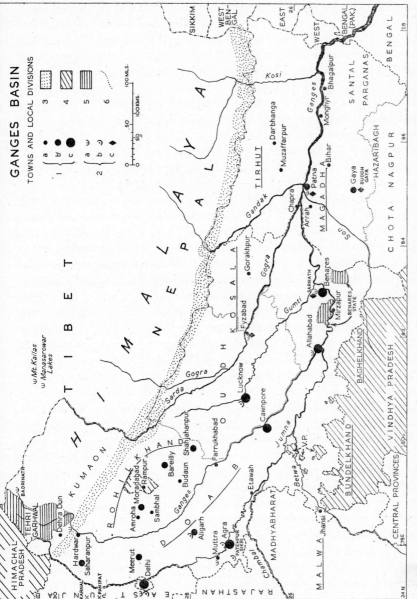

Fig. 96.—THE GANGES BASIN: GENERAL. 1, towns of (a) 50–100,000, (b) 100–250,000, (c) over 250,000 popⁿ; 2, religious or cultural centres (a) Hindu, (b) Muslim, (c) Buddhist; 3, bhabar and terai; 4, old states now under centre; 5, old states merged in UP (Rampur should now be added); 6, Agra/Oudh and Bihar proper/Chota Nagpur boundaries. Historic and regional names underlined.

level, and that depraved. "Buildings, which look like marble by moonlight, are shown by the disillusioning sun to be degraded examples of stucco and brick. Flying buttresses to support nothing but one another, copper domes gilt from top to bottom, burnished umbrellas, and balustrades of baked clay" form a gallery of architectural horror perhaps matched only in the Indo-British buildings of Bombay. The city was of little importance until the 18th century; modern Lucknow (**496,861**) sprawls over an immense area S of the Gumti, which is bordered by a belt of open spaces surrounding the tawdry palaces. Lucknow has a considerable industrial development, including rail shops, paper and cotton mills, sugar-refineries, and a wide range of light consumption trades.

Cawnpore in the 18th century was a mere village, but between 1931 and 1941 it outstripped Lucknow and in the latter year had 487,324 inhabitants; it has since grown rapidly (without control) to **705,383** under the stimulus of the war industrial demand. In Company days a military and trade station—like Lucknow a Mutiny storm-centre—its real rise also began under war conditions, when the American Civil War created a sudden demand for Indian cotton. Cawnpore had then just been linked by rail to Calcutta and promptly became a boom town. "Lands covered with the mud huts of camp-followers were hastily taken up by the authorities. Commissariat elephants were brought out to push down the frail erections in order to clear space for the bales of cotton which, piled up level with the roofs, had been blocking every lane in the city. At the same time the ordinary country produce of the Doab and of Oudh began to pour in here instead of passing along the river." Unlike most of the riverain cities except Lucknow, Cawnpore has its close-built area a mile back from the Ganges, which is bordered on the N by the older industrial area, on the S by more open suburbs; while inland from the old city is a great mass of new factories and industrial housing, if housing it can be called. Cawnpore is now the greatest industrial city of India after Ahmedabad, and has a more varied activity than that predominantly cotton centre. It is the greatest woollens and leather centre of India, and has also cotton, flour, and vegetable oil mills, sugar refineries, small chemical works, and many minor industries, among which the manufacture of brushes (associated with its importance as a tanning centre) may be mentioned. The first cotton mills were built between 1869 and 1882, so that Cawnpore ranks as one of the older of the factory cities of India. There is a true proletariat here, and in many cases living conditions are little better than those of the first boom days, so it is not surprising that Cawnpore labour disputes have been bitter.

The Middle Ganges Plains

Reverting to the discussion of the regional division of the Ganges lowland, we may define the Middle Ganges Plains as simply what is left between the Upper Ganges Plains and Bengal: roughly the En third of UP and the Nn half of Bihar. The only real difficulty (once we have settled on the boundary in the indeterminate passage-zone of Oudh) is in the E, where there is no marked difference between Purnea Dt of Bihar and adjoining Bengal. Despite the Partition of that Province, however, the set of rivers, communications, and life in Nn Bengal is so distinctly to the S that it is better to regard the doab between the great bends of Ganges and Brahmaputra as a sub-region of Bengal; we may thus make a virtue of convenience and take the State boundary as our En limit. The Middle Ganges region thus defined is very comparable to the Upper Ganges Plains in area —about 62,000 against 65,000 sq mls—and also in topography; as already stressed, the major variable is climate.

Climate and Topography

In both these respects the region is obviously transitional between the relatively dry, mainly bhangar, doabs of the Upper Ganges Plain, and humid, largely khadar, Bengal. About 90% of the rainfall is from the monsoon, except in the extreme NE, where the hot weather 'nor'-wester' thunderstorms of Bengal bring some 6 ins. to Purnea in March–May inclusive; but even here the monsoon proportion falls only to 87%. Spatially the rainfall shows a steady decrease from 70 ins. or more on the En to a little over 40 on the Wn margins; and there is also, as in the Upper Ganges Plains, marked decrease from the Himalayas to the Ganges: while the main mass of the region receives 45–55 ins., the extreme N has around 60. Mean minimum and maximum temperatures in December–January are around 50 and 85° F, and there are no frosts; mean maxima in May exceed 100°.

Rainfall is intense in incidence, the average fall on a rainy day being 0.75–1 in.; although real droughts are rare, the monsoon is sufficiently variable to introduce insecurity. The rains tail off in October and variability is then most likely and on the whole most serious, since a premature cessation may involve both failure of standing kharif and very unfavourable sowing conditions for the rabi.

The whole area, with very minor exceptions, lies below 500 ft, falling to under 100 in the E. Physiographically it is of course much the same as the Upper Ganges Plains, but still there are some broad differences. Foremost of these is naturally the greater development of khadar, though most of Nn Bihar is still bhangar.

The monsoon rainfall on the Himalayas becomes increasingly heavy as the Bay of Bengal is approached, and the rivers draining them are consequently subject to extremely violent fluctuations in volume and course. In the E the Kosi is especially notorious, with rises of 30 ft in 24 hours. From its montane catchment of about 24,000 sq mls, largely in shales and sandstones, "the charge of detritus and sand is so great that, despite a flood discharge of about 200,000 cusecs, the river has no permanent deep channel, but . . . tears through the flat country in numerous capricious channels". Its general movement, of course with regressions, is to the W (i.e. cutting into the right bank, like other Nn hemisphere rivers), and two centuries ago it flowed by Purnea town; between 1934 and 1936 its lower course shifted 12 miles to the W. A wide tract is scarred with its abandoned channels—the numerous Burhi (old) or Mara (dead) Kosis. The Kosi has been responsible for enormous devastation by flood or by spreads of micaceous sand: "How quickly and deeply it can overlay the country is apparent from the fate of indigo factories which have been abandoned owing to its encroachments. In comparatively few years all that can be seen of them is the chimneys, for the buildings are buried deep in sand." [22] It is no wonder that the taming of the Kosi has caught the imagination of *India*.

Devastating also, but to a less extent, have been the other great rivers, Gogra, Great Gandak, Burhi Gandak, Kamla. Their khadar floodplains are wider than in the Upper Ganges Plains, and even on the doabs there are many *jhils*, more or less permanent lakes, and *chaurs*—"long semi-circular marshes which develop into a vast and intricate chain of temporary lakes during the rainy season"; one such chain, an old course of the Great Gandak, covers 140 sq mls when full. The landscape is thus rather more diversified and of distinctly more humid aspect than that of Wn UP. Perhaps associated with this is the fact that Bihar has the biggest output of freshwater fish in *India*.

S of the Ganges the alluvial filling is shallow, a mere veneer; the Peninsular edge is very ragged, and many groups of small craggy hills (up to 1600 ft) form islands of bare rock or scrub. This alluvial strip is some 85 miles wide in the W, where the Son makes a great deltaic re-entrant into the older rocks; but in the E the Rajmahal Hills, the extreme NE of the Peninsula, abut almost directly onto the Ganges. Most of this fringing plain is bhangar, and inundated areas are fewer than N of the Ganges in Tirhut. But they are not unimportant. The Ganges bank itself lies high, except in Shahabad Dt, and at high water the tributaries are ponded back; the Punpun valley, parallel to the Son on the E, is thus annually flooded. Both N and S of Ganges the construction of railways athwart the drainage causes local, but sometimes disastrous, waterlogging and flooding. Some of these temporary inundations, however, are agriculturally useful; rabi crops are grown on them when they dry out, or they are bunded for dry-weather rice.

The khadar consists largely of light sandy loams; most of the area more

---

[22] L. S. S. O'Malley, *Bengal, Bihar and Orissa, Sikkim* (1917), 49. This may throw some doubt on Strickland's clear distinction (522–25 *passim*) between deltaic (depositional) and paradeltaic (erosional) areas; unless indeed we regard such areas as inland deltas, which in many ways they are. The scale, and the gentleness of slope, are perhaps too great for the terms alluvial fan or cone to be appropriate; might not 'pediment delta' be useful?

than 20 miles N and E of Great Gandak and Ganges is *matiyar* clay with some loams. The *diaras* or alluvial islands in the great rivers are mostly sandy, as is the wide tract wasted by Kosi. S of Ganges heavier loams and clays prevail.

Very little of the natural vegetation is left. In the N the terai carries sal forest and tall reedy grasses; but most of the unreclaimed terai lies beyond the Nepal border, Bihar having a mere ribbon E of the Kosi and some 4 miles wide. The riverain strips and *diaras* have of course the usual jungle of sissoo, tamarisk, and reeds.[23]

Agriculture

The region is perhaps rather less diversified agriculturally than is the Upper Ganges Plain, although most of the drier crops of the W continue into Bihar, and in the E a new one, jute, appears; since Partition it has been forced into En UP, in the wetter terai.

Of a total area of about 37·5 m. ac. the NSA amounts to about 22 and TSA to about 30 m.—the big difference reflecting increased humidity and the greater area of easily inundable khadar. Rice easily leads with 10 m. ac. (NSA), followed by barley ($3\frac{1}{2}$), wheat (3), and gram ($2\frac{1}{2}$); oilseeds and sugar (each $1–1\frac{1}{4}$) are also important. Cotton fades out—there are only about 25,000 ac.—but in the E jute is increasingly important and no longer confined to Purnea; Bihar and UP had between them 555,000 ac. in 1951–52.

The broad change from W to E can perhaps be best seen by comparing the six Divisions wholly or mainly within the region: Benares, Fyzabad, and Gorakhpur in UP, Tirhut, Patna, and Bhagalpur in Bihar (Fig. 97). Rice is easily the dominant in all of them; in Fyzabad wheat acreage is still over half that of rice, but in the E it has fallen to 12–15%. Except in Benares and Fyzabad jowar and bajra are negligible, and in these two Divisions oilseeds are of little importance. Sugar, with its heavy demand for moisture, is a crop of the N; gram is strongest in Patna, which has considerable areas of the Peninsular Foreland, not readily separable from the plains.

It is unfortunately impossible to make a direct comparison of the role of irrigation in the Upper and Middle Ganges Plains, since the statistics of irrigation in Bihar appear to mean something quite different from those of UP.[24] The increase in irrigated rice might be taken as referring to the double paddy harvest, but the decrease in irrigated wheat is not so easily

---

[23] This section is largely based on P. Dayal, *The Agricultural Geography of Bihar* (London Ph.D. thesis, 1947), Chs. I–IV. These chapters give an interesting revelation of the amount of variety—or rather perhaps repetition of standard variations—found in what appears at first sight a nearly featureless plain.

[24] It is indeed quite impossible to say what they do mean, as may be seen from the remarkable figures for Bhagalpur quoted on 200 above. Obviously the usual warnings about agricultural statistics apply with peculiar force here. . . .

explicable. In Bihar some 25% of the NSA is irrigated, against 31% in UP; but the former figure is swollen by primitive irrigation on the plateaus on Sn Bihar, and in the main lowland N of Ganges the figure is under 20%, falling to under 5% in Purnea. Large-scale canal irrigation is almost confined to the Son Valley, where climatic conditions are normally insecure but topography exceptionally favourable, with a slope of 2–3 ft per mile and no drainage lines to cross. The Son Canals irrigate some 600,000 ac., including some 30% of the NSA of Shahabad Dt. The rest of the plain S of Ganges is mostly irrigated by *pynes* or *pains*, small private canals, for the most part mere inundation cuts. Some are larger and more elaborate, but they suffer from the changing and conflicting interests of the many landholders concerned, and often pass out of repair. In S Bhagalpur, Patna, and Gaya Dts they irrigate some 20–30% of NSA. The same Districts, with Shahabad, contain most of the irrigation from tanks or *ahars*. These are usually formed by bunding small streams; again they are more or less temporary, and like the

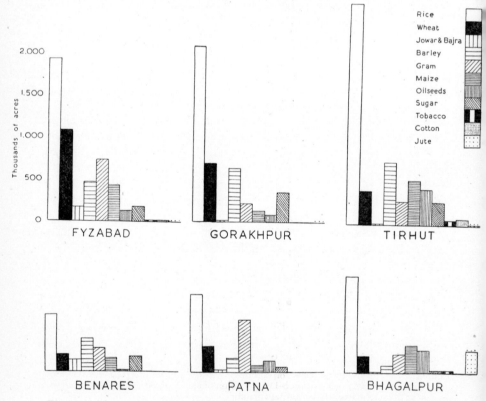

Fig. 97.—MIDDLE GANGES PLAINS: CROP DISTRIBUTIONS. By Divisions, figures for 1938–40; main change since then is the extension of jute, indicated by dots outside rectangles. Note that the lower tier includes portions of the Peninsular foreland.

pynes they suffer from neglect due to lack of co-operation. Wells are less important except in Saran, the angle between Gogra, Great Gandak, and Ganges, where they irrigate some 150,000 ac.; unlike *pynes* and *ahars*, which mainly inundate paddy-fields, the wells are chiefly used for the rabi.

The appearance of a three-harvest year marks a further stage in the transition to the humid delta: the kharif of the W is replaced by a *bhadai* (autumn) and *aghani* (winter) harvest. The gradual shift is well described by Dayal: [25]

> On account of an earlier monsoon and pre-monsoon showers in May, the agricultural season starts here earlier than in the United Provinces with the result that in place of two well-marked seasonal crops 'kharif' and 'rabi' as in the latter, we have three seasonal crops in Bihar. But the early rainfall in Bihar is neither so early nor so heavy as in Bengal. Consequently not only is the 'bhadai' harvest much less important in Bihar than in Bengal, but the crops grown are different. Moreover, while it is possible for an East Bengal cultivator to harvest his 'bhadai' crop so early as to transplant the 'aghani' rice crop on the same land, this sort of double-cropping is generally impossible in Bihar . . . the cultivator must choose between a 'bhadai' and an 'aghani' crop just as is to be found to a certain extent in Western Bengal. Further, while the area under 'rabi' crops is very small in the Ganges Delta, they occupy in Bihar an even larger acreage than the 'aghani' crops. . . . But there is a difference between the 'rabi' crops grown in Bihar and those grown in the United Provinces especially west of Allahabad. In the latter they are valuable crops like wheat, barley, oilseeds, but in Bihar a considerable amount of the 'rabi' harvest consists of inferior catch-crops such as 'khesari' [chickling-vetch] and gram, grown on the 'aghani' rice lands.

The bhadai crops—quick-growing rice, maize, millets, jute—are sown May–July and harvested August–September; they are most important in the NE, approximating to Bengal conditions. In the W the rabi acreage exceeds kharif, bhadai, and aghani combined, but in central Tirhut aghani predominates; some 90% of it is rice sown at the beginning of the rains and harvested November–December. The rabi crops are much more varied than those of the rains-sown harvests, but contribute comparatively little to local food supply, being largely cheap catch crops such as pulses or cash crops such as oilseeds, tobacco, and wheat. "Good bhadai and good rabi go hand in hand," but aghani rice stays too long on the ground to leave time for the better rabi crops; the bhadai-rabi combination also offers better security against the mischances of the seasons.

The detailed crop distribution, implicit above, calls for little comment, or else for much more than can be attempted here. We may, however, note: (i) the remarkable concentration of maize on the wedge of light loams

---

[25] *Op. cit.*, 262–63. Dayal's analysis of the correlations of soil, climate, topography, and harvests is extremely interesting, but unfortunately too detailed to summarise.

between Ganges and Burhi Gandak and on the sandy Kosi soils, and its corresponding absence on the heavy *matiyar* with its tendency to water-logging; (ii) the somewhat similar distribution of barley in En UP and Wn Bihar, but more restricted towards the E than is maize owing to the increasing rainfall and the increasing dominance of rice, barley being essentially a 'rabi after bhadai' crop; (iii) the strong localisation of sugar in Tirhut, which has 60% of the cane area and 80% of the refineries of Bihar. Finally we may note that indigo, once the greatest cash crop, has practically disappeared, the total now amounting to under 2000 ac. and apparently still declining. Opium also is now extinct. The reasons, of course, are external, the competition of synthetic dyes and the suppression of opium-growing after the agreement with China in 1911. There is some Ganges-side market gardening for the Calcutta market, 400 miles away, a very unusual development.[26]

Population and Industry

Density is very high: of the 24 Districts wholly or mainly within the region, 2 have *c.* **505** to the sq ml: these are Bahraich and Purnea in the extreme NW and NE respectively. Bahraich has a considerable area of terai, Purnea the Kosi, and both are highly malarial. Most range from **600** to **975**, while Ballia, Darbhanga, Saran, and Muzaffarpur form a block of 10,224 sq mls with densities of **1010-1182**, and this with little urbanism: Darbhanga, largest of the three towns with over 50,000 people, had only 69,203 in 1941. Benares (**1009**) and Patna (**1168**) are small Districts inflated by their eponymous capitals.

The Middle Ganges Plains showed a remarkable gap in the distribution of large towns (Fig. 26A); the whole region had only 13 towns of over 50,000, aggregating no more than 1,200,233 out of a total population between 40 and 45 m. The 88 "towns" of Bihar contain (1951) only 6·3% of its people, of major units only Assam and Orissa falling below this proportion; and, while it is true that this town population is mostly concentrated in the Middle Ganges Plain, the region as a whole is under-urbanised. The vast mass of the people, some 90–95%, live in compact villages; owing to the far more numerous water-points, however, these are generally smaller than those of the Upper Ganges Plain, most of them probably with 500–1000 inhabitants. The standard ills of the Indian countryside prevail.

Industrially the region has little importance. The most important lines are sugar-refining, mainly in the Nn zone (En UP and Tirhut), and rice-milling along the Nn borders of the region, the paddy being drawn largely from Nepal. Benares, of course, has its luxury crafts; Patna and other Ganges-side towns cotton, silk, and oil mills, railway and general engineering; at Monghyr is the largest tobacco factory of India. At Dalmianagar, in the

[26] RCAI, 595.

Son re-entrant, are cement and other industries, but these really belong to Peninsular Foreland (below, 584). Practically speaking the industrial significance of Bihar, which is immense, springs from the Damodar and the mineralised plateaus to the S. The plains may become more significant should the Kosi scheme ever come into full operation; though it has been pointed out that no survey of power demand was made. The project, designed to provide ultimately 1·8 m. kW and to irrigate 3 m. ac. (a third of it in Nepal), involves a 750 ft high dam at the Chatria gorge in Nepal, together with two other barrages. Flood and erosion control are also among the primary objects. Some progress has been made with a preliminary railway to Chatra and bridge and dam works there; this is the first of ten stages in the project, and "will pave the way for taking up subsequent stages as finances permit."[27]

As late as 1911 indigo manufacture, with 78 factories and 27,000 workers, was the leading industry of Bihar; in 1941 there were only 4 factories and 250 workers, but the presence of the old plantation tradition played some part in the growth of sugar production.[28]

Of the three important towns, Benares has already been described. Patna (**283,479**) is an ancient city; as Pataliputra it was described by Megasthenes and it was of great importance in Mauryan and Guptan days; remains of an Asokan palace lie at a considerable depth below the present level. Primarily an administrative centre, it has some, but not very significant, industry, and has given its name to the finest-quality rice. Gaya (**133,700**) lies on the very margin of the plain and is most famous for its Buddhist associations: the Enlightenment took place at Buddh Gaya, 6 miles to the S. It has a few mills (rice, cotton, oil) and railway shops, and craft industries are still carried on, largely, of course, the manufacture of small images for the pilgrim trade.

Sarnath, near Benares, and Gaya are the places most associated with the life and work of Buddha, greatest of all teachers who have walked Indian roads; and for a few centuries on either side of the beginning of the Christian era this region, Magadha, was the focus of the most flourishing civilisation of India. But in modern times the Middle Ganges Plain seems to lack individuality. It has indeed great interest for the geographer, but this is as illustrating the transition from the drier plains of the W to the Delta rather than by any distinctive regional quality of its own.

BIBLIOGRAPHICAL NOTE

Most of the works used are cited in the footnotes. To them may be added:
R. K. Mukerjee, *The Regional Balance of Man* (Madras, 1938). A very full study of 'human ecology'.

---

[27] *IR* II. 23 (17.6.50).
[28] S. A. Majid, *The Industrial Geography of Bihar* (London Ph.D. thesis, 1949), 41.

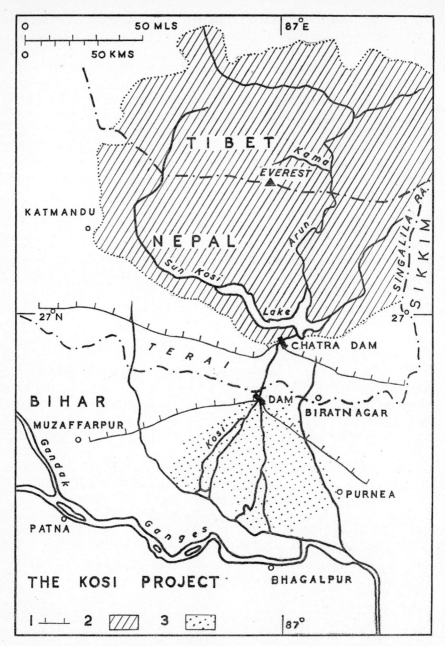

Fig. 98.—THE KOSI PROJECT. 1, proposed canals; 2, catchment; 3, approx. area liable to Kosi floods. Adapted from map in *New Projects for Irrigation and Power in India* (Simla, 2nd ed., 1948); courtesy of CBI.

B. Ganguli, *Trends of Agriculture and Population in the Ganges Valley* (1938). A very thorough and detailed study of the agricultural economics of the whole valley from Delhi to Dacca.

R. McLeod, *Impressions of an Indian Civil Servant* (1938). Rather thin, but gives some background.

Report of the Terai and Bhabar Development Committee (UP Govt, Allahabad (1947)).

The extremely interesting history of indigo planting is set out in D. H. Buchanan, *The Development of Capitalistic Enterprise in India* (1934), Ch. III.

For the Indo-Gangetic Divide, as well as the Darling references (see Bibliographical Note to Ch. XVII), there are F. L. Brayne's books on the 'Gurgaon Experiment'—*The Remaking of Village India* (1929) and *Socrates in an Indian Village* (1929).

The section on the Middle Ganges Plains owes much to theses by my old students Drs P. Dayal and S. A. Majid; between them they cover nearly all aspects of Bihar geography in admirable detail. Other London theses worthy of note are: S. M. T. Rizvi, *Economic and Regional Geography of UP* (Ph.D., 1937); V. N. S. Mathur, *Economic Geography of Western UP* (M.A., 1938); S. M. Ali, *A Geographical Study of the Ghaggar Plain* (Ph.D., 1939).

CHAPTER XIX

BENGAL
(Region XIII)

The Region and its Sub-divisions

ALMOST the entire area of the old Province of Bengal is, in a popular sense, deltaic—it has been succinctly described as "new mud, old mud, and marsh"—and if we take in all the areas of generally deltaic aspect, including the Surma Valley, it is probably the largest delta in the world. But in a strict sense the Ganges, Ganges-Brahmaputra, or Bengal Delta is much smaller, and by no means easy to define. The whole of Bengal [1] (apart from the highland fringes in the extreme N, SW, and SE) has, however, a common structural history and a very similar way of life based on rice; it had for some centuries possessed an historic entity, and, except for the brief interlude of Curzon's partition (1905–11), it was until 1947 a linguistic and cultural unit focussed on Calcutta. It would therefore be difficult to divide it into more than one region, on the scale on which that term has to be used in a book treating of a sub-continent.

Nevertheless there is a good deal of physiographic variety within the general pattern of alluvial and detrital plains, and sub-division is necessary. The general limits may be taken as roughly those of the Province, less the Himalayan fringe in Darjeeling Dt and the definitely non-alluvial margins of the Peninsular block in the W, but plus most of Sylhet Dt of Assam. The regional boundary is then that of the alluvium and the older rock of the surrounding hills; in the NE and NW, where the alluvium is of course continuous into the Brahmaputra and Ganges Valleys, the political boundaries of Assam and Bihar respectively are taken for convenience. The area thus defined is approximately 80,000 sq mls with a 1941 population of 63,000,000.

The main bulk of the region is taken up by the true Delta and the great mass of alluvial fans—Strickland's paradelta—to the N. There have been many attempts at defining the Delta, most of which appear decidedly odd to a geographer. No purpose would be served by reviewing them here; this has been done by Bagchi, and on the whole his delimitation and sub-division appear valid, and in fair conformity with Strickland's distinction between "the area of transcendent deposition", the delta, and "that of corrasion", the paradelta.[2]

---

[1] Bengal used without qualification of E or W refers to the Province as existing before the 1947 Partition.

[2] Kanangopal Bagchi, *The Ganges Delta* (Calcutta, 1944), Chs. I–III; C. Strickland, *Deltaic Formation with special reference to the hydrographic processes of the Ganges and the Brahmaputra* (Calcutta, 1940), 8.

We have then (Fig. 99):

I. the sub-montane terai, here known as the Duars;

II. the Nn paradelta, or the Ganges-Brahmaputra doab and the Barind;

III. the En margins: the Surma Valley, the plains along the Meghna and
      along the Chittagong coast;

IV. the Wn margins: (i) the largely lateritic piedmont plain between

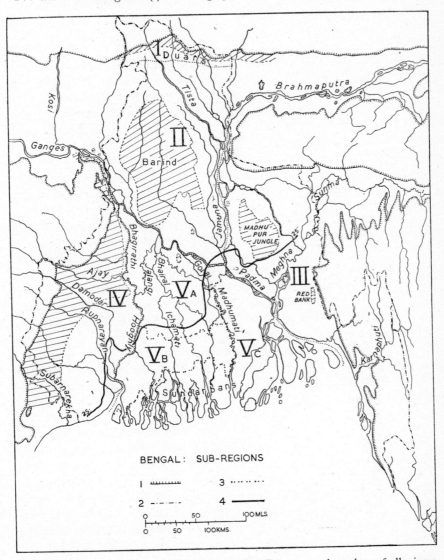

Fig. 99.—BENGAL: PHYSICAL FEATURES AND SUB-REGIONS. 1, boundary of alluvium;
2, of undivided Bengal; 3, of sub-regions; 4, 25 ft contour. Shaded areas older (largely
lateritic) alluvium.

the Hooghly and the Peninsular block; (ii) the Contai coastal plain;

V. the Ganges Delta proper (hereafter 'the Delta') between Hooghly-Bhagirathi, Padma-Meghna, and the sea; further sub-divided into (A) moribund, (B) mature, and (C) active sections.

Before considering these individually it will be appropriate to discuss generalities: hydrography, climate, agriculture.

The Rivers

It will be evident already that "the deltaic plain of Bengal has a double, or even a multiple, origin: one should not say the delta, but rather the deltas".[3] The literature of hydrographic change in Bengal is vast and confused as the subject itself; only brief reference can be attempted here, and it will not be necessary to go back to the days of the Indobrahm nor even to those of the more legendary King Bhagirathi who is said to have excavated the eponymous Bhagirathi distributary about 2000 BC.

The cardinal factor in the later history of the Delta has been the Ewds shift of the Ganges waters from a main outlet along the Wn margins—the Bhagirathi-Hooghly—to the present main course, the Padma-Meghna, with such streams as the Ichamati, Jalangi, Matabhanga, Gorai, representing intermediate (not necessarily successive) positions of the most important channel. Whether this is mainly due to alluviation at the heads of successive main spillways, to tectonic change, to shifts in the balance of the Delta due to changes of course elsewhere (e.g. the great shift of the Tista), or to a secular swing to the E, are questions which admit of large and inconclusive debate. The exact sequence of events also remains an open question, the evidence depending largely on the interpretation of obscure literary texts; it seems possible, for example, that although Sanskrit tradition ascribes an early and special significance to the Bhagirathi, in Ptolemy's day the main outlet was in the E: we might then envisage a swing to-and-fro analogous, on a vaster scale, to the lateral wanderings of an individual stream meandering across its floodplain.

It is at least clear that the Bhagirathi, or one of its several branches (Hooghly, Sarasvati, Adi Ganga or 'Tolly's Nullah') was the most important distributary in the 17th century, but has been silting at least since 1770, when the Damodar, which helped to keep it clear, shifted its mouth 80 miles to the S. The lower reaches of this line, the Hooghly proper, retain their vitality, being fed by streams from the Peninsula such as the Damodar and the Rupnarayan. More recently the most striking event has been the diversion of the Tista into the Brahmaputra, about 1787. This led to a relative decline in the old Brahmaputra course E of Dacca, already ponded

---

[3] A. Geddes, *Au Pays de Tagore: La Civilisation rurale de Bengale occidentale et ses facteurs géographiques* (Paris, Colin, n.d. (?1928)), 45.

back by the waters brought from the Surma Valley by the Meghna. The main Tista-Brahmaputra outlet was by the Jamuna, and the immense volume of water and silt brought down to the Padma near Goalundo backed up the Ganges waters and opened up the Gorai, in 1764 a mere creek, in 1863 the main steamer route from Calcutta into the upper Ganges.[4]

From all this follows the well-known contrast between the decayed W, scarred with silted or stagnant *bhils*, the *disjecta membra* of dead rivers, and the active E; with all the secondary consequences, of which the prevalence of malaria and the absence of fertilising silt in the W are the most important. The mechanism of deltaic deposition is discussed in stimulating detail (and obstetric terminology) by Strickland. Perhaps his most interesting point is the explanation of the more or less continuous line of large bhils Ewds from the Salt Lakes of Calcutta, with the associated slightly higher 'ledge' towards the seaface. This ledge corresponds to a zone in which the tidal masses rise about 18 ft throughout the year, leading to rapid silting of the interior basins of the saucer- or horseshoe-shaped banks which are the beginning of land-building; the result is the formation of this belt of more continuously firm ground.[5] Behind the ledge deposition is less sustained since flooding varies with the vagaries of rainfall.

The transverse channels between distributaries are largely kept open by tidal flushing, and are thus best developed (as in the Irrawaddy delta) towards the seaface, or at least the ledge: "The tidal influence is the most important factor in their preservation, for they do not appear in lake deltas or in deltas in tideless seas, and as the delta is elevated out of tidal influence the cross-channels disappear." [6] The varying hydrographic conditions of the Delta give to some of these channels a considerable tidal gradient; thus while the tidal range at Chandpur on the Meghna during the spring equinox of 1935 was only 3 ft, on the Hooghly the mean ranges of ordinary springs are 10–14 ft.[7]

Climate and Vegetation

Juxtaposition to the Bay of Bengal, and the lie of the surrounding highlands, are the proximate determinants of the climate. On the one hand temperatures are modified: cold weather means are around 64° F., hot weather only 80–85°. The Calcutta figures are typical:

J.	F.	M.	A.	M.	J.	J.	A.	S.	O.	N.	D.	Rang
65·3	70·3	79·3	85·0	85·7	84·5	83·0	82·4	82·6	80·0	72·4	65·3	20·4

This moderation in the hot-weather temperature, however, is paid for by excessive humidity from mid-March through October.

In general rainfall is at least adequate, although on the Wn margins, with about 55 ins., there is enough variability to make an extension of irriga-

---

[4] Strickland, *op. cit.*, 103.   [5] *Ibid.*, 62–64.   [6] *Ibid.*, 14.
[7] *Ibid.*, 111; and cf. Bagchi, *op. cit.*, 62 footnote.

tion desirable. W Bengal (excluding its wetter Nn exclave) gets between 50 and 60 ins.; most of E Bengal between 60 and 95. The highest falls are naturally in sub-montane Jalpaiguri, around the Meghna mouth (100–120), and in the Sylhet funnel between the Shillong Plateau and the Tripura-Lushai Hills (c. 150 ins.).

The usual Indian régime is, however, modified by violent cyclonic disturbances—the 'Nor'-westers'—in March and April, often accompanied by heavy rain, sometimes by hail. These months generally receive 2–3 ins. each, but in Dacca and Chittagong April has 6–7. These rains are of considerable value to the *aus* paddy and the jute crops. On occasion, however, these storms are catastrophic, especially when they coincide with high spring tides in the funnel-shaped Meghna estuary: on the night of May 25th, 1941, between 5000 and 10,000 people lost their lives around Barisal and Noakhali. The turn of the monsoon is also a period of intense cyclonic activity; the Calcutta hurricane of October, 1864, which destroyed much of the shipping in the port, drowned 48,000 people, while in October 1876 large areas around the Meghna estuary were flooded to 10–20 ft: in Bakarganj Dt 74,000 people were drowned and 50,000 fell victims to cholera, while the total loss of life, direct and indirect, has been put as high as 400,000. In the paradelta the Tista floods of 1787 cost the lives, by drowning, disease, or famine, of one-sixth of the population of Rangpur Dt. The indirect suffering and the economic dislocation of such catastrophes can hardly be estimated or exaggerated.

Except in the sal forests of the terai, little natural vegetation remains on dry land, though the lateritic areas of the Barind, the Madhupur Jungle, and the Wn shelf carry some degraded forest or scrub jungle, and what Geddes calls "the arid tropical steppe succeeding to the destroyed forests", stretches of all but useless grass and bush. But the countryside is in general far from treeless: villages, semi-dispersed hamlets, or separate homesteads carry their clumps of bamboo, the toddy-palm and the Indian date, banyans, *pipal*, tamarinds, and mangoes. The aquatic flora is richer: bhils are often choked with reeds and sedges, while on the seaface (with protrusions along the streams) are the great tidal jungles of the Sundarbans. These take their name from the *sundri* (*Heritiera* spp.), a pneumatophore reaching 80–100 ft and supplying useful constructional timber; mangroves provide fuel, and the huge fronds of the nipa palm thatching. In the past two or three decades the water hyacinth has spread with its usual disastrous proliferation, blocking many waterways to navigation and drainage.

The Agrarian Life of Bengal

The agriculture of Bengal is dominated by paddy and jute, accounting respectively for c. 29 m. and 2–4 m. ac. of a TSA of about 40 m. ac. (NSA 32 m. ac.).

Of other crops tea is marginal to the region, though grown in the Duars and Sylhet; tobacco and sugar have 300–350,000 ac. each, oilseeds about 1 m., three-quarters rape and mustard. In general greater diversity would be an advantage, especially in the practically monocultural Wn margins: in Birbhum and Midnapore the acreage under crops other than paddy is as low as 4%. Cotton, once a great crop here, has virtually disappeared before the competition of more favoured areas; but sugar, tobacco, and oil-seeds could be extended, at least if the pressure of the population for rice permitted; but this is a large question.

There are two main paddy crops. *Aman* is transplanted in May and June, harvested in November–January, thus corresponding to the kharif; *aus* or *bhadoi* is a quicker crop, sown with the pre-monsoon rains of April, harvested in July–September. In some areas advantage can be taken of the drying margins of the marsh to secure a hot-weather harvest (*boro*); but *aman* is about 75% of the total. Yields are low even for India, only 851 lbs. per ac. against 945 in Bombay (including Sind) and 1007 in Madras. The demand for seed paddy alone amounts to over three-quarters of a million tons a year.[8]

Jute is in competition with rice for the soil of E Bengal, and raises special problems. An exhausting crop, it is at its best in the E with its constant alluviation: the yield is also susceptible to variations in the monthly and the total incidence of rainfall, while world demand is notoriously elastic. Jute acreage and yield thus fluctuate widely, though these fluctuations are by no means comparable to the price movements. Jute production is there-fore a double gamble—on the weather and on the world market—and may be expected to meet increasing competition from substitutes, bulk loading, and possibly other areas. Yet it is almost the only cash crop of the Bengali peasant, although owing to the proliferation of middlemen far too small a proportion of the price comes back to the cultivator. It is not too much to say that the solvency, even the viability, of E Pakistan is bound up with this one highly speculative crop. As we have seen, jute is an economic battle-ground between *India* and Pakistan (above, 283–84).

The usual wearisome catalogue of agrarian miseries holds—small hold-ings (average 7 ac. for Bengal as a whole, of which 1·7 are fallow), fragmen-tation, debt, collectively excessive and individually inadequate cattle, and the rest. But in addition Bengal has suffered the crushing burden of the Permanent Settlement of 1793. The intention was good: to create from the *zamindars*, the semi-feudal class responsible for collecting Mogul land revenue, enlightened and improving landlords after the model of the English Agrarian Revolution. The results were disastrous in the extreme. *Vis à vis* the *zamindars* the EIC voluntarily limited itself to a revenue laid

[8] M. A. Huque, *The Man behind the Plough* (Calcutta, 1939), 52. Of course all these figures are probably underestimated to some extent.

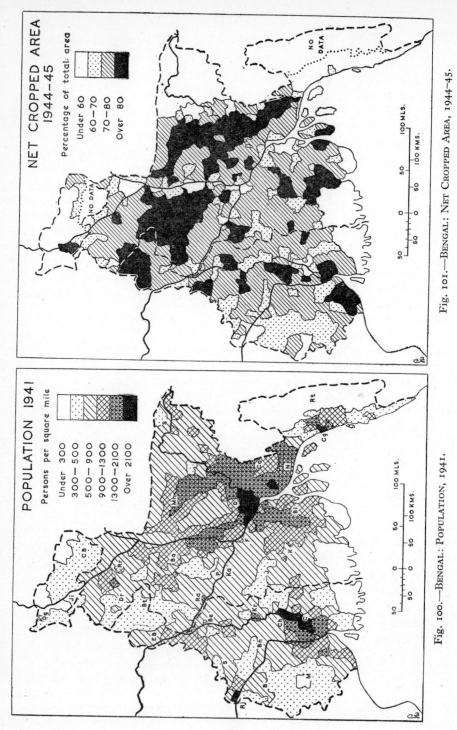

NET CROPPED AREA
1944–45

Percentage of total area

Under 60
60–70
70–80
Over 80

NO DATA

Fig. 101.—Bengal: Net Cropped Area, 1944–45.

POPULATION 1941

Persons per square mile

Under 300
300–500
500–900
900–1300
1300–2100
Over 2100

Fig. 100.—Bengal: Population, 1941.

528

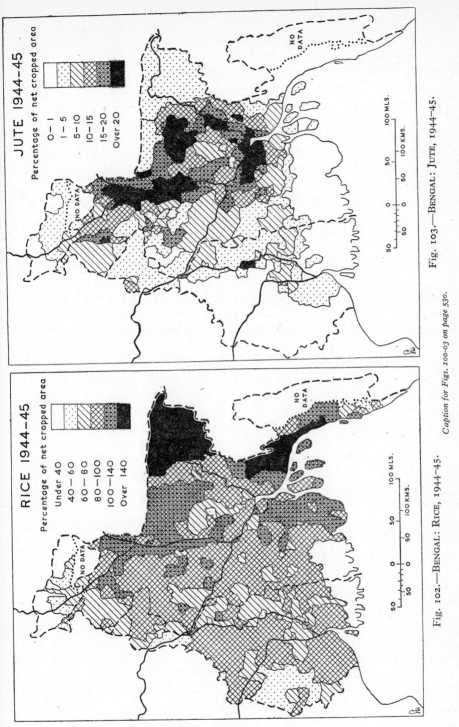

RICE 1944-45

Percentage of net cropped area

Under 40
40 — 60
60 — 80
80 — 100
100 — 140
Over 140

NO DATA

Fig. 102.—BENGAL: RICE, 1944-45.

JUTE 1944-45

Percentage of net cropped area

0 — 1
1 — 5
5 — 10
10 — 15
15 — 20
Over 20

NO DATA

NO DATA

Fig. 103.—BENGAL: JUTE, 1944-45.

Caption for Figs. 100-03 on page 530.

529

down for all time as a fixed demand, not variable with output or land values. The Company specifically reserved the right of intervention on behalf of the *rayats* or peasantry, but although, after the middle of the 19th century, this right did not remain altogether a dead-letter, it was exercised to the accompaniment of noble rhetoric in the Council Chamber and stultifying timidity outside. The *zamindars*, who after all in Mogul days were essentially removable officials (though with the usual feudal tendency to keep the job in the family), became hereditary absentee, and often all but absolute, sovereigns of the soil. In 1793 there was more land than labour available; but with settled conditions and the consequent increase of population this situation was soon reversed and the lord of the land had the whip-hand, and used it. The details of rack-renting, extortion, and legal (sometimes physical) harassment amounting to terrorism, make sickening reading: the landlords' agents were often hardly paid at all and naturally made their living by every kind of corruption, and various extra-legal and often sheerly illegal dues (e.g. on the marriage of the landlord or of the tenant, just as in feudal Europe) in practice added one-third to one-half to what already amounted to rack-rents. While the *zamindar's* contribution to the state changed not at all—in fact really decreased with the fall in the value of money—rents increased four- or five-fold, or even more. Subinfeudation created in some cases as many as six or seven layers between the government which claimed and the peasant who ultimately paid the revenue; and each took his share.

Nor were the absentee landlords themselves exempt from the effects of this vicious social system. In many cases they became parasitic hangers-on of the Anglicised culture of Calcutta, contributing to the contemptuous picture of the Bengali which is so recurrent a theme in old-style Anglo-Indian literature. There have of course been shining exceptions, the Tagore family for one, or Ram Mohan Roy, the first modern thinker of India (fl. 1815–40.) It is fortunate that the Permanent Settlement has not long survived British rule, though its lesions have penetrated deep into the very tissue of Bengali life and it will be many years, perhaps decades, before its effects cease to be felt.

Caption for Figs. 100–03 adapted from *Bengal in Maps* (1949), courtesy S. P. Chatterjee and Orient Longmans. Initials on Fig. 100 indicate District capitals (eponymous except where Dt name given in parentheses). Key: *W Bengal*—B, Bankura; Be, Berhampore (Murshidabad Dt); Bn, Burdwan; Bt, Balaghat (W Dinajpur); Ch, Chinsura (Hooghly); Dg, Darjeeling; EB, English Bazaar (Malda); Ji, Jalpaiguri; Kr, Krishnagar (Nabadwip, ex-Nadia); M, Midnapore; S, Suri (Birbhum); *E Bengal*—Ba, Bogra; Bl, Barisal (Bakarganj); Ca, Comilla (Tippera); Cg, Chittagong; D, Dacca; Dr, Dinajpur (E); F, Faridpur; J, Jessore; K, Khulna; Ka, Kushtia (ex-Nadia); Mh, Mymensingh; N, Noakhali; P, Pabna; Ra, Rampur Boalia (Rajshahi); Rr, Rangpur; Rt, Rangamati (Chittagong Hill Tracts); S, Sylhet. Other initials: Rj, Raniganj; CB, Cooch Behar; C, Calcutta, which is a Dt in itself. The capital of 24 Parganas Dt is Alipore, a Calcutta suburb, and Howrah, opposite Calcutta, is also a Dt centre. On Fig. 102, areas with over 100% give a rough indication of main double-cropped areas, except for two tracts: along the Meghna and in the triangle English Bazaar–Pabna–Berhampore.

The total population of Bengal was 60,306,525 in 1941, the density of 779 giving an average of about half an acre of cultivated ground (including fallow and double-cropping) per person. In 1951 W Bengal had **24,810,000** and E **39,047,000** (excluding **3,072,000** in Pakistani Sylhet); the density would thus seem to have risen to **798**, but the 1951 W Bengal total includes over 1300 sq mls of relatively sparsely peopled country in Cooch Behar. Although the total area "available for cultivation" amounted to 33·5 m. acs, 72·5% of which was in fact cultivated, we have seen that in general "culturable waste" is a derisory term; but even were it not so, in the most densely populated areas there is little which even in the imagination of secretariat statisticians could be brought under the plough. Six Districts have over 90% of the area "available" already cultivated, and in Faridpur and Bakarganj the figure rises to 99%: these Districts have respectively densities of 1003 and 834. In the N of the paradelta there is perhaps some scope for extension of agriculture; elsewhere the only hope, and that slight, lies in diversification and intensification. The 1943 famine was, it is true, due to an altogether exceptional combination of factors: the impounding of country boats to deny them to the Japanese (which naturally dislocated paddy movements); crop failure; hoarding and revolting malpractices on the part of some trading groups; the deprivation of the small but qualitatively important 'pump-priming' rice import from Burma. But this disaster, in which certainly one and perhaps two millions perished, is all too clear an indication of the razor-edge on which is balanced not the prosperity but the mere existence of many of these 60 million human beings.

The Duars

In Bengal the terai, which is found mainly in Jalpaiguri Dt, is known as the Wn Duars, the "doors" of Bhután. The Duars have the usual features of terai country, and about a quarter of the 2000 sq mls is still under forest, mainly sal; but much of the grass and reed jungle has been cleared for rice, jute, and tobacco. Soils are naturally much coarser than farther S, often sandy or even gravelly. The Siwaliks are absent in N Bengal, great Himalayan thrust-masses abutting directly on the plain, and the fierce erosion (rainfall is 120–150 ins.) may also contribute to this breach of continuity. In the N wooded plateaus at 1200–1500 ft form a transition to the mountains; some have been cleared for tea plantations, but most of these lie farther N and higher up in Darjeeling. Politically Darjeeling and most of Jalpaiguri Dt form an exclave of W Bengal.

The Ganges/Brahmaputra Doab; the Barind

The country between the Ganges and the Brahmaputra-Jamuna is essentially Strickland's 'paradelta': a vast plain falling from about 300 to

100 ft, scarred by innumerable old river-courses, and liable to disastrous floods, especially along the Tista which, like the Kosi, is an exceptionally violent stream, its large ice- and snow-fed Himalayan catchment debouching onto the plain through narrow gorges. In the heart of the doab lies the Barind, a large island or terrace of older quasi-lateritic alluvium. The Barind still carries much scrub and degraded remnant forest, and forms a marked negative tract on the population map (Figs. 30, 100).

Soils are varied: old alluvium, clayey silts, sandy clays and loams; naturally they become finer and more fertile towards the Ganges. Most of the area gets 60–80 ins. On the whole the agriculture is rather more diversified than in the rest of Bengal, except in the overwhelmingly jute/paddy tract around the Tista-Brahmaputra confluence. Most of the barley and a large proportion of the sugar, pulses, and oilseeds of Bengal are grown here, while tobacco as a money crop is largely confined to Rangpur Dt. Most of the sub-region lies in E Pakistan; parts of Dinajpur and Malda Dts, and the state of Cooch Behar, are *Indian*. The most important line of communication (apart from the Jamuna navigation) is the BG East Bengal Rly running N to Jalpaiguri and Siliguri, whence a 2 ft 6 in. mountain line runs to Darjeeling; Jalpaiguri town is on the Tista, with a ferry to Barnes Ghat on the E bank, railhead for the old metre line into Assam. Communications in this area have, however, been badly cut up by quite irrational boundary delimitation[9]; but the new railway into Assam bridges the Tista (above, 313). Apart from the eponymous District headquarters, not one of which attains 50,000 inhabitants, there are no towns of importance.

The Eastern Margins

The area E of the Jamuna-Padma-Meghna line forms a great embayment of lowland—the Meghna-Surma Valley—between the Shillong Plateau and the parallel ranges which extend from just E of Comilla to beyond the Burma border. All of it, except a small strip of Sylhet Dt (which before Partition was in Assam) and the plains section of Cachar (which still is), is in E Pakistan, the boundary of which approximates very closely to the limit of the plains, except in the SE where the Chittagong Hill Tracts are included.

The country along the Padma and the lower Meghna is of course very similar to the active Delta across the estuary. But it is backed by the Madhupur Jungle, a much-dissected older alluvial terrace rising some 40 ft above the general level. This interruption of the slope down to the sea, the ponding back of the local water by the main Ganges-Brahmaputra current, and the high rainfall (75–95 ins.), combine to make the Meghna-Surma embayment perhaps the most amphibious part of Bengal during

---

[9] O. H. K. Spate, "The Partition of the Punjab and of Bengal", *GJ* CX (1947), 201–22; map at p. 214.

the rains. The lower tracts are flooded to a depth of 8–15 ft, and homesteads are built on earth platforms 15–20 ft high (Fig. 105 (C and E)). "The water is green with jute. . . . In the height of the inundation no land is to be seen, and all travelling has to be done by boat. To say that travelling has to be done by boat gives, however, but an inadequate idea. . . . Half a dozen huts are clustered together on a hillock a few yards square, and the inhabitants cannot proceed beyond that hillock, whether to visit their neighbours or their fields, to go to market or to school, without wading, swimming, or travelling in or on something that can float", including "circular earthenware pipkins, more difficult of navigation than a coracle." [10]

Apart, then, from the grass and scrub of the Madhupur Jungle, the area is a sea of paddy and jute, except in Sylhet where some marsh and jungle still await reclamation, and where there are about 70,000 ac. of tea. Sylhet indeed is now the only outlet for population-saturated E Bengal, and it is limited—only 4655 sq mls, which had already in 1941 a density of 587.[11] In the other Districts 90% or more of the land "available" is already cultivated. Jute normally accounts for some 25% of the cultivated area in Mymensingh and along the silt-bringing Brahmaputra. Average holdings are under 5 ac., but this is to some extent compensated by the constant accretion of fertile silt and by the profits of jute, which can sometimes be grown as a second crop in paddy-fields.

Swds, along the Bay shores, Chittagong Dt and the E of Noakhali are not really deltaic: Bagchi speaks of the area as being made up of coalesced alluvial cones; it is in fact a narrowing coastal plain, backed by low Tertiary ranges, built up by independent streams of which the most important is the Karnaphuli, at the mouth of which stands the port of Chittagong. Rainfall is high (100–120 ins.) and Chittagong is practically monocultural, with no jute and with only 2% of the cropped area not paddy.

Communications, other than the superb net of waterways, are at a discount in this land of great rivers, universal inundation for much of the year, and no road-metal: the straight-line distance from Dacca to Calcutta is about 150 miles; by rail it is 380 miles, with a break of gauge as well as a long ferry across the Jamuna; and there is no through road. Such railways and roads as there are tend to hug the piedmont (e.g. the line from Chittagong to Comilla, Sylhet, and Assam) or to follow the rather higher ground along the old Brahmaputra course (Jamalpur-Mymensingh-Dacca or Bhairab Bazar). On the other hand an immense volume of jute and paddy traffic is carried by sailing country craft as well as by steamers, and there are several small ports—Cox's Bazar (hardly more than a jetty), Noakhali,

[10] Quoted in L. S. S. O'Malley, *Bengal, Bihar and Orissa, Sikkim* (1917), 8–9.

[11] Between 1931 and 1941 the population of Sylhet (undivided) grew from 2,724,342 to 3,116,602 (density from 497 to 569). Much of this increase was due to Muslim squatter families from the adjoining Dacca Division. According to *IR* II. 6 (11.2.50), 450,000 Muslims entered Assam between Partition and November 1949.

Chandpur, Narayanganj (the port for Dacca), and the tiny new port of Chalna on the Pussur.

More important than these is of course Chittagong (91,301), the Porto Grande of the Arab-Portuguese Mugh pirates of the 17th century.[12] Before Partition it was not really much of a port: four jetties only, with berths. But already its capacity has been nearly quintupled, to 2·5 m. tons a year, and it is planned to raise it to 3·3 m. But it would surely seem that the improvement of its long and tenuous rail link (metre ST) is as urgent as the provision of turn-round facilities at waterside. Chittagong lies in a very excentric position with regard to E Pakistan, but is the obvious outlet for most of Assam, a factor which seemed likely to grow in importance with the opening up of that last pioneer fringe of the sub-continent. Assam tea had been its most important export for a long time before 1947 and imports showed the same bias, being largely tea machinery and packing material. But Partition is now congesting Chittagong with jute (though much still has to go via Calcutta) and Calcutta with tea. Pakistan lays much store on her plans for developing Chittagong, but, although prospects are good, talk of its rivalling or even outstripping Calcutta obviously ignores broad positional factors as well as the weight of vested interest (and capital and business acumen) in the going concern on Hooghlyside. Nevertheless 'Greater Chittagong' in 1951 had **269,000** people.

Dacca (213,218), the capital of E Pakistan (as of the short-lived E Bengal and Assam Province of 1905–11), is by far the largest town. The 17th-century headquarters of the Mogul governors of Bengal, it was famous for the almost incredible fineness of its muslins,[13] a trade ruined by machine competition in the 19th century. More recently it has been perhaps most notable as the University centre for the Muslim E of Bengal, and now of course as a regional capital; with its port Narayanganj it now numbers **401,000.** Plans for industrial development, and the layout of a great administrative centre, are being worked out but obviously depend very largely on the general possibilities, or lack of them, in E Pakistan. Industry in E Pakistan will depend very largely on the Karnaphuli hydro-electric scheme (160,000 kW); and it is planned to set up a paper mill on the Karnaphuli using Chittagong Hill Tracts bamboo to make 30,000 tons a year (about Pakistani demand), and 3 jute mills of 1000 looms each are being set up at Narayanganj.

Urbanisation is thus very slight, a fact which throws into higher relief the appalling population pressure in E Bengal. Despite the presence of the poor and relatively thinly populated Madhupur Jungle, the 15,498 sq mls of Dacca Division carried 16,258,000 people in 1941—a density of 1048. In

---

[12] The Mughs, fallen from their ancient ferocity, are now in great demand as cooks, their piratical propensities finding more modest expression in bazaar charges.
[13] Seven thicknesses were said to be necessary for decency.

1941 the four largest towns had only 383,491 people in all, and subtracting these there was a *rural* density of over 1000 on an area twice
the size of Wales. In the Padma-Meghna angle S of Dacca 550 sq mls
have a density of 3000. Clearly this raises problems which will tax E
Pakistan's resources (which except for jute and paddy are exiguous) to
the utmost.

The Western Margins

This sub-region may be defined as the area between the Bhagirathi-
Hooghly and the surface outcrop of the solid rocks of the Peninsula; like
the En margins, it falls into a Nn and a littoral section; but there the resemblance ends. The W is a shelf of lateritic old alluvium (the Rarh), flanked
by the coalesced fans of rivers draining the Peninsular plateaus—Ajai,
Damodar, Rupnarayan, Kasai—which in turn fall to a 'dead delta' zone
below the higher land along the Hooghly banks. In the S, lowland Midnapore is only partly deltaic, with a prograding coastal plain marked by lines
of old beach-ridges, which give rise to linear settlement patterns around
Contai.

The lateritic areas (*khoai*) are very poor, with a decidedly xerophytic
aspect. The firm shelf has been from early times an avenue of settlement,
between the dense jungle of the plateau and the marsh of the delta; and
forest destruction has brought the usual nemesis of erosion. On the lateritic
interfluves poor short grass, thorny bushes, scattered wild dates, and the
rust-red laterite in roadside cuttings combine to present a landscape of
drought and desolation, relieved only by the countersunk paddy-floored
valleys.[14] Farther E the area within the great bend of the Damodar is
especially liable to floods, breaching levées and embankments, and between
the Damodar elbow and the Hooghly is a most typical dead delta zone.
Here the small streams, some formerly spill channels of the Damodar, have
lost their headwaters by silting or shifts of that river, while the Hooghly
has probably been pushed to the E by the detritus of the plateau streams.
This is thus a region of silted and stagnant bhils: "the villagers laconically
remark that their land is infested by blind, dying, and choked rivers." [15]
Incompetent embanking and river-training, the numerous culverts on
roads and railways (which generally run athwart the drainage), and the
spread of water-hyacinth have added to the dislocation of drainage. Add to
this the great floods of the Damodar (which has a wide catchment area on
impervious rock, funnelled down through a narrow valley succeeded by a

[14] A small area around Tagore's *ashram* at Santineketan is the field of what is probably
the best geographical (and historical) analysis, in real detail, of any area in India: Arthur
Geddes, *Au Pays de Tagore* (Paris, n.d., ?1927). Unfortunately space prevents me from
rifling this fascinating study as liberally as I should like.
[15] S. C. Bose, *The Damodar Valley Project* (Calcutta, 1948), 31. Again I wish I could
quote more from this very useful study.

right-angled bend) and it is not surprising that the Damodar is a problem river second only to the Kosi, nor that the sub-region, with its poor rainfall, is in general perhaps the most wretched and poverty-stricken part of Bengal, with malaria hyperendemic. The reformation of the Damodar by a TVA-type scheme is discussed elsewhere (below, 591).

If not flood, drought: the rainfall of between 50 and 60 ins. is irregular enough for crop failures to be not infrequent. This is the more serious in that the area is again almost monocultural: there is practically no jute, and although dry crops (wheat and barley) are of some slight importance on the uplands, secondary crops of all kinds (including those just mentioned) cover only 4–9% of the cultivated area in this tier of districts. The growth of the Hooghlyside conurbation, however, has led to an extension of market gardening irrigated from the *kanas*, the blind rivers of the Damodar-Hooghly belt. Irrigation in the sub-region has a history of bad planning, and its remodelling and extension form a much-needed part of the Damodar project.[16]

The sub-region is largely a transit zone: along or across it radiate the main railways from Howrah to the Ganges Plains, to the Damodar coalfields, through the Jamshedpur Gap to Bombay, and S along the coast to Madras. The towns, such as Midnapore and Burdwan, are mainly administrative and commercial, except the largest, Kharagpur (**129,636**), originally merely the railway suburb of Midnapore, now an important junction with workshops and much larger than its parent. The Hooghlyside towns are of course in a different category.

The Ganges Delta Proper

The contrast in health and prosperity between the W and the E of the Delta is well known—the former a region of decadent rivers, stagnant bhils, and malaria; the latter continually revivified by the silts of a very active river-system, which enables it to support, if perhaps precariously, a denser population. But of course the tidal influence along the seaface introduces a third aspect, and Bagchi's threefold sub-division of the Delta seems on the whole most in accord with the general development.[17]

(i) *The moribund Delta.* This lies mainly in Nadia, Jessore, and Murshidabad Dts, the NE quadrilateral bounded by Bhagirathi, Padma, and Madhumati, and on the S by a line roughly along the Nn boundaries of 24-Parganas and Khulna. Here the off-takes of the old distributaries in the N have been silted up, and the rivers themselves flow on old levees. Even in flood the country in general is not inundated; on the other hand the interfluves are ill-drained owing to their saucer section, and their decayed bhils

[16] *Ibid.*, 34–41, 61–62.
[17] Bagchi analyses the population thana by thana (Chs. XI–XIV); cf. also the elaborate discussion and maps in A. Geddes, "The Population of Bengal, its Distribution and Changes," *GJ* LXXXIX (1937), 344–68.

are the epicentres, as it were, of malaria. Population in Nadia is stagnant, and in Jessore shows an actual decrease from 1881 to 1931, though this was succeeded by an increase in 1931–41. Densities are 6–800.

(ii) *The mature Delta.* Between the moribund Delta and the Sundarbans is a belt, roughly the Nn half of 24-Parganas and Khulna, where the rivers are more 'live' and some silting occurs along the larger ones. They still carry a good deal of water from the local rain, but in general they are deteriorating, and are becoming more and more brackish or saline in the dry weather. Along the Wn and the En confines—Hooghly and Madhumati —the land is still being built up to some extent. The demographic conditions are thus variable. Densities in Khulna and 24-Parganas are 404 and 957 respectively, but the former is reduced by the large empty area in the Sundarbans, the latter inflated by the Hooghlyside towns.

(iii) *The active Delta.* The Sn boundary between the mature and the active Delta is approximately the line of large bhils running E from Calcutta (cf. above, 524–25); the active Delta consists of the Sundarbans (Sn Khulna and 24-Parganas) and of the country between Madhumati and Meghna (Faridpur and Bakarganj). The great tidal forests stretch along the seaface for about 170 miles, and reach 60–80 miles inland; they are, however, subject to recession along the Nn border as land is reclaimed for paddy. The Sundarbans themselves are almost devoid of habitation; Faridpur and Bakarganj, on the other hand, the deltaic districts *par excellence*, have densities of 1024 and 938 respectively.

There is some debate as to whether the Delta is still advancing seawards, or whether it is losing by marine erosion more than it gains. Local erosion doubtless exists, but on the whole it would seem that accretion predominates. It is true that there seems little difference between the general lie of the coast shown on Rennell's map of 1770 and by modern surveys; but the presence of old beach-ridges in the Sundarbans certainly points to accretion, and in the E, where Padma, Meghna, and above all Brahmaputra bring down vast quantities of silt, all stages in the process of land-building are very clearly seen from the air.

The soils of the Delta naturally show a good deal of variation. The moribund Delta is mainly sandy loam, with some areas of stiff clays; the Sundarbans (and a strip to the N, now reclaimed) are clays, with fresh sands along the seaface, and of course strongly saline. Between these, in the mature Delta and along the Madhumati, are clayey loams, becoming more sandy towards the Meghna mouth, while farther up along the Padma are pure silt-loams. In detail, of course, there are numerous complications; for example, in the W "on all the higher parts of the levees the soil is mainly sands and sandy loams which grade into pure loam on the lower slopes, which in its turn merges into the depressed clayey bhil areas. . . . Corresponding to this is a gradation of crops, e.g. vegetables, pulses, and *aus* paddy on the higher levees, jute and oilseeds on the lower slopes, and winter rice on the lower marshy areas".[18]

The three sub-divisions, and the soil zones which by and large correspond with them, have differing agricultural emphases. Nadia and Jessore have 30 and 21% respectively under secondary crops (including jute); Murshidabad 46%, but half of this Dt lies W of Bhagirathi, merging into the plateau. Jute, however, accounts for only 8, 11, and 4% of the cropped area in these three. In Khulna and 24-Parganas under 10% is in secondary crops, of which jute is dominant in the latter only, doubtless on account of the proximity to Hooghly mills. Faridpur has 27% secondary crops, half being jute; Bakarganj only 12%, 2% jute. Jute is thus associated with lighter, loamier, but not too sandy soils.

Densities, as we have seen, run high; the moribund Delta is almost certainly over-populated on any view, while Khulna's low figure masks the congestion on the cultivated area by including the Sundarbans wastes. The very high figures for Faridpur and Bakarganj, like those of Dacca Division, are attained with practically no towns of any size—only one, Barisal (61,316) exceeds 50,000. Urbanism indeed is at a discount, apart from Hooghlyside, and that is obviously to a large extent grafted onto rather than growing out of Bengal. The basis of its industry is of course jute, but the impetus was originally and in some measure still is that of alien commerce and capital, and the bulk of its industrial labour is immigrant. Land communications, except along the Hooghly banks, are very poor, waterways excellent, feeding the jute mills by thousands of small country craft. The towns, then, are administrative and market centres, the more important such as Faridpur, Barisal, and Khulna with river port functions. Hooghlyside deserves a treatment of its own.

Politically most of the Delta has gone to E Pakistan, W Bengal's share being a strip 30–50 miles wide adjoining Bhagirathi-Hooghly. The economic dislocation is obvious, and in detail the division is sometimes inexplicable; there seems, for example, no warrant for allotting to Pakistan the NW of Khulna, which strangely enough has good land communications with Calcutta and was predominantly Hindu, the whole District being only 49·3% Muslim.

The Countryside

The settlement-pattern of much of Bengal (especially the E) is distinctive in lowland India in that the homestead, and not the compact village, is the unit. There are of course exceptions, especially in the poorer W where the terrain of lateritic interfluves and paddy valley-floors favours some con-

[18] Binapani Mukerjee, *The Hooghly and its Region* (London Ph.D. thesis, 1949), 80; cf. N. Ahmad, "The Physiography and Crops of Eastern Pakistan", *Agriculture Pakistan* I (1950), and Map 6 in S. P. Chatterjee, *Bengal in Maps* (Calcutta, 1949).

centration. But for the rest there are few nucleations, and such clusters and hamlets as exist (Fig. 104 A) are not tight-packed in the Punjab or UP manner. Yet where densities are so high it would be an abuse of language to speak of the population as dispersed; this may be the case in the newer reclamations of the Duars and the Sundarbans fringes, but in general there is a close stipple of homesteads—often very close indeed, and yet never more than two or three together (Fig. 104 B). Over large areas there is no

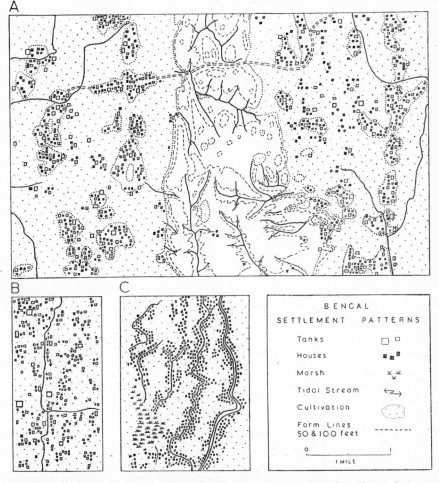

BENGAL
SETTLEMENT PATTERNS

Tanks

Houses

Marsh

Tidal Stream

Cultivation

Form Lines
50 & 100 feet

0   1
I MILE

Fig. 104.—BENGAL: SETTLEMENT PATTERNS. **A,** 2–12 mls SW of Comilla; settlements dispersed or in amorphous clusters, many tanks; in E some linear, probably on higher ground of old creek-bank. Upland part of 'Red Bank of Comilla', an island of older lateritic alluvium. SOP 79 M/3; courtesy SOP.

B, 9 mls NE of Noakhali; close stipple of homesteads with tanks. SOP 79 N/1; courtesy SOP.

C, inside Damodar bend; linear along banks of past or existing creeks. From B. Mukerjee, *The Hooghly and its Region* (thesis), Fig. 40b.

real "pattern" at all, so homogeneous is the environment; elsewhere river levees or the margins of an upland (Fig. 104 A and C) or, as in Contai, old beach-ridges, impose linear layouts.

No less striking is the aspect of the homesteads themselves. Huts are universally gabled, usually high-pitched to shed the rain, with thatching of palmyra or nipa leaves, or with corrugated iron where this is readily available and within the means of the householder. Corrugated iron has the great merit of being fireproof, but otherwise is obviously far less suited to the climate than is good thatching, whether in the hot weather, the cold weather, or the rains. Walls are of split bamboo, reed, or jute-stalk matting (the last none too weatherproof), or of mud, more rarely of wood and very rarely indeed (except in towns) of brick. Floors are of mud, often scrupulously clean. Altogether the matting/thatch combination gives an airiness very desirable in the humid heat.

"The homestead is neither a cottage nor a house as Europe knows them. . . . It never consists of a single hut—even the poorest families always have a separate kitchen. . . . A prosperous family builds larger huts and more of them",[19] up to half a dozen or so, grouped round a little court with a tank for bathing and domestic water supply. Sleeping, living, and cooking quarters, and reception rooms, are under separate roofs, although any room may be used casually as a store or a sleeping-place, and much of the life of the family is carried on in the open air or on verandahs. A great variety of mats and baskets, large storage jars, a few chests, form the most of the furniture, and, in areas where the streams are tidal or flood in the rains, nets and other fishing gear are prominent.

The individual buildings are universally on mud plinths, and in the active Delta and the Meghna-Surma Valley the annual inundation forces the homestead, or the hamlet where such rough groupings exist, to be itself on a platform up to 15–20 ft above the general level, the necessary earth being obtained from the excavated tanks. The countryside in the E is thus dotted with scores of thousands of tiny islets. These would form in aggregate a very substantial reduction of the area available to support the dense population, but they are themselves not unimportant agriculturally (or rather horticulturally), carrying vegetables, tobacco, mango and other fruit trees, as well as the indispensable bamboo and (S of a line roughly Howrah-Jessore-Khulna-Comilla) coconut palms. This varied bush and tree culture and the many small bodies of water give an extremely agreeable diversity to the landscape, and indeed nothing can well be more beautiful than the E Bengal countryside seen from the air after the mango-showers and just before the rains—a vivid carpet of various green, inset with countless

---

[19] J. C. Jack, *The Economic Life of a Bengal District* (Oxford, 1916), 21. Ch. I of this book gives a very detailed (if rather idyllic) account of the Bengali home as seen in Faridpur; conditions on the other side of the Hooghly are described in Geddes, *op. cit., passim,* but especially Ch. III (Les Villages).

tanks, the homesteads nestling in groves of feathery bamboo, coconut, or the darker masses of mango trees, all with the precise delicacy of a Japanese colour-print. The reality of life on the ground is doubtless different.

In this environment the great mass of Bengalis lives: under 10% of the population is urban, and of the urban population over half is in the great Hooghlyside conurbation. This indeed completely overshadows town development in Bengal; only Dacca and Chittagong (and the latter is still very provincial) have anything much in the way of independent status. The sparsity of sizeable towns is most noticeable (Fig. 26A); of the 18 with over

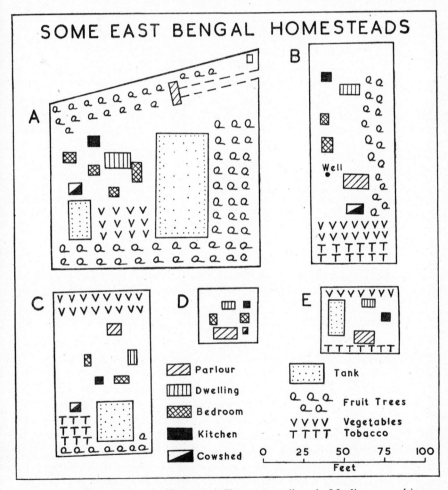

Fig. 105.—Some E Bengal Homestead Types. **A,** well-to-do Muslim non-cultivator in drier N; **B,** Muslim, and **C,** Hindu, cultivators 'in comfort'; **D,** poor Muslim, and **E,** poor Hindu, cultivators. C and E are on platforms above marsh. Adapted from J. C. Jacks, *The Economic Life of a Bengal District* [Faridpur] (1916); courtesy Oxford University Press.

50,000 inhabitants, 10 are on the Hooghly and only 5 (Dacca, Chittagong, Barisal, Narayanganj, and Mymensingh) in E Pakistan, these 5 accounting for only 1·2% of the 1941 population. In W Bengal the area immediately around Calcutta had in 1941 over $4\frac{1}{4}$ m. people on 470 sq mls, while the Hooghly-Bhagirathi strip in general had some $7\frac{1}{2}$ m. on 3000 sq mls—54% of the population of W Bengal on 13% of the area. This figure has undoubtedly been much increased by the refugee influx. The six major towns of Hooghlyside alone contain nearly 3·5 m. people, of whom over two-thirds are in Calcutta. This, perhaps the only true conurbation in India, but for Bombay demands a separate survey.

CALCUTTA AND HOOGHLYSIDE

Despite its excentric situation, in the littoral which after 1869 was the farthest from Europe, Calcutta remained the British capital of India from 1773 until 1912. This peculiar site for the seat of Government was hardly improved by the costly annual migration of most departments to Simla (1100 miles away) for the hot weather; although of course the energetic (largely Scots) commercial oligarchs who really made Calcutta were less migratory. As Reclus remarked, Calcutta is not the natural centre for "the concentration of local energies" even for Bengal alone; such a centre would be near the Delta-head, and here in fact were the indigenous capitals of Bengal, now mostly jungle-smothered ruins: Gaur, Tanda, Pandua, Rajmahal. Although individual sites were at the mercy of shifting streams, this node retained its importance in the early European phase, when Murshidabad, Cossimbazaar, and Malda (English Bazaar) were still the leading trade counters; the selection in 1608 of Dacca as the Mogul provincial capital exemplifies the duality of the Delta. Dutch and English shipping developed bolder courses across the Indian Ocean than did the Portuguese, who had come well up the African coast before striking across for India: hence the En littoral came to be of more immediate access than the Wn, and of course penetration upcountry by the great rivers was easier than on the W coast, shut in (except around the Gulf of Cambay) by the steep wall of the Ghats. Once off Bengal energetic European traders anxious to tap the wealth of the Gangetic Plain, with its flourishing Mogul cities supplying (it is ironic to recall) fine textiles for European markets, fixed on the Wnmost and shortest entry as the all-important one. This is attested by the list of early factories, which includes Hooghly town (Portuguese, earliest of all), Chinsura (Dutch till 1825), Serampore (Danish till 1845), and Chandernagore, which remained French until 1949 when it voted by 7473 to 114 for accession to *India*. Even the feeble Austrian Ostend Company tried its hand at Cossimbazaar.

Calcutta, destined to dwarf all these, was originally the least significant: when Job Charnock located the English factory in 1692–94, the site was occupied by three petty villages, its only positional advantages being the deep water on the outer side of the meander and (a little later) the intervention of the Hooghly between it and possible Maratha raids—which did not exclude the desirability of a defence (the Maratha Ditch) on the En side. The approach, some 120 miles from Sandbanks up a trickily shoaling estuary, was difficult, not to say dangerous, in sailing days, and to-day is feasible thanks only to costly and unremitting pilotage, conservation, and dredging services. In fact, "its situation is so bad by nature that there is little that man could do to make it worse, but that little has been faithfully and assiduously done".[20]

On this unpromising site, pent narrowly between the river and the Salt Water Lakes (of some use as a vast cesspool), there rose a "city of palaces" —and a far larger city of hovels. The nucleus is Fort William (rebuilt in 1758–73—after Plassey—and a notable museum-piece of 18th-century fortification) and the Maidan, a vast open space littered with statues of generals and philanthropists. N from the Maidan lie Dalhousie Square, on the site of the great tank which was the 18th-century water supply, Government House, and the commercial and banking core around Clive Street—now, by one of time's revenges, Netaji Bose Street, after the leader of the Jap-sponsored National Army. Flanking the Maidan on the E is Chowringhee, the main shopping and entertainment thoroughfare. Central Calcutta has at least some space and dignity, even though the neo-Grecian palaces (except the really fine Government House) seem now overwrought and faded, and Curzon's white marble Victoria Memorial has little to recommend it but its impressive (or oppressive) size.[21]

Around this nucleus the mass of the city presents the standard features of Indian urbanism: flat-topped buildings, the taller blocks of offices and flats crazy with balconies, teeming bazaars, trams and bullock carts and bulls, the cinema and the shrine; villas hidden in great gardens in the better suburbs; and, despite decades of piecemeal improvement, vast areas of *bustees*, the hovels of the submerged proletariat, areas which rank with similar zones in such cities as Osaka and Johannesburg as the most revolting expressions of our industrialism.

Calcutta proper had **2,548,677** inhabitants in 1951. Across the river lies the great industrial town of Howrah (**433,630**), hardly to be regarded as a suburb, with the terminals of the railways to the W and S; since 1943 the famous bridge of boats has been replaced by a great structure of steel. The Hooghly wharves and moorings in Calcutta itself are mostly used by smaller

[20] A writer of the 1880s, quoted by Sir Torick Ameer Ali in *Journal of the Royal Central Asian Society*, Vol. XXXII (1945), 177.

[21] Reclus and Sion both note the parallel with St Petersburg, with a slight shift of emphasis significant in view of Reclus' political views; see Reclus, *L'Inde* (Nouvelle Géographie Universelle, T. VIII (1883)), 375; Sion, *Asie des Moussons* (1929), 306. The later version is inferior.

shipping; the main port activity is now centred round the docks at Kidder-pore. Farther down river are specialised installations such as the oil depot at Budge Budge. The conurbation extends as far up river as Hooghly town, 25 miles from Calcutta itself (Fig. 106).

In the orientation imposed on the economic geography of 19th century India by its gearing to British needs, the advantages of the Calcutta neigh-bourhood were many: the sea-entry to the areas of greatest population and (at least until the rise of Punjab and Deccan cotton) of highest agricultural productivity—including that of the great early staple exports, opium, tea, indigo; a monopoly of world jute supply at its doors; the only well-developed network of internal navigation in India; the region where British territorial power on any large scale was oldest; the seat of Government and above all of a forceful, not to say ruthless, dominant minority of British business-men. Calcutta soon outstripped Madras and was not seriously challenged by Bombay until the cotton boom of the American Civil War and the open-ing of the Suez Canal. By then the mineral wealth of the Bihar-Orissa border, so accessible to Hooghlyside, was realised, and its exploitation provided the incentive to a more diversified and increasingly Indian-owned industrial development in this century, so that by 1921 a third of the factory population of India was concentrated in the narrow strip from Hooghly town to Budge Budge; with the spread of industrial development generally this had fallen to about a quarter by 1941.[22] In 1939 the industrial popula-tion of Hooghlyside was about 465,000—82% of that of Bengal; but it had only 57% of the factories; units, especially in jute, are large. By 1945 war expansion had brought the number of workers to over 650,000, in 1450 factories against 961 in 1939. With all this the fact that even in the trun-cated province of W Bengal industrial workers are only about 10·5% of the occupied population is a reminder that, in relation to area and population, India is still backward industrially. Agriculture accounts for 68·3% of workers, trade and transport 8·5%, administration 5·1%. Calcutta proper is more commercial and administrative than industrial, being outstripped in this regard by Howrah, while such towns as Titagarh and Bhatpara are solidly industrial, factory workers and their dependants forming 65–85% of the total population.

Jute of course is dominant: in 1949 there were 94 jute mills out of an Indian total of 105, employing around 300,000 workers. Mills are strung out along the river from below Budge Budge to Naihati, with notable con-centrations N of Howrah and above all in and around Bhatpara. The indus-try has a long history, the first mill dating from 1855, though power was not introduced until 1859: the Crimean War had blocked hemp supplies to Dundee, and the Scots connection then established is unbroken: although most of the capital is now Indian, the firms of Managing Agents

---

[22] Cf. Tables I and III in B. C. Ghose, *Industrial Location* (OPIA No. 32, 1945).

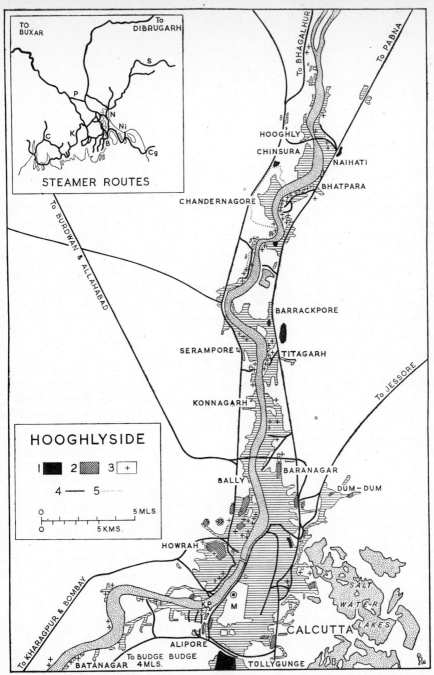

Fig. 106.—Hooghlyside. 1, rice-milling areas; 2, jute mills; 3, main concentrations of engineering works; 4, railways; 5, old Franco-Indian boundary; KP, Kidderpore (docks); M, Maidan and Fort William (circle). Based in part on map in B. Mukerjee, *op. cit.* for Fig. 104.

Inset: B, Barisal; C, Calcutta; Cg, Chittagong; K, Khulna; N, Narayanganj; Ni, Noakhali; P, Pabna; S, Sylhet. Note much greater development in E. Based on *Bengal in Maps*, Fig. 99; courtesy S. P. Chatterjee.

who actually run the industry are still mainly Scots in spirit and personnel.[23] By 1910 Dundee itself was outstripped, and manufactured jute is now India's leading export, its value being about five times that of raw jute.

The Partition, however, left some 80% of jute acreage and output in En Pakistan, which is naturally disposed to industrialise in order to retain the profits of manufacture. It will be some time, given E Bengal's general backwardness and special poverty in power, before competition is intense; but in the meantime the politics of jute, so vital to both the Bengals, have given rise to serious friction: *Indian* efforts at producing more jute have spread as far as En UP and have been so far successful as to enable buyers to delay purchases, depressing prices in Pakistan; *Indian* devaluation introduced further complications, and in 1949 Pakistan imposed a standstill on exports in an endeavour to maintain the price. All this bodes very ill, and in view of the vulnerable nature of the monopoly may prove suicidal: bulk-loading and substitutes [24] have already made inroads on the demand, other tropical countries (e.g. Brazil) may well turn seriously to production of raw jute, and finally the cheapness of labour, a prime factor in the success of the industry, is becoming less significant in view of the general rise in Indian costs and money wages.

Other textile industries include hosiery and silk, but are of little account, though cotton has increased two- or three-fold since 1932 and now employs some 30,000 workers. Of much greater importance are the very diversified engineering and metallurgical industries, developed in close association with Asansol-Raniganj coal and Jamshedpur iron and steel. There are over 600 engineering works of all sizes and types, employing about 95,000 hands; all but a few are in Calcutta or its immediate suburbs and Howrah. Machine parts for the jute mills and a wide variety of light machinery are manufactured; a recent development of interest is the rolling of aluminium sheets and bars from ingots at Belur. Railway workshops, ship repairing, motor assembly, and allied industries are important; a motor-vehicle plant is projected at Konnagar.

With so large a market there is naturally a great variety of consumption goods; this of course is typically metropolitan, but Greater Calcutta is distinctive in having practically all of one of the major industries of the country. Perhaps the most important miscellaneous lines are rubber, chemicals (Calcutta is perhaps the leading Indian centre), rice-milling (especially in the Sn suburbs of Calcutta, close to the market and with access by country boat from the Delta), and paper. The last is of exceptional importance, the mills at Titagarh and Naihati producing nearly half the Indian output; this is doubtless connected with the importance of Calcutta

[23] For a description of the system, and discussion of its advantages and drawbacks (the latter are now perhaps the greater), see D. H. Buchanan, *The Development of Capitalistic Enterprise in India* (1934), Ch. VIII *passim*.

[24] Cement, for example, is now almost entirely bagged in paper.

as a publishing and educational centre. Finally we may note the large boot
and shoe factory at Batanagar, a name which explains itself.[25]

This concentration of industry has not been gained without the exaction
of a heavy price in human suffering. The population of Calcutta itself grew
between 1931 and 1941 from 1,164,000 to 2,109,000; Howrah from 225,000
to 379,000; seven of the minor towns of the conurbation increased by 500%
in 50 years. Central Calcutta, it is true, shows the normal metropolitan trend
to a stationary or declining population, but the city as a whole showed an
increase of 81% in 1931–41, and four of its immediate suburbs increases of
138–158%, extraordinary figures even allowing for some exaggeration due
to the intense communal interest in inflating the 1941 figures. Yet in 1941
the birthrate in Calcutta was 25·7 per mille against a deathrate of 31·7; the
ratio of still to live births was 8·2%; and mortality under one year 673 per
1000 births.[26] Conditions in the 1943 famine are unimaginable. Truly these
cities are eaters of men, and the increases are supported practically entirely
by continual immigration of new victims for the smoky altars of industrialism: in Titagarh and Bhatpara, two of the most purely industrial units of
the conurbation, in 1931 the percentages of population born outside Bengal
were 86 and 72 respectively.

The reason is not far to seek: it lies in the remark of a very well-travelled
journalist that, of all the cities he knew, Calcutta cared most for money and
least for men. Much of the population still lives in *bustees*, grossly overcrowded single-room huts some 10 ft square, huddled together by the
hundred in lanes a yard wide; as Binapani Mukerjee remarks, the internal
structure of a *bustee* area can only be photographed when half of it has been
burnt in a communal riot. Open drains lead to stagnant pools full of decay-
ing garbage; natural necessities are attended to on scraps of fetid waste
ground; standpipes are so few and distant that the pools too often serve as
the local water supply. The 'lines' of the organised factories, both *Indian* and
European owned, are usually much better, sometimes with really good
pucca (brick-built) quarters, and some riverside jute mills have even a
certain aesthetic appeal. But others are nearly as bad as the *bustees*.[27] The
appalling figures quoted above represent some—not, fortunately, all—of
the reality behind the commercial and industrial progress of what used to
boast itself the second city of the British Empire.

The future of Calcutta is hardly likely to be as brilliant [28] as its past. It is
indeed unlikely to be dethroned by Chittagong, as some ardent or appre-

---

[25] Details drawn largely from Binapani Mukerjee, *The Hooghly and its Region* (London
Ph.D. thesis, 1949), and S. P. Chatterjee, *Bengal in Maps* (Calcutta, 1949), 88–93. Cf.
also Ch. XI, Sections II and III above.

[26] B. Mukerjee, *op. cit.*, 328.

[27] In one case cited by Mukerjee 373 workers were provided with 8 seat-latrines, 18
urinals, and 2 taps for drinking and bathing. These revolting details are, after all, part of
the "cultural" landscape.

[28] After the last two paragraphs, readers may feel that this is not quite *le mot juste*.

hensive writers have suggested; but at least there will be a rival near the throne, and the transfer of the bulk of the jute area and much of its food area to a different political entity cannot fail to affect it adversely. Still, the trade of the Ganges valley will remain and probably expand; Calcutta had generally some 35% of the seaborne trade of India before the war, running neck and neck with Bombay. Moreover the immense vested interest of Hooghlyside, the accumulation of capital, financial skill, enterprise, and the technique and installations of trade, represent a solid asset. The projected hydro-electric development in the Damodar Valley may further the industrial development of the Hooghly region as a whole, while permitting a desirable decentralisation. Yet in the long run it seems that the division of Bengal and the spread of modern industry in *India* generally will probably spell some lessening of Calcutta's relative position among the foci of *Indian* economic activity. The city's increase 1941–51 was only 22%, and Bombay is now larger.

The Partition and its Problems

The Radcliffe Award of 1947 gave W Bengal 29,370 sq mls with a 1941 population of 21,196,453 [29], leaving E Bengal with 48,072 sq mls and 39,110,072 people, plus 4621 sq mls and 2,733,202 from Assam, being the major portion of Sylhet Dt. As already noted, the 1700-mile-long boundary is most arbitrary and, especially in the N, paid no attention whatsoever to communications, necessitating the building of a 140-mile railway linking Assam with *India*. The rump of W Bengal is itself divided into two fragments. Of the old states adjoining En Pakistan, Cooch Behar (1321 sq mls, 1941 poptn 640,842) has been merged with W Bengal, and Tripura (4032 and **639,029**) is, perhaps significantly, now a province under Chief Commissioner responsible directly to New Delhi.

It is ironical that Bengal was perhaps the only province in India with a real linguistic unity, except possibly Sind: in 1931 some 86% of Bengali speakers were within its borders, and they in turn formed 92% of the provincial population, the rest being tribesmen in the extreme N and E, and the immigrants (Biharis very largely) to Hooghlyside.

Neither of the Bengals is a strong unit. W Bengal, with its enormous urban concentration on Hooghlyside, now swollen by refugees, is a food-deficit area, its agriculture being qualitatively as well as quantitatively inferior to that of E Bengal. Economically there seems very little justification for its continued existence: the Asansol coalfield is only a fragment of the much more important Bihar fields, and the Damodar Valley project cuts across the provincial boundary and would probably be simpler to administer were that boundary not there; while in the N the reconstruction

---

[29] There have probably been at least 3 million immigrants from E Bengal since Partition.

of communications with Darjeeling will obviously bring that outlier into the orbit of Bihar rather than of Bengal, and the new railway to Assam will impose an E/W orientation on Jalpaiguri, to replace the old N/S links severed by the Partition.

But less tangible factors are far stronger than these material considerations. Calcutta was the heart of Hindu Bengali culture, a culture which, with all its faults of excitability and emotionalism verging on hysteria, had played a great part in the development of Hindu nationalism, of pride in the cultural heritage of Mother India, and in the literary renaissance of this century; nor does it lack self-consciousness and sensibility. The tradition is too strong for a merger to be practical politics. But for some time it has seemed that the vitality of Bengal lay in the E rather than in the over-sophisticated society of Calcutta. Certainly the Bengali Hindu, with all his good points (alertness of mind and a fine ironic humour are notable), is regarded in India as the very type of the *babu*, a talker inveterate even by Indian standards. Certainly also the political scene in Calcutta during the war years was not likely to engender optimism in outside observers: factionalism which would have been ludicrous had it not struck at the root of all government, corruption and profiteering in the midst of famine and on a scale which made the most toughened journalists stand aghast. The virtual removal (by the Partition) of the communal element does not seem to have exorcised the evil. And, in any case, the teeming life of Hooghlyside is kept alive only by a continuous blood transfusion, largely of Biharis.

E Bengal is in some ways more promising, or rather would be so were it not so isolated from the rest of Pakistan—and in that other body of Pakistan resides most of the drive which made the new state. There is a real danger that E Pakistan may become a mere poor relation: though it has four-sevenths of the population, the central Government is in the W, and proximity to the seat of Government means much. It is arguable that, like W Pakistan, E Bengal depended on the export beyond her own limits of primary products, jute and some tea, and that therefore the high protectionism characteristic of industrial *India* would not be in accordance with the interests of E Bengalis. But that is not the end of the economic argument. At the time of Partition E Pakistan had not a single jute mill, and hardly any other industry; apart from raw jute, some tobacco, and tea, there were hardly any industrial resources. Some haematitic laterite has been reported N of Dacca, but even ardent Pakistanis cannot work up much enthusiasm about it, with no coal except some rather doubtful lignite. As for power, projects are on foot for developing some 160,000 kW on the Karnaphuli, but there is little else, and even this is obviously not very well placed; it will, however, materially assist the development of Chittagong. But industrial progress will be slow, for lack of basic power and mineral resources, of capital, and of technicians.

Yet, without industrialisation, E Pakistan is a miserable, overcrowded agrarian slum. It was claimed to be self-sufficient in food; this is untenable and natural disasters can still tip the balance towards famine. To attain any self-sufficiency, even on low standards, will involve intensification of agriculture and in all probability a restriction of jute acreage—and raw jute is the one solid fiscal resource, apart from land revenue itself. Bengal was almost always a deficit province, and relied heavily on the proceeds of the Jute Export Duty [30]; and E Pakistan has not, of course, the immense reservoir of taxable capacity represented by the trade and industry of Hooghly-side. Her dilemma, then, is obvious: rice or jute, food or cash. In any case the pressure on land is acute: Sylhet will offer some relief, but the potential *lebensraum* of Assam is lost. On the whole the alternatives appear to be injurious friction with surrounding *India* or special economic arrangements which might eventually bring E Pakistan *de facto* into the orbit of an *Indian* imperialism. This would mean a sub-continental crisis, and E Pakistan is a militarily indefensible enclave. To avert such an evolution might call for subsidies from W Pakistan (itself not over-wealthy) on a scale that could not or would not be supported.

These are very long-term views, which may be belied by events. There is indeed one probable gain—intangible but perhaps by reaction not without an economic effect—in escape from the hegemony of Calcutta, a feeling that the agrarian problems of the E will no longer be lost sight of in the unspeakably petty squabbles of the council chamber. Still, the entanglement remains, as the history of jute since Partition amply shows. By and large it seems impossible to avoid the conclusion that on every logical and rational criterion the Partition of Bengal was a profound mistake. But in view of the general irrationality of human affairs, to say that does not mean that there was any alternative to Partition, still less that what is done should be undone.

BIBLIOGRAPHICAL NOTE

The most important sources are indicated in the notes—Strickland, Bagchi, Jacks, Geddes, Chatterjee's very useful *Bengal in Maps*. Other useful works are:

C. A. Bentley, *Malaria and Agriculture in Bengal.*
R. K. Mukerjee, *The Changing Face of Bengal* (Calcutta, 1938).

There is a recent study, optimistic but not unreasonably so, by Nafis Ahmad: "Prospects of Industrial Development in Eastern Pakistan", *Economic Geography* XXVI (1950), 183–95.

[30] More illuminating than statistical tables are the sidelights on Bengali finance in R. G. Casey, *An Australian in India* (1947).

CHAPTER XX

THE EASTERN BORDERLANDS: ASSAM

(Regions VIII, XV, and XX)

The Individuality of NE India

As in the W, the En marches of India present a difficult problem of description: hills sharply marked off from the plain physically and culturally, yet so linked locationally that they have to be treated together to some extent. The State of Assam possesses a very marked individuality. It is in a sense transitional towards High Asia and Indo-China (in the broad sense), and even to China itself; the word 'Assamese' as applied to the people conceals a multitude of ethnic groups with strong Mongoloid elements, and it is significant that to mediaeval India Assam was *mlechha*—foreign. Nor were even the Moguls able to reduce the kingdom of the Ahoms, a branch of the Shan peoples of the Sino-Burman marchlands. Geomorphologically Assam consists of three entirely distinct regions, belonging to all three of the structural macro-divisions: besides the Himalayan fringe, little known and of little account, the ranges of the Assam/Burma border belong to the Extra-Peninsular mountains; the Assam or Brahmaputra Valley is an extension of the Indo-Gangetic trough; while the Shillong Plateau is essentially an outlier of the Peninsula, separated from it by the shallow Rajmahal sill stretching across the head of the Bengal Delta (Fig. 2). Finally, from the economic point of view, Assam presents the phenomenon, unique in India, of an undeveloped or even underpopulated monsoon country. Nowhere in *India* does the term "culturable waste" approach nearer to reality, and there is still room for expansion of agriculture and also (if the hydro-electric resources can be developed) of industry.

The three regions will be treated separately but, with some violence to their macro-affinities but with obvious practical convenience, in juxtaposition, followed by a discussion of some general matters affecting the whole. The fragment of Sylhet left to Assam, and lowland Cachar, are simply an extension of the Surma lowlands already treated in Bengal, and will be ignored except as they enter into statistics.

The Assam Valley

Physical Considerations

The great ramp-valley, from Dhubri to its blind end beyond Sadiya, extends for over 400 miles, with a remarkably even breadth of about 60 miles, except where the Mikir and Rengma Hills narrow it slightly. Most of this great area is formed of the detrital terraces of the Brahmaputra and its numerous tributaries. On the Nn flanks the outer ramparts of the Himalaya tower up abruptly; on the Sn the margin is less precise, the alluvium giving way to the Tertiary foothills of the Patkoi and Naga Ranges, with some outlying fragments of the older Shillong rocks along the river between Gauhati and Dhubri. On either side of the Mikir Hills the Kapili and Dhansiri Rivers form re-entrants of alluvium in a complicated area which may once have been occupied by the main Brahmaputra cutting across the Barail Range to the Barak (Surma) valley.

The master-stream is undoubtedly one of the most astonishing rivers in the world, whether we consider its immense hairpin-shaped bend (some 1800 miles from the Tsangpo sources to the Meghna confluence), the wild Dihang gorges cut some 18,000 ft below Namcha Barwa (25,445 ft) and linking the Tibetan Tsangpo with the Indian Brahmaputra, or the width and power of the main stream. Already at the Dihang-Dibong-Lohit confluence, nearly 900 miles from the sea, the stream even in the dry season is broader than Rhine or Rhone in their lower courses. At high stage, after snow-melt and in the rains, it is an immense corridor of waters five miles and more wide, with a discharge at Goalpara of over half a million cusecs. "During the second half of the monsoon period . . . the main river rises by about ten to fifteen feet, near Gauhati. Such a rise in level may not appear great if one forgets the general dimensions of the river, viz. an average width of fifteen hundred yards." [1] The channel is of course braided and shifting on a scale proportionate, a factor which hampers steamer navigation (which extends for 800 miles, to Dibrugarh) and compels settlements as a rule to lie well back, with in some cases a dry-weather extension to the shore. The great floods are a chief factor in inhibiting the clearing of the waste.

The climate shows some slight modification of the standard monsoonal type, the hot season being shorter than usual and with the low average temperature of about 85° F. This is due to the relatively large rainfall (up to 20% of the total) received in April and May from the 'Nor'-westers' (cf. p. 43); the actual amounts are 10–20 ins. or more, and are of great importance to the tea crop. Rainfall is high enough to obviate irrigation, flood being far more dangerous than drought, but there is something of a rain-shadow effect along the Sn flanks of the valley, especially in the lee of the Shillong Plateau: Sylhet gets 159 ins., Cherrapunji on the Plateau 428 (35 ft!), Gauhati only 67; this is about the minimum. Farther up the valley, however, perhaps owing to the Barail saddle, 80 ins. and more are received. Precipitation is naturally higher on the Himalayan slopes and generally the

[1] V. S. Gananathan, "Physical Environment and Human Responses in Assam", *IGJ* XXV (1950), No. 3, 1–9.

tributaries have pushed the Brahmaputra over to the S; but in the extreme E the blind end is another pocket of very high rainfall and the lie of the valley is here somewhat different.

Large areas are covered with sal forest and with tall reed-jungle in the swamps and *jhils* of the immense floodplain. In these swamps the one-horned white rhinoceros, elsewhere extinct, survives.

Indigenous Agriculture and Settlement

Of peasant-grown crops, rice and jute were by far the most important; but about 14% of the jute and 40% of the rice were in Sylhet, and the bulk of this has gone to Pakistan. Hardly any other cereals were grown; mustard (for oil), pulses, and small amounts of cotton and sugar are grown.

Agricultural Statistics, 1948–49 (thousand acres)

Total	Forest	Unculttd	NSA	Rice	Jute	Mustard	Cotton	Sugar	Tea
33,400	4,200	17,038	5,371	4,008	225	314	31	61	389

Settlements are for the most part large hamlets rather than villages, sited usually on rises or along levees; according to Ali and Lambert, Assam possessed the largest village in the world—Baniyaganj, with a population of 42,000! The settlements are surrounded by fruit trees (plantain, popaya, mango, jackfruit) and bamboo—another indication, perhaps, of the approach to the Indo-Chinese lands, where the multitudinous uses of bamboo are the most striking feature in the material culture.

Holdings are not large—perhaps 5 ac. of paddy plus small patches of vegetables, sugar-cane, areca and betel for home consumption. Goalpara Dt, however, is (or at least was) parcelled out into about 18 great *zamindari* estates, the largest covering over 1000 sq mls. It is perhaps significant that Goalpara has about a third of the jute. A notable feature of Assamese rural life is the strong hold retained by handloom weaving. The hills, of course, were hardly reached by bazaar goods until the war, which with its lavish distribution of silver rupees and large demands for paid labour has prob-ably changed all this. In 1921 there were still over 500,000 handlooms in the Province, which, with a population of 7,500,000, indicates that the great majority of families still made their own clothes. Except in the railway and river-port towns manufactured cloth only recently has seriously competed with local production. Sericulture—again on a very small scale—is also important; these crafts, of course, are mainly women's work.

The whole State below 5000 ft is highly malarial, except for the upper end of the valley where the active nature of the streams is probably respons-ible for freedom from the disease.

Tea

The most individual feature of Assamese agriculture is the great extension of tea estates; about 390,000 ac. of an *Indian* total of 780,000. The estates, 10 or 11 hundred in all, are generally located on the higher terraces of the plains/hills margins; they employed in 1941 about 450,000 hands, and tea factories employ about 80% of the pitiful total of 60,000 or so industrial workers (excluding extractive industries). Production is generally around 300 m. lbs.

The wild plant is perhaps indigenous to this Indo/Tibetan/Chinese borderland, but although experiments were made at the time of the first Burmese war (1824) the EIC had then a legal monopoly of the China trade, in which the main item was the import of tea to Europe; it is not surprising that little was done until the monopoly lapsed in 1833. The Company then started trial estates using Fukienese labour. In 1838, 12 chests reached the London market; by 1871 the total Indian output was over 6·25 m. lbs. The early days of the industry were marked by frantic speculation, non-existent estates in the midst of unmapped jungle being sold over and over again. Scarcity of local labour (except hillmen for initial clearing only) was acute, and was met by a virtual slave-trade: labour was beguiled from Bihar and Madras by glowing promises, convoyed under guard, and often kept in what were virtually concentration camps. In 18 months over 18,000 out of 50,000 coolies died or vanished into the jungle.[2]

All this is now a thing of the past. Legislation, and some degree at least of public spirit among the planting community, have made the tea-gardens almost a sheltered occupation with, as a rule, better housing, medical care, and maternity facilities than are usually the lot of Indian labour.[3]

Other Resources

The other resources of Assam, apart from oil and to a less extent coal, are virtually untapped. Although the State as a whole has more forests than any other (21,000 sq mls, of which only about 300 in Sylhet, as against 19,000 in Madhya Pradesh (CP) before the addition of the states), relatively little use is made of them. Only 6600 sq mls are Reserved Forest and the out-turn of both timber and fuel and of minor produce (bamboos, lac, resin, etc.) was about a fifth of that in Madhya Pradesh; in fact Assam

[2] In one notorious case a planter convicted of causing the death of a coolie by flogging was sentenced to 1 year's imprisonment and a fine of Rs.500. The jury was composed of tea planters. D. H. Buchanan, *The Development of Capitalistic Enterprise in India* (1934), 63.

[3] Probably the increase in the number of British wives on the plantations has had something to do with the improvement; and much relief work was done for the scores of thousands of refugees from Burma in 1942. This section of the British community appears to be a shining exception to the generally correct view of the memsahib as Britain's worst ambassador.

stands ninth on the list of timber-producing provinces. The war, of course, saw a great deal of felling for local military purposes, but this is not likely to have been well-managed from the forester's point of view. Sal and (to a small extent) teak are exploited, and tung oil trees have been introduced on some plantations. The forests are of course mainly, but not exclusively, on the hills (cf. Fig. 18).

The main extractive industry is oil. The field at Digboi is the only producer in the *Indian* Union, the tiny one at Badarpur (Sylhet) having become exhausted in 1933. The oilsands (Eocene-Miocene) are associated with the coal measures of the Eocene-Oligocene Barail series, which change laterally from hard sandstones in the Barail Range itself to carbonaceous shales and coal in the N.[4] Oil production is 65–80 m. gallons a year: coal, rather soft but of fair calorific value, about 300,000 tons (over 2% of Indian output), mainly at Margherita near Digboi. Most of it is used on the Assam railways. There are further and larger reserves, unexploited owing to lack of transport, in and around the Shillong Plateau, which may become important in the near future.

But the most important potential resource of Assam is hydro-electric power. The alliance of terrain and climate all round the flanks of the valley speaks for itself. But the economic terrain is less favourable. "To profit by [this resource], however, it is necessary to break the deadlock of industrialists declining to come to Assam owing to the absence of hydro-electric power, and Government being naturally unwilling to undertake its initiation because there are few industries." [5] At a long interval after the numerous tea factories come the wells and mines of Digboi-Margherita, employing together perhaps 15,000 workers; apart from these there are only the usual petty saw, rice, and oil mills, a little printing, and so on. But, given power, there might be a fairly wide development of fertilisers, bamboo paper, cement, and chemicals using the limestone of the hills. But at present "the industries are so scattered and so seasonal that any power scheme loaded with high capital and maintenance charges could not hope to be a paying concern for many years, and then only, perhaps, if the cheap power supply enabled considerable industrial development to take place." [6] The circularity of the argument faithfully reflects the facts. It is true that recent and forthcoming advances in long-distance transmission might make development much more practical; but the Hooghlyside market will presumably be supplied from the Damodar, and although En Pakistan urgently needs power if a jute-manufacturing industry is to be built up, this is not, perhaps and unfortunately, an argument likely to induce *India* to grant high priority to Assam schemes.

[4] D. N. Wadia, *Geology of India* (1939), 249–50, 338, 342.
[5] A. Ali and E. Lambert, *Assam* (OPIA No. 37 (1946), 20).
[6] G. Kuriyan, *Hydro-Electric Power in India* (Indian Geog. Soc. Monograph No. 1, 1945), 54.

Towns and Communications

The urban geography of Assam may be dismissed very briefly. Apart from the tiny mining towns of Digboi and Margherita, and the anomalous centres as Shillong and Imphal, the towns of any significance—Dhubri, Gauhati, Tezpur, Dibrugarh, Sadiya—are railheads and/or river ports on the Brahmaputra; and few are of any size. The great length of the valley in relation to breadth does not favour any particular centre, and the nature of the river and its floodplain offer few good sites: it is significant that Dhubri, Gauhati, and Tezpur are all on tiny outliers of the older rock of the Shillong Plateau. Gauhati, however, has grown rapidly since 1947 and has now about 75,000 people.

Roads, as a result of the war, are now numerous, but perhaps of more strategic than economic value. The Ledo Road into the Hukawng Valley, for example, has probably disintegrated under the monsoons by now. Its American builders generously presented the Hukawng section to Burma (they could hardly have taken it away); but as no conceivable gift horse could be less acceptable to the Burmese than a road by which Indians could enter, it is unlikely that its maintenance has had a high priority from a government sufficiently preoccupied by internal revolt. The old roads to such local centres in the hills as Kohima and Imphal were greatly improved during the war, and are probably more useful. Railways—about 1200 miles—are all metre gauge and ST; their most important function is to carry tea to Chittagong and packing materials back. A new railway (metre) has been built to replace the old Jalpaiguri–Dhubri line, cut by the Indo-Pakistan boundary; this gives direct access to *India* and replaces the old Jalpaiguri–Barnes Ghat ferry by a bridge.

The Shillong Plateau

The Shillong or Assam Plateau is also known as Meghalaya—'Abode of Clouds'—and is divided into the Garo, Khasi, and Jaintia Hills; but these are merely administrative or tribal divisions of one unit. Here, for the first time since leaving Potwar and the Salt Range, we meet (not without relief) some solid geology. The Plateau is in fact a detached block of the Peninsula, some 150 by 60 miles, with summit levels at 4500–6000 ft.[7] To the N the Mikir and Rengma Hills are further and more dissected outliers. The bulk of the Plateau is formed by Archaean (Dharwarian) quartzites, slates, and schists, with granite intrusions and some basic sills; but in the S these are overlain by horizontal Cretaceous and Eocene sandstones, which on the outer flank dip steeply Swds. This steep edge overlooking the Surma Valley is extremely straight and precipitous, rising over 5000 ft in 10 or 12

---

[7] The plateau is studied in detail in S. P. Chatterjee, *Le Plateau de Meghalaya* (Paris, 1936), which I have not, unfortunately, been able to consult.

miles; scoured by the highest rainfall in the world it is naturally wildly dissected and covered with dense jungle. To the E the Plateau is linked to the Barail and so to the Assam-Burma Ranges by a saddle, geologically extremely complex, which sinks below 3000 ft and is used by the Assam-Bengal railway. The recent discovery of (?Tertiary) coal on the Plateau may prove of some importance to the Assam tea industry.

Much of the Plateau is under heavy forest—with pines on the higher ridges—but centuries of shifting cultivation have produced a mixture of woodland and secondary bush (rhododendrons and orchids are prominent) with some more or less open downland.

The tribes—Garo, Khasi, Jaintia—have Mon-Khmer or Tibeto-Burman affinities: they are generally matriarchal and amongst some of them the initiative in the affairs of life, including marriage, rests of right with the

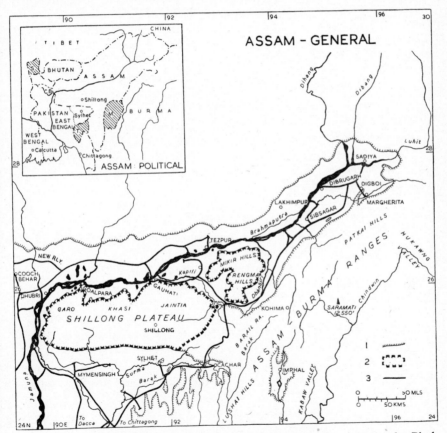

Fig. 107.—ASSAM: GENERAL. 1, boundary of alluvium; 2, outlier of Peninsular Block (small relics black); 3, railways, metre ST except Mymensingh–Dacca.
Inset: CB, Cooch Behar (now merged in W Bengal); S, Sikkim (*Indian* protectorate); M, Manipur; T, Tripura (both 'C' states under New Delhi).

women, instead of being merely usurped, as is more usual. They live by shifting subsistence agriculture (*jhuming*); the villages often shift with the fields. As in the not dissimilar Shan States, potatoes and oranges are the chief cash crops.

Shillong, the capital of Assam, is a hill station (*c.* 5000 ft) which, with its cantonments, has a population of about 60,000. It is about 45 miles from the nearest railway, but lies about half-way on the important road from Sylhet to Gauhati.

The Assam-Burma Ranges

The Shillong Plateau, with its extensions indicated by the Mikir and other outliers, plays in the NE the same role as the concealed extension of the Peninsula in the NW: around it are wrapped the Tertiary ranges of the mountain wall. The great Arakan arc consists of tightly-packed parallel ridges and valleys, in a belt 80–150 miles broad, formed of Cretaceous and Tertiary sandstones, limestones, and shales. The drainage shows an extraordinarily regular trellis-pattern, of Jura rather than Appalachian type since the folding is open and regular and relief is usually not yet inverted. The ridges are rarely over 7000 ft, though Saramati (Mt Victoria) on the actual Indo-Burmese boundary reaches over 12,000 ft.[8]

With a normally-distributed monsoon rainfall of up to 80–100 ins. the hills have a heavy forest cover, ranging from tropical evergreen with giant dipterocarps in the wetter and lower S, through monsoon deciduous to some pine and even rough grass on the highest ridges. But it has been much affected by *jhuming* (the Burmese term *taungya*, 'mountain field', is perhaps better known), resulting in very dense secondary scrub-jungle and, on the Arakan border, vast stretches of *kayinwa* bamboo, "like a hayfield 40 ft high". This is reputed to be about the most impenetrable type of jungle.[9]

The hill peoples are a mosaic of tribes, mainly Mongoloid, of whom the various Naga clans are perhaps the most prominent. Villages are on the whole more stable than on the Shillong Plateau, the houses occupying a commanding height, partly to avoid the malarial valleys and partly for defence: many are still stockaded, and head-hunting was practised until recently. Around the village the fields, in use or abandoned, spread out along the spurs, the only areas of more or less level ground. Tracks follow the ridgeways as much as possible. From the air the whole arrangement looks like a giant amoeba, the village as the nucleus, and the fields as the pseudopodia.

The peoples are attractive for the most part, with high standards of

[8] Saramati sometimes carries snow. This sudden phenomenon on an air-photo, in the midst of jungle, once gave a great deal of trouble to the topographers of South East Asia Command.

[9] But cf. Wingate's order, "No jungle is to be reported impenetrable until it has been penetrated".

courtesy and decency (perhaps moral rather than physical). But normally they contribute little or nothing to the economic life of Assam—as indeed why should they? Millet, maize, dry hill rice, buckwheat, sugar-cane, tobacco; buffaloes, goats, and poultry; and the innumerable products of the jungle, from bamboo to honey and wax, provide them with the essentials of an existence not without culture.

Routes across the hills, until the war, were for the most part mere trails: the Taungup Pass road, further S in Burmese territory, was adventurously motorable: the main route in Assam ran through Kohima to Imphal and on to Tamu, the border town in the Kabaw Valley. The main administrative centre is Kohima, a hill-top village with a few official bungalows: the District Commissioner's tennis-court, one of the few level patches, was the prize of some of the fiercest fighting in the Japanese war. But in the extreme E is a distinctive area, the state of Manipur, now directly controlled by the central Government. Here an intermont basin, floored with paddy, of about 100–150 sq mls around the reedy Loktak Lake, provides the base for a political organisation more advanced and stable than that of the jungle tribes, yet too small to stand of its own. Manipur is indeed the only parallel to the larger Shan States, with similar basin-bases, on the other side of Burma; it was bound to fall into either the Burmese or the Indian orbit, and the war of 1824–26 brought the Indian boundary to the foot of the Wn wall of the Kabaw valley, only 12–15 mls from the purely Burmese Chindwin. The lake is of course silting up; on the rather older and firmer ground to the N lies the capital, Imphal, in a sense a freak agglomeration in these scantily-peopled hills, although perhaps rather a collection of villages round the ruler's seat than a real town. None the less it is the largest settlement in *India* or Pakistan E of Dacca, with a 1941 population of 99,618.[10]

The State as a Whole: Population

In the first quarter of the 19th century large areas of the valley, especially in the E around Sibsagar, the Ahom capital, were virtually depopulated as a result of incessant Burmese incursions, and Assam is still the pioneer province of *India*. As a result of the Burmese war Assam came definitely under British rule in 1824–26, although the hills were long quasi-independent, and some were hardly administered even by 1947: there is still a small blank on the map in the Patkoi Hills. In 1892 the total population was only 5,364,000; by 1941 it had risen to 10,204,733—an increase of 90% against 39% for India as a whole. Excluding Pakistani Sylhet, the population was 7,593,037 in 1941; by 1951 it was **9,043,707**: some 20% increase in the decade. Some of this was no doubt due to better enumeration and its extension to new areas, but most to two factors; the long-standing

---

[10] The Census was taken in March, too early for military occupation to affect these figures seriously.

immigration to the tea-plantations, and a more recent drift (in the last four decades or so) of Muslim family squatters from overcrowded E Bengal, especially Mymensingh. This has affected particularly Sylhet and Cachar Dts, in the Surma-Barak valley; in 1941 these two had together 37% of the population on 17% of the area.

This immigration also affects the valley Districts, with decreasing intensity Ewds: in 1921 the Census Superintendent wrote, ". . . Darrang is being invaded. Sibsagar has so far escaped completely, but the few thousand Mymensinghias in North Lakhimpur are an outpost. . . . Where there is waste land there flock the Mymensinghias. In fact the way in which they have seized upon the vacant areas in the Assam Valley seems uncanny. Without fuss, without tumult, without undue trouble to the district revenue staffs, a population which must amount to over half a million has transplanted itself from Bengal to the Assam Valley in the last 25 years".[11]

The total area of Assam (excluding Manipur and Khasi states)[12] was 54,951 sq mls giving a density of 186. The hills together accounted for 21,816 sq mls and about 750,000 people, a density of 35 compared with 240 for the valley Districts, 569 for Sylhet, and 266 for Cachar, which includes some hill country. As a result of Partition Assam has lost the major portion of Sylhet—4621 sq mls with 2,733,000 people; but this area included over a quarter of the cultivated land of the State; and it must further be remembered that the intrusive Mymensinghia cultivated far more intensively than the Assamese, getting yields perhaps twice or even thrice as great as those of the Assam Valley folk.[13]

Sylhet was naturally the most Muslim District of Assam—61% in 1941, followed by Goalpara with 46, Cachar 38, and Kamrup 29%. Even neglecting any subsequent movements, the Partition reduced the percentage of Muslims on a 1941 basis from 34 to c. 20%.[14] This is not unimportant, as the continual influx of Mymensinghias had given rise to fears that it would "destroy more surely than did the Burmese invaders of 1820 the whole structure of Assamese culture and civilisation"[15]; especially as the intruders brought their women. Realisation of the value of this *lebensraum* led to the general inclusion of Assam in the demand for Pakistan, and specifically to the exaggerated Muslim claims before the Radcliffe Commission; and

---

[11] Quoted in Census of India 1931, Vol. I, Part 1 (India, Report), 65.

[12] Manipur 8620 sq mls, 512,069 poptn, density 59; Khasi 8788, 213,586, and 24.

[13] Ali and Lambert, 18.

[14] A fact which doubtless gave joy to Mr. V. S. Savarkar, President of the Hindu Mahasabha and old enough to know better, who in the height of the Bengal famine spoke of the influx of Muslim vagrants into Assam: "It is regretfully true that maddening hunger has driven hungry, homeless people in Bengal and Orissa in all directions in search of food. *But as far as Assam is concerned, even this madness has method in it.*" (Indian papers of 10/12/43; Mr. Savarkar's grammar, my italics.) These illiterate and starving peasants were, of course, thinking of the 1951 Census. This quotation illustrates the depths to which communalism had poisoned Indian public life: *tantum religio potuit suadere malorum.*

[15] 1931 Census, *loc. cit.*

the squatters had already given rise to serious friction between the governments of Bengal and Assam. Obviously the movement was a very salutary relief to population-saturated En Bengal, and the immigrants were agriculturally excellent colonisers; but the Partition has eased Assam's problem of assimilation, while it leaves E Pakistan with a more desperate problem of adjustment of excessive numbers to land—so desperate that some Muslim migration to Assam has persisted.

Urbanism is very slight indeed—in 1951 only 4·6% of the people lived in towns, a smaller proportion than in any other units except the very isolated and backward Punjab Hill and Orissa states. Only 200,000 were in settlements of over 10,000 inhabitants (1941).

The peoples of Assam, both valley and hills, are extremely diverse ethnically, Tribes accounting for some 33% of the 1941 population of the State as it now stands—a larger proportion than in any other large unit of *India*. In the hills of, course, they overwhelmingly outnumber other communities. Their fragmentation is extreme, some 120 languages (many, of course, closely related "splinters") being spoken. Before Independence the hills were either partly or wholly excluded from the jurisdiction of the elected provincial government; but the pious hope, voiced as recently as 1937, that the hill people might "long be spared from the terrible consequences of Western Civilisation"[16] was soon disappointed: in 1942–45 modern civilisation descended on the Assam hills in strange forms. In the new *India* the assimilation of the tribes to a more advanced economy, without their exploitation and without the loss of the many valuable elements in their own culture, will be a most delicate and difficult task. Looking to the precedents of the Gonds and the Santals, and to the general context of Indian society, it is impossible to be very sanguine of the outcome.

The State as a Whole: Prospects

Assam until 1948 did not possess a University, symbol of respectability and maturity in Indian States. Yet, as we have seen, it has a strong individuality, unique possibilities of agricultural expansion, and at least fair industrial prospects if its hydro-electric potential can be tapped. How little has been done can be seen from the extraordinarily low degree of urbanism and the fact that some 75% of the people are directly dependent on agriculture. Such development as exists has been almost entirely due to aliens, British or Indian: the Assamese themselves appear to have their share of Indo-Chinese insouciance, pleasant indeed but unpractical. The profits of production have gone largely beyond the borders: the offices of the tea companies are in Calcutta, the Provincial royalty on crude oil is negligible compared with the Central excise.[17]

[16] E. T. D. Lambert, "From the Brahmaputra to the Chindwin", *GJ* LXXXIX (1937), 32–33.
[17] Ali and Lambert, *op. cit.*, 27.

Assam was obviously more directly affected by the war than any part of India except E Bengal. It could be wished that the hillmen's introduction to modern devices had been less catastrophic; yet for the State as a whole the net effect of the war was probably a healthy stimulation of economic activity owing to the inflationary effect of the military demand for goods and services. Communications were greatly improved (even if these included a superfluity of airfields); some military installations may be of permanent use; food production was increased; technical knowledge was more widely spread. Some of these things will remain.

Materially, therefore, the possibilities are great. Yet the gains of peace may well be accompanied by loss. Assam is now *India's lebensraum*, the last frontier of settlement of any significance. The irruption of alien enterprises, the unleashing of an expansionist capitalist economy, cannot fail to have disintegrating effects on what appears to have been a reasonably well-adjusted society, in both valley and hills. Is the alternative to "an undeveloped monsoon country" with too few men to be a developed one with too many? Precedents, unfortunately, suggest that the answer will be yes.

BIBLIOGRAPHICAL NOTE

In addition to the footnote references, R. C. Muirhead-Thompson: *Assam Valley: Beliefs and Customs of the Assamese Hindus* (1948), though of little geographical interest, has two chapters on Village and Town Life. There is of course a considerable ethnographic literature, especially by Professor J. H. Hutton on the Nagas. The war also produced many books on the Burma campaigns which give an idea of the country: perhaps George Rodgers, *Red Moon Rising* (1943), is especially notable for its fine photographs.

CHAPTER XXI

THE ARAVALLIS AND CENTRAL INDIA

(Regions XV–XIX)

The Heart of India

THIS heart of India—roughly the triangle between Delhi, the Gulf of Cambay, and Bengal—is an area of great physical complexity, including as it does the very ancient Aravalli Ranges and a great series of scarped plateaus and troughs which represent the buckling of the Nn foreland of the Peninsular Block under the stress of the Himalayan mountain-building. Other elements are the peneplains of Chota Nagpur, the complex topography of the Maikal block, the highly dissected gneissic terrain of Bundelkhand, and the great Nn salient of Deccan Lava in Malwa. From a human point of view the area is transitional between the Indo-Gangetic Plains and the Deccan, lying between the two great structure-lines of Indian historical geography, that from the middle Jumna axis to Cambay, and that along the Narbada-Chota Nagpur line; and it includes the Malwa passageway from Hindustan into the Deccan. In social organisation it exhibits a widespread archaism with relatively few sectors of modern development, although it contains the most productive coalfields of India; but the general cast of society is still represented by the tribes of the junglier hills and the ancient feudality of Rajputana, with the economically more active Malwa states (Gwalior, Indore, Bhopal). This is changing rapidly, and the recent simplification of the political structure—until 1948 as complex as the physical—will bring more rapid changes.

This indeed was a great shatter-zone, stretching from Kathiawar to Orissa and containing the great majority of the nearly 600 Indian states, none of them very large in either area or population.[1] Except for Bhopal and Kathiawar, all are now either merged (nearly all into Madhya Pradesh (CP)) or have joined the three great Unions of states: Rajasthan, which corresponds to the old Rajputana Agency less Sirohi and Palanpur (to Bombay); Madhya Bharat, the largely Maratha-ruled Wn half of the old Central Indian Agency, plus Gwalior; and Vindhya Pradesh, the more backward En part of the CIA. The area also includes the major part of the Chota Nagpur Division of Bihar, E and W Khandesh in Bombay, the old British enclave of Ajmer-Merwera, the Nn Districts of Madhya Pradesh (CP), and the long, ragged projection of the UP in Jhansi Dt—presumably a

---

[1] Exception might be made for Marwar (Jodhpur) with its 36,120 sq mls; the largest population was that of Gwalior, 4,006,159.

strategic bridge of British territory to meet the Central Provinces in Saugor
Dt. Although the excessive fragmentation of British days has gone, the
area is still much sub-divided politically, and boundaries are still arbitrary
and in places fantastic, with a number of en- and ex-claves; though these
will probably be exchanged. Its political geography, then, still carried a
reflection of its past as the marchland between the powers based in the
Indo-Gangetic Plain and those of the Deccan (Fig. 112).

It seems best to begin with a general description of the whole area in its
physical aspects, since the various definite regions which it contains are
much interlinked; details will be reserved for separate sections on the nine
regions into which it may reasonably be divided.[2]

Physique. The structural setting has already been discussed (Ch. I, pp.
8–9, 11–13). The area as a whole is often termed the Peninsular Foreland
('North Indian' by Wadia; much is included in Stamp's 'Rajput Foreland'); but it seems desirable to emphasise the separateness of the Aravallis,
and for the rest the neutral 'Central India' avoids illegitimate extensions and
implications such as might be raised by the attractive term 'Vindhyan India',
which expresses the general latitudinal grain of much of the area and the
wide exposure of Vindhyan rocks.

The dominant factors in the geomorphological evolution of the area—
apart from the general opposition of Gondwana block and Himalayan folding—are probably the gnarled Aravallis in the NW, the gneissic block of
Bundelkhand in the N, the massive Archaean peneplains of Chota Nagpur
in the NE; and over against these the great Deccan table. These rigid
masses have probably controlled the layout of the plateaus and troughs
squeezed between them. Working N from the Deccan and excluding the
Thar we have:

(a) the faulted Tapti trough [3];
(b) the Satpura block, linked Ewds by the Mahadeo Hills to the
    Maikal 'culmination';
(c) the Chota Nagpur peneplains, continuing the Satpura-Maikal trends
    still farther E [4] and carrying the higher Hazaribagh Range and the
    faulted Damodar trough;
(d) the great Narbada-Son furrow, bounded sharply on the N by
(e) the *Vindhyan Hills* (Deccan Lava) and
(f) the Bhanrer-Kaimur Hills (Vindhyan *rocks*);

---

[2] The regional division is exceptionally difficult, and, although that adopted here is the
result of a good deal of permutation and combination of various possible layouts, and seems
a refinement on earlier schemes, I would emphasise that it makes no claim to be more than
convenient and provisional.

[3] From a human point of view this area might well go with the Deccan, to which it is
transitional; but the Narbada-Tapti parallelism justifies its treatment here: the Ajanta
Hills on its Sn border are the last major E/W line.

[4] 'Continuing' obviously implies no genetic relationship, merely a continuation in plan;
the links between (b) and (c) are exceedingly obscure.

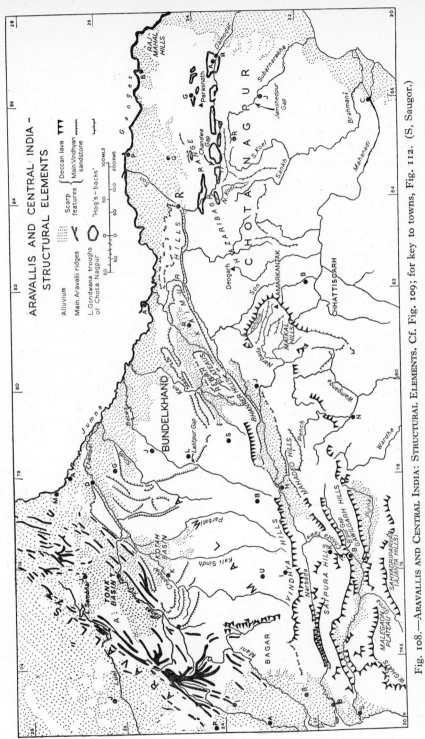

ARAVALLIS AND CENTRAL INDIA – STRUCTURAL ELEMENTS

Alluvium

Main Aravalli ridges

L.Gondwana troughs of Chota Nagpur

Scarp features

'Hog's-backs'

Deccan lava

Main Vindhyan sandstone

Fig. 108.—ARAVALLIS AND CENTRAL INDIA: STRUCTURAL ELEMENTS. Cf. Fig. 109; for key to towns, Fig. 112. (S, Saugor.)

(g) the long slope of Deccan Lavas in the Chambal basin N of the *Vindhyan Hills*, masking the Sly continuation of

(h) the triple outward-facing Vindhyan rock scarps of Nn Malwa, with a great boundary fault marking them off from

(i) the Aravallis;

(j) E of Malwa is gneissic Bundelkhand, and between it and the Narbada-Son furrow are

(k) the scarped plateaus of Vindhyan sandstone in Rewah.

It will be noted that the latitudinal belts tend to break up into En and Wn sections, shown very clearly by the difference between the Narbada and the Son Valleys. It seems likely that some deep-hidden structural feature lies transverse to the generally latitudinal lines, perhaps indicated by (i) the Gondwana Godavari trough; (ii) the Jubbulpore Gap; (iii) the Narbada/Son contrast, with the change in rock-type (Deccan Lava/exposed Vindhyan) and in direction (W/E to WSW/ENE) on the Nn flanks of the furrow, between Hoshangabad and Jubbulpore; (iv) the great E-facing scarp of Vindhyans overlooking Bundelkhand; (v) the Nn side of the Jodhpur-Jaipur saddle. Far away in the same direction [5] are the Kirana-Sangla Hills in the Punjab, which, as we have seen, attest a concealed extension of the Peninsular block. The coincidences seem too many to be fortuitous, and we have here yet another addition to the immense agenda of Indian geomorphological problems.

Grouping together some of the physical components set forth above, we may divide the whole area apart from the Thar into the following regions, some of which might, however, rank strictly as sub-regions:

1. THE ARAVALLIS
2. MALWA AND THE VINDHYAN HILLS
3. BUNDELKHAND
4. THE REWAH PLATEAUS
5. NARBADA-SON FURROW
6. SATPURA/MAHADEO/MAIKAL HILLS
7. CHOTA NAGPUR
8. THE TAPTI VALLEY

Some sub-division will, of course, be necessary in the detailed treatment.

Climatically the area ranges from the very arid Thar (5–10 ins.) to reasonably humid conditions in Chota Nagpur (45–55 ins.); the 20-inch isohyet runs roughly along a line Gwalior town–Cambay, while the country S and E of a line Rohtas–Lalitpur–Bhopal has over 40 ins. Temperatures vary to some extent with altitude and aspect: January means are around 60–65° F., May 90–95°. Daily ranges are high, as much as 20–30° F. in both of these months.

All except the more arid margins was originally forested; and even the semi-desert often carries a very open acacia scrub. Considerable areas of forest remain, especially in Chota Nagpur, and on all the higher country

[5] Hardly, as Wadia has it, "on a prolongation of the Aravalli strike".

thence to the Satpuras (cf. Fig. 19). Thorn forest prevails in the W, closed monsoon deciduous forest (largely sal) in Chota Nagpur, more or less open dry deciduous in the intervening areas; in the Thar, of course, a practically semi-desert open thorn scrub.

The Thar

Between the irrigated lands of the Indus and Sutlej riverain and the En edge of the Aravallis stretch the desert and semi-desert wastes of the Thar, covering approximately 100,000 sq mls. Most of the Thar lies in the large Rajasthan states of Bikaner, Jodhpur (Marwar), and Jaisalmer; but it also includes the En half of Bahawalpur, most of Khairpur state, and Thar Parkar Dt (Sind), these three being units of W Pakistan. The desert is not total, but bad enough; Jaisalmer has a density of under 6.

Most of the Thar is presumably a sanded-over peneplain. The strike of the great sand-ridges is generally transverse to the SW winds, but in the S, where winds are stronger, they are longitudinal to the wind-flow and up to 500 ft high. Through the sand project Vindhyan, Jurassic, and Tertiary inliers, themselves largely sandstones, and the Lower Gondwana Talchir Boulder Bed is also represented. In Jodhpur are bare rocky hills of granite and rhyolites, extrusions onto the old Aravalli surface. Of the recent deposits, the calcareous conglomerates found along the larger wadis, such as the Luni, suggest earlier more humid conditions. In the *pat* desert, adjoining Khairpur, impervious clays beneath the sand hold up groundwater, *dhands* (saline lakes) are numerous, and there is a relatively thick grass cover in the valleys.

Except in the extreme S rainfall is under, generally well under, 10 ins. Mean monthly temperatures range from 60° F (January) to 95° (May), but diurnal ranges are naturally high—20–30° at all seasons. Vegetation is extremely stunted and thorny open scrub, largely acacia: "the term 'tree' is rather a courteous acknowledgement of descent than an indication of size." [6] In the S conditions are rather better, and in good monsoons there is good grass; the limestone ridge country on the Jaisalmer/Jodhpur border N of the Luni is to some extent sheltered from sand-drift and so is rather less waste than the 'great desert' to the W or the 'little desert' to the E. But the desert seems to be gaining on the sown, perhaps by 50 sq mls a year, and it has been suggested that afforestation in the Sirohi gap, whence sand-laden winds break out on a wide front, is a primary need.

Along the old Ghaggar bed canal irrigation, mainly for wheat, has doubled the population of Bikaner in 20 years (660,000 in 1921, 1,293,000 in 1941). Elsewhere a primitive and precarious dry cultivation is carried on in the damper lows where the finer soil-particles accumulate

[6] *Rajputana Gaz.* (Calcutta, 1908), 9.

between the sandhills; bajra is the most important crop. But permanent cultivation depends on tapping the water-table, which lies deep—at 200 or 300 ft 60 miles N of the Rann. Pithawalla and Rainsinghani estimate the culturable area of the Sind portion at 15% of total area, but as this is based on a single sample of 400 ac. (about ·00058% of the area considered, and place not specified) no importance can be attached to it, and in any case both *India* and Pakistan have more urgent problems than uplifting the Thar and providing bone buttons.[7] There is, however, a more serious project for tapping by tube-wells the great underground reservoir which almost certainly underlies the upper Luni. Pastoralism is important, sheep and goats providing raw materials for the crafts of the few towns; and the camel is still one of the chief means of transport.

An economic activity of more than local significance is the exploitation of the brine pits of the Pachbhadra lake, or rather marsh; this and other salt-pans are apparently concentrations of salt particles wind-borne from the great tidal flats of the Rann of Cutch. The pits are served by a railway.

Although the population probably does not exceed 4,250,000, there are two large towns, Bikaner (**117,113**) and Jodhpur (**180,717**). These were essentially nodal centres on caravan routes, and their isolation has enabled indigenous trading families and methods to survive and flourish. Bikaner and Jodhpur have their own state railways, though the part of the Jodhpur railway outside the state boundaries and leading to Hyderabad (Sind) has been taken over by Pakistan. In the N the Ghaggar irrigation is served by separate lines in Bikaner and Bahawalpur, producing a marked 'strategic' pattern on the map. The Jodhpur railway links the Indus at Hyderabad with the better-developed E of Rajasthan, via the Sambhar saddle through the Aravallis; another link goes to Bikaner whence lines diverge to Bhatinda and Hissar in E Punjab. All these are metre ST, except the BG ST Fort Abbas loop in Bahawalpur.

The Aravallis

The Aravallis are one of the oldest mountain systems, still retaining some relief, in the world; their tight-packed synclinoria in quartzites, schists, etc., of Delhi-Dharwar age (Algonkian-Huronian) were probably first uplifted in pre-Vindhyan (pre-Torridonian) times.

From Gujarat to Delhi (430 miles) the main SW/NE strike is remarkably regular, though the steep front to the aeolian plains of the Thar is formed of discontinuous and sometimes echelonned ridges: the highest point, the great granitic mass of Mt Abu (5646 ft) lies off the main axis in the extreme

---

[7] M. B. Pithawalla and G. S. Rainsinghani, "A Plan for the Development of the Thar Desert in Sind", *IGJ* XVIII (1943), 169–96.

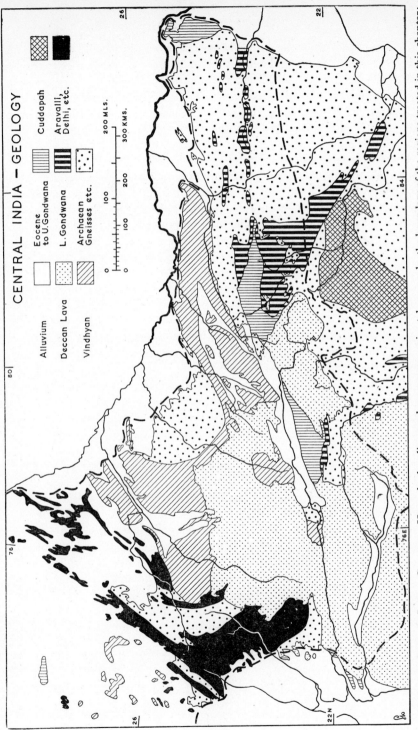

CENTRAL INDIA – GEOLOGY

Alluvium	Eocene to U.Gondwana
Deccan Lava	L. Gondwana
Vindhyan	Archaean Gneisses etc.
Cuddapah	
Aravalli, Delhi, etc.	

0   100   200   300 KMS.

0   100   200 MLS.

Fig. 109.—CENTRAL INDIA: GEOLOGY. Heavy broken line marks, very approximately as a rule, the boundary of the regions treated in this chapter; in the Thar/Rajasthan marchland no boundary is possible.

569

SW.[8] Around Udaipur the Aravallis reach their culmination (3500–4000 ft) in a great node of spurs and curving ridges; thence another series of ridges strikes off ENE along the Great Boundary Fault, enclosing the alluvial basin of Tonk and finally linking up with the Wn axis in the extremely tangled country of small quartzite hills half-smothered in the Gangetic alluvium, which lies N of the important saddle (c. 1200 ft) between Jaipur and Jodhpur.

The whole area was peneplaned in the later Mesozoic and afterwards warped, so that in Udaipur summits are around 4000 ft, S of Delhi around 1000. A probable second peneplain (on rather softer schists and gneisses) is found on the plains E of the Wn axis and in the strike valleys; much of it is covered by a thin veneer of older alluvium, which, according to Heron,[9] has itself been recently peneplaned. These Tertiary and Pleistocene peneplains meet at about 1400 ft in central Rajputana; W of the main axis the alluvium is at about 1000 ft, and smothered by the blown sand from the Thar. All the hills are dissected by generally dry but at times torrent-filled nullahs, and surrounded by pediment-fans.

There is obviously much room for human diversity in so large and physically complex an area. In the W, in Jodhpur or Marwar ('region of death') and Bikaner it merges into the Thar. Here, with a rainfall around 10 ins., "the people are semi-nomadic in habit, and on the advent of a period of scarcity they drive off their animals to other parts of the State, going as far as Kathiawar, Central India, and the Punjab in search of grazing for their cattle and work for themselves; at such times their villages are left in the charge of a few of the older men and women. . . . villages are small and consist for the most part of quite unsubstantial huts of beehive form roofed with thatch".[10] The water-table may be as much as 400 ft down, and life is harsh in the extreme.

It is easier, but not much, in the Godwar, the long daman skirting the main ridges and dissected by numerous nullahs (of which a few are perennial) flowing to the Luni, which itself reaches the Rann of Cutch—sometimes. Here, with about 20 ins. of rain and despite encroachment by blown sand (and in the Jaipur-Jodhpur saddle dunes come right across the main axis; cf. Fig. 110), irrigation is possible by wells and small tanks; possible, but difficult, since the average depth of wells in Jodhpur is estimated by Fergusson at 150 ft, and except when wells are unusually full it takes a long time to bring up the often saline water by the 30–40-gallon sacks hauled by a

[8] See Stuart Pigott, *Some Ancient Cities of India* (1945), 65–70, for a vivid description: the exfoliated boulders round the Jain sanctuary "look like nothing so much as the Creator playing at being Mr. Henry Moore."

[9] A. M. Heron, "The Physiography of Rajputana", *Proc. 25th Indian Science Congress* (Calcutta, 1938), Pt. II, 119–32. The physical account above is based on this excellent presidential address to the Geography section of the Congress.

[10] F. F. Fergusson, "Famine and Water Supply in Western Rajputana", *GJ* XCIII (1939), 39–53. This and the succeeding paragraph are based on Fergusson's work.

pair of bullocks or a camel. Hence these wells are used mainly for stock, but nearer the hills and along stream-beds Persian wheels can be used. As for the tanks, they are shallow—merely bunding across nullahs—and with an annual rate of evaporation of 7·5 ft only a few hold water for more than three or four months in the year. Their improvement by deepening and providing better drainage into them has had good results: "The annual evacuation of a number of villages has been entirely arrested, and in cases the population has shown a tendency to increase owing to former inhabitants drifting back." The effects of famine, formerly very severe, have been mitigated by the construction of metre-gauge railways. But in Jodhpur only some 700 out of 36,000 sq mls are irrigated: in good years this area could produce sufficient rabi grain (mainly wheat) to support half the population. The rainfed kharif (millets and gram) is obviously an essential part of the economy of Rajasthan W of the main Aravalli Range, and it will be equally obvious that the kharif is at best precarious.

Around the Jaipur-Jodhpur saddle are several small basins of interior drainage, of which the most important is that of Lake Sambhar, the major source of salt in N *India* now that the Salt Range has gone to Pakistan. Sambhar covers 90 sq mls when flooded, but is really a playa, almost dry in the hot weather. The salt is possibly brought by wind from the Rann of Cutch; annual output is about 250,000 tons and the reserves in the upper-most 12 ft of mud are estimated at 50 m. tons.

E of the main axis the topography is more varied. In the N the tough Delhi Quartzites form a series of flat-topped ridges, gaunt bony fingers half buried in the alluvium. Around the Banas river lies Mewar, a dissected plain of Archaean gneiss; the Banas is superimposed in a most striking manner, turning at right angles to cut through a strong Delhi Quartzite ridge at Rajmahal; its course appears to antedate the Mesozoic warping. These gneissic plains have poor, thin soils, but the numerous pegmatite (sometimes micaceous) and quartzite dykes facilitate the construction of small tanks. From Sambhar to Udaipur the Aravallis form the Gangetic/Cambay watershed; the tributaries of the Mahi, with only about one-tenth as far to go to base-level as the Banas headstreams, have dissected Sn Udaipur into a very confused terrain of innumerable valleys. This area, the Bagar, is extremely isolated, inhabited largely by Bhil tribes practising shifting agriculture.

A gnarled, dry land on the whole: rainfall varies from 11 to 25 ins. (up to 50 on Mt Abu) and is highly variable; droughts and dearths are frequent, and, on occasions such as the cloudburst of 1943, floods may burst the tanks and devastate the little cultivated valleys below. There is a good deal of forest on the hills, but of an open xerophytic type with much thorny acacia: and where it is naturally denser, in the slightly more humid SW, it has been much depleted in many places by Bhil shifting cultivators. Yet

Rajasthan is not without its favoured areas: essentially a land of refuge, last stronghold of the chivalric Rajput tradition, but with the bases for fairly extensive and solid states like Jaipur, Jodhpur, and Udaipur (Mewar).

Statistics are too incomplete for any quantitative review of agriculture. Bikaner, as we have seen (p. 567 above), has added greatly to its cultivated area by extension of irrigation from the Punjab, and more is possible: while the population of Rajputana increased by only 9% between 1891 and 1941 (against 39% for All-India), Bikaner's increase was over 55%: evidence of the generally precarious conditions of life in Rajasthan as well as of Bikaner's exceptional advantage. In the two large states of Jodhpur and Jaipur, with a total area of 33 m. ac., the cropped area fluctuates between 1·75 and 2·25 m. This is *par excellence* the millet area of India; in Jaipur about 40%, in Jodhpur about 66%, of the foodgrain area is either jowar or bajra. Wheat, gram, and pulses come next; other crops of some importance are sesamum, cotton, and sugar. Camels are important W of the main Aravalli axis, goats everywhere, with deleterious results on what vegetation cover there is.

Other resources are not great; perhaps the most important is Sambhar salt. Bikaner has a little Tertiary coal (50–75,000 tons p.a.). Small quantities of mica and graphite are mined; exploitation of the copper and zinc deposits of Zawar has begun; Jodhpur and Bikaner have considerable playa-deposits of gypsum; now that Salt Range supplies are in Pakistan, these may become more important in connection with the fertiliser factory at Sindri in the Damodar Valley, at the other end of central *India*. Ajmer-Merwara produces *c.* 100 tons of beryl a year—world output is 1000–2000 tons. The Aravallian series also contains very fine marbles of many colours, including the dazzling white Makrana marble beloved of the later Moguls and used for the Queen Victoria memorial at Calcutta.[11] But they find little demand in an India enamoured of ferro-concrete.

The 1951 population of Rajasthan (including the Thar) was *c.* 15·3 m. on 130,272 sq mls (density **117**).[12] Urbanism was a little lower than in *India* generally—rather over 14%; but a fifth of the urban population was in the three cities of Jaipur (**291,130**), Bikaner (**117,113**), and Jodhpur (**180,717**). Ajmer, capital of the tiny province of Ajmer-Merwara (2400 sq mls) had **196,633**: this was in its origin (1818) a British strategic outpost in the heart of the Rajput country. Jodhpur and Bikaner were really large caravan towns with craft industries originally dependent on their princely courts; Bikaner's growth since 1891 has been remarkable (132%), a reflection of the general development of the state. Jaipur, the capital of Rajasthan, is

---

[11] See the discussion on Fergusson's paper for an account of the probably unique occasion on which Lord Curzon was *left* in a minority of one.

[12] Besides the Aravallian states, Rajasthan also includes: Jaisalmer in the Thar; Alwar and Bharatpur on the margins of the Upper Ganges Plains; Dholpur and Karauli on the Vindhyan Plateau along the Chambal; Kotah and Jhalawar in Malwa; and Tonk, scattered about all over the place. 1941 population; *c.* 13 m. (increase 1941–51, 20·5%).

perhaps the most interesting of the towns; in an excellent position on the more favoured side of the saddle, it was the centre of the finest flowering of Rajput culture under the remarkable astronomer-prince Jai Singh (*fl.* 1699–1743); like Udaipur in the S, it attracts some tourist traffic, to Amber or Old Jaipur, a romantically beautiful fortress and palace town on the hills above. Modern industry is negligible in Rajasthan, except for the state

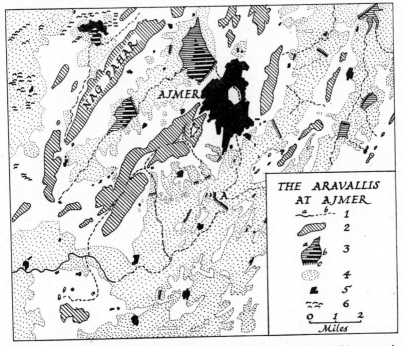

Fig. 110.—THE ARAVALLIS AT AJMER. 1, streams (a) perennial, (b) seasonal; 2, over 2000 ft; 3, (a) seasonal and (b) perennial tanks, (c) bunds; 4, cultivation; 5, settlement; 6, sand-dunes creeping in from Thar. Some of the larger ridges carry rather open forest; the *daman* around them (area left white) is mostly open scrub and waste, dissected by many dry stream beds, and W of Nag Pahar ('Snake Hill') very badly ravined. Cultivation mainly by bunding valleys; note how tanks have been silted out of existence, e.g. at A. SOI 45 J/11; courtesy SOI.

railway workshops, but the old Court-fostered crafts—fine textiles and metal work—retain some importance.

Tonk is ruled by the descendant of a particularly shifty 18th century Muslim freebooter, sufficiently adroit to be more or less in with and more or less a nuisance to both British and Marathas. The other princes are Rajputs, the flower of the Kshatriya or warrior caste, claiming descent from the Sun, the Moon, or more modestly from the heroes of the *Mahabharata* epic: at all events, their genealogy is of respectable antiquity in a country where (contrary to popular belief) most of the princely states represent simply the more successful bandits of the moment when British hegemony froze the 18th century chaos. The Rajputs were forced into their hills by Muslim invasions into Hindustan proper; Rajput princelings are also found to the N of the Delhi doab, in the Himalayan foothills. Favoured by Akbar, they still, perhaps, represent the values of a feudal age, on the whole in its better aspects. Of the peoples of Rajasthan, the great majority are Hindus; but aboriginals (mostly in the S) number over 1,500,000, and Jains over 325,000—a quarter of the Indian total. Their devotional life centres on the temples of Mt Abu, fantastically sculptured and fretted in white marble; their more mundane interests take them as far afield as Calcutta and Rangoon, where 'Marwari' traders and moneylenders are a power in the land, and, if common repute be true, by no means always a beneficent power. The exaggerated sanctity attached even to insect life apparently does not extend to the livelihood of less adroit men.

Malwa

Malwa forms a great triangle, based on the *Vindhyan Hills* [13] and bounded on the NW by the Great Boundary Fault of the Aravallis, on the E by the sharply-defined scarp overlooking Bundelkhand. Most of it is drained by the Chambal and its right-bank tributaries; but it includes in the SE the upper courses of the Ken and Betwa, in the SW a very irregular and dissected Deccan Lava brow overlooking the wild Bagar.

Physically it falls into two very different divisions, which might indeed form separate regions but for the practical difficulties of treatment on a reasonable scale. These are the Vindhyan scarplands of the N, the great Deccan Lava plateau in the S (Figs. 108, 109).

The major Vindhyan scarps (1500–1900 ft), formed in massive sandstones and separated by shales, are three, facing outwards—to the SSE between Banas and Chambal, to the E over Bundelkhand; the general effect is that of a syncline pitching S. In the NW there is a strong scarp-feature flanking the left bank of the Chambal, and beyond this a scarped block occupying the states of Dholpur and Karauli. Here the usually almost horizontal Vindhyans are folded and faulted, presumably by the rigid Aravallis which are overthrust onto them along the Boundary Fault. This contact may have been responsible for the warping of the Mesozoic peneplain in the Aravallis; warping and the displacement of the Boundary Fault are of the same order, 4000–5000 ft diminishing NE and SW. [14]

The river system is interesting. The Chambal, Ken, and Betwa rise within 20 miles of the Narbada and appear as consequents on the Mesozoic surface, superimposed on the scarps: the Chambal in particular cuts

[13] In this chapter *Vindhyan Hills* is italicised to avoid confusion with the large areas of Vindhyan rocks.
[14] Heron, *loc. cit.*, 123, 129.

straight across them, with subsequent tributaries on the softer shales. In the E the Kunu and Kunwari appear subsequents, but the former cuts through the innermost scarp at Nayagaon; it may have developed as a consequent on an older surface and reached its present position by lateral shifting down the dip. The Chambal and its tributaries Kali Sindh and Parbati have formed a triangular alluvial basin at about 700–900 ft in Kotah, above the narrow trough of the lower Chambal; gullying along their banks suggests slight recent rejuvenation.

The Deccan Lavas of the S abut on the outer scarp, and their eroded edge suggests that the main lineaments of the underlying Vindhyans are similar to those exposed on the N. They form a great table-land, rising gently from about 1400 ft in the N to 2500 in the great brow overlooking the Narbada. This 'scarp' is known as the *Vindhyan Hills* but it hardly deserves that name: big, bold, and impressive from the trough below, from above the existence of the scarp is hardly suspected until one is almost on the edge: at Mhow, only 12 miles to the N, there is nothing to suggest that the gently undulating plateau does not extend indefinitely Swds. S of Bhopal the scarp is formed in a window of Vindhyan rocks; here the main Bombay–Agra railway climbs it by a narrow transverse valley. In places there are sheer precipices of 400–600 ft; but even here the box-like Vindhyan Sandstone mesas soon give way to the gentler outlines of the lavas.

Such are the general features of relief: in aspect, of course, there is a great contrast between the Vindhyan and the Deccan Lava landscapes. The former is harsher, bonier, more rugged and more arid in appearance: an alternation of large or small basins with large or small plateaus, often with sheer walls of 200–400 ft. Large parts of it have only a few inches of soil, or even bare peneplaned rock-surfaces in places: poor grassland and open acacia scrub interspersed with rather poor agriculture. The lava country as far S as Indore is practically a peneplain; beyond this it rises into gentle swells, with few of the mesas so typical of Maharashtra (below, 646). Cultivation appears much more widespread and flourishing; it might almost be an E Anglian landscape minus its hedges, but a little too big and coarse in scale. Along the *Vindhyan Hills* the country becomes wilder; woodland (with teak) predominates, but is very open in many places, with almost more glade than trees, and the rounded hills give a Hercynian effect.

In the N, except in the larger alluvial plains, villages show marked topographical preferences, nestling at the foot of scarps, at gaps, grouped around forts on little isolated hills. On the more homogeneous lavas topographical influence is naturally less marked; settlement is so confined to rises, and rises to settlement, as to suggest that the hillocks on which the villages stand are simply the accumulated rubbish of generations. Houses are of stone (especially in the Vindhyan country) or mud, roofs of thatch or stone slabs or, in the S, semi-cylindrical tiles reminiscent of the Deccan. Fields in the Vindhyan country are sometimes bounded by mud or dry-stone walls capped with thorns. The *Vindhyan Hills* themselves are very empty, and in places wood-cutting for fuel or charcoal appears a main activity.

Again there is little quantitative information on agriculture; only Gwalior, Indore, and two or three minor states published statistics. With rainfalls of 25–35 ins., and fairly high variability, millets—mainly jowar— are of course dominant, with cotton a strong second on the moisture-retaining black soils (regur) of the lavas. The contrast suggested in the preceding

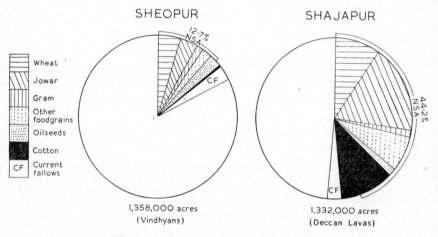

Fig. 111.—The Lava/Vindhyan Contrast.

paragraphs is strikingly brought home by the land-use figures for two Districts of Gwalior. Sheopur is entirely Vindhyan, lying along the right bank of the Chambal from the Parbati to beyond the Kuni confluence; Shajapur entirely Deccan Lava. The areas are very comparable, but Shajapur has much the greater population—382,897 against 144,313 (densities 155 and 61) (Fig. 111).

Agricultural Statistics in thousand acres, 1938–39

	Total	NSA	CF	Irrig.	Wheat	Jowar	Gram	All FGs	Oilsds	Cotton
Sheopur	1358	173	37	7	61	47	17	153	36	0·5
Shajapur	1332	589	37	24	124	237	19	464	15	153

Only about 4% of the cultivated area (*c.* 8·5 m. ac.) of Madhya Bharat is at present irrigated, but the Chambal multi-purpose scheme proposes to irrigate 1·1 m. ac. and to develop 72,000 kW. Half of the Central Government's reclamation of "culturable waste" by tractors is being carried out in Madhya Bharat.

Historically Malwa displays a curious duality: the Deccan Lavas provide the only really extensive agricultural base in central India, and so it has retained its individuality; yet, as a land of passage, it has constantly changed hands, "the invariable appanage to the domains of every monarch, native or barbarian, who became the master of the Gangetic plain".[15] This is too strong; but Fig. 33 (Ch. VI) indicates that the frontiers are least persistent in the N. This is, in part at least, inherent in the geography of Malwa compared to that of its neighbouring regions. On the one hand lie the burning wastes of the Thar and the natural and artificial strongholds of the Aravallis; on the other the mass of excessively broken and jungly terrain around the Maikal Hills, and farther E the broad forested plateaus of Chota Nagpur. The Son, pent in between Vindhyan cliffs and Gond jungles, has never been an important entry; in any case it leads backwards, as it were, in relation to the drive of invaders down the Ganges. The centre of power in the N—continuously since the Muslim conquests, and often before them —was in the Delhi-Agra region: the way into the S Country, Dakshina or Deccan, was over the more open Deccan Lavas. The *Vindhyan Hills* and the Narbada once crossed, the Burhanpur gap and the broad embayment of Chalisgaon led on to Nasik. The more difficult part of the Malwa passageway is in the Vindhyan N: it is significant that the railways avoid the funnel of the lower Chambal. One line crosses the Karauli Plateau into the Tonk basin, reaching the Chambal well up, almost on the Deccan Lavas, by the gap at Indorgarh (which incidentally looks as if the Aravalli/Vindhyan boundary ranges have been breached by superimposition or river capture); the other goes through Bundelkhand and reaches the lava plateau by a well-marked gap S of Lalitpur, where the Vindhyan outcrop is reduced to a single narrow scarp.

In peace, as in war, the Malwa route was one of the most significant in India; alike in Ptolemy's day and in that of the Discoveries, it led from the Cambay sea-entry at Barygaza (Broach) or Surat to Ujjain and so by Bhilsa, with its great Buddhist monuments, to Pataliputra (Patna), later to Agra and Delhi. With the coming of the railway and the concentration of so much of India's trade on Bombay the actual lines of movement shifted, but they remain within this broad zone.

Karauli, Dholpur, Kotah, Jhalawar are Rajput; the Madhyabharat states nearly all Maratha 18th century foundations by chiefs of that great but loose confederacy. The most important are Gwalior and Indore, which

[15] 1931 Census, Vol. XX, Pt. I, 3.

together accounted for *c.* 77% of the area and of the population of the union.[16] Bhopal was Muslim-ruled; it is probably in virtue of the isolated position of the Nawab of Bhopal that the state has come under direct Central control. These three states were among the most progressive in India, and the formation of the Union cannot fail to improve standards of administration and services. Some 80% of the population of Malwa is Hindu, the rest mainly tribal.

Indore (**310,859**) is the largest town, outranking Gwalior (or rather Lashkar, **241,557**); but the latter, as capital of the largest unit and of the union, has rather more general importance. Bhopal (**102,333**) is less significant. Indore reflects the generally higher standards of the cotton-growing lavas; it has a number of cotton mills and other light industries. Lashkar, 'the Camp', is the new (18th century) town below the old stronghold on the astonishing Rock of Gwalior, a cliffed plateau nearly two miles long rising sheer 300 ft from the plain, fortified all round the periphery, and carrying in the cliff rock-cut Jain statues nearly 60 ft high. This stranded Gibraltar is one of the most impressive holds in a country liberally provided with *tours-de-force* of fortification.[17] Lashkar itself is a flourishing industrial centre, with cotton, leather, pottery, light engineering, quarrying, and cigarette-making; the flying-boat station on Tigra reservoir is a useful half-way-house on the Karachi–Calcutta run. The only other town of note is Ujjain (**129,817**), the traditional capital of Malwa, in a Sn outlier of Gwalior on the lavas. It also has cotton mills, but is more famous for its brilliant past, whether commercial as an important stage on the Jumna–Cambay trade route, or cultural as the half-legendary seat of King Vikramaditya, the traditional patron of Kalidasa who immortalised the city in the most splendid of Sanskrit lyrics, the *Meghaduta* or *Cloud-Messenger*. Through Ujjain, regarded as the centre of the world, ran the prime meridian of Sanskrit geographers; Jai Singh of Jaipur could hardly overlook so fitting a site for an observatory, and his calculation of its latitude, 23° 10′, was only one minute out.

Bundelkhand

Bundelkhand need not delay us long: physically it is a homogeneous dissected upland, politically it is occupied by some of the more obscure states of backward Vindhya Pradesh, with a tongue of UP territory in Jhansi Dt. The country is recognisable at once, without a geological map: a mass of rounded hummocky hills, with almost a *roches moutonnées* effect,

---

[16] Areas and populations (1941): Madhya Bharat, 46,710 sq mls and 7,151,502 (Gwalior, 26,367 and 4·0 m.; Indore, 9934 and 1·5 m.); Bhopal, 6921 and 0·8 m. 1951 poptns: M.B., **7,954,154**; Bhopal, **836,474**.

[17] The aspect of central India, where every tactical strongpoint carries its keep, hardly corroborates the view of a mythical golden age when such wars as there were passed harmlessly over the peasant in his fields. Robber barons were probably much the same on the Chambal or on the Rhine.

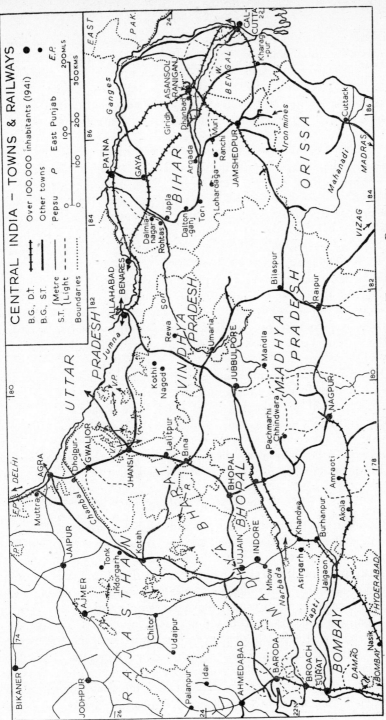

Fig. 112.—Aravallis and Central India: Towns and Railways.

typical tropical exfoliation-weathering in the reddish Bundelkhand Gneiss, cut across by innumerable white quartzite dykes, in all sizes from veins of a few inches to massive walls. The frequent constriction of drainage by the dykes favours a multiplicity of small half-natural half-artificial tanks and so enables agriculture to be carried on with some security in a region of variable rainfall, around 45 ins. The vegetation is largely open scrub and bush.

Agriculture is extensive, and pulses and gram bulk large. "Proper soil preparation has to give place to hurried tillage, and single crops to mixtures like gram and wheat, or gram and linseed, or even gram, linseed, and wheat in the rabi, and sesamum and arhar, or jowar and arhar, in the kharif. In the hope of striking a lucky combination of a large sown area and a favourable season more land is farmed than can be properly controlled with the man and bullock power available." [18] Hence the spread of *kans*, a weed of creeping habit, which is controlled—again extensively—by grazing it for 15 years or so, or flooding it for a couple of monsoons. There is much rough grazing, and the number of cattle owned is often evidence of status.

Villages are small, stoutly built, often of stone; outer walls are blind and doorways massive and low—relics of the old insecurity visibly attested also by the hill-top holds which are easily the most striking features of the cultural landscape.

The only centre of any importance is the railway town of Jhansi (**127,365**). The last Rani of Jhansi is a romantic figure in the gallery of Indian national heroes: described by her opponent Sir Hugh Rose as the best and bravest of Mutiny leaders, she was killed in action at the age of 20, riding as a trooper; she is not alone as a reminder that generalisations about Oriental subjection of women are generalisations after all, and that human realities will break through the forms of social convention.

The Rewah Plateaus

The country between Bundelkhand and the Son is occupied by a great series of wall-sided plateaus, a belt 300–400 miles long and 50 wide, terminating very abruptly in the S in the Kaimur scarp dominating the Son; less abruptly, but still sharply enough, in the N. The Vindhyans are mainly massive sandstones, with some limestones and shales. The Kaimur crest lies at 1500–2000 ft, rising 1000 ft above the Son; except for a very narrow strip along the Son, discussed in the next section, most of the drainage is to the Ganges via the Ken or the Tons: these rivers cross the Nn scarp in a series of falls and cascades. Above the scarp they are mature, and much of the region is a high alluvial plain at about 1000 ft.

Rainfall is 40–50 ins.; there are many tanks, but probably more ground is

[18] W. Burns (ed.). *Sons of the Soil* (ND, 1941), 46. Arhar is a highly nitrogenous pulse (*Cajanus indicus*).

cultivated by bunding valleys and sowing in the moist soil after the rains: this gives relatively high yields. Much of the alluvium is a fertile black loamy soil well adapted to wheat. The margins and much of the higher ground within the plateau are forested.

The whole area is extremely isolated and backward, and recent information on it is almost nil. Despite the fair rainfall and soil conditions, probably not more than 20–25% of the area is cultivated. The principal crop is probably *kodon*, the smallest of the millets, which is adapted to poor soils with fairly good rainfall. Rice, wheat, and maize account for the bulk of the remaining cultivation. Other economic development is negligible, and the only town of any size is Rewah (26,008), capital of Vindhya Pradesh. State capitals such as Kothi and Nagod are mere villages of 4–6000 people. So backward is Vindhya Pradesh that its administration was soon taken over by Delhi.

The Narbada-Son Furrow

This "region" falls into two very distinct sections: the alluviated fault-trough of the Narbada, and the much narrower but more complex immediate valley of the Son. The two are curiously interdigitated N of Jubbulpore. To the N the Vindhya-Kaimur scarps flank the trough for 600 miles or more.

(a) The *Narbada* rises on Amarkantak, most prominent of the Maikal Hills, and has a complex course as far as the Marble Rocks gorge, below Jubbulpore. Below this it enters the great trough; the rift character is illustrated by a boring, only four miles within the alluvium, which found no solid rock at 491 ft. The geomorphological problems presented by the Narbada and Tapti have been discussed in Ch. I (pp. 9–10 and Fig. 4); we need note here only that the steepness and straightness of the lower Narbada gorges suggest a recent origin, and that it seems likely that the Narbada originally flowed out on the Tapti line via the Burhanpur Gap.

The human interest of the Narbada is considerable. Its sanctity is rivalled only by the Ganges; indeed local patriotism avers that mere contemplation of the Narbada is as efficacious as bathing in the Ganges, which, in the form of a black cow, must be washed white of her annual accumulation of sins in the Narbada. High merit may be obtained by the *pradakshina*, a pilgrimage up one bank from Broach to Amarkantak and down the other; the round trip is about 1600 miles. The river historically was considered as the boundary between Madhyadesa and Dakshinapatha, the Middle and the S Land; to the Marathas all to the N was foreign—and indeed, as we have seen, the river forms part of the most persistent internal frontier in India.[19]

The *Vindhyan Hills* rise steeply to heights of 1000 ft above the valley-floor. To the S the Satpura and Mahadeo scarps are less well-marked and

[19] *Central India Gaz.* (1908), 104–5.

less continuous, yet bold enough. The valley-floor is some 20-40 miles wide
and the river is countersunk some 20-40 ft within it. This is unfortunate
since rainfall is only about 30 ins. and irrigation would be useful, but is thus
inhibited; the hill streams on either side offer no scope for dams, and the
valley-floor is badly gullied by the Satpura torrents. Wheat, cotton, jowar,
and sesamum are the chief crops. Lumbering and charcoal-burning are
important on the bordering hills, particularly perhaps on the Mahadeo
slopes. The lower gorges run through almost empty forest country, inhabited
mainly by Bhils.

The Sn side of the trough is followed by an important railway between
Jubbulpore and Khandwa, whence it crosses to the Tapti. Two lines cross
the Narbada: a metre line Khandwa–Indore (and so to the N by Kotah), and
the BG Itarsi-Bhopal, part of the main Bombay–Agra–Delhi line.

Khandwa and Hoshangabad are local centres: the site-values of the
former, at the debouchment of the Burhanpur Gap and the bifurcation of
the two railways, are obvious; the latter is on the actual main-line crossing
of the Narbada. Both are outshadowed by Jubbulpore (**256,998**), occupying a commanding position at the head of the Narbada trough, with
relatively easy routes N around the end of the Bhanrer Hills to Allahabad,
S between the Mahadeo and Maikal Hills to the Wainganga Valley and the
Deccan: Narbada and Wainganga headwaters approach to within 2 or 3
miles of each other, in a col not much over 1500 ft above sea-level. The
Bombay–Allahabad line was the first through rail route in India (1870),
linking Bombay with both Calcutta and Delhi; not till 1888 and 1889
respectively were more direct lines opened. These have to some extent
weakened Jubbulpore's relative position, but its advantages of centrality and
nodality have led to some canvassing of its suitability as a capital. The tradition of Delhi is too strong, however; meanwhile Jubbulpore remains as the
only large town in a very wide area, with railway shops and some modern
industry, chiefly cotton.

(b) The *Son*, in sharp contrast to the Narbada, is not followed by a railway, nor even a road; the physical interest of its valley far outweighs the
human, and it has a very different history from that of the Narbada.[20]

For some 300 miles the river runs close under the Kaimur scarps rising
500–1000 ft above the narrow valley-floor. Mainly resistant sandstones
interbedded with porcellanite (volcanic ash), the Kaimurs are practically
the watershed, only a few very short obsequents cutting back and developing subsequents along the shales between the more massive sandstone
members; here and there Ganges drainage has been captured (Fig. 113 (A)).

---

[20] R. D. Oldham analysed the evolution of the Son landscape in detail in "Notes on
the Geology of the Son Valley" (*Mem. GSI* XXXI (1901), 1–178). This excellent paper,
with some by Vredenburg and others, is evidence of an early but unfortunately short-
lived interest in geomorphology among the Survey geologists; in recent years only Wadia
and Heron have shown any special interest in this aspect.

Nor are there any deeply-cut windgaps to suggest an originally Nwd consequent drainage dismembered by the growth of the Son as a strike stream. This lack of windgaps is an anomaly in so long a scarp, and the asymmetry of the valley is also very striking: although the Nn watershed is so close to the river, there are several right-bank tributaries rising 100 miles away. In places the Son is definitely superimposed (Fig. 113 (B)). Oldham envisaged a peneplain with very open relief of the order of 300 ft, with the Kaimur scarp already outlined but much lower: general uplift and a lowering of the valley-floor later etched it out.

There is little alluvium along the Son; in Mirzapur (UP) the river is sunk in a low terrace, which disappears Wwds in Rewah. Farther up there are, of course, alluvial patches, and in some places fine unstratified loams which seem aeolian. There is evidence of slight recent rejuvenation, but Oldham thinks that it is at least as likely that the change is due to the extensive clearing of forests as to a general movement of elevation.[21]

[21] *Loc. cit.*, 51. This remark has probably a wider application.

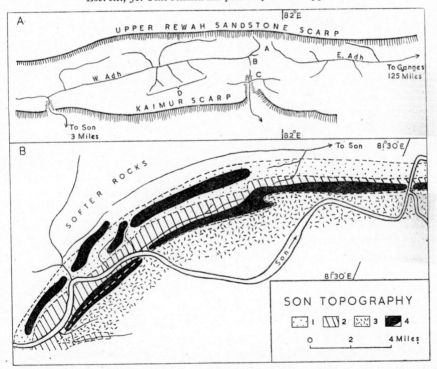

Fig. 113.—SON TOPOGRAPHY. **A:** A, broad open valley; B, recent steepening; C, gorge with boulders too large for transport by misfit stream (originally flowing to N); D, main valley cut down, side valleys rejuvenated owing to capture by W Adh.
  B: 1, volcanic ash (porcellanite); 2, shales with hard quartzite capping; 3, crystalline gneisses, etc.; 4, high ridges.
  Based on R. D. Oldham, *Mem. GSI* XXXI (1901); courtesy GSI.

The Son Valley is in general an empty land of great sal forests, with isolated patches of subsistence cultivation. Only where it begins to open out into the Gangetic Plain is there much development. Here, near Rohtas, an outcrop of 'fat' (80% calcium carbonate) limestone in the Kaimur scarp has been exploited for cement works at Japla (connected with the quarries by a 5-mile ropeway across the Son), Dalmianagar, and Kalyanpur. Clay is available locally, coal from the little Daltonganj field some 40 miles away; only gypsum has to be brought from the Punjab or Rajasthan. Dalmianagar, founded by the self-made magnate Seth Dalmia, is a model industrial town with over 5000 factory workers: the largest unit is the paper factory. This, with 1600 employees and a capacity of 10,000 tons a year, is the third largest in India, producing in 1944 about 9% of the total Indian output. The raw materials are mainly bamboo, largely from the Kaimur talus-slopes and rafted down the Son, or by rail from the N Koel Valleys. Other lines in a well-integrated set-up are alkalis and sulphuric acid, a vegetable ghee factory, sawmilling, carpentry, and so on.[22]

The Satpura-Mahadeo-Maikal Ranges

The Narbada is flanked to the S by a series of scarped plateaus, generally at 2000–3000 ft. In the W the Satpuras ('Seven Folds') proper are simply a steep-sided Deccan Lava block, sinking between Burhanpur and Khandwa to 1200 ft in the gap followed by the main Bombay–Agra railway and guarded by the great hill-fort of Asirgarh. As we have seen, the Narbada may have flowed through this gap; the Chhota Tawa valley suggests the actual course. In the angle between the upper Tapti and its tributary the Purna the Gawilgarh Hills are another Deccan Lava horst: the displacement along the fault which bounds them to the S is between 1800 and 4000 ft. Farther E, in the Mahadeo Hills (sometimes included in the Satpura Range), is a great window of Archaeans and Middle Gondwanas, thick masses of red sandstones forming small plateaus with precipitous scarps. E again, beyond the Jubbulpore Gap, the great bastion of the Maikal Range is crowned by Amarkantak (3493 ft), the sacred mountain in which the Narbada rises. Most of this dissected plateau drains by deep-cut valleys into the Narbada; but in the extreme E the Johilla tributary of the Son has a curious course separated from the broader parallel valley of the upper Son by a narrow ridge of Deccan Lava. The plateau is tilted to the NW, falling from 3000–3500 ft in the abrupt scarp overlooking Chhattisgarh to about 2000 ft around Mandla where the Narbada headstreams converge.

Economically this is on the whole a poor area. Some manganese is worked on the Sn Mahadeo flanks, and there is a small coalfield near Chhindwara in the Pench Valley (output c. 0·75 m. tons p.a.). In the Maha-

[22] Details from S. A. Majid, *The Industrial Geography of Bihar* (London Ph.D. thesis, 1949), Ch. VIII and pp. 327–32.

deos the upper Wainganga and Pench Valleys widen out into small plains where wheat, jowar, kodon, and a little cotton and sugar are grown; elsewhere agriculture is very patchy, except perhaps in the Burhanpur Gap, while on the higher hills to the E shifting cultivation is carried on by the various Gond tribes who have given their name not only to all the area between the Son and Chhattisgarh, but (through the Gondwana rocks) to the great ancient landmass which bulks so large in geological history. There is some good grazing, and lumbering is important: the hills still carry much forest, though on their lower skirts this is very open and scrubby, and in many places shifting cultivation has had serious effects. Sal is important in the E, except on the lavas; there is some teak in the W, and bamboos are widespread. The most striking features of the cultural landscape in the tiny towns strung out along the Khandwa-Itarsi railway are timber yards and charcoal kilns.

Pachchmarhi (c. 3500 ft) is a local hill station; Chhindwara a very minor administrative centre. Otherwise there is no urban development worth mentioning, except Khandwa and Burhanpur, and these are really in the Narbada and Tapti Valleys respectively. The whole region is in fact a barrier broken by the two gaps, at Asirgarh and S of Jubbulpore.

Chota Nagpur and the Damodar

(a) *The Plateaus*

E of the ridge separating the Johilla and the Son is a mass of extremely confused hill country around Deogarh (3365 ft) on the very irregular Son-Mahanadi watershed. It is formed mainly of Gondwana rocks with patches of Archaeans and Deccan Lavas—the last outposts of these; at Umaria is an extraordinary occurrence of marine Permians, and a tiny coalfield. There is no doubt that geomorphologically this country would be extremely interesting if it were known; but geographically speaking it is *terra incognita*, rocky, jungly, isolated, backward, and almost empty.

Beyond the Behar tributary of the Son, however, we have firmer lines: a great rectangle of some 40,000 sq mls, mainly Archaean gneisses forming rolling peneplains, bisected longitudinally by the fault-trough of the Damodar with its Lower Gondwana coal. Most of this area lies in the Chota Nagpur Division of Bihar, which extends beyond it into the Jamshedpur Gap.

The Hazaribagh peneplain N of Damodar lies at about 1300 ft.[23] Across it, and slightly diagonal to its E/W extension, runs the Hazaribagh "Range", really a higher plateau (c. 2000 ft) with some monadnocks rising to 2800 ft. The plateau on the whole is rather open, and there is a fair amount of cultivation. On the N it falls abruptly, but with many irregular spurs and outliers covered with open jungle, into the Gangetic Plain; to the SE the

[23] The succeeding paragraphs are based on P. Dayal, *The Agricultural Geography of Bihar* (London Ph.D. thesis, 1947).

descent is more gradual and the upper Ajai and Damodar-Jamunia Valleys provide routes across the plateaus giving Calcutta direct access to the Middle Ganges Plain. In the NE the Rajmahal Hills, highly dissected plateaus of basalts of Gondwana age, rise steeply from the alluvium in the great bend of the Ganges. Considering the terrain they are well cultivated and densely peopled[24]; the Santals occupy the broader valleys, keeping large herds of buffaloes in the smaller side-valleys, while on the higher ground the Paharias ('Hillmen') cultivate remarkably steep slopes.

The Damodar Basin will be treated separately. S of it lie the Ranchi peneplains. In the E is the country of the *pats*: little plateaus, largely basalt, with intricately fretted and extremely steep sides, the relics of a peneplain at about 3600 ft. Some of their flat tops are cultivated, but soils are lateritic and their jungle-covered walls make many of them practically inaccessible. The main peneplains are at about 2500, 2000 (the most extensive), and 1000 ft, the last bordering the Subarnarekha; open, broadly rolling country, with mature valleys (Sankh, S Koel) bordered, however, by low gullied terraces.[25] They are broken by monadnocks, fantastic cones and domes of gneiss "looking as if they had been exuded from the earth as gigantic bubbles that had become solid instead of bursting."[26] E of the Subarnarekha the plateau sinks gradually into the deltaic alluvium, and is generally veneered with laterite.

Much of Chota Nagpur, especially perhaps the centre and the W, is forested; 10,000 sq mls, or about one-third of the area of the whole Division. But about 80% of this forest was not protected, and much of this is of course bad scrub jungle. Nevertheless the collection of minor forest produce is an important occupation; the flowers of the mahua tree are collected for the distillation of country spirit, and they may become a valuable source of power-alcohol. Chota Nagpur is the most important Indian producer of lac—a sticky exudation from insects parasitical on certain trees, used for shellac, varnishes, etc. Bamboo and *sabai* grass for the Dalmianagar paper mill, pit-props for the coalfields, are also important. But agriculture is far from negligible.

Soils, indeed, are for the most part thin and poor—sandy or clayey red soils on the gneisses, badly leached and deficient in organic material, nitrogen, and lime. In enclosed fields around the villages, however, even these upland soils, highly if erratically manured, can give two crops a year—often maize followed by rabi mustard. On the valley-slopes terracing for paddy catches the soil-wash, checking erosion and retaining sub-soil water.

---

[24] Density of Santal Parganas (including a very narrow alluvial fringe) 408, against 240 for Chota Nagpur excluding Manbhum with its coalfields.
[25] Rejuvenation, or erosion by greater run-off due to forest clearance?
[26] G. C. Deprée (1868), quoted Dayal, *op. cit.*, 31. The area is described by S. P. Chatterjee in the *Calcutta Geographical Review* II, No. 1 (1938), 45–48; VII, Nos. 2–3, 31–35.

Rainfall is generally adequate, though not too reliable: only the Nn fringe of the Hazaribagh Plateau and the lowest part of the Damodar Basin receive less than 50 ins., and the higher plateaus S and W of Ranchi have over 60; as usual 85–90% falls in the monsoon months, but in the SE there are 4–5 ins. in March–May inclusive, a continuation of the Bengal régime. But much of the rice is not irrigable, and there is a certain precariousness. The general agricultural pattern is indicated by the following figures for the five Bihar Districts considered here [27]:

	Total 1000 ac.	Forest 1000 ac.	Forest %	TSA 1000 ac.	TSA %	% TSA:			
						Rice	Maize	Gram	Oil-seeds
Palamau .	3139	1345	42·8	627	20	28·2	10·8	7·8	12·6
Hazaribagh	4471	2525	56·5	1055	23·6	46·4	7·8	1·1	10·9
Santal Ps .	3507	278	7·9	1940	5·8	47·8	9·2	1·8	6·7
Ranchi .	4540	1216	26·8	1883	41·5	61·1	0·9	1·3	7·7
Manbhum .	2620	502	19·2	556	21·2	67·8	6·2	0·2	4·8

Forest, of course, is official forest and probably much less than the wooded area, especially in Santal Parganas.

As in the adjacent lowlands of Bengal there is a three-crop year: *bhadai*, *aghani*, and rabi, of which the first is by far the most important, except in Santal Parganas and Manbhum; rabi is relatively unimportant as it needs deep moisture-retaining soils. In the Ranchi and Hazaribagh Plateaus, however, over 60% of the cultivated area is *tanr* or dry upland. Owing to the relatively small proportion of cultivated ground, pressure on the land is nearly as severe as on the plains: Saran (in the Gandak-Gogra-Ganges angle) and Hazaribagh Dts have densities of **1182** and **276** respectively, but for TSA the figures are **1272** and **1172**. Forest occupations afford some relief, but the dry weather is a time of agricultural idleness. Many cultivators find work in Damodar mines or Hooghlyside factories, but this, of course, raises new social problems.[28]

Chota Nagpur Division has by far the most important mineral concentrations of India. Apart, however, from the Hazaribagh mica and Damodar coal most of the mining localities lie S of the Jamshedpur saddle (below, 667); but recently the vast reserves of bauxite in the laterites of the *pat* country have been exploited; the metre-gauge railway from Lohardaga takes them to the new smelter at Muri S of the Damodar. Palamau also produce   and there are large limestone deposits.

[27] Based on Dayal, *op. cit.*, Appx. II.
[28] Studies of the rhythm of life in Chota Nagpur will be found in A. Geddes, *Comptes Rendus du Congrès International de Géographie*, Amsterdam (1938), Sec. III c., 365–80.

By far the most important mineral (reserving Damodar coal for separate treatment) is the mica. The deposits occur along the dissected Nn fringe of the Hazaribagh Plateau, in pegmatite veins in a discontinuous belt of Dharwarian rocks. Much of the production is from primitive digging following the veins deep into the hillside; transport facilities are poor, the mica belt being barely skirted at one end by the railway to Gaya and having hardly any internal communications beyond unmetalled tracks. Work in smaller mines ceases in the rains, owing to waterlogging, poor roads, and the return of labourers to their fields. Working conditions are extremely poor; most of the mines are exploited by *zamindars* or petty syndicates, and the miners' temporary camps are mere barracks in the jungle. Improved methods are being introduced, however, and 25–30% of the output now comes from about a dozen large mines. *India* produces some 75% of the world's mica, and Bihar's share of *Indian* production is usually about 65%, and that of better quality; 75% by value of the output of dressed mica in *India* comes from this small area. Production is 80–200,000 cwts. a year[29]; labour difficulties sometimes hamper production, even managers being wretchedly underpaid, and labour is often lorried from a considerable distance. On the other hand the large supply of female and child labour is an asset to the splitting and dressing side of the industry: wages are lower than for almost any other occupation, except perhaps *bidi* (cheap cigarette) making in S India—another sweated home industry. But the work is not strenuous and can be done at home at any time. The number of miners is 20–40,000, processing workers at least three times as many, and of these about three-quarters are home workers; the "factories" are for the most part tiny workshops. No mechanical process has yet been devised to equal the skill of the women and children of Hazaribagh, who can split sheets to 1/1000th of an inch. On their fingers the electrical industries of the world largely depend.[30]

Away from the coalfield there are no large towns in the Chota Nagpur region except Ranchi (**106,849**); lying at about 2200 ft and accessible from Calcutta, it is the educational and administrative centre of the Division and the hot-weather capital of Bihar.

(b) *The Damodar Basin* (Fig. 114, p. 592)

The Damodar Basin occupies only a small area, some 7500 sq mls, but its human significance is immense. In the past this has been expressed positively by its use as a railway corridor and by the exploitation of the coal preserved in its down-faulted basins, accounting for some 90% of Indian output; negatively by the devastation brought to W Bengal by its

[29] This is an understatement: false returns are often made, and illicit production and pilfering are rife.

[30] All these details from Majid, *op. cit.*, Ch. VI. See also P. J. Thomas, *India's Basic Industries* (1948), Ch. VII.

frequent floods. These are the natural consequence of the convergence of the drainage from the impervious crystallines of the plateaus into the 15-mile-wide bottleneck at Asansol, and of the right-angled bend where the lower Damodar emerges onto the plains below Burdwan; but they have been much aggravated by deforestation and severe soil erosion. In the near future this negative will be transformed into a positive by development on Tennessee Valley lines.

The Gondwana rocks of the basin form generally low undulating terrain. The main stream runs W–E, providing a col at little over 1500 ft into the N Koel Valley; the railway through this Chandwa Gap, however, is of small significance except to the little industrial concentration in the Son Valley (above, p. 584). But the larger tributaries, all on the left bank, provide chord routes cutting across the great Ganges bend. The watershed between the Damodar and the upper Ajai at Asansol is a mere height of land, and the interfluve is followed by a railway with a branch to the small coalfield at Giridh in the Barakar valley. This, the largest Damodar feeder, is followed by a road only; but E of the striking isolated peak of Parasnath (4480 ft, a Jain sanctuary) the Jamunia opens a direct line, across the upper Barakar, from Calcutta to Gaya and Patna: this is used by the E Indian Railway's 'Grand Chord' line and by the Grand Trunk Road. Both lines have summit levels about 1200 ft. SE again the Bokaro enables the E/W railway to avoid a jungly stretch along the Damodar and to open up the Bokaro field; and to the S the recession of the Ranchi peneplain scarps gives easy access to the Subarnarekha and Jamshedpur. The W of the Damodar Basin, around Tori and the Karanpura coalfields, is as yet undeveloped jungle country.

The Coalfields.[31] The production of the Damodar fields alone actually exceeds that of any other Indian Ocean country. The coal is preserved, thanks to displacements which are of the order of 5000–9000 ft along the Sn flank of the basin. The coal-measures are little folded or faulted, though in the E they have been adversely affected by ultra-basic dykes and sills; some seams are 15–30 ft thick or more, and working is generally easy. The coal is sub-bituminous to bituminous, but often with rather high ash content and friable. The best coking coals are in the Barakar seams on the Jharia field; although reserves as a whole are good, anxiety is felt as to future supplies of coke (cf. Ch. X, p. 259).

After an abortive beginning in 1774–75, production in Raniganj, the first field to be developed, has been continuous since about 1815. But it was negligible until the development of railways after the Mutiny, and it was not until the real beginnings of modern industry in the 1890's that production reached considerable figures: in 1900 All-India output was over 6 m. tons. The two wars and the establishment of Tata's iron and steel works

---

[31] Again following Majid, Ch. V.

provided further stimuli: Jamshedpur now takes *c.* 900,000 tons a year.
The relative importance of Damodar coal in India, and of the individual
fields of the basin, can be seen from Figs. 56 and 114. On the Raniganj
and Jharia fields, almost alone in India away from the greater cities, there
is a real industrial landscape: collieries with their attendant spoil heaps
and many subsidence flashes, the irregular and squalid settlements of
the miners, a dense rail and road net, ropeways bringing sand from the
Damodar for stowage and for sealing-off fires by surface spreading.

The most important problem facing the industry is probably labour. The
labour force fluctuates widely from year to year and also—more significantly
—with the seasons: most of the colliers are still cultivators as well. Normally
seedtime and harvest spell absenteeism: coal raisings in slack agricultural
months exceed those in the planting season (June–July) by 30–50%; and it
is only in years of deficient rainfall that labour is abundant for the mines.
In the war years, with high agricultural prices, the labour shortage became
so acute that the Government, despite severe criticism, permitted female
labour underground—a practice which had been prohibited as late as 1939.
The human price for economic advance has been shamefully high. Most
of the miners were tribesmen (Bauro or Santals) who were said, probably
with truth, to be reluctant to leave their wives at the surface, and in some
cases to have two: a butty in the pit and a housewife at home, which is presumably a long way off. Casual absenteeism and sickness take a great toll;
the average miner is a miner for only about 190 days in the year. But if the
indiscipline of the tribal workers inhibits reasonable working of the mines,
it also militates against any organisation of their own, and working and
housing conditions (a few very recent model pits and villages apart) remain absolutely appalling. Output per worker is naturally very low, about
half that in Britain; mechanisation is hampered by lack of capital, the
general backwardness of many mines (especially perhaps on the convey-
ance side), and the fact that labour is after all cheap on a short view.

The general technical level is not high; wastage, bad stowage, avoidable
fires, robber exploitation of the best seams, poor grading, are prominent
features. To a large extent this is due to lack of capital and the farming out
by the *zamindars* of concessions to small operators, who may in turn
have sub-lessees. As in agriculture, indeed, fragmentation of the most
uneconomic sort imaginable is rife.

Until recently industrial development, other than that strictly connected
with coal exploitation, was limited to the manufacture of firebricks, mainly
at Mugma on the Jharia field, and glass, located here because of accessible
fuel and refractories, and proximity to Calcutta for sales and for the import
of soda ash. Since the war there have been two developments of the greatest
importance on an *Indian* as well as a local scale: the opening of the Indian
Aluminium Company's smelter at Muri and of the great state fertiliser

factory at Sindri near Dhanbad on the Jharia field. Muri lies well to the S; its rail connection is with the W rather than the E of the basin, and this may lead to increased coal development there. It draws its bauxite from the Lohardaga *pat* country, 75 miles to the E by the metre railway through Ranchi; coal from Argada on the Karanpura field. The alumina produced is shipped from Calcutta to Alwaye in Travancore, formerly dependent on imported alumina; here hydro-electric power is available for its reduction to aluminium. Sindri was planned to draw its gypsum from Khewra in the Salt Range, but now must obtain it from Rajasthan. Capacity is *c.* 350,000 tons of ammonium sulphate a year.

The towns of the Damodar Basin, of which the largest is Asansol (55,797) in W Bengal, call for little comment: they are almost solely colliery and communication centres.

The Damodar Valley Project.[32] The taming of the Damodar and its harnessing to productive purposes is perhaps the most interesting and certainly the favourite among *India's* post-war development projects. The objective is threefold: flood control, irrigation, and power production. The first two are provided for mainly by a barrage and a weir between Raniganj and Burdwan; some 1,325,000 ac. on either side of the lower Damodar will come under perennial irrigation, adding 125–150,000 tons of rice to W Bengal's annual production. In the upper basin it is proposed to impound 4,500,000 ac.-ft of water; the hydro-electric installations will provide 275,000 kW, thermal plants on the coalfields another 150,000. This will be fed into a grid serving Hooghlyside and the coal towns. Other aspects of the project include malaria control and the provision of a navigable canal from Raniganj to Calcutta.

The Tapti Valley

The Tapti Valley [33] is essentially a transitional zone between central India and the Deccan; Khandesh was not infrequently a debatable land between Malwa and Maharashtra. Physically the region falls into two parts: the main Tapti trough continued in that of the Purna, and the upper Tapti Valley in its NE–SW course through the Burhanpur Gap. But the E/W climatic division is of more significance.

The main valley-floor lies at 600–900 ft, with the river itself entrenched as much as 50–60 ft below; to the N the steep face of the Satpuras and (in the Purna Valley) the Gawilgarh Hills mark it off sharply, except at the Burhanpur Gap; to the S the Sahyadriparvat or Ajanta Hills are set farther back, but no less boldly formed, except in the SW where there is a more gentle rise, in the Girna Valley, to the little gap-town of Manmad; but here,

---

[32] S. C. Bose, *The Damodar Valley Project* (Calcutta, 1948); W. Kirk, "The Damodar Valley—'Valles Opima'", *GR* XL (1950), 415–43. Both these excellent studies cover much more than the project itself.

[33] See C. D. Deshpande, *Western India* (1948), 148–54.

on the Malegaon plateau, we are at the threshold of the open plains of Nasik in the upper Godavari basin.

The entire area, except for the alluvial filling of the trough, is Deccan Lava terrain. Rainfall is 40 ins. on the Wn margin, but falls below 25 ins. in

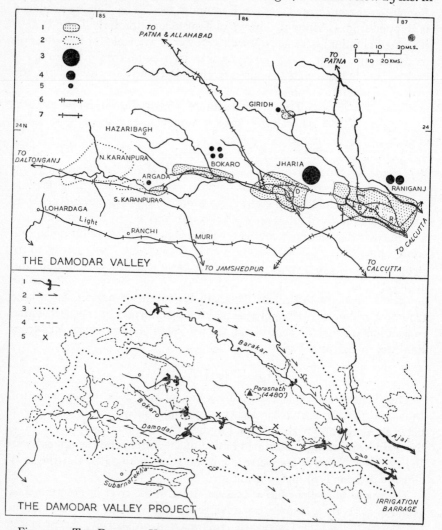

Fig. 114.—THE DAMODAR VALLEY AND PROJECT. *Valley:* 1, worked, 2, unworked, coalfields; 3, 10–12 m. tons p.a. coal output; 4, 2·5–4 m. tons; 5, 0·5–1 m. tons; 6, BGDT; 7, BGST (except light Lohardaga line). D, Dhanbad; B, Barakar; A, Asansol; R, Raniganj.

Project: 1, dams and reservoirs; 2, power transmission lines; 3, Damodar watershed; 4, contours at 200 and 500 *metres*; 5, thermal electric stations (installations under 1, 2, and 5 all projected or building).

Based on maps and text in S. A. Majid, *The Industrial Geography of Bihar* (thesis, 1949), and S. C. Bose, *The Damodar Valley Project* (Calcutta, 1948).

E Khandesh, where variability is over 25% and agriculture not too secure. However, the moisture-retaining regur offsets this; jowar, oilseeds, and pulses are prominent, but the dominant until recently was cotton. There is a distinct difference between the moister, but hillier and more forested, W and the open plains of the E. W Khandesh, E Khandesh, Buldana, Akola, and Amraoti Dts, with comparable TSAs of between 1·6 and 2 m. ac., had the following approximate percentages under leading crops [34]:

1939-40:	Cotton	Jowar	Bajra	Wheat	Rice	Oilseeds
W Khandesh .	30	16	18	8	3	8
E Khandesh .	34	17	12	2·75	—	18
Buldana . .	36	32	3	8·5	—	9
Akola . .	43	32	—	7	—	4
Amraoti . .	47	31	1	5·5	—	4

The margins of the area are poorer; in the Burhanpur Gap villages are few and far between and there is rather broken country with light woodland; the Malegaon plateau in the SW is dryish, with much grass, thorny scrub, and big masses of euphorbia; here cultivation is confined to valley-bottoms below the marked break of slope at the foot of the lava mesas, and is aided by well irrigation.

But on the whole the heart of the region is flourishing enough. This is perhaps due in part to the emphasis on cash crops—as the table shows, cotton was rarely less than one-third of TSA and oilseed percentages are fairly high. This emphasis is fostered by the good rail connection to Bombay, and has led to the growth of a small local cotton industry. Settlement avoids the eroded banks of the entrenched Tapti, but on the broad valley-floor is a remarkable concentration of small towns and large compact villages, often walled and with a generally fort-like appearance, a reminder of the march-land role of Khandesh which is most strikingly displayed in the enormous fortress at Asirgarh on its spur projecting into the Burhanpur Gap. Railway towns like Akola (62,564), Amraoti (61,971), and Burhanpur (54,987), in Madhya Pradesh (CP), Dhulia (53,308) and Jalgaon (42,000) in Bombay, have developed into minor commercial centres with a little textile industry. It is perhaps significant of their close relation with their region that, unlike so many Indian towns, their male and female inhabitants are nearly equal in numbers. The lower Tapti itself, although followed by a railway, is now of little importance, the trade which once went down it to Surat having long ago been drawn to Bombay. But the importance of the area as the vesti-bule of the Deccan from the N, lying athwart the routes from Bombay into its Nn hinterland, remains a significant feature in its life.

[34] But see below, 649, for recent changes.

CHAPTER XXII

THE WESTERN LITTORAL

(Regions XXI–XXV)

THE Wn coast of India has been historically the most active, partly for reasons inherent in its own nature—a coast with numerous havens, creek or roadstead, a narrow immediate hinterland with a few well-defined routes into the interior—and partly by virtue of its location facing the intercontinental nodes of SW Asia. Maritime activity goes back to the beginnings of history, and this was the first part of India to receive the attention of Renaissance Europe; indeed some fragments of the Portuguese empire here have survived the British. But, in contrast to the E coast, geographical and political factors impeded territorial expansion, and the development by Dutch and British of more Sly routes from the Cape of Good Hope led to a relative decline as against the Bengal entry. Later the cotton boom of the American Civil War (1861–65) brought a few years of very rapid development, and the ensuing slump was followed closely by the opening of the Suez Canal (1869), which revived the older locational values.

The whole area falls into five major regions: Cutch and Kathiawar; Gujarat; the Konkan; Goa and Kanara; Kerala. Of these Goa and Kanara form a distinctive transitional zone between the Konkan and Kerala; Kerala itself is more or less coterminous with the Malabar coast, but as this is also the name of a Madras District it seems preferable to use the local name Kerala, which is standard among Indian geographers. The Wn Ghats are treated in the next chapter, but as their seaward scarps are intimately connected with the lowland beneath them, some reference to them is essential here.

The Coast in General

As we have seen (Ch. I), subsidence on a macro-regional scale and at a late date seems necessary to account for the hydrography of the Ghats, with an almost total absence of large-scale river capture in conditions apparently exceedingly favourable to it. Except just S of Goa the great fault-line scarp of the Ghats is continued as a remarkably sharp feature on the Archaeans, and although the watershed recedes in places from the coast, so also do the Ghats: watershed and crest are never very far apart except in the breach S of Goa. The old theory, still in some vogue in India, that the Ghats are old sea-cliffs can hardly survive examination of large-scale maps; nevertheless the coast has some difficult complexities. S of the Goa-Kanara transitional zone there is not much difficulty: the land is obviously in the ascendant.

But the Konkan coast appears to suggest a plane of marine erosion, with bevelled surfaces in Deccan Lava surmounted by isolated hills which look very much like old offshore islands. On the other hand the submerged forest at Bombay and the ria-like appearance of the Deccan Lava coast strongly suggest recent depression; though there is also the low platform of littoral concrete seen on the Wn side of Bombay Island, at Bandra Head, and other places, and there has been sufficient stability to allow great mangrove-flats to grow up behind bayhead bars.

Summing up the scattered pieces of evidence (which are hardly ever presented with any clue to sequence) we seem to have: some submergence in the N (Cambay submerged forest) but a seawards advance of the land (Rann mudflats, linking of Kathiawar with mainland, miliolite belt on S coast); prograding shores of the Gulf of Cambay; in the Konkan macro-regional subsidence of Arabian Sea, emergence of plane of marine erosion, with some sinking followed by a still-stand as the latest phases (not excluding minor oscillations); a 'hinge' around Goa; definite uplift assisted by prograding on a low shoreline of emergence in the S.

That movements of these types in the various regions have taken place is obvious from the map, but in the absence of any precise data as to levels and sequences it is impossible to attempt to trace their origins and history, whether mainly isostatic or eustatic. The sagging which would appear natural as a result of the weighty outpourings of Deccan Lavas would seem too early (Eocene)[1]; the macro-faulting *might* be associated with the Miocene Himalayan orogeny, but the problem of the Ghats watershed suggests a very late date; in the S the uplift might be connected with the punching-up of the Nilgiri, Anamalai-Palni, and Ceylon horsts, if that be indeed their origin. The one thing that is clear is that we have here one of the most fascinating geomorphological problems that even this geomorphologically almost virgin sub-continent has to offer.[2]

Cutch and Kathiawar

The quadrilateral of some 46,000 sq mls between the Rann of Cutch and the Gulf of Cambay is a world apart; and this is, of course, especially true of Cutch.[3] The Rann is a vast expanse of naked tidal mudflats, a black desolation flecked with saline efflorescences, or the sudden flights of great flocks of flamingos; here and there the banks of dead creeks are picked out

---

[1] But Sahni, on the evidence of the flora of some intra-lava beds, would place much of the extrusion in the Miocene.

[2] Without claiming a detailed knowledge of local scientific papers, I think it unlikely that any modern analysis of the problem exists. There are of course hints in R. B. S. Sewell, "The Oceans round India", in *An Outline of the Field Sciences of India* (ISC, Calcutta, 1937, 17–41) and in A. N. Harris, "Factors Controlling Port Sites, with Special Reference to Western India", *Geography* XVIII (1933), 118–25.

[3] The arrangement of this section is my own, but the facts are mainly from C. D. Deshpande, *Western India* (Dharwar, 1948), 208–22.

in a white skeletal outline of salt or scum. To the N the desert of mud and the desert of sand in the Thar merge almost imperceptibly. The normal dendritic pattern of the creeks has been interrupted by earthquakes, notably that of 1819 which interrupted the old Indus distributaries into the Rann by the formation of a fault-scarp 10–18 ft high and some 50 miles long, the Allah Bund ('God's Dyke'). Yet isolation is not complete nor the waste entirely trackless.[4]

To the E there is no such barrier: gas seepages on the Cambay shores suggest that the Gulf was part of the Sind depositional area in the late Tertiary, and Kathiawar may have been semi-insular as late as the 17th century.[5] But prolonged silting by the mainland rivers [6] and tectonic uplift have attached it to the mainland, despite very high tidal ranges in the Gulf. The old channel (doubtless tidal or seasonal) joining the Little Rann (SE of Cutch) and the Gulf of Cambay is marked by the lakes and marshes of the Nal depression. Entry was easiest in the N, by the low plateau between Drangadhra and Wadhwan, the latter anciently a fortified strategic centre and still of trading importance owing to its rail nodality.

Physique, Climate, Vegetation

Within this framework of sea and marsh the broad outlines of relief and geology are simple enough, but the detail complex. Cutch has a discontinuous backbone (up to 900–1100 ft) of Jurassic-Miocene rocks, mainly sandstones with intrusive and interbedded basalts, flanked by alluvial and aeolian deposits; the highest point (1525 ft) lies away to the N on Pachham Island in the Rann. Physically it is an alternation of little flat-topped steep-edged plateaus, much dissected round the margins, and tiny alluvial basins. The Rann itself appears to be a broken anticline.

The great mass of Kathiawar is formed of sheets of Deccan Lava intersected by swarms of trap dykes (Fig. 115, inset); in the N the Drangadhra-Wadhwan Plateau is mostly sandstone of Jurassic age. Except in the N the basalt platform is flanked by younger rocks—Tertiary clays and sandy limestones in the extreme W (Dwarka) and E (Bhavnagar), and between these a belt, 20–30 miles wide, of alluvium and miliolite. This latter is a wind-blown sand, largely formed of foraminiferal casts, in a calcareous matrix; at Junagadh, 30 miles inland, it is 200 ft thick. It is an attractive building-stone, creamy-white and easily worked, and is exported as 'Porbandar stone'. The actual edge of the lavas is marked by a discontinuous strip of laterite, and there is of course a good deal of alluvium. Most of Kathiawar lies below 600 ft, but there are two hill-masses, E of Rajkot in

---

[4] See the splendid description in E. Reclus, *L'Inde* (Nouvelle Géographie Universelle, Tome VIII, 1883), 226–29.

[5] D. N. Wadia, *Geology of India* (1939), 228; *Bombay Gaz.* (1909), II. 346.

[6] ". . . currents setting into the Gulf of Cambay prevent the free movement of Narbada and Tapti silt out of the gulf." A. N. Harris, *loc. cit.*, 119.

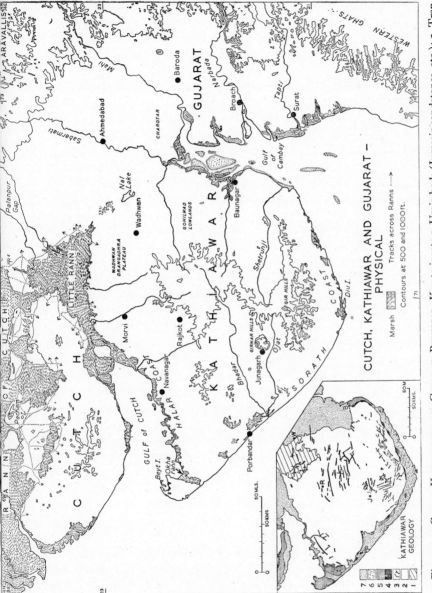

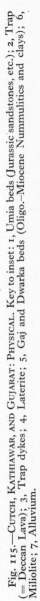

Fig. 115.—CUTCH, KATHIAWAR, AND GUJARAT: PHYSICAL. Key to inset: 1, Umia beds (Jurassic sandstones, etc.); 2, Trap (= Deccan Lava); 3, Trap dykes; 4, Laterite; 5, Gaj and Dwarka beds (Oligo.-Miocene Nummulitics and clays); 6, Miiolite; 7, Alluvium.

the N (1100 ft) and the higher and bolder Gir Range (up to 2100 ft) in the S. These two dissected plateaus have a perfect radial drainage pattern; they are linked by a narrow and sinuous neck over 600 ft separating the two major rivers of Kathiawar, the Bhadar (110 miles long) flowing W and the Shetrunji E. A few miles W of this watershed rises the remarkable circular group of the Girnar Hills culminating in Goraknath, the highest point of Kathiawar (3666 ft). This igneous complex (gabbros, diorites, and syenites) seems to be intruded through the Deccan Lavas, but from the same magmatic reservoir.

Despite the areal preponderance of the lavas, the numerous dykes and the fairly wide range of younger rocks, with aeolian and alluvial deposits, introduce considerable local diversity of terrain, soils, and hydrology. The environment is generally arid enough, but the region lies between the dry shores of Sind and the fluctuating flank of the Arabian Sea branch of the monsoon, and there is some climatic variation. Cutch averages 12–15 ins., and as little as 1·4 have been recorded; from the air the arid aspect of its erosional features is striking. The Kathiawar coastlands, except in the SE, receive 15–20 ins., but the highland centre and the Cambay coast have over 25 and Junagadh, lying close under the Wn side of the Girnar Hills, about 40. The rainfall is precarious, variability being everywhere over 50%. Mean temperatures run high, 80–85° F in January and 90–95° in May, when mean maxima are around 110°. The natural cover of most of the region is dry thorn forest, very open and stunted, with small patches of dry deciduous on the Gir and Girnar Hills; on the N coast of Kathiawar and in Cutch the scrub breaks down into poor grass and bush, almost desert in places. Mangroves are exploited for fuel along the coast. In the Gir forest the lion, extinct in the rest of India, survives, thanks to state protection.

Agriculture

Over most of the region agriculture is naturally dominant, but in Cutch it shades off into a semi-pastoral economy. Water is of course the primary determinant of agriculture, but the influence of terrain in the narrower sense is often striking: much of the land is waste not only on the hills but also, at least in the N of Kathiawar, along the streams, the banks of which are often badly gullied on the plateau and marshy, often saline, farther down. The larger blocks of cultivation are thus often located at the foot of the ridges or low plateaus, or on the broader interfluves. Altogether about 50–60% of Kathiawar is cropped, no small proportion given the low and unreliable rainfall, and obviously possible only by careful exploitation of all available sources of water. There are no large irrigation works in this area which, until very recently, was split up amongst scores of statelets; but tanks, valley-bunds, and especially wells are used. Wells are often aligned along the dykes in the Deccan Lavas; in some cases the intrusive traps are themselves aquifers, but more often perhaps they hold up the movement of water in the country rock, producing local rises in the water-table.

In the E the alluvial Gohilwad lowland along the Nal depression is one of the more favoured areas; the relatively high rainfall (20–25 ins.) indeed sometimes causes flooding in this tract where the drainage-lines are obviously impeded by the greater amounts of silt brought down by the mainland rivers. Wheat is the main crop here, followed by millets. Along the Cambay coast ground-water is brackish or saline and soils sandy; but inland large areas are devoted to bajra, wheat, cotton, and jowar. On the Drangadhra-Wadhwan Plateau cotton covers half the cultivated area and jowar a quarter. The Sn coast (Sorath) is very unequal in agricultural potentialities; rich where alluvial, it is poor on the laterites and miliolites. Casuarinas (for fuel) and coconuts are important here. Around the lower courses of the Bhadar and Ojat are large areas of salt marsh, but above them the *gher* or 'sweet water' lands raise rich crops of jowar and bajra, cotton and oilseeds, and some rice. The Bhadar basin is perhaps the richest agricultural area of Kathiawar, owing largely to the regur soils and the numerous dykes: cotton, oilseeds, jowar are the chief crops.

Dwarka and the Halar coast in the N represent a transition to definitely marginal agriculture. Dwarka, almost cut off by the Okha Rann, is formed largely of clays and marls with higher limestone areas; soils are light, rainfall poor, and under a third of the land is cultivated, 70% to bajra and the rest jowar. The Halar is mainly marshy creeklands or dry thin-soiled interfluves; millets and oilseeds are grown, but pastoral activities tend to be more important than tillage. In Cutch these tendencies are accentuated; there are belts of irrigated alluvium (wheat and cotton), but livestock are more important, especially in the arid Banni country in the N; Cutch is, or at least was, noted for its breeds of horses and camels. Holdings in the light sandy soils are large, but in any one year about half lie fallow, and the land actually cropped is less than a quarter of the total area.

Villages over much of Kathiawar are strongly nucleated and tend to be large, sited on rises, bluffs along the valleys, hill-foot fans, or river crossings. In Halar and Cutch, however, they are often mere hamlets, and great stock corrals are prominent features of the cultural landscape.

General Development: Towns

Cutch (8461 sq mls, 1951 poptn **567,606**) forms a single political unit, administered by a Chief Commissioner directly responsible to Delhi: perhaps significant in view of its situation marching with Pakistan.[7] Density is **67** and the only places of any importance are Mandvi port (27,000) and the capital, Bhuj (25,000), which has a light railway to the tiny port of

---

[7] The Nn boundary follows the Sind coast of the Rann, and as the limits of 'sea' and 'land' are highly ambiguous there is a technical dispute, in practice utterly unimportant.

Tuna. The most interesting thing about Cutch culturally is the eclectic attitude of its ruling Rajput tribe, which has evolved a curiously distorted mixture of Hinduism and Islam.

Kathiawar is very different. Until the formation in 1948 of the Union of Saurashtra it was politically the most fragmented portion of India [8]; the Union welds together 450 states (many styled such by courtesy) which, with ex- and en-claves, represented 860 distinct territorial units; this in an area of 21,451 sq mls with a 1951 poptn of over **4,137,000**. There still remain several pieces of Baroda—now merged with Bombay—of which Amreli in the S and Okha Mandal (Dwarka) in the W are the most important. On the S coast Portugal holds three villages and the island of Diu (20 sq mls), entirely useless but treasured for the memory of the magnificent defence against the Sultan of Gujarat in 1545. Lying off the main routes of war and trade in India, Kathiawar has been a land of refuge, but its peninsular situation has invited overseas contacts—Arabs, Portuguese, even Africans.

The almost incredible *morcellement* of Kathiawar obviously impeded any really well-found development, administrative or economic; Junagadh, the largest state by both area and population, had only 3337 sq mls and 670,719 people in 1941. On the other hand, the administrative demands of the half-dozen or so larger states, and their desire to cut some small figure in the world, led to an urbanisation nearly double that of all *India* (**33·8**% against **17·3**%), some local industry, some port activity, and a fairly close net of metre railways. Industries include quarrying of Porbandar stone, cotton textiles (especially at Bhavnagar), leather, matches, potteries, cement, and chemicals, the last two particularly at Dwarka, with accessible salt and limestone; here Tatas manufacture soda ash, bleaching powder, and hydrochloric acid.

Minor ports, as is natural in a peninsula of such dimensions, have been of great importance; but they are now overshadowed by the growth of Port Okha and Bhavnagar at the extremities of the peninsula. Bhavnagar (**137,951**) is the largest town of Kathiawar: it is situated where firm ground abuts on its creek, and is not so liable to silting as ports farther up or across the Cambay Gulf, but the main anchorage is 8 miles away; small coasting steamers can lie on the mud in the creek itself. Local cotton and oilseeds provide the staple exports and some industry. Okha has been developed by Baroda, superseding the sacred island of Beyt: it is completely modern in equipment, if on a modest scale, and was fast becoming an entrepôt by 1939–40. The war years saw a sharp decline, but the unification of most of its hinterland augurs well for its future as the outlet for most of Kathiawar, although for wider relations it suffers from isolation: Gujarat traffic must pass through Wadhwan, 231 miles by rail. Cement exports account for

[8] Cf. Fig. 15 (p. 147) in W. G. East and O. H. K. Spate (eds.), *The Changing Map of Asia* (1950).

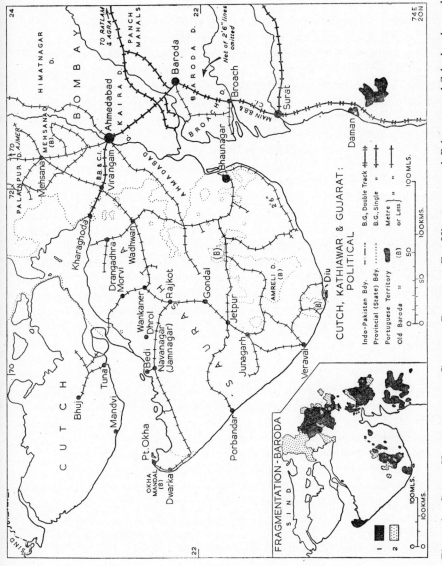
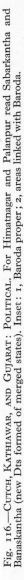

Fig. 116.—CUTCH, KATHIAWAR, AND GUJARAT: POLITICAL. For Himatnagar and Palanpur read Sabarkantha and Banaskantha (new Dts formed of merged states). Inset: 1, Baroda proper; 2, areas linked with Baroda.

about half the total volume of trade; cotton, oilseeds, and salt are also exported; imports are mainly oil, sugar, china clay, textiles, construction and transport material.[9] The only other port which calls for mention is Bedi, a few miles from Jamnagar town, and little more than a tidal basin with warehouses and a railway. Bedi and other "ports" of the Halar coast are handicapped by the low marshy shores and shallow waters of the Rann of Cutch, and also by the development of the Wadhwan-Rajkot-Okha railway which takes traffic out E and W. They are in fact mere break-of-bulk points for goods lightered to shipping in the roadsteads; all commercial functions are carried out at the inland centres. But a new port is being developed at Kandla (Cutch) to relieve Bombay of the added burden of E Punjab trade diverted from Karachi (Kandla is the railhead E of Tuna, Fig. 116).

Of the inland marts the largest and most important is Jamnagar (**104,419**), capital of the old Navanagar state. Of its older crafts dyeing has survived, and some new light industries have been added; but it is more important as a commercial centre. Morvi (36,000) is the centre of an important cotton tract on the Drangadhra-Wadhwan Plateau, Wadhwan (21,000) the main point of entry on the Gujarat side. Rajkot (**132,069**), though commercially limited by the competition of Jamnagar and Gondal on either hand, is the administrative centre of Saurashtra. On the S coast the little ports—Porbandar, Veraval, Diu—have decayed before the competition of Okha and Bhavnagar, except perhaps for Mahuva, but there are a number of flourishing inland centres, generally on defensible sites of past strategic significance; the most important is Junagadh town (58,111), the centre of the Bhadar basin.

Gujarat

Gujarat might almost be described as an intrusion of Indo-Gangetic conditions into the Peninsula: a great tract of alluvium formed by the Sabarmati, Mahi, and minor parallel streams, actively prograding into the Gulf of Cambay. Historically it was for long periods a flourishing independent kingdom, controlling the seaward terminals of the great Cambay-Agra route and marked off from Malwa by the dissected jungly country where the Aravallis and the Deccan Lavas break down into the plain: this zone has been a minor shatter-belt, as shown by the very numerous 'states' and statelets (down to a population of 96 and areas of a square mile!) which existed before 1948. Nwds the limits of the region lie in the Palanpur Gap between the Aravallis and the Ranns; Swds the impingement of the Deccan Lavas on the coast is taken as the boundary with the Konkan.

Except for the Portuguese enclaves of Damão the entire area now forms part of Bombay, which has taken over not only the petty states—most of them in two new Nn Districts, Banaskantha and Sabarkantha—but also

---

[9] *Baroda Administration Report 1944–45* (Baroda, 1946), 139.

the 8176 sq mls and 2,855,010 people (1941) of Baroda, the main block of which lies central in the plain.

Climate and Agriculture

Physically there is little need for comment. The region falls into three N/S belts: the alluvial piedmont (above 200 ft) between the highland and the plain; the coastal marshes; and between them the great shelf of firm alluvium, some 250 miles long and up to 60 wide. This is of course the main agricultural area; the great estuaries are surrounded by unreclaimed tidal marshes, the E is still largely under dry deciduous jungle, much degraded by the shifting cultivation of tribes such as the Bhils.

Climate is more difficult to evaluate: the region lies in a critical position on the flank of the Arabian Sea branch of the monsoon. Rainfall thus decreases rapidly from 60–70 ins. in the extreme S to 41 at Surat and 29 at Ahmedabad; the higher E, of course, receives rather more, but this is offset by the broken terrain and poor soils. Reliability also decreases, and NW of a line from a little N of the Narbada mouth past Ahmedabad variability is over 30%; there seems also some evidence of diminution of amount during this century. Rainfall is often very local and patchy, both at any one time and over a run of years. The village of Atgam, near Bulsar in the S of the region, has about 75 ins., but annual falls have varied from 40 to 116. Here even 45 ins. can give good crops if well distributed seasonally; but the right distribution is extremely delicate, as the following table shows [10]:

Period	Desirable Rainfall	Agricultural Work
	ins.	
June 13–20	8	Preparing for sowing
26–30	2	Broadcasting paddy
July 1–7	7	Growth of seedling paddy
7–15	10	Preparing beds for transplanting paddy
15–31	3	Transplanting paddy
Aug. 1–31	10	Crop growth
Sept. 1–30	10	Crop growth, and rabi planting
Oct. 1–31	2	Rabi crops

This is of course a minimum demand; but the point is that even with a normal total for the year, maldistribution in the growing months may be disastrous; and in fact at Atgam good, fair, and bad years are equally common. N of the head of the Gulf lies an area traditionally liable to famines; that of 1630–32 was perhaps the worst in all India's long history of such calamities. Flooding is also a risk. Probably not more than 150,000 ac.

[10] G. C. Mukhtyar, *Life and Labour in a South Gujarat Village* (Bombay, 1930), 26–30.

are irrigated (mainly in the N), and that chiefly from tanks and wells. But there are schemes to irrigate 120,000 ac. from a tributary of the Mahi in Kaira, and if the Tapti multi-purpose project at Kadapadah is carried out several hundred thousand acres will be irrigated, mainly in Surat Dt.

Lack of statistics from the old state areas, and the fragmentation of Ahmedabad, Broach, and Surat Dts, render quantitative analysis difficult. Gujarat is of course one of the most famous cotton areas of India, yet the crop is not so dominant as this reputation would suggest, the highest District percentage (in Broach) being under 30% of TSA even in 1939; but locally it covered 47% of the cropped area around Broach town. Rice is strong in the more humid S but in the N exceeds cotton only in Kaira, where it is dependent on large tanks. This is anomalous; adjoining Ahmedabad has only 3% rice against 24% cotton. By and large jowar is the most important cereal, followed by wheat; but Kaira has 19% bajra against 5% jowar, clear evidence of its arid marginal nature where not protected by tanks. The new Districts probably have larger proportions of the inferior millets and pulses. Oilseeds (mainly groundnuts) and tobacco are minor cash crops. But it will be evident that there are no clear lines, rather a mosaic of differing crop associations dependent on local water-supply, soils, and markets, with variable proportions of food and cash crops and of the cereals. The proximity of the Bombay and Ahmedabad markets has also given rise to some dairying, especially in Charotar, probably the richest tract of Gujarat, an area of very fertile and well-watered alluvium between the lower Sabarmati and Mahi Rivers.

Villages are especially large in Kaira, where their average population in 1931 was 1027: elsewhere it was 6–700 except in Panch Mahals (in the backward E) where it was under 500. The siting in estuarine areas is typically on low sandy rises, at once dry- and water-points as fresh water is held in the sand above the denser saline ground-water of the marsh. Social factors provide interesting variations: the overwhelmingly Hindu population is much caste-ridden, but the castes fall into two great divisions— Kaliparaj, the 'black races', embracing most of the lower strata, and the socially superior Upaliparaj. The Kaliparaj live in little hamlets (*falias*) of 8–10 houses, lying within three or four miles of the village nucleus, which is very small and inhabited mainly by Upaliparaj. At Atgam "The vernacular school, patel's office, and the Post Office are located here. In this space are found two grocers' shops and an open space in front of the village where, under a tamarind tree, some villager occasionally sets up a temporary shop selling chillies, onions, garlic, and a few vegetables. Here also are seen a temple of Rama and a mosque. On its outskirts to the east dwell the untouchables." This hamletted occupance is not without advantages in an area where holdings are small and much fragmented, as the average distance from house to field is much shorter than in a nucleated village with the same field and holding pattern. Poorer houses are generally of mud and grass, with thatched roofs; tiles are an indication of individual economic advance.[11]

The Industrial Towns of Gujarat

Four great towns dominate Gujarat: Ahmedabad, Baroda, Broach, Surat. The last two, in their day the most flourishing ports of India, have long ceased to have any significance as such, but have taken a new lease of life as minor industrial centres; Baroda owes its importance largely to its functions as the capital of its state; the architectural glories of Ahmedabad are now overshadowed by the mills of the largest inland factory city of India.

Ahmedabad (**788,333**, the sixth city of *India*) was originally a strategic centre, commanding the first easy crossing of the Sabarmati above the Cambay marshes. Under Gujarati Sultans and Mogul viceroys it was one of the most brilliant Indian cities; its magnificent mosques and tombs represent a remarkably successful fusion of Islamic, Jain, and Hindu traditions, and are especially notable for the fine stone tracery of windows and screens. These monuments of the past consort strangely with the grim cultural landscape of the new industry; but this industry has transformed the post-Mogul decline and stagnation into rapid growth: in 60 years the city grew by 446% from a total of 144,451 in 1891. The first mills were opened about 1859–61; there are now more than in Bombay city itself (84 to 74), though Bombay units are larger. Large-scale development started later than in Bombay, and the Ahmedabad millowners had the benefits of the Bombay experience as well as their local advantages: cheaper land, cheaper labour, raw cotton on the spot. A larger proportion of Ahmedabad's production is in the finer counts than is that of Bombay. A peculiar feature of the city is the building plan in *pols*, self-contained blocks of houses which may contain up to 10,000 people, often inhabited by members of one caste only and forming virtually self-governing neighbourhood units. The larger ones indeed are almost little towns, traversed by a street with gates at either end and with separate courts on each side of the thoroughfare.

Baroda (**211,407**), lying on the Mahi/Narbada doab, is central to its fragmented state; this, and a local eminence, led to its development as the capital of the Maratha Gaekwars. The surrounding country includes some of the richest land of Gujarat; the town itself is well laid out, with the amenities of a progressive educational and cultural centre; there is some industry, mainly textiles, chemicals, and pottery. The merging of Baroda into Bombay will obviously reduce the city's importance to some extent, but it will of course remain the administrative and commercial focus of this central portion of Gujarat.

[11] Mukhtyar, *op. cit.*, 24–25, 61, 150–52.

Broach (55,810) and Surat (**223,182**) occupy strategic points at the lowest crossings of the Narbada and Tapti respectively. Surat, seat of the first English factory in India (1608–13), was the most active port of India in the first half of the 17th century, centre of a bitter triangular conflict between Portuguese, Dutch, and British; its outport Swally Roads was the scene of hard fighting. After the great sack by Sivaji in 1664, when the Dutch and English factories alone held out, "a Maratha raid was almost an annual certainty". Already Broach was declining before Surat; Cambay silting, the increased size of ships, the shift of trade routes and European interests to the Bay of Bengal coasts, local warfare, and the rise of Bombay brought both towns to a state of all but complete decadence.[12] But as late as 1695 Surat could be described, doubtless with exaggeration, as "the prime mart of India. . . . no ship trading in the Indian Ocean but what puts into Surat".[13] It recovered before Broach, mainly as the centre of railway-building in Gujarat in the 1860s when the American Civil War cotton boom brought prosperity and wild-cat speculation to all this part of India. The old gold- and silver-thread crafts and silk-weaving are still carried on; there are over 50,000 handlooms and some modern cotton and other textile mills, but Broach has more factory industry. The core of Surat is the once fortified area on the high Sn bank of the Tapti; Ewds lies an industrial zone along the railway, to the SW well-to-do suburbs extend along the estuary. As a port Surat is dead, and despite the Tapti Valley railway the trade of Khandesh is never likely to be diverted from Bombay to its old channels down the river. But lying as it does at the gateway from the Konkan into Gujarat, where the plain widens out, Surat remains an important centre of internal trade.

The Konkan

The Konkan [14] is the coastal lowland as far S as Goa: lowland, not plain, though it has some of the features of a plane of marine erosion. The lowland, 330 miles long and 30–50 broad, is much broken by hills, some of considerable extent and elevation. In the N indeed there is a flat alluvial belt along the coast, but this is only 4–8 miles wide, and behind it lies a series of parallel ridges reaching 1500–2000 ft, in which rivers like the Vaitarni, Ulhas, and Amba have lower courses more or less parallel to the coast before reaching it transversely. The Ulhas and its tributaries form a great amphitheatre between the Ghats and the Matheran outlier. S of Bombay the pattern changes: streams are shorter and directly transverse, though some, like the Vasishti and Savitri, have also formed amphitheatres

[12] Populations: Broach in 1777, c. 50,000; 1812, c. 38,000; Surat in 1811, c. 250,000 (?), 1816, 124,000; 1847, 80,000; 1881 and 1891, 109,000.

[13] *Bombay Gaz.* (1909), I. 331.

[14] Thana, Kolaba, and Ratnagiri Dts, with Bombay and the old states of Janjira and Savantwadi.

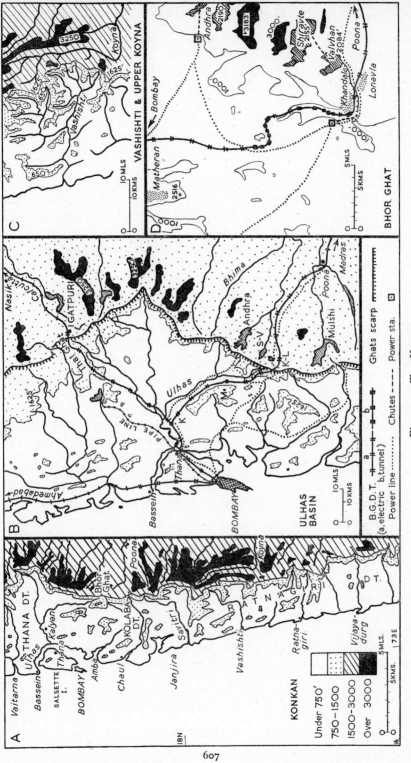

Fig. 117.—THE KONKAN.

607

under the Ghats. Active headward erosion in the massive horizontal lava
flows is obviously taking place, and it is clear, for example, that the upper
Koyna cannot long survive, geologically speaking (Fig. 117). S again, in
Sn Ratnagiri, the great feature is the series of extensive laterite-capped
residual plateaus. And throughout its length the Konkan is dominated by
the tremendous scarps of the Ghats, rising sheer a matter of 3000 ft in a
mile or two, fretted into wild canyons at the valley-heads.

Rural Konkan

With a rainfall of 75–100 ins. practically everywhere, rice is the dominant
crop.[15] A good way after come ragi, pulses, and fodder crops; coconuts are
increasingly important as we go S; and the Bombay bazaars call for some
market gardening. But the valley-bottoms are given over mainly to paddy,
with some ragi on the upper margins and pulses intercropped. Jute has
been introduced since 1947. In the estuaries mangroves are important for
fuel. The laterites are very barren, in places merely a surface of iron-stained
pebbles and slabs. The hills and the tangled country below the Ghats, like
the Ghats themselves, are covered with tropical semi-evergreen forest.

The whole region is dominated by Bombay, and apart from its satellites
Thana and Kalyan no town has 20,000 people. There is a string of tiny
ports, mostly decayed; some once Portuguese (Chaul, Bassein), others once
strongholds of Mogul or Maratha piratical chiefs, such as Vijayadrug,
which dominated 150 miles of coast and was reduced only by a full-scale
naval attack in 1757. Bassein had a good strategic position guarding the
approaches to Salsette Island; the typical market town (14,000), with its
wooden houses and carved balconies, lies in a countryside still dotted with
wayside crosses, but Bassein Fort was inhabited in 1943 by two Franciscan
fathers and a score or so of orphans, two or three families of peasants, and a
Hindu hermit, living in the midst of ruined baroque churches and surrounded by the complete 16th century walls of what was once a town of
35,000 people.

In the S the string of ports is paralleled by a string of towns at the head of
river navigation, once trading stations on the pack-routes through the
fortress-crowned spurs of the Ghats. Ratnagiri (18,000) is the only place
of much importance—for fishing, the coastal trade, and the emigrant
traffic to Bombay. This migration is an index of the poverty of the District:
in 1931 it provided 204 out of every 1000 immigrants into Bombay, and the
migrant population was about one-sixth of the total. Most of the migrants
go to the cotton mills, the police, and domestic service, and most are
young men. Remittances probably form a substantial part of the local
income.

[15] Total area, TSA, and rice (all in thousand acres): Thana 2195, 643, 336; Kolaba 1385,
422, 277; Ratnagiri 2564, 903, 768.

BOMBAY

The setting of Bombay forms as complete a contrast as can be imagined to that of Calcutta, its only rival as a commercial and industrial metropolis: an island site, dominated by the blue wall of the Ghats and the nearer hills across the broad harbour, as against the flats of Hooghlyside. The large-scale locational advantages of Bombay are obvious: centrality on the active littoral facing the SW Asia portages revivified, after long eclipse by the Cape route, in 1869. The link between these continental/oceanic values and the more local positional factors is the Ulhas basin (Fig. 117 B), the watersheds of which lead up to the Thal and Bhor Ghats (1900 and 1800 ft) used by the railways to Nasik and Poona respectively. As for the site itself, the island is now rather cramped, but the harbour, with an effective area of about 75 sq mls of sheltered deep water, is unrivalled in India.

The Rise of Bombay

The seven Deccan Lava islets which are now joined to form Bombay Island were held by the Portuguese, who made little use of them, though the local officials were aware of their value and put every obstacle in the way of their cession as part of Catharine of Braganza's dowry in 1661. Bombay soon supplanted Surat as the chief English base on the W coast, but although commercial progress was steady no territorial expansion took place until the seizure of Salsette in 1774, and no considerable expansion until the collapse of Maratha power in 1818. In the second quarter of the 19th century the population rose from under 250,000 to over 500,000: the opening of the improved Bhor Ghat road to Poona (1830) and the steamer service via Suez for home mails were the chief events of this period; by 1843 Bombay was within 30 days of London. In 1853 the first 20 miles of railway in India, Bombay to Thana, were opened, and by 1864 the rail had reached Ahmedabad and Poona. At the same time the blockade of the South in the American Civil War led to a spectacular boom in cotton prices, and the population in 1864 was over 816,000—a figure not reached again until 1881. The collapse in 1865 was catastrophic; but the opening of the Suez Canal to some extent mitigated the disaster, and meanwhile the bases of a modern textile industry had been laid: one mill in 1854, 7 by 1860; by 1885 there were nearly 50 with over 30,000 workers. Apart from Hooghlyside and (in cotton alone) Ahmedabad the primacy of Bombay as an industrial centre is unchallenged, and the initiative and drive have been indigenous to a much greater extent than in Calcutta. The place originally held by the Scots in Bengal belongs in Bombay to the Parsees, who built up the 18th century shipbuilding industry. It is sufficient to mention the great house of Tata, which has some share in nearly all the major modern activities of India, from soap to aviation, and a quasi-monopoly of some of the most important.

Apart from some minor state schemes in Mysore and Kashmir, Tatas led the way in the development of hydro-electricity in India, their first plant dating from 1915; and this has been the most significant feature of the recent industrial development.

The Port

Bombay has been by far the leading W coast port for two and a half centuries, and only recently has a rival appeared in Cochin—a rival not likely seriously to challenge Bombay's hegemony. From the bulk oil storage at Sewri to Alexandra Dock, a straight-line distance of 5 miles, the En side of the island is given over to port installations; the Port Trust estates cover nearly 1900 ac., about one-eighth of the whole island. The three main docks—Prince's (1880), Victoria (1888), and Alexandra (1914)—contain over 100 ac. of water with depths of 28–37 ft and 31,000 ft of quayage, to which the bunds or wharves add another 30,000. These are served by about 120 miles of Port Trust railway. The layout is shown on Fig. 118; the Cotton Depot, descendant of the famous 'Cotton Green' of early days, alone covers 127 ac. and its godowns have a capacity of a million bales.

The trade of the port has changed greatly since Reclus' day, when raw cotton, wheat, and opium were the chief exports, and Bombay had lost its place as an exporter of cotton goods—a line regained with the rise of factory industry. Cotton still has its place in the export list, but is outranked by cotton goods; other main lines are oilseeds and manganese. Imports, which normally exceed exports, consist mainly of constructional and consumption goods and mineral oil from abroad, grain and raw materials by the coasting trade.

The hinterland of Bombay extends roughly as far as Delhi, Jubbulpore, Nagpur, and Hyderabad; for exports as far as the oilseeds areas of the Madras Deccan. No small proportion of its considerable entrepôt trade is carried on by hundreds of sailing country boats; nor is this merely coastal, though of course the bulk of it is with the minor ports from Dwarka to Cape Comorin: the *baghla*, a high-pooped lateen-rigged craft of up to 400 tons, sails as far as the Persian Gulf, Aden, and Zanzibar. These vessels are the little-changed descendants of the 'Arab' boats which handled the traffic of the Indian seas before the dawn of history.

Industry [16]

As we have seen, Ahmedabad leads Bombay in number, but not in size, of cotton mills; but this is far outweighed by the 'metropolitan' diversification of industry in the greater city.

Textiles, indeed, are dominant, with some 200 factories of all types and

[16] Deshpande, *op. cit.*, 174–75, 250–52; cf. T. R. Sharma, *Location of Industries in India* (Bombay, 2nd ed., 1949), Chs. II–III.

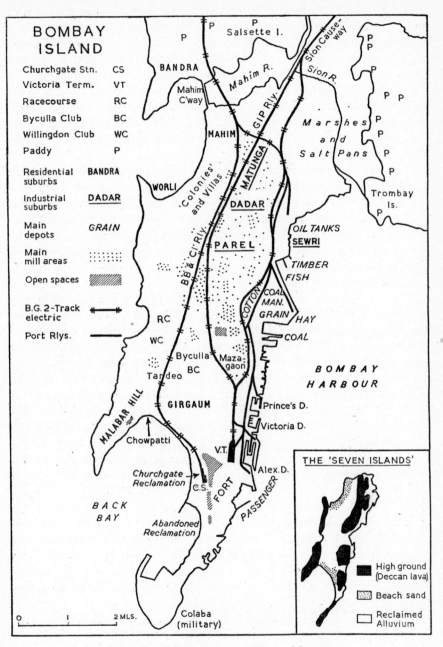

Fig. 118.—BOMBAY ISLAND. Man = Manganese.

200,000 workers: the heart of the industry is in Parel, where land was cheap in the earlier decades. Bombay yarn is mainly coarse, and piecegoods (apart from the home demand) are exported mainly to low purchasing-power markets, especially SW Asia and E Africa. The industry's adjustments to meet new competitors have been to some extent handicapped by the Managing Agency system, and there are definite signs of at least relative decline, attributable to high overheads in this intensively developed area and to competition in the immediate market by imports landed on the spot. Since 1915, however, economies have been effected by the change to hydro-electric power.[17]

Next comes engineering (over 400 works, 40,000 workers), largely located in Mazagaon, close to the port and railway installations. The *raison d'être* of the machine trades is obviously the general demand of a great conurbation and the special needs of the textile mills. Other important lines are printing (largely in the commercial Fort area), food, drugs and chemicals, and of course a host of consumption industries, large and small, catering for the metropolitan market. The film studios in the Nn suburbs are the most important in India.

Hydro-electrification has been most significant in recent years (Fig. 117 B and D). There are three power stations, fed by great storage reservoirs on the reverse slope of the Ghats—Andhra, Shiravte-Valvhan, and Mulshi Lakes (see Fig. 117 B and D). The water is led through the Ghat crest by tunnels—that from Mulshi is nearly three miles long—and the head at the three stations ranges from 1660 to 1740 ft. All are controlled by Tatas; the total normal capacity is 183,500 kW. They power most of the industry of Greater Bombay, as well as the Bombay trams and the electrified sections of the BB & CI to Virar beyond Bassein and of the GIP up the Ghats to Igatpuri and Poona; the latter, opened in 1929, was the first main electric line in India. The domestic supply companies in Bombay and Poona, originally thermal, now take their electricity in bulk from Tatas.[18]

The City

Bombay Island covers about 25 sq mls[19] with a 1941 population of 1,489,883; the Bombay Suburban Dt (S Salsette) added 250,000, and Greater Bombay has now **2,839,270**—not far behind Hooghlyside. The density of the city proper is about 50,000 to the sq ml, and in one area reached 375,000 in 1931.[20] The ordinary phenomenon of central depopula-

---

[17] Originally the power came from Durban coal.

[18] G. Kuriyan, *Hydro-Electric Power in India* (IGS Monograph 1, Madras, 1945), 21–23.

[19] The 1941 Census gives 30 (without explanation); this seems to include marginal semi-reclaimed land.

[20] Consistent in ill-doing, the 1941 Census not only has nothing comparable to the large volume on *The Cities of the Bombay Presidency* of the 1931 Census (Vol. IX), but even omits Bombay from the few sample tables, although sample slips were taken and figures are given for the next five towns.

tion exists, though distorted by the fact that the commercial 'centre'—the Fort and surrounding Esplanade area, roughly that shown on Fig. 119—is geographically excentric. Large open spaces and blocks of offices bring the density of much of this zone below 30 per acre. Sion in the NE, still largely marsh, had a similar figure; the densest belt (400–700 per acre) lay in the geographical heart of the city, between Girgaum and Mazagaon.

The Island is really formed of two lines of Deccan Lava hills; the intervening valley, originally tidal marsh, has been reclaimed, but the location of the most close-built areas in this central plain implies serious drainage and sewerage problems. The Island is separated from Salsette by the Mahim River, a broad tidal stream, and the largely silted Thana creek. These are crossed by road and rail (BB & CI) from Mahim to Bandra, and by the Sion Causeway carrying the main Poona road and the GIP. The population of over **2,000,000** is thus restricted to two links with the mainland, apart from coastal shipping. Rail, bus, and tram routes converge on the Fort—the commuting core, despite its peripheral location—and the narrowness of the Island behind Back Bay and the harbour adds to the resultant congestion.

Setting aside the docks and related areas in the E, the city falls into three or four main sections:

(i) the Fort and lower Bombay;
(ii) the densely populated area between Malabar Hill and Mazagaon;
(iii) the Nn suburbs: (a) residential in the W, (b) industrial in the centre and E.

(i) *The Fort*.[21] This, as the name implies, is the original European settlement around the Portuguese Castle, a part of which still remains intact. The line of the 18th-century enceinte (demolished 1862) is marked by Hornby Road and Rampart Row (RR); within it is the old town, an area of small businesses and shops, with a marked concentration of banking and insurance around Elphinstone Circle (E),[22] the first Cotton Green. NE of this core is the 'Big Business' of the Ballard Reclamation, housing the greater banks and international firms. S of the old town is the old cantonment of Colaba; N is the Victoria Terminus (VT), a building of stupendous size and astonishing ornament; but indeed the more grandiose architecture of the Fort as a whole is an Arabian Nightmarish medley of styles, all bad, and several groups would certainly be on the short list for the most hideous architecture in the world.[23] Beyond the main European shopping streets

[21] Letters in parentheses refer to Fig. 119.
[22] Now Horniman Circle, after a local English editor who threw in his lot with Indian nationalism.
[23] Holdich's reference (*India* (1904), 309) to "a city adorned with architecture worthy of the Government of an Indian Empire", if not so obviously sincere might well count as one of the bitterest gibes ever levelled at the British Raj. But exception must be made for the pleasantly Doric Town Hall, built—significantly—in 1833, before the booms. Much better is the remark (p. 308) that "a dirty picturesqueness (which is almost Italian) pervades most of the back premises of Bombay".

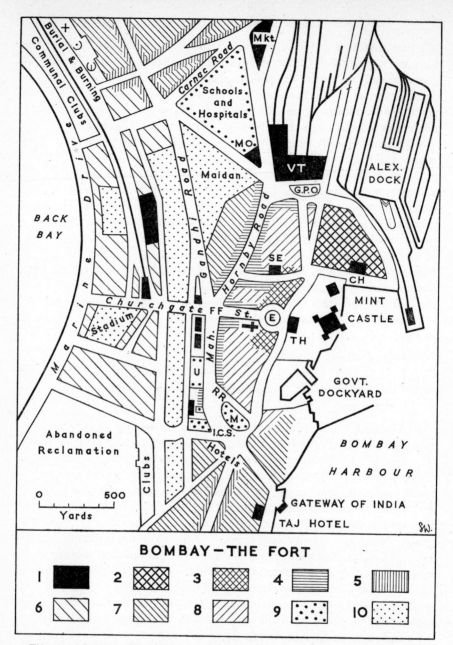

Fig. 119.—BOMBAY: 'THE FORT'. 1, public buildings; 2, 'Big Business'; 3, banks and offices; 4, main shops; 5, minor retailing; 6, modern residential (Churchgate flats); 7, middle-class residential, largely Anglicised; 8, poorer residential; 9, educational, etc.; 10, open spaces.

MO, Municipal Offices; VT, Victoria Terminus (GIP Rly); CH, Custom House; SE, Stock Exchange; TH, Town Hall; E, Elphinstone (now Horniman) Circle; FF, Flora Fountain; U, University; ICS, Indian College of Science; M, Museum; RR, Rampart Row.

(Hornby Road and lower Mahatma Gandhi Road) are public buildings—Courts, Secretariat, the weird Italo-Gothic University clock-tower and library—and a belt of open spaces. Beyond these again lies the Churchgate Reclamation, begun to give space for the BB & CI and added to in a long history of wild-cat speculation. As in so many double-fronted coastal towns, there is a complete contrast between the harbour and the Back Bay waterfronts: the latter is occupied by vast blocks of "modernist" flats along the great promenade of Marine Drive; from Malabar Hill the sweep of Back Bay looks like nothing so much as a vast toothy grin of too-regular dentures.[24] This is an upper-middle class and rather cosmopolitan residential area, with clubs, hotels, and restaurants; but the main hotel area for foreigners is S of the Fort, by the Gateway of India, a large and not unimpressive but pointlessly-sited triumphal arch.

(ii) *The Main City Mass.* Immediately N of this excentric core lies the vast amorphous mass of Indian Bombay; the cultural divide at Carnac Road is extremely sharp. At the head of Back Bay, N of the recreational area devoted to Gymkhana Clubs catering for the various communities, is the little bayhead beach of Chowpatti, Bombay's Marble Arch, venue for political and religious meetings and for general recreation on high days and holidays. Back Bay is closed on the NW by the heights of Malabar Hill, covered with the houses of the wealthy, generally hideous Indo-Baroque palaces but with a few older and pleasantly rambling bungalows and the inevitable piles of luxury flats.

Ewds across to Mazagaon is the densely-peopled zone of petty commerce, artisan crafts, bazaars, and so on. Byculla is a fossil 19th century outer suburb, left behind by the industrial expansion: a middle-class area with clubs and other recreational facilities. Amorphous as this main mass of the city appears, however, it is internally well segregated, not so much on class or economic lines (though these play their part) as by religion and language.

(iii) *The Northern Suburbs.* Nwds the development becomes looser, with islands of densely-built industrial housing as in Parel and Dadar: the skyline is broken by mill chimneys and the vast blocks of workers' tenements (*chawls*), often unspeakably congested and insanitary.[25] Such development is mainly E of the railways; to the W, in Mahim, is the usual untidy villa and garden-and-shack zone found on the outskirts of a great city. These outer suburbs also contain planned suburban estates or 'colonies'

[24] Some of this speculative building was so jerry-built that it collapsed before completion.
[25] In 1931 no fewer than 256,379 people lived in rooms housing 6 to 9 persons each; 80,133 in rooms with 10–19 inhabitants; 15,490 in rooms actually tenanted by 20 or more persons—a total of over 30% of the population in the three classes, and this does not represent the full extent of overcrowding, which is not of course confined to the industrial zones: there are slum enclaves in the Fort itself, the low density of which is offset by the large area of public and office buildings and docks (1931 Census, IX. 86). Any statistical improvement in 1931–39 has probably been swamped by the increase of street-dwellers.

sponsored by communal building societies. Mahim, like Bandra across the bay, has a considerable Portuguese Christian element, largely descended from refugees from the fall of Bassein. The NE of the Island has still much tidal marsh, with important salt-pans along Sion Creek.

Greater Bombay

The relationship between Salsette Island and Bombay is complex. In the W, along the electrified BB & CI, is a string of dormitory suburbs such as Bandra (71,789, of whom nearly 18,000 Christians; it is dominated by its three big Portuguese churches), Santa Cruz, Ville Parle, Andheri, Juhu, the last with the Bombay airport and fine bathing beaches. Even Bassein on the mainland is within commuting distance. These W Salsette towns have developed between the coastal marshes and the hills (over 1500 ft) of the NE; in the E there is little development between Kurla (39,066), with its slaughter-houses and leather industries, and Thana, but it is from this area, where land is poor and cheap, that Bombay's milk-supply comes, with water from reservoirs in the hills.[26] Elsewhere, as well as the usual paddy, there is a good deal of fruit and vegetable culture for the city's markets.

Thana (29,751) commands the most important crossing to the mainland; Kalyan (31,356), the natural route-focus of the Ulhas basin, was one of the leading ports of Wn India at the beginning of our era. Both are now mere satellites of Bombay, but since hydro-electricity became available there has been a considerable development of light industry, which "tries to avoid the high land values and overhead costs so characteristic of Bombay proper, and yet tries to retain the benefit of high finance and management of the 'city', and the advantages derived from bulk handling in the premier port of India. The Kurla Match Factory and the Ambernath Chemical Works are two leading examples of this kind. Even the port of Bombay at times finds a serious rival in these Salsette ports where the cargo of the ocean-going vessels is unloaded and 'broken' in transport by means of country craft to avoid the dock charges." [27] Other local industries include brick and tile works at Kalyan and, across Bombay Harbour, at Mora; these again use country boats as cheap transport for their bulky products. The whole of Salsette is thus directly subsidiary to Bombay, either as a commuting or as a supply zone; as Deshpande remarks, the difference between the dormitory and the producing sides of the island represents an extrusion of the similarly differentiated NW and NE of Bombay Island itself.

The immediate influence of Bombay extends as far as Matheran: a hill station in complete miniature on its little plateau (2500 ft) reached by a tiny 2 ft 6 in. 'mountain' railway. Not until the resorts and sanatoria of Khandala

---

[26] The main water-supply is now from the Tansa reservoir, farther out, and a dam is being built across the Vatarna.

[27] Deshpande, op. cit., 170.

and Lonavla, at the top of the Bhor Ghat, is there another urban pull, that of Poona; and even this tract, with its great hydro-electric plants powering the metropolis, is clearly more directly tributary to Bombay.

An Indian Microcosm

In many ways Bombay is a microcosm of Indo-British society, or rather societies, though East and West were more integrated here than elsewhere owing to the invaluable social lubricant provided by the Parsees, occupying a key intermediate position.

The street-plan and street-names of the Fort still reflect the layout of the 17th century trading station; here are the official monuments of John Company in an area remarkably tidy and compact and with a tendency to the grandiose which for the most part achieves only the grotesque. Here, too, there are the international contacts of the great trading houses on Ballard Estate and the slick modernity of Churchgate, yet near at hand the tight-packed streets of the old town with its sailors' taverns: Cosmopolis and the sea.

Malabar Hill represents the picturesque half-splendid and half-shabby India of Government House and Civil Lines, Cantonments and the Princes, an always-afternoon land with a touch of weirdness in the Towers of Silence where the Parsees expose their dead to the scavenger fowls of the air. North of this the densely-packed mass of Indian Bombay, still tightly organised but leading its own life, bound up with the world market and yet aloof: bazaars, temples, mosques, communalism. There is little European about it, but not a little Eurasian in islands of Victorian provincialism.

Beyond the close building the cultural landscape of the alien bureaucracy can still be recognised in the framework of roads and railways and public works; but in the interspaces, chaotically untidy, hives the real life of India. Mostly (and this is atypical) it is the new industrialism, spawned from the West but growing up outside the British environment, if within the steel frame of British imperialism: the mills and the chawls, the Hindu masses. Here and there are the relic villages to remind us that India is a land of villages; and in the harbour, on Elephanta Island, there is another India in the cave temple where the colossal three faces of Siva Trimurthi, Creator Preserver and Destroyer, brood eternally in darkling majesty.

Goa and Kanara

The Ghats Breaches

Between 16° and 12° N, Goa and the Dts of N Kanara (Bombay) and S Kanara (Madras) are in most respects transitional between the Konkan and Kerala. The coastal topography cannot be evaluated without more detailed studies than are available. Around the island of Goa conditions are more deltaic than anywhere else on the Wn Littoral, but both N and S the high ground comes down to the sea and the estuaries have a definitely ria aspect. But a few miles S of Karwar, at the Tadri mouth, we get the first hint of the spit-and-lagoon shoreline characteristic of Kerala. Inland the lateritic topography of Ratnagiri continues, and there are signs, in river terraces and possible planes of marine erosion, of negative shoreline movements. All this tends to confirm the suggestion of a 'hinge' of the whole coast about Goa.[28]

The Ghats themselves are exceptionally interesting in this section. Near the Nn boundary of Goa the Deccan Lava gives way to the Archaeans and the change is marked by a series of breaches in the mountain wall: the Kalinadi, Gangavali-Bedti, Tadri, and Sharavati have all definitely encroached on the Kistna-Tungabhadra drainage, setting the watershed some 80 miles back from the coast instead of the usual 25–35; more significantly, this also marks a major recession of the watershed not only from the sea but also from the Ghats crest (Figs. 2, 120), while in other embayments the watershed and the scarp swing back together. Possibly this has developed on an older surface not buried by the Lavas; but the continuation of the very strong Ghats scarp on the Archaeans well to the S of the Sharavati is a major difficulty on this view. At all events the 2750–3000 ft crest of the Lava Ghats breaks down here for about 200 miles, before rising again to 6215 ft in Kudremukh (S Kanara Dt) and more in the Nilgiris; and indeed between the Bedti and Varada Rivers the col is only c. 1600 ft.

This lower altitude, however, does not make access to the interior much easier, since the valleys are deep gorges two or three miles (or less) across and 1000 ft (or more) deep. Moreover it is precisely in this section that the coastal lowland is narrowest and most broken, affording but a small base for commercial activity other than piracy; 30–45 miles wide behind Goa, it narrows to 3 or 4 miles at 14° N, where Bombay, Mysore, and Madras meet on the Ghats crest only 8 miles from the sea. Tracks, and even roads of a sort, do cross the Ghats in this sector, and contributed to the old importance of Karwar and Honavar; but only the Bedti valley is used to any extent by these routes, and it is more significant that the chief towns in the Ghats (Yellapur, Sirsi, and Siddapur) are all on strongly-marked ridgeways. The most important economic value in this area, apart from forestry, is likely to be the Mahatma Gandhi power station at the Gersoppa or Jog falls on the Bombay/Mysore boundary, where the Sharavati has the most spectacular

---

[28] It might be hazarded that the deltaic conditions around Goa are associated with this relative stability, and possibly also with the position at the centre of the broad front on which the monsoon drift of the Arabian Sea impinges on the coast. It seems significant that, on the whole, coastal depositional forms at river mouths tend to run S–N in the Konkan and N–S in Kerala.

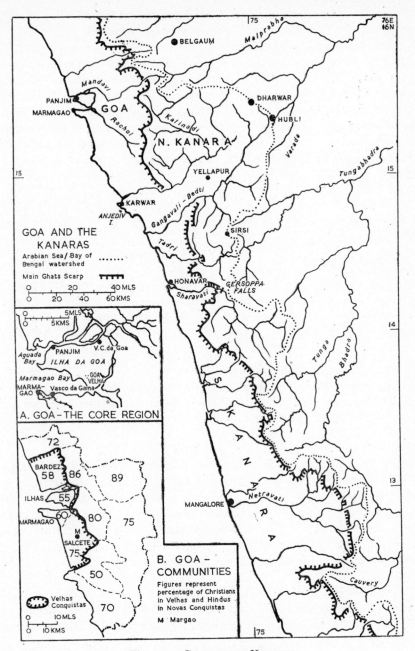

Fig. 120.—GOA AND THE KANARAS.

waterfalls in India, one of the four having a straight leap of 829 ft. Of the projected 120,000 kW, 48,000 are already being generated.

From the human point of view also this is a transitional zone. The solid Marathi of the N is succeeded by its regional version Konkani, which in Goa has a strong infusion of Portuguese loan-words; in the Kanaras Dravidian speech is dominant, Kanarese in N and Tulu in S Kanara; beyond, in Kerala, is another solid block, of Malayalam. Keralan conditions are also foreshadowed by the increasing importance of the coconut.

Climatically the entire area is hot and humid. Once more the transition is clearly shown, this time by the increasing length of the rainy season to the S:

Rainfall in Inches:	Total	May	%	June–Sept.	%	Oct.–Nov.	%	
Ratnagiri 16° 59' N	100·0	1·4	1·4	93·6	93·6	4·6	4·6	Konkan
Marmagão 15 25	94·9	2·6	2·7	86·1	90·7	5·1	5·4	Goa
Karwar 14 49	120·1	3·2	2·7	108·5	90·3	7·5	6·3	N Kanara
Mangalore 12 52	125·7	6·2	5·0	106·8	85·0	10·6	8·5	S Kanara
Calicut 11 15	118·6	9·5	8·0	88·5	80·5	15·2	13·0	Kerala
Cochin 9 58	114·7	11·4	10·0	74·8	64·5	19·6	17·1	Kerala

The human geography of each of the three components of this region is highly distinctive, and physically also they are sufficiently distinct to rank as sub-regions; it seems best to abandon the standard regional layout and give each a general treatment.

Goa

Goa, with 1268 sq mls and some 550,000 people, is the only considerable component of the Portuguese 'State of India'.[29] Small as this territory is, however, it has a tangible as well as a sentimental value. Marmagão is the best (and best-equipped) port between Bombay and Cochin, and the complete colonial hierarchy in an area the size of an English county gives plenty of patronage for deserving friends of the régime in Portugal, and (in the past at least) for deserving enemies against whom nothing could be proved.

At the beginning of the 16th century Goa was part of the Bijapur kingdom. The Portuguese had already factories and forts farther S—notably at Cochin and Cannanore—in which, however, they probably felt themselves

[29] Deshpande, 186–91; information from the Agencia Geral das Colonias, Lisboa, and other Portuguese sources. A lively account of Goa in its prime will be found in Maurice Collis's *The Land of the Great Image*. Portugal also holds the nearly deserted islet of Anjediv, off Karwar, where Vasco da Gama careened and where most of the English force sent to take over Bombay died while waiting.

straitened. The geopolitical eye of Afonso de Albuquerque at once grasped the advantages of the island site: large enough to give a secure food-producing base but with the defensible moat of the Mandavi and Rachol estuaries; central to the active littoral and well-placed with respect to the important NW sector of the Arabian Sea. He took the city by assault in 1510; in 1543 the rest of the Velhas Conquistas (Bardez and Salcete) were added. By this time Goa Dourada, 'Golden Goa', was at once fortress and mart, a Renaissance city transplanted to the East. The Portuguese decline is a part of general history; so far as Goa was concerned the subjugation of Portugal by Spain (1580) laid it open to the attacks of the Dutch.[30] By the mid-18th century the old city, Velha Goa,[31] was so decayed that it was gradually succeeded as the capital by Panjim or Nova Goa (11,153). The melancholy beauty of Old Goa has often been described, a city of baroque churches half-hidden by jungle, dead except for the great pilgrimage to the tomb of St Francis Xavier in the magnificent cathedral of Bom Jesus. Incessant warfare with the Dutch and the country powers, Muslim or Maratha, silting of the river and increase in malaria, reduced the population, said to have reached 200,000 in its prime, to a handful of clergy.[32]

The deltaic area—Ilhas, 'the Isles'—between Aguada and Marmagão Bays has the dense populations associated with rice/coconut culture; so also have the coastal tracts of Bardez to the N and Salcete to the S. The inland Novas Conquistas (acquired in an intermittent warfare with the Marathas in the 18th century) have large areas of laterite and rise through jungle-clad foothills and scarps to the crest of the Ghats; they are thinly populated, mainly by Hindus (Fig. 120 inset), and economically backward. The Marmagão peninsula has an interesting urban development, tiny as the towns are. Marmagão and Vasco da Gama, two miles apart, are practically one town in two distinct functional parts. Marmagão (3865) consists of little but harbour buildings with an airport on the low (200-ft) laterite plateau behind The harbour is well protected by breakwaters; ships of 22–30 ft draught can come alongside the quay, which has good cranage and warehousing and the wharfside railway (metre, connecting with the Indian railways between Belgaum and Dharwar). Vasco da Gama is larger (6719) and more residential, but has large oil installations. Towards the root of the peninsula Margão (11,002) is the nodal and market centre of Salcete. The economic activity of Goa, apart from agriculture, is largely concentrated

---

[30] So strict was the Dutch blockade that the ship bearing news of the regaining of independence (1640) had to send in its message by a small boat at night.

[31] Strictly Velha Cidade da Goa, the Portuguese keeping 'Velha Goa' for the ruined pre-Muslim city in the S of the island.

[32] There is a good description in Reclus (*Nouvelle Géographie Universelle*, Tome VIII (1883), 476–78); but it should be remembered that Reclus was a Communard, and the clerical dominance so often alleged as a main cause in the Portuguese decline was more probably a collateral.

in this little peninsula, and is not inconsiderable. Manganese is mined near Marmagão, and salt production exceeds 25,000 tons a year; coconuts and copra, fresh and dried fish, cashew nuts, and salt are exported, and there is further the transit trade from the Deccan. Some 3000 ships (aggregating half a million tons) enter and clear annually. Exports, however, greatly exceed imports, amounting to £1·5–2·25 m. sterling against imports of £0·25–0·5.[33] The colony is kept going by remittances.

The social geography of Goa is indeed fascinating. Dense population and high taxation lead to much emigration, some as far afield as Mozambique, though some two-thirds of the emigrants go to Bombay City, which has generally a Goanese population of about 40,000 as well as its own local Luso-Indians. Educational standards are reasonably high, and Goanese are prominent in clerical occupations, teaching, medicine, and in the Indian marine, as well as in entertainment and domestic service; a large proportion of the emigrants are females, and the hotel staffs of Wn India are largely Goanese. Their earnings play a large part in Goanese economy, and in Bardez the cultural landscape is somewhat anglicised, with the modern bungalows of returned emigrants and a fair prevalence of English speech. Emigration is of course mainly from the crowded, and Christian, coastal areas.

Here four and a half centuries have produced a high degree of cultural fusion, extending even to the peculiar Goanese language. Christians form 43% of the total population (Fig. 120 inset),[34] and there is probably a considerable metropolitan sentiment among the Catholic Goanese. Nevertheless the claim of *India* to round off her national territory meets a response from within Goa, a response which cannot be indefinitely overcome by mere repression; nor, clearly, could Portugal hope to maintain her footing by force of arms. It is ironic that the Portuguese empire in India should have survived the British; how long it will do so is an open question. But whatever the political fate of Portuguese rule in India, culturally it has struck deep roots; nor can a certain immortality be denied to a city which knew St Francis Xavier, the Apostle of the Indies, and Camões, the greatest poet of his time in any country and of his country in any time. The grandeur and the decadence of Goa meet in his work: she is at once "Senhora de todo o Oriente" and the Babylon of those bitter sonnets which are perhaps the most poignant utterances of genius exiled in an alien land.

N Kanara: Coastlands and Ghats

(a) *The Coast.* Alone of the Wn Littoral sub-regions, N Kanara is more essentially highland than lowland.[35] The lowland is indeed almost restricted

[33] *Statesman's Year Book* (1949), 1284. The port is managed by the Madras and Southern Mahratta Railway.

[34] The Roman Catholic Archbishop of Bombay was by convention alternately a Portuguese and a British subject; this has now been abrogated with other Portuguese patronage in *India.*

[35] Here we rely more heavily than ever on Deshpande.

to pockets along the lower courses of the rivers which break the Ghats and, *per contra*, thus warrant an extension of the 'Wn Littoral' well inland. The alluvial lower section of each valley is a unit focussing on the small port at or near its mouth; places of great historical interest but almost completely insignificant to-day.

The coastal taluks have densities of 240–340, but only about half (or in the S a third) of the land is cultivated, and densities in relation to arable land are high—about 1200. Rice is dominant, covering 60% of the cultivated area, with coconut on the sandier coastal soils and ragi millet on the poorer laterites inland. The low-level laterite (200–400 ft) is indeed largely given over to scrub and poor grass; S of the Sharavati it dominates the lowland. The Ghat forests reach down to the sea in several places.

Karwar (15,300) on the Kalinadi is the most important of the little ports, with a fairly well-sheltered harbour in Baitkul Cove. But the immediate hinterland is poor and rugged, and such activity as exists, mainly timber rafting, is not in the Cove but on the Kalinadi estuary itself, two miles to the N. The construction of the Marmagão railway has completely inhibited any serious development at Karwar. The Sharavati is navigable by small craft to Gersoppa, and the estuarine plain is very fertile, but again the complete lack of any wider hinterland keeps Honavar (9000) hardly more than a village; though a link with the Mysore railway might revivify it. For all these little ports the wider hinterland of the Bombay Karnatak, once tapped by pack-bullock trails, has been drained off to Bombay itself by the railways; but it is planned to construct a modern port at one or other of them.

(b) *The Ghats.* Differential erosion, river capture, faulting, lithological variety combine to render this an extremely dissected area; the high rainfall favours a dense forest growth. The lower Wn spurs and terraces are largely lateritic, with poorish teak and bamboo; above them is the evergreen zone with the best teak stands; the drier En slopes carry stunted or pole forests and grass. In the S sandalwood is important. Much of this forest has been badly damaged by shifting cultivation (*kumri*).

In this jungly and malarial terrain densities are naturally low (20–100) and cultivation sparse (6–15% of total area). Rice is the most important crop, but spices are important, though declining—about 12,000 ac., mainly in the S (Sirsi and Siddapur taluks). The spice-villages have a distinctive settlement pattern, generally linear along the break of slope above the valley-bottom, with holdings running across the valley to secure equitable allotment of soils and water; houses are widely spaced.

Of more importance is the forest, on which indeed the spice-gardens are dependent for their heavy demands in leaf-manure, while dwellings, household utensils, and decorative crafts are mainly of wood or bamboo-based. The best teak is in the N around Yellapur; to the E light timber is obtained from the pole forests. Some of the timber goes out to the E by rail, but most down the convenient rivers to Karwar and Honavar.

The area has a declining population and is essentially negative, a barrier to movement. Roads and tracks follow the lower reaches of the rivers, then climb the terraces and tend to keep to high ground; Ewds, on the open Deccan, movement was and is mainly on N/S lines. Such towns as exist are points of convergence for the plateau roads before they pitch steeply down the Ghats: such are Yellapur (15,000) and Sirsi (10,500), both centres of the spice trade which, owing to its high value for bulk, is relatively well adapted to the poor transport facilities.

S Kanara

S Kanara,[36] like the Ulhas basin and Goa, is an embayment of lowland, widest (*c.* 45 miles) in the Netravati valley behind Mangalore. The setting back of the Ghats permits a greater development of alluvium than in N Kanara, broad wedges rather than narrow strips. These are backed by a low (150–400 ft) plateau of laterite, covering perhaps half the area, and essentially sterile despite the heavy rain. Towards the lower margin of this platform the laterite appears redeposited rather than formed *in situ*, but nearer the Ghats this detrital form overlies that weathered directly from the gneissic or granitic country rock. The laterite in general appears to correspond in age to the late Tertiary Warkalai beds of Kerala; in the extreme S it has lignite beds similar to those of the Warkalais. The laterite platform, like the Warkalai surface, is held by local observers to be a plane of marine erosion, and two terraces in the major valleys also point to a general negative movement.[37]

The laterites, and in places the alluvium also, are broken by ridges and isolated hills of Archaean gneisses and granites, some of which appear to have been offshore islands. In the N the Ghat scarp (here formed of Dharwars) is very sharply defined; but although it is higher in the S (rising to 6000–6500 ft) the headwaters of the Netravati and other rivers have etched it into a series of deep coulisses; the drainage-pattern along the watershed, especially across the border in Coorg, is of a beautiful complexity. In the extreme S, as in the N, Ghat spurs reach nearly to the coast.

Rainfall is everywhere over 125 ins., and on the Ghats over 200. The extensive laterite and the Ghat foothills, however, limit agriculture, and less than a quarter of the 4000 sq mls of the District is cultivated. Of the rest some 2400 sq mls are forested, but only a third of the forest is Reserved. The relations of forest and cultivation show interesting peculiarities. The jungle is largely occupied by tribal remnants practising shifting *kumri* cultivation: they have wandered over the land to such an extent that only some 10% of

[36] Based on 10 papers in *JMGA* XIII (1938). The extreme S (Kasargod taluk) is Malayalam in speech and belongs culturally to Kerala.
[37] V. D. Krishnaswamy, *JMGA* XIII (1938), 253–55.

the forest is untouched, mainly on the wildly dissected and inaccessible main Ghats scarp. The remainder is badly degraded secondary jungle. Before 1860, however, the forest was protected by the settled cultivators of the valleys, who used it mainly as a source of leaf-manure. The forest land up to the ridgetops bounding the valleys was known as *kumki* (= 'aid' to cultivation) and in it the cultivator had considerable rights. But in 1860 this privilege was restricted to a distance of 100 yds from the fields; all beyond this became unoccupied Government land, and before the creation of the Forest Department in 1882 was exploited without control: what the shifting cultivator spared the timber speculator gutted. The results of this spoliation are still visible, and the indigenous tradition of conservation has been so undermined by the influence of a money economy that—as elsewhere in India—there is agitation not only against an expansion of the Reserves, but actually for their diminution.[38]

Forestry, however, remains a chief source of wealth. Teak is increasingly becoming a plantation rather than a natural crop; and, besides other timber trees, minor products such as sandalwood, bamboos, canes, cutch, honey, and wax are important. The cashew nut, introduced by the Portuguese in the 16th century, now grows wild all over the District and is being planted; it offers great potentialities, as the oil (used locally as caulking for boats and as a wood preservative) is in some demand in the United States as a plastics base and for paints and varnishes, and the tree also yields a fleshy fruit from which power alcohol can be distilled.[39]

Agriculture displays the usual features of the humid littoral: concentration on rice in the loamy alluvium, with coastal coconuts, and ragi and pulses on the laterites, where these are not given over to coarse grass and bush or secondary scrub-jungle. The contrast is well shown by the difference in density between Mangalore taluk (excluding Mangalore town), which has 764, and Karkala, mainly laterite, which has 244.

There are no towns of any importance except Mangalore (**117,083**). The "port" is a mere roadstead two or three miles offshore, useless in the monsoon; small country craft can harbour in the creek. Owing to its proximity to the Mysore plantations, however, it handles about three-quarters of the coffee trade of India; other exports are pepper, tea, and cashew nuts. It has an interesting local industry: Mangalore tiles are famous throughout Sn India, and the industry has some geographical localising factors: demand for roofing on this rainswept coast, good local clay, and transport on the rivers between which Mangalore lies. But the change from petty artisan to factory production seems to have been a mere historical accident, a result of the initiative of the Basel Mission which established the first factory in 1865 and still runs two of the three largest. There are altogether 30 or 40 factories

---

[38] E. V. P. Pillai, "The Forests of S Kanara", *JMGA* XIII (1938), 269–78.
[39] Pillai, *loc. cit.*, 275; A. K. Menon, *ibid.*, 280.

with an output of 5–600 m. tiles a year; local sailing coasters supply markets from Karachi to Colombo, and there is some export via Bombay to E Africa, Persia, and Malaya. But competition from Malabar and, much more serious, from cement and asbestos roofing is adversely affecting the industry, which appears to be declining.[40] Other industries are of little importance: iron-founding (ancillary to the tile factories), and soap, based on local and imported copra; Mangalore is the main port for the Laccadive islanders. A feature of some interest is the prominence of Portuguese names among the larger concerns, both in coffee-curing and in tile-making.

Kerala

Both physically and culturally Kerala is one of the most distinctive regions of India.[41] Historically it has been somewhat isolated from the rest of the Peninsula, but accessible to maritime influences. Homogeneous in speech, it is probably more caste-divided than any other area, and it is here that 'untouchability' developed the more fantastic extremes of 'unapproach-ability' and even 'unseeability', while the Nairs who form the bulk of the minor gentry preserve a matrilinear organisation in which both polygamy and polyandry play a part.[42] Perhaps by reaction against caste, the region has the highest percentage of Christians in all India—28·8 in Cochin and 32·3 in Travancore. This element long antedates the vigorous Portuguese missions, which succeeded in bringing into the Roman fold most of the 'Syrian' (i.e. Nestorian) Christians, whose traditions go back to St Thomas the Apostle; there were Christian communities 1500 years ago. The 'White Jews' of Cochin are another ancient fossil kith; their number is only a few hundreds, but their origin is claimed to be from a Solomonic colony and is undoubtedly very ancient. But there is no end to the ethnographical fascinations of Kerala.

The Physical Setting

Tokens of uplift are numerous and decisive, including the existence of coral reefs below the alluvium some miles from the present coast.[43]

---

[40] U. Hammaba, *ibid.*, 291–99.

[41] Based mainly on a series of papers by G. Kuriyan in *JMGA* and *IGJ*: "The Indus-trial Crops of Kerala" (XI (1937), 283–90 and XII (1937), 1–8); "Population and its Distri-bution in K." (XIII (1938), 125–46); "The Geographic Basis of the Legendary Origin of K." (XVI (1941), 340–54); "Some Aspects of the Regional Geography of K." (XVII (1942), 1–41). On Cochin I am indebted for first-hand information to Sir Robert Bristow, CIE, to whom the development of the modern port is largely due.

[42] The best easily accessible account for geographers is in C. D. Forde, *Habitat, Economy and Society* (1934 and later eds.), Ch. XIII. See also G. Slater, *Southern India* (1936), Chs. XVI–XVII.

[43] Legend ascribes the formation of Kerala to the impatience of a local saint ("during the thousandth year after the [biblical] flood") with the unspecified improprieties of his aged mother. He threw an axe from Gokarna (near Goa) over the sea; it flew to Cape Comorin and the sea retreated beneath its flight. This does correspond with the actual area of emergence.

Literary and place-name evidence points to continuing growth of the land within proto-historic or even historic times. It seems likely that there were at least two phases of relative upward movement, represented by erosion surfaces in the laterite at around 250 and 600 ft, while the last stage—that reflected in legend and literature—added the eight miles or so between the existing shore and a line of villages of whose names 'sea' or 'island' is a component; some places mentioned by Ptolemy as sea-ports now lie at a similar distance inland. But all these are near the great Cochin backwater, which suggests—as do the large-scale maps—that normal prograding on a low shoreline of emergence is responsible for this accretion, rather than an actual change of levels. Probably associated with this are the Malabar mudbanks, which lie off all the river mouths. They are up to eight miles long, and their extremely finely comminuted lateritic mud forms as it were an emollient which deadens the ocean swell; in their lee are safe roadsteads for the small ports of the coast.

The general tripartite longitudinal division is found: alluvial coastland, low lateritic plateaus and foothills, gneissic highlands. The division is indeed rather more clear cut than in the more complex Nn lowlands, but each zone has certain peculiarities. In the alluvium is the great development of lagoons and backwaters, saline or fresh, which, with some artificial cuts, form splendid waterways for some 150 miles from the Ponnani mouth to Trivandrum. The largest of these, behind Cochin, widens out Swds into Vembanad Lake. The laterites (including the ?Pliocene Warkalais) form plateaus at 200–600 ft, with much grass and scrub; into them project spurs of the Anaimalai-Cardamom Hills which, S of Palghat, have a very strong SE–NW trend, shown by the Periyar Valley. The hills themselves, rain-swept and forested, will be treated in the next chapter, but it may be noted here that the plantation agriculture of Kerala is confined to them, and the development of hydro-electricity from Pallivasal is of great importance to the agriculture and industry of the lowland.

The Ponnani, the headwaters of which rise on the Nn slopes of the Anaimalais, leads up to the Palghat Gap, nearly 20 miles wide and not much over 1100 ft on its broad sill, which lies beyond the regional limits. Farther S the higher (nearly 1500 ft) and much narrower Shencottah Gap gives access to the extreme S of Madras. It is noteworthy that in both these gaps there were exclaves of Cochin and Travancore territory, extending well E of the watershed in the latter; these, with the ancient walls across the Comorin lowland, emphasise the importance of these sole easy points of contact between Kerala and Tamilnad.

Climate and Agriculture

The climate represents the nearest approach in India to equatorial conditions. Maximum temperatures rarely exceed 90° F., minima rarely fall

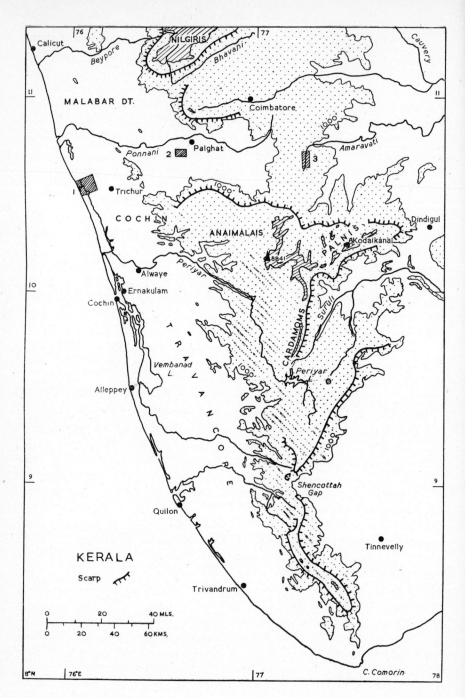

Fig. 121.—KERALA. 1, area of Fig. 122; 2, of Fig. 123; 3, of Fig. 146. 1000–6000 ft
stippled, over 6000 ft shaded.

below 70°, the annual range at Cochin is only 6° and the diurnal is about 10°. Apart from the high falls (180 ins. plus) in the hills, rainfall decreases from N to S (Calicut 119, Trivandrum 64 ins.) and the extreme S, around Comorin, falls below 40: here alone are there major irrigation works. But this decrease is balanced by a better seasonal distribution in the S: Trivandrum has 24·85 ins. in June–August, 21·32 in September–November, and 18·23 in December–May—28% in what is an almost completely dry season in nearly all the rest of the sub-continent.

Kerala as a whole (including the hills) has an area of about 15,500 sq mls, of which some 20% (mainly on the Travancore hills and foothills) is forested and 45% NSA. The TSA is about 15–20% greater than NSA in Cochin and Malabar. The question of 'culturable waste' is, as usual, difficult; but it seems that in the alluvial and lateritic zones respectively about 75–80 and 65–70% of the total area, or 90 and 80% of the 'cultivable', are in fact cultivated.[44] It is clear that what is left will be marginal and that there is very little room for expansion.

Rice is dominant, occupying about 260,000 out of a TSA of 550,000 cropped ac. in Cochin, 860,000 out of 1,790,000 in Malabar, but only 655,000 out of 2,200,000 in Travancore. The area under rubber, tea, and pepper in the Travancore hills accounts for this in part; but in Cochin and Malabar a good deal of rice is grown on the lateritic hills after burning the jungle; the heavier rainfall has probably a bearing on this. The local variations in cropping, analysed in detail in Kuriyan's 1942 paper, deserve summarising:

(i) In the extreme S rice is grown by canal- and in Shencottah taluk (E of the hills and really outside the region) by tank-irrigation. With intensive watering and careful transplanting crops can be obtained both in September–October and in February–March. In Chittur taluk—the Cochin outlier in Palghat—there is also a little irrigation by *anicuts* or weirs feeding canals, and here cotton and groundnuts are grown. These three areas are strongly influenced by Tamil methods.

(ii) Along the backwaters (*punja* and *cole* areas) the problem is not to get water on the land but to get it off. These areas are divided into blocks of up to 50 (exceptionally 100) ac., bounded by double dykes enclosing a channel. From July to September–October the ground is submerged, sometimes to a depth of several feet; after the rains the water is lifted into the bounding channels by Persian wheels; latterly oil-driven and still more recently electric pumps powered from Pallivasal have been introduced. The land lies three or four feet below the water-level in the channels, and sluices regulate various inundations during the growing season. Should the bunds be burst the half-drowned crop may be reaped from boats by cutting off the heads.

(iii) Along the backwaters on the Cochin-Malabar boundary the soil on areas liable to salt-water inundation is heaped up into mounds about one foot

[44] Kuriyan (1938), 133; (1942), 29.

high and five feet round, on which the paddy is sown just before the rains. When the monsoon bursts the surrounding water is freshened and transplanting takes place. This is a rather precarious method, illustrating the devices enforced by severe population pressure.

(iv) In the wet lowlands above the backwaters more normal methods prevail, but the early onset of the rains enables planting to take place in April–May and harvest in September; the continuance of the rains then often permits a poor second crop (not necessarily paddy) harvested in January; very occasionally a third is possible.

After rice, coconut is the chief crop, accounting for nearly 1 m. ac., typically, of course, in the sandy coastal strip but also on alluvial loams and (with more careful preparation) on laterites. In Travancore the coconut acreage is nearly equal to that of rice; in Quilon taluk, indeed, it covers 85% of cropped area. After rice as the essential food, the coconut palm is the basis of life in Kerala: "Apart from the several uses of the chief products, viz., coir, copra, coconut oil, oil-cake, the hollowed trunk serves as a canoe, the nut forms a staple article of diet, the leaves may be used for many of the purposes of paper, are frequently employed as thatch and for the manufacture of brooms, baskets, umbrellas, tattis [screens kept soaked to cool rooms], and fans, and utilised as crude torches in a dried form, or burnt as fuel, as it is [sic] or in the form of charcoal. In addition, the fresh or fermented juice of the stem is consumed as a beverage, by evaporation it is made into jaggery and by subsequent treatment even sugar is obtainable. When distilled, the toddy becomes arrack and finally vinegar." [45] Of the "industrial" workers of Kerala—most of them, of course, cottage workers—about a third are in various processes connected with coconut products, and of these two-thirds are women. The coir 'yarn' is almost entirely cottage-produced, its working-up into mats and so on largely a small factory industry.

The most important other crops (apart from plantation rubber and tea in the hills), are cassava (tapioca) and pepper, mainly in the foothills. The former is grown as a food crop on poorer lateritic soils; pepper is perhaps the chief peasant-produced cash crop after coconut. Cereals other than paddy are negligible, as are oilseeds except for a little sesamum (gingelly), often as a third crop on the higher wet-rice lands. Nearly every homestead has its plantains and other fruit trees, and ginger and the betel vine, with its associated areca palm, are also grown widely but in tiny patches.

Tapioca deserves special mention. Introduced about 1920, it is grown on the lateritic soils ("about as attractive for agriculture as railway ballast") in tiny holdings by the poorest of the poor. As Gourou points out, there is a sort of social inversion: the better-off rice farmers in the valley-bottoms, and a hundred feet or so above them a very wretched (largely Christian) peasantry.

[45] Quoted in Kuriyan, 1937 (Vol. XI), 286. Cf. P. K. Paniker, "The Coconut—its Cultivation on the Malabar Coast", *IGJ* XVIII (1943), 78–88.

Other Occupations

Fishing, both sea and freshwater, plays a big part in the life of Kerala but, as usual in India, is primitive in technique and organisation. It has, however, some interesting features: Portuguese influence is obvious in the so-called 'China nets' and the crossbow used for shooting fish from river-banks, [46] and there are many varieties of basket-work fish-traps. The catch of 'sardines' is largely used for manuring coconut; prawns are taken in flooded paddy-fields, the skins used as manure and the pulped flesh exported. Normally Burma was a good customer for prawns; the time of transport raised no difficulty as a high degree of putrescence was regarded with favour.

Travancore has a hydro-electric plant at Pallivasal on the Mudrapuzha River, with a capacity of 21,000 kW which can be increased to 36,000. The power is used for the industries of Cochin town and Ernakulam, of which the production of soap and cosmetics from copra is the most important. It also powers the sole Indian aluminium works, at Alwaye, formerly dependent on imported alumina but now increasingly supplied from Muri in Bihar (591 above); and a recent development is the use of electric pumps for 'de-watering' the *cole* lands. The great reservoir impounding the Periyar headwaters was built to supply irrigation water, by tunnel, to the Madras side, but may possibly be developed for power in the future.

Except for local clays and laterite, the only mineral deposits are the ilmenite, monazite, and zircon sands of the Travancore beaches from Quilon to Cape Comorin. These contain 8–10% thorium oxide and were exploited for the manufacture of gas mantles; the spread of electric lighting ruined this demand, but there has been a remarkable recovery. Titania from the ilmenite and cerium from the monazite are essential to some highly specialised electrical and chemical manufactures (electrodes, tracer bullets, and as a catalyst in benzine synthesis, amongst others) and recent developments in atomic research have made these deposits of great strategic significance. Production, which in 1925 fell to one hundred-weight of monazite, amounted in 1944 to 200,000 tons ilmenite, 2000 monazite, and 1600 zircon.

Population and Settlement

Population problems are very serious in Kerala; the density of Cochin in 1941 was the highest for any political unit in India—953 on a total area of 1493 sq mls—locally reaching 2000–4000 in a purely rural environment. Elankunnapuzha village had in 1941 no fewer than 18,173 people on its 3·8 sq mls—a density of 4782. The rate of increase has been very high—for

[46] A. K. Menon, "Fisheries of Cochin" (*IGJ* XIV (1939)), 229–36; C. D. Forde, *op. cit.*, 269.

Malabar, Cochin, and Travancore respectively 14, 23, and 27% in 1921–31, 11, 18, and 19% in 1931–41. The decrease in rate seems to be associated with later marriage. Females outnumber males in Cochin (1042:1000) and in both Cochin and Travancore the proportion of unmarried females over 15 years old is several times greater than that of India as a whole—in 1941 Cochin had 172 per mille and Travancore 107 against an All-India rate of 36. In Cochin also the proportion of children under 10 had been stable in the last two Censuses.[47] The rate of increase, however, turned upwards again in 1941–51, which added to Travancore-Cochin 1,772,264 souls— an increase of 23·6% compared with an *Indian* average of 13·4. Population is now **9,280,425** with a density of **1015** on 9155 sq mls.

The situation is grave; on the 1931 figures Kuriyan calculated that taking a liberal view of the potentialities of 'culturable waste' only another 2,000,000 souls could be supported. Holdings are extremely small—96% under 10 ac., 87% under 5, 38% less than 1; and 5 ac. is regarded as the minimum for a family to live in reasonable comfort.[48] In Cochin the total area per person in 1941 was 0·67 of an acre, of cultivable land 0·36, of land actually cultivated 0·29; and the rice grown is sufficient to feed the people for only 7 out of 12 months.[49] During the war the Cochin and Travancore governments prided themselves, with some justice, on the efficiency of their procurement and rationing, but the ration was minimal even by Indian standards. As we have seen, agriculture is in many respects extremely intensive; yet in many areas there is a slack season from May through August, and this coincides with the slack season in sea-fishing owing to the stormy monsoon.

Diversification and expansion of agriculture are thus urgently necessary. But the density on cultivated area in the lowland is now at least 2250, and there is here very little land available for expansion on the most optimistic view imaginable. Various plans exist for irrigating perhaps 100,000 ac., mainly in the foothills; but these will not go very far, and it is difficult to see where the 15,000 ac. allotted to jute in 1950 can be fitted in. Even in the foothills there are well over **1000** persons to the cultivated square mile. Here, however, there is perhaps some room for diversification by expansion—perhaps of poorer crops on the poorer soils. Gram, soya, and other pulses, fodder crops, and buckwheat are suggested by Kuriyan, together with more tapioca and fruit. Other occupations may play an ancillary role in relieving pressure, but their scope is limited.

As for settlement patterns, the extreme density of population (as in Bengal) produces a close stipple of habitations; there are no grouped villages (other than mere thickening of homesteads) except in the tran-

---

[47] 1941 Census, Vol. XIX (Cochin), 18–24; the discussion is largely based on Cochin figures since this, by exception in 1941, is an excellent report.
[48] *Ibid.*, 31; Kuriyan (1938), 140, where 8–10 ac. is given as the 'economic' holding.
[49] 1941 Census, Vol. XIX, 31.

sitional areas—Comorin, Shencottah, Palghat, parts of Malabar. The importance of food-producing trees (coconut, areca, plantain, jackfruit) fits in with this: they are grown in the house compounds, so that the actual dwelling-space subtracts hardly anything from the cultivation-space, while

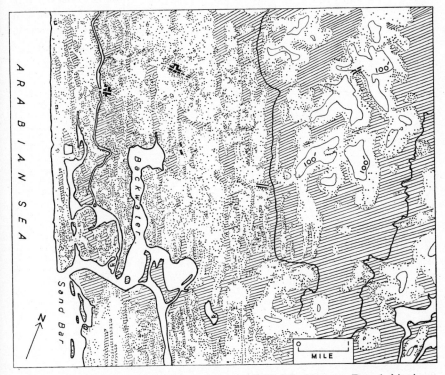

Fig. 122.—KERALA: COASTAL SETTLEMENT. 40 mls N of Cochin town. Dots, habitations; shaded, paddy. Note contrast between linear settlement on beach-ridges (under coconut) in W and ring settlement around lateritic rises in E. SOI 58 B/2; courtesy SOI.

at the same time the compounds ensure that the 'village' is loosely built, and may indeed spill all over the village lands. (Fig. 122.)[50]

Along the coast there is a marked linear tendency, houses and coconuts on the sandy ridges with their fresh ground-water, paddy in the lows. Inland the lateritic topography exercises a marked effect, settlement being strung out along valley-flanks or interfluves or forming a complete ring around the rises. (Fig. 123.)

[50] The 14th and the 20th centuries tell the same tale. "Mulaybar, which is the pepper country, extends for two months' journey along the coast. . . . there is not a foot of ground but what is cultivated. Every man has his own orchard, with his house in the middle and a wooden palisade all round it." (Ibn Battuta, *Travels in Asia and Africa, 1325–1354,* trans. H. A. R. Gibb (1929), 231–32). Along the 40 miles from Quilon to Trivandrum one is never out of sight of habitations or foot-travellers; G. Slater, *op. cit.,* 172.

Towns

The towns of Kerala are for the most part either ports or crossing-points on the backwaters. There is virtually no indigenous maritime tradition, but from very early times spices attracted traders from E and W: Arabs, Graeco-Romans, Chinese.[51] With the Discoveries the Malabar coast became the scene of a fierce struggle between the Portuguese and their Muslim and European rivals. Relics of the era of European conflict are the tiny French settlement of Mahé (26 sq mls, poptn (1941) 14,092) and the exclaves of former British territory at Cochin itself and in Travancore

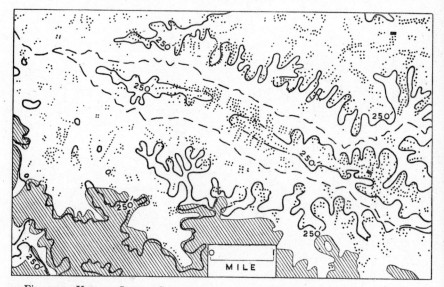

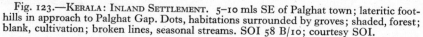

Fig. 123.—KERALA: INLAND SETTLEMENT. 5–10 mls SE of Palghat town; lateritic foot-hills in approach to Palghat Gap. Dots, habitations surrounded by groves; shaded, forest; blank, cultivation; broken lines, seasonal streams. SOI 58 B/10; courtesy SOI.

at Anjengo and Quilon (Tangasseri), which last had an area of 99 acres!

In Malabar Dt Tellicherry (36,320) exports most of the Coorg coffee and some pepper and copra; Calicut (**158,724**) has a similar trade but is more important administratively. Both ports are mere roadsteads, ships lying two or three miles offshore and lighters working from one or two piers, but at Tellicherry the shelter of offshore reefs enables some traffic to be carried on during the monsoon.

Cochin is far more important: it really consists of two adjacent towns, ex-British Cochin (26,320) and Cochinese Cochin or Mattancheri (53,346). Cochin is in fact the oldest European settlement in India; on Christmas

[51] On the Chinese shipping, see Ibn Battuta, *ed. cit.*, 235–6.

Day 1500 Cabral arrived, and from then until the Dutch supplanted them in 1663 the Portuguese were in alliance with the rulers of Cochin against the Muslim Zamorin of Calicut. The port has considerable locational advantages: it is central on the backwaters, the Palghat Gap lies about 125 miles (by rail) to the NE, and it is about 300 miles nearer Aden and Durban than is Bombay. It may even rival Colombo as a transit port, as a call at Cochin adds only 40 miles to the Aden-Fremantle run.[52] The development of the modern port was for long impeded by its curious political situation; it lies on a breach in the long spit separating the great backwater from the sea, but while the major installations and the approaches lie in what was British territory, the inner harbour—in which much of the trade is carried on—is in Cochin state, and much of the backwater was Travancorean. Real development—including the cutting of a channel through the bar across the natural breach, and much reclamation—began only in 1920–23; later a 3-mile approach channel was dredged to a width of 450 and a depth of 37 ft, so that the inner harbour is now accessible to any ship which can pass Suez. Rail and road bridges cross the backwater, and a large airport has been built on reclaimed land; the old metre line to the SIR through the Palghat has been changed to BG. The volume of trade increased from 450,000 tons in 1920 to about 1,250,000 in 1950, while the number of ships using the port has more than trebled. Normally rice from Burma and Indo-China formed two-fifths in bulk of the total trade; mineral oil is also a major import. The exports are the usual Kerala ones: coconut products, especially coir and copra, tea, rubber, cashew nuts. Across the backwater is Ernakulam (46,790), capital of Cochin, with important soap factories, the largest owned (naturally) by Tatas: rice milling, as at Mattancherri, is also important. Trichur (57,524), the largest town of Cochin, has cotton spinning and weaving mills and tile factories; it shares with Palghat (55,160) command of the gap.

Travancore is less urbanised than Cochin, but Trivandrum (**186,931**) is the capital of Travancore–Cochin state. Alleppey (**116,278**) and Quilon are ports of ancient fame now decayed; mere roadsteads, they still carry on a considerable backwater traffic. Alleppey, protected by a mudbank, is slightly the better port, but Quilon has the advantage of its situation on the metre line from Trivandrum through the Shencottah Gap.

The Maldive and Laccadive Islands

These groups of coral atolls extend from the Equator to about 15° N, 180–300 miles from the Malabar coast. The Laccadives and Minicoy are attached to Madras, the Maldives (which have their own Sultan and constitutional government) to Ceylon: these affiliations represent historical

[52] *Handbook of Commercial Information for India* (Delhi, 1937), 79; personal information from Sir Robert Bristow.

accident merely. The submarine swells on which they are based show opposing gravity anomalies, positive in the Laccadives, negative in the Maldives. Glennie concludes that the former occupy an upthrust, possibly on a continuation of the Aravalli strike; the Maldive ridge is possibly the result of volcanic extrusions on a crustal downwarp.[53]

The Laccadives (*Laksha divi*, 'hundred thousand isles') have in fact nine inhabited islets, plus Minicoy which is really the most Nly of the Maldives; the total population was 15,230 in 1941. Minicoy is about the largest: $1\frac{3}{4}$ sq mls. They are of course formed of coral detritus, but (except on Minicoy) the humus from the coconut palms is used for garden cultivation of millet, yams, jackfruit, and plantains; there is no rice. The people are Malayalam-speaking but Muslims; fine seamen, they obtain rice and other necessities by taking coir, turtles, sea-slugs, and other marine products to the Malabar ports. The people of Minicoy have a different language, are akin to the Sinhalese, and use a duodecimal numeration instead of the universal binary counting of India. Though Muslims they are monogamous, and "the women take the lead in everything but navigation". The 12 inhabited Maldives have a population of 93,000; again the population is Muslim, and the economy is similar to that of the Laccadives.

BIBLIOGRAPHICAL NOTE

There is little to add to the text citations. The wealth of material in the *Statistical Atlas of Bombay State* (Bureau of Economics and Statistics, Bombay, 1950), may be noted; and there is a most suggestive comparison between Goa and Kerala in P. Gourou, "Quelques observations de géographie tropicale dans l'Inde", *Revue de l'Université de Bruxelles* (1950–51).

[53] R. B. S. Sewell, *loc. sit.*, 22. The standard reference is J. S. Gardiner (ed.), *The Fauna and Geography of the Maldive and Laccadive Archipelagoes* (Cambridge, 1903).

CHAPTER XXIII

THE PENINSULAR INTERIOR

(Regions XXVI–XXXII)

Generalities

THE vast mass of the Peninsula is difficult to divide into satisfactory units of study. The Deccan Lavas have indeed a characteristic physical aspect and a high degree of cultural individuality as the Maratha homeland; but for the rest plateau merges with plateau, river-basin with river-basin, and the border ranges are discontinuous in the E, a mere fillet in the W. Much of the NE is imperfectly known, and as a whole the Peninsular Interior has been neglected by Indian geographers. Any division, therefore, can but be tentative, and must give more than usual weight to factors of location and mere convenience of handling. As the criteria are so empirical, the *raison d'être* of the division must appear in the treatment of individual regions. It may be noted, however, that the broad outlines are similar to those of Stamp, Richards, and Baker, although with some refinements. The regions adopted are then:

1. The Western Ghats, including Coorg.
2. The Southern Blocks (Nilgiris, Anaimalais, Cardamom Hills).
3. Maharashtra (Deccan Lava country).
4. Karnataka (Sn Bombay Deccan and Mysore).
5. The Upper Mahanadi and adjacent basins: (a) Wainganga Valley; (b) Chhattisgarh; (c) Upper Brahmani and Jamshedpur Gap.
6. Telangana (SE Hyderabad and Madras Deccan).
7. Anantapur-Chittoor Basins.
8. The Eastern Hills: (a) Orissa and Bastar Hills; (b) Cuddapah Ranges and Valleys.

Some of these are clear and legitimate enough, but it must be admitted that the 'Upper Mahanadi' is something of a monster. It has a recognisable core in the irrigated Chhattisgarh Plain, but the area described extends from the Wainganga to the Subarnarekha, and these extensions E and W are linked with Chhattisgarh simply because they can hardly stand (on our scale of work) as regions by themselves, and cannot very well be linked with anything else. Yet the area has a certain unity of function in that it forms a corridor lying between the Chota Nagpur plateaus and the wild Orissa highlands, linking Bengal and Maharashtra. This, however, is a development of the railway age; historically the great movements of war and trade have been N/S, or between the interior and the nearest accessible coast, not across the root of the Peninsula.

Structure has been described in Ch. I. We may note briefly the extraordinary maturity of the Peninsular rivers, graded almost to their heads in the Wn Ghats, but cutting through the En Hills or descending precipitously from the high Mysorean plateaus in gorges. The major relief features are usually no more than the flanks of plateaus or of fault-troughs, or residual crests on the heights of land between the main river-basins; but there is a good deal of local diversity, the mesas and buttes of the Deccan Lavas, the fantastic tors and gnarled ridges of the Archaeans.

Climatically the entire area, except for the En Hills, the Wn Ghats, and the rain-shadow of the latter, could be described as Tropical Savannah with monsoonal modification. There is a broad distinction between the NE, with 40 ins. plus and considerable humidity, and the drier (20–40 ins.) and more variable W and S, which in the lee of the Ghats receives less than 20 ins. in places.[1] The boundary between these is a line running roughly along the lower Godavari and produced to the NW. Temperatures practically everywhere range from means of 65–75° F. in January to 85–95° in May; except, of course, where modified by high altitude.

The Western Ghats and Coorg

The astonishing contrast between the scarp and the plateau faces of the Ghats is brought out by Fig. 125: on the one side deep ravines and canyons, on the other flat-topped spurs intersected by mature valleys. The spurs lose height to the E fairly rapidly, becoming mere flat-topped relic ridges on the watersheds, with outlying mesas and buttes; the actual dissected belt, the Ghats proper, is only a few miles wide as a rule; generally 2500–3000 ft high, it reaches 4500 or more in the culminations whence spring the transverse spurs, such as the Tryambak massif at the root of the Balaghat Hills. It is a negative area: in some places, as the Peint forests and the Dangs (S of the Tapti) and behind Ratnagiri and Goa, a tangle of dense jungle, including teak on terraces and valley-floors; elsewhere it carries more open forest with not a little bare rock on the flanks of the more massive lava flows. On spurs E and W are the great hill forts, bases whence the 'mountain rat' Sivaji gradually extended his power over the Konkan and the more open Maharashtra country. Except in the Kanara sub-region already discussed (pp. 617–26), there is little economic activity apart from jungle agriculture, forestry, and the increasingly important hydro-electric development around the Bhor Ghat and Gersoppa. The only places of much importance are the little gap towns and sanatoria behind Bombay (Igatpuri, Lonavla, Khandala; above, 616–17) and Mahabaleshwar (5000), a hill-

[1] For a more detailed analysis see E. Simkins, *The Agricultural Geography of the Deccan Plateau of India* (n.d., ?1926), 13–22.

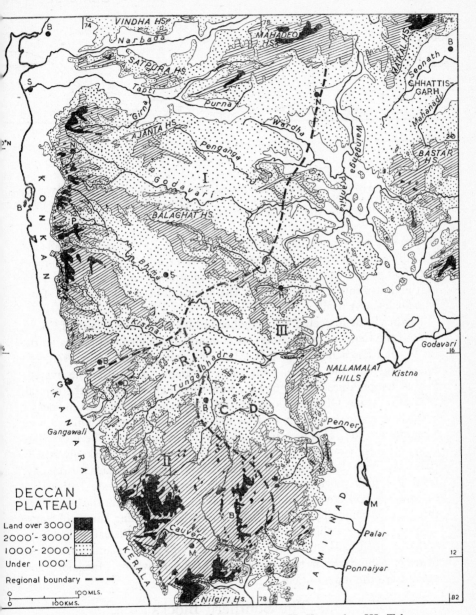

Fig. 124.—THE DECCAN PLATEAU. I, Maharashtra; II, Karnataka; III, Telangana; RD, Raichur Doab; CD, Ceded Districts.

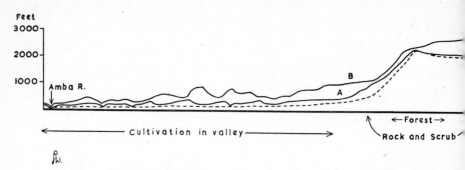

Fig. 125.—SECTION ACROSS THE GHATS. The scarp is here 32 mls WNW of Poona, interfluve 1 ml N of A; C, crest of spur between Pauna R. and Lonavla. Note that Paun from SOI 47F/6; vertical exaggtn 2·1.

station at 4000–5000 ft, used by Bombay officials. Its excessive rainfall (260 ins.) gives it a short season; Panchgani, only 12 miles E, receives no more than 60 ins. and has a less fluctuating population, receiving not only some of the hot-weather exodus from the plains, but a rains exodus from Mahabaleshwar itself.

Farther S the dissected belt is higher and wider in the coulisses of Coorg, around the Cauvery headwaters; some points in the girdle of ranges on the N, W, and S reach over 5500 ft. Most of Coorg was originally evergreen forest and bamboo jungle, with some parkland to the E. The average annual temperature is only 60° F., humidity high, rainfall at the capital, Mercara, 133 ins. Of the million acres of Coorg a third are forested and nearly a third cultivated, though of that about half is generally fallow. Rice accounts for 56% of the cropped area, coffee about 30%. The little State (1593 sq mls, 1951 poptn **229,405**) is inhabited by a remarkably sturdy peasantry, with their own language (Kodalu): isolated, perhaps fortunately, from the main currents of Indian life, they half-cultivate half-gather cardamoms, collect wax and honey, and hunt, to supplement the product of their paddy-fields: it is typical that even the backbreaking labour of trans-planting paddy seedlings ends in a race.[2] The Wynaad Plateau links Coorg with the great boss of the Nilgiris; the tea and coffee plantations of the plateaus extend down the slopes into Malabar, where Mangalore and Calicut are the main outlets.

The Southern Blocks

On either side the Palghat Gap is dominated by the highest mountains of the Peninsula, Nilgiris to the N and the Anaimalai-Palni-Cardamoms

[2] For a full and interesting, if disjointed, account of Coorg see L. A. Krishna Iyer, "Coorg Ethnology" (*IGJ* XXII (1947), 157–225).

WEST OF POONA

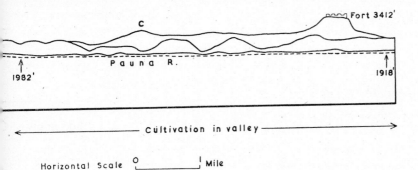

mls S of Bhor Ghat. Broken lines, thalwegs; A, general line along valley flanks; B, along
is graded almost to its head; base level at Poona (Mula confluence) only 1820 ft. Drawn

group to the S. According to Wadia these are great horsts, corresponding
to similar structures in Ceylon: "one cannot but ascribe such extraordinarily
abrupt inequality of the ground in an ancient Archaean terrain to mechanical dislocation and recent block uplift." [3] But there are difficulties in accepting this view.

These are the great plantation areas of the Peninsula, and the power
from their rejuvenated streams is a main factor in the modern industrial
development of Tamilnad.

(a) *The Nilgiris*

The Nilgiris ('Blue Mountains'; Fig. 126) form a compact plateau of
about 1000 sq mls, with a summit level of 6000–8000 ft, rising with
extreme abruptness on all sides: on the En slopes there is a fall of 6000 ft in
1½–2 miles, the face to the Coimbatore Plateau is hardly less steep, and on
the N the Nilgiris are cut off from the 3000–4000-ft Mysore plateaus by
the deep straight gash of the Moyar (the 'Mysore ditch'), the narrow floor
of which lies at 1000–2000 ft. The massif is as it were islanded between
the Moyar and the Bhavani to the S; the headwaters of these rivers have
obviously been captured by the shorter Malabar streams.

With a rainfall of 60–160 in., according to aspect, and temperatures of
38–68° F. in the cold weather, 55–75° in the hot, the Nilgiris form a little
botanic realm of their own, with affinities to the Assam flora. Half the area
is under forests containing teak and sandalwood; but much consists of
open, boldly rolling downland interspersed with woods (*sholas*) presenting
a parkland aspect. Quick-growing eucalypts have been introduced from
Australia to supply fuel to the hill-stations, and there are Government

[3] D. N. Wadia, "The Making of India" (Presidential Address, 29th ISC; Calcutta,
1942), 17.

chinchona plantations (1500 ac.): the Indian demand for quinine would warrant extension. "In the *sholas* grow rhododendron, ilex, ferns of many varieties, bracken, tree-orchids with delicate blossoms, the hill gooseberry, blackberries, the sweet-scented Nilgiri lily, the alpine wild strawberry. . . . Hedges are often made of heliotrope, fuchsia, and geraniums."[4] With the added attraction of shootin' and fishin' it is no wonder that the Nilgiris are the leading holiday resort of S India.

TSA is only about 100,000 ac., and of this at least 60% is plantation crops (tea 40,000, coffee 20,000 ac.). Foodgrains cover only 20,000 ac., a quarter of which is rice land. The economy of the Nilgiris is thus thoroughly

[4] *Madras Gaz.* (1908), II. 296–97.

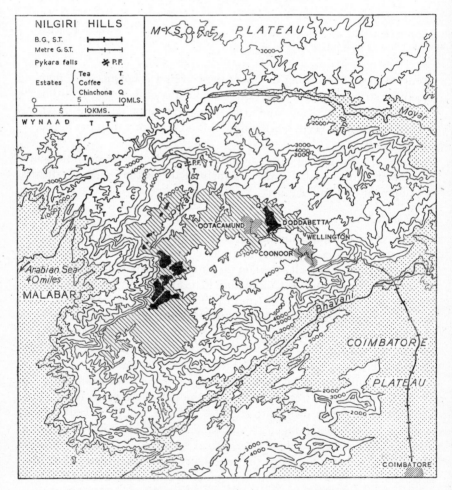

Fig. 126.—THE NILGIRI HILLS. Contours at 1000 ft interval; under 2000 ft stippled, 7–8000 ft shaded, over 8000 ft black. SOI 1/253,440 58 A; courtesy SOI.

atypical. Much of it indeed revolves around the hill-station of Ootacamund, lying under the highest point of the plateau, Dodabetta (8760 ft). 'Ooty' and its satellites Wellington and Coonor have the usual hills layout of straggling bungalows; they are reached by a metre-gauge rack-railway with gradients of 1 in 12½. There is a little local industry of the kind associated with resort functions: breweries (now presumably under a cloud), sodawater factories, and so on; tea, quinine, and eucalyptus oil are processed, and at Wellington the Government cordite factory had one of the earliest hydro-electric installations in India. Of much greater importance is the power station at Pykara Falls, with an installed capacity of 38,750 kW; large extensions are planned, and in addition the utilisation of the Pykara tail-water over a 1200-ft drop in the Moyar Valley, to produce another 36,000 kW, forming a new link with Mettur. This is in the future; but already the leisure resort of S India has become one of the most vital nodes in its workaday life.

(b) *The Anaimalais, Palnis, and Cardamoms*

This remarkable group of hills (Figs. 121, 150) is more complex than the Nilgiris, and in Anaimudi itself they have the highest peak of the Peninsula, 8841 ft. The front to the Palghat Gap is remarkably steep and in the E remarkably straight; the SE flanks of the Palnis, overlooking the upper Vaigai re-entrant, are also remarkably abrupt, as are the Cardamoms and their protrusions (Varushanad Hills) S of the Vaigai. But to the NW the hills fray out into long SE–NW ridges; and indeed over much of the area this trend is most marked, the rivers (e.g. the Periyar) having longitudinal stretches of such straightness as to suggest control by faults, with transverse gorges producing a perfect trellis-pattern. Between 10° N and the Shencottah Gap the active streams of the exposed Arabian Sea front have pushed the watershed back to within 4 or 5 miles of the En edge of the hills: here the change from jungle-clad mountains to the tank-pitted Tamilnad Plain is very sudden (Fig. 150).

Again, apart from the shifting cultivation of tribes some of whom (e.g. Cochin Kadars) are hardly more than hunters and gatherers, the economy is atypical: forests, plantations, hydro-electricity. The most exploited forests, served by special light railways, are in the NW, the Cochin slopes of the Anaimalais. As for plantations, these are not confined to the Wn flanks but are more numerous there, where there is a broader plateau development than on the E. A little coffee and tea are grown in Cochin and in Madura Dt (Madras), but the major share of the plantations (78,000 ac. tea, *c.* 6000 coffee) is in Travancore, which is also by far the most important rubber-producing area of India, with nearly 100,000 ac. bearing against 13,000 in Malabar and 10,000 in Cochin (1945). It is grown on the lower slopes, generally below 1000 and never above 2000 ft, with 80–120 ins.

rain. Above the rubber, tea extends to nearly 6000 ft, and indeed more than half of it is grown above 4000 ft; rainfall is usually 100–150 ins. It is note-worthy that over half the rubber is produced on Indian-owned estates, but only a small fraction of the tea.

As for hydro-electricity, the hills are dotted with falls and rainfall on the Wn flanks is everywhere high and reliable. So far the most important large development is at Pallivasal in Travancore (installed 21,000 kW, potential 36,000), which powers the aluminium smelters at Alwaye and also works pumps draining the flooded paddy-fields of Kerala. A project of great interest is that for utilising the great Periyar Reservoir (Fig. 150) for power. The Periyar headwaters have been impounded and are taken through the watershed by tunnel to irrigate the Suruli-Vaigai Valley in Madura; some 40,000 kW might be developed, and altogether the region has a potential of at least 200,000 kW.

The Wn flanks of the hills are too rain-swept to have much settlement except on plantations, forest camps, and power installations. In the E Kodaikanal, lying at 7000 ft on the Palnis, is a minor hill-station, noted for its mission schools and an old-established physical observatory.

Maharashtra

Maharashtra, the Maratha country *par excellence*,[5] may be taken as roughly coterminous with the main mass of the Deccan Lavas above the Ghats. To the N the Tapti Valley, flanked by typical lava plateaus but floored by alluvium, forms a transition to the central Indian scarplands; in the S, along the Malaprabha, there is another belt where Archaeans and lavas interdigitate and where cultural allegiance is divided between the Marathi and Kannada (Kanarese) languages. But to the E, in Hyderabad especially, the boundary of Marathi speech shows a striking accordance with the edge of the Lavas (Fig. 127); hence the division of the state into Marathwara and Telangana, a rare instance of official recognition of regionalism. This great area thus includes all central Bombay, the NW third of Hyderabad, and SW Madhya Pradesh (CP) as far as Nagpur.

The Terrain

It is a region of extraordinary physical homogeneity, in the gross at least, although (as Deshpande points out) detailed study would undoubtedly re-veal significant differences in erosional features, soils, vegetation, and farm-ing practice depending on the varying petrology of the lavas. The general slope to the E and SE is gentle: Poona lies at 1800 ft, and it is over 100 miles down the Bhima to the 1500-ft contour. From the Ghat culminations long tongues of higher ground (over 2000 ft) run E and divide the plateau

[5] The etymological connection of Maratha or Mahratta and Maharashtra, if any, is still controversial.

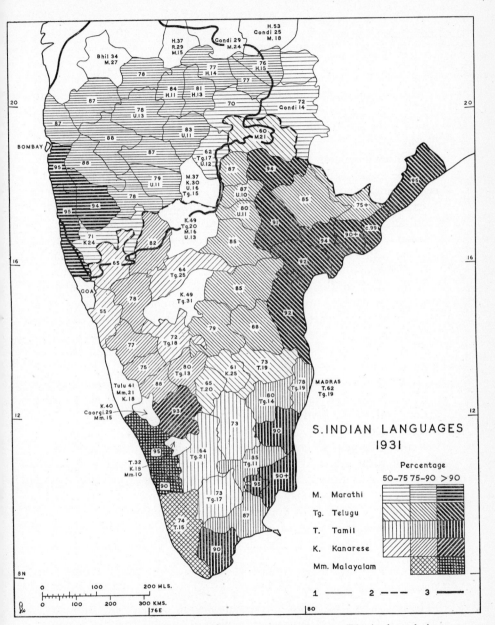

Fig. 127.—S Indian Languages. Figures = % speakers. 1, District boundaries; 2, boundary between Aryan- and Dravidian-speaking majorities; 3, boundary of Deccan Lavas. H, Hindi; U, Urdu; R, Rajasthani.

into compartments which (except on the upper Kistna) are mature or even senile in aspect: the plains of Berar and Nagpur, the great basin of the upper Godavari, the Bhima from Poona to beyond Sholapur. But these "ranges", prominent as they appear on small-scale maps, are quite unlike the sierras which compartmentalise the Meseta: they are really only flat-topped tablelands with more or less steep flanks. The most prominent up-lands are the Sahyadriparvat or Ajanta Hills, but their eminence is owed mainly to the faulting-down of the Tapti trough below. S of these is the Balaghat "Range"; one can drive from Poona onto its "summit" at Ahmad-nagar without noticing more than a bolder modelling of the relief, which looks like an impossibly idealised textbook block diagram. Poona itself has been variously described as a 'hill-girt city' and as lying in a landscape so flat as to make one believe in the flat-earth theory; either statement is true according as one looks S or N. Everywhere the Deccan Lavas carry their sign-manual: mesas and buttes, the tops remarkably accordant, often as if sliced off with a knife; slightly incised streams, with some definite valley-bottoms bounded by the bevelled edges of the little plateaus (Figs. 125, 130). The flanks of the hills are often stepped by the great horizontal lava flows and/or constructional benches, and the whole country then looks ridiculously like a relief model so badly constructed that the cardboard layers show through the modelling. The valleys are graded to local base-levels at the confluences with the main rivers; the general effect of the flat floors and relatively steep sides where they impinge on the plateaus strongly suggests lateral corrasion. The upper Kistna and its tributaries (especially the Koyna), however, have steeper profiles and show more signs of vertical erosion, and on the Hyderabad border the Kistna descends in rapids of 400 ft in 3 miles.

Despite this general homogeneity, the uplands are less mature, more dissected, with greater available relief than the basins; and these factors introduce important variations in value. The steep slopes, and in places the summits, of the plateaus may be stony and barren, and elsewhere carry but poor vegetation, often short grass; cultivation is mainly millets. Soils in the valleys are deeper, more mature, and more fertile than the thin washed-out soils of the plateaus; the valleys also have more trees, though even there these are rather scattered.

Climate and Cultivation

The region as a whole lies in the rain-shadow of the Ghats, though the NW fringe (Purna and Wainganga Valleys) is reached by Bay of Bengal influences and receives over 40 ins. Good rainfall spills over the Ghats as far as Poona and Belgaum; beyond this a roughly N/S belt 50–60 miles wide is the most marked rain-shadow area (20–30 ins.) and is also the area of maximum variability. Belgaum, in this Malvad or Ghat foothill strip, has

50 ins. (probably the lowering of the Ghats by the Kanara breaches has some effect); Poona, on the inner edge of the better-watered belt, 27. Bijapur and Ahmadnagar, with 20 and 22 ins., represent the rain-shadow area, Akola, with 31 ins., the transition towards Nagpur. The retreating Bay of Bengal monsoon showers are important for rabi crops as far inland as En Bombay.

Soils are of great importance. The more mature black earth of the alluvial Tapti trough extends across the Amraoti height of land (Purna/Wardha watershed), with some change in appearance but little in agronomic value, onto the lavas and to the En limits of the region around Nagpur; but elsewhere it is found mainly in the larger valley-bottoms (Fig. 128). Most of the soil is 'medium regur', and the higher ground carries immature regur or even red soils; these are notably poorer. As we have seen (Ch. III), the black soil is by no means confined to the Deccan Lavas; but here the limits of Lava and regur do coincide fairly closely. The characteristics of the regur are well described by Simkins; we may recall the high moisture content, and the aeration and 'working-over' of the soil layers by deep cracking in the hot weather.

The agriculture presents some highly individual features. For so large an area of mainly non-alluvial land, not very humid, a very high proportion is cultivated; nominally perhaps two-thirds,[6] but there is also a high proportion of fallow, and on the areas of poorer and drier soils one might almost speak of an approach to the long-fallow *chitamene* type of shifting cultivation. Yet the area of stable cultivation is very large, accounted for by terrain and soil—the wide flattish expanses of good regur—together. There is relatively little difference between NSA and TSA, irrigation being as yet little developed and mainly by wells, except in some of the Maval valleys. The most important existing works are the Mutha and Nira Canals in Poona Dt; but the District has only about 70,000–75,000 ac. of canal- and 80,000–90,000 ac. of well-irrigation in a TSA of over 2·25 m. ac., and the canals are for protection rather than for intensive culture. Only Ahmadnagar and Sholapur Dts approach the Poona figures, while the four Berar Dts (Akola, Amraoti, Buldana, Yeotmal) have only 34,000 ac. irrigated out of nearly 2·75 m. cropped. At present in the region as a whole, even a bad year has no more than 5% of TSA irrigated, and that mainly on the margins —in the Malvad, and the marches with Telangana and Karnataka where Archaeans and Lavas interdigitate locally. Yet the unreliability of the rain-

---

[6] Quantitative survey is more than usually difficult; the inclusion here of the Tapti Valley may be balanced against the omission of the old Deccan states, but the area of Hyderabad 'by village papers' was 5262 sq mls more in 1938–39 than in 1937–38; and the figure for the former year was 6718 sq mls less than the area by survey. Much of Hyderabad was in *jagirs* or fiefs which did not return village statistics; but this cannot explain why the surveyed area should be 385 sq mls more than the standard figure of 82,313 sq mls given in Census and other official reports. The search for precision in crop figures is obviously a romantic ideal rather than a practical objective.

fall warrants the extensions now proposed. Of these the most important is on the Ghataprabha, in the S, which will ultimately command 300,000 ac. in Belgaum and Bijapur Dts. There are also schemes in Nasik and Khandesh, but the 0·5 m. ac. of the Kadapadah project on the Tapti will be mostly outside the region, in Surat Dt. Unfortunately the scope for irrigation is most limited where it is most needed, away from the Malvad; and the hygroscopic virtues of well-developed regur themselves render it not very suitable for irrigation, since it becomes very heavy and sticky to work when wet.

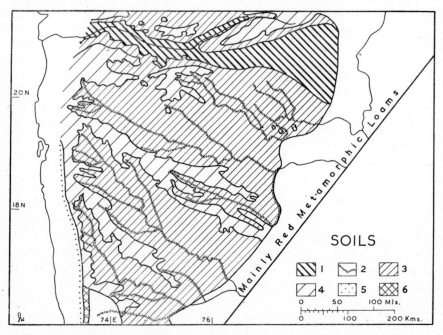

Fig. 128.—MAHARASHTRA: SOILS. 1, deep regur of Tapti trough and (2), of main valleys (agriculturally first class); 3, medium regur (good); 4, thin black or red soils (poor); 5, laterite (very poor); 6, forest loams (first class). Adapted from Fig. 2 in E. Simkins, *Agric. Geog. of the Deccan Plateau*; courtesy of the author and the Geographical Association.

Probably no region of the sub-continent, comparable in size, has so little rice, only about $2\frac{1}{2}\%$ of the cropped area, nearly all in the irrigated pockets under the Ghats. In the heart of the region no fewer than 8 Districts have under 10,000 ac. each under paddy—exceedingly low figures for India. Amraoti and Wardha, on the whole the most fertile, and well watered, have only 5000–6000 ac. each. With local exceptions wheat is the great irrigation crop; in Wardha the irrigated rice area is returned as one acre! But increasingly sugar is grown by irrigation, in some cases 'factory cane' grown by the refining firms on land leased from the cultivators.

This is pre-eminently the realm of jowar and cotton (Fig. 129), which before the war covered respectively 33 and 18% of TSA, followed by bajra 10, oilseeds 9, and wheat 6%. Cotton has now fallen, say to 10–12%, and the others must be scaled up somewhat, though not all land lost to cotton has turned to foodgrains, some lying fallow. But these five crops still account for over three-quarters of the arable, the rest being mainly under gram, other pulses, and fodder crops, all mainly on the poorer uplands. Jowar has the most general distribution, being the leading crop in 13–15 of

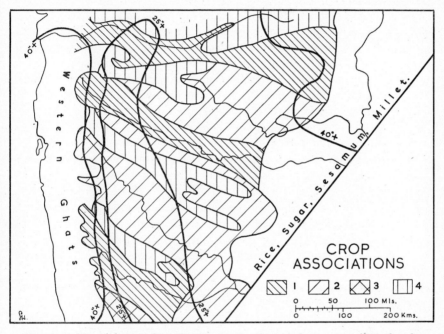

Fig. 129.—MAHARASHTRA: CROP ASSOCIATIONS. 1, jowar, wheat, cotton, linseed, pulses; 2, jowar, cotton, bajra, pulses; 3, rice, sugar, cotton, millets; 4, bajra, pulses; 5, approx. isohyets. Cf. Fig. 128. Adapted from Fig. 26 in Simkins, op. cit. as for Fig. 128.

the 22 Districts considered here, and in 3 (Ahmadnagar, Bijapur, Sholapur) it has over 1 m. ac.; in Sholapur, indeed, it is over three-fifths of TSA. It is of course the staple foodgrain, and the large stalks and the leaves are very useful fodder; indeed it is sometimes grown for stalk and leaf rather than grain.

In its main concentration, on the deep regur of the N, cotton before the war locally exceeded 50% TSA. Its recent decline is shown by the following figures of its percentage of TSA in (i) 1939–40 and (ii) 1946–47: Buldana, 36 and 30; Akola, 43 and 28; Amraoti, 47·5 and 32; Yeotmal, 39 and 30. Only in Wardha has it remained stable at 33%. Even so, the later figures are very high for a cash crop in *India*, and provide an index of the extent to

I.P.—21*

which the economy is tied to outside markets. The cottons here are mainly
the short-stapled ($\frac{3}{8}$ to $\frac{5}{8}$ in.) 'Oomras'. Beyond the Ajantas is a second
zone in the upper Godavari Valley, but neither intensity nor yield is as high
as in the Nn zone. A third area in the S (Belgaum and Bijapur) has a much
smaller acreage, but its 'kumpta' strains have a longer staple, up to $\frac{7}{8}$ in.
Cotton stays long on the ground, being planted in July–August and not
harvested until February or March.

Bajra is especially strong in the W (it is the leading crop, with over 37%
of TSA, in Nasik), and tends to replace jowar on the higher ground and
thinner soils. The distribution of wheat (rabi) follows that of cotton fairly
closely; the other great rabi crop is one or other of the oilseeds. In E
Khandesh oilseeds are actually the second crop. Generally groundnuts
(often kharif) predominate in the W, linseed in the E, with sesamum (*til*)
on the Telangana border in Adilabad and Nizamabad Dts, neither wholly
Maharashtran. A new crop of interest is *mesta*, a wild plant some 10 or 12
ft high with a fairly good fibre which can be mixed up to 20% with jute;
it is now being grown on a small but increasing scale as a jute substitute.

Agriculturally, then, the region is outstanding in India by the insignificance of irrigation and rice, by the very great importance of cash crops, and
in some areas (such as the Kistna/Panchganga doab) by increasing specialisation backed by industry, e.g. for sugar. The wide expanse of good land in
the open regur plains, their easy communications, and the metropolitan
stimulus of Bombay, have fostered this commercial bias. The total foodgrains proportion of TSA is remarkably low; in the great cotton belt only
about 60%, in Amraoti not much over half, against an *Indian* average of
about 77%. Fortunately the main cotton tract is the most secure of the
region; most risky are Ahmadnagar, Sholapur, and Bijapur Dts, where one
year in five is likely to be too dry; Bijapur especially is liable to severe
dearths.

Prosperous as Maharashtra is, it is not immune from the usual risks and
ills of Indian agriculture, and the emphasis on cash crops may itself be a
source of weakness. Efforts are being made to increase the food proportion
(though demands for more cotton acreage are not lacking), and the rolling
terrain provides some opportunities for expansion: much of the mechanised
preliminary preparation now being sponsored by Government is taking
place on the old fallows of this region, and Bombay State's food deficit is
at least being reduced. The existing garden cultivation in the Malvad, for
Bombay and Poona markets, favours an extension of dietetically valuable
fruits and roots such as plantains and sweet potatoes.

Population and Settlement

District densities generally lie between **170** and **320**, and are naturally
highest in the Malvad close under the Ghats, and in the deeper regur.

Villages are usually large and compact, but more widely spaced than in the Ganges valley or the En littoral plains. Houses are often stone or brick, the latter with attractive detail in doorways and recesses, and have low-pitched roofs of semi-cylindrical tiles, or flat mud roofs. Many villages are grouped round a little fort or retain the old gates. Water-points are favoured sites; tanks, other than village ponds, are few, but the Lavas include good aquifers and wells in the valleys are usually reliable. The discontinuous lines of trees in the valley-bottoms give some variety to the wide and open landscape. Fig. 130 illustrates some of these points.

As a general rule the larger towns of Maharashtra were strategic in origin and took on administrative and commercial functions in consequence; they are generally grouped round a massive citadel. Such are Ahmadnagar (54,193), the old Bahmani capital, and Aurangabad (60,924) in the N, Kolhapur (**136,835**), until 1948 state capital, and Bijapur (48,000) in the S. Bijapur indeed is an extraordinary misfit; the capital of the Adil Shahi kingdom (15th–17th centuries), its immense domes look out over a poor and precarious countryside, the administrative offices occupy part of the citadel, and the rest of the modern town is lumped in a corner of the vast enceinte, with straggling village-suburbs in the ruins.[7] In the NW Nasik (52,386), an old religious centre, owes its continued importance to its situation on the upper reaches of the Godavari, midway between the little gap towns— mere railway colonies—of Manmad, controlling the entrance from the Tapti, and Igatpuri (8000) at the top of the Thal Ghat. Under the new pro- hibitionist régime its distillery is being converted to power alcohol (there will doubtless be some leakage); its leading industry is probably the great Government press for security printing, but it may add to its stature as irrigation and small power schemes are developed on the Godavari head- waters. Deolali, a few miles away, was probably the largest military transit camp in India—the first high and open (hence healthy) ground on the rail- way from Bombay into central India.

Other towns are primarily collecting centres and administrative head- quarters, with a little industry, owing their rise to cotton and the railway: Akola (62,654), Amraoti (61,971), and Wardha (28,359) in Madhya Pradesh (CP); the last was famous as the site of Gandhi's *ashram*. Similar is Bel- gaum (58,319) in the S, the junction for the transit trade to Marmagão, and really a contact town on the Karnatak border; it too has hopes from power development on the Kalinadi.

There are only three really large towns: Nagpur (**449,099**), Poona (**480,982**), and Sholapur (**266,050**). The last is of least general importance, an isolated phenomenon, a predominantly industrial town with no *raison d'être* save its position in a cotton tract. Originally a strategic centre com- manding the Bhima route into or out of Maharashtra, it is now one of the

[7] C. D. Deshpande, *Western India* (1948), 111–12.

few predominantly industrial towns of India, and perhaps the most homogeneous, since its life revolves around its cotton mills. Otherwise there is
little industrialisation in Maharashtra, and not very much scope for
development: except for bauxite and the excellent building stone there are
no noteworthy minerals. The bauxite is mostly in Kolhapur, and reserves
are large; but their exploitation must wait on power development. This
would presumably be from the projected 300-ft high dam across the narrow

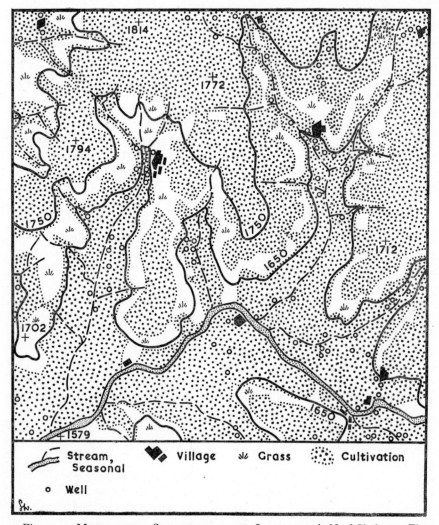

Fig. 130.—MAHARASHTRA: SETTLEMENT ON THE LAVAS. 30 mls N of Sholapur. Flat
plateaus and graded valleys cultivated (cotton, millets); grass on steeper slopes. Wells and
few trees mainly in valley bottoms. Villages compact, evenly spaced, but much farther
apart than in Gangetic Plains. SOI 47 N/16; courtesy SOI. Scale as on Fig. 131.

Koyna valley, which could probably develop a continuous output of some 250,000 kW, and ultimately 600,000 kW seasonal, and irrigate 800,000 ac.

Nagpur, meeting-place of the GIP and Bengal-Nagpur Railways, is the focus for the Purna and Wainganga valleys: essentially a contact town. Originally the capital of the Maratha Bhonslas, it remained the administrative centre of the Central Provinces (now Madhya Pradesh) when the

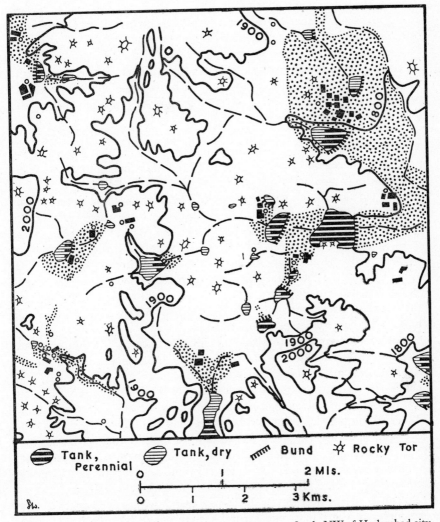

Fig. 131.—TELANGANA: SETTLEMENT ON THE GNEISSES. 8 mls NW of Hyderabad city. Rocky terrain (original map shows 437 'tors'); cultivation (ragi, rice) in small tank-fed basins. Blank area rocky ground, with very open scrub and bush, largely acacias and euphorbias. Other symbols as on Fig. 130. Note that on this map and Fig. 130 *all* streams are dry half the year. SOI 56 K/7; courtesy SOI.

Bhonsla territory lapsed to the EIC in 1853. Apart from centrality in Madhya Pradesh and its position on the edge of the Lavas, there is little of note about its site; nor can it claim much antiquity. Its importance is mainly administrative and commercial, with some cotton mills and minor industries, which find some support in the coal from very local fields in the Wainganga valley.

Poona is of little importance industrially but of great and growing significance as the cultural and educational focus of the very considerable regional consciousness of Maharashtra; this, of course, is an inheritance from its past as the seat of such central authority as the Maratha confederacy possessed. Marathi literature has an exceptionally strong historical wing, and this is based largely on the archives of the Peshwas at Poona. It was also a centre of British-Indian society, connected with its wide-spreading military establishments, which form a fascinating contrast (analysed in Ch. VII) with the old Maratha town.

The Individuality of Maharashtra

The whole region bears the imprint of the Marathas: a tough, cheerful, hard-working peasantry, ably served by an adroit Brahmin élite which maintained close touch with the people. The Marathas first defied Muslim and Mogul power from the great holds and petty forts which command the spurs and river-crossings of the Ghats and the Malvad, and later overran most of India on horses light-built and wiry to match the men; and here, too, aggressive Indian nationalism was launched in the 1890s by Tilak. All is distinctive: the terrain of wide rolling swells and abrupt mesas, the simple but extremely pleasing village and small-town architecture, even the women's dress, with business-like saris tucked up between the thighs to make breeches when real work must be done.[8]

The correlation of Marathi speech with the Lavas is not simply a matter of political power based on their splendid light cavalry country; much of the Deccan is just as suitable for their mobile guerilla warfare, and Maratha chiefs founded principalities in Gujarat, Malwa, and Tanjore. Nevertheless it does seem to be a matter of terrain. The Marathas were essentially a millet-eating people, jowar and bajra; beyond the Lavas, with a rainfall of over 40 ins. to the NE, and better terrain for tanks on the Archaeans to the SE, rice becomes much more important, even though the masses may be limited to ragi.[9] And with this goes a complex of cultural as well as agricultural aptitudes. The contrast is shown in Figs. 130 and 131.

With a strong historic personality, a distinctive agriculture, the power resources in the Ghats, and a rural society which (despite its integration

---

[8] But it could be wished that they would favour some colours other than the muddiest purples and dingiest browns.

[9] We may recall the contrast between the Maratha and Kanarese rats, cited above, 213.

with cotton prices) seems on the whole healthier and better balanced than the average, Maharashtra would certainly become one of the most important units of *India* should the long-discussed scheme of linguistic provinces come into being.

Karnataka in Bombay and Mysore

This is the real 'Carnatic', which name came to be entirely misapplied to the Madras littoral.[10] The region extends from the Deccan Lavas on the N to the Moyar in the S; the Wn limit is of course the Ghats crest, and to the SE the border hills and scarps of the Mysore plateaus provide a fairly sharp boundary between the Moyar and the Palar. But in the NE the high plateaus break down into the isolated basins S of the Penner and the Cuddapah Ranges, and in the N the Raichur Doab, between Kistna and Tungabhadra, was the marchland between the Muslim Deccani Sultanates and Hindu Vijayanagar, which city occupied a forward position on the Tungabhadra, near Hampi village. The Doab is still a marchland between Karnataka, Telingana, and to a less extent Maharashtra. In general the region corresponds with the area in which Kannada (Kanarese) speech is dominant; but the lower levels of the Raichur Doab and Anantapur Dt (Madras) go more naturally with Telangana. There is of course a belt of 'cultural conflict' with Maharashtra in the N, and the breaches of the Ghats S of Goa make for some overlap with the Wn Littoral. There is thus some vagueness in the N and NE, but the region covers Mysore together with Dharwar and parts of Belgaum and Bijapur Dts in Bombay.

Within this area there is some diversity, e.g. between Malnad and Maidan (see below), and there are a number of peneplains at altitudes from about 2000 to about 4000 ft; but in the absence of any precise data about them it seems not unreasonable to treat the region as essentially one, with perhaps a sub-division into the Bombay Karnatak, the Malnad, and the Maidan.

Physique

The entire area, apart from a fringe of Cuddapah (Algonkian-Torridonian) rocks along the Deccan Lava boundary, consists of a basement of Archaean gneisses and granites, intersected by great belts of much metamorphosed Dharwarian (Huronian) sediments, mostly phyllites, schists, and slates, occupying the bottoms of tight-packed synclinoria (Fig. 141). The precise relationship of the Dharwars and the gneisses is difficult to unravel; although the former are in general erosion products of an Archaean land-mass, they are sometimes interbedded with the gneisses. "The complex foldings of the crust in which these rocks have been involved have obliterated nearly all traces of their sedimentary nature, and have given to

[10] See *Madras Gaz.* (1908), I. 182–84.

them a thoroughly crystalline and schistose structure, hardly to be distinguished from the underlying gneisses and schists. They are besides extensively intruded by granite bosses and veins and sheets, and by an extensive
system of dolerite dykes." [11] They are naturally well mineralised, iron,
manganese, and gold being especially important.

The plateaus or peneplains rise from about 1500–2500 ft in the N to
3000–4000 ft in the S. The Nn border is more complex; here the great
scarps of the Kaladgi (Cuddapah) sandstones and limestones, cut across by
the superimposed Ghataprabha and Malaprabha, form a belt of poor
scrub-clad hills, a barrier zone marked by a great proliferation of ancient
forts and local capitals on sites "more defensible than the open plain, less
cramped that the jungle".[12] S of these hills is a plain of good black soils (on
gneisses), the Dharwar cotton tract.

In Mysore there is a fundamental division—again recognised in both
traditional and official nomenclature—between the high forested Malnad
in the W and the more open 'champaign' country of the Maidan (here =
'parkland') in the E: the transition is in places remarkably abrupt. In the
extreme W, N of Coorg, the Malnad really overlaps into the Ghats, here
reaching 5000–6000 ft. It is highly dissected by the headwaters of the Tunga
and Bhadra, and of the Cauvery, all of which rise on the very crest of the
Ghats, only 30 miles or so from the Arabian Sea. The drainage system
would repay study: the rivers (e.g. upper Tungabhadra, Hagari, upper
Penner and Chitravati) flow in long S–N stretches, apparently structurally
controlled, to the middle Tungabhadra or in the NE to the Penner. Some
of the Penner tributaries have a SW–NE trend—parallel to the presumed
faulting of the trough between the Mysore plateau-scarp and the Javadi-
Shevaroy axis (below, 704), but this is cut across by the NW–SE trend of
the upper Palar and Ponnaiyar. In the S the Cauvery breaks right across
the plateau in a more or less W–E direction, but between the great Cauvery
falls at Sivasamudram and the Bhavani confluence it has reaches in both the
NW–SE and NE–SW directions. The highest peneplains—4000 ft plus—lie
S of the Cauvery, separated from the Nilgiris by the Moyar trench. Here,
where the great scarp is most strongly marked, is another important power
node, developed at Sivasamudram and Mettur.

A strip about 6–14 miles wide in the extreme W carries tall evergreen
forest, but most of the Malnad (roughly Shimoga, Kadur, and Hassan Dts)
has a mixed deciduous cover, with teak, sissoo, and the most important
sandalwood forests of India. The most interesting of the many complex
small ranges of the Malnad is the Babu Bhudan group. These hills reach
6317 ft—the highest point in the region—and were the first home of coffee
in India, the seeds being brought from Mocha by a 17th-century Muslim

---

[11] D. N. Wadia, *Geology of India* (1939), 69.
[12] Deshpande, *op. cit.*, 115. This is Deshpande's home ground.

saint who gave his name to the hills: the first European plantation dates only from 1840. The Babu Bhudan Hills are now more important as the source of ore for the iron works at Bhadravati (output *c.* 25–30,000 tons p.a.); charcoal is used for smelting and limited quantities of high-grade steel are produced. Other industries include paper, cement, and wood-distillates (see Ch. XI).

The Maidan consists in general of rolling plateaus rising in the E (between Tumkur and Kolar) into disjointed granitic hills of fantastically irregular plan and elevation. But there is a great deal of local diversity. "The level plains, of blackish soil, in the north, are covered with plantations of sugar-cane and fields of rice; those irrigated by tanks have groves of coconut and areca palm; the high-lying tracts of red soil, in the east, yield ragi and other 'dry' crops; the stony and widespreading pasture grounds, in the central part of the country, are stretches of coarse grass, relieved by shady groves of trees",[13] among which acacia and wild dates are prominent.

The N is rather precarious climatically, with a rainfall of around 25 ins. The Mysore plateaus have 30–35, but an important feature is that while most of the rain falls in the standard five months (June–October), there is a peak of *c.* 5 ins. in May followed by a drop until the major peak is reached in September or October; and there is appreciable fall in November. In the W (e.g. Shimoga) there is also a double peak, but the régime is nearer the normal W-coast pattern, with most rain in July. This extension of the rainy season is of the greatest agricultural value, the May 'mango showers' being essential to the flowering of coffee.[14] Figures for Bangalore illustrate these points:

J.	F.	M.	A.	M.	J.	J.	A.	S.	O.	N.	D.	Total
0·2	0·3	0·6	1·2	4·5	3·0	4·1	5·8	7·4	6·2	2·4	0·4	36·0 ins. (J.–O. 26·5)

The retreating monsoon has thus some influence in the E. Temperatures range from a mean of 69° F in December to 81° in May. Night frosts are not unknown on the higher levels.

Agriculture

Deshpande's work on the Bombay Karnatak brings out a degree of sub-regional diversity to which justice cannot be done here. The most striking feature is, or was, the prominence of cotton in Dharwar Dt, which as a whole has only 13% of TSA under that crop, but in some taluks 30%. But jowar and oilseeds are the main crops by acreage, wheat follows cotton, and sugar is also important. There are interesting variations: in the Kistna floodplain, 3–4 miles wide, specialised crops (vegetables, green fodder) are exceptionally important. Most of the area is unsuited to irrigation, for both physiographical and pedological reasons; but on some of the Kaladgi rocks

---

[13] *Mysore Gaz.* (1908), 2.   [14] Simkins, *op. cit.*, 18.

and the high-level laterites of Belgaum irrigation is possible, and on crystalline rocks in the Varada Valley both tanks and wells are used.[15] Indeed in a "belt of territory about 20 miles wide running almost parallel to the Poona-Bangalore railway . . . practically everything is transitional. Valleys open out to form the undulating surface features of the plateau. A rapid decline in the rainfall favours the growth of transitional vegetation type of medium sized trees and open grasslands. Tank irrigation is possible since narrow streams can be easily bunded. A variety of agricultural products, ranging from rice the representative of subsistence agriculture to commercial crops of tobacco and cotton, is grown." [16]

Tank-irrigation is extremely prominent in Mysore; there are about 37,000 tanks, large and small but mostly small. Over half the irrigated area of more than 1 m. ac. depends on tanks, and only in Mysore Dt, with its great Krishnaraja reservoir, is the canal area larger than the tank. Of the total area of Mysore—29,326 sq mls or about 18·75 m. ac.—over 10% is forest, and it is probable that a large proportion of the 7·75 m. ac. uncultivated is also under forest of a sort. The NSA is about 6·25 m. ac.; irrigation brings the TSA to about 6·5 m. ac. Rice and jowar are respectively a little over and under 700,000 ac.; but the poverty of much of the area is shown by the high figures for ragi (over 2 m.) and gram (800,000). The chief cash crop is groundnut, with a third of the 600,000 ac. of oilseeds. The fallow proportion is high, about 1·7 m. ac.; a drive is being made to bring half of it under more permanent tillage. Coffee (100,000 ac.) is confined to Hassan and Kadur Dts, but the Wynaad Plateau, politically in Malabar, adds 8,000. These bald figures conceal important diversities.[17]

A feature of interest is the importance attached to cattle-breeding. This stems from the days of Haidar Ali, who developed a strain of tough fast-trotting bullocks for use in his very mobile warfare. Pastoralism is particularly important in the forests of the SE scarps, spilling over into Hosur taluk of Salem Dt (Madras), where the bulls at least are half-wild. The Mysore breed is a very valuable strain and there is a large export to the plains.

The settlement geography is complicated. In the N larger villages and main roads tend on the whole to avoid the immediate river banks, owing to flooding on the Kistna and intense gully erosion on the smaller streams. But waterpoints are the fundamental siting factors, and houses are 'arid' in aspect, with mud walls and flat roofs. Villages, however, are large and on the whole prosperous except in the drier parts, e.g. the Bijapur border, and on the higher infertile ridges. In the Mysore Malnad there is a strong tendency, except in the larger valleys, to semi-dispersal, tiny hamlets or

[15] Not to be confused with the larger Varada in Mysore.
[16] Deshpande, op. cit., 105.
[17] They are analysed in detail in H. K. Ghori, The Agricultural Geography of Mysore (London Ph.D. thesis, 1950).

even scattered homesteads. In the Maidan, with its dependence on tanks, there is more nucleation, but even here dependent hamlets are common. Houses are generally mud-walled or stone, usually low-built around a courtyard which may be surrounded by carved and painted verandahs. As so often, thatch is the rule and tile the exception which indicates individual prosperity, but in the drier E flat roofs are common.

Towns and Industry

The Bombay Karnatak is in many aspects a transitional zone between Maharashtra and Mysore, and between the Wn Littoral and the Deccan. Its towns are thus for the most part contact settlements: Belgaum is on the very edge of the Lavas, Dharwar and Hubli actually on the Arabian Sea/Bay of Bengal watershed. The local sites of all three are at the margin of hill and plain; and they are all essentially depots for the transport of cotton and oilseeds to Bombay or Marmagão. Belgaum has already been mentioned (above, 651); Dharwar and Hubli are interesting as twin and rival cities, only 10 or 12 miles apart on the junction of a Dharwarian syncline with the gneissic black soils. Hubli (95,512; **129,609**) is growing much more rapidly than Dharwar (47,992); the latter's functions are mainly administrative, while the larger town has added to its old commercial importance modern industries: cotton ginning, pressing, and weaving, railway shops employing 6000 hands. Farther E Gadag-Bettegiri is so typical of the collecting centres of the Deccan as to merit an extended quotation [18]:

> Gadag dominates the southern cotton tract and cotton dominates the town and its annual rhythm of activity. Its cotton market is the focus of urban life. By the beginning of the picking season the town bursts into activity; commercial agents flock in; there is a flow of cart caravans bringing cotton into the market; the market bustles with activity and the rest of the town follows the pace; ginning mills and cotton presses lying idle for a long time are now set to work; cotton finds its way out in a compact and well-graded form to the metropolitan city of Bombay for export, or to cities like Sholapur for industrial consumption. By the middle of June this activity is at its zenith. The town accomplishes its major ambition and settles down to a quiet life during the next eight months. . . .

Gokak (13,600), also on the Lava edge, is more industrial, its old handicrafts, textiles and toys, being supplemented by cotton mills powered from the Ghataprabha; the hydro-electric supply is not as yet too reliable, but there are prospects of expansion when the river is fully harnessed.

In Mysore minerals and hydro-electricity have given rise to considerable industrial development, mainly of light consumption goods but with the important iron of Bhadravati and assembly plants (telecommunications

[18] Deshpande, *op. cit.*, 118.

equipment, motor-vehicles, aircraft) of Bangalore. Nearly all India's gold comes from fields around Kolar (**159,084**); the ore occurs in quartz reefs in the Dharwars, and mining has been carried down 7400 ft. Annual output is about 330,000 ounces fine gold. The Baba Bhudan field raises about 30,000–40,000 tons of iron ore (55–64% Fe), and Shimoga Dt about 20,000 tons of chromite—the great bulk of *Indian* production now that the Baluchistan output, which was three-fifths of All-India's, has gone to Pakistan. Manganese output fluctuates but is at times considerable; small amounts of magnesite and silver and even smaller of copper, graphite, and mica (from Wynaad) are mined. Other minerals include kaolin, corundum, garnets, and ochre.

The famous Cauvery Falls (320 ft in all) around the little island of Sivasamudram were the first in India to be exploited on any large scale (1902). But development is limited, by agreement with Madras, to 35,000 out of a potential 42,000 kW, in order to prevent undue abstraction of water. Since 1927 Sivasamudram has been linked with the great barrage at Krishnarajasagar; this, $1\frac{3}{4}$ miles long and 130 ft high, is partly for irrigation but also helps to maintain the flow at Sivasamudram, where the natural *monsoon* discharge has varied between 18,000 and 200,000 cusecs. These installations, linked with Shimsha and Mettur, supply Kolar, Mysore, and Bangalore cities; the 93 miles to Kolar was one of the longest transmissions in the world when opened. In the N the Gersoppa development already noted (above, 620), and in the centre Shimsha, are largely for Mysore; at Gersoppa 48,000 kW are already generated, about a half of the potential. There are a number of minor schemes, e.g. on the Bhadra.

The Mysore government was one of the most progressive in India; it had 750 miles of metre railway and had developed an unusually good road net for S India, as well as fostering industrial development. There are some 400 factories with 50,000 workers, but over half are seasonal. Cotton and silk, leather and tea, ceramics and chemicals are the main lines; and electric power may revivify some of the craft industries.

Bangalore (**778,977** including cantonments) is the capital: a close-packed old town, with over-planned gridiron suburbs N and S, and the vast sprawling cantonments to the E. In addition to its electrical and assembly industries it is of significance as a place of retirement, combining climatic attractions with urban amenities; this accounts in part for the large Tamil proportion of its population. Bangalore is also the seat of the important Tata Institute of Science. Mysore (**244,323**), the old capital, is much more 'Indian' and much more humanely planned.

Karnataka as a Whole

With the Telugus of Andhra Desa, the Kannada people have been in the forefront of the movement for a linguistic division of *India*: convenient enough when it was a question of attacking the British Raj for its arbitrary mutilation of living cultural entities in the interests of mere administration, the issue is now embarrassing to realistic statesmen. Clearly at present *India* cannot afford any new separatism, though later on, when a common Hindi allegiance has developed (if it ever does in Dravidastan) a secondary tier of cultural provinces might be reasonable.

The core of Karnataka is obviously Mysore; though it should be observed that Fig. 127 conceals the fact that the Tamil population was nearly 5% in 1931; apart from Bangalore valetudinarians, they form important professional and official groups in the towns. Still, some 70% of the people of Mysore are Kannada speakers. There are outliers in Madras and Hyderabad, most notably in Bellary and Raichur. But the Bombay Karnatak is in large part a debatable land, the theatre of very interesting inter-ramifications of geographical and historical factors. The destruction of Vijayanagar by the Muslim Deccani kingdoms, and their short-lived supersession by the Moguls, followed by Maratha dominance and the rise of Hyderabad, fatally weakened the unity of Karnataka. The towns in the Nn frontier zone, Maratha administrative centres and border-fortresses, are mainly Marathi-speaking, and Marathi has also spread along the hill country of the Ghats. Moreover, a century of administration from Bombay and—even more important—commercial ties with that metropolis have forged very strong links. "It would be difficult to claim that without the aid of Bombay Port and the market of Western India, Northern Karnatak would be able to maintain its economic progress. The very geographical position and the political position of Northern Karnatak have placed it in a peculiar position: it owes a cultural allegiance to the south and an economic allegiance to the north." [19] The path of regionalism is by no means easy.

The Upper Mahanadi Basin and its Annexes

The plains and basins which extend E of the Deccan Lavas and lie between the Maikal Range and Chota Nagpur to the N, and the Orissa Hills to the S, have really no regional cohesion—rather they are what is left over when the well-defined regions mentioned have been delimited. In the W the Wainganga valley is separated by low discontinuous hills (running S from the Maikal Range) from the upper Mahanadi basin, the heart of which is Chhattisgarh. Beyond lies the much smaller basin of the Brahmani, E of which again the Orissa Hills and Chota Nagpur approach each other on either side of the Jamshedpur Gap; the lower Subarnarekha is transitional to the lateritic shelf of W Bengal.

---

[19] Deshpande, 121–22. Here we must say farewell to a most valuable guide.

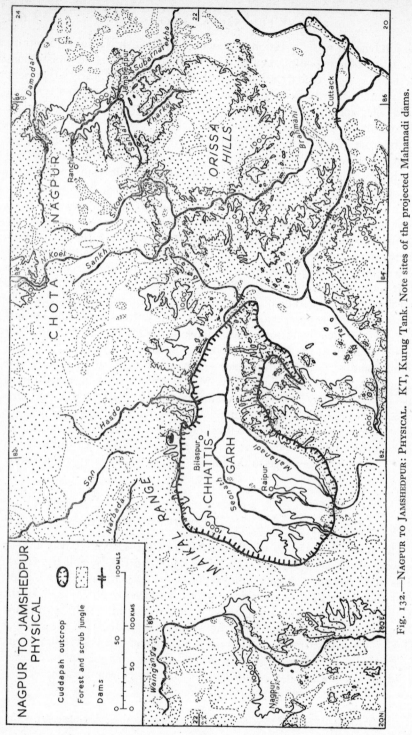

NAGPUR TO JAMSHEDPUR
PHYSICAL

Cuddapah outcrop

Forest and scrub jungle

Dams

0   50   100 MLS
0   50   100 KMS

Fig. 132.—NAGPUR TO JAMSHEDPUR: PHYSICAL.   KT, Kurug Tank. Note sites of the projected Mahanadi dams.

662

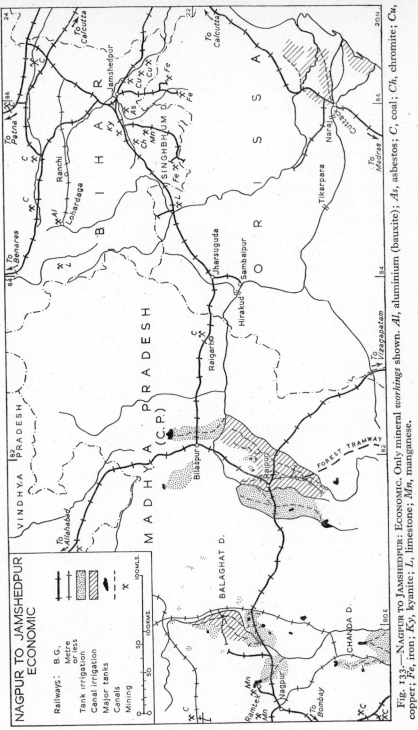

NAGPUR TO JAMSHEDPUR
ECONOMIC

Railways: B.G,
Metre
or less

Tank irrigation
Canal irrigation
Major tanks
Canals
Mining

0   50   100 KMS.

0   50   100 MLS.

Fig. 133.—NAGPUR TO JAMSHEDPUR: ECONOMIC. Only mineral *workings* shown. *Al*, aluminium (bauxite); *As*, asbestos; *C*, coal; *Ch*, chromite; *Cu*, copper; *Fe*, iron; *Ky*, kyanite; *L*, limestone; *Mn*, manganese.

663

(a) *The Wainganga Valley*

Immediately E of Nagpur the Deccan Lavas give place to generally Archaean terrain, irregularly undulating country at about 900-1100 ft, broken by small disconnected hills up to 500 ft high and rocky or covered by scraggy open forest. Rainfall is 44–55 ins. with a strict monsoonal distribution; Bhandara (54 ins.) has 7·5, 16·5, 15, 9·5 ins. for the months June–September, just 90% of the total. There is some tendency to variability towards the end of the rains and irrigation is at least desirable for security, and is mainly from thousands of small tanks formed by bunding the irregular little valleys; a handful of the larger ones are really small lakes of 5–10 sq mls.

A considerable proportion of the valley itself, as well as the hills to N and E, is heavily forested. This is the great domain of sal; minor products— bamboo, charcoal, myrobolans, lac, the leaves used for covering *bidis* (cheap 'cigarettes'), fodder—are extremely important elements in the economy of the whole of this region, except Chhattisgarh itself. The Districts of En Madhya Pradesh (CP) show even less than the usual relation to natural sub-divisions, and it is difficult to present a quantitative picture of the agriculture. Bhandara, however, lies wholly within the sub-region and may be taken as typical, with the qualification that adjacent Districts show higher proportions of forest (Balaghat 30%, Chanda 50%). Bhandara, with a total area of *c.* 2,283,000 ac., has some 322,000 under forest (14%), NSA 830,000 ac. and TSA 1,100,000. Rice accounts for nearly half the TSA, followed by wheat and oilseeds (nearly all linseed), each with about 90,000 ac. The Wainganga marks the transition from the agriculture of Maharashtra, with its uncertain rain but moisture-retentive regur, its wide plains and commercial bias, to the realm of paddy in the better-watered but more broken NE Peninsula.[20]

The most important mineral exploited as yet is manganese; Madhya Pradesh production is about 280,000 tons p.a., or around 60% of the *Indian* total. The great Gondwana trough, which continues the line of the lower Godavari Valley, has a number of small coalfields, extending from the Pench and Son Valleys in the N (above, 584) to Singareni and Tandur in Hyderabad. Production is of the order of 250,000–500,000 tons, most notably at Warora and Bellarpur in Chanda. In the S there are great reserves of good haematite (60–67% Fe), as yet little exploited. The haematite forms monadnocks such as the Dholi and Rajhara Hills in Drug Dt (on the Chhattisgarh border) and Lohara in Chanda: the Rajhara Hills alone contain some 7,500,000 tons of ore, while Lohara, in area 700 by 200 yds, is practically a solid mass of haematite. The focus of economic life is Nagpur (above, 653–54).

[20] Simkins, *op. cit.*, 34.

(b) *The Upper Mahanadi: Chhattisgarh*

Between the Maikal and Orissa Hills lies the great plain, 80–100 miles wide, of the upper Mahanadi. Most of the plain lies W and N of the Mahanadi and is drained by the Seonath; on the NW it is sharply limited by the Maikal scarps, on the S it rises into the jungly hills of Bastar, but W and E the watersheds with the Wainganga and Sankh-Brahmani are mere residual crests, bold but broken hills. For a good deal of its W–E course the Mahanadi hugs the Orissa Hills before plunging into them SE of Raigarh, which lies in a corridor, 20–25 miles wide, between the river and the tangled Chota Nagpur foothills.

The heart of the plain is occupied by a great basin of Cuddapah rocks (Fig. 132) (grits, quartzites, sandstones, shales), resting on the Archaeans which form the irregular margins, and bevelled off in perfect peneplains at about 900–1000 ft. The rivers are extraordinarily mature as a whole; but here and there the master-streams are incised, not very deeply, in gullied banks. This suggestion of rejuvenation may be due to renewed erosive power consequent on forest destruction, or perhaps to rains in tributary catchments when the base-level is lowered a few feet by the dry-weather shrinkage of the main streams.

This plain of Chhattisgarh ('36 Forts') is girdled by more or less broken forest country, and until the coming of the Marathas was historically an isolated Gond kingdom; it stands out vividly on forest and population maps (Figs. 19 and 30). "The surface is an expanse of small embanked rice-fields, sometimes 50 to an acre . . . over large areas there are few trees other than the mango groves adjoining the more important of the frequent clusters of mud-roofed huts which form a Chhattisgarh village."[21]

With a rainfall of about 55 ins. irrigation is desirable. Canal irrigation is important but recent; it is practically confined to the Seonath/Mahanadi doab, the margins being dependent on tanks, many of which are of large size, such as the 8-mile-long Kurug Tank N of Bilaspur.[22] On the fertile black silts of the central plain paddy is dominant; in Raipur Dt as a whole it accounts for over 1,500,000 of a TSA of about 2,600,000 ac.; the NSA is under 2,000,000 ac., testimony of the importance of irrigation. In Bilaspur the corresponding figures are 1,300,000 paddy, 2,250,000 TSA, 1,750,000 NSA. Pulses, linseed, and wheat follow. A feature of farming practice is the extensive use of silt from the tanks as fertiliser; cultivators are also adepts in the siting of ditches sub-parallel to the contours to bring water to the fields. Well irrigation with pole-and-bucket lift is used for specialised crops such as betel vines, and the sandy river-beds are used for dry weather garden cultivation.

[21] *CP Gaz.* (1908), 3.
[22] It is impossible to be more precise since the agricultural statistics for CP include Government Canal and tank irrigation under private canals!

Villages are definitely at waterpoints, close-packed, mud-built with mud or tiled roofs; they have a pueblo aspect enhanced by mud walls joining up farmstead buildings and separating the fields; in places dry-stone walls, and slabs of rock 'mortared' with mud, are used.

The most important mineral is coal, mainly on the NE flank of the basin where a long Gondwana trough lies between the Mahanadi and the Brahmani. Some seams are of great thickness (100 ft or more) but much of this is made up of carbonaceous shale. The whole of this belt, down to Talchir on the lower Brahmani, contains probably about 200 m. tons of coal; but it is hardly exploited except near Raigarh, where the Bengal-Nagpur Railway crosses it, and even there production is very small. There is some limestone and dolomite quarrying around the margins of the basin, particularly towards the Jamshedpur side.

Densities are fairly low (**192–223**) and this has been one of the least urbanised areas of India, but there are some signs of change, consequent on irrigation and railway development and perhaps the general economic changes influenced by the proximity of Jamshedpur. The main Calcutta–Bombay railway skirts the Nn margin of the plain to Bilaspur, whence a line strikes NW to the Son valley. Beyond Bilaspur the main line runs along the Seonath/Mahanadi doab to Raipur (63,465) which, since the construction in 1932 of the line to Vizagapatam, has developed rapidly as the regional centre of Chhattisgarh. Most of the railway towns have now a little industry; at Jharsuguda in the extreme E is one of the largest paper-mills in India (Fig. 133).

(c) *The Upper Brahmani and Jamshedpur*

E of the Mahanadi-Brahmani watershed the hills to N and S converge, leaving a corridor of hilly lowland, drained by the Sankh and the S Koel (which unite to form the Brahmani) and the Sanjai and Kharkai, tributaries of the Subarnarekha. Except for Singhbhum Dt (Bihar), the area was parcelled out amongst various petty states, which have now been merged into Madhya Pradesh and Orissa, except Seraikela and Kharsawan, which have gone to Bihar. These two had an area of only 600 sq mls, but their mineral wealth is not an unimportant addition to that of Singhbhum.

The confused topography is developed mostly on Dharwarian rocks. In the N, on the Chota Nagpur flanks, the main ridges reach nearly 3000 ft, with a rough E/W trend cut across by the N–S valleys which lie at about 1500–2000 ft. On the Sn flank the main trend of the Orissa Hills is SW/NE, but the spurs are extremely irregular. A very large proportion of the sub-region is under forest, much of it sal and much of it open. Population density is thus generally low and the people largely tribal—66% in Singhbhum, 70% in Gangpur and Bonai on the Mahanadi/Brahmani watershed. Agriculture is for the most part primitive and backward.

JAMSHEDPUR

From every point of view the Jamshedpur area is by far the most important part of the sub-region. Here the convergence of Sanjai, Kharkai, and Subarnarekha forms a fair-sized (though broken) lowland, with a good deal of tank-fed, or at least tank-secured, paddy-land in the valleys, which show a marked trellis-pattern (Fig. 135). The passage-function of the sub-region is also very clearly shown here: railways from W Bengal come from the NE (Asansol) and SE (Midnapore) into the Jamshedpur basin, and the main line to Bombay uses the Sanjai to cross over to the Brahmani valley by a col at no more than 1100–1200 ft (Fig. 134). But above all, of course, this tract is significant as the seat of the largest individual industrial undertaking in India, the Jamshedpur (Tatanagar) iron and steel works which are among the largest in the British Commonwealth: an island of heavy industry in a sea of jungle and subsistence cultivation, an outpost of monopoly capitalism in a human environment still mainly tribal. In 1911 Jamshedpur had a population of 5672; in 1941 it was 148,711, an increase of nearly 2500%; and by 1951 it was **218,162** (nearly 3500%).

The locational advantages are striking, and are sufficiently displayed by Fig. 134, which shows the position of Jamshedpur in relation to its fuel and raw material supplies, all of which except the flux lie within 70 miles, and to the important Calcutta market. The 'Iron Ore Belt' in Singhbhum and the adjoining states has reserves estimated at not less than 2700 m. tons of haematite (Fe 60%).[23] Of alloy metals, sufficient manganese is found locally, and some chromite and fluorspar, while new deposits of chromite and manganese are reported from Keonjhar in Orissa, and fluorite in Singhbhum. Magnesite comes from S India, especially Salem, though possible local sources are being investigated. For furnace linings the Raniganj and Jharia coalfields supply excellent fireclay, and silica is available from nearby Manbhum. The Bihar copper belt—the only important worked deposits in the sub-continent—lies in the Subarnarekha Valley, about 25 miles away. To the N is the alumina-plant at Muri, to SW possibly large deposits of bauxite in the Orissa Hills. There can be few heavy metallurgical centres so advantageously situated from the point of view of access to materials. Unskilled labour is drawn from the Santal tribes; more skilled workers from all parts of *India*, but especially Bengal and Bihar, and the British and American technicians of the early days are now almost entirely replaced by Indians: but labour efficiency, while it has increased remarkably in the last two decades, is still below western standards and this offsets low money wages. The various Tata enterprises connected with Jamshedpur employ

[23] Most of the details given here are drawn from S. A. Majid, *The Industrial Geography of Bihar* (London University Ph.D. thesis, 1949), Ch. VI. A lively account of the growth of the industry is given in J. L. Keenan, *A Steel Man in India* (1945); not much direct geography, but one of the 'climates' of Indian life given with any amount of verve.

at least 50,000 workers, 20,000 of them in the town itself. Jamshedpur-Tatanagar really consists of a number of separately planned, but integrated, settlements around the great steel works and the associated plants; the standard of housing and amenity is far higher than in most Indian industrial centres (Fig. 135).

There had been numerous false starts before Jamshedji Tata launched his project in 1908, and expert opinion held that in the economic climate

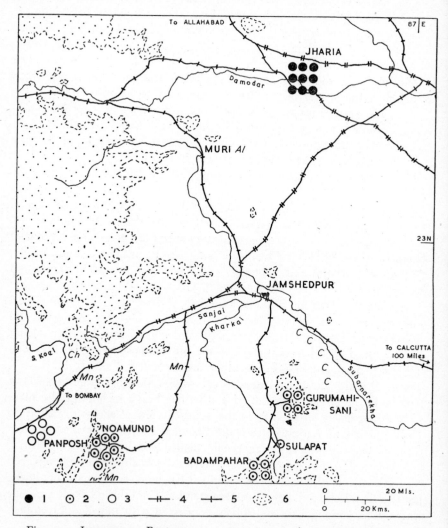

Fig. 134.—JAMSHEDPUR: RESOURCES. 1, 100,000 tons coal; 2, 100,000 tons iron ore; 3, 10,000 tons dolomite (1–3 consumption p.a. 1945–47); 4, BGDT; 5, BGST; 6, over 500 *metres*; *Al*, alumina; *C*, copper; *Ch*, chromite; *Mn*, manganese. For the 2′ 6″ ST to Lohardaga, see Fig. 133. Based on map by S. A. Majid.

of India visions of a great heavy metals industry were visions and no more. The preliminary reconnaissance was thorough; operations started in 1911, and in 1914 some 160,000 tons of pig-iron were produced. The 1914–18 war almost cut off iron and steel imports and gave Tatas a flying start, and with the aid of protection the depression of the 1930s was surmounted. Tatas have never produced less than 50% of the Indian total of pig iron and have reached 80%. Railway, bridge, and constructional materials have

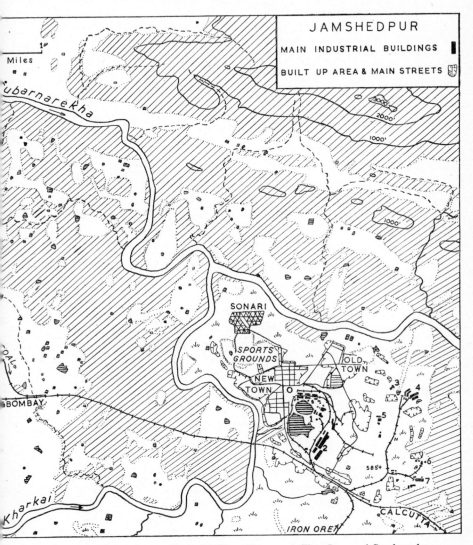

Fig. 135.—JAMSHEDPUR: THE SITE. O, Tata offices; 1–2, Tata Iron and Steel works— 1, furnaces and cooling tanks, 2, rolling mills, etc.; 3, agric. implements; 4, tinplate; 5, cables; 6, steel wire; 7, loco works. Jungle shaded; courtesy SOI.

always been prominent lines; bars and light structural steel comprise about a quarter of the finished products, rails and fishplates about 14%. The 1939–45 war saw a great expansion in quantity and range, including the production of light armoured vehicles. Associated industries include tin-plate (developed in association with the Burmah Oil Co., production 40,000 tons in 1947), cables, wire and wire nails, agricultural implements, enamelled and galvanised sheets, and all types of castings. Most of the undertakings responsible for these products, as well as the mines and quarries on which they are based, are part of the multifunctional 'Tata group' which has wide ramifications, from soap to aviation. The metallurgical and engineering side has thus elements of both vertical and horizontal monopoly. In Bombay is the general staff of this industrial empire, and its service corps; here, set down in the incongruous jungle, is its arsenal.

Telangana

The remainder of the Peninsular Interior, within the bordering En Hills, is perhaps best regarded as the Deccan component of Andhra Desa, the country of the Telugu-speaking peoples; a component which differs widely from the littoral districts of 'Andhrastan'. The area here considered con-sists of the Hyderabad Telangana (with Raichur, officially in Marathwara) and the Madras 'Ceded Districts' of Anantapur, Bellary, and Kurnool. The fourth Ceded District, Cuddapah, lies mostly in the Cuddapah Ranges region, as indeed does much of Kurnool. The limits, except where formed by the Deccan Lava edge and the front of the Cuddapah Ranges, are very vague; pending serious work on the Mysore peneplains, we may take the Madras/Mysore boundary as an approximation, though this includes Kanarese-speaking populations of 64 and 49% in Raichur and Bellary, which nevertheless go physically with the rest of the present region. In the SE the little river basins lying between the Cuddapahs and the Mysore plateau, in E Anantapur and W Chittoor, are really another 'left-over' sub-region, in Chittoor transitional to Tamilnad; they will receive separate treatment. With these rather wide qualifications, the name Telangana seems appropriate, or at any rate least inappropriate.

The Physical Aspect

The bulk of the region consists of peneplains developed on the Archaean gneisses. In the N, however, faulting has preserved a belt of Gondwanas (with some coal) along the lower Godavari trough: much of this is below 500 ft, but with its dissected terrain it has remained very largely under forest of a dryish deciduous type.

The most general levels lie between 1600 and 2000 ft; in the S, below the rather ragged break of slope down from the Mysore plateau, the Kistna and Tungabhadra valleys lie at 1000–1500 ft, and to the NW the watershed between the Bhima and the Godavari is a great swelling upland reaching 2400 ft in places. But the general aspect nearly everywhere is that of practically senile peneplains, intersected by broad, open, almost completely graded valleys, and littered with monadnocks which range from considerable hill-groups to innumerable fantastic tors which look like dumps of gigantic road-metal. Around Hyderabad City these form "a chaos of granitic boulders . . . piled up in bizarre heaps, as if giants had amused themselves with childish games"; in places these rocky belts form a wilderness wide enough to act as a marchland.[24] With the poor sandy red soils of the gneisses and granites, a variable rainfall of 25–35 ins., and May mean temperatures in the 90s, life is hard except in favoured basins, where soilwash and tank irrigation give some prosperity. Bare hills, reddish-khaki plains with scattered thorny scrub, rivers merely ribbons of sand for half the year or more, tanks bunded into the little valleys, all combine to produce a landscape with a desolate and brooding charm. The contrast between Hyderabad Marathwara and Telangana is extremely striking, and is brought out by Figs. 130 and 131.

The Ceded Districts are if anything worse.[25] In Marathwara there is hardly any surface water in the hot weather, except in the bigger streams; in Sn Telangana even this exception hardly holds. The railway bridges are stoutly built to withstand the immense volume of monsoon water in rivers which are then half a mile or more wide; in the hot weather they traverse great flats with a yard or so of water in the middle, and the herds of cattle or goats crossing the bed are recognisable from afar by their great clouds of dust.

Except for the jungles of the N, the region presents a decided savannah aspect, poor savannah with widely spaced acacias. Most of the tors are absolutely naked, and their skirts (with much of the more or less level ground) carry only a thorny scrub, in which euphorbias are prominent, while in damper depressions there are scattered palms, toddy or the wild Indian date. The scrub is secondary, on ground long subject to the depredations of sheep and especially goats, or once cultivated.

Agriculture

Rainfall, by and large, is much the same in Telangana as in Maharashtra; if anything more favourable, since the region lies farther from the lee of the Ghats and more open to Bay of Bengal influences. But differences in terrain and soil are decisive. The area here considered is about 75,000 sq mls, of which the TSA is only about 43% (approximately 20,250,000 ac.).[26] Forest

[24] E. Reclus, *L'Inde* (1883), 506; cf. *Hyderabad Gaz.* (1909), 2.
[25] For some vivid remarks, see J. C. Molony, *A Book of South India* (1926), 166.
[26] Figures even more approximate than usual, as those of Hyderabad are internally suspect.

covers over 14,000 sq mls, largely on the indeterminate En marches of the region. Irrigation, though more important than in Maharashtra, accounts for only 8–9% of NSA and is over 60% from tanks. Fig. 136 brings out some points of the Maharashtra/Telangana contrasts, the Districts selected being comparable in area, while Ahmadnagar is not too specialised to cotton. The most striking features are the much smaller proportion of cultivation in Anantapur, and the far higher proportion of 'other food-grains', i.e. the poorer millets and pulses such as gram.

There is, however, considerable internal variation. Rice everywhere plays a much more prominent role than in most of Maharashtra, but still accounts for only 7% of NSA: dependent on the tanks, it is the food of the better-off agricultural classes. Jowar has the largest acreage (c. 5·4 m.), followed by bajra (c. 1·5 m., largely on lighter soils); significantly enough, gram is third with 600,000 ac. Maize is important in some Hyderabad Districts, nearly 10% of TSA in Karimnagar. Oilseeds are the dominant cash crop, approaching 4 m. ac. Groundnuts account for some 60% of this,[27] and in the Ceded Districts play something of the role of cotton in Maharashtra:

	NSA, 1948–49	% of total area	Groundnuts		
			"Normal"	1948–49	1948–49, % of NSA
Kurnool . .	2,074	41·5	476	267	12·5
Bellary . .	2,225	61·4	320	324	12·9
Cuddapah . .	1,000	26·3	187	182	16·9
Anantapur .	2,026	47·0	341	372	17·7
	7,325	43·7	1,324	1,145	15·6

Figures in thousand acres; the 1948–49 groundnuts total was 31% of that for Madras. Figures supplied by Mr C. D. Deshpande.

Jowar takes the heavier soils: "In a tract with just the minimum rainfall, 20–30 ins., groundnut is the most valuable kharif crop on light soils, where the soil is not heavy enough for jowar and rainfall not high enough for rice." Cotton has only half the acreage of oilseeds, and except on the black soils of the greater rivers, extrusions from Maharashtra, it is largely limited to the Raichur (Kistna/Tungabhadra) Doab: Raichur and Bellary Dts account for well over half the total acreage. In this area a high proportion of the rain comes late in the wet season; at Anantapur, a little to the E, 8·6 ins. fall in September alone, and July–September inclusive account for 15·6 of a total 27·4 ins. The rabi crop therefore tends to be more important than the

[27] S. Velayudham, "Groundnut in Madras", IGJ XXI (1946), 100–12 and 153–73; refce at p. 157.

kharif, especially on heavier soils which, with the intense May heat and late start of considerable rains, may not be workable till August. While groundnut is the kharif cash crop, cotton is entirely rabi. Jowar is grown for fodder as well as grain; ragi and other millets as well as rice are often wet crops; and millets are sown mixed with pulses, which take longer to mature and are a safeguard against the failure of the cereals. Most of these features point to the general precariousness of the agriculture in the region, which as a whole is a food-deficit area.

Differences of expert opinion in the two states long impeded work on the great dam, $1\frac{1}{2}$ miles long and 160 ft high, being built across the Tunga-

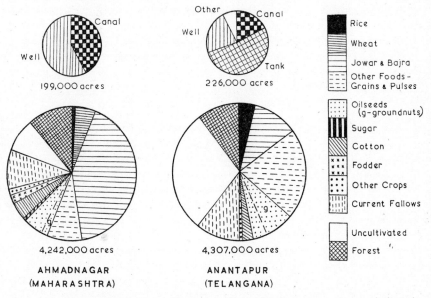

Fig. 136.—THE LAVA/ARCHAEAN CONTRAST. Upper circles represent areas irrigated.

bhadra: this will irrigate 600,000 ac. in Hyderabad and 300,000 in Madras, as well as generating about 150,000 kW. But the execution of the 7 major and some of the 32 minor projects in Hyderabad, which together might command 3·5 m. ac. and produce 500,000 kW, probably lies in an indefinite future. Terrain and climate impose severe limitations on Telangana, and the unlucky history of the Kurnool project (below, 680) suggests that a cautious policy may be essential for real progress.

Other Resources; Settlement and Towns

The mineral resources of Telangana are scattered and little exploited. The most important production is probably that of Gondwana coal, mined chiefly at Singareni; in NE Hyderabad are some outliers of the great iron zone of the Orissa Hills. There are small deposits of lead (Nalgonda), copper and mica (Raichur), and graphite (Warangal), while the Ceded Districts have non-ferrous metals (manganese, antimony), corundum, and barytes; but most of the minerals here are associated with the bordering ranges to the E, and in any case are almost untouched. Golconda diamonds belong to history—and legend—rather than to modern economy. The forest resources around the Godavari are not very accessible, though it would seem that more use might be made of the river itself as an outlet, and power might be available from the rapids where it crosses the En Hills.

Population densities are not high—**170–200** in the Ceded Dts, **160–220** in Hyderabad. Villages are essentially tied to waterpoints, often in association with tanks, and generally built of mud or stone set in mud, with thatched roofs.[28]

Apart from Hyderabad City, towns are few and small. Warangal (**133,130**) is the largest, and of merely local importance; Bellary (56,148) is an important railway town and has small sugar and vanaspati (vegetable ghee) mills. Otherwise, except for cotton ginning and so on, industrial development is negligible: in 1949 Hyderabad had only 60,000 factory workers (probably mostly in the capital), 26,000 miners, 22,000 railwaymen.

Hyderabad (**1,085,722**) was in 1941 the fourth Indian city; it has since been outstripped by Delhi (Old and New together). Founded in 1589 by the Muslim king of Golconda, it was the capital of the Mogul Viceroyalty of the Deccan and of the independent state which arose on the Mogul ruins; old Golconda, an impressive hill-fortress, lies 5 miles to the W. The significance of Hyderabad is essentially administrative and cultural, as is evidenced by the high proportions of Urdu and Tamil speakers; the former represent the semi-feudal class dominant in the state until 1948, the latter the clerkly bureaucracy. The city is close-packed, mostly unplanned, with palaces perhaps more remarkable for size than beauty, surrounded by vast tanks. Most notable of modern buildings is perhaps the fine Osmania University. Six miles to the N is the enormous cantonment of Secunderabad, designed to afford protection to Our Faithful Ally the Nizam, and perhaps not less to ensure his continued faithfulness—a precaution not unwarranted in the stirring and in all senses intriguing days when the rising British power was at grips with the Marathas and the Mysore of Haidar Ali and Tipu, and when French influence was not altogether dead in the Deccan.

Telangana: Aspect and Prospect

Hyderabad, with its 82,313 sq mls and **18,655,108** people, its own internal posts (with yellow pillar-boxes), its integration of road services with the Nizam's State Railway, and with a reasonably good administration, was a

[28] W. Burns (ed.), *Sons of the Soil* (1941), 5.

state of weight not inferior to that of many a sovereign member of UNO. But large parts of it were still under practically feudal *jagirs*, and the tension between a Muslim aristocracy and bureaucracy, and the Maratha/Telugu peasantry, was a fundamental weakness. As the only notable survivor of the Muslim Mogul succession-states, it was an Islamic cultural and political outlier fatally isolated from the Islamic bases in the NW and NE. These things were obvious to the casual traveller: as one passes from the lava mesas of Maharashtra the cultural landscape changes as much as the physical. At Gulbarga, on the lava edge, the tombs of the Muslim Bahmani Sultans dominate the gently rolling country, their domes rising like giant bubbles over the flat skyline; on the station platforms the local petty bourgeoisie and bureaucracy, gathered to meet the train and always easily recognisable, no longer wore the dhoti or completely anglicised office clothes, but were clad in the long tight-fitting Muslim *sherwani* coat. But the Muslim hold was thin, and they were a minority of 12·8%. Geographically the weakness of the state was of course its separation from the sea—doubtless not accidental on the EIC's part; hence its interest in Masulipatam on the Godavari delta, linked by rail and only 60 miles from Hyderabad territory by the easy gap where the Gondwana trough breaks the En Hills.

To-day it seems possible that all the Telugu country may be united into an Andhra state, despite the great gap in economic development, and perhaps in economic interests, between the harsh and arid plateau and the paddy-plain of the Madras littoral. It would probably be difficult enough to weld together peoples of such divergent environment; but the major objection to Andhra Desa is not so much the thing in itself as the difficulty of stopping such particularisms from spreading. The detachment of Telangana from Hyderabad leaves Marathwara to be disposed of; presumably there would be a move to attach it to a Maharashtra state. This would involve in turn the creation of Karnataka for the Kanarese, and there is an important overlapping zone between the two [29], while, as we have seen, the Bombay Karnatak has important ties with Bombay. That city itself is the natural outlet for Maharashtra and is in historically Maratha country; but commercially it is also closely allied with Gujarat, and indeed Gujarati is probably the main business language of Bombay. Clearly to such separatisms there is no end territorially; they probably raise as many problems as they solve; and from an *Indian* point of view the result of creating linguistically homogeneous states might be a grave weakening of national unity. (Cf. below, 682,692).

In any case, the development of the essentially poor land of Telangana will call for great capital expenditure without, perhaps, much prospect of cash returns. The future depends largely on the progress of the great

[29] Deshpande, *op. cit.*, Fig. 20 (p. 86).

Tungabhadra scheme; but the history of large-scale irrigation here is discouraging, though of course much experience has been gained since the Kurnool failure. With the development of hydro-electricity there may come decentralised industrial development on the Mysore model; but Mysore had a more solid backing in at least some industry, sericulture and Bhadravati iron for instance, to give a base. Telangana is not without resources such as oilseeds and fibres (including sheep and goat wool), and in view of *India's* shortages in non-ferrous metals development of the poor communication net might lead to at least some exploitation of the scattered minerals. But when all is said, it seems likely that Telangana will remain, if not a backward, at least a poor country.

The Anantapur-Chittoor Basins

Between the bold scarp of the Palkonda Range and the higher Mysore levels are a series of basins around the middle courses of the Penner tributaries—Chitravati, Papagni, Punchu/Cheyyeru, the last two with a remarkable confluence-gorge in the Palkondas. To the SE the sub-region breaks down to the Nellore/Coromandel plains through the little intermont basins of the Nagari Hills (up to 2800 ft) and through the broader Swarnamukhi valley, which may occupy a fault-trough under the Palkondas. The whole area is crossed by N/S or NE/SW trap dykes, which may also have some influence on the remarkable drainage-pattern.

The area is isolated and poor, except in the extreme SE—the Nagari valleys, culturally transitional to Tamilnad. Only 20% of Chittoor Dt is cultivated—less than any other Madras District except the Nilgiris—but the density is **304,** intermediate between the Ceded Districts (*c.* **185**) and the coastal plains (**450–650**). Millets account for over 40% of the cropped area, followed by rice and groundnuts (24 and 14%).

There is no urban or industrial development worth mentioning. The Nagari basins are better cultivated than those of the plateau, but even they are not very impressive agriculturally: their flattish floors are broken by patches of sandy soil, almost bare but for a thin grass/acacia cover, and by naked rock exfoliation surfaces, looking like *roches moutonnées* and often used as threshing floors. Around the plain a lateritic piedmont slope fringes the craggy hills, with boulders as big as a small house on the talus slopes. Below the lateritic apron is a better-watered and more fertile piedmont strip, which is in places a solid belt of paddy, the zone of bush and trees along the laterite margin being a favoured settlement-line. It is a strange landscape: fantastic hills, stacked and pinnacled, long ridges capped by massive quartzites, reflected in the still waters of the big tanks with their borders of toddy palms; an eerily attractive picture under iron-blue or grey skies.

The Eastern Hills

The term "Eastern Ghats" is honoured by time but by nothing else; its use gives a misleading impression of comparability with the Wn Ghats, and suggests an entirely non-existent homogeneity. The hills which border the Peninsular Interior on the E have in fact no continuity, structural or topographic. In the N they are elevated highly-dissected peneplains (largely Charnockite) cut across by the Gondwana Mahanadi/Brahmani trough; but S of the similar lower Godavari trough there is an absolutely different element in the Cuddapah Ranges. S again are the Javadis, Shevaroys, etc., cut off from the Mysore plateaus by the middle Palar/Ponnaiyar trough; these are better considered as a separate group in Tamilnad. The word 'ghat' was applied to the En hills by historic accident; it must be remembered that one signification of 'ghat' is a pass or way through, and it was down the ghats in this sense that the armies of Haidar Ali and Tipu descended to the "Carnatic"—another misnomer. By extension all the hill-masses were lumped together as "Eastern Ghats"; but it seems best to confine the term to the Mysore scarp overlooking the Palar/Ponnaiyar trough, which is indeed analogous to the Wn Ghats, and to use the non-committal term 'Eastern Hills' for the groups discussed here.

(a) Orissa and Bastar

Between the Jamshedpur Gap and the Godavari breach lies a great tract of wild hilly country, mainly on Archaeans with an extensive development of Charnockites in the higher portions. It falls into three main masses. (i) The most Nn (old Keonjhar and Mayurbhanj states) is largely Dharwarian and reaches 3824 ft in Meghusani in the NE; but much of it is an extensive dissected peneplain at 1800–2000 ft (once continuous with Chota Nagpur?) lying W of the Kharkai. In the irregular monadnocks along its N edge are the main iron supplies of Jamshedpur, notably at Gurumahisani (Fig. 134). This mass is separated from the others by a remarkable transverse trough, partly floored by Gondwanas (including the famous Permo-Carboniferous glacial boulder-bed at Talcher) and flanked by the gorges of the Mahanadi and Brahmani, which are paralleled to the N by the smaller Baitarni Valley; the drainage-pattern here would repay careful study.

S of the Mahanadi the mountain mass widens to c. 125 miles, divided into (ii) a definitely NE/SW-trending section in the E and (iii) the lower and less defined plateaus of Bastar in the W. The En section is largely formed of Khondalites (gneisses and schists, perhaps the oldest rocks of India) and Charnockites; most of it lies at over 3000 ft with a few summits at nearly 5000. The NE/SW trend is well shown by the line of the Tel-upper Indravati-Sabari and Sileru Rivers, marking it off from Bastar (2000–3000 ft, a few points 4000). Bastar is a highly dissected and almost entirely forested plateau, most of which drains to the Godavari via the Indravati; it contains a few Cuddapah inliers, but is for the most part a mass of un-differentiated gneiss, covered by a mass of jungle.

Nearly all this area was divided amongst a multiplicity of very backward states which, except for Bastar and Kanker (which have gone to Madhya Pradesh (CP)), are now merged with Orissa, increasing its area by 85% but its population by only 58%. A large proportion of the region consists of dense or open deciduous forest, with some sal; in Bastar, indeed, open ground amounts to only a small fraction of the state's 13,701 sq mls. The largest, indeed the only extensive, non-forested area is in the Tel valley. Koraput Dt may be regarded as typical: here nearly 4·75 m. ac. of a total of 6·39 m. are forest or scrub,[30] and of the TSA of about 1·42 m. ac. over half is rice—dry hill-rice, or terraced in the valleys—and the only other single crops of much importance are ragi and gram. Shifting agriculture, supple-mented by forest produce, is prevalent; mahua flowers are distilled, and mango-stones ground for flour. Taken as a whole, and despite the mineral reserves (iron especially, chromite, bauxite, manganese), the region is probably the most jungly of all India.

The Mahanadi gorge, however, offers sites for joint hydro-electric/irriga-tion development at Hirakud, Tikarpara, and Naraj (Fig. 133). The first of these sites is already being developed to irrigate 1 m. ac. (mostly in Sambalpur Dt) and to generate 350,000 kW—ultimately! It will be linked with the Pipri (UP) and Tilaya (Damodar) dams and provide power as far as Cuttack and Nagpur. In the S a smaller scheme (100,000 kW) has been initiated, or at least surveyed, on the Machkund River.

(b) *The Cuddapah Ranges and Basins*

Another Gondwana trough lies along the lower Godavari, and for about 100 miles the rampart of hills is completely breached, the plateau breaking down through dissected and forested country to the Godavari/Kistna deltas. Beyond the Kistna (which is in fact superimposed across their tip) lie the most interesting of the En Hills, which from their rocks and position may be collectively styled the Cuddapah Ranges and Basins (Figs. 137, 138).

The region forms a great crescent, the heart of it being the wide Nandyal valley (*c.* 700–800 ft), drained by the Kunderu, formed on Kurnool (L. Vindhyan) limestones and shales and extending from the Kistna/Tunga-bhadra confluence to Cuddapah. To the W this trough is marked off from the Deccan plateaus by the out-facing scarps of the Erramalais/Seschalam Hills/Palkondas, formed of massive quartzites interbedded with slates and lavas; in the S especially the Palkondas, here reaching 3000 ft, form a very fine scarp overlooking the Anantapur-Chittoor basins (Fig. 137). The En limb of the central Kunderu basin is formed by the parallel Nallamalais and

---

[30] Including uncultivated and 'not available for cultivation'.

Velikondas ('outside hills'), 2500–3000 ft high and separated by a beautifully regular development of longitudinal valleys. The evolution of this remarkable drainage-pattern, with its elements of superimposition and of strike subsequents, would make a fascinating geomorphological study; especially notable are the gorges of the Kistna, Penner, and Cheyyuru (Figs. 137, 138). In the E, especially in the Velikondas, the Cuddapah rocks have been subject to great Wwds overthrusting and inversion; the lithology here in-

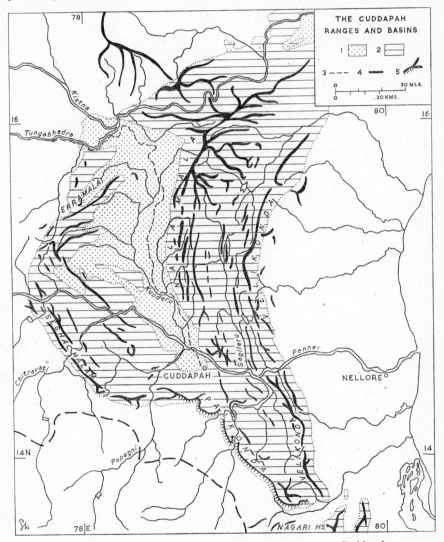

Fig. 137.—THE CUDDAPAH RANGES AND BASINS. 1, Vindhyan; 2, Cuddapah, outcrop; 3, Kurnool–Cuddapah Canal; 4, approx. edge of Mysore plateau; 5, main ridges and scarps.

dicates deposition in shallow but not sheltered waters, and the general lie of the E coast may thus be of great antiquity. The change in strike between the Orissa Hills and the Cuddapahs is very closely followed by the coast.

The hills are wooded and the pattern of relief stands out clearly on forest and population maps (Figs. 18, 30); but the forest is thin, rainfall being only about 40 ins. and the rocks porous or fissured. The few inhabitants are mostly Chenchus, an aboriginal tribe living a semi-pastoral existence eked out by the collection of honey, bamboos, fuel for the railways, and other minor forest produce.

The valleys, however, though on the whole poor enough, have a fair amount of cultivation, mostly jowar (25–30% TSA), other millets, groundnut (16–20%), with some irrigated paddy. The topography in the longitudinal valleys favours the construction of large tanks by bunding a transverse tributary gorge. The main (GIP) Madras–Bombay railway strikes diagonally across the S of the region, and is one of the most interesting traverses in India. The hill country is first entered in the Nagaris, which are the last Cuddapah outliers; here Renigunta and Tirupati are little towns controlling at once the route up the Swarnamukhi, the crossings of the river, and the col to the N between the Palkondas and Velikondas. Beyond, in the Razampeta corridor, the contrast between cultivated floor and barren hills is exceedingly sharp. The generally arid aspect is mitigated by groves of mangoes around the tanks; houses are stone- or mud-walled, and round beehive huts, striped vertically in white and rusty red, attest the Telugu country. After crossing the wide bed of the Cheyyeru, the line emerges at Cuddapah from grey and arid hills into a greyer plain, a vast ash-coloured expanse largely given over to dry cultivation. The region lies on the margin of the October–December rainfall area of the Madras littoral, and the rivers rise in the dry Mysore Maidan, not in the Wn Ghats as do Kistna and Tungabhadra; hence, even in August, the great streams—Penner itself, Cheyyeru, Papagni, Chitravati—may be spreads of quartzite boulders, shingle, or sand, several hundred yards wide with a line of water a yard across, or even not a drop; while only 90 miles to the N the Ghats-fed rivers are full, great ribbons of muddy water half a mile or more wide.

Through the Kunderu valley runs the ill-starred Kurnool Canal, constructed in 1860–76 by a private company which apparently failed to notice the difference in the régimes of Peninsular and extra-Peninsular rivers; the complete, but inefficient, canal had eventually to be taken over by the government in 1882 after two decades of mismanagement. The topographical layout is obviously encouraging, and it is now proposed to recast the whole project, with reservoirs on the Kistna and at Someswaram in the lowest of the Penner watergaps; the project, if carried out in full, would irrigate no less than 3 m. ac., mostly, however, in the coastal plain of Nellore.

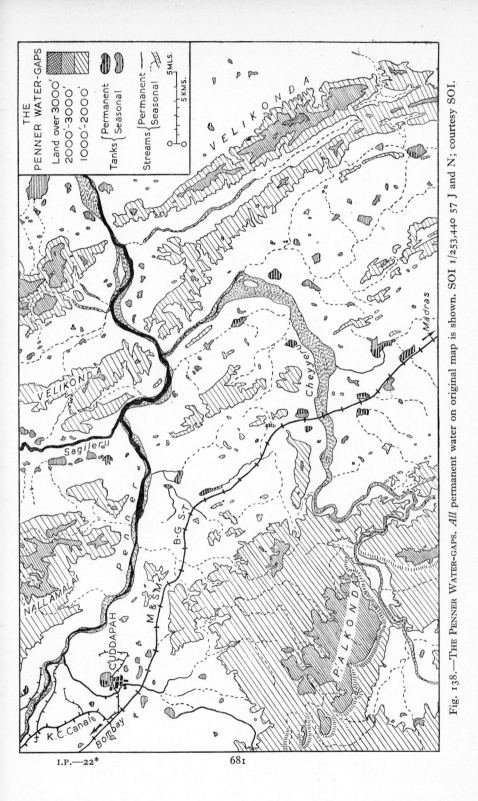

Fig. 138.—The Penner Water-gaps. *All* permanent water on original map is shown. SOI 1/253,440 57 J and N; courtesy SOI.

The mineral wealth of the region is probably considerable in the aggregate, but scattered and not very accessible. It includes unworked copper and antimony; in asbestos and barytes the region produces practically all India's output, but the amounts are only *c.* 1200 cwt. and 1800 tons p.a. respectively. Cuddapah, with a little industry, is the only town of any significance; or was until the selection in 1953 of Kurnool on the Tungabhadra for the capital of the new Andhra State, to consist of the Ceded Districts and the Northern Circars. This selection, against the claims of say Bezwada (below, 691) makes sense only if it is intended eventually to bring in the Telugu portions of Hyderabad. Kurnool has only about 13,000 people; it is perhaps significant that strong opposition came from the left-wing parties. The motivation was perhaps a desire to give the Ceded Districts some token that they would not be neglected.

CHAPTER XXIV

THE EASTERN LITTORAL: ORISSA AND ANDHRA DESA

(Regions XXXIII and XXXIV)

Generalities

THE En Littoral forms a strong contrast to the Wn. The lowland is in general much wider, and much of it is a true coastal plain structurally, with in-facing cuestas developed on Cretaceous and Tertiary epeirogenetic deposits; elsewhere it is formed of the great deltas of the Mahanadi, Godavari, Kistna, and Cauvery. In the S the coastal lowland is no less than 60–80 miles wide, and is backed not by a steep more or less continuous wall but by the broken Tamilnad Hills (Javadis, Shevaroys, etc.) and by the low (1000–1500 ft) plateaus around the middle Cauvery.

The climatic variation on this 1200-mile coast is highly significant. The N lies full in the track of the Bay of Bengal branch of the summer monsoon and receives *c*. 60 ins.; but Sn Orissa already lies on the fluctuant flank of this great current and receives a lower (*c*. 50 ins.) and less reliable fall. As we move S we enter the largest area of anomalous rainfall régime in the sub-continent, the SE which has its rainy season in the months of the retreating monsoon, October–December. From the great bend of the coast S of the Kistna delta this régime is dominant, and the lie of the coast—sub-parallel to the track of the rain-bearing depressions—contributes to generally low figures. The extreme S, Ramnad and Tinnevelly, is sheltered from the Arabian Sea branch by the high Anaimalai/Cardamom block, while to the N the great projection of the Cauvery delta, low-lying as it is, yet shuts off some at least of the retreating monsoon rain. Here we have remarkably low figures (25–30 ins.) for a coastal area in sub-equatorial latitudes.

The agricultural contrasts which would normally result are to some extent masked by irrigation in the great deltas, but are nevertheless striking enough (Fig. 139). Orissa is as typical a paddy-land as Bengal—indeed in Balasore Dt over 95% of TSA is *unirrigated* paddy, and millets are totally absent. S of the Kistna, however, they generally exceed the area of *unirrigated* rice, and in places all rice; paddy dominates the landscape only where irrigation is possible on a reasonably large scale. There is further the difference between tank- and canal-irrigation, the former dominant everywhere away from the deltas.

The primary division, then, is that between the areas of normal and of anomalous season of rain; but this is cut across by the deltas and, in the S especially, there is considerable regional diversity. Culturally also there is the great distinction between the Aryan-speaking (Oriya) lands N of Vizagapatam and the Dravidian S, itself divided into Andhra Desa(Telugu)

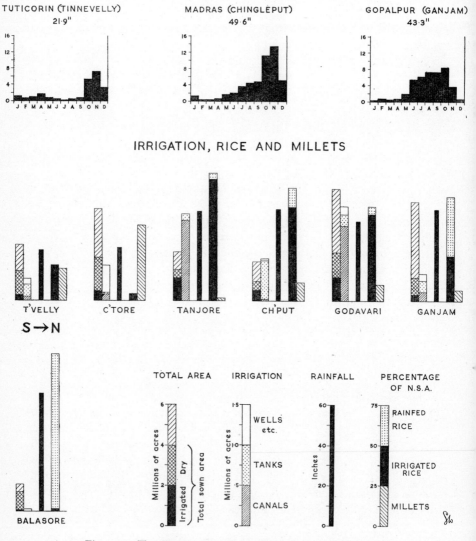

Fig. 139.—THE EASTERN LITTORAL: RAIN, RICE, AND MILLETS.

and Tamilnad, the latter area having the highest development of Dravidian culture. The great quadrant of Tamil country, between the Mysore Plateau, the Sn blocks, and the sea, is indeed very complex; and on the whole it seems best to separate its treatment from that of the rest of the En Littoral, especially as the activities of the Madras Geographical Society enable it to be handled in rather more detail.

With all this in mind the N can be divided as follows:

1. Deltaic Orissa.
2. Northern Circars: (a) Vizagapatam/Ganjam Coastal Plain.
                     (b) Godavari/Kistna Deltas.
                     (c) Nellore Coastal Plain (transitional to Tamilnad).

Deltaic Orissa

Three rivers, Baitarni, Brahmani, and Mahanadi, combine to form a great alluvial salient, 125 miles across the base (Chilka Lake-Balasore) and generally over 50 miles wide. The Mahanadi indeed is one of the most active depositing streams in the sub-continent, and its discharge is extraordinarily irregular—the maximum near its mouth is as large as that of the Ganges, nearly 2,000,000 cusecs, while it has dwindled to 1125. Flood is the greatest hazard of agriculture in Orissa, but the silt is some recompense.

There is the so frequent three-fold division: swampy jungle on the prograding seaface; a zone some 40 miles wide of firm older alluvium; the lateritic shelves on the irregular upland margin. Towards the W there are many outliers of the gneissic hills, which in the Nilgiris of Balasore, and again N of Chilka, reach nearly to the sea. Chilka itself varies in size from 350 to 450 sq mls, and is salty and fresh alternately. Only a few feet deep, it is cut off from the sea by a long spit, on which, and to the S of the lake, is a raised beach 20–30 ft above present flood-level. It is an important fishing ground and a source of thatching reeds.

Rainfall is 60 ins., and the fairly extensive canal-irrigation has never paid its way, being of value essentially as a guarantee against the occasional years of drought. The main headworks are at the head of the Mahanadi delta proper, above Cuttack; the canals were originally designed for navigation as well as irrigation, in order to break down the notorious isolation of the province, which until 1912 was a part of Bengal and thence till 1936 united with Bihar—surely one of the most unnatural administrative groupings ever devised. But the railway destroyed the *raison d'être* of the coastal canal, and the High Level Canal which skirts the landward margin of the plain is of most use as providing some outlet for upland flood water; as Reclus pointed out, control at the debouchment of the valleys is the real essential here.[1] Rice is naturally the dominant crop, its cultivation supporting some 80% of the population of the whole State. Other crops are almost negligible areally, except for jute, the cultivation of which has expanded rapidly since Partition (1938–39, 8321 ac.; 1951–52, 161,340 ac.). Sugar and oilseeds are of local significance. In the three Districts of Balasore, Cuttack, and Puri, which practically correspond to the region, the TSA is about 3·16 m. out of a total area of 5·85 m. ac.; of the cropped area 84% is paddy, or 93% if NSA only is considered.

The region is the heart of Orissa State; its area (9000 sq mls) was under a third of the area of Orissa before state mergers but contained well over half the population—in 1941 these three Districts had 4,562,796 of a total of 8,728,544. Densities are high: Cuttack 536, Balasore 501, Puri 442. Orissa is linguistically one of the most homogeneous of the States of the *Union*, the great majority speaking Oriya; and it is almost solidly Hindu, in the three Districts 95%. But it has always been isolated, as shown for example by the great famine which followed droughts in 1865 and floods in 1866. This took the authorities completely unawares; it is said that one District Commissioner knew nothing of it until he found a starving woman eating his soap. "The only road, leading to Calcutta across a country intersected by large rivers and liable to inundation, was unmetalled and unbridged", and the monsoon practically inhibited import through the few open roadstead-ports. Only with great difficulty were 10,000 tons of rice imported in 6 months; mortality was between a quarter and a third; in Puri Dt at least 36% of the population died. The State is not now so isolated, but despite—or because of?—its homogeneity it remains backward, while the large coolie emigration is an index of its poverty. Industry, except for a few rice and oil mills, is entirely negligible; the first large-scale factory, a cotton mill, was opened only in 1949. Urbanism was only 3·6% in 1941— less than any State except Assam, while that of the hill states was the lowest for any large political unit in All-India, only 2%.

Apart from Cuttack, the only place of any but local note is Puri, where the Jagannath ('Juggernaut') temple is still one of the most famous shrines of India, although the tales of suicides under the great temple car (which has given a journalistic metaphor, happily dead from overwork, to the English language) were almost wholly unfounded.[2] Cuttack itself, at the very head of the Mahanadi Delta, occupies, as Reclus again remarks, what would be an admirable position were the rivers of any use. Its population (**102,505**) is less than that of any Provincial capital except Shillong and

---

[1] E. Reclus, *L'Inde* (1883), 420.

[2] The 'suicides' were probably involuntary, due to pressure of the crowds, and in any case hardly favoured by the priests since they obligated complicated purificatory observances. The cult at Puri is syncretic and includes very ancient, possibly pre-Hindu, features; Reclus (430) gives a vivid but fairly balanced description: "Religion is in fact the great, almost the only, industry of Puri, whose 20,000 inhabitants live directly or indirectly on the exploitation of the Faithful."

Mercara in tiny Coorg, and it is in any case being superseded as the seat of government by a new town at Bhuvaneshwar, 20 miles S of Cuttack.

There may, however, be a brighter future for Orissa. The merger of the hill states increased the area by 85% (to 59,869 sq mls) and the population by 58% (to **14,645,946**); these are the largest gains by merger in all *India*. The ending of the fantastic fragmentation of the State may facilitate co-ordinated development of the Mahanadi power projects and flood control (above, 678); it also gives some hope for the development of the forest resources of the excessively backward hills: timber (floated down the Mahanadi), lac, tussore silk.

The Northern Circars

This region, which corresponds to littoral Andhra Desa, is a transition zone in every respect. In the N we have the normal monsoon rainfall distribution; but the October–December proportion increases steadily in importance Swds, together with a decrease in total amount and in rainy days. Already in Kistna Dt a third of the rain comes in the last quarter of the year, but these rains are more uncertain than those of the more usual monsoon months. In Ganjam Oriya is still dominant, but where the coastal plain narrows beneath the abrupt peak of Mahendragiri (4923 ft) the Aryan tongue gives way to Dravidian Telugu, which holds sway as far as the Nagari Hills (Fig. 127). To the S Nellore represents a further stage in the transition.

Ganjam, Vizagapatam, Godavari E and W, Kistna and Guntur Dts form the Northern Circars, brought under Muslim rule by the Golconda kings about 1575, ceded to the French in 1753; 12 years later the EIC obtained a grant of the whole from the Mogul Emperor, though of course his nominal subordinate the Nizam had exercised what government existed, apart from that of warring petty rajahs; this was the Company's first considerable territorial acquisition outside Bengal. Despite the Telugu culture and the modern historical identity, the region seems to lack unity. The proliferation of small ports and trading stations in the early European phase was perhaps a reflection of this; the Dutch factories at Bimlipatam and Coconada were not ceded to the EIC until 1825, and they had forced the early English settlement at Pulicat to move in 1625 to Armagaon, the parent of Madras. In Masulipatam the factory at French-pettah was not handed over to *India* until 1947, while English-palam and Volanda (Holland)-palam mark the settlements of those nations in the same town. Nizampatam was the first English station on the E coast (1611), and Yanaon (area 5 sq mls, poptn 5711) in the Godavari Delta survives as the last relic of the 18th century French holdings.

The total area is about 25,000 sq mls with a 1941 population of c.

12 m.; densities increase from Ganjam (420) to E Godavari (714) and then decrease to Guntur (393); beyond the regional limits Nellore, with more Archaean terrain than the central parts of the Circars, and less (and less reliable and well distributed) rain than the Nn, had only 204. On the whole it seems best to treat Ganjam/Vizagapatam and the deltas separately.

(a) *The North*: *Ganjam and Vizagapatam* (*Vizakhapatnam*)

Essentially this is the area with over 40 ins.: the three Sn taluks of Vizagapatam fall a little short of this. The lowland narrows to 12 miles under Mahendragiri, but on either side of this gate are the embayments of the Rushikulya (Ganjam) and the Languliya and Vansadhara (Vizag) valleys. The plains are floored by red lateritic soils near the hills, shading off into black loams and clays; but they are cut up by numerous irregular outliers of the En Hills: thus Vizagapatam itself lies between the 1600-ft Kailana Ridge to the N and the 1100-ft Yaroda to the S; the latter runs out to sea in the bold cliffs (300 ft) of Dolphin's Nose which shelters the port, while in the Nn suburbs of the town are the peculiar Waltair Highlands, *c.* 150 ft high and formed largely by the accumulation, since the Pleistocene, of red loams partly fluviatile and partly perhaps aeolian.[3]

Of a TSA of some 4 m. ac., rice accounts for about 1·65 m. ac., ragi 390,000, oilseeds (chiefly groundnut) 500,000, the balance being widely distributed amongst millets and pulses mainly. Irrigation is on the whole unimportant, much of it being dependent on temporary mud-and-brush-wood dams across the short rivers.

Mineral resources are few—graphite, manganese, kaolin, mica—and hardly developed; a potential resource of some interest in this atomic age, though limited in amount in comparison with other *Indian* occurrences, is the ilmenite and monazite in the dunes and beaches around Vizagapatam.[4] Industrial development—with the important exception of the Vizag shipyards—is again negligible: two or three jute and sugar mills in the Vizagapatam plains. Hydro-electric development in the hills might alter this.

Again there is only one real town, 'Vizag' itself (**108,042**), which has developed considerably since the opening of the railway up the Languliya valley to Raipur and the subsequent dredging of a deep-water harbour in the tidal marshes. The accommodation at quayside is limited, but it is more up-to-date than at most E coast ports. The selection of Vizag as the main shipbuilding centre of *India* is presumably because of its situation as the nearest *ocean* port to Jamshedpur, but it is still a long way round. Ships up to 8000 tons have been launched. The hinterland extends to Nagpur and the chief trade is in Madhya Pradesh (CP) manganese, and oilseeds and their products. The small ports of Bimlipatam and Gopalpur are quite

[3] See the very original paper by C. Mahadevan and N. Sathapathi, "The Origin of the Waltair Highlands", *IGJ* XXIV (1949), 26–51.
[4] *Ibid., loc. cit.,* 29.

dead, especially since the cessation of coolie emigration to Burma and Malaya.

(b) *The Deltas*

These, like N Kanara on the W coast, form an 'overlap' region, the breaching of the En Hills by the Godavari and the Kistna leaving the limits in the hinterland indeterminate where the hills virtually disappear for about 100 miles. There is of course a marked break of grade where the rivers cross the line of the hills—the Kistna, as we have seen, is actually superimposed across the Nn end of the Cuddapah Ranges, and here the gradient is $3\frac{1}{2}$ ft or more to the mile, against 7–9 ins. near the sea. Their discharge is of course irregular; it has been estimated that in high flood the Kistna carries enough silt "to cover daily an area of 5 sq mls to a depth of one foot".[5]

[5] *Madras Gaz.* (1908), I. 167.

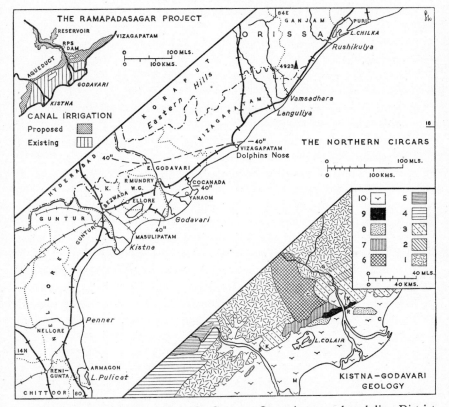

Fig. 140.—ANDHRA DESA: THE NN CIRCARS. On main map, dotted line District boundaries—K, Kistna, WG, W Godavari Dts; all railways ST, BG (thick line) or metre. *Geology*: 1, Archaean gneisses; 2, Charnockites; 3, Khondalites; 4, Cuddapah; 5, Vindhyan; 6, Lower, 7, Upper, Gondwana; 8, Tertiary; 9, Deccan Lava outlier; 10, alluvium. G, graphite; K, kaolin; C, coal (doubtful value); other initials towns, as on main map.

The worn-down margin of the Archaean hinterland is poor country: undulating plains broken by little hills, with much waste and stony ground; soils are mainly lateritic with some loams. The coast for several miles inland is largely fringed with mangrove swamp (valuable as a fuel reserve) or sand-dunes rising to 30 or 50 ft. Between the relatively negative upland and the completely negative coast lie the rather limited areas of true delta. At Bezwada (Vijayarada), 45 miles inland, the Kistna crosses a low gneissic ridge in a 1300-yd-wide gap; this is utilised for the headworks of canals irrigating about 900,000 ac. The Godavari Delta begins 40 miles inland at Dowleshwaram, where a dam $2\frac{1}{4}$ miles long feeds canals for another 1 m. ac. (TSA; NSA 800,000). The deltas are of course liable to flood, at times disastrous; and cyclones are also a danger, that of 1864 causing 30,000 deaths and ruining the prosperity of Masulipatam port for ever. In the Kistna delta the land slopes away from the main distributaries at about 18 ins. to the mile, and in that of the Godavari below Dowleshwaram "the country is a vast expanse of ricefields dotted with gardens and villages. During the rains the greater part of this tract becomes one sheet of water, only village sites, canal banks, roads, and field boundaries appearing above it. Later in the year, as the rice grows higher, the dividing boundaries are hidden; and the whole country looks like a single ricefield, the groves around the villages, the road avenues, and the white sails of the boats gliding along the main canals breaking the uniform sea of waving green crop." [6] There is still a certain amount of local traffic, chiefly paddy, on the canals.

Between the deltas Colair Lake occupies a depression not yet silted up, though constantly diminishing by natural and artificial encroachment; covering about 100 sq mls in the rains, it has at times dried out. Its numerous islands are intensively cultivated, and there is a good deal of fishing.

Rainfall exceeds 35 ins. only in the seaward half of the Godavari Delta, and the tendency to October maxima is unfavourable to the groundnut and early paddy harvests, while cotton sowings must be late. Irrigation, if not essential, is at least highly useful; its importance is reflected in the high densities (up to 1100 plus) of some delta taluks. The following figures (in thousand acres approximately) give a summary view of the agriculture:

	Total area	NSA	TSA	Rice	Total foodgrains	Ground-nuts	Total oilseeds
E Godavari .	3981	1072	1380	692	1070	4	142
W Godavari	1511	800	1111	697	823	42	115
Kistna .	2270	1119	1225	572	877	185	195
Guntur .	3684	2092	2384	400	1405	365	395

[6] *Ibid.*, 268–69.

For the purely delta taluks, of course, the rice proportion would be higher. Tobacco covers some 200,000 ac. in all, the best being grown on temporary sand-islands in the larger streams. Some sugar is grown, but this tall and long-standing crop must be protected from cyclones by expensive fencing with bamboos.

Again mineral potentialities are slight and development slighter. There are two tiny unworked coalfields, of dubious value, in the Gondwanas along the Godavari; graphite and kaolin are worked in a small way, mainly for Rajahmundry paper mills (which use paddy straw as well as bamboo from the hills) and for the small crucible industry at the same town. Salt evaporation at Cocanada might lead to a chemical industry. Industry itself, though very small-scale, is interesting; as well as the Rajahmundry works just mentioned, and the rice and tobacco trades to be expected, there are cement, silk, fruit canning, and vegetable ghee works. Most of these are congregated along the Kistna below Bezwada and between Rajahmundry and Cocanada. Varied as it is, the total is not impressive: the crucible industry has 150 skilled workers, the paper mill a capacity of 3000 tons p.a.; the 77 rice mills in E Godavari employ only 1800 workers, the three silk factories 122; and the total industrial population of this District is only 7200—0·39% of total population, and at that not much below the figure for Madras State (0·42%). Such as it is, this industrial development has yet led to an ominous, if incipient, competition for land in a few tracts between tobacco and paddy; fortunately the region, except for Guntur, has a sizeable rice surplus (about 400,000 tons less 110,000 tons deficit in Guntur); and counting all foodgrains Guntur also has a surplus.[7]

The industrial, and to some extent the agricultural, future of the region will depend on whether or not the great Ramapadasagar multi-purpose scheme is executed; at present financial difficulties stand in the way. The proposed dam, 428 ft high with foundations 190 ft below the river bed, and 1½ miles long, would impound 15·6 m. ac.-ft of water, irrigate for paddy some 2·35 m. ac. of un- or under-developed land, improve the supply to 2 m. ac. already irrigated, and develop at least 100,000 kW; it might also, and less beneficially, trap the silt.

There are a fair number of minor towns. The site-significances of Bezwada (**161,198**) and Rajahmundry (**105,276**) are plain; Guntur (**125,255**) and Ellore (64,911) are trading centres with a little industry. The ports of Cocanada (75,140) and Masulipatam (59,146) are of little use. At Masulipatam large ships must lie 5 miles offshore (weather permitting!) and the half-dozen wharves are three miles up a winding creek; yet in early European days it was a place of great importance, famous for carpets and

---

[7] This discussion is based on (i) Dr. V. L. S. P. Rao's interesting summary of his doctoral dissertation, "Industrial Problems, Development, and Planning [in] ... the Lower Godavari Region" (*IGJ* XXIII (1948), 1–15); (ii) V. V. Ramanadham and V. L. S. P. Rao, *Economic Atlas of Andhra Desa* (Calcutta, 1949).

chintzes. The opening of the coastal railway completed the ruin of the cyclone of 1864; yet it is still generally known as Bandar ('the port'). Cocanada is rather better, with many more wharves and jetties; but again the anchorage is 5–6 miles offshore. The ports might—at large expense— be developed as outlets for En Hyderabad, should that backward area itself be developed; but obviously the actively prograding deltas impose severe difficulties on any reconstruction; at Cocanada constant dredging is necessary to keep a depth of 4–6 ft (LWOST) on the bar. In the great days of the coolie traffic, before the depression and the Indo-Burmese race-riots of the 1930s, Cocanada had an enormous migrant turnover.

(c) *Nellore*

The traditional Sn boundary of the Telugu country lies along the Tiru-patti escarpment, overlooking the Renigunta basin; beyond is Tamilnad, a country, almost a nation, on its own. The transition is reflected in the increasing importance of tank-irrigation, though this will be changed if the Penner is ever fully utilised. Physically also the transition is marked by patches of marine Jurassics and the coastal belt of sub-recent Cuddalore sandstones; both become more important in the Madras coastal plain (Fig. 141).

Most of Nellore is poor country: low peneplains of Archaean gneisses and schists, stony or lateritic and largely covered with scrub. Even allowing for the large part of the District in the Velikondas, agriculture is severely limited. The coast is fringed by a belt of alluvium 2–14 miles wide, between low-level laterites and the blown sand of the shore. The most interesting coastal feature is the great salt-water lagoon of Pulicat; the islands of the lagoon are used for burning lime from the great shell-banks (this is a main source of *chunam* plaster for Madras building) and salt smuggling is or was important.

The Penner and its associated tanks (Fig. 138) are already important for irrigation, and will be more so when the old scheme for an anicut at the Someswaram watergap through the Velikondas is carried out.

Away from the Cuddapah Ranges (above, pp. 678–82), the only mineral wealth consists of laterite, building-stones, the coastal salt and shell-lime, and mica from the Archaean schists: output of mica is about 11,000 tons p.a., rather under 10% of *Indian* production. Nellore (56,315) is almost entirely administrative and commercial; it has a little pottery, but other industrial development is practically absent.

The Circars form the nucleus of the new Andhra State which neverthe-less is to be administered from distant Kurnool. This is the first experiment in "linguistic states", and it can hardly be said that its geographical foundations are very sound or imposing (cf. 126, 675, 682).

CHAPTER XXV

THE EASTERN LITTORAL I: TAMILNAD

(Region xxxv)

THE Tamil country consists of the great quadrant, approximately 50,000 sq mls, lying between the sea and the Deccan plateaus, here well recessed from the coast. This is the "Carnatic" of the 18th-century Franco-British wars.[1] The coastal plain proper extends from the Kistna to Comorin; but as we have seen Nellore is transitional and the Cauvery delta makes a great breach in the continuity of the *emergent* lowland, while the area S of the Cauvery has distinct differences from that to the N. Inland we have the discontinuous Tamilnad Hills, sufficiently distant and distinct from the Mysore plateaus to receive separate treatment; and behind them is the trough which extends from the Cauvery across the Ponnaiyar[2] basin to the Palar; across the middle Cauvery lies the Kongunad or Coimbatore plateau leading up to Palghat.

There is thus considerable regional diversity, and Tamilnad can best be described under six sub-regions:

1. The Coromandel Coastal Plain (Madras hinterland).
2. The Tamilnad Hills.
3. The Ponnaiyar/Palar trough.
4. Kongunad.
5. The Cauvery Delta.
6. The Dry SE:
   (a) Upper Vaigai Basin.
   (b) Madura-Ramnad Tank Country.
   (c) Tinnevelly Black Soil Plain.
   (d) The Tamprabarni Basin and its surroundings.

The distinctive characteristics of the entire region are its Tamil culture and its rainfall régime with most of the rain falling in October–December inclusive; with these goes (in most regions) a great development of tank irrigation. Physically the structure is probably much more complex than the straightforward emergent coastal plain which Cushing took it to be[3];

---

[1] This is a misnomer which will not be used here. The Muslims who overran much of S India after the fall of Vijayanagar extended the term Karnataka from its true seat on the Mysore plateau to include all the S (except Kerala or Malabar); and from them Europeans took over the name, applying it to the land 'below the Ghats'. See *Madras Gaz.* (1908), I. 182–84.

[2] Also known as the S Penner; to avoid confusion Ponnaiyar only will be used here.

[3] S. W. Cushing, "The East Coast of India", *Bulletin of American Geographical Society*, XLV (1913), 81–92.

it is unfortunate that early publication in an authoritative American journal, by a pupil of W. M. Davis himself, has beclouded the active Tamil school of Indian geographers ever since, though some with geomorphological interests (e.g. Dowie, Kalyanasundaram) have dissented. It may well be that the low outer peneplain (*c.* 500 ft) fringing the Tamilnad Hills and the Sn blocks is a plane of marine erosion, and the area more coastward still is undoubtedly an uplifted coastal plain; but Cushing's interpretation is absolutely inadmissible for what may be called the inner peneplains of the Ponnaiyar and upper Vaigai. The marked parallelism between the

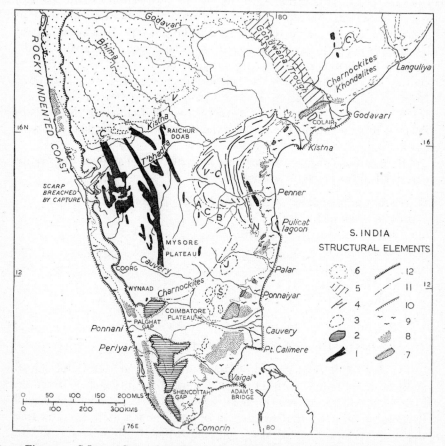

Fig. 141.—S India: Structural Elements. All blank areas undifferentiated Archaean gneisses, etc. 1, Dharwarian synclinoria; 2, Sn Blocks; 3, outliers of higher plateaus; 4, Cuddapah ranges; 5, Gondwana trough; 6, Deccan Lavas; 7, marine Jurassic and Cretaceous, cuestiform on coastal plain; 8, late Tertiary Cuddalore (in E) and Warkallai (in W), shelves or low cuestas with some laterite; 9, alluvium; 10, definitely prograding or emergent shorelines; 11, approx. boundary of Mysore plateau; 12, main Ghats scarp. C, Cuddapah, V, Vindhyan, outcrops. ACB, Anantapur-Chittoor basins; N, Nagari, J, Javadi, S, Shevaroy Hills.

Tamilnad Hills and the Palni/Varushanad trends, with the strong NW–SE and SW–NE lines of the drainage in both areas, certainly call for a general structural explanation.

The Coromandel Coastal Plain

Structural History

This seems a reasonable name for the portion of the coastal plain centred on Madras: Chingleput, most of S Arcot, the E of N Arcot and the N of Trichinopoly Dts.[4] It is a true structural coastal plain, but the geomorphological history is not yet fully worked out. The lowland below 500 ft is 50–60 miles wide and falls into five belts:

   (i) the peneplaned gneisses below the Tamil Hills (250–500 ft);

  (ii) remnants of marine deposits (Cretaceous–?Eocene);

 (iii) the Cuddalore Sandstone/laterite shelf;

 (iv) a young alluvial plain, with embayments behind Madras (Korteliyar/Cooum/Palar valleys) and Pondicherry (Ponnaiyar), with the Vellar basin as a transition to the Cauvery delta;

  (v) the very recent alluvial strandplain, still prograding in places.

Of these (ii) and (iii) are discontinuous; the older rocks come close to the sea S of Madras, where the plain is broken by numerous abrupt Charnockite *inselbergen*, generally 250–500 ft high but reaching 700–800 and trending NE/SW, "the stocks of very ancient folded chains".

The first belt is very probably a marine erosion surface, although this rather facile explanation must be regarded as not quite proven even here and as more than doubtful when extended as far as Cushing takes it. The marine deposits consist of argillaceous or calcareous sandstones, and often carry scrub jungle. The Cuddalores—probably mid-Miocene—have a wider exposure and in S Arcot form distinct cuestas up to 250–300 ft; they are much lateritised and carry a generally xerophytic scrub of euphorbia and bamboo, with palmyra and coconut palms.

The coast follows the main strike of the Deccan Charnockites, with the great change in trend at 16° N. The coarse nature of the outer Velikonda deposits suggests that the general line was early established; from the later Jurassic onwards emergence seems to have been dominant, with of course local and temporary regressions. The embayments of the young alluvial plain often widen out inland, presumably as a result of the filling of

[4] Numerous papers, amongst which may be mentioned: in *JMGA*—N. Subrahmanyam, "The Human Geography of the Post-Tertiary . . . Madras Coast", XI (1937), 275–82; V. D. Krishnaswami, ". . . Prehistoric Man near Madras", * XIII (1938), 58–90; P. G. Dowie, "The Physical Aspects and Geology of the Neighbourhood of Madras", * XIV (1939), 319–402; in *IGJ*—N. Subrahmanyam, "Seasonal Control . . . in the Conjeeveram Region", XVII (1942), 100–09; V. Kalyanasundaram, "The Physical Geography of South Arcot District", XIX (1944), 107–15. Those marked * are especially important.

temporary basins as the consequent drainage was impeded by the slight Cuddalore uplift: this probably accounts for their rich black loams, contrasting vividly with the rusty reds and yellows of the more or less lateritised soils around them.[5] There is, as usual, evidence for both emergence and submergence in the later phases. At Pondicherry the alluvium is over 550 ft thick, and there is archaeological and literary evidence for submergence in the S. Thomé/Mahaballipuram area. On the other hand Krishnaswami has definitely established the following sequence on the Korteliyar (heights from present valley-floor):

main laterite peneplain, 100 ft plus.		.	. Abbeville–Acheulian
60 ft terrace	.	.	.	. Acheulian
20 ft terrace	.	.	.	. Acheulian–Levalloisian
8 ft terrace	.	.	.	. Upper Palaeolithic

The main formation of laterite (100–125 ft peneplain) was the result of an intense pluvial period, and in part at least antedates human settlement in what was probably heavily forested country; Krishnaswami's subsequent pluvials correlate well with de Terra's Kashmir/Potwar glacials. Krishnaswami's work clearly indicates uplift of 100–125 ft since the early Pleistocene.

The 'strandplain' is very narrow, and still being added to by marine and aeolian deposition; the beaches and dunes of Madras, for instance, have grown up as the result of the interruption of longshore drift by the harbour walls. Behind is a lagoon and backwater belt which, except at Pulicat, is very restricted compared with that of Kerala.

Before the 11th century AD the Palar appears to have taken a line well to the N of its present course, perhaps debouching N of Ellore. The Korteliyar, Cooum, and Adyar, misfits in relation to their wide alluvial belts, probably represent old channels of the Palar; the diversion would seem to be the conjoint result of exceptional floods and human interference.[6]

Agriculture

The gneissic fringe has generally red sandy soils, leached and lateritised, with black clays and loams in wetter depressions where oxidisation is inhibited (Fig. 142). The remainder of the region has generally black loams, best in the 'inner' alluvium, e.g. of the Vellar, behind the line of higher Cuddalore terrain in the Capper Hills behind Cuddalore and the Red Hills at Pondicherry. But N of Madras the red soils predominate, and of course the calcareous or sandy Cretaceous–Eocene uplands and the lateritised Cuddalores are very poor. The immediate coastal strip is almost pure sand, often saline.

[5] Cf. Vageler's views (Ch. III, 87–88).   [6] Dowie (1939), 371–81.

The rainfall is less effective than its amount (40–45 ins.) would suggest, as about two-thirds of it is concentrated into three or four months. With taluk densities of 5–700 (even 900 in parts of S Arcot) irrigation is clearly essential to extend the growing season. The rivers contain hardly any water for nine months of the year, and recourse is therefore had to tanks and 'spring channels'; the tanks are fed by the cold-weather rain and by leats taken off from springs and waterholes in the river beds, and these spring-

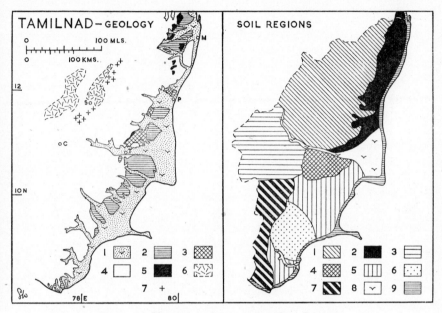

Fig. 142.—TAMILNAD: GEOLOGY AND SOIL REGIONS.

Geology: 1, recent; 2, Cuddalores and laterites; 3, Cretaceous; 4, unclassified gneisses, etc.; 5, U. Gondwana; 6, Charnockites; 7, granites. Initials for Madras, Salem, Coimbatore, Pondicherry, and Trichinipoly.

Soils: 1, red, sandy, leached and lateritised, some black soil in depressions; 2, loamy, black in S to red in N; 3, thin Archaean soils; 4, poor red soils, alkaline in S; 5, red soils, saline in places; 6, black cotton soils; 7, colluvial red loams; 8, alluvium; 9, grey littoral sands.

Adapted from maps by K. Ramamurthy, *IGJ* XXIII (1948); courtesy G. Kuriyan.

channels are independently used for specialised high value crops such as garden produce. Chingleput, the only District entirely within the region, has NSA *c.* 0·75 m. ac., TSA *c.* 1 m., out of a total of nearly 2 m. ac.; of the TSA about 70% is paddy, 11% millets (mainly *cumbu* = bajra), 5% groundnut; but in S Arcot, behind Cuddalore, is one of the great groundnut areas of the State, second only to the Ceded Districts on the Deccan. Forests are negligible, covering about one-eighth of Chingleput with the scrubbiest scrub, mainly used for grazing and even so very poor.

Agricultural rhythms differ notably from those of more normal rainfall régime. In the hot weather (March–May) the country is completely parched and purely agricultural work is at a standstill, except for garden crops, irrigated by wells, jaggery-making, and so on. This is the season for fuel-cutting, building, thatching, work on tanks wells and weirs, pilgrimages, religious plays, and the great games of match-making and marriage. With June's two or three inches of rain the village as it were clears for action: new tenancies are taken out, cattle bought, ploughs repaired.[7] "The half-built house, the half-raised wall, are all left off suddenly to be taken up for completion at the next slack season. The Indian peasant knows instinctively the immense importance of taking time by the forelock so far as cultivation is concerned. . . ."[8] The *kar* paddy crop, and such dry crops as ragi, sesamum, groundnuts, and pulses are now sown, to be harvested in September–October when the real rain begins. Then the main (*samba*) paddy crop is transplanted; harvest is about mid-January—again a marriage season. There remains a short and relatively cool (70–75° F.) season in which another crop may be grown—the third on really good wet land, but more usually the second; this crop of course depends on tanks since the total rain from January through May is not more than 3–4 ins.

Other Activities

The narrow coastal strip has its own life: tree cultures, fishing, salt-making. Coconuts and toddy (palmyra) palms thrive on the sandy soils; the casuarina is grown as the main source of fuel. Remarkably quick-maturing, the tree can yield annually about 5 tons of good fuel-wood per acre; the little plantations have now spread to the sandier soils and laterites inland. The casuarina checks the inland movement of dunes and, where not gleaned by the village women for kitchen kindling, the fallen leaves (like pine-needles) give much-needed humus; the root nodules also add nitrogen. This improvement of the soil may enable an extension of pasture or even dry crops. The men from the tiny fishing-hamlets are adept in the use of their exceedingly primitive log catamarans; most of the catch is dried and salted. At Ennore, just N of Madras, and at several smaller places there are salt-pans; the Pulicat lime-burning has already been noted.

Casuarina fuel, Pulicat *chunam*, salt, dried fish, make up almost all the traffic on the Buckingham Canal, which was constructed piecemeal (1806–82) along the backwaters and reaches 200 miles N of Madras and 60 S. Despite expensive reconstructions after 1880, the Canal is a poor piece of work, unfit for craft drawing over 3 ft, and cost of maintenance has always exceeded receipts. Such as it is, however, it is the main avenue by which these cheap but bulky commodities come to Madras. Mineral

---

[7] The village carpenter, a person of importance in Adi (June–July) becomes unpopular when he has to be paid in kind at harvest in Thai (January–February); as the local proverb has it, "The master-carpenter of Adi becomes the carpenter-boy of Thai."

[8] Subrahmanyam (1942), 106.

resources, apart from laterite, are negligible, if we except the 100-sq-ml lignite area in S Arcot. This is estimated to contain 500 m. tons.[9]

Conjeeveram (74,635) has already been described (Ch. VII); Cuddalore (60,632) is the usual creek-and-roadstead port, with an important trade in groundnuts and some associated industry (oil-pressing etc.); Saidapet (41,347) is simply an outer suburb of Madras. Away from the coast Vellore (**106,024**) has nodal advantage, where the Palar route around the N of the Tamil Hills is crossed by a N/S piedmont route; its main importance is as a grain mart. The coast is dotted with decayed relics of early European activity—Armagon, Pulicat, Fort St David, Porto Novo; of these Pondicherry alone retains some importance simply by historic accident: it is doubtful whether it would have been developed had it been under the same political jurisdiction as Madras.

Pondicherry, largest of the French possessions, has an area of 113 sq mls divided into about 16 fragments; there is, or was, even a village held jointly by British and French India; with such a 70-mile frontier, it is probable that smuggling contributed largely to the flourishing trade. The chief cash crop of the territory and its hinterland is groundnuts, exported to Marseilles; the town "also exploits its political connections. Its most important manufacturing enterprise . . . exported yarn to the hand-loom weavers of French Indo-China, and coloured cloths to Madagascar, in each case getting the benefit of free entry into a protected market."[10] There are also small foundries and rolling-mills using scrap. There is a 300-yd-long pier, and ships can anchor within 2–300 yds of it.

About a quarter of the 205,000 inhabitants of the territory live in the town itself, which contrasts remarkably with the standard Euro-Indian urban type. Most of the Indian workers live in the outlying villages; Pondicherry town, closely but regularly built, is largely French or at least Gallicised, an enclave of Mediterranean culture. Its political future is at present uncertain, though there can be little doubt of its eventual union with *India*.

MADRAS

Madras [11] (Fig. 143) was the third city of India (777,481) in 1941, and retains its position, nearly doubling by 1951 to **1,416,056**. Strictly speaking its site has no advantages whatever, except that its position

[9] It was reported in *India News* (15/7/50) that the field would be exploited without interruption by sinking 100 artesian wells, which would also irrigate 3000 ac. For *exploited* read *explored*?

[10] G. Slater, *Southern India* (1936), 162–64.

[11] This section is based largely on personal observation, but the following papers may be mentioned: in *JMGA*—G. C. Armstrong, "Madras Harbour", V (1930), 16–22; N. Subrahmanyam, "Some Aspects of the Growth of Greater Madras", XIII (1938), 22–31; G. C. Armstrong, "The Port of Madras", XIV (1939), 146–54; P. S. Loganathan, "The Industries of Madras", *ibid.*, 155–63; G. Kuriyan, "The Distribution of Population in the City of Madras", *IGJ* XVI (1941), 58–70. The description in the *Madras Gaz.* (I. 497–521) is very good and by no means entirely out of date.

midway between Penner and Ponnaiyar probably counts for something. But in the general setting of early English activity along this coast some commercial and administrative centre was bound to develop, and any site once developed was bound to maintain its position since, if it had no special values itself, no possible rival had any either, and a going concern had a certain pre-emption. But it is obviously and solely a matter of history that Madras is to-day more important than Pondicherry.

There were, it is true, two very local factors which may have influenced Francis Day in his choice in 1639: the Cooum creek, capable of taking ships up to 50 tons burden, and the defensive values of a shallow lagoon paralleling the coast about a mile inland. But later in the 17th century East Indiamen already ran up to 1500 tons or more, and half a dozen places offered similar site values, though some, such as Porto Novo, were already taken up by Portuguese or Dutch. The really decisive factor seems to have been nothing more nor less than the cheapness of local cloth.[12]

The city owed its earlier importance to the opportunities of the Franco-British conflict in the Peninsula; even so, while it was far from being an isolated laggard like Bombay, it is significant that Calcutta—the gateway to really profitable aggrandisement—supplanted Madras as the nerve-centre of British power as early as 1773, only 15 years after Plassey and the first serious territorial acquisitions. Nevertheless, at the first Census in 1872 Madras was returned as the fifth city of the British Empire.[13] It is astonishing that this position was attained by a port of which the "facilities" were a jetty and a roadstead, from which most passengers and goods were landed by not too safe surf-boats. Nor has industry ever been of much significance.

The morphology of Madras, if such it can be called, is as bizarre as its development. The city area was unchanged from 1798 until 1923, when a small extension was made. Within its 30 sq mls the 1941 density was only about 40 per acre, very unequally distributed: ward densities in 1931 were from 175 per acre down to 11; since at least 1921 increment has been most rapid on the periphery, but the centre remains congested. Such a distribution implies gaps in the building pattern, and in fact Madras is rather a congeries of more or less contiguous suburbs and even rural villages than a city; Georgetown apart it might almost be called, in Robert Graves' phrase, the suburbs of itself. It is not only an absence of planning, but almost an absence of structure.

There is a nucleus: Fort St George and Georgetown. The Fort is typical 18th-century work and contains the Secretariat, barracks, and so on, as well as the oldest Anglican church in India (St Mary's, 1678–80). On the landward side is an irregular maidan, with courts, colleges, and hospitals

---

[12] C. S. Srinivasachariar, *JMGA* XIV (1939), 134–35.
[13] In thousands: London 3254, Calcutta 795, Bombay 644, Liverpool 493, Madras 398 Manchester 351, Birmingham 344.

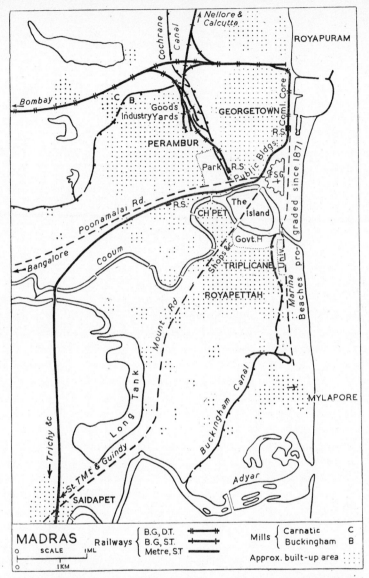

Fig. 143.—MADRAS. Crosses indicate St Mary's Church (Fort) and St Thomas's Cathedral (Portuguese, Mylapore). Ch'pet = Chintadripet; St T. Mt = St Thomas's Mount; F.S.G., Fort St George.

skirting it. Georgetown [14] is close-built, but on fairly regular lines and contains some modest but not unattractive building, mostly *chunam*, with the commercial core facing directly onto the harbour. Georgetown and the

[14] Previously Blacktown, renamed in 1906 in honour of the visit of the then Prince of Wales.

Fort are marked off from the rest by the Cochrane Canal (the first section of what became the Buckingham Canal) and the meandering Cooum, which except in November–December is a foul green backwater. Beyond lies the sprawl. W is the suburb of Egmore, cultural and residential, the ribbon-development along the Poonamalai Road, and industrial Perambur, with the famous Buckingham and Carnatic cotton mills.

The Cooum Island is open development—parade-grounds and clubs—and to the S are the Government House grounds.

S of the Cooum, for the three or four miles to the Adyar, is an extra-ordinarily mixed area: Chintadripet is an unbelievably squalid slum, and yet more village than town; Triplicane simply a normal Indian provincial town; Royapettah an agglomeration of pleasant old-fashioned small-town bungalows. Mount Road, the main axis, runs from Government House to St Thomas's Mount, through the anarchically developed suburb of Saidapet (headquarters of Chingleput Dt) and Guindy, with the race-course,[15] another Government House, and various clubs. In the central part of Mount Road is the main shopping, hotel, and cinema area. The Gazetteer's description of 1908 is still largely valid: ". . . anything but typically urban in appearance. Most of the roads of this part run through avenues, and are flanked by frequent groves of palms and other trees; the shops in the wide Mount Road, though many of them are imposing structures, often stand back from the street with gardens in front of them; the better residences are built in compounds which have almost the dignity of parks; and rice-fields frequently wind in and out between these in almost rural fashion." This extraordinarily open development, as compared with Calcutta and Bombay, is probably a function of unimpeded terrain and cheap land.

The Sn suburbs are historically interesting. St Thomas's Mount is the reputed site of the martyrdom of the Apostle, and here a Christian (Nestorian) inscription has been found, written in Pahlavi, probably of the 8th century. The existing church on the summit of the Mount is Portuguese (1547), as is the great church at Mylapore (Ptolemy's Meliapuram) where the reputed tomb of the Apostle may be seen; Mylapore has still some Lusian connections.

Although Madras was more nearly dependent on trade alone than most cities of its rank, nothing was done to provide it with a harbour until 1871, when the great breakwaters were begun, replacing the old iron jetty. Originally the harbour entrance faced E, straight out into the Bay, and in 1910—only 20 years from completion—it was found necessary to shift it to the NE, mainly to avoid shoaling. As late as 1904 conditions were almost fantastically primitive.[16] The present facilities are inadequate for a great

---

[15] Now fallen on evil days; the present governing class is decidedly Puritanical.
[16] For a vivid description see Armstrong (1930), 20.

port, with room for only 12–15 large ships in the harbour (and only 7 of these berths are actually alongside the wharves) and some 16 ac. of warehouse accommodation. But large extensions are planned. The import trade is very miscellaneous, Madras being the great entrepôt for S India; exports include groundnuts, hides, raw and manufactured cotton. Cochin is already proving a rival, and Madras is far behind Bombay and Calcutta.

Industrially also Madras is outstripped not only by Bombay and Calcutta, but by several towns within the State, such as Madura and Coimbatore. Yet the Madras government was far in advance of the Centre and of other Provinces in its encouragement of indigenous manufacturing, starting an aluminium utensils industry, for instance, as early as 1906.[17] Private enterprise also made an early start; the Buckingham and the Carnatic Mills date from 1874–83 and have been among the most progressive in India. These two are the only cotton mills in Madras (there were four in 1911) and employ about 11,000 workers—the largest single organised industry. A feature of their policy is that recruitment is mainly from the children of employees, and this stable labour force is probably a factor in the high reputation of the product.

The simple fact is, of course, that Madras is not well placed as regards either raw materials or (unless and until linked with Mettur) power. Assembly and small consumption factories are spreading, in the city itself or in satellites within 20 miles or so: matches, chemicals, glass, pencils, and so on. Leather is important, though tanning is not allowed within the city itself: the large factory at Chromepet owes its existence to the initiative of the provincial Department of Industry in experimenting with chrome tanning, and there are perhaps 200 more indigenous tanneries. Among the crafts handloom weaving (especially *lungyis* for overseas Bay of Bengal markets) and *bidi*-making are notable. *Bidis* are accurately described by Loganathan as "tobacco dust rolled into a cigarette-like thing", and as the poverty of the Indian masses compels production at the cheapest possible rate, it is not surprising that *bidi*-making is one of the most sweated occupations in the world. "No adult worker can hope to earn a living wage even by working 12 hours a day," and the manufacture is carried on almost entirely by boys in a multitude of tiny sweat-shops. There are, of course, the usual metropolitan trades: foundries and workshops (the largest those of the M&SM Rly at Perambur), minor metal crafts, and printing. Current innovations include motor assembly plants at Ennore and at Vandalop, 20 miles to the W. But the sum total of Madras industry, except perhaps for tanning, is not impressive.

This account has perhaps over-stressed the negative aspects of the city's life: there are others. Electrification of the local railways has led to some

---

[17] The deliberate suppression of this initiative in the interests of *laissez-faire* is described in Slater, 33–39.

good suburban development, especially to the SW whence come most of
the commuters. The inner Wn suburbs are for the most part depressing,
and the most degrading poverty is terribly apparent in places like Chintadripet, divided from cultured Egmore merely by the Cooum. Yet there
is space as well as scope for rehabilitation; "congestion is not due to
scarcity of land but to failure in providing for an ordered city growth,"
and here there are at least signs of change. Above all Madras is the conscious centre of modern Dravidian culture, especially of course Tamilian;
about two-thirds of the people speak Tamil, one-fifth Telugu, and English
is widespread. There are no keener or more cultured intellects in the
world than those of many Madrassi Brahmins, and educationally Madras
is a centre of the first rank; the city which has produced a statesman like
Rajagopalichariar, a mathematician like Ramanujan, is no mean city,
whatever it may look like. The Indo-British architecture (as usual when the
PWD goes gay) indulges in a profusion of comic cornices and futile volutes,
but the colleges of the University along the Marina (the old seafront now
faced by wide prograding beaches) are not unworthy of their setting. With
all its muddle and (as compared with Bombay, Calcutta, or Delhi) its air
of provincialism, Madras is perhaps a more likeable and more liveable-in
city than any of the three; its charm is odd and irritating, but charm none
the less.

The Tamilnad Hills

Between Palar and Cauvery the coastal plain is backed by a discontinuous
line of highland, made up of small but bold hill-masses of which the chief
are the Javadis, Shevaroys, Kalrayans, and Pachaimalais (Fig. 144). There
seems to be no collective name for them, and 'Tamilnad Hills' seems
reasonable. N of the Palar smaller and even more broken hills link up with
the tail of the Cuddapahs in the Nagari Hills; across the Cauvery further
detached massifs N of Madura lead on to the long Varushanad-Andipatti
Range and so to the Cardamoms. Behind this disjointed wall lie the inner
plateaus of Tamilnad, in the Palar/Ponnaiyar trough, the mid-Cauvery
valley, and the upper Vaigai embayment. This layout is itself suggestive,
and it will be convenient to take up here some of the structural relations
hinted at in the opening of this chapter (Fig. 141).

The more prominent ridges in the hills are usually Charnockites,
"intruded as sills along the foliation planes of the older gneisses"; the
general strike is NNE/SSW, as shown e.g. in the remarkably straight and
wall-sided Cheyyur/Agaram through-valley which bisects the Javadis and
appears to mark the line of weakness of the Charnockite/gneiss contact.
These NNE/SSW trends are cut across perpendicularly by other structure-
lines, seen in the parallel courses of the Palar and Ponnaiyar and many of
their tributaries down the Mysore Ghat. Similar alignments are seen on

the Vaigai/Periyar watershed, far to the S (Fig. 150), while the Cauvery
between Sivasamudram and Erode swings from one trend to the other in
great right-angles. It is probably significant that the middle Palar, the
section of the Cauvery below Hagenakal Falls, with the tributaries entering at each end of this section, and the upper Bhavani all lie in the same
straight line (A–B on Fig. 144). The whole pattern, on both the Mysore
Ghat and the Cardamom flanks, strongly suggests control by reticulate
faults—macro-jointing, as it were.

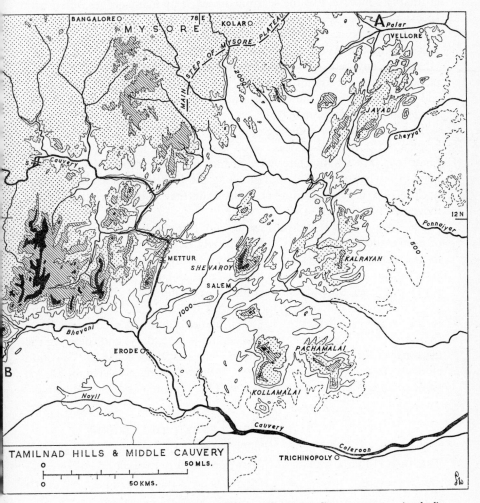

Fig. 144.—The Tamilnad Hills and Middle Cauvery. Contours at 500 (pecked),
1000, 2000, 3000, 4000 ft (2–3000 stippled, 3–4000 shaded, over 4000 black). Mettur
Lake cross-hatched. J, Jalarpet gap; S, Sivasamudram; H, Hagenakal Falls. SOI 1/1M
57, 58; courtesy SOI.

I.P.—23

W of the middle Palar the Mysore Ghat descends in a series of steps, from a general level of 3000 ft plus through a broad shelf at *c*. 2250 ft. Both the Ghat scarps and the line of the Javadis have in general straight trends, and the Tamilnad Hills have flattish surfaces at heights comparable with those of the plateau. All this suggests a former contiguity of plateau and outlier, a contiguity now disrupted by rift-faulting. There is also some evidence of faulting on the SE faces of the Shevaroys, Nilgiris, and Palnis; as we have seen, in the last two Wadia thinks in terms of horsts. There is the further point that the valleys above and below the Mysore Ghat are at least late mature, but the scarp is dissected by many gorges, often with spectacular falls. Kalyanasundaram [18] very reasonably suggests that this feature must be at least post-Cretaceous, and it is tempting to go on to link it with the Arabian Sea subsidence and the formation of the Wn Ghats. At any rate it is clear enough that Cushing's theory of marine planation cannot account for the inner plateaus—the steep Ghat is stepped [19] and would have been the cliff of a narrow land-locked sea, to which it is altogether disproportionate.

The Tamilnad summits are generally rather higher than the opposite heights of the Mysore Plateau: 3600–3800 ft in the Javadis, 5–5400 in the Shevaroys. The Charnockites were formed at greater depths than the main mass of Archaean gneisses, but all along the E of the Peninsula the charnockite zone is relatively higher. This again may point to relative vertical movement.

The steep flanks of the hills are usually forested, but within this girdle of jungle the plateaus carry a surprisingly large agricultural population: in the Shevaroys [20] Yercaud taluk (practically equivalent to the main plateau) had a density of 289 on its 60 sq mls, and only 2–3000 of the 17,000 people were in the tiny hill-station of Yercaud itself. The Malayalees (= 'hillpeople'; not to be confused with the Malayalams of Kerala) are mainly agriculturalists, growing ragi, cholam, gram, oilseeds, and fruit; there is some terraced rice. Cattle-keeping is secondary, and there are the usual minor forest products, including some sandalwood and lac. The mild climate (range *c*. 60–87° F.) with its good rain (128 ins. at Yercaud) has led to a certain amount of coffee-growing. There is some unexploited bauxite.

The Ponnaiyar/Palar Trough and Salem [21]

The general limits of the trough between the Mysore Ghat and the Tamilnad Hills are well defined, but in the S the area around Salem raises

---

[18] "Some Aspects of the Physical Geography of the North Arcot District", *IGJ*, XVIII (1943), 204–12.

[19] The question of the origin of all the peneplains as erosion surfaces is obviously a different issue from the simple one presented by Cushing.

[20] V. Natarajan, "The Shevaroys Region", *JMGA* XI (1936), 162–73.

[21] Based mainly on 11 papers in *JMGA* XI (1936), No. 2.

difficulties. It might well be better to link the plateau [22] around Salem with that of Coimbatore and the Palghat across the Cauvery; but on the whole the river seems to make a marked divide from an economic if not from a physical point of view, and the links of Salem are mainly to the N and E.

The geomorphological relationships of the region have been indicated in the preceding section; it may be added that the Palar originally flowed out to the S, by the broad col at Jalarpet into the Ponnaiyar. In general the region is a plateau, known as the Baramahal, at about 1300 ft, sinking in the S to *c.* 1000 ft; here it is separated, as we have admitted rather arbitrarily, from the Coimbatore plateau by the Cauvery. To the W Dharmapuri and Krishnagiri taluks of Salem Dt lie on a shelf (1500–2250 ft) below the main Ghat steps, while in the NE the Palar valley widens out and falls below 1000 ft: Vellore, as a typical contact town, may be taken as the limit here.

Climate and Agriculture

Shut in as the region is, the rainfall of 30–33 ins. is at least as much as can be expected. Where it opens out to the S Salem town gets 39 ins. with a puzzling distribution:

J.	F.	M.	A.	M.	J.	J.	A.	S.	O.	N.	D.
0·3	0·3	0·5	1·8	4·7	3·0	3·8	6·8	6·6	6·7	3·7	1·0

This is very clearly not a typical SE Littoral régime; but the area is not particularly open to Arabian Sea influences since, as we shall see, the effect of the Palghat Gap is much more narrowly restricted than might be expected. Mean temperatures at Salem range from 76 (December–January) to 98° F (April), and humidity is always relatively low (72% April, 81% October). Soils are generally red and sandy but on the whole not infertile: soil wash from the Ghat slopes is probably responsible for this.

Rainfall is not too reliable, but only about 14% of the cultivated area of Salem Dt is irrigated, 80% of the irrigation being equally divided between small tanks and wells. The ingenious device known as the *kabalai* is widely used here and elsewhere in the Tamil country. This consists of a large leather bucket ending in an open tube; when the bucket is drawn up the tube discharges directly into the irrigation channel. The advantage of this is that both filling and emptying are automatic, and only one man is needed, to drive the bullock, against two with the *mhote* of N India, one of whom has to control the bucket.[23] This is essentially a dry crops area: the three main millets are the staple food crops, rice being really important only

---

[22] Or peneplain; probably intensive geomorphological work would disclose several erosion surfaces extending from Comorin to the Penner and beyond, now made discontinuous by the erosion of the main valleys and probably vertical movements. But in the absence of serious fieldwork (except in very limited areas) it is perhaps better to be non-committal and to speak of plateaus as it were *ad hoc* and without any genetic implications. More agenda!

[23] For a fuller description see Slater, *Southern India,* 76–77; and cf. Fig. 89 in C. D. Forde, *Habitat, Economy, and Society* (1931 ed., p. 269).

towards the margins of the region—where the Palar opens out and on the Sn flanks of the Tamilnad Hills. In the S, around Salem, groundnuts and some cotton are grown. An interesting feature is the intrusion of the Telugu-speaking Reddis along the Ghats margin; these are skilled tank cultivators, perhaps especially for ragi, and appear to have worked along the piedmont even across the Cauvery into Madura.

On the shelf below the main Mysore Ghat much land is still under forest, mostly rather open and used mainly for grazing. This is geographically, and perhaps historically, an offshoot of the famous cattle-breeding of Mysore; the Dharmapuri/Krishnagiri cattle markets are the main source of heavy draught animals for an area stretching from Malabar to Chittoor, while the best animals are sold as far afield as Madura and Tinnevelly as coach bullocks. "The breeding herds live on the forests for the greater part of the year, where they are kept in pens at night time. They are brought back to the village at harvest, when the harvested fields provide grazing for some time, and the cattle supply the necessary manure for the succeeding ragi-crop. . . . The breeders . . . cannot be considered as ryots. They . . . certainly grow crops for their own requirements, but by profession they are breeders of cattle, dependent on the sale of their calves for their livelihood. . . . A good number of the breeding bulls . . . live in a semi-wild state."[24]

Minerals

Gold, mica, corundum, and copper occur here and there on the flanks of the Mysore Plateau, but the most important mineral deposits are around Salem town. Large quantities of magnetite iron ore are found in the Kollamalais and Talamalais (Sn outliers of the Pachamalais); nearer Salem in the isolated 3200-ft-high Kanjamalai to the SW and Godumalai to the E; and in the conical Tirthamalai (3500 ft) rising sharply out of the outer (Coromandel) peneplain just S of the Ponnaiyar Gap. In all these little mountains the massive magnetite beds stand out from the gneissic country rock; the Fe content varies (apparently) from 30 to 70%; limestone is available. These deposits are interesting as providing the basis of one of the EIC's few displays of economic initiative. Talus from the slopes had been immemorially worked in primitive furnaces, and in 1826 Josiah Heath set up extensive works, powered by bullocks and fuelled by charcoal; the foundries were at Porto Novo. The Madras jetty was built of Salem iron; but irrigation obstructions on the Cauvery (used for transport) and the exhaustion of the more accessible forest made success impossible, and a long history of failure ended in 1867: though projects for revival were under consideration as late as 1925.[25] Unless hydro-electricity can be used

---

[24] R. W. Littlewood, "Alambady Cattle", *JMGA* XI (1936), 126–29.

[25] The Madras pier was sold for scrap to the Pondicherry rolling-mills, and this suggested the last scheme, which involved electrical concentrating on the Cauvery and the co-operation of Schneiders. For details see Slater, 81–84, and *JMGA* IX (1934), 104–07.

for at least preliminary smelting, Salem cannot hope to compete with Jamshedpur.

Corundum is still worked to some extent, and steatite (used locally for pots and exported as a refractory) is obtained from some of the hills. Far more important is magnesite; the 'Chalk Hills' between Salem and the Shevaroys contain large quantities (c. 90 m. tons?) of this ore, 95% $MgCO_3$ and easily worked open-cast. The demand for magnesia in paper, glass, pharmacological, alloy, and plastic industries is increasing, and the Salem deposits are the second most important source in the Commonwealth, with an output of 40–50,000 tons.

Communications and Towns

Despite its girdle of hills, the region has been far from isolated historically. The Baramahal ('twelve forts' or palaces, and by extension administrative areas) represents the farthest Muslim advance after the destruction of Vijayanagar: and in the 18th century this was a debatable land between the rising British power and the new and very virile dominion of Haidar Ali and Tipu Sultan in Mysore: sweeping down the Ghat and through the gaps in the Tamilnad Hills, especially the remarkable break by which most of the drainage of the region leaves it via the Ponnaiyar, Haidar exploited to the full his advantages of mobility and local knowledge. To the British the Nn entry, by the Palar, was the most important as nearest to the Madras base; hence the significance of Clive's defence of Arcot and that of Vellore in 1780–82.

Salem (**202,235**) increased by 287% in 1921–51; it is rapidly developing as a textile centre, powered by Mettur and Pykara. The Attur gap (1250 ft) between the Kalroyans and the Pachamalais gives easy access to the coast.

THE CAUVERY VALLEY

The Cauvery (Fig. 145) is physically, perhaps, the most remarkable river of the Peninsula; its delta presents some extremely distinctive physical and human features; its power is a main factor in the remarkable recent growth of the Tamilnad towns. It is thus intimately associated with the life of all its border regions, and we may break off the regional description to look at its basin as a whole, and to gather up the scattered notices of hydro-electric development in Sn India, on the whole the part of the sub-continent most advanced in this use of water.

The Cauvery is not a large river by Indian standards, only about 475 miles long and draining about 28,000 sq mls. Above the great Krishnarajasagar reservoir, 12 miles from Mysore city, it is simply a rocky mountain stream; below it becomes increasingly important as an aid to cultivation. Just above the confluence of the Shimsha, the main left-bank tributary, the Cauvery crosses the 2000-ft contour at Sivasamudram Island, on either side of which is a succession of falls and rapids with a total drop of 320 ft; the wider fall "in the rainy season pours over the hillside in an unbroken sheet a quarter of a mile wide". [26] At Sivasamudram the first fair-sized hydro-electric plant in India was installed as early as 1902. Below the island the river plunges through a succession of wild gorges, with right-angle bends conforming to the NW/SE and SW/NE stresses of the plateau-edge; the Hagenakal Falls (70 ft) may be taken as the end of its plateau course. There is, however, another narrow straight gorge, W of Salem, and this provides the emplacement for the Mettur Dam. Mettur was the first combined power and irrigation project in India (1925–34) and its dam is one of the world's largest: the river here was 1100 ft wide, the dam itself is 5300 ft long and 176 ft high, impounding a 60 sq ml lake of 93,500 m. cubic ft capacity.

The Cauvery now enters its plains course, the 500-ft contour being crossed between the Bhavani confluence and Erode: the Bhavani and its tributary the Moyar drain the Nilgiris, and on their Nn flank is the Pykara power station, shortly to be extended by an installation on the Moyar; Mettur and Pykara are the main links in the expanding S Indian grid.

A few miles above Trichinopoly the river bifurcates around another sacred island, Srirangam, the Nn (Coleroon) branch being the larger. From here on is deltaic country, mainly in Tanjore Dt, which has been irrigated since at latest the 11th century, when the Chola kings constructed the Grand Anicut—a mass of masonry 1080 ft long and 40–60 broad. The Mettur Dam was projected primarily to add to the delta irrigation, but it has not perhaps been entirely satisfactory from this point of view, and its power function is equally important (Fig. 145).

The Cauvery basin indeed accounts for about two-thirds of the hydro-electricity generated in S India. Apart from the relatively small Shimsha plant (12,000 kW) the main installations, with their 1945 installed and potential capacities in thousand kWs, are:

	Installed	Potential
Sivasamudram (Mysore) . .	42	45
Pykara (Madras) . . .	44	69
Moyar (Madras/Mysore) . .	—	36
Mettur (Madras) . . .	37·5	50
	123·5	200

Sivasamudram was developed in the first place to power the Kolar Gold Fields, 92 miles away—an immense transmission distance for 1902—and

[26] *Madras Gaz.*, I. 175.

to light Bangalore. Of the total Mysore power, nearly 90% is devoted to industry—with a strong sector in decentralised light industry and an agricultural demand which in 1945 was estimated to be increasing by 1700 HP a year.[27] Pykara (1932) led to an immediate development of textiles and cement at Coimbatore, with some as far as Madura; this station also serves the Nilgiri tea factories, and already in 1941 there were 2200 irrigation pumps in Coimbatore Dt. At Erode Pykara and Mettur are linked; a light

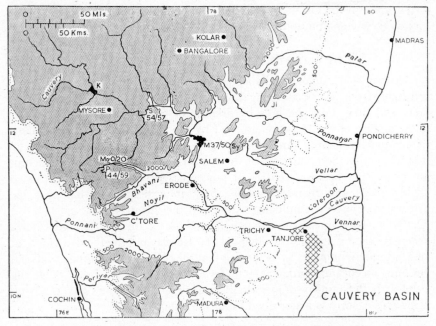

Fig. 145.—THE CAUVERY BASIN AND POWER DEVELOPMENT. Black, reservoirs; crosshatched, new Mettur irrigation. Figures indicate actual/potential hydel in 1000 kWs. K, Krishnarajasagar; P, Pykara; M, Mettur; Mo, Moyar; S, Sivasamudram; Ji, Javadis; Sy, Shevaroys. Shimsha (12,000 kW) included in Sivasamudram figures; later figures for Shimsha and Mettor potential are 51,000 and 36,000 kW.

industrial estate has grown up at Mettur itself, which also supplies Trichinopoly (textiles, cement, rail-shops), Salem and small towns in Salem Dt (textiles), and Negapatam (rolling-mills); lighter lines go as far as Vellore. Wide fluctuations in the Cauvery discharge to some extent limit the regular supply from Mettur, but this is being remedied by the integration with Pykara and ultimately of the resources of the hills S of Palghat, which include Pallivasal (Travancore; installed 21,000 kW, potential 36,000) and Papanasam (Tinnevelly; 21,000 and 28,000).

Altogether Sn India has a probable potential of the order of 1,000,000 kW (Madras 500, Mysore 300, Travancore 200 thousand), of which only

[27] G. Kuriyan, *Hydro-Electricity in India: A Geographical Analysis* (Madras, 1945), 32.

20–25% is as yet developed; thermal sources account for about 50,000 kW, about 20% of total, but this proportion is declining, and the hydro output is expected to be doubled by 1954–55.

The results have been especially notable in the growth of the four great Tamilnad towns, Coimbatore, Salem, Madura, Trichinopoly. Of perhaps even greater importance in the long run are the possibilities of rural electrification for wells, sugar-crushing, and (in Kerala) drainage. Again, in view of the complete absence of coal in S India, and the obvious dangers of burning up the forests as loco fuel, the possibility of railway electrification is receiving attention.[28]

The Coimbatore Plateau and Palghat

Between the Cauvery and Palghat lies an extensive low plateau, rising gradually from 400–600 ft along the river to 1200–1500 in the W, and broken here and there near the hills by granitic or gneissic monadnocks.[29] The individuality of the region is attested by the survival of its ancient name Kongunad—roughly Coimbatore Dt and SW Salem; but it was never an historic entity. Some at least of the reasons for this are perhaps inherent in its location between centres of power based on intensively-cultivated paddy-plains and themselves less open; it is significant that near the Amaravati-Cauvery confluence three of the greatest and most stable Dravidian kingdoms marched together: those of the Cholas and Cheras who gave their names to Coromandel and Kerala, and the Pandya kingdom of Madura. Significant also is the fact that the place-name ending -*palayam*, meaning an encampment, occurs no fewer than 94 times in Erode taluk, the gateway both from Mysore via the Ponnaiyar, and from the Cauvery Delta. This area again was a storm-centre in the Anglo-Mysorean wars.

Relief and Climate

The topography is simple enough. In the W the broad Palghat sill is eaten into by the Ponnani headwaters, and from the watershed three rivers, each about 100 miles long, drain very mature valleys into the Cauvery. Of these the Bhavani and the Amaravati,[30] drawing from the rainy heights of the Nilgiris and the Anaimalais, are fairly perennial, though the Amaravati gets very low towards the main river. Between these two, however, the Noyil (or Noyyal) is dry for most of the year, with practically no water in its lower course and little in its middle: it rises in a horseshoe of hills W

---

[28] The difficulties of both water- and fuel-supply are illustrated by an incident—clearly a routine one—at Sidhout in the Cuddapahs in May 1945, when the writer saw 20–30 women collecting water in brass pots from an engine tender, and paying for it at the rate of one billet of wood per pot. The wood was quite likely taken from railway piles anyway, but not all got their water, and it was a pathetic business to watch.

[29] This section is based mainly on 14 papers in *JMGA* V (1930), Pts 2 and 3.

[30] The *Wn* Amaravati; as often there is another river of the same name rising in the same watershed but flowing in the opposite direction.

of Coimbatore and is effectively cut off from much precipitation. What water it had was very carefully conserved—it had more *anicuts* than the other two put together—but it has now been almost completely ruined by deforestation around its sources, so that its spring channels have decayed.

The climatic effects of the wide and low Palghat Gap are much less than might have been expected. The rainfall in general is 27–30 ins., but although Pollachi taluk, actually athwart the gap, gets 36, its plains portion is not much better off than its neighbours. Significant, however, is the seasonal distribution:

	June–Sept. %	Oct.–Dec. %
Pollachi taluk	48	32
Central plains	19	54
Bhavani and Cauvery valleys .	30	43
Kollegal taluk (Mysore Plateau) .	43·5	26

All stations have a double maximum, in May and October, the latter everywhere the wettest month: this may represent, as it were, a convergence of SW and "NE" monsoons. The central plains are on the arid side: Dharapuram has only six months (April–May, September–December) with over one inch. Altogether, however, the distribution is puzzling; even the taluks on or bordering the Mysore Plateau have more rain in May than in June and July put together. Air masses at various levels are obviously involved, and there is a subject for intensive research here.

The influence of Palghat is better seen in other factors than rainfall. The temperature range is remarkably slight for an inland (if low) plateau—the December–January mean is 73·7° F., April 83·3; the heat is tempered by the breezes and light showers of the SW monsoon.

Agricultural Individuality

Agriculturally the region has some very individual features: the negligible position of rice, the importance of wells, millets, and pastoralism. Coimbatore Dt (which includes some hill country both N and S) has a NSA of about 1,825,000 ac., TSA about 2 m. Of the TSA only 5% is paddy, the three main millets accounting for about 45%, of which in turn 50–60% is usually cholam (jowar). Of cash crops cotton and groundnut (*c.* 18 and 9% respectively) are the most important. The irrigated area varies from 400–450,000 or more acres; tanks are of little importance (only some 20,000 ac.) but wells account for 300–350,000 ac.[31] Practically 100%

[31] The projected 5½-mile-long dam at the Bhavani/Moyar confluence is designed to give a further 200,000 ac. canal-irrigation.

I.P.—23*

of the rice is irrigated, about 24% of the cholam, and 14% of the cumbu (bajra), but only a few thousand of the 2–400,000 ac. of cotton.

This broad quantitative statement conceals very interesting adjustments. Soils are varied: the E and a good deal of the W are occupied by the usual thin red sandy Archaean soils, but on the Palghat sill there is a good deal of medium regur, and valley-bottoms often contain good black loams which amply repay the careful culture they receive. The Anaimalais are often fringed with lateritic shelves, but there is also some 'colluvial'— rain-wash—soil of much higher value.

Paddy is practically confined to *ayacuts* (areas supplied from *anicuts* or weirs) in the major valley-bottoms. Coimbatore has the largest cumbu acreage of any Madras District, followed closely by Salem with Trichinopoly a fair third; for cholam and ragi only the Ceded Districts outrank this region. Much of the cholam is for fodder. As for cotton, the Coimbatore concentration is third to the Ceded Districts and Ramnad/Tinnevelly. The local *Karunganni* cotton is intermediate in staple between the usual Indian varieties and the long-stapled Cambodia, which is grown only on irrigated red soils. A large area is covered by the drought-resistant strain CO_2 evolved from Cambodia by the Coimbatore Agricultural College; this is exceptionally well adapted to Tamilnad conditions and has spread widely in the last two decades. *Karunganni*, a dry crop on black soils, is still areally dominant, however.

Perhaps the most notable success of the Agricultural College (one of the most important in *India*) has been with sugar, but this has benefited the N rather than Madras, although the harvesting might be spread over ten months instead of the four of the Gangetic Plain. As we saw (above, ooo) the existence of a plantation/factory tradition for indigo played an important part in the evolution of the sugar industry in Bihar and UP; in the S high costs and absence of factories seem to act as a vicious circle: it is not worth while to grow sugar in small lots, nor to build a factory unless there is extensive cultivation, and sugar-cane remains negligible. There is also the not unimportant competition of jaggery from the palmyra, particularly in Tinnevelly.

In irrigated garden cultivation the region is pre-eminent. The Coimbatore ryot is an exceedingly assiduous gardener, fencing his compact holdings and temporarily at least living in field-huts on them—a factor of significance for this type of culture. Cereals, cotton, sugar are grown in rotation with sweet potatoes, onions, turmeric, chillies, and a variety of other intensive cultures; betel-vines are expecially noteworthy. All this is dependent on anicuts with spring-channels or leats and on wells; Fig. 146 shows something of the irrigation and settlement pattern in the Amaravati valley-bottom. The Kongunad farmers are adept well-sinkers, some of their shafts going down 100 ft into solid rock.

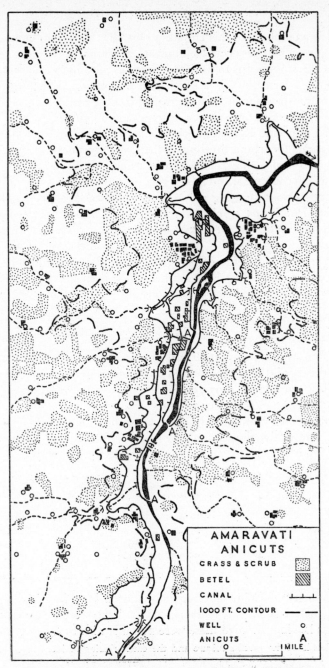

Fig. 146.—Amaravati Anicuts. 40 mls SE of Coimbatore.
Solid lines perennial, broken seasonal, streams. Note (i) absence
of tanks; (ii) moderate relief (only two tiny residual hills on whole
sheet, c. 275 sq mls). Canals follow contours, large settlements at
edge of floodplain. SOI 58F/6; courtesy SOI.

There is a corollary to this emphasis on wells. Unless oil-engines or the increasingly numerous electric pumps are available, the deeper wells need exceptionally stout beasts to work them, and in the almost arid centre of the region animal husbandry is a specialised occupation. Kangayam, on the Noyil/Amaravati watershed, is the main breeding centre: it lies in a tract of light rainfall, with few streams or trees, and a light red loam with some kanker. The specific Kangayam stock is reared only by a handful of well-to-do peasants for whom breeding is their main business; but the general Kongu breed is also an excellent animal when well cared for. "Kangayam looks down on communal and mixed grazing, and cattle have been provided private and enclosed grazing grounds on which the famous grass" *Kolai-kattai pul* (*Pennisetum cenchroides*) is grown. Cholam is grown by well-irrigation for fodder in February–March—just before the most trying season for cattle—and cumbu-, paddy-, and ragi-straws are also used for feed; the black soil tracts and the garden grounds are dotted with cholam stacks at this time of year. The Kangayam bullock is in great demand in the garden lands and in the black cotton soils of the SE, as far as the Tamprabarni.[32]

Coimbatore Town

Erode (39,483), an important rail crossing of the Cauvery, has some textile industry and may be expected to develop rapidly with expansion at Mettur. But Coimbatore (**197,755**) is the only town of real importance; its population has more than trebled since 1921, mainly owing to industrial growth based on Pykara power and local cotton. This is strikingly shown by some comparative figures for 1932 and 1937,[33] between which years the Bombay Presidency cotton industry actually declined slightly:

	Mills			Spindles			Hands		
	1932	1937	Incr. %	1932	1937	Incr. %	1932	1937	Incr. %
Coimbatore .	8	20	150	177,408	352,040	97	6,793	14,228	109
Madras Prov.	26	47	81	820,870	1,150,866	40	34,753	49,110	42
All-India .	340	370	9	9,506,083	9,730,798	2·3	403,226	417,276	3·5

The industry at Coimbatore actually started in 1888 with two mills; local raw materials, labour, markets, and capital [34] were there; only cheap power was lacking. In 1938 there were 26 mills with over 21,000 workers.

[32] For details of the garden culture and the cattle rearing of Kongunad, see K. C. Ramakrishnan, "Agricultural Geography of Coimbatore District", *JMGA* V (1930), 95–107, and A. S. Ayyar, "Cattle of Kongunad", *ibid.*, 108–11.

[33] C. M. R. Chettiar, "Growth of Modern Coimbatore", *JMGA* XIV (1939), 101–16; refce at 113.

[34] It is true in strange hands—Multanis to exploit raw millowners, 'Kabulis'—Pathan moneylenders—to exploit their workers (*Ibid.*, 110–12).

This initial spurt has died down, but there are a number of other industries —coffee mills, tanneries, oil-presses, and a large cement works (Tata's once more) in the vicinity.

The town itself has little of interest. It is in a fairly healthy situation at 1300–1400 ft on the Noyil, but the Palghat Gap, only a few miles away, hardly affects the climate, and water is brought in a tunnel from a small catchment on the windward side of the surrounding horseshoe of hills. The original core, as often in Tamilnad, was the intersection of the four large streets for temple cars. The recent growth has been disorderly, slums and congestion are rife. A minor point of urban morphology is interesting: the original cotton mills, dependent on export, cling to the railway, in the heart of the town; ginneries and presses, with their bulky import, congregate on the En outskirts, towards the source of supply.

The Cauvery Delta

This region (Figs. 147, 148) covers some 4000 sq mls, with a 1941 population of nearly 3,750,000; most of it lies in Tanjore Dt.[35] The build of the delta is remarkable; from the Coleroon (also called Kollidan) the seaface runs straight S for about 80 miles to Pt Calimere, where it makes a right-angle bend and runs W for 30 miles, until it abuts on older ground at the mouth of the Agniar. The tendency in Coromandel for a Nwds deflection of river mouths, influenced by the dominant of the SW monsoon, is here inhibited by the bulge of the delta, like a vast groyne across the limited fetch of Palk Bay, shutting off these generally stronger currents. Hence the Nn half of the E face is exposed to the open NE and is suffering some erosion; the rivers are normal to the coast, debouching directly into the sea with little or no deflection. But S of Negapatam the belt of dunes (50 ft high or more), backed by a long marshy low, strongly suggests pro-grading, and W of Pt Calimere the material that is brought by the SW longshore drift piles up, so that the shoreline is backed by a mass of fetid mudflats 5–6 miles wide, the Vedanniyam Salt Swamp. In conformity with this view of the coast is the lie of the 5-fathom line: $\frac{1}{2}$–1 mile offshore from the Coleroon to Karikal, $2\frac{1}{2}$ miles at Negapatam, and 8–13 miles off the S face. Pt Calimere itself is a blunt cuspate foreland, a complex of beach-ridges which would repay detailed study, affected as they obviously are by the alternating dominance of the monsoons.

The drainage-pattern also is interesting, with its bundle of streams packed into 8–10 miles between Trichy and Tanjore but fanning out into a quadrant 75 miles across; it must be remembered, however, that the whole area has been intensively worked over by man for at least 10 centuries; the

---

[35] This section is based mainly on: 15 papers on Trichinopoly Dt, *JMGA* VIII (1933); 7 papers on Tanjore Dt, *JMGA* XII (1937). It may be noted that Trichinopoly is more formally styled Tiruchirapalli, more familiarly just 'Trichy'.

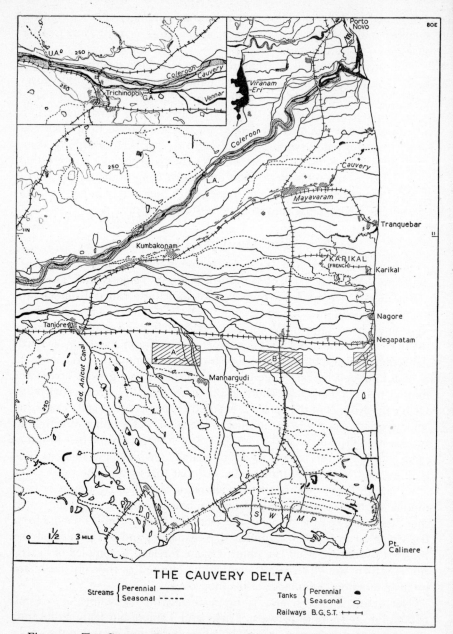

THE CAUVERY DELTA

Streams { Perennial ——— Seasonal - - - - -

Tanks { Perennial ● Seasonal ○

Railways B.G, S.T. ┼┼┼┼

Fig. 147.—THE CAUVERY DELTA. Inset: continuation to W. LA, GA, UA, Lower, Grand, Upper Anicuts; *all* permanent water on original shown. A–C, area of Fig. 148. SOI 1/253,440 58N; courtesy SOI.

Grand Anicut was constructed in the 11th century AD. The slope is steep for a delta: Trichy, at delta-head, is on the 250-ft contour, 30 miles from Tanjore which at 50 miles from the sea is at 150 ft, and this slope is maintained right to the coast; indeed heights of 25–30 ft (not dunes, but possibly old beach-ridges) are found within 3–4 miles of the sea.

The alluvium extends far to the W of Trichy in a highly fertile belt about a mile wide; to the E it varies in quality. The Coleroon/Cauvery doab from Trichy to Kumbakonam is the richest part of the delta, but S of the Vennar underlying calcareous deposits reduce fertility, and towards the coast soils are markedly sandy. Within the deltaic area a patch of laterite and/or Cuddalores forms the low (180 ft) 'Vallam Tableland' in the SW, and around the delta on W and S is the usual fringe of low gneissic terrain with thin red soils tending to red loams in the more favoured portions. Soils in general are open, porous, and permeable, on the whole very 'thirsty'. The area W of Trichy may be considered as topographically, climatically, and agriculturally a transition zone to the Coimbatore/Salem plateaus.

A belt about 10 miles wide along the coast receives over 50 ins. of rain; indeed a small tract S of Negapatam has over 55. Inland this decreases regularly: Negapatam 55 ins., Kumbakonam 43, Tanjore 37, Trichy 33. It has a very typical SE littoral distribution, the stations mentioned having respectively 72, 54, 50, and 45% of their fall in October–December inclusive. All of them have a small secondary peak (1·5–3 ins., *increasing* inland) in May, 'mango showers' associated with thundery pre-monsoon cyclonic disturbances. An interesting concomitant of the rainfall distribution is the belt of dry evergreen forest which survives in small patches, as at Pt Calimere (cf. Ch. III, 70 above).

Irrigation and Agriculture

The agricultural economy of the delta and its margins is complex. Paddy is dominant—77% of TSA in Tanjore—but falls off rapidly towards the margins, accounting for only 21% in Trichy Dt; but even in Tanjore we have the rather odd phenomenon (for a fairly humid delta) of 4% under groundnuts, admittedly largely on the higher inner margins but also associated with sandy soils near the coast. It will be simplest to write off the marginal areas briefly and to concentrate on the old and new irrigation of the delta proper.

N of the Coleroon the deltaic area between that river, the Vellar, and the Viranam tank is mainly paddy, and paddy extends as the major crop up the Vellar as far as the Willingdon Reservoir. But the paddy belt farther along the Coleroon is narrow, and the high and dry Coleroon/Vellar interfluve is mainly dry crops, cumbu, groundnut, some sugar. Between Trichy and Karur the agriculture rapidly becomes poorer (cholam and ragi as food, castor as a cash crop) and in Karur taluk, on the Coimbatore plateau/ Cauvery delta border, gram is perhaps the leading crop. In all these areas, of course, rice is grown where irrigation facilities permit, as also cotton, chillies, and tobacco.

The older irrigation of the delta was a combination of inundation canals and, in the higher W, tanks fed from them; tanks of any *agricultural* significance are not found E of a line Kumbakonam/Mannargudi. This highly integrated system was dependent on the great *anicuts* at either end of Srirangam Island. The Coleroon has a straighter course and a lower level than the Cauvery, and by the 19th century the Cauvery offtake was silting and its branches deteriorating. The Upper Anicut (1836–38, remodelled 1899–1904) was designed to offset this, and is supplemented by regulating dams across all main offtakes.[36]

The dominant irrigated crop was of course paddy, but there was an interesting specialisation on plantains "rotated with paddy on wet lands with an unfailing supply of water from irrigation channels, the rainfall alone being insufficient and ill-distributed for the very high water require-ments of the quickly growing and bulky plantain." In contrast to the usual view of the banana as conducive to laziness, the cultivation here is ex-ceedingly intensive: "the labour that is demanded is indeed prodigious compared with that involved in the case of paddy or of any other intensively cultivated crop except sugar-cane. . . . The village itself is rarely able to supply all the labour needed" [37], and there is some seasonal immigration from the surrounding uplands. Other intensively cultivated crops are betel and sugar-cane.

The Mettur scheme was intended to protect the delta irrigation against floods, to regulate supplies in the older-irrigated region (where previously the period of available water shortened to the E), and to add to the irrigated area a further 300,000 acres W of Mannargudi. The essential principle is to substitute for direct flow, dependent on the irregular natural levels of the river, storage enabling supply to be regulated to the differing needs of the delta; the semi-saline soils near the coast, for instance, require frequent flushing to wash away the salts, and this cannot be attained satisfactorily by inundation methods. But the results attained illustrate the complex problems involved in new-modelling an already highly developed system, problems far more difficult than those of breaking in new ground, as in the Punjab.[38]

[36] A description of the main channels is given by K. Ramamurthy, *IGJ* XXIV, No. 2 (1949), 30–33.
[37] K. C. Ramakrishnan, "A Model of Intensive Cultivation in the Cauvery Valley", *JMGA* VIII (1933), 179–87.
[38] The remainder of this section is based on the remarkable analysis by T. Krishna-swami, "Recent Irrigation Changes in the Cauvery", *JMGA* XIV (1939), 237–71. The caution should be added that, as Krishnaswami admits, the period of five years between the opening of Mettur and his paper is too short for a final evaluation.

The main feature of the scheme was the construction of the Grand Anicut Canal, turning S at Tanjore town and running along the contours down the higher flank of the delta; its length is 66 miles, that of its distributaries nearly 700 miles; full discharge at offtake 5000 cusecs, at tail 300. Perhaps the chief difficulty is that due to interference with the water-table. "With the Canal flowing for more than six months of the year, and the monsoon rains, the proper drainage of the area has become an acute problem," despite siphons where the canal cuts across drainage-lines, as a contour canal must. The distributaries naturally follow the higher levels, to command wider *ayacuts*, and this seems to have overcharged the natural drainage below them. The problem is further complicated, though to a less extent than in W Bengal and Bihar, by the construction of railways and roads transverse to the natural slope. Already there seems to have been an increase in malaria.

The newly irrigated area was previously mostly rainfed, with some tanks, growing coarser paddy, groundnuts, gingelly (sesamum), millets, and pulses. Soils are varied and difficult to manage. In the circumstances the risks of over-irrigation, with consequent waterlogging and alkali panning, are very real. The rise in the water-table is reported to have adversely affected the important jack-fruit and casuarina groves of the area. There is also a conflict of interest between the activities of inland fishermen (building bunds, scoops, etc.) and the needs of canal maintenance.

A further difficulty lies in the disturbance of a well-established agricultural rhythm:

. . . the cultivators in the deltaic tracts complain of the shrinkage in the volume of water supplied to them and the present system of irrigation interferes with their normal agricultural operations. During the natural flood season under the direct flow system, operations commence almost simultaneously both at the head and tail of the delta area. Thus with the first freshes in the river there is bound to be an all-round and sympathetic activity throughout the entire villages. There is, however, much truth in the complaint that the control system makes the tail-end cultivator wait indefinitely long . . . so there is considerable uncertainty regarding the method of cultivation to be adopted and the crops to be raised. . . . Errors in calculation of the 'duty' have also been responsible for the failure of the control system to meet the requirements of agriculture especially in critical times . . . in 1935 'the low level sluices could not meet the demand at a critical period during the transplantation season, even though they were fully open.' Added to this, the popular misconception that the greater the irrigation the greater the produce has to be removed, if the 'duty' is to approximate to the actual needs. The difficulty of the tail-end cultivators is more pronounced in the case of double-crop areas under paddy.[39]

[39] Krishnaswami, 263–64.

In the long run, of course, such initial difficulties are likely to be more than offset by greater regularity than can be attained by relying on natural flood, taking one year with another.

This last conclusion, however, may not apply to the very serious matter of loss of silt. It has been argued that most of the silt is actually supplied by the Amaravati and the Bhavani. But as we have seen (above, fn. 31) there is a scheme to dam the Bhavani,[40] and against this view is the provision for adding to the height of the Mettur Dam to allow for an estimated accumulation of 10 feet of silt in 50 years; as Krishnaswami says, this certainly suggests that the complaints of cultivators have some substance. On the other hand, "with the limitation and regulation of water in the Coleroon, . . . larger quantities of sand are now brought down the Cauvery, or deposited by its distributaries in the lower reaches", a long-standing difficulty, which has led to increased flooding in the delta. It seems that too little attention has been paid to the problems of aggrading river-beds.

Much of the dissatisfaction is doubtless the reaction of rural conservatism to a sudden change in conditions, and one feels at times that Krishnaswami is a devil's advocate. But on the whole it is difficult to resist his cautious conclusion that "it is not possible to definitely assert that the Canal irrigation is under all circumstances an unmixed blessing."

Settlement and Towns

The delta is densely populated: the deltaic portions of Tanjore Dt, excluding towns of over 20,000 people, have an average density of 705, and in Kumbakonam taluk this rural density is 1104. Nevertheless there is an export of rice to Ceylon, mainly through Negapatam.

The settlement patterns are extremely interesting (Fig. 148 A–C). In the W (Tanjore to Mannargudi, A) there is a tendency to fairly strong nucleation associated with large semi-perennial tanks; there is a fair amount of waste, casuarina groves are common, and the pattern is rather coarse. This area will be affected by the new irrigation. Beyond the Kumbakonam/ Mannargudi line the pattern of the channels is much closer and more rectilinear (cf. E portion of Fig. 148 A), settlements on the whole are smaller and more scattered, but although there is thus some 'loosening' there is nothing like the close stipple of homesteads in Bengal. Casuarinas are very few in this tract, but coconut palms begin to join the ubiquitous toddy; tanks are small, merely for domestic supply, and practically all perennial. There is the usual deltaic tendency to settlement along levees, but also some linear *across* the drainage lines (B), and towards the SE of the delta at least a strong suggestion of old beach-ridge settlement. Finally (C) there is the negative area of the old lagoons along the line of the Vedaranyam

[40] There is also agitation for the construction of major works on the Amaravati. But it seems likely that with the harnessing of the Bhavani the Cauvery basin would be utilised to the fullest extent possible.

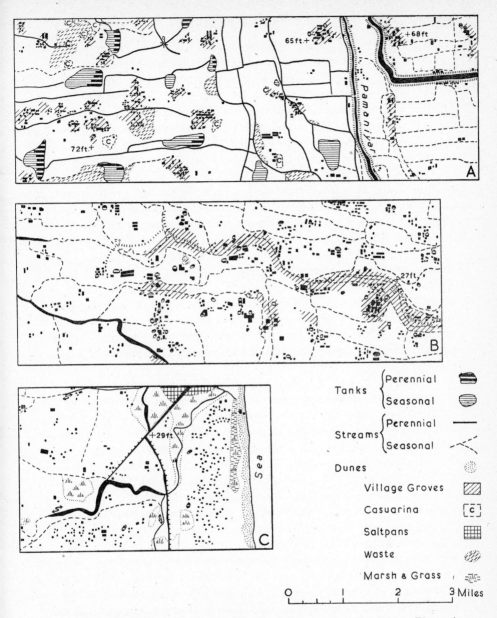

Fig. 148.—THE CAUVERY DELTA: SETTLEMENT. All 3 maps on 10° 45′ N (see Fig. 147).
A: old delta, large tanks, nucleated villages; E of Pamaniyar older canal irrigation, in W
new irrigation from Grand Anicut Canal; few palms W of Pamaniyar, toddy palms in fields
to E; linear settlement along levees beginning in E.

B: mainly linear. Size and position of tanks (nearly all perennial) very different from
those of A. Most palms toddy but coconut coming in to E; no casuarina.

C: dunes coast; semi-linear (approach to Kerala type, cf. Fig. 121) on sandy belt
(paddy/coconut/casuarina) between marsh and dunes. Dunes about 30 ft high; better
marked, with linear settlement on old beach-ridges, to S of area. SOI 58N/6, 10, 14;
courtesy SOI.

Canal, succeeded by an approximation to the Kerala settlement type in the sandy littoral strip, with its paddy/coconut/toddy/areca economy.

The delta is reasonably well served by communications, but from Erode to the sea the Cauvery/Coleroon has only three rail crossings (Erode, Trichy, and near the coast) and two complete road bridges, at Trichy and the Lower Anicut. The Grand and Upper Anicuts have roadways, but these cross only the Cauvery and the Coleroon respectively, and so give access merely to Srirangam Island. The numerous ferries use coracles.

The towns of the region fall into three groups: interior markets, ports, and, in a class by itself, Trichinopoly. Those of the first group are not of much importance, except for Kumbakonam (67,008) and historic Tanjore (**100,680**). Many of the coast towns are most interesting as survivals of the European intrusion: thus Tranquebar has still some buildings of the Danish occupation (until 1845); the seat of the first Protestant mission to India, it retains a Lutheran bishopric. The French enclave of Karikal (53 sq mls, poptn 60,000) is not fragmented like Pondicherry, but its licit trade in groundnuts is supplemented by high-value low-bulk smuggling; on the Sn border Karikal merchants have established "a town entirely of shops and nothing else", and S. R. Pandyan formally, and doubtless correctly, includes smuggling among the indigenous industries of adjacent Negapatam.

Negapatam (52,936; Fig. 149) has suffered from the removal of the SIR workshops to Trichy, but this has to some extent been offset by the establishment (with Pykara power) of steel rolling-mills, which share the old railshops with a cinema. The town has still many traces of Portuguese and Dutch occupation; as usual, the latter left a few buildings and the former a more intimate cultural and ethnic influence, including a whole village of Roman Catholic fishermen. The port is a mere roadstead, with a couple of cranes on a creek-side wharf, but it flourishes as the outlet of the delta. Trade is mainly with Ceylon, Burma, and coastwise, much of it by country craft, in which connection the large number of Muslims is significant: in 1941 they were over 22% of the population, against 7·9% in all Madras. Most of them are merchants and seamen. Negapatam is mainly an exporting port (groundnuts, rice and gram, tobacco, cotton); after Madras it is indeed the leading groundnut port of the State, outstripping Cuddalore which is nearer the main Tamilnad groundnut area but even worse as a port; before the war 90% of the groundnut trade was to Hamburg and (doubtless under Pondicherry influence) Marseilles. Cottons from Madura are dyed and printed (by Muslims) and exported to SE Asia markets; a minor but interesting import is "betel" (areca) nuts from Ceylon and Malaya.[41]

[41] S. R. Pandyan's very interesting and well-mapped paper (*JMGA* XI (1937), 291–318) is the warrant for this extended note, presented as a type-specimen of the minor Indian ports.

Trichinopoly (**218,921**) commands the most important crossing of the Cauvery, and has besides the attraction of the great shrine of Srirangam (26,676), a town mostly built four-square within the vast temple enceinte. Trichy itself is dominated by the famous Fort on an isolated rock towering 270 ft above the town. Modern industry started late and lags behind that

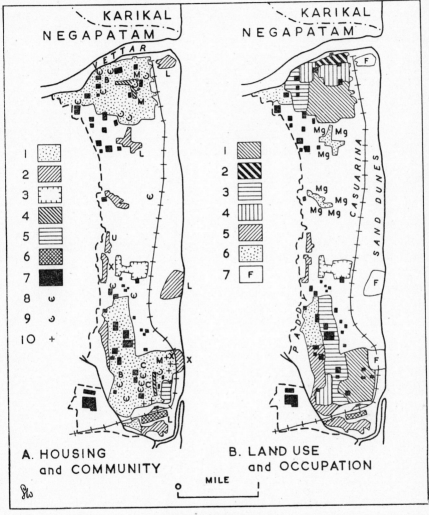

A. HOUSING and COMMUNITY

B. LAND USE and OCCUPATION

MILE

Fig. 149.—NEGAPATAM.

A: 1, tiled houses; 2, thatched huts; 3, European-style bungalows (local officials, etc.); 4, shops; 5, godowns; 6, old SIR works (now steel rolling mills and cinema); 7, tanks; 8, temples; 9, mosques; 10, churches. B, Brahmins; C, Chettiars and traders; X, Christians; M, Muslims; L, lower castes (coolies, fishermen); U, Untouchables.

B: 1, traders; 2, smugglers; 3, clerical and professional; 4, priestly class; 5, poor working class; 6, cultivators; 7, fishermen. Mg, market gardens.

Adapted from maps in S. R. Pandyan, "Negapatam", *JMGA* XI (1937), 291-318.

of other Tamilnad cities; there are some textiles, cement works at Dalmian-agar, and the loco and carriage shops in the well-planned railway colony of Garden Rock.

The Dry Southeast

Generalities

This is a complex area, and but for considerations of scale its sub-regions might well be promoted to full regional rank. The dominant factor is low rainfall: sheltered by the Cardamoms from the Arabian Sea monsoon, off the main track of the advancing Bay of Bengal branch, and to some extent at least losing the full effect of the cyclones of the retreating monsoon by reason of its position in relation to the Cauvery delta bulge and Ceylon.

This is the main cotton region of Tamilnad, the three Districts (Madura, Ramnad, and Tinnevelly) accounting for nearly a third of the acreage in Madras State. Tank-irrigation reaches its peak in Madura and Ramnad, while Tinnevelly has the most important black soil tracts outside the Deccan. Historically the region has the distinction of having never been subject to a central power before that of the British Raj.

Physique

Physically we have the standard pattern: low gneissic peneplain beneath the hills; alluvial and marine/aeolian deposits along the coast, up the major valleys; and between these the discontinuous Cuddalore/laterite shelves. The NW of the region, however, is complicated by the layout of the hills: the Suruli/upper Vaigai Valley is set within the arms of the Palnis (WSW/-ENE to SSW/NNE) to the N, the Varushanad and Andipatti Hills to the SE. These ranges almost converge around the great curve of the Vaigai, and are continued to the NE by fairly large outliers (up to 3000–4000 ft) on the Cauvery watershed—the Surumalais, Karandamalais, Nattam and Alyar Hills.

The parallelism of the trough between the Mysore Ghat and the Javadis, and of the upper courses of the Bhavani, Noyil, Amaravati, and Suruli/Vaigai, is very striking, as is the sharp SE front of the Palnis: can this upper Vaigai embayment be structurally analogous to, or even connected with, the Palar/Ponnaiyar trough? In any case, though the *outer* peneplain may be a marine erosion surface, Cushing's general theory appears nowhere less convincing than here, where he describes the 7000-ft scarp below Kodai-kanal as a "sea-cliff".[42] A cliff of this height is startling enough in all conscience, and no less so when we note that the hypothetical sea washing the foot of the Palnis was 15–20 miles wide, since the Andipattis would be out of the water; the extreme fetch would be about 50 miles, and that parallel

---

[42] See especially Cushing's Plate 5; the caption of which reads in part "the ancient sea cliff, which here plunges directly down nearly 7000 ft to the plain of marine denudation".

to the "cliff". The only escape, on Cushing's view, would be to postulate extremely obscure vertical movements of a magnitude and recency sufficient to make the whole theory merely an unnecessary complication.

E of the Surumalais and Nattam Hills a broad apron of laterite and old alluvium links the Cauvery delta and the Vaigai; here, between the Varshalei and the Vaippar, is tank country *in excelsis*. The Vaigai itself thrusts great wedges of alluvium NW and SE, up between the hills and down to form the Ramnad Peninsula. The great bulge of alluvium S of the Tamprabarni may mark a formerly more Sly embouchure of that river, which has ancient bunds on the S bank, while black soils, probably formed in a marshy valley-bottom, occur in a strip between the present and the possible old course—the only occurrence S of the river. Here, from the Vaippar Swds, the Cuddalores and laterites disappear, only small patches occurring in the extreme S, around Cape Comorin.

The determinants of regional differentiation here are largely soil factors, but allowance must be made for positional and physiographic factors. The area can be sub-divided as follows:

1. Upper Vaigai valley.
2. Madura-Ramnad tank country.
3. Black Soil tract.
4. Tinnevelly: (a) piedmont, (b) Tamprabarni basin, (c) red soil and *teri*.

Before discussing these we may deal with the coast in general.

The Coast and the Teri Tracts [43]

The coast as a whole shows strong evidence both of prograding and of uplift. Apart from patches of doubtful Cuddalores in Tinnevelly Dt, there are extensive outcrops of undoubted marine calcareous sandstones, in places pure limestone, false-bedded and dipping gently seawards; their fossils are recent and there are records of interbedded pottery, though this may have been washed down from still more recent beach-rock. S of the Tamprabarni these are overlain by the remarkable red *teri* (= 'sandy waste').

The *teri* deposits are definitely aeolian, though capillary oxidisation has consolidated them, so that in general only a thin surface layer is now being re-worked by wind. The *teris* form rolling little plateaus, up to 15–20 sq mls in area, at 100–220 ft. They carry a thin vegetation of palmyra (toddy) palms and thorny scrub, and in some places are still active, advancing to the ESE at 5–15 yds a year and ponding up (but eventually filling) small lakes around their margins, and sometimes overwhelming tanks. Naturally

[43] P. G. Dowie, "Geology of the Tinnevelly District", *JMGA* XV (1940), 303–29; V. Kalyanasundaram, "Changes in Level in the S.E. Coast of Madras", *IGJ* XVIII (1943), 30–36.

there is hardly any surface water, but their ground-water emerges in springs along the flanks; these springs are sometimes led off into irrigation channels, while in depressions, which are sometimes loamy, well-irrigation is possible. Some of the *teris* appear to be a thin veneer over the marine sandstones at 200 ft plus; this indicates an uplift to this extent since the Pleistocene. In the *teris* chert cores and flakes and sherds of pottery have been found.

The coastal dunes speak to prograding; they reach 178 ft, the highest parts being consolidated by solution and redeposition of comminuted shells. Old islands off Tuticorin are now attached to the mainland, and there is also direct and incontrovertible literary evidence of advance of the land. Korkai, identified with Ptolemy's port of Kolkhoi, is now 4½ miles inland; Kayal (= 'backwater' or 'lagoon'), Marco Polo's Coel, 2¾ miles. Here the settlement level is two or three feet below the alluvial surface, and in it fragments of Arabian and Chinese pottery have been found.

In 1881 Bishop Caldwell estimated an emergence of 45 ft, as fossils of species of pectens and oysters now living about the 5-fathom line are found 17 ft above sea-level near Tuticorin. This is exactly confirmed by similar evidence from Pamban (Rameswaram) Island. On the N of the island are a fringing and a raised reef, the latter forming a scarp 3–5 ft high, continued on the mainland across Pamban Strait. These straits themselves are nearly bridged by a reef of coral sandstone, so regularly jointed as to give the appearance of an artificial mole, and indeed it is to all intents used as such by the railway.[44] Adam's Bridge itself is basically a coral reef killed by uplift and consolidated into coral rock.

For all that, one can hardly avoid preferring the account in the *Ramayana*: the bridges were built by the admirable monkey-king Hanuman and his followers to aid Rama in the expedition to regain his wife Sita, abducted by the ten-headed Ravana, the demon king of Lanka or Ceylon. On his return Rama built the vast Rameswaram temple, its quadrangle of 650 by 1000 ft flanked by pillared corridors exceeding in length St Peter's nave. Unfortunately stylistic experts coldly assign a 17th-century date—AD 1550 at earliest—to this magnificent work.

The Upper Vaigai (Fig. 150)

The headwaters of the Vaigai rise in the broad but rugged Varushanad Valley, as it were the aisle to the nave formed by the main embayment, which it joins tranversely. This main valley, about 50 miles by 15, is flat-floored at about 1000 ft, and from its relations to the surrounding hills would seem structural in origin. The upper (Kambam) valley is in fact drained by the Suruli, one of the headstreams of which actually rises to the W of the straight Cardamom scarp (X on Fig. 150). The fall is indeed very

---

[44] Kalyanasundaram, *loc. cit.*; personal observation.

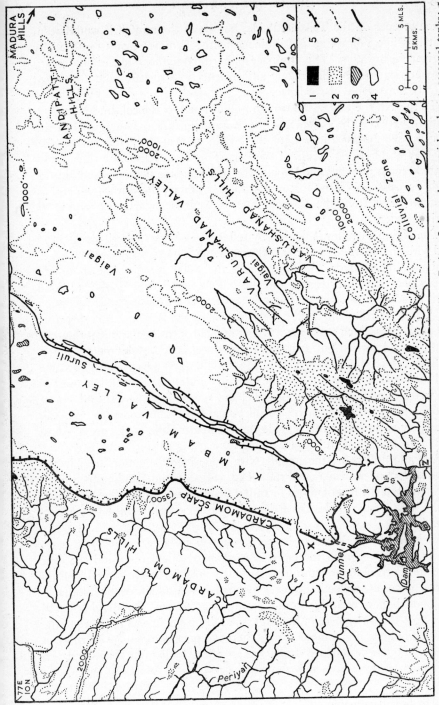

Fig. 150.—Upper Vaigai/Periyar Watershed. 1, over 6000 ft; 2, 4000–6000 ft; 3, Periyar Lake and perennial tanks; 4, seasonal tanks; 5, permanent, 6, seasonal canals; 7, perennial streams (*all* shown; seasonal streams, numerous in E, omitted). X, fragment of old E-flowing drainage above scarp; Y–Z, probable old course of U. Suruli, now captured by Periyar headwaters. Source of Periyar is about 16 mls S of Z. SOI 1/253,440 58 G; courtesy SOI.

much steeper on the Tamilnad side, but given the rainfall it would seem
that this is a relic of an old drainage to the E, now mostly captured by
Periyar headwaters. The drainage-pattern on either side of the scarp
presents some very remarkable adjustments to structure, and this is an
equally remarkable discordance.

To the NE the axis of the trough is continued by the col (under 1000 ft)
leading between the Palnis and the Karandamalais to Dindigul: but the
Vaigai itself breaks through to the SE in a great sweeping curve. The
NE/SW and SE/NW trends of the Palar/Ponnaiyar region are thus duplicated here. It may be noted finally that the Vaigai is perennial only in the
high Varushanad Valley, in contrast to its tributary the Suruli, which has
feeders direct from the Cardamoms, as well as an artificial supply of
Periyar water.

The Kambam valley is floored by red loams—'colluvial' soil-wash, deep
and with an underlying layer of rock fragments. These are thus well watered,
drained, and aerated; "into these soils the water draining the mountain
slopes penetrates very easily, and the soil climate is comparatively humid
even in adverse seasons".[45] There is some tank-irrigation, wells are much
used, and the Kambam Valley is also served by the Periyar reservoir across
the mountains. Such a scheme was first mooted at the beginning of the 19th
century, and carried out at its close; hydro-electric development has not
yet taken place. The masonry dam, 173 ft high, impounds a lake of 8000 ac.,
and the water is taken through the crest in a mile-long tunnel, but most of
the water-body lies below tunnel-level and simply lifts the rest up.[46] Some
13,000 ac. are irrigated in the Suruli/Vaigai Valley, but most use is not in
this fairly secure tract but outside the Andipatti Hills in the great Vaigai
bend; the water has the negative quality of being entirely silt-free.

Rice and millets are the staples, with a considerable cotton area. In the
N, on the Cauvery watershed, the tobacco area around Dindigul is limited
in extent, but the most famous in India. Betel is also grown. The proximity
of the hill forests enables the irrigated area to be well fertilised with leaf-
mould.

An isolated area, much of it was given over to large *zamindari* estates,
one of which occupied the entire Varushanad valley. But good soil, fair
rain, and Periyar water combine to produce densities of 450–650. The little
market towns are collecting centres for the forest products of the hillmen—
bamboos, honey, wax, dye- and tan-stuffs, cardamoms. Dindigul (56,275)
lies across the watershed, in the Amaravati drainage, but its links are to the
S with Madura; it is famous for its cheroots, poor compared with those of
Burma but the best which India has to offer. Unlike the Tamilnad *bidi*
manufacture, this is a factory industry.

---

[45] K. Ramamurthy, *IGJ* XXIII, No. 4 (1948), 31; cf. Vageler's views, above, 87–88.
[46] Details in Ramamurthy, *IGJ* XXIV (1949), 33–35.

The Madura/Ramnad Tank Country

The topography of this area is shown in Fig. 152, which covers an entire quarter-inch sheet (one degree square, 4625 sq mls) between the Varshalei and the Vaippar. On the ground the landscape is not striking: coconut and palmyra, paddy and millet, not a little bare ground or short ragged grass and low bush, lateritic surfaces gravelly or actual 'pan', carrying low but locally dense thorny scrub. On the Ramnad–Trichinopoly railway one does not see a hill for the first 80 miles, and then it is a hummock 50 ft high at most; not until Pudukottai—continuation of the 'Vallam Tableland'—is reached can the ground be called even undulating. On this flat, gently-sloping shelf (the 250-ft contour is 30–40 miles from the sea) the only noticeable elevations are the tank-bunds, and in the dry weather at least only the biggest of these are very noticeable. In fact such swells and hollows as exist are as it were flattened out by the surpassing skill with which even the shallowest depressions are bunded, producing a skyline of flat planes imperceptibly merging into one another.

From the air, however, this is certainly one of the strangest landscapes in the world. Fig. 151 shows some of the possible arrangements of tanks in relation to relief; Fig. 152 the remarkable over-all pattern. Among the more notable features are the way in which a large tank inhibits the formation of smaller competitors within its domain; the string of large gibbous tanks, often paired, on either side of the main rivers, which obviously have levée characteristics; the alignment along contours, which could almost be interpolated from the pattern; the suggestion of an old deltaic fan on the lower Vaigai; the crescent or fish-tail shapes of the majority of tanks. This last is due to the obvious economy of bunding below a confluence, so that the resulting tank has two arms wrapping around the blunt end of the interfluves; the paired crescents usually lie on either side of a larger stream. Except after heavy rain, usually in November–December, practically all tanks and streams are dry; and from above the landscape is a medley of all shades of khaki, ochreous yellow, and rusty red, with a few bottle-green blobs below the less-silted tanks: the whole looks like a surface of vast over-lapping fish-scales. For most of the year the impression is arid and desolate in the extreme; the dune-fringed coast is relieved to some extent by patches of dry thorny scrub or, more pleasantly, by coconut and palmyra groves. But even so the contrast between the wall of green standing almost straight out of the water at Talaimanaar on the Ceylon side, and the almost Red Sea coast at Dhanushkodi, is more striking than enlivening.

Apart from this astonishing terrain, little need be noted. With a rainfall of only 34 ins. and poor lateritic or gneissic soils, this would indeed be a poor country were it not for its intensive refashioning by the hand of man; and this refashioning has been so intense that no streamlet, however miserable, escapes unchecked to the sea without yielding up its toll of water. Even as it is, the region is hardly prosperous; most of the tanks are more or less silted up and there is scarcely room for new ones, while loss by evaporation from these water-bodies of small volume in relation to surface is very

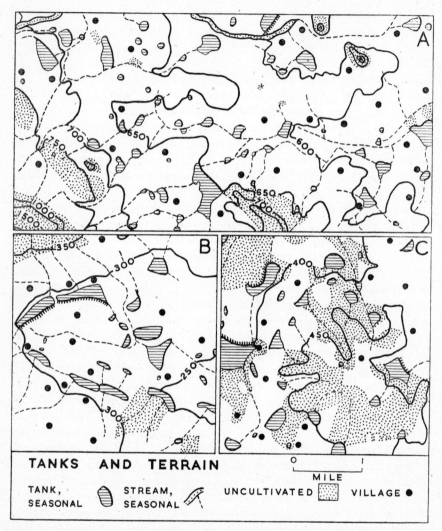

Fig. 151.—TANKS AND TERRAIN.   Three types of tank pattern:

A, 30 mls SW of Trichy: tanks along streams near hills, villages on valley sides.   SOI 58J/6.

B, 8 mls W of Pudukottai: tanks on flanks and around head of valley.   SOI 58J/10.

C, 18 mls S of Trichy: tanks and villages radial around lateritic rise.   SOI 58J/10; all courtesy SOI.

All tanks and streams seasonal, generally holding water July–Dec. in A, Sept.–Feb. in B and C.

high. Ramnad Dt, except for its extreme W, lies entirely in this region: of a TSA of about 1,275,000 ac., some 375,000 ac. are under rice and 150,000 cumbu; cotton accounts for 200–250,000 ac. and oilseeds (60% ground-nuts) 100,000. No other single crop, except sometimes ragi, reaches 100,000 ac., the balance being made up largely of the poorer foodgrains and pulses. The percentage of the total area returned as cultivable is 71, but only 41% is cultivated; and, more significant, the percentage of cultivable area double-cropped in 1930–40 was only 2·4—less than that of any other

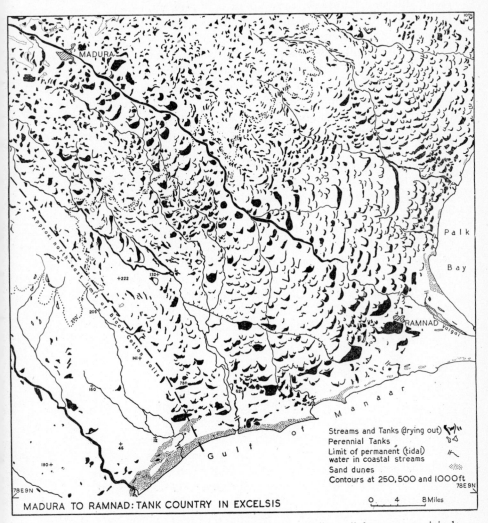

Streams and Tanks (drying out)
Perennial Tanks
Limit of permanent (tidal) water in coastal streams
Sand dunes
Contours at 250, 500 and 1000 ft

MADURA TO RAMNAD: TANK COUNTRY IN EXCELSIS

0   4   8 Miles

Fig. 152.—THE MADURA-RAMNAD TANK COUNTRY. All "water" features on original map shown; they "usually contain water after heavy rain". Note relative absence on black soils in SW. SOI 1/253,440 58K (whole sheet); courtesy SOI.

Madras Districts except Anantapur and Nilgiris. And it is fairly safe to assume that even this small fraction was in the 'colluvial' zone of the far W, where the whole piedmont is commanded by tanks of which many are perennial (Fig. 150).

Settlements are fairly compact, usually under the tanks; a notable feature is the large number of tiny market towns; Ramnad Dt has half a dozen larger centres with 25–50,000 inhabitants. Most of the area was *zamindari* and rather backward. The only places of more than local importance are on Pamban Island: Rameswaram as a place of pilgrimage, Dhanushkodi as the ferry port for Ceylon. But Rameswaram is only a large village (*c.* 6000), and Dhanushkodi not even that.

Closer to the hills conditions are rather better, and in the Madura taluks within the Vaigai bend there is a fair amount of Periyar irrigation. Madura itself (**361,781**), the second city of Tamilnad, dominates the entire SE, which was the domain of the Pandya dynasty from the 3rd century BC till the 10th AD, when it fell under Chola sway. Madura was sacked by Ala-ud-din's general Malik Kafur in 1310, but Pandynad and adjacent Kerala formed the only part of the Peninsula not subject to Asoka, Muhammed bin Tughluk, or Aurengzeb. The city's most brilliant period was under the Naik dynasty (16th–18th centuries), when the great temple with its nine towering *gopurams* was built, and also the 1200-ft square Teppakulam Tank, walled and revetted of granite. But with almost pre-eminent sanctity in S India goes a strong indigenous craft tradition and modern industry. The Naiks introduced silk-weavers from Gujarat (a Gujarati dialect was still spoken in the first decades of this century), and the handloom and dyeing tradition of the city may have played a part in the rise of factory methods in the 1890s. Especially since the advent of Pykara power, Madura has rivalled Coimbatore as the leading textile centre of Tamilnad; in marked contrast to its neighbour Trichinopoly, it nearly trebled its population between 1921 and 1951.

Tinnevelly: the Black Soil Tract

Some 10 or 12 miles E of the Vaippar the tanks end almost abruptly (Fig. 152); this is associated with the occurrence of an extensive regur tract, mainly in the N of Tinnevelly (or Tirunelveli) Dt.[47] It is true that tanks reappear in the 'colluvial' belt, into which the black soil tract grades; but they are much fewer, and a fair proportion are perennial.

This is well brought out by the following figures for 15-minute squares (each *c.* 296 sq mls) on the 1/253,440 sheets, 58G and 58K; the squares analysed form an E/W strip about 120 by 16 miles from the Varushanad Hills to the sea. Sheet 58K is represented on Fig. 152, which shows about

---

[47] The following sections are based mainly on 10 papers in *JMGA* XV (1940) and S. M. Das, "The Tamprabarni Basin", *ibid.*, XIII (1938), 161–68.

2600 tanks, of which only 30 or so are perennial, and these include some coastal ones which are probably partly lagoons.

¼-in. sheet	Square	All tanks	Perennial	Remarks
(West) 58G	B/3	46	21	Half hills, half colluvial.
	C/3	111	nil	Tanks concentrated in colluvial W.
	D/3	41	nil	Largely black soil.
58K	A/3	52	17	Largely black soil; most tanks very small.
	B/3	149	3	Only parts of 3 perennial; most very small; adjacent square to N has 315 tanks, none perennial.
	C/3	168	nil	Some up to $4\frac{1}{2}$ sq mls.
(East)	D/3	83	9	This square includes Ramnad and is largely sea; the 4 completely perennial perhaps rather lagoons; dry tanks up to 6 sq mls.

This area has almost the lowest rainfall of Tamilnad; Tinnevelly Dt as a whole has an average of 29 ins., but in the regur tract it is only 25–27 ins., at Tuticorin as low as 22. The regur developed on the gneiss has not the transitional *murum* found between rock and soil on the Deccan Lavas; it is less moisture-retentive than the Maharashtra deep regur, but more easily worked. It cracks deeply, and the soil-layers are well aerated and mixed. The best black soil, locally known as *karisal*, is about 3–6 ft deep, and on the whole is rather deficient in organic and nitrogenous compounds.

The major crops are cumbu, cholam, and cotton, grown in rotation. Cumbu is more intensively cultivated and manured than is cholam, so that the following crop is better, and hence the rotation is usually cumbu–cotton–cholam. The varieties grown are much the same as in Coimbatore; Cambodia has a yield $2\frac{1}{2}$ times that of *karunganni*, but it thrives only with irrigation, and is thus largely limited to the piedmont colluvial belt: here, in Sankaranayinkovil, Tenkasi, and Koilpatti taluks, under the hills, are most of the District's 36,000 wells and a third of the tank-fed area. CO2 has a wider tange than pure Cambodia, while the poorer *vepal* soils of the E, with lower and later rain, concentrate on the relatively inferior 'Tinnies'. Well-irrigation may be extended when Papanasam power becomes available to tap underground sources. Farming practices are good: much use is made of tank silt and cowdung (the fuel situation is obviously easier than on the Gangetic plains), ploughing is early, the rotation gives little slack time. Cattle—largely the Kangayam breed from Coimbatore—are well cared for, fed on cotton seed, gram, and cumbu and cholam straw. Pulses are often intercropped with the millets. With all this yields are relatively good, and with the emphasis on millets in mind, it is interesting to note the presence of a fair proportion of Telugu Reddis in the District.

Such industrial activity as exists in the small towns is associated almost entirely with cotton: ginneries, a few small mills. The most important centre is the port of Tuticorin (75,614). The town received its main impetus with the American Civil War cotton boom; its surroundings are unattractive in the extreme, marsh and sand, and the development has been very haphazard. As usual, the roadstead is 5 miles offshore and goods have to be lightered to the three jetties; two-thirds of trade and shipping is purely coastal. There is some industrial development, mainly cotton; the Madura Cotton Mills employ about 5000 hands, while some 2000 are engaged in salt-pans and stevedore work.

The port facilities of Tuticorin are antiquated and Cochin has made inroads on its trade, which in 1939–40 amounted to only £7 m. but has several interesting features. Raw cotton, yarn, and piecegoods are the chief exports, raw to Europe and manufactured to Ceylon and Malaya. Chillies (to Ceylon), cardamoms and other spices, oilcake and cattle food, even bonemeal figure in the export list; rice is normally imported from SE Asia for local consumption and some re-exported to Ceylon. Highly specialised local products include senna leaves, palmyra fibre, and chank (conch) shells for the Calcutta bracelet trade. Pearling on the Indian side of the Gulf of Mannar was never very important and is now dead. Fishing and shell-diving are practically a monopoly of the Roman Catholic Paravans (tribe, caste, or sect?), who form a quarter of the population in Tuticorin and a considerable element along the coast.

Tinnevelly: Red Soil and Teri

Little need be said of the red soil area proper; much of it is simply waste, poor acacia scrub; paddy is grown under the many rain-fed tanks, but more often only poor crops of the poorer millets, gram, and gingelly are possible. The only specialised crop is senna. Here and there well-irrigation, with tank-silt and farmyard manure, enables better crops to be grown; oil-pumps have been introduced; and there are hopes from Papanasam.

More interesting is the palmyra economy of the *teri*. The palmyra or toddy palm (*Borassus flabellifer*) is widespread throughout Tamilnad, more important on the Tinnevelly red soils, and of prime importance in the *teri*, which as a rule produces nothing else whatever. There are some 10,000,000 palms in Tinnevelly, providing full- or part-time employment to a large fraction of the population. The palmyra here is probably only less useful than the coconut in Kerala. The broad fan-shaped leaves are used for thatching and even fencing, as fans and sun-shades, for basketry and mats, or, when dyed, to make toys; the fibres of the stem for brushes, ropes, and webbing. But the juice of the stem is the most valuable element: it is the main source of toddy or 'country spirit' [48] and large quantities are used to make jaggery; the District has or at least had several sugar factories based on palmyra. The curious light railway in the extreme SE was laid down in 1905 by the East India Distilleries Co. to convey palmyra juice and jaggery from the *teri* to its sugar refinery at Kulasekharapatnam.[49] This went out of production in 1927, and the line was taken over by the local authorities for passengers and goods. With the advent of freedom and Prohibition distilling has fallen under a cloud, and the depressed caste of toddy-tappers, the Shanars, are probably now still more depressed: but the presence of 10,000,000 palmyra trees suggests that enforcement may well prove inordinately expensive, not to say oppressive.

Tinnevelly: The Tamprabarni Valley

"A splash of green to the naturally dull brown of the vegetation map of Tinnevelly", the Tamprabarni Valley, with that of its tributary the Chittar, accounts for three-quarters of the 50,000 ac. of canal-irrigation in the District.[50] The river is exceptionally favoured: rising at 6000 ft, its sources receive rain from both the main and the retreating SW monsoons, and its bed is never dry; and the valley moreover coincides almost exactly with a narrow E/W belt which receives 30–35 ins. of rain.

There are 8 *anicuts* on the main river, 18 on the Chittar, 12 on other tributaries; nearly all are ancient works. With the regular régime, the cultivating season lasts for 10 months and 94% of the irrigated area is double-cropped, generally with two rice crops. Other wet crops are plantains, betel, turmeric, and sugar-cane; chillies and gingelly are occasionally irrigated. Ragi and cholam are rain-fed, or irrigated from wells in the off-season on the lower reaches of the Chittar, which has really plentiful water only from October to January.[51]

Apart from agriculture, there is little of note in the present human geography of the area: a little oil-pressing, and an interesting local craft (entirely in Muslim hands), the weaving of grass mats which before the war were exported as far as Burma and Malaya. The only large towns are the District capital Tinnevelly (60,676) and Palamcottah (30,967), across

[48] Which smells like ammonia, but when fresh has a cinnamon flavour and might pass as an aperitif; not fresh it is probably deadly.

[49] The company also used a pipeline, but the chemical reactions were disastrous.

[50] But of the 314,000 ac. irrigated, tanks supplied 187,000 and wells 73,000.

[51] For the sake of completeness, we may note that the extreme S of Travancore is also Tamil country, and here, in the Kodayar valley, are 300 miles of modern canals and distributaries and 50,000 irrigated ac.

the river and indeed so practically contiguous that the towns are virtually one.

The real interest of the Tamprabarni, its irrigation apart, lies in the future. The Tamprabarni is probably unique among Indian rivers in that it was harnessed to provide direct hydraulic power for cotton spinning: the first of two turbine-driven mills was set up in 1885. At Papanasam there is a 300-ft fall which is being developed to produce 21,000 kW (ultimate capacity 28,000). The actual engineering work is completed, and full development is limited only by doubts as to the need of conserving water for irrigation; but the possibilities of cheap electricity in this area are manifold: foremost perhaps an increase of well-irrigation in the half-dead edaphically arid tracts, and industrially the revivification of the palmyra sugar industry, the extension of cotton in all its branches. Oilseeds could certainly be more widely cultivated in the red soil area, possibly leading to soap and allied industries, and the hills contain vast reserves of bamboo for paper-making.

The Andaman and Nicobar Islands

These two groups, directly under Delhi, continue the trend of the Arakan Yomas, linking them to the Sumatran ranges. They differ between themselves to a marked extent, both physically and culturally.

1. *The Andamans*

These number over 200, extending NNE/SSW for some 220 miles between 10° and 14° N; the total area is 2500 sq mls, of which the great bulk is in the three major islands of North, Middle, and South Andaman. These three, indeed, are separated only by narrow mangrove-fringed inlets, so that they are often referred to as virtually one island, Great Andaman. The islands are formed of sandstones, limestones, clays, and some serpentines, probably mainly Tertiary, and are highly dissected, rising to 2400 ft. With a temperature never far from 85° F, rainfall over 100 ins., and a monsoonal distribution with no really rainless season, they are naturally jungle-covered: mangrove along coasts and inlets, tropical evergreen along valleys and on steeper wetter slopes, elsewhere moist deciduous. Forestry is perhaps the most important economic activity and is fairly well organised; a match factory was set up about 1930.

The total population in 1941 was 21,316, but this included a strange medley: aboriginals, convicts and ex-convicts with their 'local-born' children, officials. A century ago the aboriginals probably numbered about 5000; in 1931 they were estimated at about 460, in 1941 at 62; many tribes have died right out. At once shy and savage, they had a reputation for ferocity, and early settlement was avowedly to protect shipwrecked mariners from massacre. Despite efforts at conciliation there was violence on both sides; attempts were made indeed to settle some of the more friendly groups in an 'Andamans Home' as fishers of trepang (sea-slug) and collectors of edible bird-nests, both for the Chinese market. But the only result was to civilise them out of existence, largely by venereal disease.[52] The Andamanese are—perhaps one should say were—Negritos, and as they represented perhaps the nearest approach to a 'pure primitive' society, both ethnically and culturally, these hunters and gatherers have attracted anthropological attention out of proportion to their numbers.[53]

Transportation of convicts to the Andamans began after the Mutiny. Latterly there was a change of emphasis, hopeless criminals being re-transported to India and the settlement becoming in effect an open prison for young men condemned to life sentences for more or less excusable homicide. After a few months in jail convicts were allowed to become wage-earning employees of Government, to wear ordinary dress, and to marry or bring out their wives. These changes were reflected in the sex composition of the population: 15,158 males to 2980 females in 1901, 14,872 to 6444 in 1941. The cultural landscape also changed: "Everywhere the ephemeral huts of former times are giving way to well-constructed two-storeyed houses of sawn timber and iron roofs," and a good deal of reclamation of malarial swamp took place around Port Blair. The communal composition of the population was an odd reflection of social conditions: in 1941 Muslims were about a third, largely Moplahs from Madras deported after their 1921 rebellion; Sikhs were 3·5% against an All-India total of 1·5%, Buddhists—i.e. Burmese—over 13%. This corresponds to the prevalence of dacoity in Burma and to the Sikh *penchant* for "liquor, love, and fights".

Practically all the economic development is in the Settlement of Port Blair, an area of about 500 sq mls in the S of South Andaman; here is 90% of the population, the remainder being in forest camps. About 75,000 ac. are more or less cleared, of which about 10–15,000 are cultivated and as much grazing land. Paddy and coconuts each account for about a third of the cultivation, and there are (or were) struggling plantations of rubber and coffee, negligible in area.

The war and the Japanese occupation saw a fall in population to about 16,000, and on re-occupation the penal settlement was formally abolished. From time to time schemes of Anglo-Indian agricultural settlement have been mooted, and in March 1948 a batch of 132 families displaced from E Bengal arrived. It may be noted that some Burmese politicians periodi-

---

[52] 1931 Census Vol. II (Andamans and Nicobars), 11–23.
[53] The classic treatments are those of Sir Richard Temple in the 1901 Census and of A. R. Brown in *The Andaman Islanders* (1922). There is unfortunately little geography in the latter book; what there is is largely summed up in L. Garrard's 'sociograph' in *Studies in Regional Consciousness and Environment* (ed. I. C. Peate, 1930), 82.

cally put forward a vague claim to the Andamans, whether on geomorphological or penological grounds is unknown.

2. *The Nicobars*

This group extends from about 6 to 10° N, Car Nicobar lying 75 miles
from Little Andaman, Great Nicobar 91 miles from Sumatra. Of the 19
islands 12 are inhabited; Great Nicobar, with 133 sq mls, had in 1931 only
300 people; several islands run to 40–60 sq mls and Car Nicobar (49 sq mls)
had the largest population, 7492. The greatest density, 205, was on Chaura,
which supported 615 people on 2·8 sq mls: as we shall see, Chaura is of very
peculiar significance. All these figures are for 1931, when the total population was 10,240; by 1941 it had risen to 12,452. Of these perhaps 200
belong to the Shompen, a jungly inland tribe ('pre-Dravidian'?) on Great
Nicobar, and traders and officials number perhaps 500. The rest are
Nicobarese proper, whose affinities seem to be with the Mon-Khmer
peoples of the Indo-Chinese Peninsula.

The basis of the islands is formed of (? Tertiary) soft micaceous sandstones and clays, but there are extensive slightly raised coral flats. None of
the islands is very high, but Great and Little Nicobar are very much
dissected and forested; the others are mainly covered with tall *lalang* grass
or coconuts, and abandoned coconut groves around Great Nicobar tell of
a former larger population; conflict with the Shompen is apparently
responsible for this abandonment.

With extreme temperatures of 65–98° F and a rainfall of 90–170 ins.
(more on Great Nicobar) conditions are ideal for the coconut, and with fish
and imported rice it forms the staple diet. "In a rich man's household often
as many as 300 coconuts are consumed in one day. Some 200 of these are
used in feeding the family's many pigs in the jungle."[54] The Shompen
practise a primitive agriculture with fire-sharpened digging sticks, though
they also obtain iron *dahs* (Burmese choppers or knives) by raid or trade
from the coastal villages.[55]

Dutch pirates and French Jesuits had contacts with the islands before
the Danish East India Company took on the task of 'civilisation' in 1756.
The British occupied the islands during the Napoleonic wars, but spasmodic and rather inept Danish efforts at colonisation and evangelisation
continued until they admitted defeat in 1848: the chief relic of their interest
is the herd of half-wild buffaloes on Kamorta. In 1867 and 1876 Prussians
and Austrians made gestures towards developing the islands, which in the
intervals were used by Malay pirates (led by a deserter from the Royal
Navy) who concealed their activities by only attacking ships actually
calling at the islands and by leaving no survivors: they seem to have been
responsible for the ill-deserved Nicobarese reputation for ferocity. Finally in

---

[54] 1931 Census, Vol. III, 74.   [55] *Ibid.*, 87–88.

1869 the British accepted responsibility for the protection of mariners. After the failure of a penal settlement and of an attempt at importing Chinese colonists, administration was practically confined to keeping out "firearms and firewater" and to licensing traders. These are mainly Penang Chinese, but country craft come from Burma, the Maldives, and even Cutch.

Coconuts are by far the most important export and are in effect the currency; by 1915 the Nicobarese were in debt to the tune of 29,000,000 nuts or four years' output. The Government allowed five years to collect debts and then closed accounts and forbade credit. This admirably simple fiscal reform has doubtless been evaded, but has certainly improved the economic situation. Other exports, in which a Chinese bias is evident, include trepang, edible nests, trochus shells, areca nuts, and rattans; imports rice, tobacco (which is also grown on some islands), *dahs*, and cloth, much of the last item being destroyed in funerary ceremonies.

The internal economy of the islands is highly developed but pays little attention to economics.[56] The lively inter-island trade is dominated by Chaura, which, owing to its insignificance to normal commerce, is practically untouched by administration. The key position of Chaura is only in part due to its situation between the most populous island, Car Nicobar, and the central group; much more important is the fact that it is the centre of the peculiar cults of the Nicobarese. Trade is largely governed by tabus: thus canoes must not be made in the Nn islands (including Chaura), and the lime for betel-chewing (obtained by burning shells) must not be produced on Chaura or Teressa. But only Chaura can make pots, though the exhaustion of local supplies compels the Chaura people to get their clay from Teressa. Further, canoes for Car Nicobar must either be bought through Chaura or their whole value in nuts, cash, or kind must be paid to anybody on Chaura. This is enforced by an embargo: "unless this price has been paid a canoe may never visit Chaura, and as a pilgrimage to Chaura is as important as the *haj* to Mecca" this is as good a sanction as can be devised.[57] The system is perhaps more ingenious than rational, and murmurings have been heard on Teressa; but perhaps if the trading agreements of the modern world were preserved unchanged for a couple of centuries the results would look much the same. . . .

BIBLIOGRAPHICAL NOTE

The activities of the Madras Geographical Association (later the Indian Geographical Society) permit of fuller documentation than usual. Apart from papers on special areas, cited in the text, attention may be drawn to: N. Subrahmanyam, "Regional Distribution and Relative Growth of the Cities of Tamil

---

[56] As understood in the London School of Economics.
[57] *Ibid.*, 70–76; H. S. Montgomerie, "The Nicobar Islands", *GJ* LIX (1922), 36–50. The fascinations of the Nicobars are by no means exhausted in the paragraphs above.

Nad", *IGJ* XVI (1941), 71–83; and K. Ramamurthy, "Some Aspects of the Regional Geography of Tamilnad", *IGJ* XXIII (1948), No. 2, 6–39 and No. 4, 24–33, and XXIV (1949), No. 2, 28–41.

Ethel Simkins deals with the agricultural geography of both the En and Wn littorals in "The Coast Plains of South India", *Economic Geography* IX (1933), 19–50 and 136–59.

G. Slater's *Southern India* (1926) (cited simply as 'Slater') does for Tamilnad something of what Darling does for the Punjab; slighter, but with many good points, is J. C. Molony's *A Book of South India* (1926). Slater's *The Dravidian Element in Indian Culture* (1928) is suggestive, and his *Some South Indian Villages* (1918) initiated village surveys; see also P. J. Thomas and K. C. Ramakrishnan (eds.) *Some South Indian Villages: A Resurvey* (Madras, 1940).

CHAPTER XXVI

CEYLON

By B. H. Farmer

(Fellow of St John's College and Lecturer in Geography in the University of Cambridge)

ALTHOUGH Ceylon is separated from India by a strait only some twenty miles wide, it has a very marked individuality. This is not primarily a matter of physical geography, for Ceylon is essentially a detached portion of the Deccan, with land forms, climatic regions, natural vegetation, and soils which can be matched in S India; but it is, in the main, a cultural phenomenon, a matter of differences between the society and economy of Ceylon and those of adjacent areas of India.

It is not that the insularity of Ceylon has kept it apart from India, for throughout history almost every phase of Peninsular Indian civilisation has found its way to Ceylon, from early Buddhism and ancient architecture to the modern renaissance of art and music. There have also been actual movements of peoples across Palk Strait; Tamil immigration in mediaeval, and perhaps in ancient, times has made its mark on the racial composition and language of the Sinhalese,[1] and founded a distinctive community of 'Ceylon Tamils' in the Jaffna Peninsula,[2] while more recently labourers have come to work on plantations.

The island nature of Ceylon has, however, reduced the intensity of cultural change and allowed local differentiation. (Here an analogy may be drawn with the relations of Britain and continental Europe.) Thus the Sinhalese have retained their Buddhism and in so doing have had considerable influence on other Buddhist lands; and, in spite of continual coming and going between Jaffna and S India, the Ceylon Tamils have themselves grown different from their Indian cousins. Again, the presence of the sea undoubtedly reduced the pressure of settlers from India, so helping to produce the relative emptiness of the Dry Zone between the Jaffna Peninsula and the Sinhalese areas of the centre and SW.

Much of the individuality of Ceylon may be attributed to the fact that it is not only an island but an island in a prominent position in the Indian Ocean. It lay on early shipping routes between the two coasts of India, and between the Graeco-Roman world, and later the Arab world, and China; later still, it lay in the track of Europeans sailing round the Cape, while in modern times it is, of course, on the Suez route to Australia and the Far

---

[1] Sinhalese (Singalese, Cingalese) = member of, language of, the majority community in Ceylon; Ceylonese = any native of Ceylon.

[2] For place-names see Figs. 154 and 160.

East. Maritime influences are therefore strong. It is fairly certain, in fact, that the Sinhalese themselves came by sea from N India and not across Palk Strait, for they speak a tongue which is recognisably Aryan. The great differences between Sinhalese and the Dravidian languages of S India have helped to maintain Sinhalese culture. The island was later visited by Arab traders, whose descendants, the so-called Moors, are prominent in the coastal population to this day, and later still by the Portuguese and the Dutch. All of them were attracted by intrinsic wealth as well as by positional advantage. The two European powers in turn controlled the maritime regions, where they left a strong mark on society (e.g. the Roman Catholic religion and Roman-Dutch law); but they failed to conquer the highlands. The British took over from the Dutch in 1795–96, mainly in order to control Trincomalee, and at first attempted to govern the island under an arrangement with the EIC. But by 1802 it was apparent that Madras-trained officials were, apart from other disabilities, quite unable to understand the language and customs of the Sinhalese, and Ceylon became a Crown Colony. The British, having thus recognised the distinctiveness of Ceylon, made it even more distinctive, especially when, after 1815, they came to control the whole island. British influence varied in intensity with local conditions, but, by and large, was greater than in any but the most exceptional parts of India. To mention only a few of its effects, a plantation economy was superimposed on the older subsistence economy, the English language became well established, and English systems of education were adopted by the new urban middle class to the detriment of indigenous culture; and in many other ways British rule modified the cultural and economic pattern of Ceylon, continuing a process begun by the Portuguese and Dutch and further differentiating Ceylon from near-by India. Since February 4th, 1948, the distinctiveness of Ceylon has found a new political expression, and the country has become an independent entity within the British Commonwealth. Although there are forces making for union with *India*, it seems unlikely that such a union will take place voluntarily and in the conditions prevailing at the present time.

I. THE PHYSICAL SETTING

Structure and Relief

Although systematic geological mapping in Ceylon is by no means complete, enough has been done to establish the main lines of the geology and structure of the island and to demonstrate its kinship with S India.[3] The whole of Ceylon, with the exception of the Jaffna Peninsula and the NW coast, and of small, mainly coastal strips elsewhere, consists of crystalline pre-Cambrian rocks. The Khondalite Series, similar to the

[3] See especially L. J. D. Fernando, "The Geology and Mineral Resources of Ceylon" *Bulletin of the Imperial Institute*, Vol. 46 (1948), 303–25. See also Fig. 153.

series of the same name in Madras and Orissa, is folded into a complex synclinorium and is now believed to occupy a broad belt in the interior of

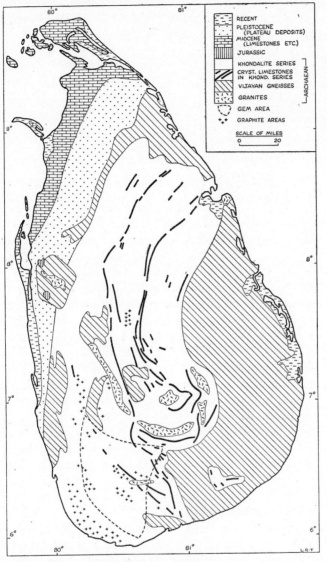

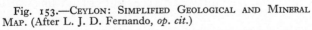

Fig. 153.—CEYLON: SIMPLIFIED GEOLOGICAL AND MINERAL MAP. (After L. J. D. Fernando, *op. cit.*)

the island (see Fig. 153). It is made up of metamorphosed sediments, largely quartzites, schists, and crystalline limestones which have a considerable influence on relief, hydrology, and human geography; and, in the SW

I.P.—24*

especially, contain the island's principal mineral, graphite or plumbago. (The Khondalites also contain gem-bearing veins, but most of Ceylon's precious stones are obtained from secondary sources, i.e. alluvium.) The Vijayan Series underlies the Khondalites and consists mainly of biotite-gneisses and schists; its discontinuous outcrop fringes that of the Khonda-lite Series and there are also apparently Vijayan intrusions in the Kandy and Kurunegala areas. There are also certain other ancient intrusive rocks, including charnockites similar to those of India.

Geographically important outcrops of sedimentary rocks are confined to the Jaffna Peninsula and the NW coast, where almost horizontal Miocene limestones have a dominant effect on water-supply and human activity. Gondwana deposits are limited to one or two tiny outcrops of sandstones, which unfortunately contain none of the coals which make the series so important in India.

The solid geology is masked in certain areas by superficial deposits which are frequently of importance because, in a country of generally impermeable crystalline rocks, they provide limited supplies of under-ground water. Thus in the NW many of the interfluves are capped with "plateau deposits", comprising "gravels" (really a rubbly débris) and red earths,[4] both of uncertain age and origin; they may in part be residual.

In the pre-Cambrian terrains of Ceylon observers have seen three more or less eroded peneplain-like surfaces,[5] rising from the sea like the treads of three steps, and separated from each other by mural scarps (Fig. 154). The lowest surface is developed mainly in the Vijayan Series, is maturely dis-sected, and may be recognised in the higher hill-tops of the coastal plain; its remnants lie generally below 400 ft, and are narrow in the W and S but wider in the E, and cover most of the N of the island. The second surface is found in both the Khondalite and the Vijayan Series, and has a less mature relief; its altitude is about 1700–1900 ft. The third, with juvenile relief, lies entirely in the Khondalite Series or in intrusions in it, at about 4000 to 6000 ft; it slopes appreciably Nwds, so that the scarp which bounds it disappears in the same direction. The origin of the "peneplains" is uncertain. Adams [6] considers that they are subaerial and represent successive stages in the uplift of the island, the lowest being the youngest. Wadia,[7] on the other hand, considers that they are the result of block uplift of an ancient erosion surface in two stages, the earlier lifting the second "peneplain" above the first, and the later stage lifting the third above the second. If this is so, the mural scarps are fault or fault-line scarps. Wadia's

---

[4] See E. J. Wayland, "Outlines of the Stone Ages of Ceylon", *Spolia Zeylanica*, Vol. II (1921), 85–125. They are classed as Pleistocene on Fernando's map (Fig. 153).
[5] See D. N. Wadia, "The Three Superposed Peneplains of Ceylon", *Records of the Department of Mineralogy, Ceylon*, Professional Paper No. 1 (1943), 25–32; see also F. D. Adams, "Geology of Ceylon", *Canadian Journal of Research*, I (1929), 425–511.
[6] Adams, *op. cit.*   [7] Wadia, *op. cit.*

view certainly finds support in the evident youth of the highest "peneplain" and in the form, often reminiscent of step-faulting, of the scarps; but

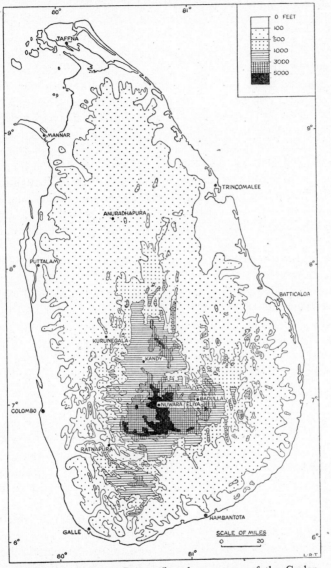

Fig. 154.—CEYLON: RELIEF (based on a map of the Ceylon Survey Department, by kind permission of the Surveyor-General, Ceylon).

certainty awaits detailed work. The denudation chronology may in fact be very complex.

The stepped nature of the relief of Ceylon has important corollaries.

Thus the mural scarps and deeply eroded valleys form obstacles to communications, while there are many waterfalls of great beauty along the scarps. These falls are potentially sources of power.

In detail, the dissection of the "peneplains" is very clearly influenced by the strike of the underlying rocks; this is especially true in the outcrop of the Khondalite Series, where quartzite ridges stand high above deep vales cut in schists, crystalline limestones, or other less resistant materials. Particularly fine ridge-and-valley topography of this kind may be studied in the Ratnapura Dt,[8] while a series of quartzite ridges stretches NNE from the Matale area to the sea at Trincomalee; Trincomalee harbour is, in fact, a series of ria-like embayments between low quartzite headlands. Grain is less evident, but still present, in country formed of Vijayan gneisses; this is well demonstrated in the broken relief of Bintenne, the hinterland of Batticaloa. N of about the latitude of Vavuniya there is virtually no relief at all. The Jaffna limestone region also has very slight relief, and nowhere rises more than 50 ft above sea-level; hence shallow wells reach the water-table, and the region does not suffer the fate of high-pitched tropical limestone areas such as those of Java.

Finally, a word may be said about coastal forms. In most parts of the shoreline except the very exposed SW, the coast of Ceylon is characterised by a series of offshore bars, spits, and tombolos, often covered with blown sand, enclosing lagoons which have become more or less silted up. The Kalpitiya spit, enclosing Puttalam Lagoon, and the long bar S of Batticaloa, are good examples. The silting of lagoons often gives wide alluvial stretches, as does also the discharge of the Mahaweli Ganga, Ceylon's biggest river, into Koddiyar Bay, S of Trincomalee.

Climate [9]

As might be expected, mean monthly temperatures in lowland Ceylon are high, and show little variation from month to month or from station to station. Thus the mean monthly temperature at Colombo (altitude 24 ft) varies only from 77·5° F in December to 82·1° F. in May, and at Trincomalee (altitude also 24 ft) from 77·8° F in January to 85·4° F in June. (These examples also illustrate the fact that mean temperatures in the hottest month are higher in the N and E than in the SW.) Reliable uniform temperatures, with the intake of solar radiation which they betoken, are among lowland Ceylon's greatest assets, and approach the optimum for the growth of rice. In the hills, lower temperatures are of course experienced; thus at Nuwara Eliya (altitude 6170 ft) the mean daily temperature hovers around 60° F, but the temperature when the sun is shining is much higher.

---

[8] See the excellent quarter-inch and one-inch maps published by the Ceylon Survey Department.

[9] For climatic data for Ceylon see the *Reports* of the Colombo Observatory.

Broadly speaking, Ceylon is under the sway of the SW monsoon from late May until August or September, and of the NE monsoon from November until January. Between the monsoons local convectional circulations tend to spring into action. The SW monsoon wind is on the whole stronger than that of the NE monsoon, and, descending from the hills with something of a föhn effect, is partly responsible for the higher temperatures on the NE coast, which may reach 100° F in the daytime during the SW monsoon.

Relative humidity at Colombo and other SWn stations remains high at all seasons (70–80% by day, 85–95% by night); the same is broadly true of NWn stations. In the N and E, however, relative humidity falls to a monthly mean of 60% or less during the SW monsoon; this helps to lower the sensible temperature, but increases the loss of water by evaporation. Relative humidity, as measured by monthly means, shows little change with altitude. The physiological effects of high humidity are in many places mitigated by wind.

Fig. 155 shows that SW Ceylon, the region usually known as the 'Wet Zone', has a much higher average rainfall than other sectors of the country, with totals exceeding 200 ins. in parts of the hills. On the other hand, in much of the N and E (i.e. the 'Dry Zone') the mean annual rainfall is below 75 ins. For the geographer, however, the mean annual figure has much less significance than the seasonal distribution, variability, and effectiveness of the rainfall. Of these, the first is illustrated by the diagrams which accompany Fig. 155. It will be clear that the Wet Zone tends to have some rain at all seasons; Colombo has two maxima, one in each inter-monsoon period, and is typical of lowland Wet Zone stations; the higher up-country stations have a single maximum during the SW monsoon, while certain intermediate stations have a triple maximum, one for each inter-monsoon period and one for the SW monsoon; all, however, tend to receive some rain during the NE monsoon, although they are on the lee side of the island. (The reasons for this are not altogether clear.) In the Dry Zone, on the other hand, conditions are very different. The SW monsoon brings very little rain, and the months June, July, and August constitute the dry season. The September–November inter-monsoon period registers fair amounts in the mean monthly rainfall graph; these are due to convection and to the passage of depressions. In all Dry Zone stations a large proportion of the mean annual rainfall comes in the NE monsoon months (60% of the annual total at Jaffna and 54% at Trincomalee). Finally, a secondary maximum, due to the so-called 'little monsoon' and its convectional and cyclonic rains, occurs in some areas in April and May; the 'little monsoon' effect is prominent at Anuradhapura, but a very minor feature at Jaffna.

The rainfall of Ceylon is subject to considerable variability. Even in the Wet Zone, there are apt to be occasional disastrous droughts, but the

problem is far more serious in the Dry Zone.[10] There the dry season nearly
always has, of course, a low rainfall, and, moreover, the mean expectancy is

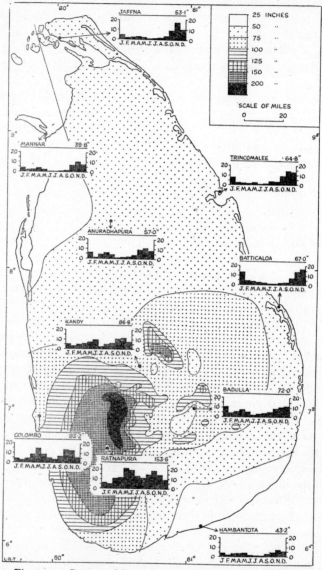

Fig. 155.—Ceylon: Mean Annual Rainfall, with diagrams
showing Mean Monthly Rainfall. (Isohyets by kind permission
of the Director of Meteorology, Ceylon.)

a great deal lower than the arithmetic mean. But spells of drought are apt
to occur at other seasons too, and the annual total of days of absolute

[10] See E. K. Cook, "A Note on Irrigation in Ceylon", *Geography* XXXV (1950), 75–85.

drought [11] is apt to be a high one (e.g. a mean of 118 days annually at Anuradhapura in the years 1931-44). The rainfall of the inter-monsoon period is particularly unreliable at many stations, and months of low rainfall are not unknown, although not very frequent, during the NE monsoon. Variability along the Batticaloa coast is generally lower than elsewhere in the Dry Zone.

However, mere variability of rainfall tends to be a statistical abstraction, and what matters to the cultivator is the reliability of *effective* rainfall, i.e. rainfall which is sufficient to counteract evaporation and to maintain soil moisture above wilting point.[12] This is especially true in the Dry Zone of Ceylon, where because of high temperatures and, locally and seasonally, of low relative humidity and high wind velocities, evaporation is high. Rainfall in a given month may show a low statistical variability, but be in many years ineffective. Fig. 156 is an attempt to indicate the percentage of years in which effective rainfall may be expected in seven Ceylon stations; it is necessarily tentative because of lack of experimental determinations of evaporation, but serves to emphasise certain important points. Thus rainfall is rarely ineffective in the Wet Zone, but often so in the Dry Zone. In the latter, the NE monsoon appears usually to bring effective rainfall, although rather less often in January; while the SW monsoon rainfall is apparently almost always ineffective at most stations. Both of the inter-monsoon periods seem to present roughly a fifty-fifty chance of effective rainfall, a singularly tantalising state of affairs for the cultivator. (October rainfall is rather more often effective than that for other inter-monsoon months.) There is also a chance of very long spells of ineffective rainfall, say from February to November; Jaffna is especially liable to such spells, and Hambantota relatively immune.

It will be clear that climatic factors, and particularly rainfall, play a major part in the regional differentiation of Ceylon. The contrast between the Wet Zone and the Dry Zone is especially marked, and, as in so many tropical islands, the transition between the two is relatively abrupt. This is true in both highland and lowland Ceylon. It will also be clear that, in a general way, the Wet Zone climate is analogous to that of Travancore and Cochin, except that in Ceylon the seasonal contrast in the rainfall régime is less marked; the Dry Zone has climatic affinities with Tamilnad, although in the latter region the 'little monsoon' effect is, as at Jaffna, slight in most years. Quite apart from its cultural affinities, Jaffna is the most 'Indian' part of Ceylon.

[11] As defined in *British Rainfall*, viz., "any period of at least 15 consecutive days to none of which is credited 0·01 inches of rain or more."

[12] See B. H. Farmer, "Rainfall and Water Supply in the Dry Zone of Ceylon", in R. W. Steel and C. A. Fisher (eds.), *Geographical Essays on British Tropical Lands* (in the press); also P. G. Cooray, "Effective Rainfall and Moisture Zones in Ceylon", *Bull. Ceylon Geog. Soc.*, Vol. 3 (1948), 39-42.

It may here be noted that the distribution of endemic malaria in Ceylon is controlled by climate.[13] Malaria has until recently been endemic in most parts of the lowland Dry Zone, although it was perhaps not always so. It is

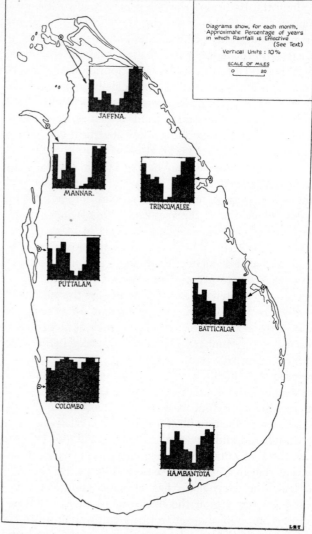

Fig. 156.—CEYLON: APPROXIMATE RELIABILITY OF EFFECTIVE RAINFALL.

carried by a mosquito, *Anopheles culicifacies*, which breeds in shallow and relatively stagnant water, and thus finds ideal conditions in the reduced streams of the lowland Dry Zone in the dry season. In the Wet Zone, on

[13] See C. L. Dunn, *Malaria in Ceylon* (1936).

the other hand, stream-beds are normally kept flushed and clear of larvae, except in times of drought; malaria is therefore epidemic in such times but not endemic.

Hydrology

The rivers of Ceylon are for the most part short and radial, rising in the highest or intermediate "peneplain" and tumbling headlong down the marginal scarps (see Fig. 157). The only really large river is the Mahaweli Ganga, which rises in the Wet Zone hill country about 30 miles S of Kandy and flows through Kandy to the sea just S of Trincomalee. Although the radial pattern is the dominant element in the drainage system, many streams show local adjustments to the strike of the pre-Cambrian rocks, especially in the Khondalite Series. The ridge-and-valley country of Ratnapura has already been remarked upon, and the long trench of the Mahaweli Ganga, in which Alutnuwara is set, may be aligned along the zone of faults between the second and third "peneplains".

Navigation on the rivers of Ceylon is unimportant except near the SW coast (e.g. on the Kelani Ganga) and the chief problem posed by their hydrology is that of controlling and using their waters in the interests of cultivation. In the lowland Wet Zone rice is the traditional crop of the peasantry, and although it could in many places and in many years be grown using only the rain actually falling on the paddy-fields, it is in practice irrigated. Irrigation, however, here presents few difficulties; the small village works take water from the local streams, most of which are perennial. There is, in fact, usually an excess of water, and much runs to waste in the sea. Since but few rivers rise in the Wet Zone and flow into the Dry Zone, and since relief in general inhibits the artificial connection of Wet Zone and Dry Zone catchments, little can be done to use this waste water where it is sorely needed. The greatest practical problem of Wet Zone hydrology is that of flood control.[14] Flooding is almost inevitable in a country where rainfall is torrential, slopes steep, and run-off from an impermeable terrain rapid, but it has undoubtedly been accelerated by the deforestation of the highlands and the planting of tea. Much has been done to protect low-lying coastal areas from floods, but the problem remains serious.

In the Dry Zone, it is seasonal shortage of water which is the main problem. The cultivation of rice using rainwater only is locally possible during most NE monsoons, but irrigation is usually desirable; while it is essential at other seasons. Direct tapping of streams, as in the Wet Zone, is usually impossible in the dry season, when most rivers are reduced to a mere string of sandy pools. Underground water is meagre in quantity; the crystalline rocks are mainly impermeable, although the relatively well-

[14] See Cook, *loc. cit.*, 76–77.

jointed limestones and quartzites and some of the schists of the Khondalite Series nourish springs which are locally valuable, if only for domestic water. The porous mantle of "plateau deposits" and residual and coastal sands is an aquifer, and many wells are sunk in it, but the water itself is scanty and impersistent, so that it is no more than a minor source of water for irrigation. Outside the Jaffna Peninsula (where conditions are clearly very different) the Dry Zone therefore has to fall back on river water, stored in tanks as in Tamilnad, and subject to a high rate of loss by evaporation. From very ancient times streams in the Dry Zone were dammed, and as technical knowledge improved the Sinhalese constructed large tanks, many of them interlinked by channels, so that those which lay on small rivers prone to dry up could be supplied from more reliable sources.[15] Many of these tanks and channels have now been restored, and a few new works constructed; to-day very large multi-purpose reservoirs are being built (e.g. on the Gal Oya). It must be realised, however, that the supply of water for irrigation is strictly limited; and much is lost by evaporation, or runs to waste (as in the Mahaweli Ganga) because relief inhibits its transference to areas suitable for cultivation. Possibly the generation of hydro-electric power at multi-purpose dams will enable water to be pumped uphill, and thus utilise resources which are at present wasted.

Very little that has been said about the problems of water-supply applies to the Jaffna Peninsula. Here the need for water is, in view of the liability to long spells of ineffective rainfall, even greater than in many other parts of the Dry Zone, but, fortunately, there are abundant, though not unlimited, supplies of underground water, kept relatively free from evaporation in fissures in the limestone. The water-table may be reached by shallow wells some 15–30 ft deep, and well-irrigation is the mainstay of agriculture. There seem also to have been some wells in ancient times in the extension of the Jaffna limestones down the NW coast.

Natural Vegetation

The natural vegetation of the lowland Wet Zone has largely disappeared, but enough patches remain to make it clear that the original covering was of tropical rain-forest. Many of the remaining stands of trees are in the ridge-and-valley country, and there and elsewhere there has been a certain amount of reafforestation. In the Wet Zone hills there are remnants of forest with more temperate species, and of recent years Australian gums and acacias have been introduced. Much of the lowland Dry Zone is covered with a tropophilous forest, adapted to the dry season; probably most of this is secondary, the original climax vegetation having been destroyed. There are, however, some valuable trees such as ebony and satin-wood.[16] Towards

[15] See Fig. 157.
[16] There were in Ceylon, in 1949, 1,362,813 ac. of forest reserves, 665,339 ac. of national reserves, and 199,829 ac. of nature sanctuaries.

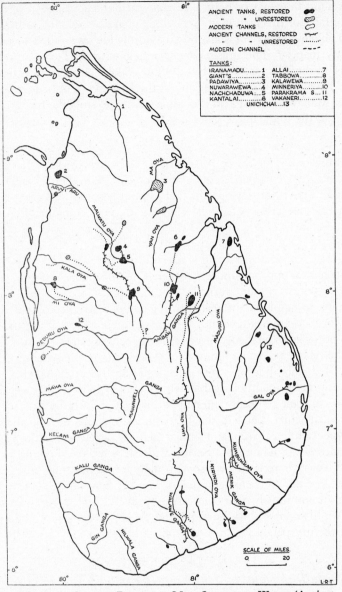

Fig. 157.—CEYLON: RIVERS AND MAIN IRRIGATION WORKS (Ancient
Irrigation mainly after R. L. Brohier; rivers based on maps of the
Ceylon Survey Department, by kind permission of the Surveyor-
General, Ceylon).

the NW, and again towards the SE, the forest degenerates into thorn scrub.
In the En parts of the hills, especially between Nuwara Eliya and Badulla,
there are large stretches of grassland, the interesting *patanas*, whose origin

is uncertain; they may be natural climax vegetation, a response to seasonally low rainfall (for this is in many ways the upland Dry Zone), to high winds, and to shallow and poor soils, but they probably owe much to periodical firing by man.[16a] The grasses are coarse and wiry. There are also 'wet patanas' in the Wn part of the hills. Other grasslands occur in various parts of the lowland Dry Zone, especially in the E; some of these (e.g. along the middle Mahaweli Ganga at Polonnaruwa) are suitable for grazing, in contrast to the unpalatable patana.

Soils

The soils of Ceylon are of great variety, and much work on them remains to be done.[17] A few guarded generalisations are, however, possible. In the first place there is, in the lowland Wet Zone at any rate, a strong tendency to lateritisation, although true laterites are not very common. Red lateritic loams are characteristic of the lowland Wet Zone and some of the wetter parts of the Dry Zone; in other parts of the Dry Zone are red loams, non-lateritic or at any rate less lateritic in character. In most of these red soils humus and calcium contents are low, phosphorus content generally poor, and potash content variable. In the second place, it seems clear that the catena principle is applicable to regions of fairly prominent relief; in other words, there is a tendency for a marked zone of leaching and eluviation to occur at watersheds, and to grade by stages into a zone of illuviated soils, the recipients of the humus, colloids, and nutrients washed down the slopes. Red soils thus pass into dark soils, by their nature fertile and by their position frequently irrigable, which are known as 'paddy soils'. In the third place, geology locally interrupts this pattern of red loams and paddy soils; in particular, parts of the Jaffna limestone area have loams of *terra rossa* type, rich in calcium, and similar soils are developed on the crystalline limestones of the Khondalite Series; wide stretches of alluvium, like those of the E coast, have their own soils, usually fertile but sometimes saline or alkaline; and the "plateau deposits" of the NW bear fertile soils on the red earths, but notoriously poor ones on the "gravels". Finally, the patanas have their own distinctive soils, humic in the 'A' horizon where well developed, but, in the dry patanas at any rate, poor in minerals.

II. HUMAN RESPONSES

The General Distribution of Settlement: Ancient and Modern

There is a great deal of evidence to show that, during the many centuries when ancient Sinhalese civilisation flourished, settlement was very largely

[16a] C. H. Holmes, "The Grass, Fern, and Savannah Lands of Ceylon", *Imp. Forestry Inst. Paper* No. 28 (1951).

[17] See, however, A. W. R. Joachim, "A Review of Progress in the Study of the Soils of Ceylon", *Proc. First Annual Session Ceylon Assoc. of Science*, Pt. 3 (Colombo, 1945), 21–30; and a series of papers by Joachim *et al.*, *Tropical Agriculturalist*, Vol. 84 (1935) to Vol. 98 (1942). (These do not refer to the catena concept as such.)

concentrated in the Dry Zone, especially in the SE and in the central region round Anuradhapura.[18] This settlement, based as it was on the growing of irrigated rice, was almost entirely rural away from the capital city, which was first Anuradhapura and later Polonnaruwa. It tended to avoid the hills and the Wet Zone alike. Probably the early Sinhalese were deterred by the scarcity of paddy-land in the former and by the difficulty of penetrating and clearing the rain-forest of the latter; and it is also possible that they were attracted to the Dry Zone because they found there a region where they could practise techniques of irrigation learnt in Nn India. Malaria, the scourge of the Dry Zone in modern times, may then have been absent or less virulent.

The glory of ancient Ceylon came to an end during a confused period from about AD 1235 onwards; thereafter Sinhalese kings ruled over an attenuated kingdom from the hills or from the SE, and Tamil kings over Jaffna and the N. It is customary to ascribe the collapse of the old order to the Tamil invasions and the consequent breakdown of the irrigation systems, but it is possible that the arrival or increased virulence of malaria may have played a part, and that soil erosion and soil exhaustion may also locally have grown serious. Certainly the effects on settlement were revolutionary. The densest areas of Sinhalese settlement came to be in the Wet Zone and in the lower hills, especially round Kandy. Apart from relatively dense settlements of Tamils in the Jaffna Peninsula, along the Batticaloa coast, and in a few places on the NW coast, the Dry Zone became for the most part a region of sparse settlement, inhabited by a few miserable remnants of the Sinhalese population living precariously around small tanks; they were too few and too enfeebled by malaria and malnutrition to repair the breaches in the ancient irrigation systems, which almost everywhere remained derelict. Early European travellers, Portuguese, Dutch, and British alike, paint a depressing picture of the decay which had afflicted the Dry Zone, making it that rare thing in the Indian sub-continent, a large region capable of supporting a greater population.

The Portuguese and Dutch,[19] important as their cultural influence was, did little to modify the settlement pattern of Ceylon, although their trading stations at such places as Colombo, Mannar, Jaffna, and Batticaloa introduced a new urban element which was especially alien when it was set amid the wastes of the Dry Zone. The British, however, conquered the mountain fastnesses of the Sinhalese, and soon began to introduce plantation agriculture. To-day the up-country regions of tea and rubber estates rival the Wet Zone and the Jaffna Peninsula in density of population (see Fig. 158).

[18] Much work on the historical geography of Ceylon remains to be done; for ancient history see Mendis and Codrington (cited in Book List, 784 below), also R. L. Brohier, *Ancient Irrigation Works in Ceylon* (3 vols., Colombo, 1934–35).
[19] For the modern history of Ceylon see Codrington, *op. cit.*, and G. C. Mendis, *Ceylon under the British* (Colombo, 1944).

During the last century or so there has also been a movement of people Nwds into the hinterlands of Negombo and Chilaw, a response to the spread of commercial coconut cultivation. The British period has also seen a growing urbanisation, especially in Colombo and adjacent townships; other towns grew too, as did villages along the new roads, but some of the smaller ports suffered an absolute or relative decline after the introduction of big ships and after the export element in Ceylon's trade began to triumph over the entrepôt trade so important in the days of the Portuguese and Dutch. In the Dry Zone, the Jaffna Peninsula and Batticaloa coast continued to have fairly dense settlement, the prosperity and population of the latter increasing especially after the coming of coconut plantations to the coastal sands and the restoration of some of the ancient tanks by the Government. The policy of restoring ancient irrigation works also attracted population to the SE coast and the Anuradhapura area, but elsewhere, until 1931 at any rate, it had but little effect on settlement. Most of the Dry Zone remained sparsely peopled, and malaria brooded everywhere.

In 1931, Ceylon received a measure of self-government which in effect gave to Ceylonese the control of internal administration, and newly roused patriotism gave a fillip to attempts to re-people the Dry Zone; a little later, the economic depression of the 1930s and the war of 1939–45 provided a further stimulus by focussing attention on the need for more home-grown food. A new policy towards colonisation in the Dry Zone was evolved: conditions of tenure were improved, and, after 1942, it became the policy to provide the colonist with a ready-cleared and ploughed farm, not merely with a patch of jungle as previously.[20] Great strides have also been made in the control of malaria. Considerable success appears to have been achieved, and settlers are now coming to the Dry Zone in fair numbers. But, as Fig. 158 shows, the main concentrations of settlement in Ceylon remain in the well-peopled Wet Zone, in the hill country, in the Nn peninsula, and in a narrow E-coast strip, with relatively sparse peopling elsewhere.

The Indigenous Economy and Society

Like Malaya, Ceylon has a dual economy and plural society; more widely than in much of India, indigenous systems are overlain by systems due to the impact of the West, and although the former are to-day much influenced by the latter, it is convenient first to consider some important autochthonous elements in contemporary Ceylonese economy and society, always remembering that in modern Ceylon it is in many areas impossible to discuss the social and economic pattern without reference to Western influence.

The indigenous economy [21] of Ceylon was, and to a large extent still is,

---

[20] See B. H. Farmer, "Agriculture in Ceylon", *GR* XL (1950), 42–67, and "Colonization in the Dry Zone of Ceylon", *Journ. R. Soc. Arts*, C (1952), 547–64.
[21] See Sir W. Ivor Jennings, *The Economy of Ceylon* (Madras, 2nd ed., 1951); and Farmer, *loc. cit.* (1950).

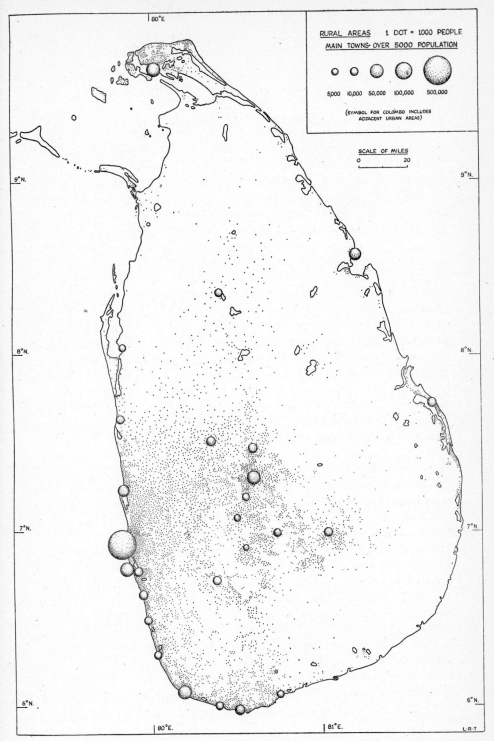

RURAL AREAS   1 DOT = 1000 PEOPLE
MAIN TOWNS· OVER 5000 POPULATION

5000   10,000 50,000 100,000 500,000

(SYMBOL FOR COLOMBO INCLUDES
ADJACENT URBAN AREAS)

SCALE OF MILES
0   20

Fig. 158.—CEYLON: POPULATION, 1946 (based on Census of Ceylon, 1946).

centred on the cultivation of rice on irrigated land; rice is the basic food-stuff, but is supplemented by various fruits and vegetables grown on unirrigable or 'high' land, and locally by grains grown by *chena* or shifting cultivation. In 1946, 912,500 ac. of Ceylon consisted of paddy-land (see Fig. 159), largely in the valley-bottoms of the Wet Zone but also in cleverly terraced fields in the hills, and in the Dry Zone. There are two main seasons for paddy cultivation, the *maha* or great season during the NE monsoon, and the *yala* or little season during the SW monsoon. In any one year, some fields are cultivated for one season only, some for both, some not at all. On the whole, land use is more intensive in the Wet Zone than in the Dry Zone. The peasants of the region W of Kandy and the Jaffna Tamils are known for their skilful cultivation, but elsewhere standards are generally low, far lower than in, say, Japan. Not enough manure is used; cultivation is poor (partly owing to the shortage and low quality of draught animals); seeds are inferior and often sown broadcast instead of in nursery beds. The Departments of Agriculture and of Rural Development are now devoting much of their energies to the technical instruction of the peasant, but the process is a difficult one.

Among 'high' land crops the coconut is especially valuable as a universal provider of food, drink, and shelter; and, with the coming of a money economy, its products may also be sold for cash; there are also peasant small holdings of tea and rubber. Another valuable palm, the palmyra (*Borassus flabellifer*), is very prominent in the Jaffna landscape. Almost everywhere in Ceylon the huts of the peasantry are surrounded by mixed gardens of palms, fruit trees, and vegetables, whose products help to lend variety to the otherwise monotonous rice diet.

In some parts of Ceylon, particularly in the Dry Zone and the hill fringes, *chena* or shifting cultivation raises special problems. Such cultivation is, of course, widespread in the remoter parts of monsoon Asia,[22] but in Ceylon it is practised by people who are well aware of sedentary methods of cultivation and who possess draught animals. *Chenas* probably existed in ancient Ceylon, and are certainly common to-day. The crops grown include millets, maize, and dry paddy, and the *chenas* are abandoned after a year of two when weeds, rather than decreasing fertility, make cultivation too arduous. Crops are grown during the NE monsoon, and, when and where possible, during the 'little monsoon'. The system has the advantages and disadvantages of shifting cultivation everywhere. In the Dry Zone especially, it tends to distract the cultivator from paddy during the rains, so that the crop is sown late and requires more irrigation water than would otherwise be the case. But *chena* cultivation is certainly one way of using unirrigable Dry Zone land, although it is clearly desirable to try to replace it with something less objectionable, and experiments have been made in rotational dry farming.

[22] See Karl J. Pelzer, *Pioneer Settlement in the Asiatic Tropics* (NY, 1945), 16–34.

Of non-agricultural occupations in the indigenous economy, fishing is one of the most important, though much more could be done to exploit the rich fisheries of the sea, the lagoons, and the tanks. The pearl fisheries of the Gulf of Mannar are historic, but variable in output. Craft industries still exist, though, as in India, they are hard hit by imported wares; the Sinhalese have long had a reputation for metalwork, especially in gold and silver. The Government is now striving to encourage cottage industries.

The production of minerals is a relatively unimportant part of the indigenous economy, but salt is obtained by the evaporation of seawater at such places as Hambantota and Puttalam. Gems are extracted from alluvium around Ratnapura, and lime is burnt from the crystalline limestones.

This essentially agricultural economy was originally one in which, as in most Oriental systems, exchange played a relatively small part; and, although there is considerable local variety, it is clear that one of the effects of Western influence has been the partial penetration of the Ceylonese subsistence economy by trade and commerce. The peasant to-day tends to exchange some part of his produce for cash or for goods, especially in the Wet Zone. Marketing methods have long been primitive and wasteful, however, and it has been an object of Government policy to encourage co-operative methods, not without success. But although the problem of marketing is much to the fore in modern Ceylon, the penetration of a money economy must not be exaggerated; it still plays only a small part in the lives of many peasant families, especially away from the linear villages strung out along main roads and bus routes. Just what part it does play is a promising subject for local research.

It must be stressed that the social pattern associated with the indigenous economy was, and is, very complex, as might be expected in an island which has received many influences from both Peninsular India and the sea. But four aspects may be selected as being of particular significance to the geographer.

In the first place, it must be stressed that the social unit is a closely-knit village society. It is traditionally governed by a *Gansabha*, or village council, which, *inter alia*, regulates irrigation and cultivation and has the authority to make every man do his share of repairs to village works. The nature of the social unit is important in many matters, from the study of settlement types [23] to the practical politics of Dry Zone colonisation, although in the towns and overgrown villages the old social bonds have largely been destroyed.

In the second place, the village society is very closely attached to its land. Land tenure in Ceylon is a very complicated matter; many systems are in

[23] For a geographical study of village patterns, see E. K. Cook, *Ceylon* (Madras, etc., 2nd ed., revd K. Kularatnam, 1951), 279–314.

force, most of them deriving from ancient service tenures. But some 60% of the paddy holdings are owned by the cultivators [24] and handed down from generation to generation, so that the attachment of the peasant to his land is understandable. It is also understandable that fragmentation is considerable; in the Kandy Dt the average holding is only three-tenths of an acre; holdings are largest (average 6·9 ac.) on the Batticaloa alluvium. Landlordism is also common, however, and some 25% of the paddy-fields are held on *ande* tenure, by which the landlord receives a share of the crop; *ande* tenure is especially common in the Kandy, Matale, Ratnapura, and Matara Dts, and hinders the spread of improved methods, since the peasant is loath to work hard and improve his yield only to hand over perhaps 50% of the increase to a landlord. In fact, as in India, fragmentation and landlordism, with their concomitant indebtedness, vastly complicate the problems of rural rehabilitation and efficient land use.

In the third place, society in Ceylon is to some extent stratified in terms of caste. The stratification is most marked in the predominantly Hindu Tamil areas, though at Jaffna it is less marked than in India. Hinduism has also left its mark on the theoretically casteless Buddhist society of the Sinhalese. The results are not so stultifying as in India, but among them a tendency to immobility of labour is important; thus fishing, a low-caste occupation, is not taken up by cultivators at times when they are not working in their fields, and a potential addition to their meagre food-supply is neglected. Labour is more mobile to-day than it used to be, but in other ways modern changes have been less beneficial. The descendants of the ancient leaders of rural society have tended to acquire Western book-learning and to move to the towns, attracted especially by Government service, so that an educational difference and a white-collar complex have been superimposed on caste, and the villages are left leaderless. Attempts to redress the balance by encouraging "middle-class colonisation" have not been particularly successful, and, till recently at any rate, educated Ceylonese have been badly out of touch with the countryside; a state of affairs not confined to Ceylon or, for that matter, to the East.

Finally, there are the related problems of literacy and of attitudes to economic and social change. According to the 1946 Census, 57·8% of the 'educable' population (i.e. those of 5 years of age and upwards) were literate in the sense that they could read and write a language, a considerable improvement on the figure of 39·9% for 1921. There was, however, a contrast between the literacy of males (70·1%) and of females (43·8%). Even more marked was the contrast between town and country; literacy reached 73% in the towns (higher still in Jaffna) but was under 40% in

---

[24] See A. G. Ranasinha, *Census of Ceylon* (1946), Vol. I, Pt. I, Colombo (1950), p. 258. The figure of 60% for the cultivator-owned paddy-fields is an average; conditions vary greatly from area to area; see, for example, the results of economic surveys quoted by Jennings, *op. cit.*, 56–57.

some rural areas; it was lowest in the Dry Zone and in the hills (especially among estate labourers. Apart from the wider issues, the importance of literacy as the first stage in the technical education of the peasant is self-evident. That is not to say, however, that literacy and technical education are panaceas; clearly, as elsewhere in Asia, deep-rooted attitudes to life and work are involved, and social research is essential.

The Impact of the West Dual Economy, Plural Society

It will be clear from what has been said that Western influence has greatly modified the indigenous economy and society, but to differing extents in different regions; in fact, the differences between the Low Country and the Kandyan Sinhalese [25] are attributable to the former group's longer and stronger European contacts. But there is also the entirely new economy and society which have been imposed on Ceylon by the Europeans, and especially by the British.

The plantation, or estate, is the chief geographical expression of this new economy; it is essentially monocultural, growing tea, rubber, or coconuts (or more rarely other crops) for export, and is worked by hired labour. (Coffee-growing, once widespread, has now almost died out.) The ownership and management are characteristically European, though much less now than formerly; and coconut estates have always been far more of a Ceylonese affair. It was estimated in 1934 that about 90% of the capital in coconuts, about 55% of that in rubber, and about 20% of that in tea, had been invested by Ceylonese.[25] Tamil labour from South India was brought in, especially to work on coffee, tea, and rubber estates, since the Kandyans were then unwilling to work for hire; the "Indian Tamil" labourers must not be confused with the "Ceylon Tamils" of Jaffna.

The hill country was the area most affected by the new agricultural system, though to varying extents in its various regions. Thus in 1946 only just over 25% of the cultivated area immediately around Kandy was under estates, but over 75% in the Badulla area and 98% at Nuwara Eliya. The low country in the triangle Colombo–Chilaw–Kurunegala was also greatly affected by the spread of coconut estates, although here a more characteristic expression of the new economy was the small holding. And around the turn of the century rubber estates began to occupy much of the 'high' land right down to the coast in the SW. Fig. 159 shows the areas under the three main plantation crops in 1946.

If the hills received the main impact of the new economy, and the lowland Wet Zone shows a less marked effect, the changes wrought by it in the Dry Zone were almost negligible. Coconut plantations have been established on the coastal sands between Negombo and Puttalam, on

[25] See Jennings, op. cit., 25–28, quoting the report of the Ceylon Banking Commission, 1934.

Mannar Island, in the Jaffna Peninsula and S of Batticaloa; and there are a few rubber estates below the En scarp of the third "peneplain" in Bintenne. But elsewhere the private capital which was attracted to the Wet Zone and the hills was repelled from the Dry Zone by its unsavoury reputation for drought and disease, and by its evident unsuitability for the staple plantation crops. And, in spite of occasional optimistic forecasts that commercial rice cultivation could be made to pay, the low price of rice conspired with the environmental hazards of the Dry Zone to discourage private enterprise. It was left to the Government to restore the breached tanks and, after the failure of one or two schemes for commercial cultivation beneath them,[26] to begin the modern era of recolonisation by peasant cultivators.

The communication pattern in Ceylon has also been greatly influenced by the coming of the newer element in the country's dual economy. It is true that early road makers (e.g. Sir Edward Barnes, 1824–31) were mainly concerned with the construction of a network which would make government possible, and that, in a later phase, the construction of such enterprises as the light railways to Trincomalee and Batticaloa were, at least in part, due to a desire to help the depressed Dry Zone [27]; but the railway from Colombo to the estate-clad hills is still the main line of the Ceylon Government Railways, and the closest road network, apart from the coastal belt of the Wet Zone, is in the estate areas. In fact, much road and rail construction has resulted from the need to move estate produce to Colombo, which has become the only major port and the undisputed focus of the island's communications system (see Fig. 160).

The products of the estates dominate Ceylon's foreign trade[28]; nearly all of the tea and rubber, and probably about half of the coconut products, are exported, mainly through Colombo, and together account for some 90% of the country's visible exports in most years. As the table shows, however, the value of these estate products fluctuates greatly from year to year with the vagaries of world prices and, more recently, as a result of international agreements to limit production and of British and American buying policy. Realisation of the dangers inherent in an economy based on such unstable foundations is one of the mainsprings of recent attempts to produce more food and to diversify the economy. But in spite of the efforts which have been made, Ceylon still has to import from one-quarter to one-third of the rice necessary to feed the population, and considerable quantities of other foodstuffs.

Efforts have also been made to broaden the base of the economy by

[26] E.g. schemes at Minneriya Tank; see R. L. Brohier, *The Tamankaduwa District and the Elahera-Minneriya Canal* (Colombo, 1941), 26–28.

[27] See G. S. S. Gordon, "Extension of the Ceylon Government Railway", *GJ* LXVI (1925), 471–72; for a more general account of the development of the railway system see G. F. Perera, *The Ceylon Railway* (Colombo, 1925).

[28] See Jennings, *op. cit.*; and B. B. Das Gupta, *A Short Economic Survey of Ceylon* (Colombo, 1949).

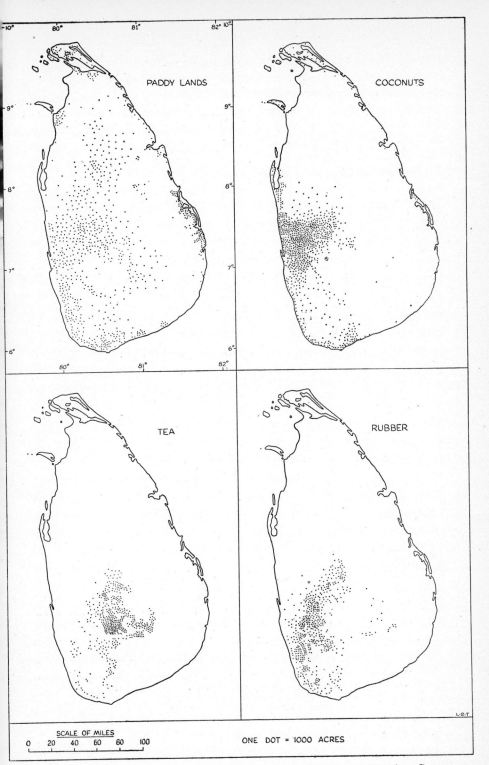

Fig. 159.—CEYLON: DISTRIBUTION OF FOUR PRINCIPAL CROPS, 1946 (based on Census of Ceylon, 1946). (Note that Paddy *Lands* are indicated: not all of these were under a crop in 1946.)

introducing manufacturing industries; but, apart from the processing of tea, rubber, and coconut products, there are few factories in Ceylon. There are private works making matches, arrack, cotton textiles, and so on; and Government factories making plywood, glass, ceramics, and other products. A new cement factory, using Jaffna limestone, has recently been opened at Kankesanturai, and the completion of the long-projected hydro-electric scheme near Hatton should help other industries which are still in the planning stage. But Ceylon is clearly not well endowed for heavy industry.

Various minerals (apart from gemstones) have been worked under the influence of the Wn economic system. The only one of any importance is graphite, of which variable quantities are mined annually, mainly in the SW.

Value of Ceylon's External Trade, 1947–50

	1947	1948	1949	1950
Exports	Rs.	Rs.	Rs.	Rs.
Tea . . .	566,522,993	590,271,396	649,845,462	751,650,630
Rubber . .	135,501,814	141,618,650	124,544,850	405,451,334
Coconut Products	93,692,306	155,600,000	190,401,611	280,998,401
Plumbago . .	3,610,792	6,734,451	6,381,146	6,222,130
Other Exports .	89,853,276	116,951,695	88,067,046	118,598,143
TOTAL . .	889,181,181	1,011,176,192	1,059,240,115	1,562,920,638
Imports				
Rice . . .	134,986,590	236,115,461	226,355,771	277,990,964
Other Foodstuffs .	350,843,033	273,619,692	284,634,982	308,290,426
Raw Materials .	79,277,432	106,607,659	110,011,273	118,432,379
Manufactures .	348,998,288	358,720,113	399,868,788	451,867,087
Other Imports .	13,975,466	10,310,907	7,972,635	10,225,397
TOTAL . .	928,080,809	985,373,832	1,028,843,449	1,166,806,253

The introduction of a plantation economy has introduced new elements into the population of Ceylon in the persons of the Indian Tamils who form the bulk of the estate labour. Their introduction was largely made necessary by the original unwillingness of the Sinhalese—independent, village-bound, and land-bound—to work for hire, at least away from his own area. The Indian Tamils numbered 780,589 in 1946, and form a distinct Hindu society with a low standard of literacy. The general problem of the immigration of estate labour has been the cause of considerable friction between the Governments of Ceylon and India. [29]

III. THE REGIONS OF CEYLON

Ceylon is capable of four-fold division, there being "low-country" and "up-country" in both Wet and Dry Zones. For convenience, however, the two "up-country" zones may be grouped together, and one may adopt a three-fold division: the Lowland Wet Zone, the Hills, the Lowland Dry Zone. These three divisions may further be sub-divided on the following scheme (see also Fig. 160):

1. *The Lowland Wet Zone.*
   (a) The coastal lowlands.
   (b) The Negombo–Kurunegala–Chilaw coconut belt.
   (c) The ridge-and-valley country of Sabaragamuwa and adjacent areas.

2. *The Hills.*
   (a) The Kandy region.
   (b) The regions of the monoculture of tea.
   (c) The Uva Basin.

3. *The Lowland Dry Zone.*
   (a) The W coast.
   (b) The Jaffna Peninsula and islands.
   (c) The E coast lowlands.
   (d) The SE coast lowlands.
   (e) Bintenne.
   (f) The N centre.

It is hoped that the scheme, although somewhat arbitrary, will justify itself in the sequel; and the student may compare it with that proposed by Miss Cook.[30]

1. The Lowland Wet Zone

The belt of transition between the Wet Zone and the Dry Zone is, both on the NW and SE of the former, a narrow one, although in some years

[29] The numerical strength of the major communities at the 1946 Census was as follows:

Low Country Sinhalese	2,902,509
Kandyan Sinhalese	1,717,998
Ceylon Tamils	733,731
Indian Tamils	780,589
Ceylon Moors	373,559
Burghers and Eurasians	41,926
Europeans	5,418
Others	101,609
TOTAL	6,657,339

[30] See E. K. Cook, *Ceylon* (2nd ed., revd. by K. Kularatnam); a summary of Miss Cook's scheme will be found in L. D. Stamp, *Asia* (7th ed., 1948), 377–85.

Dry Zone conditions may occur a little way into the Wet Zone, and vice versa. The line drawn to delimit the Wet Zone in Fig. 160 agrees well with

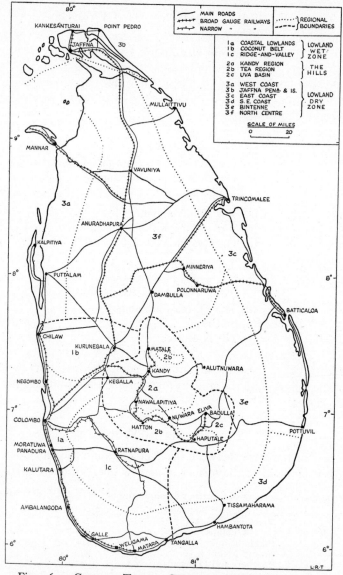

Fig. 160.—CEYLON: TOWNS, COMMUNICATIONS AND REGIONAL DIVISIONS (based on maps of the Ceylon Survey Department, by kind permission of the Surveyor-General, Ceylon).

such indices as changes in vegetation and density of settlement. A line between the Wet Zone and the Hills is less easy to draw, in spite of the presence of great mural scarps. The line chosen represents a generalised 1000-ft contour, except that it is so drawn as to include in the Wet Zone the detached mass of the Sabaragamuwa hill country.

(a) *The Coastal Lowlands*

The coastal lowlands of the Wet Zone form a narrow belt roughly parallel to the coast from Negombo to Tangalla; they also send a tongue from Colombo towards Kandy. Into this slim belt are crowded most of the towns of the island together with a very dense rural population, a fact which is clear from Fig. 158. To the N, population thins out fairly suddenly beyond roughly the latitude of Negombo.

The coastline is formed in the main of a series of sandy spits and tombolos, springing from or linking rocky headlands such as those on which Colombo and Galle are based. Inland is a discontinuous belt of lagoons, which have often become choked up with alluvium and turned into swamps, as in Muthurajawela, N of Colombo, which it is hoped to work for peat, Ceylon's only mineral fuel. Still more often they have become wide alluvial spreads which are usually cultivated as paddy-fields. These spreads send curving tongues of paddy-land up the valleys of the numerous rivers. Between the tongues, and also, island-like, in the old lagoon flats and the coastal sands, rise low, rounded lateritic hills, very maturely dissected remnants of the first "peneplain", whose summits rarely exceed a few hundred feet. Outcrops of solid rock are rare. The soils in general show the same threefold division as the relief, with sandy soils along the coast, paddy soils on the alluvium, and lateritic soils on the low hills. The three divisions may perhaps be regarded as "stows" on Unstead's scheme.[31]

Everywhere the climate is uniformly hot and humid, often depressingly so. The rainfall varies down the coast from 70 to 100 ins., and is normally well distributed throughout the year, with maxima in the two inter-monsoon seasons. Although in most years the rainfall is effective, droughts are not unknown, and may be followed by epidemic malaria. The natural vegetation must once have been mainly rain-forest or its littoral equivalent, but it has been largely destroyed except on some of the lateritic hills. The rivers are perennial, and provide readily available water for rice fields. The trouble is, however, *un embarras des richesses*, for this is the worst region of Ceylon for floods; the Nilwala Ganga is a notorious offender. Undoubtedly the floods have been made worse by deforestation and by the planting of estate crops on steep slopes in the upper reaches of the rivers.

The majority of the people are Low Country Sinhalese. Here European influence has been most intense and continuous, to say nothing of Arab

---

[31] See J. F. Unstead, "A System of Regional Geography", *Geography*, XVIII (1933), 175–87. Cf. also the threefold division in Kerala and coastal Tamilnad (above, Chs. XXII and XXV).

I.P —25

influence even earlier. Besides Colombo, towns like Galle, Matara, and Kalutara were greatly used by the Portuguese and Dutch. Not surprisingly there are many of the insignia of European contact: Portuguese surnames,[32] Roman Catholicism, burghers of mixed Dutch and Sinhalese ancestry, often a high degree of literacy in English. There is evidence that settlement in the coastal lowlands was dense in pre-European days, but the modern intense economic development has certainly greatly increased the density. There are now houses almost all the way from Negombo to Tangalla, and only in such areas as those well to the N of Galle and Matara is there fresh land for cultivation.

In spite of the concentration of places which are classed as towns, agriculture is still, outside the fishing villages, the most important single occupation in the coastal lowlands. There is the characteristic twofold division of land between paddy and 'high' land; on the latter mixed gardens of coconut, jack, breadfruit, and other trees predominate, but there are many small holdings and a few estates growing coconut, tea, rubber, and (in the S) cinnamon and citronella. The swollen villages are strung along the 'high' land, especially on the coastal sands. The impact of a money economy has been so strong that peasants tend often to rely on their perennial 'high' land crops and to neglect their paddy; for trees grow all too easily, and paddy costs effort. Yet the peasant is unlikely to make the effort until he is better fed, and that means more paddy. The problem is complicated by flooding, poor methods of cultivation, absentee landlordism, fragmentation, bad marketing, and indebtedness. In fact, despite the great density of population, land use is imperfect, and to improve it is the foremost problem of the rural coastal lands.

Of the towns, Colombo is *sui generis*, and is almost entirely a result of the impact of the West, although in its early days it owed a great deal to the Moors. For several centuries it was less important than Galle, but it pulled ahead in the 19th century with the consolidation of British rule over the Kandyan country and the establishment of estates, with the consequent Nwd shift of the centre of gravity of the island's commerce. Moreover, it commanded two relatively easy routes into the Kandyan country, one by the Maha Oya and the Kadugannawa Pass, the other by the Kelani Ganga and the Ginigathena Pass; and, with the increase in the size of shipping, it outdistanced ports like Puttalam although its own harbour is artificial. The British made it the centre of their road and rail networks, and their capital. It also, of course, became an important port of call. To-day it stands a Triton among the minnows, the one big town in the island, with 362,074 people within its municipal boundaries in 1946, and 488,535 in the whole

---

[32] Not all Portuguese surnames date, however, from Portuguese days; some are change-names adopted by Sinhalese on entering Government service because European civil servants had difficulty in pronouncing Sinhalese names.

conurbation [33]; the municipal population has quadrupled in 75 years. Limited by swamps and paddy-fields to the E, it has expanded Swds, and many of the smaller towns along the coast are in part its dormitories.

The string of towns between Colombo and Tangalla is equally a product of Western influence. Not, of course, that they are ports of consequence (with the bare exception of Galle), but that they are market towns and bazaars, foreign to the indigenous economy. Many of them have a strong Moor element, and some have small-scale industries. In fact, the light industries which seem likely to result from recent Government activity will mainly, and for obvious reasons, be concentrated in these SWn lowlands.

(b) *The Negombo–Kurunegala–Chilaw Coconut Belt*

This region, though wider, has the same three relief elements as the last, viz. coastal sands, alluvium, and interfluvial lateritic hills. But the sands recur on the inland side of some of the lagoons, and the low hills tend to cover a greater proportion of the total area. Towards the E these hills also change in character; they are higher, often relics of the second "peneplain", and as such more abrupt and rockier; and in them were formerly many primitive graphite mines, few of which now remain. The climate and hydrology are also similar to those of the previous region, although towards the N Dry Zone conditions begin to creep in and there is a greater liability to drought.

But it is fundamentally its human geography which distinguishes this region from the last. There are, it is true, paddy-fields much like those of the SW coast, cultivated in much the same unsatisfactory manner and attended by much the same social and economic evils; but they supply only about one-third of local needs, and everywhere it is the coconut which dominates both the landscape and the economy. The climate and soil are generally said to suit it, though it is noticeable that well inland, away from its natural habitat, the palm is more stunted, and drought, too, causes trouble in some areas. Coconut is largely cultivated by small holders, who often own very few trees indeed and tend them in an indifferent manner. Since the depression which set in in 1927, there has been much debt, poverty, and even emigration. Where the palm is grown on estates (these are mainly Ceylonese-owned) conditions are rather better, although mortgaging and decreasing yields, due to the age of the trees, present problems. Although there are rubber estates in the E, and although fishing is carried on along the coast, the region as a whole suffers from an undiversified economy. It is far too closely tied to the variable fortunes of

[33] The Colombo conurbation is here (and in Fig. 158) taken to include the City of Colombo together with the Urban Districts of Dehiwala-Mount Lavinia, Ja-ela, Kolonnawa, Kotte, and Wattale-Mabole-Peliyagoda.

coconut, and virtually the only industries are those concerned with the processing of coconut products.

This is a region of many small villages and fewer large ones, characteristically located on the lower slopes of the interfluvial hills; the people are mainly Sinhalese. The density of population is high, though not as high as in the SWn coastal ribbon; much of the settlement is recent, for in the years around the turn of the century there was a great growth of population, associated with the coconut boom and due partly to immigration and partly to natural increase. The largest towns are Negombo, Kurunegala, and Chilaw, with respective populations in 1946 of 32,479, 13,372, and 9108. All are marketing centres for the coconut industry, and the first and last are small ports.

(c) *The Ridge-and-Valley Country*

The rocks of this region are almost entirely of the Khondalite Series whose denudation has given rise to three types of landforms. There are first a very prominent series of parallel ridges, often very steep-sided, following the arcuate strike of the Series; across the ridges are cut presumably epigenetic transverse gorges, while between the ridges there run long "subsequent" valleys. There lies here a fascinating field for geomorphological research. The ridges become higher and wilder in the S, where they reach over 3000 ft; between them and the mural scarp of the central highlands there is a corridor uniting the Kelani Ganga and Walawe Ganga Basins. In this ridge-and-valley country lies most of the little mineral wealth which Ceylon possesses, particularly graphite and gems. There are also said to be some 5 m. tons of iron ore.

The climate here is a wetter version of that of the coastal lowlands; the mean annual rainfall exceeds 200 ins. in some places. The region still has considerable remnants of the rain-forest which once covered it, but inaccessibility hinders commercial exploitation. Reafforestation is in progress, and is vital as a measure of flood control.

The Nn part of this region is the main rubber-growing area of Ceylon. Until the rubber boom of the years after 1904 it was fundamentally a region of valleyside villages growing paddy and cultivating *chenas*. But rubber estates spread rapidly into the hinterland of Kalutara and into the country SW of Kegalle, and later into the Ratnapura area. The climate was ideal, and there appeared to be plenty of free land, though in practice the *chena*-making propensities of the peasant were locally rudely checked. There was much immigration of Low Country Sinhalese and of Indian Tamils into this traditionally Kandyan area, and the old order was destroyed. There are still many paddy-fields, but to-day the region depends mainly on its rubber. It lies at the mercy of the fickle market for that commodity, and at present also suffers from slaughter-tapping practised during the war of

1939–45. Ratnapura (12,441 in 1946) is the only fair-sized town here.

The Sn area of more rugged relief and difficult communications is one of a thinly-scattered peasant population living mainly by paddy and *chena* cultivation. There is a little rubber in small holdings, and recently a wave of new colonisation from the overcrowded coast moved into the region; one hill Division increased its population by 41% between 1931 and 1946. But the only considerable settlement is in the corridor N of these hills, where Balangoda is the centre of a tea-growing area.

2. The Hills

The relief of the central highland massif of Ceylon, developed as it is from the Khondalite Series and intrusions in them, is very complex in detail, and it is not yet possible to discuss it in genetic terms; consequently any attempt to subdivide the region on the basis of its detailed physiography is bound to be wearisome and merely descriptive. It seems better to adopt a simple threefold division, recognising each of the two main nuclei of Kandyan civilisation (the Kandy region and the Uva Basin), and the areas dominated by the monoculture of tea. There is, of course, a broad physiographic basis for this scheme, since it was areas above about 2500 ft which were not settled by the Kandyans, and hence were available for planters.

(a) *The Kandy Region*

This very beautiful region consists broadly of a basin developed in the second "peneplain" at about 1000–2000 ft, and drained by the Mahaweli Ganga in its course from Nawalapitiya to Kandy and thence Ewds into the valley known as Dumbara. Other streams fret the mural scarp of the "peneplain" and provide gates into the Kandyan fortress; the two from the W (Kadugannawa and Ginigathena) have already been mentioned, and there remains the Matale Valley, to the N of Kandy, by which the Sinhalese entered the Kandy Basin during their retreat from the Dry Zone. Above the general level of the Kandy Basin rise steep ridges of higher ground.

In the Kandy Basin temperature is moderated by altitude, but rainfall is in general as high as in the lowlands to the W, and in some places higher (75 to 100 ins.). The rain is in most places well distributed, with a tendency, as has been mentioned, to three maxima. To the N and E of Kandy, Dry Zone conditions begin to appear, and drought in the SW monsoon makes itself felt. Very little of the natural vegetation is left; uncultivated hills are mainly covered with secondary scrub or wiry grass, but forests remain in Dumbara.

The Kandyans remained unconquered and relatively out of touch with Europeans until their city fell to the British in 1815. Although affected by nearly a century of contact, they still retain many characteristics which distinguish them from the Low Country Sinhalese; greater independence, greater attachment to their hereditary lands, a better-preserved aristocracy, a lower standard of literacy but a distinctive culture; their ceremonial dancing is famous. The traditional economic basis of their life is the familiar method of cultivating both paddy and 'high' land; but here much of the paddy-land has been laboriously built *from* 'high' land on terraces which in places rival those of Java, and whose construction must seem impossible to the valley-bound Low Country Sinhalese. Associated with this laborious husbandry is, especially in the metropolitan Districts immediately W of Kandy, a higher standard of cultivation than is usual in Ceylon. The Kandyans were quick to begin to cultivate cash crops even in the early days of coffee, and still have much tea, rubber, and cacao in small holdings. One of their main problems is the pressure of population (the Districts just mentioned have over 1000 people per very hilly square mile); and perhaps in the future they will, like other highland folk, prefer to descend to the plains and live less laborious lives.

Some 25% of the cultivated land in the Kandy Dt is under estates, mainly on higher ground where, it is claimed, the land was unused by Sinhalese. (The latter, however, are apt to tell a different story.) Tea is the main crop, with some rubber and cocoa. The problems raised by hill estates can be postponed until the next section.

Kandy is the nerve-knot of its basin, and had a population of 51,266 in 1946 (with Low Country Sinhalese in the majority!). Besides its commercial function it is, of course, a cultural and religious centre of renown, and near it are being built the new buildings for the University of Ceylon to replace those at Colombo. Matale (14,090 in 1946) is also a sizeable town.

(b) *The Tea Regions*

The main region dominated by the virtual monoculture of tea lies at over 3000 ft (much of it at over 4000 ft) on the third or highest "peneplain" The mural scarp is very marked to the S, whence the magnificent views from Haputale; but on the W, overlooking the Kandy Basin, it is fretted by tributaries of the Kelani Ganga which tumble off the plateau in splendid waterfalls. The Laksapana Falls now form the site of Ceylon's major hydro-electric scheme, and there is undoubtedly room for further development near by. In detail, the surface of the "peneplain" has complex relief, for not only are dissection youthful and slopes steep, but the strike of the Khondalite Series is very variable and much broken by intrusions, so that the clear linear patterns of the ridge-and-valley country are absent or obscured. There are, however, areas of recognisable plateau surface, as around Hatton. Above the plateau remnants rise the highest hills of the island, such as Pedurutalagala (8281 ft), the spectacular Adam's Peak (7360 ft), and the detached Knuckles (6113 ft) N of Dumbara.

The mean annual rainfall is heavy, in most places over 100 ins., and with régimes as in the previous region, except that there is a tendency to a single SW monsoon maximum in the highest hills. The natural vegetation, montane forest with the probably secondary patanas, has been largely cleared, but areas of both forest and grassland remain. There has also been considerable reforestation. Soils are in general lateritic, but humic under the patanas; there are also areas of bare rock.

These upland regions were never apparently settled by the Sinhalese, and lay empty when the British arrived. In the decades after 1830 they were transformed by the wholesale clearing of natural vegetation and the planting of coffee, until disease swept away the plantations in the 1880s.[34] There followed the even more widespread planting of tea, for which the region's climate and altitude are ideal. Road and rail construction kept pace with the spread of estates, often with considerable engineering difficulty. To-day tea gardens spread almost continuously over the area within about 8–10 miles' radius of Hatton, and, after a gap, there is another large concentration to the E round Haputale; the Hatton region also sends a finger to the NE, to the Uda Pussellawa Valley beyond Nuwara Eliya; and there is finally a detached group of estates on the SE flanks of the Knuckles. In all of these regions there are many immigrant Indian Tamils, although to-day the community is in an absolute majority only in the Nuwara Eliya Dt. The population map (Fig. 158) shows that in all of these formerly empty areas there is now a considerable density of population. The two main urban centres are Nuwara Eliya and Hatton-Dikoya (populations respectively 10,828 and 5379 in 1946); the former is a famous health resort.

Of the problems now facing the tea region, three are especially significant. The first, soil erosion, is a function of the steepness of the slopes and of the heavy rainfall; many remedial measures are being taken, but much remains to be done. There is then the problem of labour; costs are rising, and fresh immigrants from India are discouraged; the number of Sinhalese labourers is growing. Thirdly, since the 1930s there have been Government restrictions on new planting, in part as a result of international regulation of production; so that any great increases in tea acreages are unlikely in the near future. There is, in fact, a casting about for new kinds of land use for the still empty areas, and there are now Government cattle farms seeking to use improved patana for pasturage.[35]

(c) The Uva Basin

This interesting, healthy, and distinctive region consists of the upper parts of the basins of a series of streams which drain to the Dumbara reach

[34] See E. C. Large, *The Advance of the Fungi* (London, 1940).
[35] See R. A. de Rosayro, "Land Utilization in the Montane Grasslands (Patanas) of Ceylon", *Bull. Ceylon Geog. Soc.*, Vol. 4 (1949), 27–38.

of the Mahaweli Ganga. (The lower parts of these catchment basins are very different, and will be considered with Bintenne.) The Uva Basin lies mainly at 1000 ft to 4000 ft; its relations with the "peneplains" are not altogether clear, though the ridge which bounds it to the E drops to Bintenne by a spectacular scarp which has every appearance of that of the highest "peneplain".

It is sometimes maintained that the Uva Basin, and not Kandy, is the real home of Kandyan civilisation. Certainly it would have appealed more to the Sinhalese trekking from the Lowland Dry Zone, since it is essentially that Zone's up-country equivalent. The mean annual rainfall is, in the Basin proper, less than 75 ins., and, more significant, there is a maximum during the NE monsoon, with a secondary maximum to correspond with the 'little monsoon'. The SW monsoon period is one of drought, and the variability of rainfall shows Dry Zone features. It is true that temperatures and therefore evaporation rates are lower than in the Dry Zone, but high winds partially offset this effect. The high winds have also been held in part responsible for the characteristic dry patana which clothes the unplanted hills of Uva, and gives them, rounded as they are, something of the aspect of chalk downland, with browns replacing greens. In many parts of the Basin trees are now confined to river banks.

It may be, then, that it was in Uva that the Sinhalese, approaching by the N/S Mahaweli Ganga trench, adapted their irrigation techniques to a region of strong relief, and terraced the hillsides. Certainly many irrigation works here are of some antiquity; they even include tunnels through hills.[36] Some of these works have been restored recently. The villages of Uva have something of the aspect of the Kandy countryside, though in a different physical setting; settlement is also much less dense and there is nothing to correspond to the metropolitan district of Kandy. Uva was also somewhat less affected by the coffee and tea booms, although there are many tea gardens here in spite of the dry climate, and over one-third of the population work on estates. The Uva estates have the same problems as those to the W, with the added danger of drought. Some Uva peasants have taken up the growing of tea on small holdings, and many have swallowed their pride and found work on the estates.

The area with most estates, i.e. that S of Badulla, has the densest population. Outside the estate areas, further restoration of irrigation works would help to attract settlement to what at present is an area of generally sparse population; and there is also the problem of utilising the remaining patanas. The regional centre, Badulla (13,387 in 1946) is an ancient city and the modern railhead.

[36] See R. L. Brohier, *Ancient Irrigation Works in Ceylon*, Pt. III (Colombo, 1935), 33.

3. The Lowland Dry Zone

The criteria by which the Dry Zone may be separated from the Lowland Wet Zone and the Hills have already been discussed. The Dry Zone itself is full of contrasts, but for the purpose of the present brief study will be divided into six sub-regions whose boundaries pass through uninhabited or sparsely-peopled territory.

(a) *The W Coast*

This is a region of very subdued relief, largely dominated by blown sand; this is especially true of the Kalpitiya spit, the Puttalam area, and Mannar Island, where the Jaffna limestones lie buried beneath dunes. Inland are some of the less fertile of the " plateau deposits", and some belts of riverine alluvium. The mean annual rainfall is comparatively low (40–50 ins.) with a November maximum and a marked dry season. The 'little monsoon' and occasional trespasses of the Wet Zone régime are felt in the S, but their effect diminishes Nwds. Variability is considerable, especially in the inter-monsoon periods, while a tendency to long spells of ineffective rainfall increases Nwds. It is not surprising that the present vegetation is largely scrub although this may not be the true climax.

It is also not surprising that rural settlement is sparse, though some areas are not without legends of past fertility. Malaria has been hyperendemic, at least until the last few years. Because of the coastal position of the region, the population is mixed, with Moors in the majority in the S and Ceylon Tamils farther N. But there are not many rural settlements outside two areas: the Nn prolongation of the coconut belt, and the lands beneath Giant's Tank in the Aruvi Aru alluvium. There are also coastal fishing settlements, some temporary, and a community of pearl fishers which varies with the fortunes of their trade. Puttalam (7792 in 1946) profits by its dry climate to make salt from sea water, but long had a reputation for insalubrity. Mannar is a decayed ancient port.

(b) *The Jaffna Peninsula and Islands*

This is a unique region with a strong personality in which traits due to its physique, its people, and its position may all be discerned. The climate is harsh in the extreme; heavy, almost excessive rains in November and December are followed by a variable tail end of the monsoon, an inter-monsoon period in which rainfall is slight or absent, and a very dry SW monsoon. There is thus a strong tendency to long spells of ineffective rainfall or of absolute drought. But fortunately the limestones of Jaffna store underground water, and the well is an essential part of the Jaffna landscape. However, the *terra rossa* soils are thin, and in many places bare rock pokes through, giving tracts where cultivation is impossible. There are also large areas of blown sand or of old dunes, equally useless except, perhaps, for coconuts; this is especially true of the En part of the peninsula and the islands.[37] The population is, in fact, concentrated into a few areas (Fig. 158).

Because of its position, the Jaffna region was one of the first to receive Tamil settlers from India; but, in spite of continual contact with India by sea, the Ceylon Tamils have over the centuries become a distinct people. They have, with their industry and resourcefulness, made a strong mark on their rocky little homeland, and are locally packed as tightly as in the SW coastlands. They grow paddy, together with palmyra and coconut palms, tobacco, and a host of other laboriously irrigated crops, and they do it with skill. The Jaffna region is one of the few in the Dry Zone to show a continual natural increase throughout the period of census-taking, and there has been much emigration. In particular, educated Jaffna men have left for Government service or for other posts both in Ceylon and overseas, in India and Malaya. Remittances by emigrants play an important part in the economy of the peninsula.

Jaffna itself is to-day the second largest town in Ceylon, with a population of 62,543 in 1946. Although it has lost the pre-eminence as a port and administrative centre which it had in Dutch days, it still retains some trade in small ships and is, effectively, the railhead. An urban study of it would be a profitable piece of work.

(c) *The E Coast Lowlands*

This region consists of two stretches of coast made up of sandbars protecting lagoons or alluvium, separated by the belt of quartzite ridges which comes out to the sea at Trincomalee. The Nn stretch, with a few exceptions, receives relatively short rivers liable to dry out, whereas the Sn stretch, the "Batticaloa Coast", receives longer and more reliable streams such as the Gal Oya; and the great Mahaweli Ganga reaches the sea just S of Trincomalee.

Most of the E coast receives a higher mean annual rainfall than most other parts of the Dry Zone (60–70 ins.), but there are the familiar wet and dry seasons separated by a 'little monsoon' with slight rains. Batticaloa's rainfall is less variable than elsewhere in the Dry Zone. All along the coast the wet season's rains are usually effective, the dry season's ineffective, and the little monsoon's effective for about half the years in a given period.

The Nn stretch of coast is inhabited mainly by Tamils, but there are very few of them. The region lacks restored irrigation works; further, it has but few ancient and unrestored works because of the nature of its

---

[37] See T. H. D. Abeygunawardena, "The Islands to the West of the Jaffna Peninsula". *Bull. Ceylon Geog. Soc.*, Vol. 4 (1949), 62–71.

rivers. This stretch is, in fact, very similar to the problem area of the Wanni which lies inland from it.

In the immediate vicinity of Trincomalee are somewhat large clusters of population near the coast, growing paddy, coconut, and tobacco. The people are mainly Tamils and Moors, who have the benefit of water from irrigation works fed from the Mahaweli Ganga; and, with modern methods of malaria control, there may well be an expansion of settlement on the fertile deltaic alluvium.

Trincomalee town stands apart from its region. Although something of a port in Kandyan days, it has recently had no commercial importance at all; wide areas of jungle cut it off from the estate areas, which are in any case orientated towards Colombo. It had no railway until the 1920s. The fortunes of Trincomalee have fluctuated not with trade but with the degree of use made of it by the British Navy. Thus the war of 1939–45 caused its population to increase from 10,160 in 1931 to 28,334 in 1946. Britain still uses it as a naval base, but its commercial future is problematical. Developments in its hinterland are likely to be aimed far more at the growing of food for home consumption than at production for export.

The Batticaloa coast has long had a reputation as a successful paddy-growing area. Numerous tanks fed from the rivers of the hinterland, and now mainly restored, bear witness to its importance in ancient times, and it will benefit from the great new scheme at Gal Oya. The alluvium behind its lagoon carries some of the largest continuous stretches of paddy in Ceylon. Here, on solid islands in the alluvium, are settlements of cultivators, usually tenants of absentee Moor landlords. But the densest settlement is on the sandbars, where there are coconut groves (Figs. 158, 159).

The Batticaloa region was one of the first to profit from the Government policy of restoring irrigation works and providing communications and the results were more satisfactory here than in remoter regions, although agricultural practices leave much to be desired. The population has grown steadily, though not without setbacks due to disease and drought. Batticaloa town, the local centre, had a population of 13,037 in 1946.

(d) *The SE Coast*

This is a region of low plains, fringed by lagoons, swamps, and sand-bars, and crossed by a series of radial streams the larger of which have laid down fertile alluvium. Like the Puttalam-Mannar coast, it is a region of low mean annual rainfall, in most places less than 50 ins., but here there are certain mitigating circumstances: the seasonal contrast of excessive rain and parching drought is less marked, variability is on the whole lower, and there is not such a tendency to long spells of ineffective rainfall; but drought is nevertheless very much to be reckoned with.[38] As in the NW,

[38] See the novel by Leonard Woolf: *The Village in the Jungle* (1913).

the vegetation is mainly scrub, though some at least of this may be due to shifting cultivation. Malaria has until recently been hyperendemic.

The SE coast was the nucleus of Ruhuna, an important part of the ancient Sinhalese realm, and had many ancient irrigation works and, presumably, a considerable population. But when it was visited by British travellers in the middle of the 19th century the belt E of Hambantota was a desolate wilderness. A great deal was done to restore irrigation works, and the population of the irrigated areas rose steadily from 1871 onwards, partly by natural increase but also by the immigration of Sinhalese from the crowded Galle and Matara Dts. But the revenue from these irrigation works did not meet current expenses, to say nothing of capital cost, and the population appears to have remained poverty-stricken. There are now two modern colonies in the region, and it remains to be seen what they will achieve. There is also a scheme for great new works on the Walawe Ganga. Hambantota, the small urban centre and minor port of the region, has a salt industry like that of Puttalam.

E of Tissamaharama is a great empty belt with no irrigation works and no coast road. Here are a national park and game and forest reserves. Irrigation may come to parts of this belt, but water is scarce.

(e) *Bintenne*

Bintenne is a region of higher and more confused relief than has hitherto been met in the Dry Zone, higher because it is largely the dissected "second peneplain", more confused because it is made up of the very ancient Vijayan gneisses which lack the alternations of resistant and less resistant bands which give pattern to so much of the Khondalite country.

Bintenne is essentially a region of difficulty. True, it has a greater mean annual rainfall than the areas just surveyed (over 75 ins. for the most part). But away from one or two of the SEwds-flowing rivers there are few large ancient irrigation works or modern restorations, largely it seems on account of relief and soil. There is thus no work fed from the right bank of the Mahaweli Ganga. (The new Gal Oya reservoir is in Bintenne, but will benefit mainly the E coast.) Moreover, the region has been extremely malarial and excessively isolated, at least away from the Badulla–Batticaloa road. It has aptly been described as the 'terai of Ceylon'.

Its population is in general sparse, except where a few tea and rubber estates have overspilled from the Uva Basin; and contains such few Vedda as remain.[39] There is very little settled cultivation, the peasants depending largely on *chena*; this practice may be responsible for the *damanas* (grass-lands) which cover so much of the country. The people have suffered much from sickness and poverty, and in most of the recent decades deaths have

---

[39] The number of Vedda is decreasing not so much because of their gradual extinction but because of their absorption into Sinhalese or Tamil communities.

exceeded births. It is not easy to see what can be done for this region. Bintenne had not by 1946 profited from measures which had helped other Dry Zone regions, although there had been some new settlement along the roads.

(f) *The N Centre*

This large region is essentially a plain, rarely rising above 500 ft, but containing many isolated hills and strike ridges which complicate irrigation but help to form soil catenas and hence to concentrate plant nutriment in irrigable areas. There is a tendency to higher temperatures in the hot season than in the other parts of the Dry Zone; and the mean annual rainfall is everywhere 50–70 ins., with a typical Dry Zone régime. There is, locally at any rate, a tendency to high variability in some months.

The whole region abounds in ancient irrigation works, including most of the complex interlinked schemes. It must all have carried a considerable density of population in ancient times, but to-day there is a noticeable concentration only around Anuradhapura (Fig. 158). Early British travellers [40] found here numerous isolated Sinhalese villages, grouped round small tanks and hence at the mercy of severe drought, and cultivating paddy and *chena* crops on a subsistence basis. Many such villages remain, though they are now more affected by a money economy, but in addition there has since 1870 been a fairly strong wave of immigration, following the restoration of irrigation works and the building of roads and railways. Until recently, however, health conditions were bad, and immigration concealed an excess of deaths over births. To-day, there is an air of great activity hereabouts, with a number of new colonies and experimental farms; but much remains to be done before the problem of living satisfactorily in this part of the Dry Zone can be solved.

SE of the series of quartzite ridges which links the Hills with Trincomalee lies the District of Tamankaduwa, with its three great irrigation works of antiquity, Minneriya, Parakrama Samudra, and Kantalai. Until very recently this region lay almost empty, and was notorious for fever. Irrigation restoration came relatively late, but alone was not enough to attract people to this remote and unhealthy area, and the provision of communications helped but little. But recent intensive efforts at colonisation have begun to have their effect. Nearly 13,000 people moved into Tamankaduwa between 1931 and 1946, and the total population increased by 163%.

There remains the Wanni N of Vavuniya, another problem area. Here climate tends towards the rigours of Jaffna, and there are few large rivers to fill major tanks. The Wanni is a Tamil area, and in addition to suffering the

---

[40] E.g. Sir J. Emerson Tennent, *Ceylon* (1859), II. 602–25. The whole work is well worthy of study by the geographer.

difficulties which afflict the Dry Zone as a whole was very badly devastated by conflicts between the inhabitants and the Dutch and British. Restored irrigation works and communications came late, and the region has had a most unsatisfactory bill of health. In decade after decade, there was an excess of deaths over births, and the region still lags behind.

Anuradhapura has changed greatly since Tennent found there a few huts only, and wrote "the air is heavy and unwholesome, vegetation is rank, and malaria broods over the waters as they escape from the broken tanks".[41] The town had 12,314 inhabitants in 1946, and it is proposed to build a new town so that archaeologically interesting areas may be preserved.

IV. THE NEW CEYLON

Ceylon gained her independence on February 4th, 1948, and the foregoing pages will form some sort of inventory of the resources with which the new state faces the future. Not, of course, that it faces it alone, for Britain, under existing arrangements, is pledged to aid in its defence, and Ceylon in return has given Britain continued rights at Trincomalee and at certain airfields. There is no sign of a general desire in Ceylon that Britain should be excluded, although future sentiments will depend on British as well as Ceylonese statesmanship. *India*, too, has many reasons to desire an independent Ceylon, although it is conceivable that at some time in the future an *Indian* imperialism might seize on the cultural affinities of Ceylon with *India* and, ignoring the individuality of the island, attempt annexation.

The external economy is still too completely tied to three commodities, two of which at any rate are produced largely on estates. True, these commodities are booming at the moment of writing (March 1951), but they may well be slumping by the time that these words are read. And, moreover, when prices for exports are rising prices for food imports may be rising too. There is, therefore, wisdom in the efforts which are being made to base the Ceylonese economy more broadly. In particular, increased food production, the processing of agricultural produce, the manufacture of cement, and a few light industries based on hydro-electric power would seem to offer suitable lines for development. Not all industrial projects, however, are unexceptionable, and one sometimes meets in Ceylon the standard Asian fallacy that industrialisation is the panacea for all ills.

Internally, it will be clear that there is the possibility of communal tensions in politics, although not, of course, of the same order as those in undivided India; moreover, these tensions appear to be less in evidence now than they were a few years before the granting of independence. But there are still occasional murmurs from the Ceylon Tamils against the majority community, and counter-murmurs from the Sinhalese against the

[41] See Tennent, *op. cit.*, 603.

Ceylon Tamil minority who secure posts in Government service out of all proportion to their numbers. The Indian Tamils, too, pose a problem for statesmanship.

The greatest problem of the new state is undoubtedly that of raising the standard of living of the people and of keeping pace with an increasing population. This is clearly not only a social and economic problem but a political one, for politically dormant as the peasant masses may be, failure to improve their lot may be to court instability. Enough has been said to show that the problem can, broadly speaking, be attacked on two fronts: the raising of standards of production in the lowland Wet Zone and the Hills, and the colonisation at a higher standard of living of the lowland Dry Zone. Neither will be easy. There is a tendency in Ceylon to look back at the ancient glories of the Sinhalese kingdom and grossly to over-estimate the possibilities of the Dry Zone; a corollary is that spectacular schemes in the Dry Zone are apt to receive more popular attention than quiet, persistent efforts to improve conditions in areas already settled. It will be clear that settlement in the Dry Zone will, in the long run, be severely limited by water-supply (although the limit can be pushed further back by pumping to previously unirrigated land and by techniques for reducing evaporation) and by the effect of variable and ineffective rainfall (which will certainly limit the very valuable efforts which are being made to develop systems of rotational dry farming). In the short-term view, the severest limit seems likely to be imposed not by lack of equipment and technical skill (although these are serious) but by shortage of capital; for great expenditure with little immediate return is implicit in Dry Zone colonisation. So far the capital has come from taxation, with an inevitable heavy burden on the export industries, and from internal loans and savings, a clearly limited source in a poor country. It remains to be seen whether the present mood of international interest in Southern Asia will last, and whether it will lead to the injection of sufficient capital without the attachment of conditions intolerable to the new Ceylon.

But, quite apart from political and strategic considerations, the whole problem has a new urgency in Ceylon because of recent population trends.[42] The population of Ceylon increased steadily from but 2,400,380 in 1871 to 6,657,339 in 1946; but now the spread of malaria control, improved medical services, and similar factors are producing an accelerated rate of increase. It is estimated that there will be a population of 10·5 m. by 1975, and this may well prove an underestimate when the recent advances in public health have had their full impact. It is true that there is likely, in the absence of political pressure, to be far less immigration from *India* than in the past, but on the other hand every advance in nutrition and in

---

[42] See I. B. Taeuber: "Ceylon as a Demographic Laboratory", *Population Index*, Vol. 15 (1949), 293–304; and A. G. Ranasinha, *op. cit.*

living standards will inevitably quicken the rate of natural increase. Except among the urban middle class, there is very little sign of a general decrease in the birth-rate. All this, of course, is a very familiar story to the student of Asia in general and of *India* and Pakistan in particular; but Ceylon's good fortune is that, given freedom from outside interference and given internal political stability, the existence of her sparsely peopled Dry Zone gives her a breathing space which is denied to India, a breathing space in which to act upon a policy which shall stabilise her population below the danger-level.

SELECT BOOK LIST

E. K. Cook, *Ceylon* (2nd edn., revd. by K. Kularatnam, Madras, Bombay, etc., 1951).

S. F. de Silva, *The New Geography of Ceylon* (4th. ed., Colombo, 1945).

H. A. J. Hulugalle, *Ceylon* (OPIA No. 6, 1944).

L. J. D. Fernando, "The Geology and Mineral Resources of Ceylon", *Bulletin of the Imperial Institute*, Vol. 46 (1948), 303–25 (with maps).

H. W. Codrington, *Short History of Ceylon* (Revised ed., 1938).

G. C. Mendis, *The Early History of Ceylon* (Calcutta, 1938).

—— *Ceylon under the British* (Colombo, 1944).

S. D. Bailey, *Ceylon*, 1952.

The Bulletin of the Ceylon Geographical Society.

Sir W. Ivor Jennings, *The Economy of Ceylon* (Madras, 2nd. ed., 1951).

B. B. Das Gupta, *A Short Economic Survey of Ceylon* (Colombo and London, 1949).

The Economic Development of Ceylon (Report of an International Bank Mission), 2 vols. (Colombo, 1952).

A SUMMING-UP

THIS book has sought to set forth the geographical facts necessary to an understanding of the life of the peoples of *India* and Pakistan. Inevitably this has involved a consideration of many social facts and trends, some directly related to the geographical setting, others with but tenuous links with the environment, or even with none discernible, yet essential to form a picture which, if it cannot hope to be a true portrait of reality, is at least free from conscious distortion, and it is hoped from hasty judgments. The length of the discussion has doubtless been wearisome to the reader, yet is certainly not commensurate with the vastness and complexity of the problems involved. Alike in its physical environment, in its economy, and in its societies, the great sub-continent is as it were a world apart; and the regional chapters have shown, or should have shown, the huge internal diversities of its regional structures and of the local societies and economies living in or based upon them. This is true even of the seemingly monotonous plains where the nuances of regional differentiation as yet defy analysis, though increasingly they are being unravelled by the labours of Indian agronomists. At every turn, both in the general and regional chapters, we noted items—a selected few only—of the immense agenda which faces Indian geographers. Almost any chapter might be the starting-point of a dozen monographs; and this is no virtue of the writer, but inherent in his theme. The abiding impression is of an intricacy fascinating by its very difficulty, challenging to the utmost the determination to penetrate the causes of things: *felix qui potuit rerum indicarum cognoscere causas.*

At this stage no more is possible than a few bold strokes towards a synthesis. The social history of the last few decades is largely summed up in two distinct but not unrelated trends: the increasing population pressure, the integration into world economy. The latter, by its substitution of cash and contract for custom and status, has meant among other things a progressive decay of that once-adjusted rural society which lies at the basis of India's future no less than of her past.

In itself the breakdown of outmoded traditions, of customs which are an affront to the dignity of man and woman, of the isolation of the village, carries capabilities for good; and at all events, in a world increasingly compacted by revolutions in transport, it cannot possibly be reversed, even by a Mahatma, unless by a catastrophe—unfortunately not inconceivable—which might reduce the world we know to a scatter of petty poverty-stricken localisms. Yet the impact of modern technique and economy on a society singularly ill-fitted to take the shock has been little short of disastrous. Paradoxically it is not only the weakness of Indian rural society which is responsible for this, but also its strength, the strength of numbers. Its mere mass and extension ruled out an easy surrender to the new forces; nothing is more striking than the unconscionable time its doomed trades and traditions take a-dying. Mass and extension again make it difficult to move on new ways: but the example of China, whether regarded as good or as evil, at least discourages overmuch reliance on commonplaces about immemorial tradition, inertia, and rural conservatism.

To counterbalance the increase of population there are considerable resources: water for power and irrigation, ores, oils, fibres, forest products, incalculable wealth in iron and manganese. Many of these are not perhaps abundant in relation to the population (they are certainly not so in Pakistan), but they are at least capable of development to a much greater extent than now exists, or indeed than seems likely in the near future, unless the tempo of development is greatly quickened. This obviously depends on many essentially political factors, both internal and external, as well as upon more purely fiscal considerations. In the last resort, however, it seems unlikely that any really stable advance will be possible without limitation of births; and in the social context of both *India* and Pakistan that is a gigantic question-mark. Yet without heroic measures it seems too probable that tentative economic advances may be whirled away in the unceasing flow of new mouths to feed.

Once more, the prime needs of *India* and Pakistan are more fertility in their fields and less fertility in their homes. If either of these could be attained, it is probable that an equilibrium would be reached, advance in some sectors, retrogression in others, stagnation at a more or less workable level for most. If both, the resources for real advance are there, and the increase in human energy, with the liquidation of disease and malnutrition, opens prospects of a new and happy culture, prospects which to-day are only a dream. But if neither, then disaster: disease, famine, social catastrophe on an unparalleled scale.

To avert this danger, to arrest the progressive decadence of the country-side, to build the better life which might be possible with the aid of modern techniques, are tasks which call for revolutionary zeal and energy; and also perhaps for a tact which does not always go with these qualities, the tact to preserve those indubitable values of the old traditions which are enshrined in thousands of rural hymns and proverbs. Energy in plenty there is in the new India; but how wisely directed may be doubtful, and much of it seems the surface energy of brave words and paper plans. How far the depths beneath have been stirred; whether, when, in what direction the tremendous latent energy of their collective mass will be released, no man can tell. Yet on the answer most certainly depends the role of *India* and Pakistan in the deep-rent world to-day; and, in the minds of the best of their leaders and thinkers, that role is the arduous and honourable one of mediator in the perilous schism. It is at least conceivable, therefore, that the whole balance of the world rests on the razor-edge of success or failure in the task of rehabilitating the life of the millions who toil in Indian fields. So great are the responsibilities of the leaders and the peoples of *India* and Pakistan, responsibilities to the world as to themselves.

APPENDIX
New or Altered Names in *INDIA*

New Name	Old Name or Location
Amravati	Amraoti Dt (CP)
Avadh	Oudh
Banaras	Benares
Banaskantha	new Dt (N Bombay)
Chickmaglur	Kadur Dt (Mysore)
Deoria	new Dt (part of Gorakhpur, UP)
Dhanbad	new Dt (part of Manbhum, Bihar)
Durg	Drug (CP)
Faizabad	Fyzabad (UP)
Himachal Pradesh	Punjab Hill States
Jabalpur	Jubbulpore
Kakinada	Cocanada
Kanpur	Cawnpore
Kozhikode	Calicut
Krishna	Kistna R.
Lakhnau	Lucknow
Madhya Bharat	Central India Agency (part of)
Madhya Pradesh	Central Provinces (CP)
Madurai	Madura
Mathura	Muttra
Nagapattinam	Negapatam
Pepsu	Patiala and East Punjab States' Union
Pratapgarh	Partabgarh Dt (UP)
Rajasthan	Rajputana
Ramanathapuram	Ramnad Dt (Madras)
Sabarkantha	new Dt (N Bombay)
Sagar	Saugor Dt (CP)
Saharsa	new Dt (part of Bhagalpur, Bihar)
Saurashtra	Kathiawar
Srikakulam	new Dt (S Madras)
Tiruchirapalli	Trichinopoly
Tirunelveli	Tinnevelly
Uttar Pradesh	United Provinces (UP)
Vijayawada	Bezwada (Madras)
Vindhya Pradesh	Central India Agency (part of)
Visakhapatnam	Vizagapatam
Zalwad	new Dt (Saurashtra)

INDEX

There is a separate Index of Authors and Works Cited. There is, of course, some selectivity in this General Index; the judicious user will not expect every mention of, say, *rice* or *Ganges* to be indexed. Attention is drawn to the following major heads, under which relevant entries are gathered: COAL, COTTON, DEVELOPMENT PROJECTS, ELECTRICITY, GEOLOGICAL FORMATIONS AND PERIODS, IRRIGATION, LAKES, LANGUAGES, MOUNTAIN AND HILL RANGES AND PLATEAUS, MOUNTAIN PEAKS AND HILLS, PASSES, RAILWAYS, RICE, RIVERS, SOIL TYPES, TRIBES AND CASTES, VEGETATION, and WARS.

Major references are indicated by **bold-face** numerals; *pm = passim*.

ABDULLAH, SHAIK, 379, 380
aboriginal tribes, 149
acacia gum, 232
Adam's Bridge, 728
Aden, 162, 610, 635
Adilabad Dt, 650
Adil Shahis, 651
administrative divisions, xxiii, 182
Afghanistan, Afghans, xxix, 130, 149, 150 fn., 156–157, 161, 190, 321, 382, **Ch.XVI** *pm*, 479, 480, **488–491** *pm*
Africa, Africans, xxix, 7, 267, 542, 600
Africa, East, 112, 161, 323, 324, 626
Africa, North, 244
Africa, South, 112, 139, 230, 258, 297
AGA KHAN, 189
Agra, 111, 119; historic importance, 150, 158, 159, 161; 182; industries, **297–299** *pm*, 310; 317; 494, 506, 508, **510**; and central India, 575, 577, 582, 602
Agra Dt, 299, 508
Agra "Province", 494
agricultural calendars: Kashmir, 376; Kumaon, 402; Oudh, 504; Gujarat, 603; Coromandel, 698 (*see also* harvests)
agricultural yields, 200–201, 213–215 *pm*, 221, **238**, **254** (*and see under* individual crops)
ahimsa, 136
Ahmadis, Ahmadiyya, 189–192
AHMAD SHAH ABDALI, 157, 161
Ahmadnagar, 158, 160, 223, 647, 651
Ahmadnagar Dt, 647–650 *pm*, **672**
Ahmedabad, 111, 116, 168, 183; industry, 246, 261, **275–285** *pm*, 304, 512; 603, **605**; compared with Bombay, 609, 610; 674
Ahmedabad Dt, 604
aircraft, 290, 305, 321
air-masses, 40, 44, 46, 49–50
Ajmer, 290
Ajmer-Merwara, 563, 572
AKBAR, 130, **158–161**, 268, 449, 462 fn.; buildings of, 509, 510; 574

Akola, Dt. and town, 593, 647, 649, 651
Aksai Chin, 26
Alaska, 48
ALA-UD-DIN KHALJI, 157, 492, 734
ALBUQUERQUE, AFONSO DE, xxx, 162, 169, 621
alcohol, 232–233, 260, 309
ALEXANDER I of Russia, 438
ALEXANDER THE GREAT, 63, 151, 153, 424–449 *pm*, 464, 480
Alexandria, 154
Aligarh, 506, 507, 508
alkali pans, 207, 266
alkalis, 292
Allahabad, 44, 150, 299; as railway centre, 313, 317; 506, 507, **509–510**, 582
Allah Bund, 596
Alleppey, 635
Almora, 255 fn., 400, 403, 404
Almora Dt, 399
Alpine peoples, 124
alp, Swiss, 377
ALTAMSH, 493
alum, 268, 270, 292, 309
aluminium, 266, **288**, 631
Alutnuwara, 753
Alwaye, 253, **288**, 292, 591, 631, 644
Ambala, 488, 490; Divn, 105
AMBEDKAR, B. R., 139
Amber, 573
America, North, 257; South, 7
Aminbhavi, 173–176
Amlekhganj, 409
ammonium sulphate, 252–255, 268, 292, 309
Amraoti, Dt and town, 593, 647–650 *pm*
Amreli Dt, 600
Amritsar, 111, 168, 284, 380, 390, 397, 472, 477, **478–480**
Amritsar Dt, 106, 478, 481
Anantapur-Chittoor Basins, 676, 678
Anantapur Dt, 655, 670, 672, 734
Anantnag Dt, 105, 378
Anarkali Bazaar, Lahore, 184, 480
Andaman Is., 97 fn., 120, **738–739**
ande tenure, 762

789

INDEX OF AUTHORS AND WORKS CITED

Footnotes which are simply citations of a name occurring frequently within a few pages are not indexed, but all containing comment are; thus Deshpande is indexed for p. 661 but not for p. 659.

Periodical titles are indexed only where *general* reference is made to them.

Classical works and authors (e.g. Ptolemy, *Mahabharata*, Kabir) are usually mentioned as social or historical facts, as it were, and so appear in the General Index except when directly cited; similarly, of course, political personalities who are also writers, such as Gandhi and Nehru, are entered in either Index according to context (see e.g. Gandhi on pp. xxxvi and 509 (Author) and pp. 104 and 140 (General)).

DS407   Spate
S67
          India and Pakistan